USING GEOMETRY

Second Edition

David W. Wells
Lecturer in Mathematics Education
Missouri Western State College
St. Joseph, Missouri

Leroy C. Dalton
Chairman, Mathematics Department
Wauwatosa Secondary Schools
Wauwatosa, Wisconsin

Vincent F. Brunner
Teacher, Mathematics Department
Nicolet High School
Milwaukee, Wisconsin

LAIDLAW BROTHERS • PUBLISHERS
A Division of Doubleday & Company, Inc.
RIVER FOREST, ILLINOIS

Irvine, California   Chamblee, Georgia   Dallas, Texas   Toronto, Canada

EDITORIAL STAFF

Project Director: Eugene M. Malecki

Staff Editors: Joan M. Davidson, Gene S. Kuechmann, Max V. Lyles, Carol A. Papke

Production Associate: Nora Gubbins-Kawa

Art Director: Gloria Muczynski

Photo Researcher: William A. Cassin

ILLUSTRATORS

Cover and Title Page: Donald C. Meighan

Text: John D. Firestone & Associates, Paul Hazelrigg, Donald C. Meighan

ISBN 0-8445-1891-3

Printed in the United States of America

23456789 10 11 12 13 14 15 098765

CONTENTS

Chapter 4 Parallel Lines in a Plane

Chapter 5 Polygons

Chapter 6 More About Proofs

Chapter 7 Geometric Inequalities

Chapter 8 Perpendicular Lines and Planes

Chapter 9 Areas of Polygons

SPECIAL TOPICS

ALGEBRA REVIEWS

GEOMETRY: WHAT AND WHY?

1

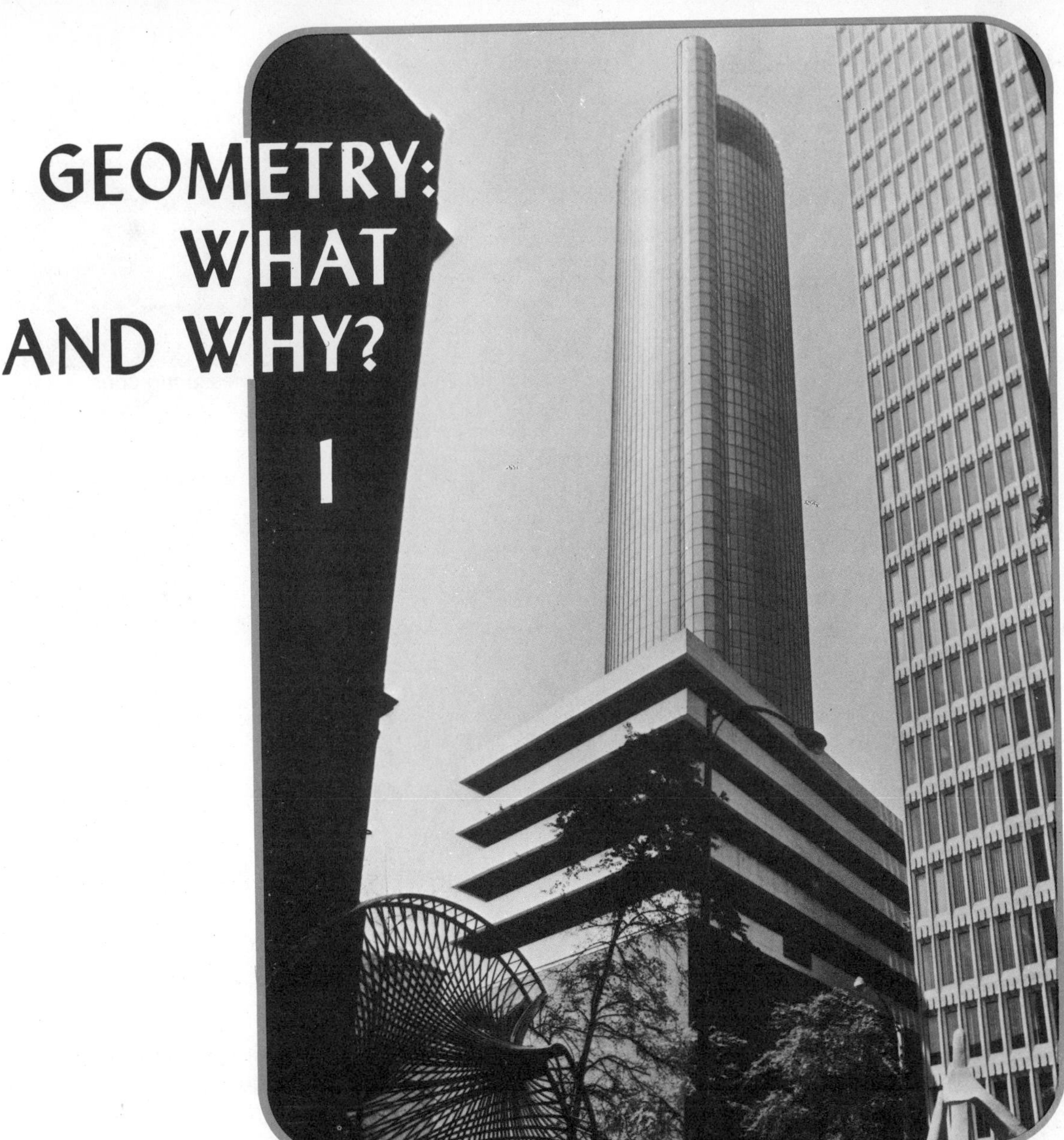

Taurus

Geometry may be thought of in two ways:

- It is the study of size, shape, position, and other properties of the objects around us.

- It is a mathematical system in which a few basic statements or ideas are agreed to and then used to discover results by logical reasoning.

Throughout this book, geometry will be studied in both ways.

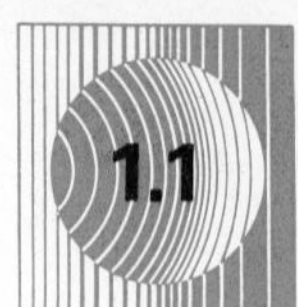

1.1 Figures—Sets of Points

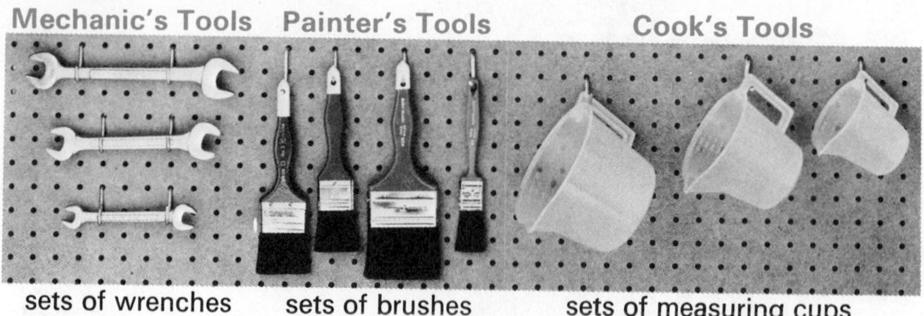

Different sets of tools are used in different kinds of work. Different kinds of mathematics use different sets of ideas.

Arithmetic	Algebra	Geometry
$1, 2, 3, 4, \cdots$	$1, \frac{3}{2}, 2, \frac{9}{4}, -3, \cdots$	$1, \frac{5}{4}, \sqrt{2}, \frac{3}{2}, \sqrt{3}, \cdots$
$\frac{1}{2}, \frac{2}{3}, \frac{3}{4}, \frac{1}{5}, \frac{7}{3}, \cdots$	$\sqrt{2}, \sqrt{3}, -\sqrt{5}, \cdots$	
$1\frac{1}{2}, 2\frac{1}{3}, 4\frac{2}{7}, 8\frac{3}{5}, \cdots$	$a, b, c, x, y, \cdots$	
sets of numbers	sets of numbers sets of variables	sets of numbers sets of points

Geometry deals mostly with points and sets of points. Here is how we draw and name them.

Model	Picture	Names	Important Notes
 a spot of light	$\bullet P$	point P P	A point has no size at all—it involves position or location only.
an endless light beam	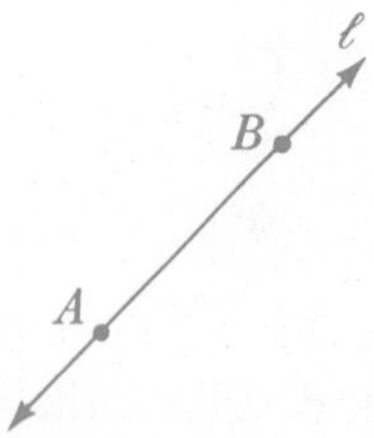 (line through points A and B, labeled ℓ)	line ℓ line AB $\overleftrightarrow{AB}$	A line extends without end in both directions. Points A and B are two points in the set. Think of a line as *straight* and as having absolutely no width or thickness.

Lick Observatory, University of California

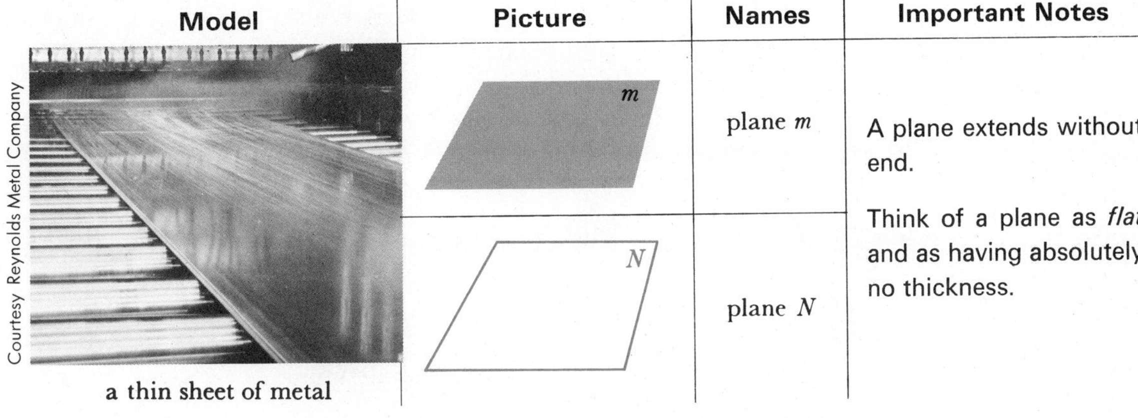

Model	Picture	Names	Important Notes
a thin sheet of metal	m	plane *m*	A plane extends without end.
	N	plane *N*	Think of a plane as *flat* and as having absolutely no thickness.

Courtesy Reynolds Metal Company

A set of points (like a line or a plane) is also called a **figure.** Objects (like lengths of thread or sheets of plastic) that help us think about geometric figures are **models**. In fact, the drawings we make of figures are also models.

Here are some basic figures and the terms we use in talking about them.

Points A and B are *on* (or *in*) line ℓ.

Line ℓ *contains* points A and B.

$\ell = \overleftrightarrow{AB}$ means that ℓ and $\overleftrightarrow{AB}$ are two names for the same line

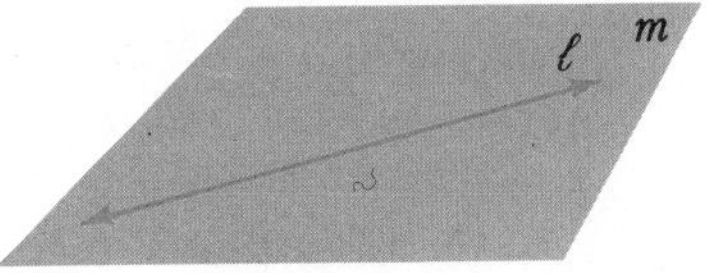

Line ℓ is *in* plane m.

Each point of line ℓ is *in* plane m.

Plane m *contains* line ℓ.

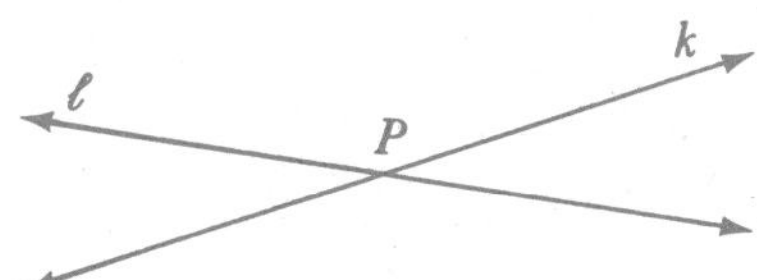

Lines k and ℓ *intersect* at point P.

Their *intersection* is point P.

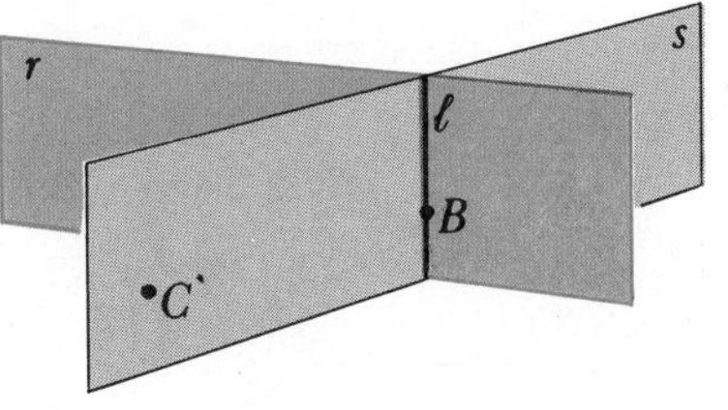

Planes r and s *intersect* at line ℓ.

Their *intersection* is line ℓ.

Point B on line ℓ is in both planes r and s.

Point C is in plane s but not in plane r.

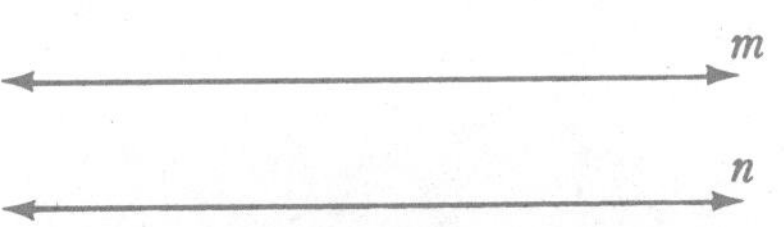

Lines m and n do not intersect.

The set of all points is called **space**. We say that space contains all points and that every point is in space.

A point is said to have *no dimensions*, a line *one dimension*, a plane *two dimensions*, and space *three dimensions*.

Exercises 1.1

Ⓐ **1–4.** For what geometric figure is the object a model?

1. a beam of light

2. a desk top

3. the tip of a pin

4. a flagpole

5–18. Using the walls, floor, and ceiling of your classroom and their intersections, describe a model of the figure.

5. a line

6. a point

7. two intersecting lines

8. two lines that do not intersect

9. a line and a point on that line

10. a line and a point not on that line

11. three lines that intersect at one point

12. three lines, none of which intersect

13. a plane

14. a plane and a line in that plane

15. a plane and a line that intersects that plane at one point

16. a plane and a point not in that plane

17. two intersecting planes

18. two planes that do not intersect

Ⓑ **19–28.** Refer to the drawing. From the list, choose a word or phrase that correctly completes the statement.

a. point

b. line

c. plane

d. contains

e. is on (or in)

f. is not in

g. intersect(s)

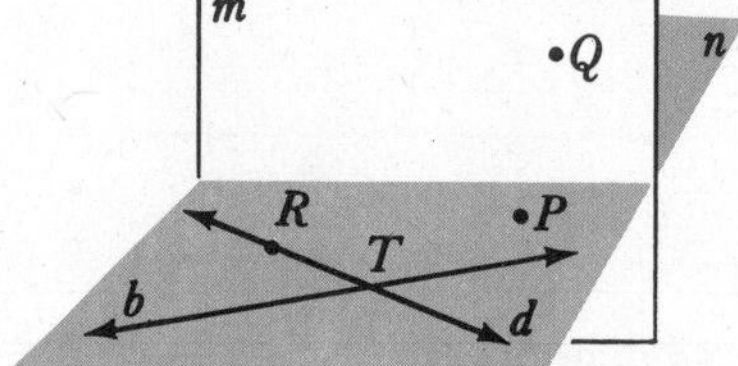

19. P is a ______.

20. n is a ______.

21. b is a ______.

22. Q is a ______.

23. Point T ______ line b.

24. Line d ______ point T.

25. Lines d and b ______.

26. Point Q ______ plane n.

27. Point R ______ line d and plane n.

28. Line d ______ plane n.

29–42. Draw and label the figure described.

29. Line ℓ intersects $\overleftrightarrow{DP}$ at P.

30. $\overleftrightarrow{SR}$ intersects line n at R.

31. $\overleftrightarrow{BC}$ is in plane m.

32. Plane r contains $\overleftrightarrow{AD}$.

33. Plane n contains lines ℓ and m, but lines ℓ and m do not intersect.

34. Lines a and b are in plane w, but lines a and b do not intersect.

Ⓒ **35.** Points A, B, and C are in plane n, but point D is not.

36. Plane r contains $\overleftrightarrow{EF}$ but not points M and N.

37. Planes m and n intersect at $\overleftrightarrow{AB}$.

38. Plane t contains line GH but not $\overleftrightarrow{CH}$.

39. Planes a, b, and c intersect at line ℓ.

40. $\overleftrightarrow{AB}$, $\overleftrightarrow{AC}$, $\overleftrightarrow{AD}$, and $\overleftrightarrow{AE}$ intersect.

41. Line ℓ does not intersect plane n.

42. Planes x and y do not intersect.

43. Does geometric space extend indefinitely?

44. What could be used as a model of a small portion of geometric space?

45. Show how you think space might be represented by a drawing.

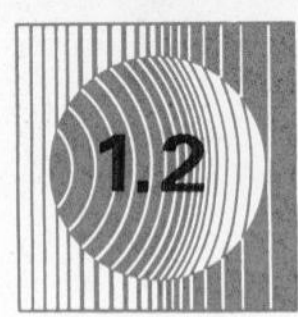

1.2 The Real Numbers

In geometry, distance and size are described using real numbers. A **real number** is any number for which there is a decimal expansion.

Integers ($\cdots$, -4, -3, -2, -1, 0, 1, 2, 3, 4, $\cdots$) have decimal expansions.	$2 = 2.000\cdots$ $-5 = -5.000\cdots$	Every integer is a rational number, since $2 = \frac{2}{1}$ and $-5 = \frac{-5}{1}$.
Rational numbers (ratios of integers) have repeating decimal expansions.	$\frac{3}{2} = 1.5000\cdots$ $-\frac{1}{3} = -0.333\cdots$	Every real number is either a rational number or an irrational number.
Irrational numbers (numbers that are not ratios of integers) have nonrepeating decimal expansions.	$\sqrt{2} = 1.414213\cdots$ $-\sqrt{5} = -2.236\cdots$	

To find a rational number between any two distinct (different) rational numbers, you can take their average (one half their sum).

$$\tfrac{1}{2}(2 + 3) = 2\tfrac{1}{2}$$
$$\tfrac{1}{2}(2 + 2\tfrac{1}{2}) = 2\tfrac{1}{4}$$
$$\tfrac{1}{2}(2 + 2\tfrac{1}{4}) = 2\tfrac{1}{8}$$
$$\vdots$$

The averaging can be continued indefinitely.

So between any two distinct rational numbers there is another rational number. (In fact, between any two distinct rational numbers there is also an irrational number.) So the set of rational numbers, and consequently the set of real numbers, is an **infinite set**. No matter how many real numbers are named, more can be named.

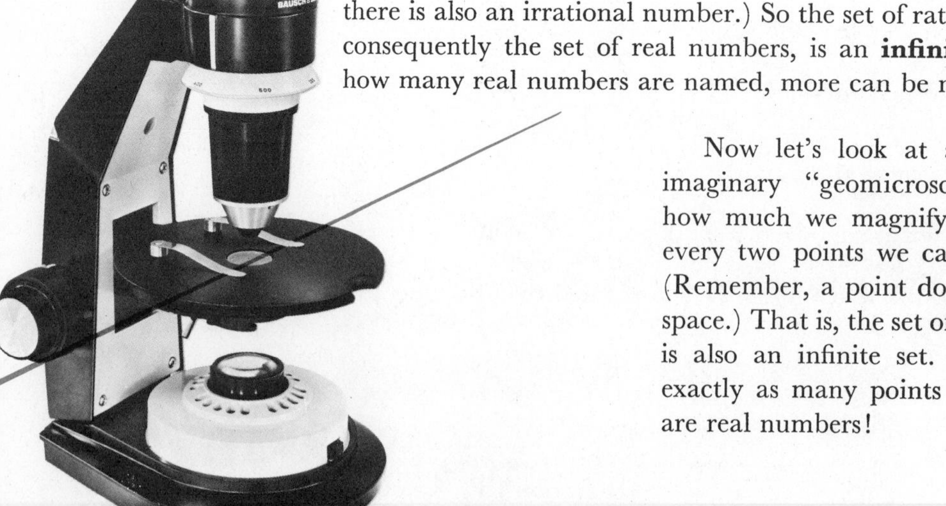

Now let's look at a line through an imaginary "geomicroscope." No matter how much we magnify the line, between every two points we can see more points. (Remember, a point doesn't "use up" any space.) That is, the set of all points on a line is also an infinite set. In fact, there are exactly as many points on a line as there are real numbers!

Courtesy Bausch & Lomb

By matching each point on a line with a real number, we can make a **real number line**. The number matched with a point is its **coordinate**. In a diagram, we label only a few of the points with their coordinates, using whatever part of the line we need, as shown below.

Examples:

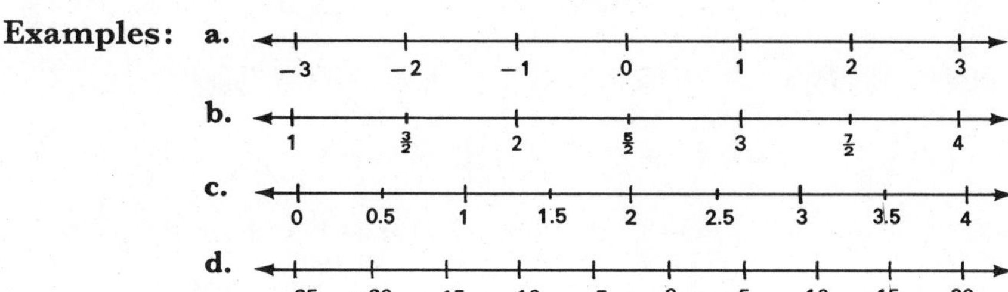

One of the ways in which real numbers are related is their **order**.

In words	In symbols	On the real number line
2 *is less than* 3.	$2 < 3$	2 is to the left of 3.
3 *is greater than* 2.	$3 > 2$	3 is to the right of 2.

The real numbers also have the following properties.

Let *a*, *b*, and *c* stand for any real numbers.	**Examples:**
$a < b, a = b$, or $a > b$ ◀ Exactly one of these is true.	• $3 < 2, 3 = 2$, or $3 > 2$ • $\frac{1}{2} < 0.5, \frac{1}{2} = 0.5$, or $\frac{1}{2} > 0.5$
If $a < b$ and $b < c$, then $a < c$.	$2 < 5$ and $5 < 6$, so $2 < 6$
If $a < b$, then $b > a$.	$4 < 7$, so $7 > 4$

Exercises 1.2

Ⓐ **1–7.** True or False?

1. All integers are rational numbers.

2. Every irrational number is a real number.

3. Some rational numbers are not real numbers.

4. Between any two points in a line there is another point.

5. There are more points on a line than there are real numbers.

6. *Is less than* is used to express order.

7. There is a smallest integer.

8–16. Tell how to read each statement. Then tell whether it is true.

8. $3 < 5$ **9.** $-4 > -2$ **10.** $0 < -3$ **11.** $2 > 0$

12. $-2 < -3$, $-2 = -3$, or $-2 > -3$ **13.** $-1 < 1$ **14.** $4 > -1$

15. If $n < 2$ and $2 < 3$, then $n < 3$. **16.** If $x < 5$, then $5 < x$.

Ⓑ **17–28.** Name a rational number that is between the two given numbers.

17. 5, 6 **18.** 7, 8 **19.** -3, -4 **20.** -6, -7

21. $1\frac{1}{2}$, 2 **22.** 3, $3\frac{1}{2}$ **23.** $3\frac{1}{4}$, $3\frac{1}{2}$ **24.** $5\frac{1}{2}$, $5\frac{3}{4}$

25. 1.2, 1.3 **26.** 2.4, 2.5 **27.** 0, $-\frac{1}{3}$ **28.** $-\frac{1}{4}$, 0

29–36. Draw a real number line and label the points described.

29. integers from 3 to 10 **30.** integers from 5 to 12

31. integers from -8 to 0 **32.** integers from -12 to -4

33. $0, \frac{1}{2}, \frac{2}{2}, \frac{3}{2}, \frac{4}{2}, \frac{5}{2}, \frac{6}{2}, \frac{7}{2}$ **34.** $0, \frac{1}{3}, \frac{2}{3}, \frac{3}{3}, \frac{4}{3}, \frac{5}{3}, \frac{6}{3}, \frac{7}{3}$

35. 0.1, 0.2, 0.3, 0.4, 0.5, 0.6 **36.** 1.0, 1.1, 1.2, 1.3, 1.4, 1.5

37–48. Which symbol, $<$, $=$, or $>$, should replace the ◍ ?

37. 13 ◍ 11 **38.** 27 ◍ 33 **39.** $4 + 1$ ◍ 5 **40.** $6 + 3$ ◍ 10

41. $\frac{17}{3}$ ◍ 5 **42.** $\frac{14}{3}$ ◍ $4\frac{1}{3}$ **43.** 2.6 ◍ $2\frac{3}{5}$ **44.** $13 + 4$ ◍ $24 - 6$

Ⓒ **45.** $\sqrt{5}$ ◍ 2 **46.** $\sqrt{5}$ ◍ 3 **47.** 1 ◍ $\sqrt{3}$ **48.** $\sqrt{3}$ ◍ 2

A B C D E F G H

0

49. Match each point with its coordinate.
3, $\sqrt{5}$, 1, $2\sqrt{2}$, 4, 2, $\sqrt{3}$, $\sqrt{11}$

CROSS-NUMBER PUZZLE

Copy the puzzle onto graph paper. Then use the numbered clues to solve it. If a result is negative, write the negative sign with the first digit. (So if either the ACROSS or the DOWN clue gives a negative result, both clues should give a negative result.)

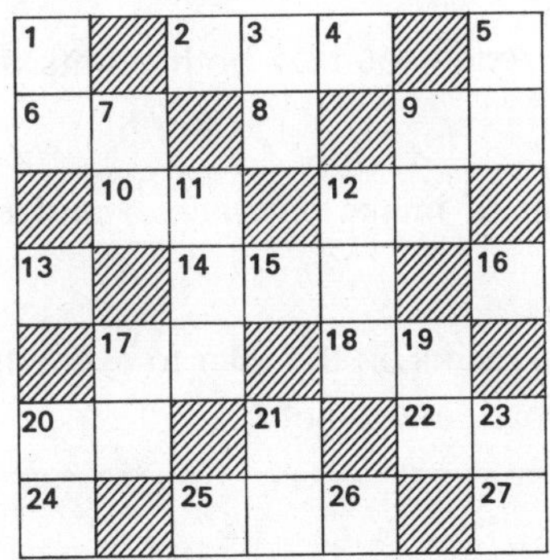

ACROSS

1. $3 + 5$
2. $21 \cdot 6$
5. $13 - 4$
6. $48 \div 4$
8. $-3 + 7$
9. $-4 - 8$
10. $1 \cdot 21$
12. $27 + (-4)$
13. $\frac{1}{3} \cdot 3$
14. 10^2
16. $(-3)^2$
17. $(-2)(7)$
18. $-7 - (-49)$
20. $-44 \div 2$
21. $-1 \cdot 3$
22. $3(13 - 4)$
24. $\sqrt{16}$
25. $1 \cdot 350$
27. 2^3

DOWN

1. 9^2
2. $-1(3 - 4)$
3. $(-4)(-6)$
4. $(-54) \div (-9)$
5. $23 \cdot 2^2$
7. $5^2 - 3$
9. $-9 + (-4)$
11. $111 - (-3)$
12. $4 \cdot 51$
13. $\frac{5}{2} \cdot \frac{2}{5}$
15. $17 \cdot 0$
16. $(-45) \div (-5)$
17. $72 \div (-6)$
19. $-11(-2)$
20. $-26 - (-2)$
21. $5 \cdot (-7)$
23. $3(-13)(-2)$
25. $\frac{1}{3} \cdot 9$
26. $-7 + 7$

Geometry Around the World

In ancient Greece, the word *geōmetrein* meant "to measure the earth." From that word came the Greek word *geōmetria* for the subject we call *geometry*.

In France it is *géométrie*.
In Mexico it is *geometría*.
In Germany it is *geometrie*.
And in Russia it is Геометрия.

See if you can find out what geometry is called in some language other than the ones shown here.

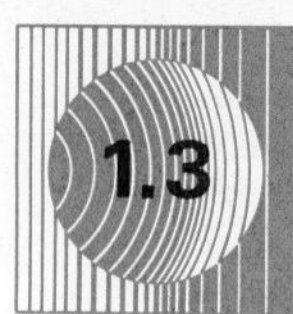

Distance

The edge of a ruler represents a real number line. To measure the distance between points A and B, you could

1. Lay a ruler so its edge touches both points and the end is at A, as shown below.

2. Count the number of marks between A and B that are labeled with whole numbers.

3. Use the additional marks on the ruler to estimate the distance between the last mark counted and point B.

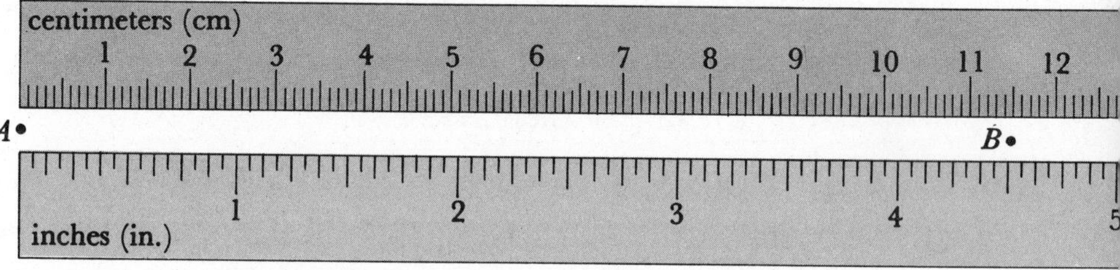

But the whole-number marks are not the same distance apart on all rulers! To state the distance between A and B, you must tell which ruler you used. That is, you must name the *unit of measure*. On one of the rulers above, the whole-number marks are one inch apart, so the unit of measure is the *inch*. On the other ruler, the unit of measure is the *centimeter*.

The distance between points A and B is about $4\frac{1}{2}$ inches or about 11.5 centimeters. (Why do we say *about*?)

Inches and centimeters belong to the two most commonly used systems of measurement. Here are some units of distance in these systems.

Customary (English) System	Metric (SI) System
12 inches (in.) = 1 foot (ft)	0.001 meter (m) = 1 millimeter (mm)
3 feet (ft) = 1 yard (yd)	0.01 meter (m) = 1 centimeter (cm)
5280 feet (ft) = 1 mile (mi)	1000 meters (m) = 1 kilometer (km)

Most ideas in geometry apply to any system of measurement. So we do not always state a unit of measure. But if no units are stated, we do assume that the same unit is used for all measurements in the same problem.

Two rulers are used to measure the distance between M and N below. This distance, written MN or NM, can be found in each case by subtracting.

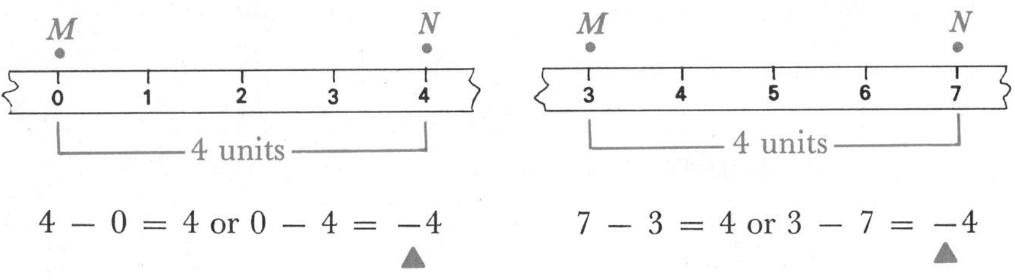

$4 - 0 = 4$ or $0 - 4 = -4$ $\quad\quad$ $7 - 3 = 4$ or $3 - 7 = -4$

To state distance, disregard the negative sign.

Harrison Forman

Another way to say *disregard the negative sign* is to say *take the absolute value*. The symbol $|\ \ |$ is used to indicate absolute value.

Examples

If a number is nonnegative, it equals its absolute value. ▶ If $n \geq 0$, $|n| = n$. **a.** $|4| = 4$ **b.** $|0| = 0$

If a number is negative, its absolute value is its opposite. ▶ If $n < 0$, $|n| = -n$. **a.** $|-4| = -(-4) = 4$ **b.** $|5 - 9| = |-4| = -(-4) = 4$

Since any real number has only one absolute value, we say its absolute value is **unique.**

The important ideas in this section and the preceding section are summarized in the following statements. We call these statements *postulates*. A **postulate** is a statement that is accepted as true without proof. We will say more about postulates in later sections.

Distance Postulate

For every pair of points there is a unique nonnegative number, called the **distance** between them.

Ruler Postulate

The points of a line can be matched with the real numbers so that

1. for every point on the line there is exactly one real number coordinate;
2. for every real number there is exactly one point on the line;
3. the distance between any two points is the absolute value of the difference of their coordinates.

Ruler Placement Postulate

> For any two points P and R on a line, a ruler can be placed so that the coordinate of P is zero and the coordinate of R is a positive number.

Two points that are the same distance from a third point are **equidistant** from the third point.

A• — 2.5 cm — •P
B• — 2.5 cm — •P

Exercises 1.3

Ⓐ **1–10.** Complete each sentence.

1. A statement that is accepted as true without proof is a ______.

2. According to the ______ Postulate, for every point on a line there is exactly one real number coordinate.

3. The most commonly used systems of measurement are the customary (English) system and the ______ system.

4. The ______ of -3 is written $|-3|$.

5. The ______ between two points is the absolute value of the difference of their coordinates.

6. The distance between two points cannot be -5 because, according to the Distance Postulate, distance is ______.

7. If the same unit of measure is used, the distance between two points cannot be both 6 and 7 because the distance is ______.

8. According to the ______ Postulate, if the coordinate of R is zero, a positive coordinate can always be assigned to another point S.

9. AB and BA both mean the ______ points A and B.

10. If MR is 3.2 and MS is 3.2, then R and S are ______ from M.

11–28. Find the absolute value.

11. $|6|$ **12.** $|8|$ **13.** $|-9|$

14. $|-10|$ **15.** $|6 - 2|$ **16.** $|3 - 1|$

Ⓑ **17.** $|12 - 5|$ **18.** $|17 - 6|$ **19.** $|23 - 9|$

20. $|21 - 7|$ **21.** $|5 - 13|$ **22.** $|4 - 7|$

23. $|13 - 13|$ **24.** $|24 - 24|$ **25.** $|2 - 18|$

26. $|5 - 12|$ **27.** $|0 - 27|$ **28.** $|0 - 19|$

29–55. The coordinates of *P* and *R* are listed. Find *PR*.

29. P: 0 R: 7 **30.** P: 0 R: 9 **31.** P: 0 R: 15

32. P: 0 R: 18 **33.** P: 12 R: 0 **34.** P: 6 R: 0

35. P: 4 R: 15 **36.** P: 7 R: 13 **37.** P: 18 R: 3

38. P: 21 R: 14 **39.** P: 15 R: 6 **40.** P: 7 R: 3

41. P: 7 R: 13 **42.** P: 8 R: 15 **43.** P: 18 R: 112

44. P: 19 R: 113 **45.** P: 23 R: 12 **46.** P: 25 R: 16

Ⓒ **47.** P: 5 R: 5 **48.** P: 3 R: 3 **49.** P: 72 R: -16

50. P: 56 R: -18 **51.** P: -37 R: 44 **52.** P: -23 R: 52

53. P: -12 R: -51 **54.** P: -13 R: -72 **55.** P: -7 R: -7

56–59. Express as an integer.

56. $2 + |-7| - |3|$ **57.** $|-5| + |5 - 2| - |-7 + 4|$

58. $||-2 - 3| + (-5) - 7|$ **59.** $9 - |3 + |-2 - 3| - 8|$

Highway Coordinates

Many highways are marked with mileposts that tell motorists how far they have traveled from some point of reference (often the state line).

A stalled car is reported at milepost 56. There is an emergency service truck parked at milepost 8 and another one parked at milepost 123. How far would each truck have to travel to reach the stalled car?

The truck closer to the stalled car goes to the aid of the motorist. It then immediately answers another call at milepost 31. How far has the truck traveled from its original location?

Gene Kuechmann

1.4 Defining Terms

Beetle Bailey accepts *greenstuff* as an undefined term. In geometry we also accept some terms, such as *point*, *line*, and *plane*, as undefined terms. This is done to avoid circular definitions. If we tried to define *point*, for example, we would eventually come back to the term *point*.

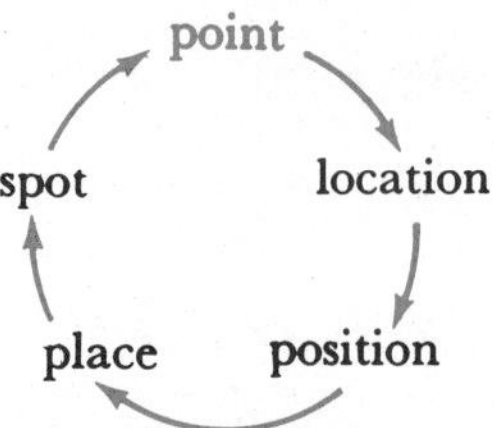

The terms we leave undefined are used, however, in defining other geometry terms. Here are some of those definitions.

DEFINITION (The word being defined is in heavy type.)	EXAMPLE
Collinear points are points on the same line. **Noncollinear** points are points not all on the same line.	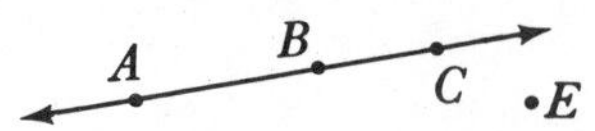 *A*, *B*, and *C* are *collinear.* *A*, *B*, and *E* are *noncollinear.*
Coplanar points are points in the same plane. **Noncoplanar** points are points not all in the same plane.	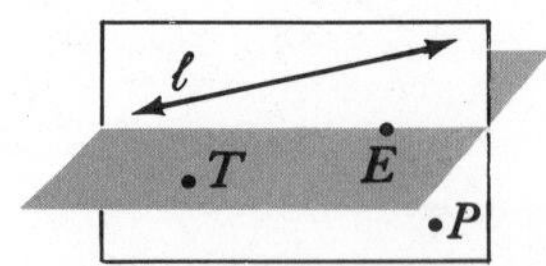 *P*, *E*, and line ℓ are *coplanar.* *P*, ℓ, and *T* are *noncoplanar.*
Let *A*, *B*, and *C* be distinct collinear points. $AB + BC = AC$ means *B* is **between** *A* and *C*. *A* and *C* are **on opposite sides of** *B*. *B* and *C* are **on the same side of** *A*.	*A* *B* *C* $\underbrace{AB + BC}_{=AC}$

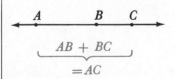

Segment DE (symbol: $\overline{DE}$) is the figure that contains D, E, and all points between D and E. Points D and E are the **endpoints** of $\overline{DE}$. The **length** of a segment is the distance between its endpoints.	D E segment DE (or $\overline{DE}$) with length DE
$\overline{DE}$ and $\overline{ED}$ name the same segment. $\overline{DPE}$ means P is on $\overline{DE}$ between D and E. $\overline{DRE}$ means R is on $\overline{DE}$ between D and E. $\overline{DPRE}$ means P is between D and R on $\overline{DE}$.	D P R E $\overline{DE} = \overline{ED}$ $= \overline{DPE} = \overline{DRE} = \overline{DPRE}$
The **midpoint** of a segment is the point that is between the endpoints and equidistant from them. Any figure that intersects a segment only at its midpoint **bisects** the segment.	ℓ D M E $DM = ME$ M is the midpoint of $\overline{DE}$. Line ℓ bisects $\overline{DE}$.
Ray FG (symbol: $\overrightarrow{FG}$) is the figure that contains F and every point on the same side of F as G. Point F is the **endpoint** of $\overrightarrow{FG}$.	F G ray FG (or $\overrightarrow{FG}$)
Opposite rays are two distinct rays that are collinear and have a common endpoint.	B P A $\overrightarrow{PB}$ and $\overrightarrow{PA}$ are opposite rays.

Notice that these definitions make use of

1. ordinary (dictionary-defined) words.

2. undefined (or primitive) terms, such as *point* and *contains*.

3. geometry terms already defined.

For example, consider the definition of **ray**.

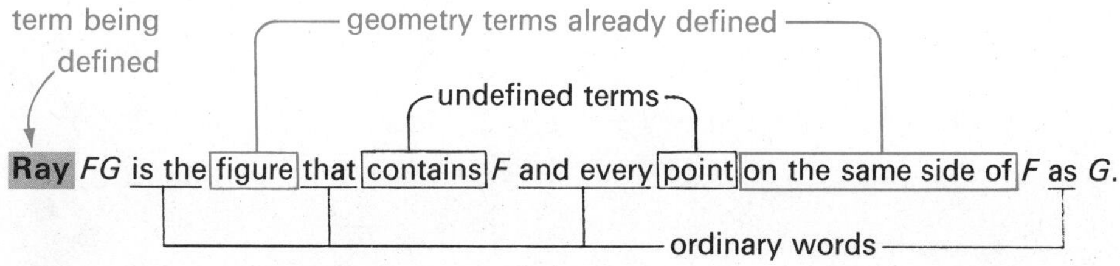

Exercises 1.4

Ⓐ **1–12.** Tell whether the term, as used in the definitions on pages 14–15, is an *ordinary word*, and *undefined term*, or a *defined geometry term*.

1. ray	**2.** every	**3.** line
4. same side of	**5.** and	**6.** bisects
7. plane	**8.** endpoint	**9.** contains
10. point	**11.** collinear	**12.** segment

13–18. Each of these terms has been defined earlier in this chapter. Give the number of the page on which each definition can be found.

13. figure	**14.** postulate	**15.** distance
16. coordinate	**17.** equidistant	**18.** absolute value

19. What term in the definition of *ray* tells you that the points on a ray are collinear?

20. What term in the definition of *midpoint of a segment* tells you that the midpoint is on the segment?

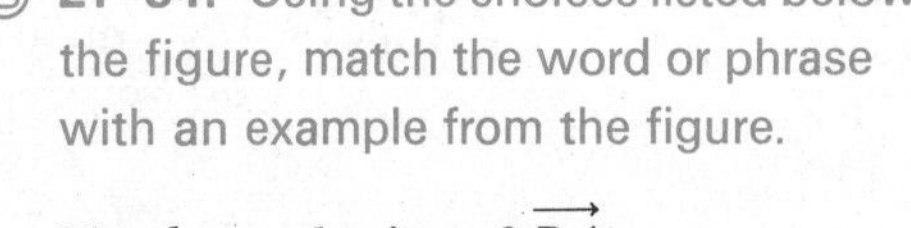

Ⓑ **21–34.** Using the choices listed below the figure, match the word or phrase with an example from the figure.

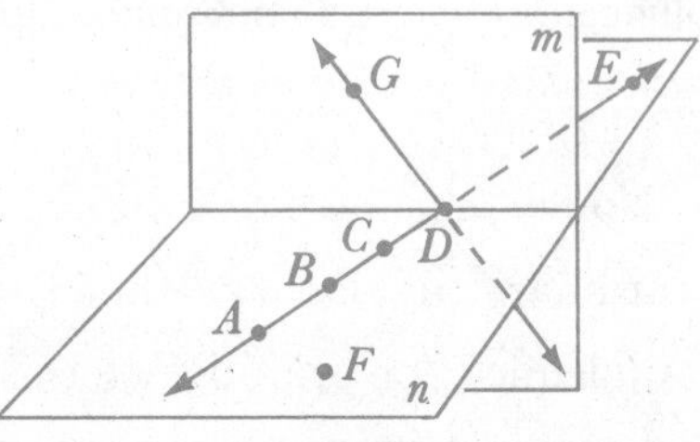

$AD = DE$

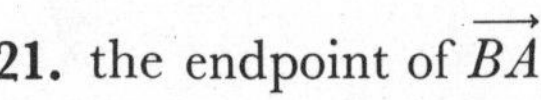

21. the endpoint of $\overrightarrow{BA}$

22. an endpoint of $\overline{AD}$

23. the midpoint of $\overline{AE}$

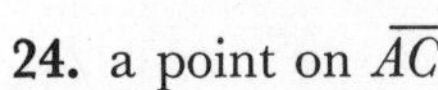

24. a point on $\overline{AC}$

25. three collinear points

26. a point between A and D

27. a point between B and E

28. another name for $\overline{AE}$

29. another name for $\overline{EC}$

a. D **b.** E **c.** B **d.** A, E **e.** $\overline{CE}$

f. A, C, G **g.** A, C, E **h.** A, F, C **i.** $\overline{ACE}$

30. a point on the same side of C as D

31. two points on opposite sides of C

32. the endpoint of the ray opposite $\overrightarrow{DC}$

33. three points not all in plane n

34. three coplanar, noncollinear points

© 35–40. Refer to the figure for Exercises 21–34. Name the following.

35. two points equidistant from D

36. a point on $\overleftrightarrow{AD}$ but not on $\overline{AD}$

37. the intersection of $\overline{AC}$ and $\overline{BD}$

38. the intersection of $\overline{FD}$ and $\overline{DB}$

39. the intersection of $\overleftrightarrow{FD}$ and $\overleftrightarrow{AC}$

40. a line that bisects $\overline{AE}$

41. Name the segment whose endpoints are M and N to show that C and D are on the segment and that C is between D and N.

Time Out

If the hands of the clock are opposite rays when the clock strikes the hour, what time is it?

1. Name three undefined geometric terms.

2–7. Refer to the figure. Name an example of:

2. a line

3. three noncollinear points

4. a segment

5. a ray with endpoint A

6. a ray opposite $\overrightarrow{PA}$

7. a point between A and B

8. $\frac{2}{3}$ is (a rational, an irrational) number.

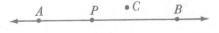

9. If $0 < 3$ and $3 < x$, then 0 ($<$, $=$, $>$) x.

10. A (figure, postulate) is accepted as true without proof.

11. The (coordinate, absolute value) of -7 is 7.

12. An endless light beam is a (model, figure) of a line.

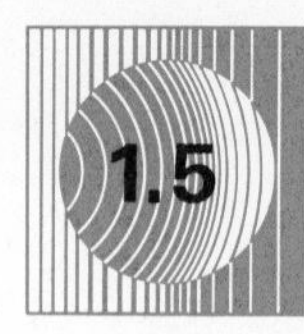

1.5 Reaching Conclusions

We've checked more than 30 of these footprints, and they've been fakes. They're all fakes.

By looking at a number of examples that have something in common, we can discover a possible conclusion. Reasoning from examples to a conclusion is called **inductive reasoning.**

- Sometimes we can check every example. Then we know that the conclusion reached by inductive reasoning is correct.

- If we cannot check every example, we cannot be sure a conclusion reached by inductive reasoning is correct.

- If we can find **one** example that does not agree with the conclusion, we know the conclusion is *not* correct.

Pictures can also suggest a possible conclusion. But again the conclusion is not necessarily correct. Most people looking at the *optical illusions* shown here reach conclusions that do not agree with the facts.

A

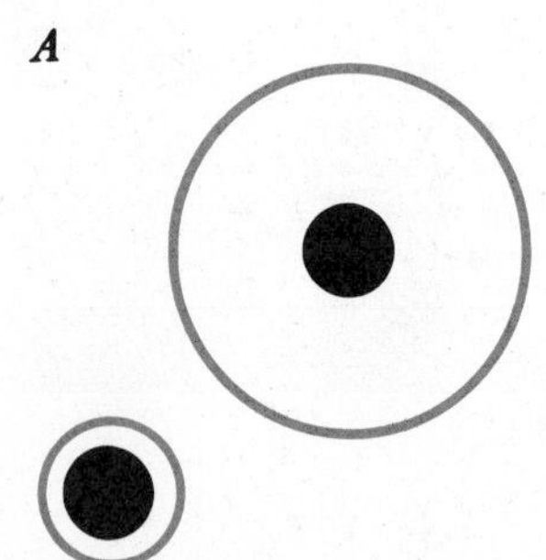

Which black spot is larger?

B

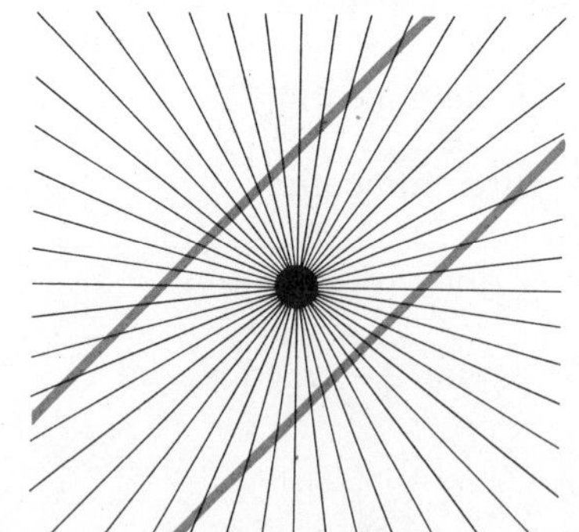

Are the heavy lines curved or straight?

C

If appearances and reasoning from examples do not always lead to correct conclusions, what does? In geometry, conclusions are accepted as true if they can be reached by *deductive reasoning*.

Deductive reasoning follows this pattern.

1. Start with agreed - upon statements (postulates and definitions).
2. Set up conditions (the hypothesis).
3. Use logical reasoning.
4. Find a result (the conclusion).

The statement of a hypothesis (step 2 above) and its logical conclusion (step 4) is called a **theorem**.

In deductive reasoning, different postulates can lead to different conclusions.

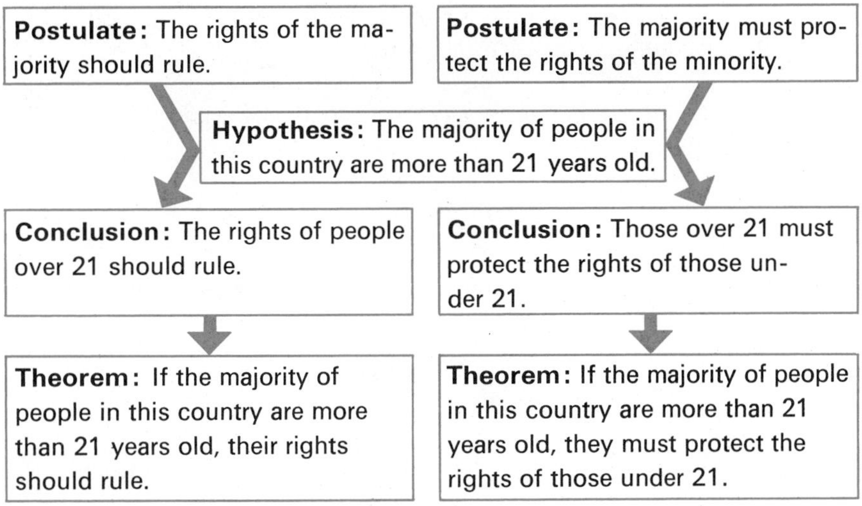

Postulate: The rights of the majority should rule.

Postulate: The majority must protect the rights of the minority.

Hypothesis: The majority of people in this country are more than 21 years old.

Conclusion: The rights of people over 21 should rule.

Conclusion: Those over 21 must protect the rights of those under 21.

Theorem: If the majority of people in this country are more than 21 years old, their rights should rule.

Theorem: If the majority of people in this country are more than 21 years old, they must protect the rights of those under 21.

Exercises 1.5

Ⓐ **1.** Reaching a conclusion on the basis of a number of examples is called ______ reasoning.

2. How many examples that disagree with a conclusion are needed to show that the conclusion is not true?

3. Reaching a conclusion on the basis of postulates, definitions, and a hypothesis is called ______ reasoning.

4. In geometry, a conclusion reached by ______ reasoning is accepted as true.

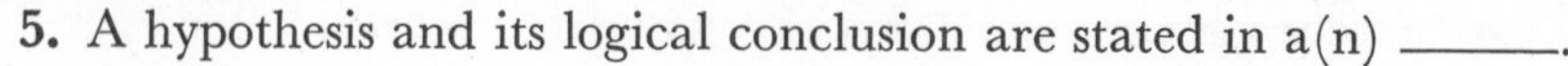

5. A hypothesis and its logical conclusion are stated in a(n) ______.

6. Using the same hypothesis but different ______ can lead to different conclusions.

Ⓑ **7–10.** What would have to happen to show that the conclusion is not true?

7. The first 39 Presidents of the United States were men.

   Conclusion: A woman cannot be President of the United States.

Grant Heilman

8. The first 36 Presidents of the United States were born east of the Rocky Mountains.

   Conclusion: A person born west of the Rocky Mountains cannot be elected President of the United States.

9. The Passenger Pigeon, a bird once common to North America, was last seen in 1914.

   Conclusion: The Passenger Pigeon is extinct.

10. Every map that has ever been drawn can be colored with four colors so that no two regions colored alike touch at more than one point.

    Conclusion: Every map can be colored with four colors.

Camerique

11–14. Use one of the postulates below and the given hypothesis to reach a conclusion by deductive reasoning.

Postulate a: An effective punishment deters crime.

Postulate b: To be protected, an animal should belong to an endangered species.

11. *Hypothesis:* Capital punishment deters crime.

12. *Hypothesis:* Bengal tigers belong to an endangered species.

Grant Heilman

13. *Hypothesis:* Capital punishment does not deter crime.

14. *Hypothesis:* Field mice do not belong to an endangered species.

15–18. Let x and y stand for real numbers. Give an example from the real numbers that contradicts the conclusion.

15. $x \cdot \frac{1}{x} = 1$ 16. $\sqrt{y^2} = y$ 17. $x^2 > x$ 18. $\frac{0}{y} = 0$

19–22. Tell which postulate, a or b, leads to the given conclusion.

Postulate a: No line intersects line ℓ.

Postulate b: Some line intersects line ℓ at point P.

19. P is on line ℓ.

20. Every line through P intersects line ℓ.

21. If ℓ and m are not the same line and point A is on line m, point A is not on line ℓ.

22. If point T is on line ℓ, point T is not on any other line.

Ⓒ 23. Find an example that contradicts this conclusion:
If n is a positive integer, then $n^2 - n + 41$ is a prime integer. (That is, the only positive integers that divide into it without a remainder are 1 and $n^2 - n + 41$.)

24. Do library research to find an example that contradicts the conclusion in Exercise 8.

Algebra Review

Review this skill:

- *solving equations using one operation*

Solve.

1. $x + 2 = 7$	2. $5 + y = 13$	3. $12 = 3 + x$
4. $n - 3 = 1$	5. $10 - t = 4$	6. $3 = y - 6$
7. $4a = 12$	8. $18 = 3n$	9. $\frac{1}{3}y = 2$
10. $8 = \frac{4}{7}x$	11. $7y = \frac{2}{3}$	12. $\frac{1}{2}n = \frac{1}{3}$
13. $\frac{7}{2} = \frac{3}{4}a$	14. $x + \frac{2}{5} = 3$	15. $2.4 = 0.6 + n$
16. $a - 2.3 = 15.6$	17. $9\frac{1}{2} - y = 4$	18. $0.5x = 12$
19. $3 = \frac{a}{7}$	20. $\frac{5}{n} = 1$	

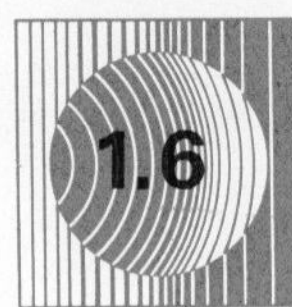

1.6 Reasoning in Algebra

The properties of real numbers on page 7 are postulates of algebra. (In algebra, the synonym *axiom* is usually used for the word *postulate.*) Here are some more postulates of algebra.

	Property of Addition	Property of Multiplication
Closure	The sum of two real numbers is a unique real number.	The product of two real numbers is a unique real number.
Commutative	Any two real numbers may be added in either order.	Any two real numbers may be multiplied in either order.
Associative	Any three real numbers may be added by grouping the first two or the last two numbers.	Any three real numbers may be multiplied by grouping the first two or the last two numbers.
Identity	The sum of 0 and any real number is the real number. (0 is the **additive identity**.)	The product of 1 and any real number is the real number. (1 is the **multiplicative identity**.)
Inverse	The sum of a real number a and its **opposite** $-a$ is 0.	The product of a nonzero real number b and its **reciprocal** $\frac{1}{b}$ is 1.

Distributive Property (multiplication over addition) When the sum of two real numbers is multiplied by a third real number, to find the result either

- add first, then multiply. ▶ $3(2 + 5) = 3 \cdot 7 = 21$
- multiply each addend, then add. ▶ $3(2 + 5) = 3 \cdot 2 + 3 \cdot 5 = 21$

There are four properties of equality that are also postulates.

Any number equals itself.	$3 = 3$
If two numbers are equal, the equation may be written with either number first.	If $2 + 1 = 3$, then $3 = 2 + 1$.
If two numbers are both equal to a third number, they are equal to each other.	If $x = 3$ and $3 = y$, then $x = y$.
If two numbers are equal, either one may be substituted for the other.	If $x + y = 6$ and $x = 2$, then $2 + y = 6$.

Many theorems in algebra result from these postulates and deductive reasoning. The Multiplication Property of Zero is one such theorem.

SYMBOLS

Imagine how thick this book would be if no symbols other than words were used! Look at these equations from the Algebra Review on page 21.

1. $x + 2 = 7$	**One.** When two is added to some number, the result is seven.
5. $10 - t = 4$	**Five.** The difference when some number is subtracted from ten is four.
7. $4a = 12$	**Seven.** Four times some number is twelve.

You can see why a word or phrase that is used over and over again in mathematics is usually replaced by a shorter symbol. Here are some symbols used in geometry. Can you read them?

$\overleftrightarrow{AB}$ $\quad \overrightarrow{DE}$ $\quad \triangle ABC$ $\quad \odot P$  $\ell \perp \overleftrightarrow{AB}$ $\quad \overleftrightarrow{DE} \parallel \overleftrightarrow{EF}$ $\quad \angle A$  $m\angle C$

If you travel in a foreign country, the words you see may look strange. But many of the symbols will look familiar. What do these symbols, all found on signs in many countries, mean?

Here are some symbols found on shipping cartons. Can you figure out what they mean?

 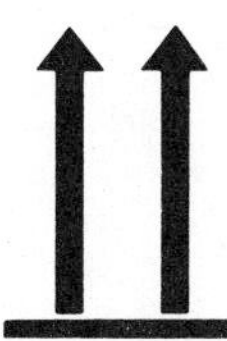 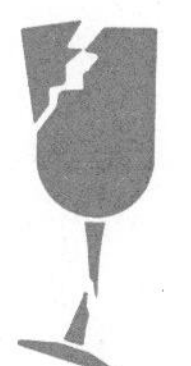 

Chemists, architects, stenographers, and people in many other occupations use symbols with special meanings in those occupations. In fact, even hobos have their own symbols.

This is not a safe place.

OK, All right

Good place for a handout

Good road to follow

Henry Dreyfuss, *Symbols Sourcebook*, McGraw-Hill Book Company

Multiplication Property of Zero If n is a real number, $0 \cdot n = 0$.

Chain of equivalent expressions	The reason each expression is equivalent to the preceding one
$0 \cdot n = 0 \cdot n + 0$	Identity Prop. of Addition
$= 0 \cdot n + [n + (-n)]$	$0 = n + (-n)$ by the Inverse Prop. of Add.
$= [0 \cdot n + n] + (-n)$	Associative Prop. of Add.
$= [0 \cdot n + 1 \cdot n] + (-n)$	$n = 1 \cdot n$ by the Identity Prop. of Mult.
$= [0 + 1]n + (-n)$	$[0 \cdot n + 1 \cdot n] = [0 + 1]n$ by the Distrib. Prop.
$= 1 \cdot n + (-n)$	$0 + 1 = 1$ by the Identity Prop. of Add.
$= n + (-n)$	$1 \cdot n = n$ by the Identity Prop. of Mult.
$= 0$	$n + (-n) = 0$ by the Inverse Prop. of Add.

Each reason in the right-hand column above is a postulate. But now that the Multiplication Property of Zero has been shown to result from the postulates, it can be used as a reason later. Definitions can also be used as reasons.

Deductive reasoning can also be used in solving equations. Usually, reasons are not written, and some steps are combined. But the solution *can be* written in as much detail as we wish. There are four properties of equality that are especially useful in solving equations.

	$a = b$	◀ Given an equation, you can:
Addition Property of =	$a + c = b + c$	◀ add the same number to both sides
Subtraction Property of =	$a - c = b - c$	◀ subtract the same number from both sides
Multiplication Property of =	$ca = cb$	◀ multiply both sides by the same number
Division Property of =	If $c \neq 0$, $\frac{a}{c} = \frac{b}{c}$	◀ divide both sides by the same number (not 0)

($\neq$: is not equal to)

We will solve $4x = 12$.

$4x = 12$	Given
$\frac{1}{4}(4x) = \frac{1}{4}(12)$	Multiplication Property of =
$\frac{1}{4}(4x) = 3$	Substitution of 3 for $\frac{1}{4}(12)$
$(\frac{1}{4} \cdot 4)x = 3$	Associative Property of Multiplication
$1x = 3$	$\frac{1}{4} \cdot 4 = 1$ by the Inverse Prop. of Mult.
$x = 3$	$1x = x$ by the Identity Prop. of Mult.

Exercises 1.6

Ⓐ 1. The additive identity is ______.

2. The reciprocal of $\frac{1}{2}$ is ______.

3. The multiplicative identity is ______.

4. The opposite of -3 is ______.

5. The property expressed $0 \cdot n = 0$ is the ______.

6. In algebra, postulates are usually called ______.

7–16. Let a, b, and c be any real numbers. Then each statement below expresses a property of addition or multiplication. Identify that property.

7. $(a + b) + c = a + (b + c)$

8. $a \cdot \frac{1}{a} = \frac{1}{a} \cdot a = 1$ if $a \neq 0$

9. $a + 0 = 0 + a = a$

10. $ab = ba$

11. $a \cdot 1 = 1 \cdot a = a$

12. $a(b + c) = ab + ac$

13. ab is a unique real number.

14. $a + b = b + a$

15. $(ab)c = a(bc)$

16. $a + (-a) = (-a) + a = 0$

17–42. Which property is illustrated? (Letters stand for any real numbers.)

17. If $4 = n$, then $n = 4$.

18. If $x = 4$, then $2x = 8$.

19. $7 + 1 = 1 + 7$

20. If $3y = 9$, then $y = 3$.

21. If $x - 2 = 9$, then $x = 11$.

22. $7 + a$ is a unique real number.

23. $x + 1 = x + 1$

24. $0 \cdot x = 0$

Ⓑ 25. $3n + 6 = 3(n + 2)$

26. $8 + (x + 2) = (8 + x) + 2$

27. $x \cdot 7y = 7yx$

28. $(n + 3) = (n + 3) + 0$

29. $(4 + x) + 0 = 4 + x$

30. $12 + 4a = 4(3 + a)$

31. $(9 + a) + 0 = 9 + (a + 0)$

32. $3 = 1 \cdot 3$

33. $\frac{1}{2 + n}(2 + n) = 1, n \neq -2$

34. $(x + 6)\frac{1}{x + 6} = 1, x \neq -6$

35. $p = 1 \cdot p$

36. $a \cdot 2b = 2ba$

37. $4(2n) = 8n$

38. $6(3a) = 18a$

39. $-(a + 1) + (a + 1) = 0$

40. $-(p + 3) + (p + 3) = 0$

41. If $x = a + b + 3$ and $y = a + b + 3$, then $x = y$.

42. If $m + n + x = 180$ and $m + n = 120$, then $120 + x = 180$.

43–50. Give a reason for each step. Let a be any real number.

43. $-1a = -1a + 0$

44. $\quad = -1a + [a + (-a)]$

45. $\quad = [-1a + a] + (-a)$

46. $\quad = [-1a + 1a] + (-a)$

47. $\quad = [-1 + 1]a + (-a)$

48. $\quad = 0a + (-a)$

49. $\quad = 0 + (-a)$

50. $\quad = -a$

51–52. Give a reason for each step.

51.
$$\begin{aligned} x + (-9) &= 3 \\ [x + (-9)] + 9 &= 3 + 9 \\ [x + (-9)] + 9 &= 12 \\ x + [-9 + 9] &= 12 \\ x + 0 &= 12 \\ x &= 12 \end{aligned}$$

52.
$$\begin{aligned} y + (-2) &= -5 \\ [y + (-2)] + 2 &= -5 + 2 \\ [y + (-2)] + 2 &= -3 \\ y + [-2 + 2] &= -3 \\ y + 0 &= -3 \\ y &= -3 \end{aligned}$$

Ⓒ 53–56. Solve as in Exercises 51–52.

53. $5 + x = 18$ 54. $8n = -320$ 55. $13 = 9 - y$ 56. $\frac{3}{5}r = 12$

57. The properties of equality on page 22 are called the *reflexive property*, the *substitution property*, the *transitive property*, and the *symmetric property*. Find out which is which.

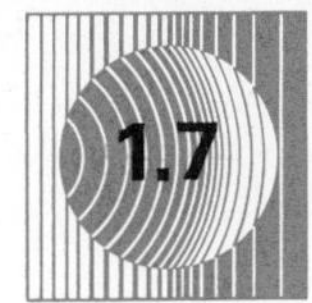

Reasoning in Geometry

Some parts of the system of geometry have already been given.

undefined terms	defined terms		postulates
point	collinear	coplanar	Distance Postulate
line	between	segment	Ruler Postulate
plane	midpoint	ray	Ruler Placement Postulate
	distance	equidistant	
	opposite rays	absolute value	

We can use the ideas above and logical reasoning to decide that the following theorem is true.

On ray *AB* there is exactly one point *P* whose distance from *A* is a given positive number *n*.

Point Plotting Theorem

Reasoning: (A drawing is usually helpful.)

Think of ray *AB* as part of line *AB*. By the Ruler Placement Postulate (p. 12), let the coordinate of *A* be zero and let the coordinate of *B* be a positive number.

By parts 1 and 2 of the Ruler Postulate (p. 11), the positive number n corresponds to exactly one point P on $\overrightarrow{AB}$, and P corresponds to exactly one positive number, which therefore must be n.

By part 3 of the Ruler Postulate, the distance between A and P is the absolute value of the difference of their coordinates: $AP = |0 - n|$. By subtraction and the definition of absolute value: $AP = |-n| = n$. So on $\overrightarrow{AB}$ there is exactly one point P whose distance from A is n.

The Point Plotting Theorem now becomes a part of the geometric system that we are developing. It can be used to help decide that the next theorem is true.

Every segment has exactly one midpoint.

Midpoint Theorem

Reasoning: C P D

By definition of *midpoint*, the midpoint P of any segment CD is between C and D and $CP = PD$

By definition of *between*, $CP + PD = CD$

Using algebra:
- Substitute $CP + CP = CD$
- Add on the left side $2CP = CD$
- Multiply both sides by $\frac{1}{2}$ $CP = \frac{1}{2}CD$

By the Point Plotting Theorem, there is exactly one point on $\overrightarrow{CD}$ whose distance from C is $\frac{1}{2}CD$. So $\overline{CD}$ has exactly one midpoint.

Before considering any more theorems, we must state some more postulates. These postulates are needed to guarantee that lines, planes, and space will have properties that we want them to have.

Straight Line Postulate For any two points, exactly one line contains both of them.

Number-of-Points Postulate A plane contains at least three noncollinear points. Space contains at least four noncoplanar points.

Plane Postulate Any three points are in at least one plane. Three noncollinear points are in exactly one plane.

Plane Intersection Postulate If two planes intersect, they intersect at exactly one line.

Flat Plane Postulate If two points are in a plane, the line through them is in the plane.

two points P and Q | points P and Q

P Q | P Q or P Q

When we refer, as above, to two points, three points, four points, or two planes, we mean that there are that many *distinct* figures. If no number is named, the figures may or may not be distinct.

We state this postulate	to get this	and not this.
Straight Line Postulate		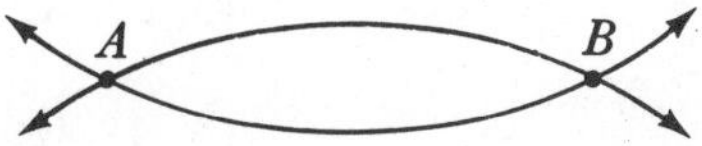
Number-of-Points Postulate	Planes with width and length: 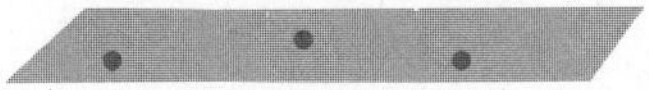 Space with width, length, and depth: 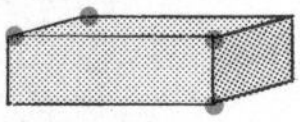	Planes that are just like lines:  Space that is just like a plane: 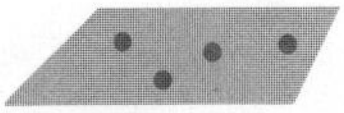
Plane Postulate	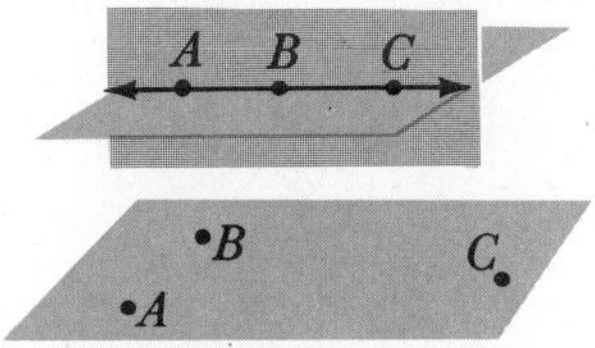	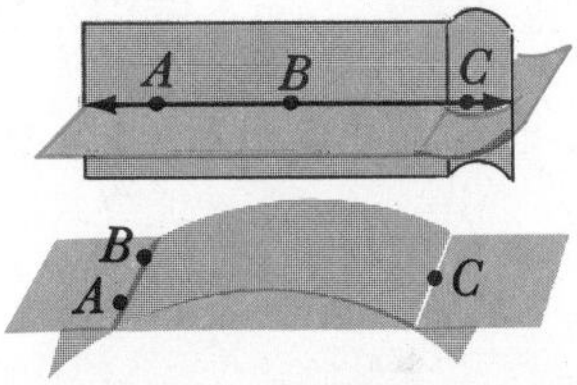
Plane Intersection Postulate	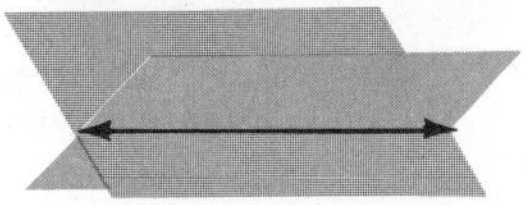	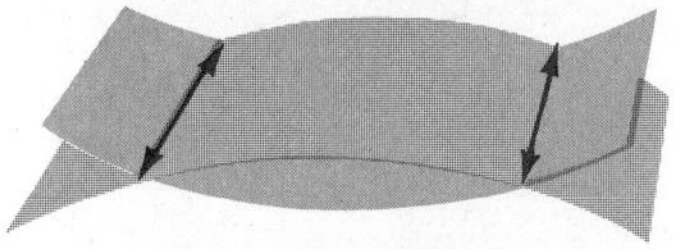
Flat Plane Postulate	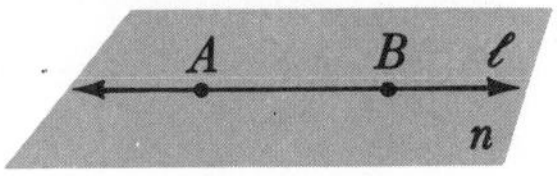	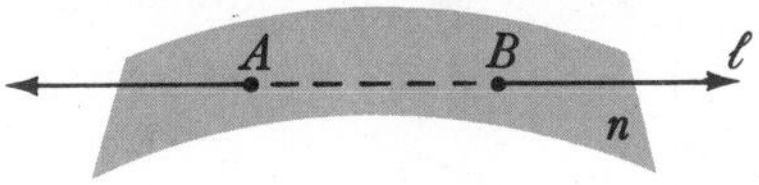

Exercises 1.7

Ⓐ **1.** Give three undefined terms of geometry we have considered.

2. Give five terms we have defined.

3–12. Refer to the figure. Which definition, postulate, or theorem shows that the given conclusion is false?

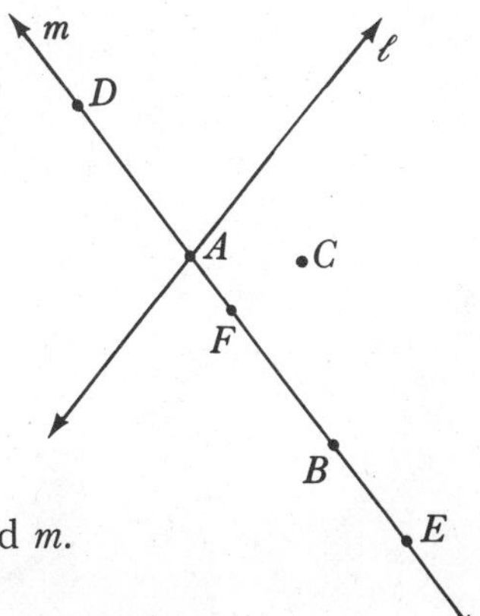

3. No plane contains A, B, and D.

4. B is on ℓ.

5. Two planes contain A, B, and C.

6. D is on $\overline{AB}$.

7. A and F are midpoints of $\overline{DB}$.

8. $AB = AE$

9. A is the midpoint of $\overline{DB}$, and DA is greater than AB.

10. Planes r and n intersect at ℓ and m.

11. $\overrightarrow{FD}$ and $\overrightarrow{AF}$ are opposite rays.

12. F is not coplanar with D and E.

Ⓑ **13–24.** Refer to the figure. Why is the given conclusion correct?

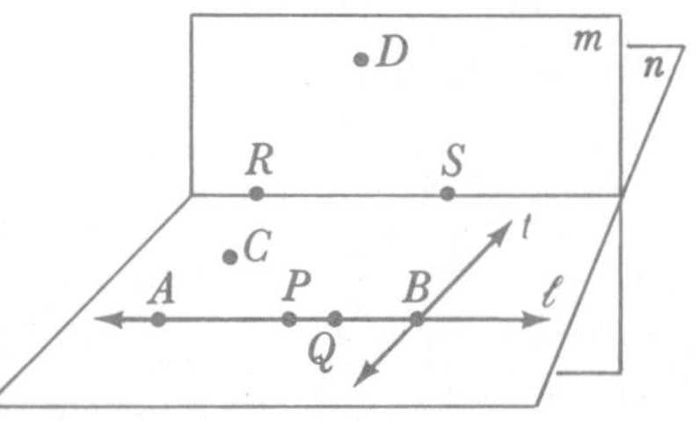

13. D, R, and S are coplanar.

14. If $AP = 3$, then $AQ \neq 3$.

15. If P is the midpoint of $\overline{AB}$, then Q is not the midpoint of $\overline{AB}$.

16. A, B, and D are coplanar.

17. If $\overleftrightarrow{AB}$ is in plane n, there is a point C in n that is not on $\overleftrightarrow{AB}$.

18. If planes m and n intersect at $\overleftrightarrow{RS}$, they do not intersect at ℓ.

19. If A and B are in plane n, $\overleftrightarrow{AB}$ is in plane n.

20. On $\overrightarrow{AP}$, there is exactly one point B such that $AB = 2PB$.

21. Since A and B are on line ℓ, A and B are not on line t.

22. If A, B, and C are in plane n, there is a point D not in n.

Ⓒ **23.** If R, S, and T are in the intersection of planes m and n, R, S, and T are collinear.

24. If planes m and n both contain R and S, they intersect at $\overleftrightarrow{RS}$.

25–27. What postulate explains why?

25. The sand yacht doesn't rock from wheel to wheel.

26. A string stretched between two stakes marks a straight row.

27. The string lies flat on the board.

Grant Follis

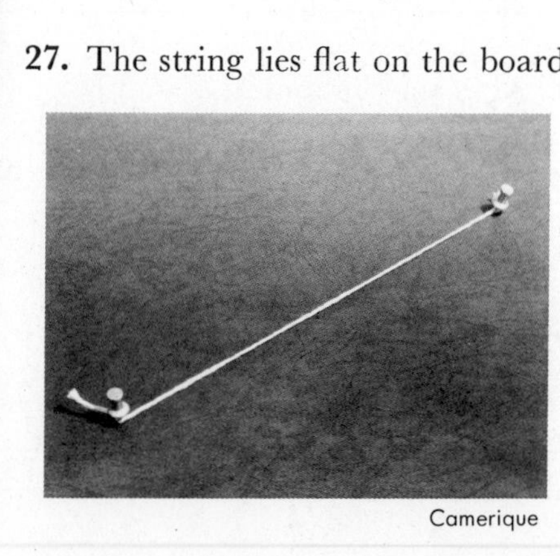

Camerique

More About Reasoning

The five postulates stated in the preceding section can be used to answer the four questions below.

If two lines intersect, what is their intersection like?

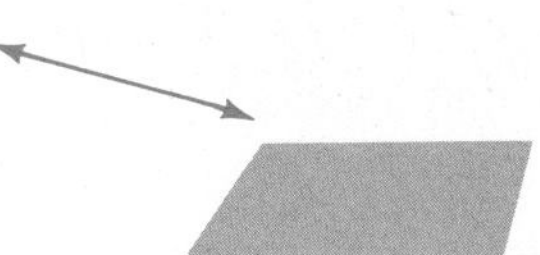

If a line and a plane intersect, what is their intersection like?

How many planes contain a line and a point not on that line?

How many planes contain two intersecting lines?

If two lines intersect, they intersect at exactly one point.

Line Intersection Theorem

Reasoning:

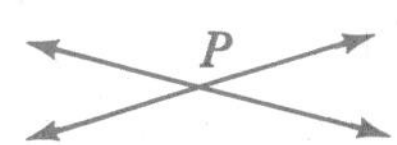

The fact that the lines intersect tells us that they intersect at *at least one* point P.

Suppose the lines intersect at two points, P and Q. Then there are two lines, each of which contains both P and Q. But, according to the Straight Line Postulate, this can't happen. So the lines do *not* intersect at *more than one* point.

Since the two lines intersect at *at least one* point but *not more than one* point, they intersect at *exactly one* point.

If you can show { there is at least one / there is not more than one } ▶ then there is exactly one.

Line-Plane Intersection Theorem

If a plane and a line not in that plane intersect, they intersect at exactly one point.

Reasoning:

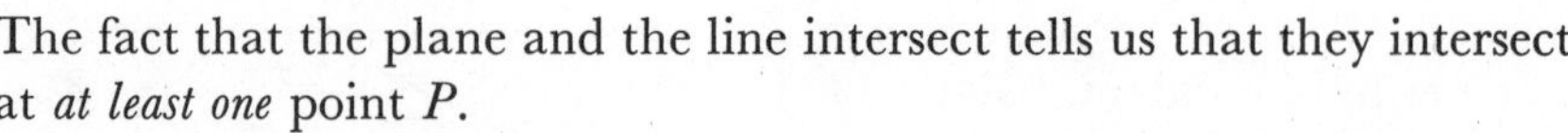

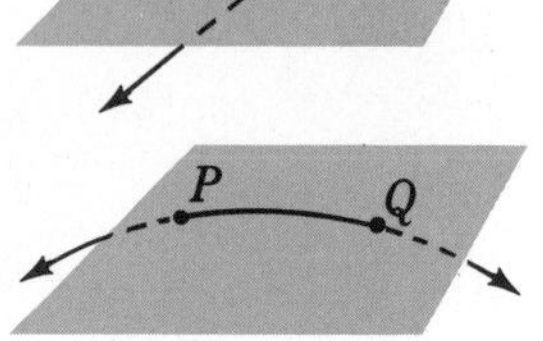

The fact that the plane and the line intersect tells us that they intersect at *at least one* point P.

Suppose the plane and line intersect at two points, P and Q. Then two points of $\overleftrightarrow{PQ}$ are in the plane, and $\overleftrightarrow{PQ}$ is not in the plane. But, according to the Flat Plane Postulate, this can't happen. So the plane and line do *not* intersect at *more than one* point.

Since the plane and line intersect at *at least one* point but *not more than one* point, they intersect at *exactly one* point.

In stating postulates and theorems, the term *determine* can often be used instead of the term *exactly one.*

This postulate	that was stated this way	can be restated this way.
Straight Line Postulate	For any two points, **exactly one** line contains both of them.	Two points **determine** a line.
Plane Postulate	Three noncollinear points are in **exactly one** plane.	Three noncollinear points **determine** a plane.

The next theorem is stated using *determine* instead of *exactly one.*

Plane Theorem

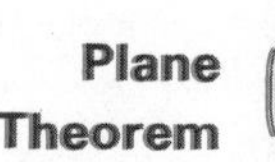

a. A line and a point not on the line determine a plane.
b. Two intersecting lines determine a plane.

Reasoning:

a.

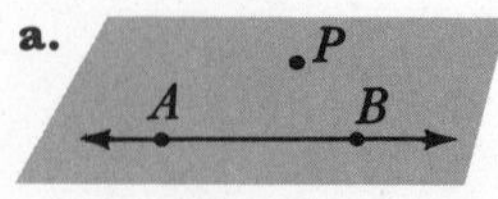

Part a. Let A and B be two points on any line ℓ. The given point P is not on ℓ, so we now have three noncollinear points. According to the Plane Postulate, these three points determine a plane. This plane contains line ℓ because it contains points A and B.

b.

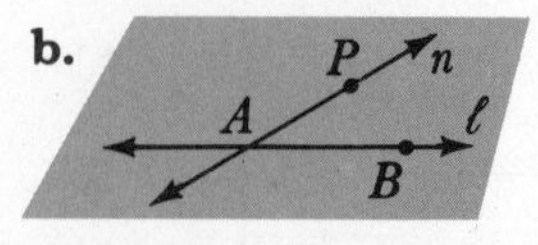

Part b. Let lines ℓ and n intersect at point A. Then let B be any other point on ℓ and let P be any other point on n. These three noncollinear points determine a plane that contains lines ℓ and n.

Exercises 1.8

Ⓐ **1.** The intersection of two lines is a ______.

2. The intersection of a plane and a line not in the plane is a ______.

3. If there is at least one figure, but not more than one, then there is ______.

4. A statement using *exactly one* can often be restated using ______.

5. A line and a point not on the line determine ______.

6. Two intersecting lines determine ______.

Ⓑ **7–8.** Restate using *determine*.

7. If two lines intersect, they intersect at exactly one point.

8. If a plane and a line not in that plane intersect, they intersect at exactly one point.

9–12. Restate using *exactly one*.

9. Two intersecting planes determine a line.

10. Two intersecting lines determine a plane.

11. A line and a point not on the line determine a plane.

12. Two noncollinear rays with a common endpoint determine a plane.

13–18. Tell which theorem lets us reach the stated conclusion.

13. Two lines ℓ and m do not intersect at two points P and Q.

14. Intersecting lines r and s are not in two planes m and n.

15. Plane p and line ℓ not in p do not intersect at two points A and B.

16. If point P is not in line t, then P and t are not both in two planes m and n.

17. Two lines ℓ and m intersect; point P is on ℓ and m; a second point Q is on ℓ. *Conclusion:* Q is not on m.

18. Two lines ℓ and m intersect; plane P contains ℓ and m; a second plane Q contains ℓ. *Conclusion:* m is not in Q.

19–22. Draw the figure described.

19. Lines m and n intersect only at point A.

20. Line s and plane T intersect only at point D.

21. Line t and point R determine plane n.

22. Intersecting lines k and r determine plane M.

© **23–24.** Which theorem explains why the picture frame sits firmly?

23.

24.

Alfa

1. Reasoning from postulates and definitions leads to conclusions in (inductive, deductive) reasoning.

2. A statement that includes a hypothesis and its logical conclusion is a (postulate, theorem).

3. The additive identity is (0, 1, x).

4. The reciprocal of 2 is $(-2, |2|, \frac{1}{2})$.

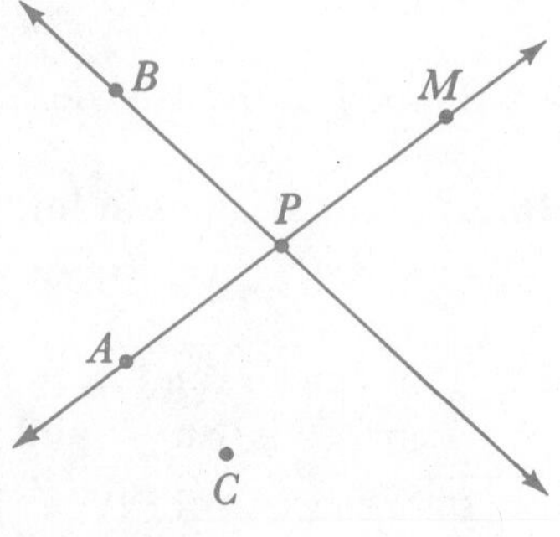

5–8. In the figure shown, which of these would determine a plane?

5. $\overleftrightarrow{AM}$ and $\overleftrightarrow{BP}$

6. A, P, and M

7. B, P, and C

8. $\overleftrightarrow{AP}$ and C

Constructions

Basketball players must not only get the ball through the hoop—they must do it according to the rules of the game. Doing a geometric construction is like playing basketball. If you don't do it by the rules, it isn't the same game.

Chicago Tribune Photo

There are two ways to make diagrams in geometry. To **draw** a geometric figure, you can use any device or instrument. But to **construct** a geometric figure, you can use only two tools besides pencil and paper. The first of these two tools is the *straightedge.*

A **straightedge** is used to construct a line through two points.

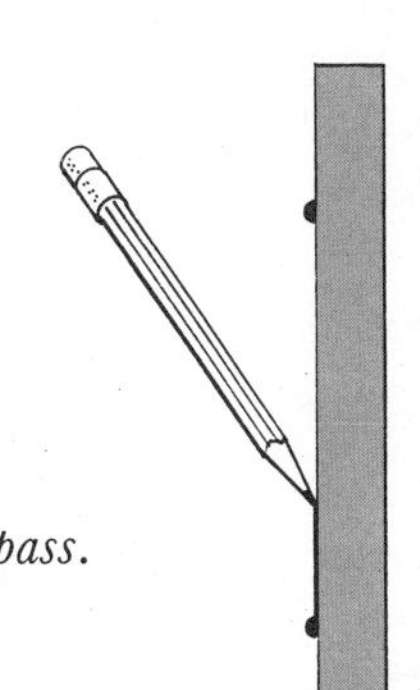

The straightedge most commonly used is the edge of a ruler. But never use the marks along the edge of the ruler. A straightedge is not used for measuring.

The second construction tool is the *compass.*

A **compass** is used to construct a circle with a given center and given radius.

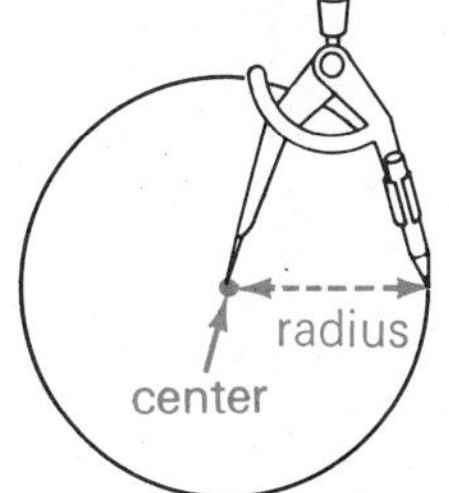

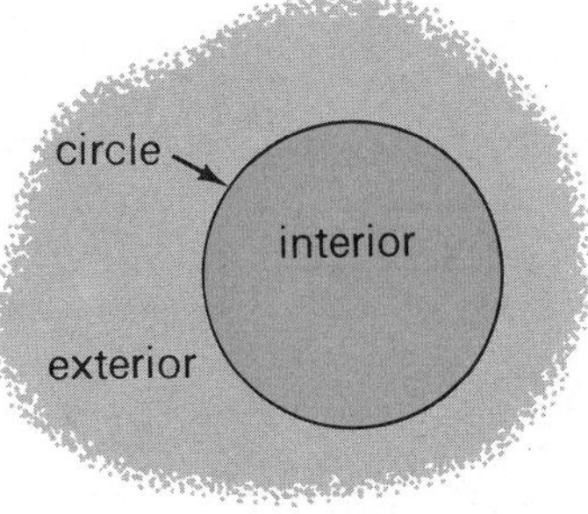

arc

Notice that the circle contains *only* the points drawn by the compass. All other points in the plane, including the center of the circle, are either in the **interior** of the circle or in its **exterior**. Only part of a circle, called an **arc**, is actually drawn in most constructions.

Exercises 1.9

Ⓐ **1.** What tools can be used to draw geometric figures?

2. What tools can be used to construct geometric figures?

3. Give three examples of a straightedge besides the edge of a ruler.

4. In constructions, a ruler must not be used for ______.

5. A compass is used to construct a ______.

6. The radius of a circle is the distance between any point on the circle and the ______ of the circle.

7. If the tips of a compass are set 3 inches apart, the compass will construct a circle whose ______ is 3 inches.

8. The center of a circle is in the ______ of the circle.

9. If the radius of a circle is 3 inches, any point 4 inches from the center of the circle is in the ______ of the circle.

10. Part of a circle is called an ______.

11–22. Refer to the construction below.

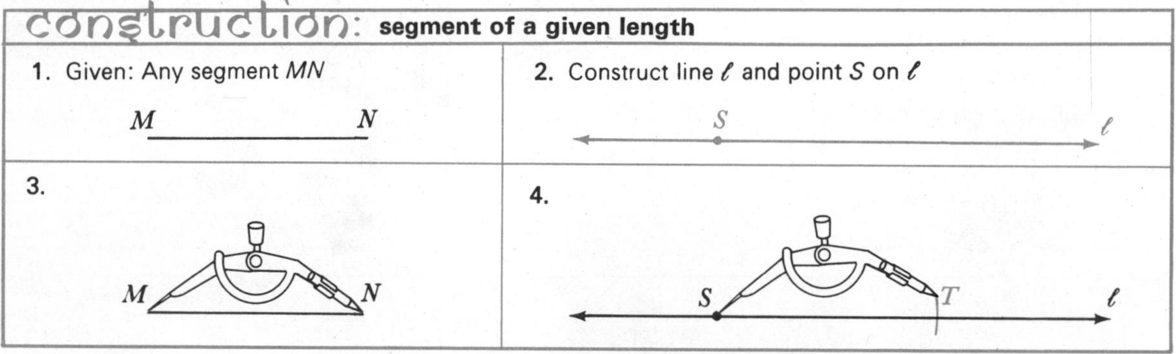

11. Describe step 3.

12. Describe step 4.

13. What segment is a copy of $\overline{MN}$?

14. Is it true that $ST = MN$?

A step 5 might follow step 4 above. Here are two possibilities.

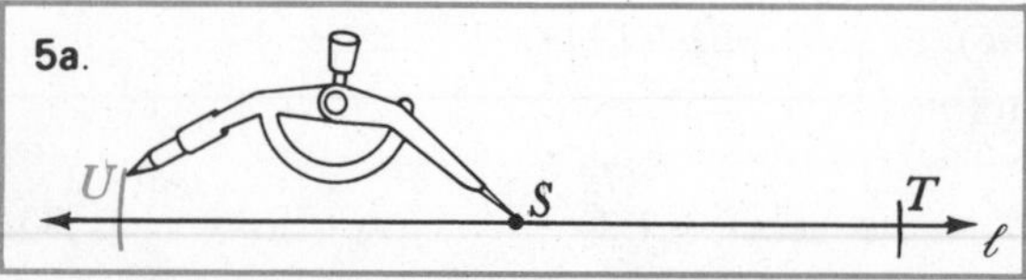

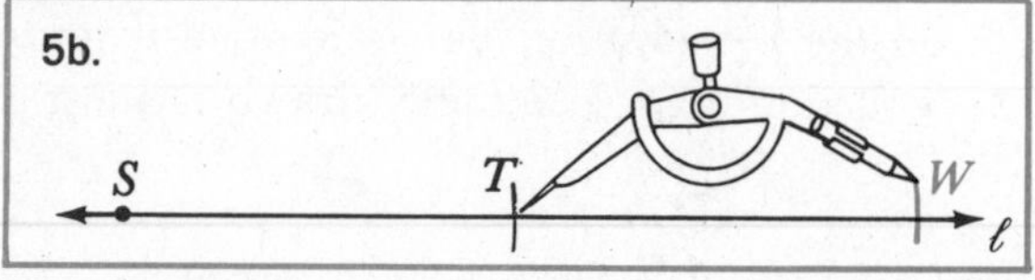

15. Describe step 5a. **16.** Describe step 5b.

17. Is the compass setting changed between step 4 and step 5a? Between step 4 and step 5b?

18. What two segments in 5a would be copies of $\overline{MN}$? In 5b?

19. What segments in 5a and 5b would be twice as long as $\overline{MN}$?

20. What segment has length $US + ST$? Is it true that $US + ST = 2MN$?

21. What segment has length $ST + TW$? Is it true that $ST + TW = 2MN$?

22. What is the midpoint of $\overline{UT}$? Of $\overline{SW}$?

(B) **23–36.** Use the given segments and the methods shown on page 36 to construct a segment of the length called for.

P ———————— Q

R ———————— V W ———————— X

23. PQ **24.** RV

25. $2RV$ **26.** $2PQ$ **27.** $PQ + RV$ **28.** $WX + PQ$

29. $2RV + WX$ **30.** $2PQ + RV$ **31.** $3RV$ **32.** $3WX$

33. $PQ - RV$ **34.** $PQ - WX$ **35.** $2RV - WX$ **36.** $2WX - RV$

37–46. Draw four noncollinear points A, B, C, and D. Then construct the following.

37. $\overleftrightarrow{AB}$ **38.** $\overleftrightarrow{BC}$ **39.** $\overrightarrow{DC}$ **40.** $\overrightarrow{CA}$

41. $\overline{BD}$ **42.** $\overline{AB}$ **43.** $\overrightarrow{AC}$ **44.** $\overrightarrow{CD}$

45. the ray opposite $\overrightarrow{CB}$ **46.** the ray opposite $\overrightarrow{BD}$

(C) **47–48.** Ruler and compass constructions can be used to make designs for tiles, quilt blocks, fabrics, and other decorative items. See if you can make patterns for the designs shown here. Then make up some designs of your own.

47.

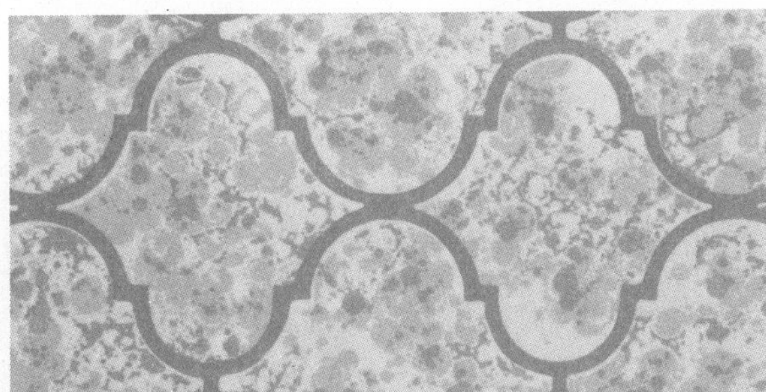

Flooring by Armstrong Cork Co.

48.

Frank Kuechmann

1.10 Transformations—An Introduction

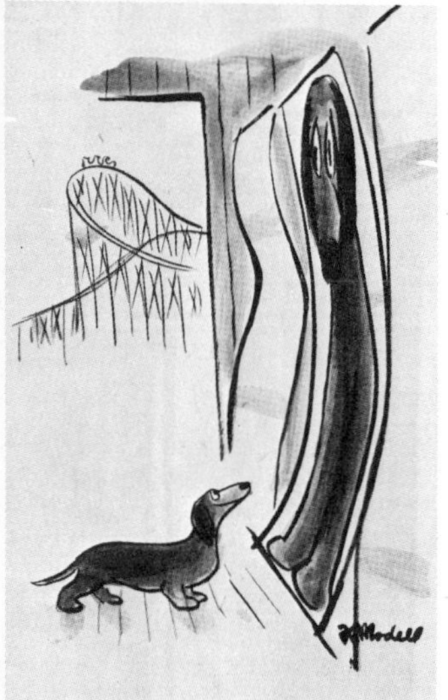

Drawing by F. Modell; © 1960 The New Yorker Magazine, Inc.

The fun-house mirror has transformed the little dog into a very big dog. Geometric figures can also be transformed. Here are a few of the ways this can be done.

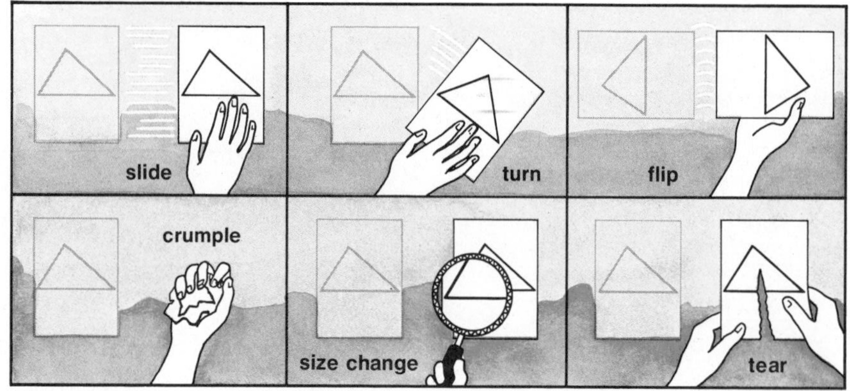

Notice that the entire plane is transformed at once. However, we usually talk about the effect of the transformation on just one figure.

The figure resulting from a transformation is called the **image** of the original figure. We often show the original figure and one or more images in the same diagram. (The original figure, like the little dog in the fun-house, is not changed by the transformation.)

Only four of the transformations shown above are important to us here. Their names describe them.

- reflection (or flip)
- slide
- turn
- size change

These transformations, and combinations of them, can be used to make many geometric ideas easier to understand. Simple paper folding shows a relation between the midpoint of a segment and a reflection.

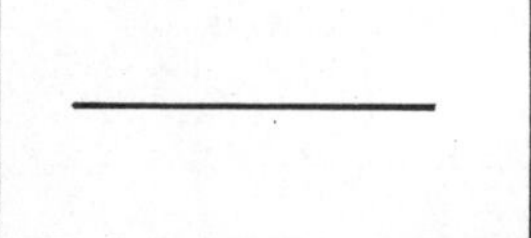

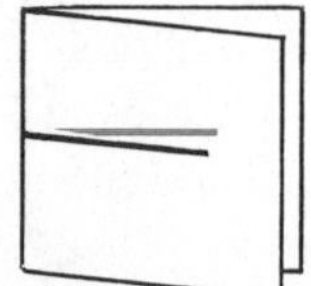

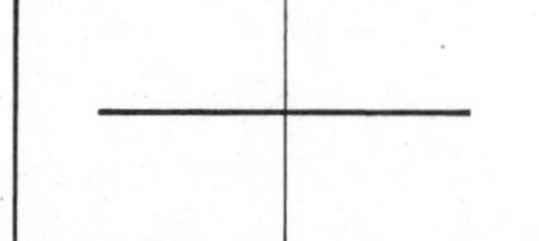

1. Draw a line segment on thin paper.
2. Fold the paper so that the endpoints of the segment match. Now the part of the segment on one side of the fold is the flip or reflection image of the other part.
3. Open the paper. Why does the fold mark the midpoint of the segment?

Exercises 1.10

Ⓐ **1–2.** Refer to the paper-folding example on page 38.

1. Are there other ways the paper could be folded once to match the endpoints of the segment? Would the fold cross the segment at the same place? What theorem about midpoints does this suggest?

2. The figure resulting from a transformation is called the ______.

3–6. Match each transformation named below with a picture at the right.

3. slide **4.** turn **a.** **b.** **c.** **d.**

5. reflection **6.** size change

Ⓑ **7–18.** Name the transformation illustrated. The image is shown in color.

7. **8.** **9.** **10.**

11.

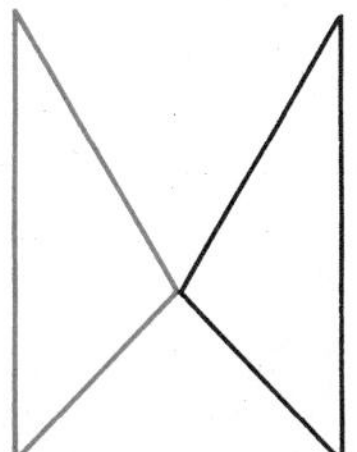

12.

13.

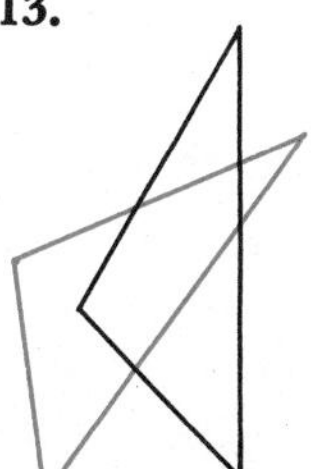

14.

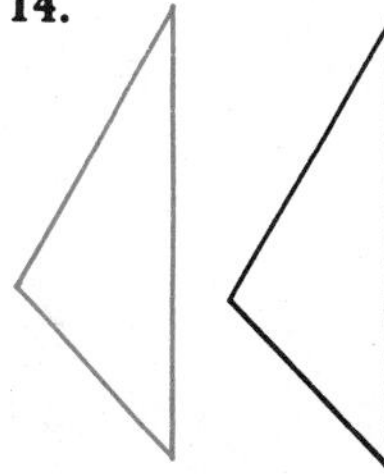

15.

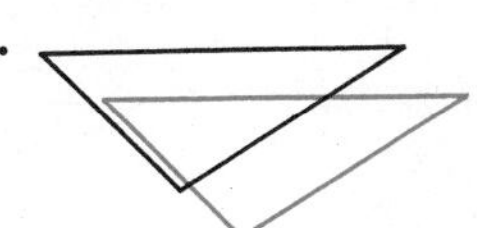

16.

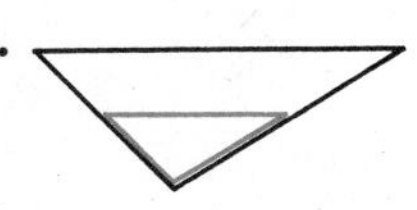

17.

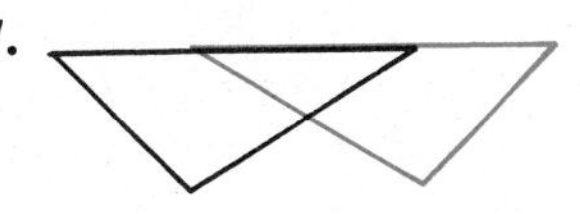

18.

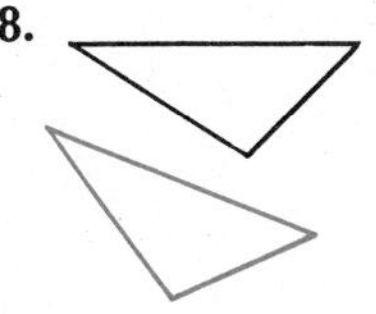

Ⓒ **19–22.** Two transformations are applied to each figure below, one after the other. The final image is shown in solid color. Name the transformations in the correct order.

19.

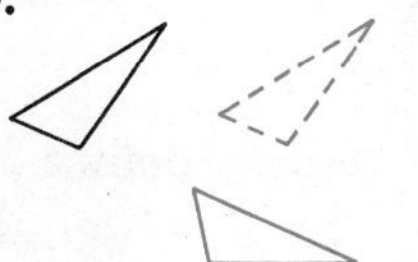

20.

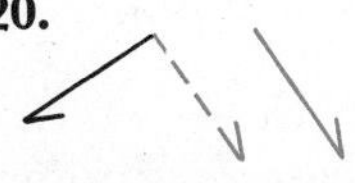

21.

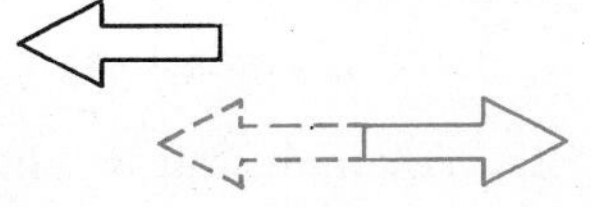

22.

■ Chapter 1 Review ■

1.1 1–3. Name the geometric figure represented by the model.

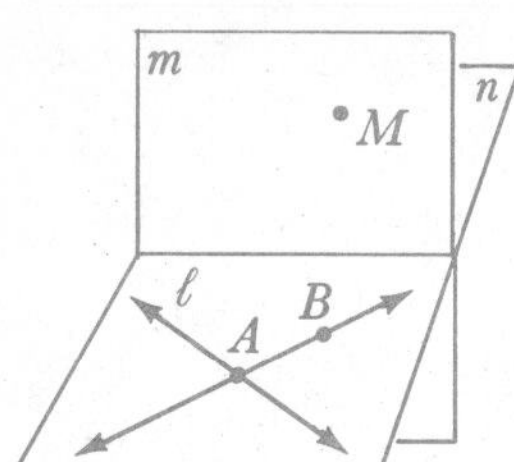

1. grain of sand **2.** endless light beam **3.** endless sheet of film

4–7. Refer to the figure to complete each sentence.

4. Line ℓ contains point ______. **5.** Point M is not in plane ______.

6. ______ and ℓ intersect at A. **7.** Points A and ______ are on $\overleftrightarrow{AB}$.

1.2 **8.** Any number that has a decimal expansion is a(n) ______.

9. The symbols $<$ and $>$ are used to show the ______ of numbers.

10. On the real number line, each point is matched with its ______.

11–13. Which symbol, $<$, $=$, or $>$, should replace the ▨? Let x and y be any real numbers.

11. $5 < x$, $5 = x$, or 5 ▨ x. **12.** If $y > 3$, then 3 ▨ y.

13. If $-2 < x$ and $x < y$, then -2 ▨ y.

1.3 **14.** A(n) ______ is accepted as true without proof. **15.** $|-5|$ is the ______ of -5.

16. $|-18| =$ ______ **17.** $|7 - 2| =$ ______

18. If the coordinates of P and Q are 12 and 3, then $PQ =$ ______.

1.4 **19.** Points on the same line are said to be ______. **20.** $\overline{AD}$ is named ______ to show that P is between A and D.

21. $AD + DM = AM$ means D is ______ A and M. **22.** Points I and F are the ______ of $\overline{IF}$.

23. If $AH = HE$ on $\overline{AE}$, then H is the ______ of $\overline{AE}$. **24.** If $\overleftrightarrow{PS}$ intersects $\overline{QR}$ at its midpoint, then $\overleftrightarrow{PS}$ ______ $\overline{QR}$.

25. If A is between B and C, then $\overrightarrow{AB}$ and $\overrightarrow{AC}$ are opposite ______.

1.5 **26.** A conclusion suggested by a number of examples is reached by ______ reasoning.

27. A conclusion reached by reasoning from postulates and definitions is reached by ______ reasoning.

28. Name the steps in the pattern of deductive reasoning.

29. What two things are included in a theorem?

30–42. Of what property is each statement an example? **1.6**

30. $5(a + 2) = 5a + 10$

31. $(n + 2) + 3 = n + (2 + 3)$

32. If $x = 2$, then $2x = 4$.

33. If $x + 1 = 2$, then $2 = x + 1$.

34. $4 \cdot 2n = (4 \cdot 2)n$

35. $a + 3 = 3 + a$

36. $3 \cdot 4 = 4 \cdot 3$

37. $0 + x = x$

38. $\frac{1}{2} \cdot 2 = 1$

39. $9 + (-9) = 0$

40. $1 \cdot 5 = 5$

41. $0 \cdot y = 0$

42. If $n + x = 12$ and $n = 3$, then $3 + x = 12$.

43–51. Refer to the figure. What postulate or theorem explains the given conclusion? **1.7**

43. If ℓ contains P and D, then $\ell = \overleftrightarrow{PD}$.

44. On $\overrightarrow{PD}$ there is exactly one point a distance MD from P.

45. If plane n contains $\overleftrightarrow{PD}$, there is at least one point in n that is not on $\overleftrightarrow{PD}$.

46. Exactly one plane contains P, D, and Q.

47. If P and Q are in plane m, every point on $\overleftrightarrow{PQ}$ is in m.

48. $\overleftrightarrow{MP}$ and $\overleftrightarrow{PD}$ intersect at exactly one point.

49. If $\overleftrightarrow{PD}$ and plane n intersect at T, they do not intersect at S. **1.8**

50. M and $\overleftrightarrow{PD}$ determine a plane.

51. $\overleftrightarrow{DQ}$ and $\overleftrightarrow{PD}$ determine a plane.

52. A statement using *determines* can usually be restated using ______.

53. Segments are constructed using a(n) ______.

54. Circles are constructed using a(n) ______. **1.9**

55. Copy $\overline{AB}$.

56. Construct a segment $2AB$ long.

57–60. Name the transformation illustrated. The image is shown in color. **1.10**

57.

58.

59.

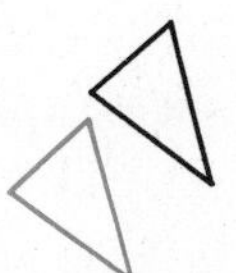

60.

Chapter 1 Test

1–8. Refer to the figure. Name an example of

1. three collinear points 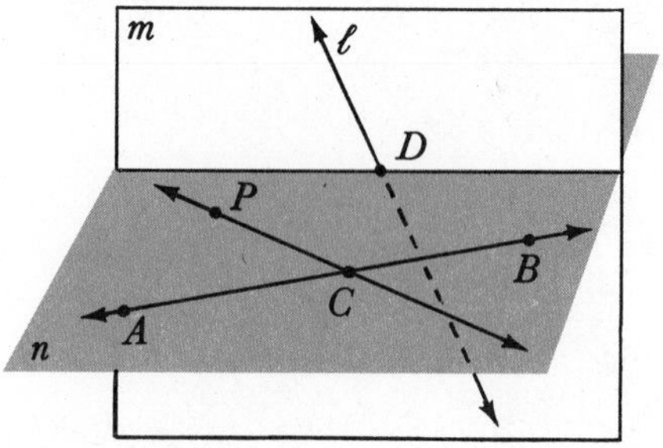
2. a line that intersects $\overleftrightarrow{AB}$
3. the intersection of line ℓ and plane n
4. three points coplanar with A and D
5. the endpoints of $\overline{ACB}$
6. a segment with one endpoint at P
7. a ray opposite $\overrightarrow{CA}$
8. two points on opposite sides of C

9. $2 < 7$ is an example of the ______ of real numbers.
10. A real number is the ______ of a point on the real number line.
11. $|-3|$ is the ______ of -3.
12. MN is the ______ between M and N.
13. If A, B, and C are collinear and $AC = BC$, then C is the ______ of $\overline{AB}$.
14. If line ℓ intersects $\overline{PQ}$ at its midpoint, then ℓ ______ $\overline{PQ}$.
15. ______ reasoning reaches a conclusion from examples.
16. Reasoning from postulates and definitions is called ______ reasoning.
17. A hypothesis and its logical conclusion are stated in a ______.
18. A statement accepted as true without proof is a ______.
19. Many statements using *exactly one* can be restated using ______.
20. The tool used to construct circles is the ______.
21. Slides and flips are two kinds of ______.

22–25. Refer to the figure for Exercises 1–8. What theorem or postulate leads to the given conclusion?

22. No line other than $\overleftrightarrow{AB}$ contains A and B.
23. No plane other than n contains A, P, and D.
24. No plane other than n contains both $\overleftrightarrow{AB}$ and $\overleftrightarrow{PC}$.
25. $\overleftrightarrow{AB}$ and $\overleftrightarrow{PC}$ intersect only at C.

2

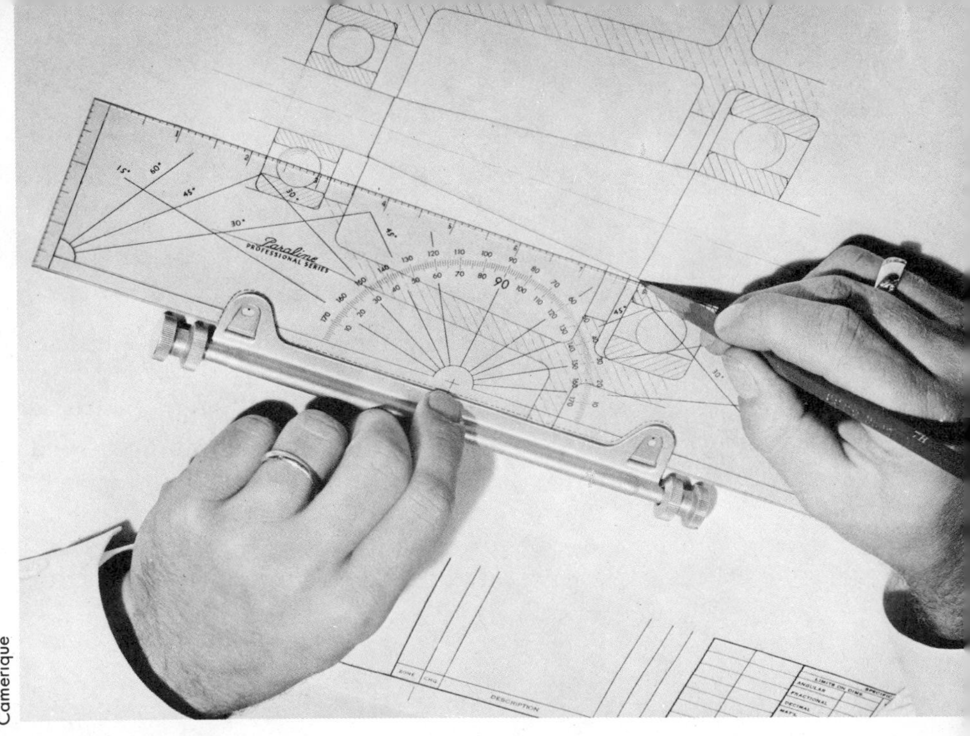

Camerique

George Franzen

ANGLES

An angle is formed by two rays that meet at a point. Models of angles can be found in designs, buildings, and various kinds of plans and instructions, as in these photos.

2.1 Convex Sets and Separation

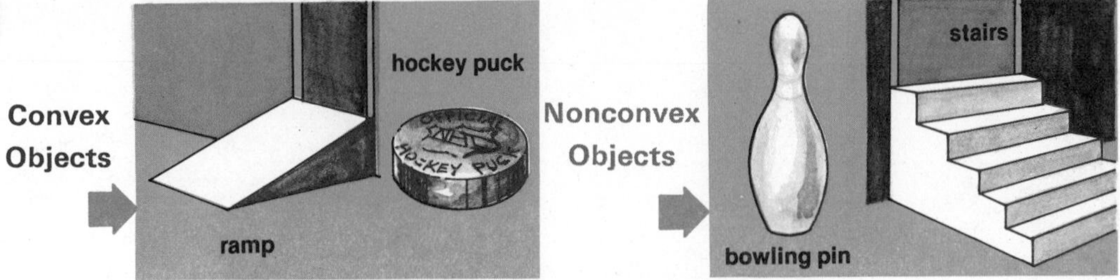

Notice that convex objects always "bend outward," but objects that are nonconvex "bend inward" in some places.

A **convex set** is a set of points with this property: For every two points of the set, the entire segment joining the points is in the set.

Convex Sets | **Nonconvex Sets**

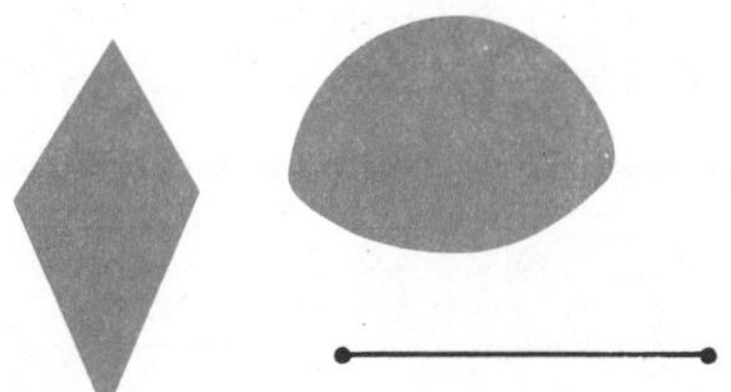

The segment joining at least one pair of points does not lie entirely inside the set.

Physical Model | **Geometric Figure**

Chicago Bears Football Club

The 50-yard line separates a football field into two convex sets.

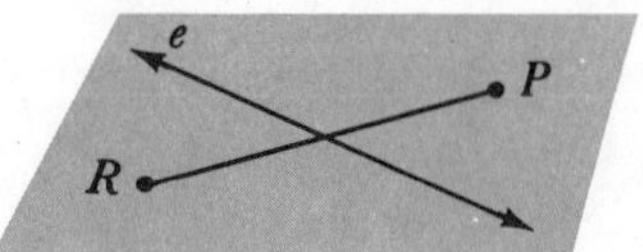

A line separates a plane into two convex sets called *half planes*.

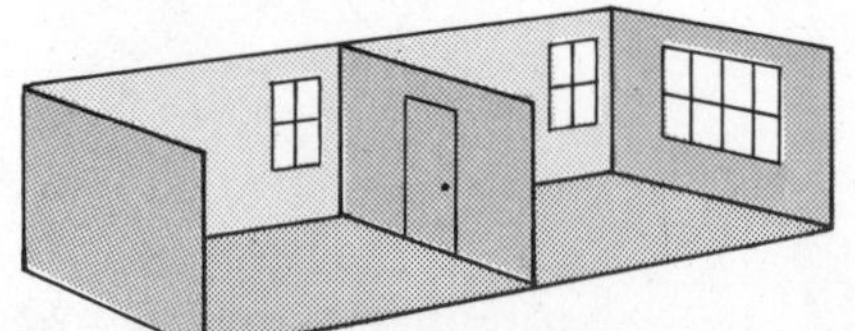

A wall separates a two-room apartment into two convex rooms.

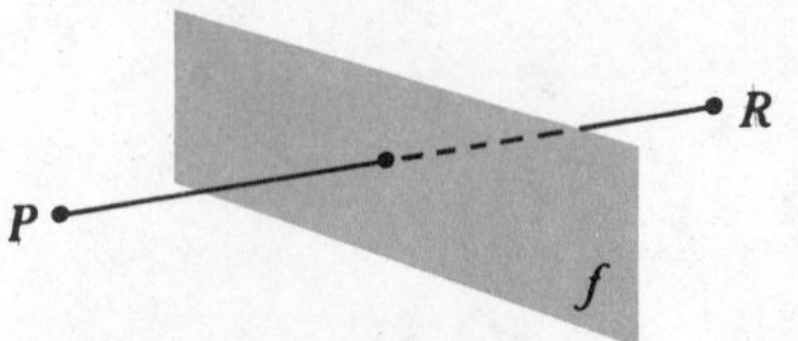

A plane separates space into two convex sets called *half spaces*.

Plane Separation Postulate

> Let e be a line in a given plane. The points of the plane that are not on line e form two **half planes** such that:
> 1. Each half plane is a convex set, and
> 2. If point P is in one half plane and point R is in the other, then segment PR intersects line e.

Line e is the *edge* of each half plane. The half planes do not contain the edge, and they are on *opposite sides* of the edge.

Space Separation Postulate

> Let f be any plane in space. The points of space that are not on plane f form two **half spaces** such that:
> 1. Each half space is a convex set, and
> 2. If point P is in one half space and point R is in the other, then segment PR intersects plane f.

Plane f is the *face* of each half space. The half spaces do not contain the face, and they are on *opposite sides* of the face.

A line is the only one-dimensional figure that can separate a plane into *two* convex sets. A plane is the only two-dimensional figure that can separate space into *two* convex sets.

Exercises 2.1

Ⓐ **1–4.** Is each object convex?

Alfa

5–12. Is each figure a convex set?

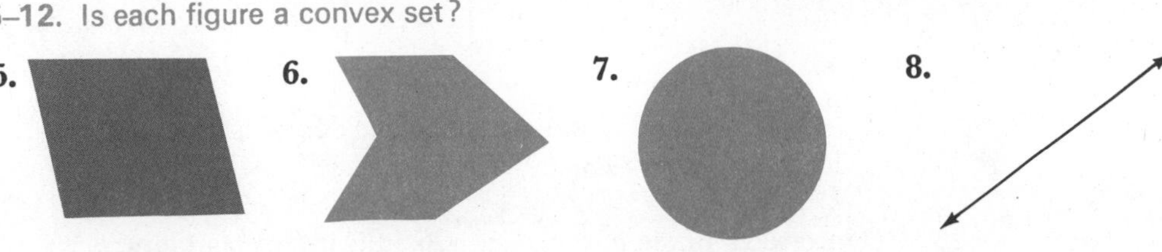

9. space

10. a line with a point removed

11. a plane with a point removed

12. a ray

13. Define *convex set.*

14–16. Complete each statement using the terms given.

a. line b. plane c. space d. half planes e. half spaces

14. A ______ separates a plane into two convex sets, called ______.

15. The face of a half space is a ______.

16. A ______ separates space into two convex sets, called ______.

Ⓑ 17–24. Line ℓ is in plane p and is the edge of two half planes p_1 and p_2. Points A and B are in p_1, and points C and D are in p_2.

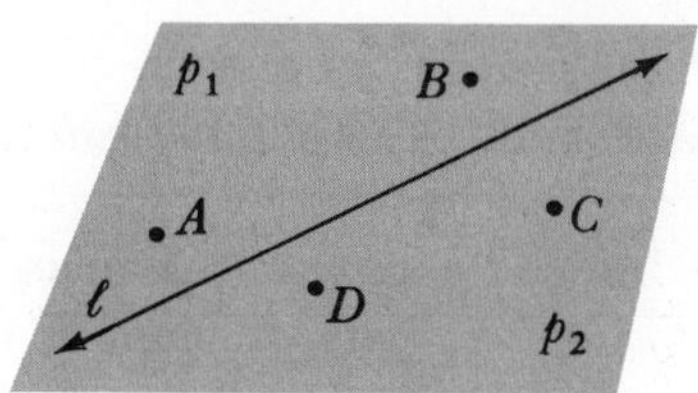

True or False?

17. $\overline{BC}$ intersects line ℓ.

18. $\overline{CD}$ is in p_2.

19. $\overline{DC}$ intersects line ℓ.

20. $\overline{AC}$ intersects line ℓ.

21. $\overline{AD}$ is in p_1.

22. $\overline{BA}$ intersects line ℓ.

23. A and B are on opposite sides of line ℓ.

24. B and C are on opposite sides of line ℓ.

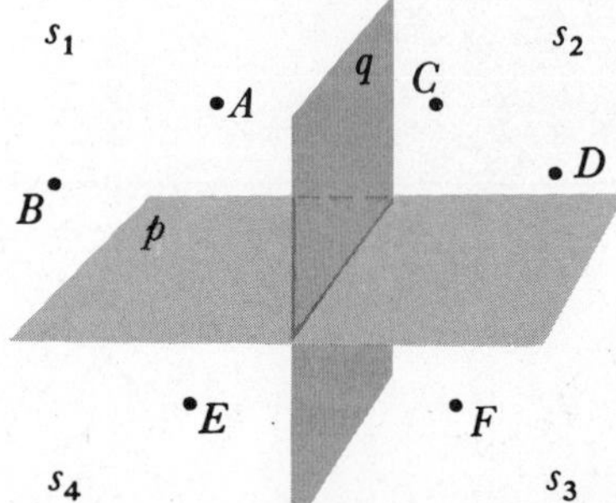

25–32. Planes p and q separate space into four sets, s_1, s_2, s_3, and s_4.

points	A, B	C, D	F	E
are in set	s_1	s_2	s_3	s_4

s_1 and s_2 are on opposite sides of p from s_3 and s_4.
s_1 and s_4 are on opposite sides of q from s_2 and s_3.
True or False?

25. $\overline{AC}$ intersects plane q.

26. $\overline{EC}$ intersects plane q.

27. Points A and C are on the same side of plane q.

28. Points E and F are on opposite sides of plane q.

29. Points B and D are on opposite sides of plane p.

30. Points B and C are on the same side of plane p.

31. A, B, and E are on the same side of plane q.

32. A, B, C, and D are on opposite sides of plane p.

Ⓒ **33–37.** Lenses are used in eyeglasses, TV picture tubes, cameras, projectors, and car headlights. See if you can match each type of lens (shown in cross section below) with its name.

a. plano-convex **b.** biconvex **c.** plano-concave

d. biconcave **e.** concavo-convex

33. 

34. 

35.

36. 

37. 

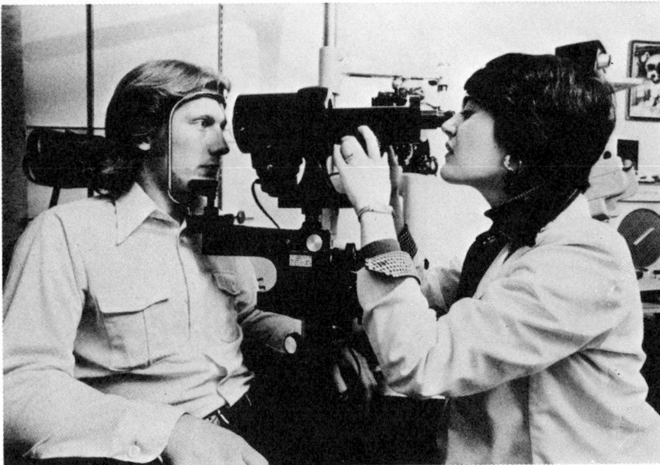

Courtesy American Optometric Association

Algebra Review

Review these skills:

- *solving equations using two operations*
- *solving equations by combining like terms*

Solve.

1. $4a + 7 = 35$
2. $-4n + 8 = 12$
3. $5m - 9 = 0$
4. $21 = 5 - 4b$
5. $\frac{1}{2}d + 4 = 8$
6. $\frac{2}{5}q - 4 = 10$
7. $3x + 2x = 90$
8. $5y - 2y = 180$
9. $14z + z = 180$
10. $d + 2d + 10 = 100$
11. $5g - 10 + g = 90$

Angles and Triangles

An **angle** is formed by two noncollinear rays with the same endpoint. Each ray is a *side* of the angle. The common endpoint is the *vertex* of the angle.

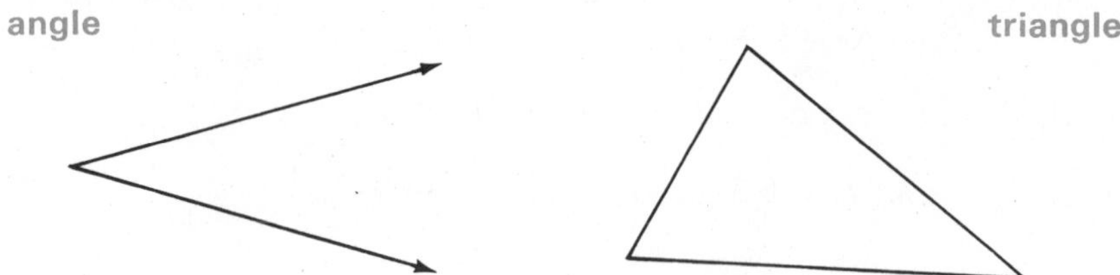

A **triangle** is formed by three segments that have three noncollinear points as their endpoints. The segments are the *sides* of the triangle. The endpoints of the sides are the *vertices* (plural of "vertex") of the triangle.

Ways of Naming Angles and Triangles

Figure	Names	Comments
A, B, C	angle ABC or $\angle ABC$ angle CBA or $\angle CBA$	$\angle$ is the symbol for "angle." The vertex letter is always in the middle.
	angle B or $\angle B$	The vertex letter may be used only when there is no chance of confusion.
D, E, 1, 2, O, T	$\angle DOT$ or $\angle TOD$ $\angle DOE$ or $\angle EOD$ $\angle EOT$ or $\angle TOE$	$\angle O$ cannot be used, since point O is the vertex of three angles.
	$\angle O_1$ (for $\angle DOE$) $\angle O_2$ (for $\angle EOT$) $\angle O_{12}$ (for $\angle DOT$)	The small numbers used in the name are called subscripts.
	$\angle 1$ (for $\angle DOE$) $\angle 2$ (for $\angle EOT$)	Numbers may be used to name angles.
F, A, M	$\triangle FAM$ (or triangle FAM), $\triangle FMA$, $\triangle MAF$, $\triangle MFA$, $\triangle AFM$, $\triangle AMF$	$\triangle$ is the symbol for "triangle." There are six different names for the same triangle.

An angle separates the plane that contains it into two sets (neither of which contains the angle). One set is convex and is called the *interior* of the angle. The other set is nonconvex and is called the *exterior* of the angle.

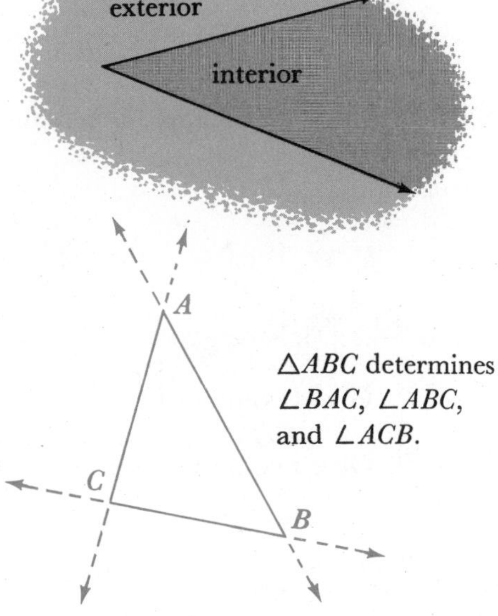

Similarly a triangle separates the plane into a convex interior and a nonconvex exterior.

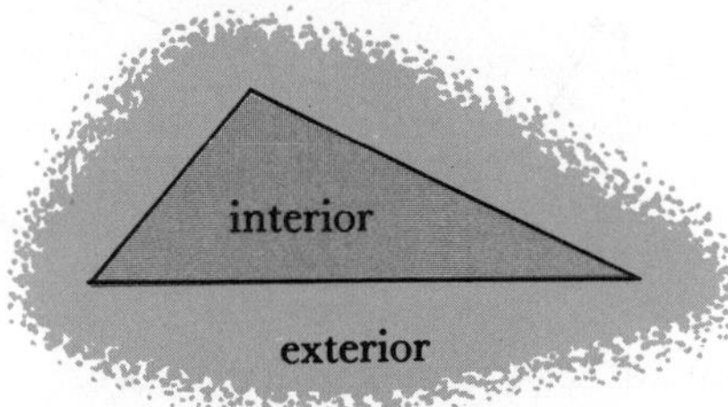

A triangle *determines* three angles called the *angles of the triangle.* Each angle has a vertex of the triangle as its own vertex and contains two sides of the triangle.

Exercises 2.2

Ⓐ **1–4.** Complete each statement.

1. Each side of an angle is a ______.
2. Each side of a triangle is a ______.
3. Each vertex of a triangle is a ______.
4. The vertex of an angle is a ______.

5. Define *angle.*
6. Define *triangle.*

7–8. Is the figure a convex set?

7. interior of an angle
8. exterior of a triangle

9–12. Use the angle at the right.

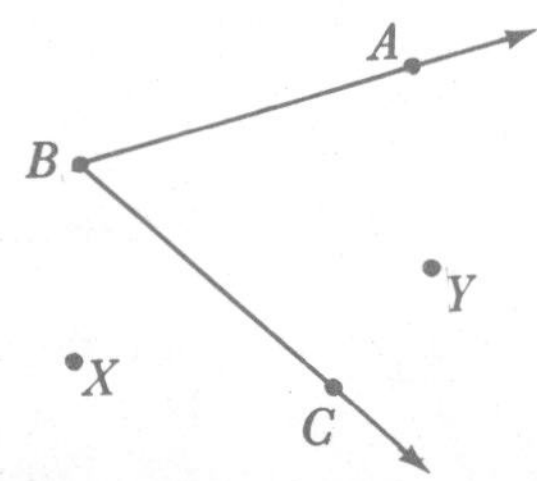

9. Give a one-letter name for the angle.
10. Give two three-letter names for the angle.
11. Name (**a**) its sides and (**b**) its vertex.
12. Name a point (**a**) in its interior and (**b**) in its exterior.

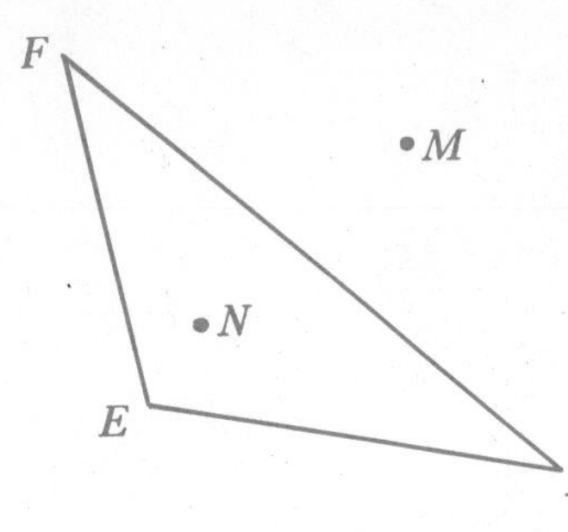

13–16. Use the triangle at the left.

13. Give six different names for the triangle.

14. Name (**a**) its sides and (**b**) its vertices.

15. Name a point (**a**) in its interior and (**b**) in its exterior.

16. Name the angles determined by the triangle.

Ⓑ 17–26. Use the appropriate figures.

17. Give two other names for $\angle B_1$.

18. Give two other names for $\angle ABD$.

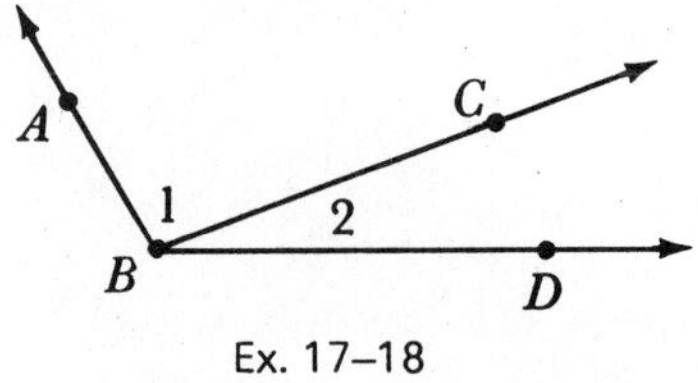

Ex. 17–18

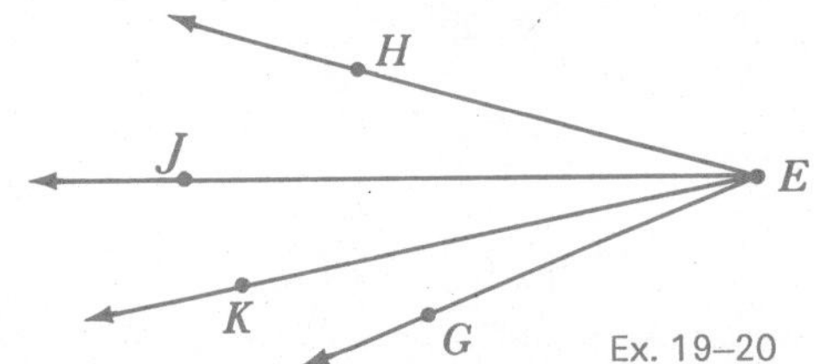

Ex. 19–20

19. Name all the angles in the figure.
HINT: There are more than 3.

20. Name 3 angles having $\overrightarrow{EK}$ as a side.

21. Name all the triangles in this figure.

22. Does $\triangle ART$ contain point S?

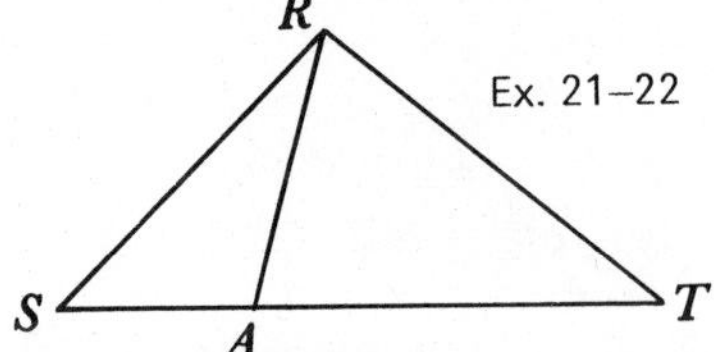

Ex. 21–22

23. Name all the points in the interior of $\angle SMG$.

24. Name all the points in the exterior of $\angle GMB$.

25. Name all the points in the exterior of $\angle SMG$.

26. Is M on $\angle SMG$?

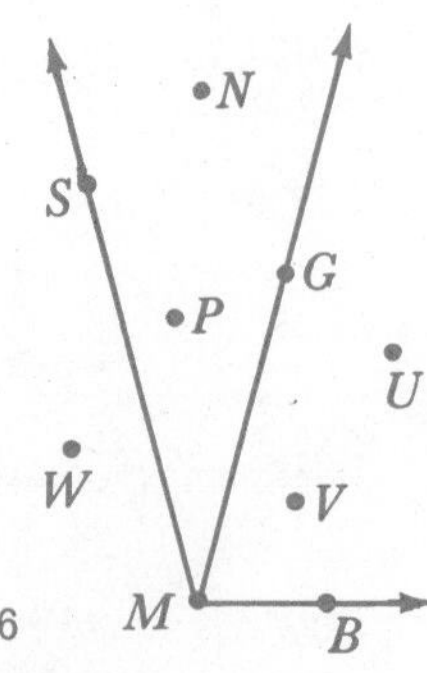

Ex. 23–26

27–30. True or False? Use the figure.

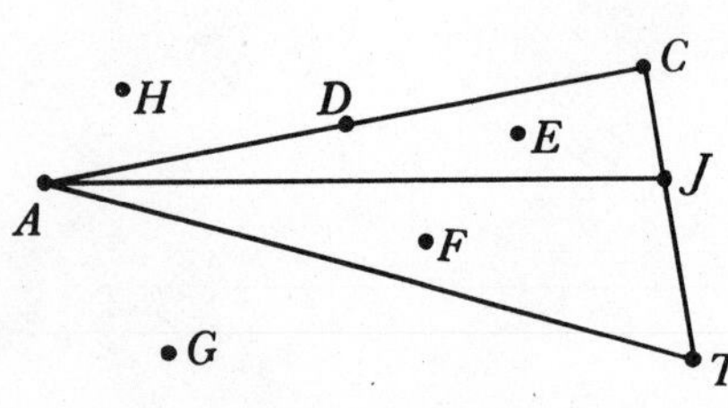

27. Points D and E are in the interior of $\triangle ACJ$.

28. Points E and F are in the interior of $\triangle ACT$.

29. Points H, G, D, and C are in the exterior of $\triangle JAT$.

30. D is in the exterior of $\triangle JAC$.

31–32. Use the figure at the right.

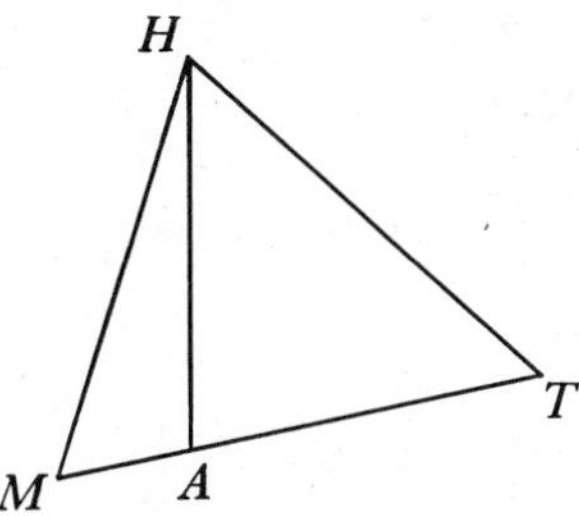

31. How many angles are determined by the triangles in this figure?

32. How many angles can be named by only the vertex letter?

33–40. True or False? $\triangle PDC$ determines the given angle.

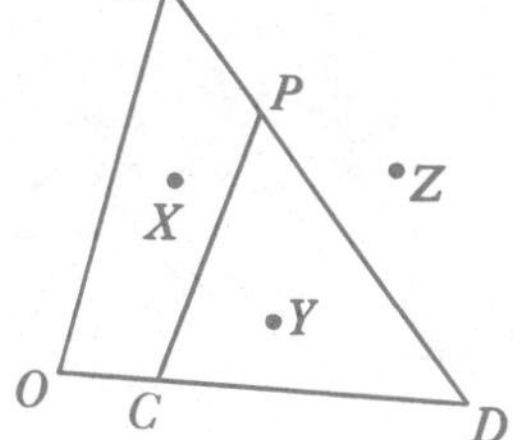

33. $\angle PDC$ **34.** $\angle OPD$ **35.** $\angle EDO$

36. $\angle EDC$ **37.** $\angle XDC$ **38.** $\angle XYZ$

39. $\angle O$ **40.** $\angle ODP$

© **41.** Can a point be in the exterior of a triangle and in the interior of one of the angles of the triangle? Draw a figure to show why.

42. Can a point be in the exterior of a triangle, but not in the interior of any angles of the triangle? Draw a figure to show why.

43–45. Draw $\triangle YOU$. Place point W so that W is on the same side of $\overleftrightarrow{YU}$ as O, on the same side of $\overleftrightarrow{OU}$ as Y, and on the same side of $\overleftrightarrow{OY}$ as U.

43. Is W in the interior of $\angle OUY$?

44. Is W in the interior of $\triangle YOU$?

45. Use these ideas to state another definition of the *interior* of a triangle.

46–47. If we pick a point on a straight line as a vertex, we could define *straight angle* as a figure formed by opposite rays.

46. Could we define the interior and exterior of a straight angle as we did for angles? Why?

47. We will not use "straight angle" in this text. What term can we use instead?

Measures of Angles

Angles are measured in units called *degrees*. Protractors are used to find the number of degrees in an angle as shown below.

Examples:

1.

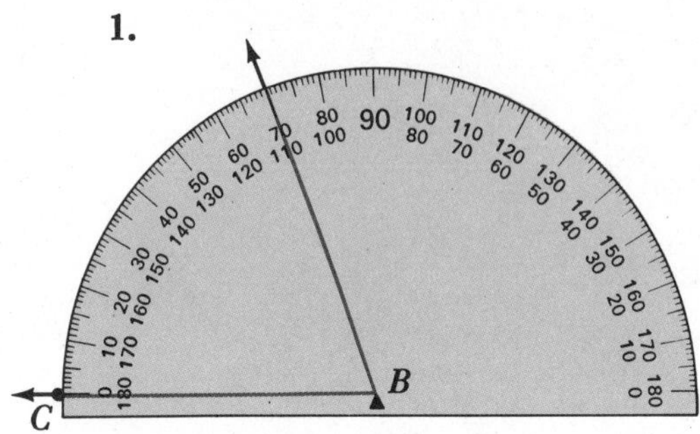

Read "measure of $\angle B$ equals 70". → $m\angle B = 70$

Use the top scale of the protractor to measure $\angle B$ because side $\overrightarrow{BC}$ intersects the top scale at 0.

2.

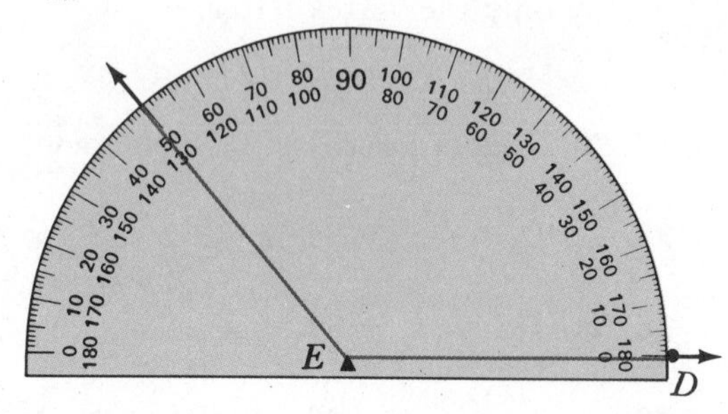

$m\angle E = 130$

Use the bottom scale of the protractor to measure $\angle E$ because side $\overrightarrow{ED}$ intersects the bottom scale at 0.

3.

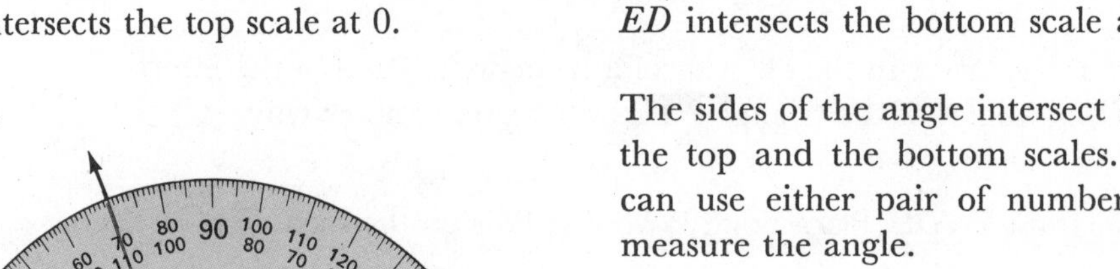

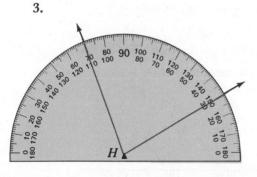

$m\angle H = 80$

The sides of the angle intersect both the top and the bottom scales. We can use either pair of numbers to measure the angle.

$$m\angle H = 150 - 70 = 80$$
$$m\angle H = 110 - 30 = 80$$

Using absolute value, we can subtract in either order.

$$m\angle H = |70 - 150| = 80$$
$$m\angle H = |30 - 110| = 80$$

NOTE: All angle measures in this book are in degrees. So we will not have to name the unit of measure or use the degree symbol (°), unless we want to make sure that a number is understood to be an angle measure.

Angle Measure Postulate

For every angle, there is a unique real number between 0 and 180 called its degree measure.

Line AB separates the plane into two half planes s_1 and s_2. Ray AB is the side of two 35° angles, $\angle PAB$ and $\angle QAB$. With respect to each half plane, we can draw only one 35° angle having $\overrightarrow{AB}$ as a side. Would this be true for an angle of any measure? Consider the next postulate.

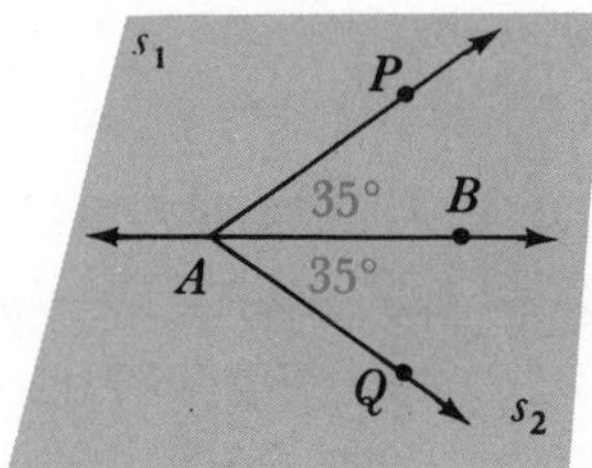

Angle Construction Postulate

> Let ray AB be on the edge of half plane s_1. For every number r between 0 and 180 there is exactly one ray AP with P in s_1 such that $m\angle PAB = r$.

Two **adjacent angles** have a common side, but no points in the interior of one angle are in the interior of the other.

adjacent angles	nonadjacent angles
$\angle ADB$, $\angle BDC$	$\angle ADB$, $\angle ADC$ or $\angle ADC$, $\angle BDC$

The next postulate refers to adjacent angles.

Angle Addition Postulate

> If B is in the interior of $\angle ADC$, then $m\angle ADC = m\angle ADB + m\angle BDC$.

We can use the Angle Addition Postulate as in the examples.

Examples:

1.

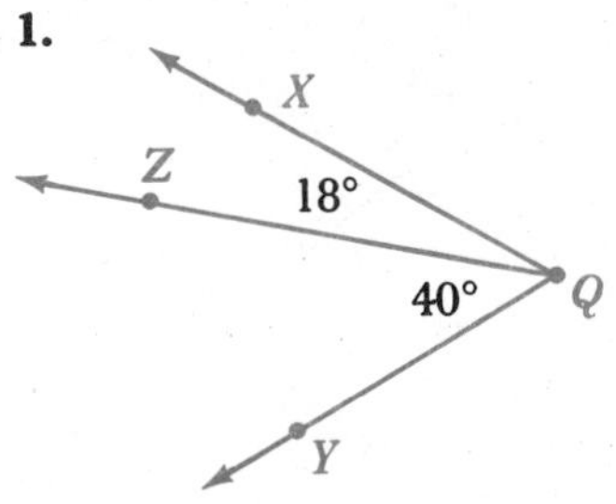

$$m\angle XQY = m\angle XQZ + m\angle ZQY$$
$$= 18 + 40$$
$$= 58$$

2.

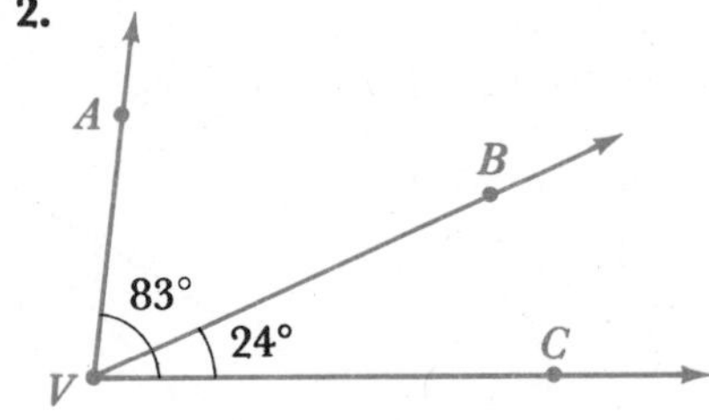

$$m\angle AVC = m\angle AVB + m\angle BVC$$
$$83 = m\angle AVB + 24$$
$$-24 \qquad\qquad -24$$
$$59 = m\angle AVB$$

Exercises 2.3

Ⓐ **1.** The measure of an angle is between ______ and ______.

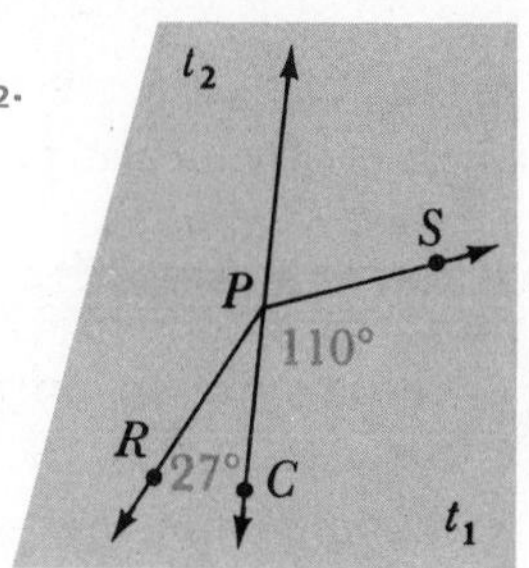

2–3. $\overleftrightarrow{PC}$ separates plane t into half planes t_1 and t_2.

2. Is $\overrightarrow{PS}$ the only ray that can be drawn in half plane t_1 so that $m\angle SPC = 110$?

3. Is $\angle CPR$ the only angle in plane t having a measure of 27 and $\overrightarrow{PC}$ as a side?

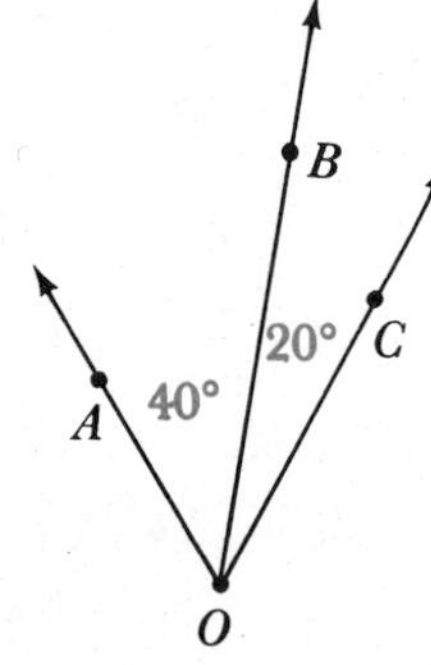

4–6. Choose the best word, number, or symbol. Use the figure at the left. (Do not use a protractor.)

4. ______ and ______ are adjacent angles.

5. $m\angle AOC =$ ______

6. The ______ ______ Postulate states that if B is in the interior of $\angle AOC$, then $m\angle AOC = m\angle AOB + m\angle BOC$.

Ⓑ **7–8.** Measure each angle with a protractor.

7. **8.**

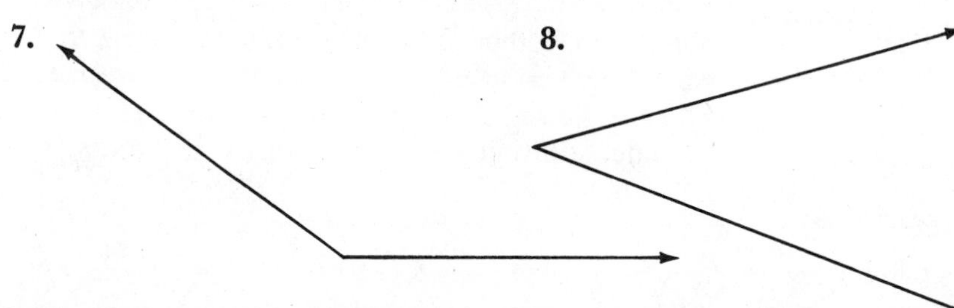

9–10. Measure each angle of the triangle.

9. **10.**

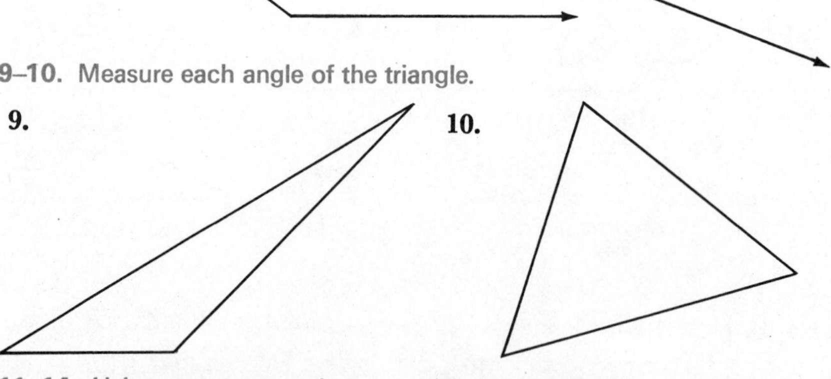

11–14. Using a protractor, draw an angle having the given measure.

11. 36 **12.** 120 **13.** 76 **14.** 155

15–18. Use the figure at the right.

15. Name two angles adjacent to $\angle TON$.

16. Are $\angle NOT$ and $\angle NOD$ adjacent?

17. Find $m\angle TOE$. **18.** Find $m\angle NOD$.

19–22. Choose the best symbol.

19. $m\angle AXB + m\angle BXC = m\angle$ ______

20. $m\angle DXC + m\angle BXC = m\angle$ ______

21. $m\angle BXD - m\angle BXC = m\angle$ ______

22. $m\angle DXA - m\angle CXA = m\angle$ ______

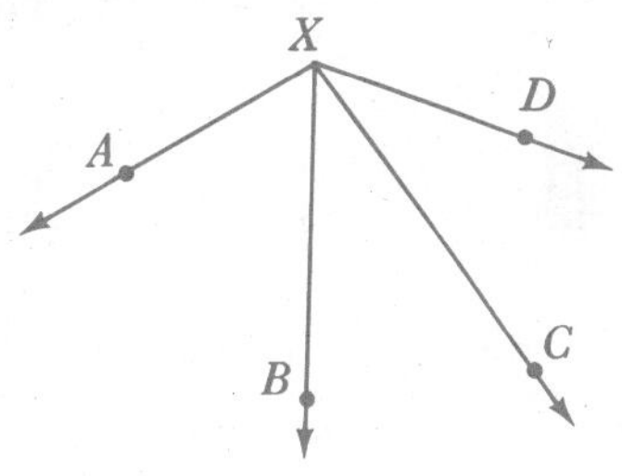

Ex. 19–26

23–26. $m\angle AXD = 131$, $m\angle BXA = 59$, and $m\angle BXC = 34$. Find:

23. $m\angle AXC$ **24.** $m\angle CXD$ **25.** $m\angle DXB$ **26.** $m\angle DXA$

© 27–32. $m\angle OGE = 100$, $m\angle CGM = 42$, $m\angle AGE = 37$, and $m\angle MGA = 72$. Find:

27. $m\angle CGA$ **28.** $m\angle MGE$ **29.** $m\angle CGE$

30. $m\angle OGC$ **31.** $m\angle OGM$ **32.** $m\angle OGA$

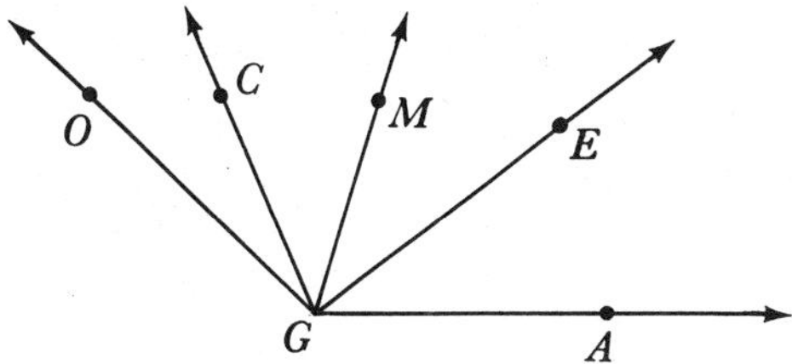

Algebra Review

Review these skills:

- *translating English to algebra*
- *setting up equations to solve problems*

1–4. Represent each number by using a variable.

1. 20 more than a number **2.** 30 less than a number

3. 2 times a number **4.** $\frac{1}{3}$ a number

5–6. Set up the equation you would use to find each pair of numbers.

5. One number is 6 more than another, and their sum is 180.

6. One number is 5 times the other, and their sum is 90.

7–8. Find each pair of numbers in Exercises 5–6.

2.4 Bisectors and Supplements of Angles

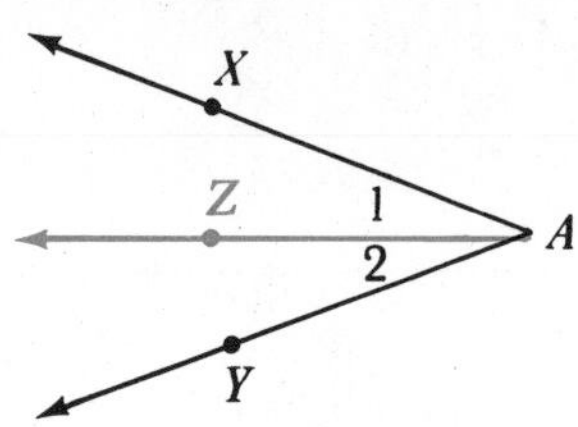

The **bisector** of $\angle XAY$ is ray AZ, where Z is in the interior of $\angle XAY$ and $m\angle XAZ = m\angle YAZ$.

We use the Angle Measure, the Angle Construction, and the Angle Addition postulates to show why the next theorem is true.

Theorem  Every angle has exactly one bisector. 

Reasoning: (See figure above.)

From the Angle Measure Postulate we know that any $\angle XAY$ has exactly one measure. Call it r. So ▶ $m\angle XAY = r$

By the Angle Construction Postulate there is *exactly one* ray AZ on the same side of $\overleftrightarrow{AY}$ as point X so that ▶ $m\angle 2 = \frac{1}{2}r$

By the Angle Addition Postulate, ▶ $m\angle XAY = m\angle 1 + m\angle 2$

Use algebra { Substitute ▶ $r = m\angle 1 + \frac{1}{2}r$
Subtract $\frac{1}{2}r$ ▶ $-\frac{1}{2}r \qquad - \frac{1}{2}r$

$\frac{1}{2}r = m\angle 1$

Since $m\angle 1 = \frac{1}{2}r$ and $m\angle 2 = \frac{1}{2}r$, ▶ $m\angle 1 = m\angle 2$

Therefore $\overrightarrow{AZ}$ is the only bisector of $\angle XAY$.

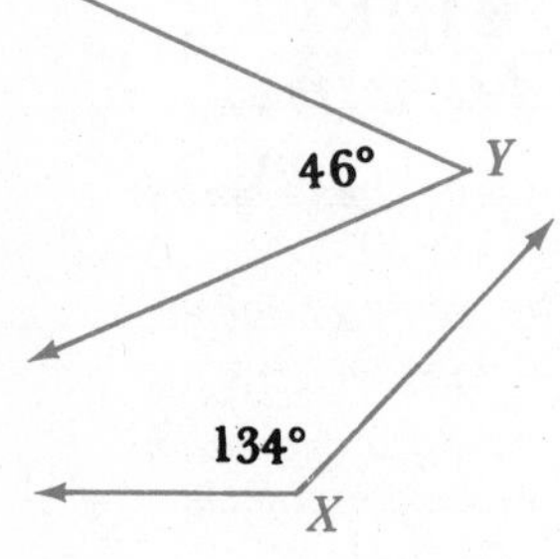

Supplementary angles are two angles whose measures have the sum of 180.

$\angle X$ and $\angle Y$ are supplementary.
$\angle X$ is the supplement of $\angle Y$.
$\angle Y$ is the supplement of $\angle X$.

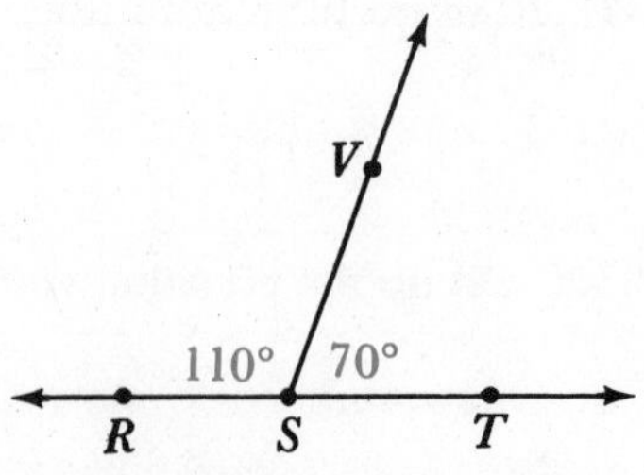

$\overrightarrow{SR}$ and $\overrightarrow{ST}$ at right are opposite rays.
Notice that $m\angle VSR + m\angle VST = 180$.

Supplement Postulate

If the noncommon sides of two adjacent angles are opposite rays, then the angles are supplementary.

Exercises 2.4

Ⓐ **1–2.** Use the figure at the right. $\overrightarrow{ST}$ bisects $\angle RSV$.

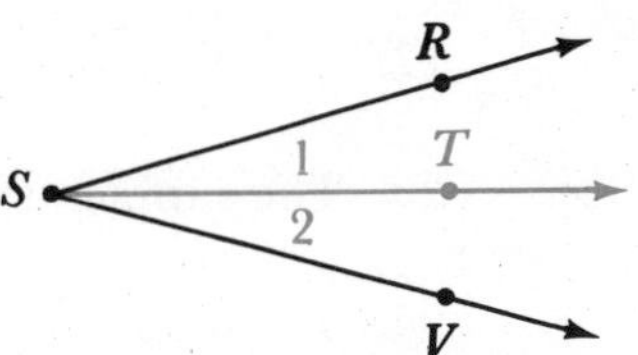

1. What is true about $m\angle 1$ and $m\angle 2$?

2. If $m\angle 2 = 27$, find $m\angle 1$.

3–5. Complete each statement. (Do not use a protractor.)

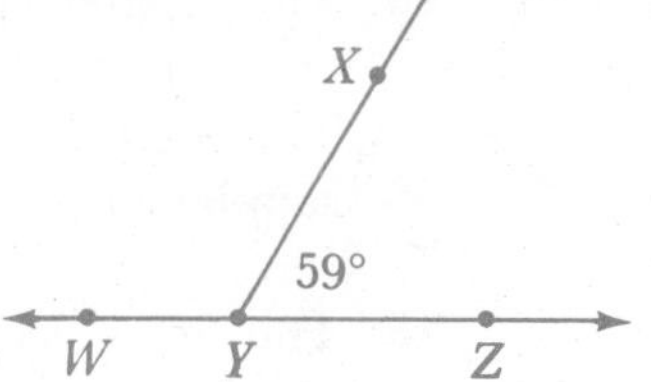

3. _____ and _____ are opposite rays.

4. _____ and _____ are supplementary angles.

5. $m\angle WYX =$ _____

6. State the Supplement Postulate.

Ⓑ **7–8.** Use the figure.

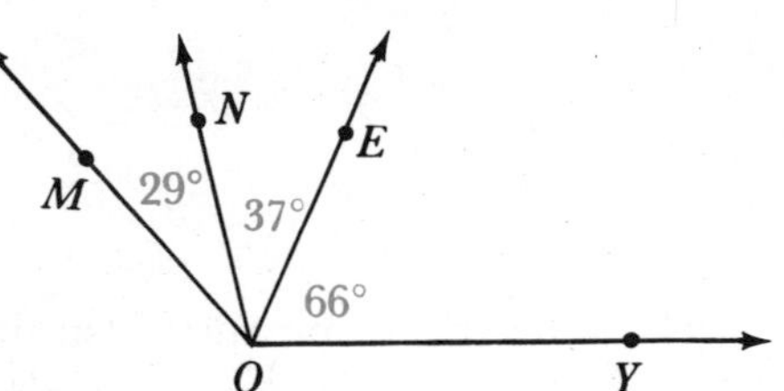

7. Is $\overrightarrow{ON}$ the bisector of $\angle MOE$?

8. Is $\overrightarrow{OE}$ the bisector of $\angle MOY$?

9. Ray AX bisects $\angle CAY$, and $m\angle CAY = 161$. Find $m\angle CAX$ and $m\angle XAY$.

10. Ray AG bisects $\angle TAP$, and $m\angle TAP = 78$. Find $m\angle TAG$ and $m\angle GAP$.

11–18. For the given angle measure, find the measure of the supplement.

11. 31 **12.** 147 **13.** 128 **14.** 41

15. 152.3 **16.** $131\frac{1}{2}$ **17.** n **18.** $(180 - n)$

19–28. Find the measure of each angle and its supplement.

19. The supplement is 3 times the measure of the angle.

HINT: Let $x =$ the measure of the angle.
Then $3x =$ the measure of the supplement.
So, $x + 3x = 180$ because the two angles are supplementary.

20. The supplement is 5 times the measure of the angle.

21. The supplement is 30 more than the measure of the angle.

22. The supplement is 72 less than the measure of the angle.

23. The supplement is $\frac{1}{3}$ the measure of the angle.

24. The angle and its supplement have the same measure.

Ⓒ 25. The supplement is 60 less than $\frac{1}{2}$ the measure of the angle.

26. The supplement is 48 more than 5 times the measure of the angle.

27. The angle has a measure of 5 more than $\frac{1}{4}$ the measure of its supplement.

28. The angle has a measure 30 less than twice the measure of its supplement.

29–30. $\angle ABC$ and $\angle CBD$ are adjacent; $\overrightarrow{BA}$ and $\overrightarrow{BD}$ are opposite rays.

29. Is $m\angle ABC + m\angle CBD = 180$? Why?

30. What is the measure of straight angle ABD? *Straight angle* is defined in the instructions before Exercise 46 on page 51.

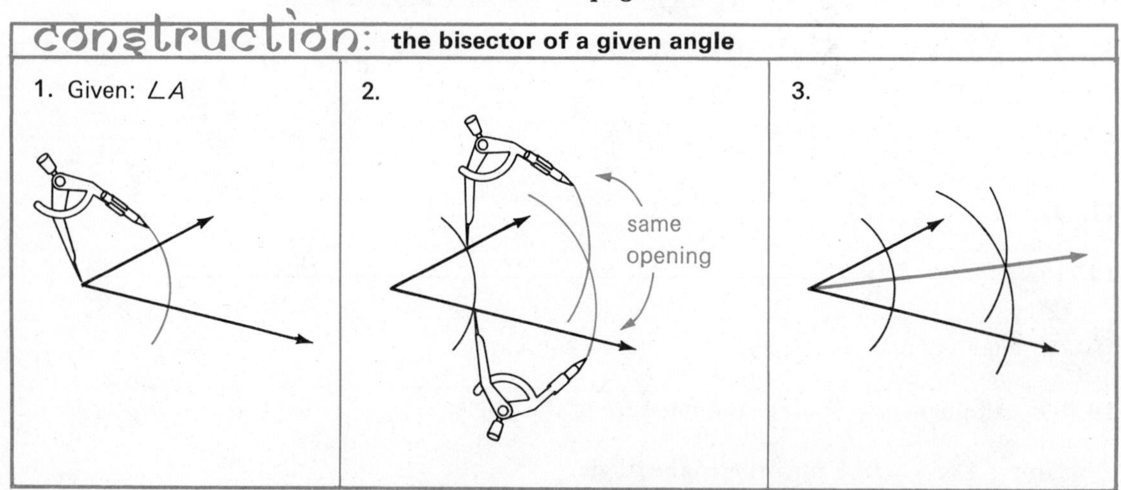

31–34. Use a protractor to draw an angle of the given measure. Construct its bisector. (Use a protractor to check your answer.)

31. 70 32. 85 33. 148 34. 115

In Other Words

Students in other countries study about angles and triangles. See if you can say their words for these terms. Pronunciations are taken from *Webster's New Collegiate Dictionary*, eighth edition.

	angle	(pronunciation)		triangle	(pronunciation)
Russian	**Угол**	('ü–gəl)	French	triangle	(trē–'än–gəl)
Italian	angolo	(än–'gō–lō)	Japanese	三角形	(san–kä–kā)
Polish	kąt	(känt)	Spanish	triángulo	(trē–'än–gü–lō)
Hebrew	**זָוִית**	(zȯ–'vēt)	Slovak	trojholnik	(trō–yü–'hōl–nik)

True or False?

1. This figure is not a convex set.

2. Points A, B, and C lie in half plane t_1.

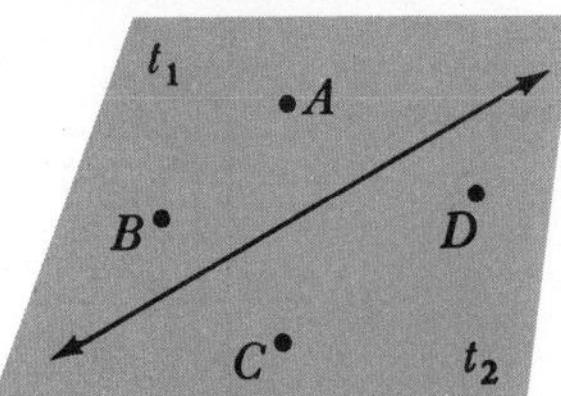

3. An angle is formed by two segments that intersect.
4. Point M is in the interior of $\angle ABC$.

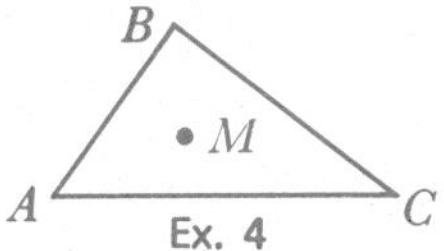

Ex. 4

5. Another name for $\angle FGK$ is $\angle G$.
6. $\angle FGH$ and $\angle FGK$ are adjacent angles.
7. $m\angle FGK = 52$
8. $\overrightarrow{GH}$ is the bisector of $\angle KGF$.

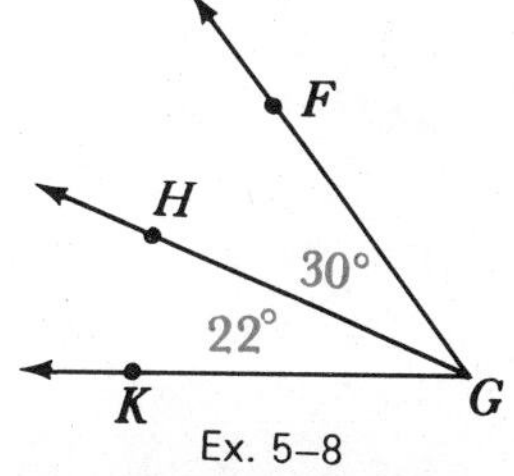

Ex. 5–8

9. If an angle's measure is 73, then the measure of its supplement is 107.

2.5 Angles and Perpendicular Lines

Definition

A **right angle** is an angle whose measure is 90.

An **acute angle** is an angle whose measure is less than 90.

An **obtuse angle** is an angle whose measure is greater than 90.

Complementary angles are two angles whose measures have the sum of 90.

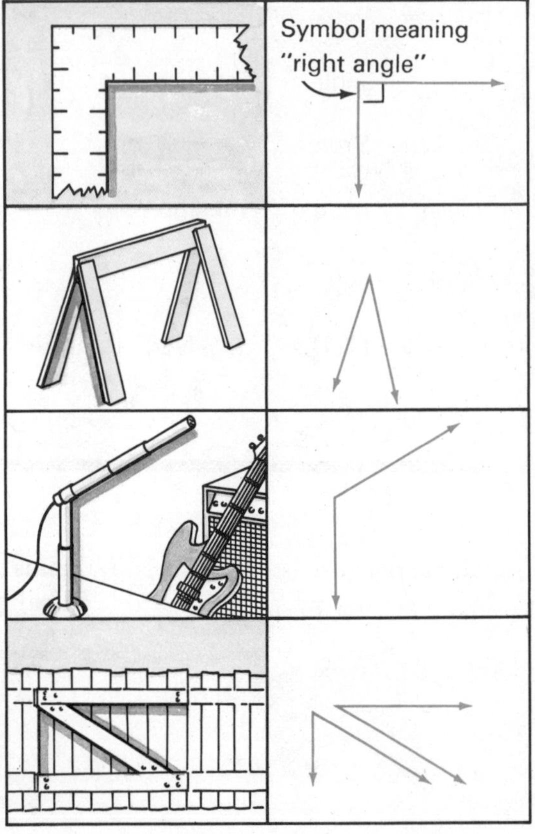

Lines, segments, and rays that meet to form a 90°, or right, angle are **perpendicular**. (⊥ means "is perpendicular to.")

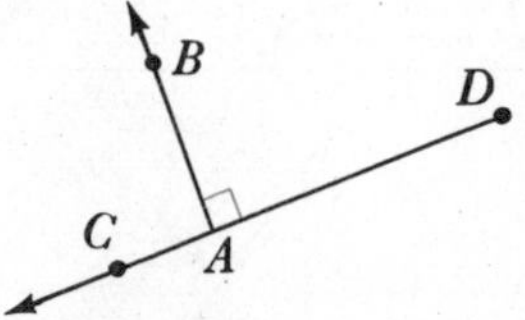

$\overrightarrow{AB}$ is perpendicular to $\overrightarrow{DC}$.

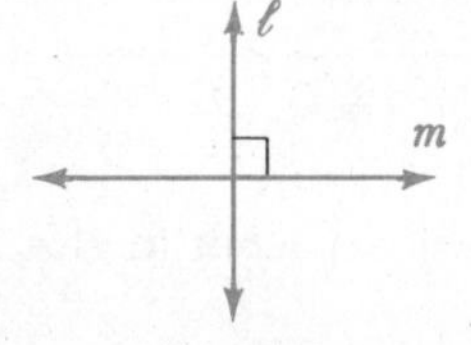

$\ell \perp m$

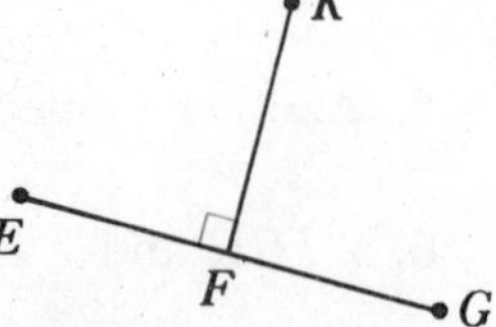

$\overline{EG}$ is perpendicular to $\overline{FK}$.

Perpendicular Line Postulate

In any plane containing a given line and point, there is exactly one line through the point perpendicular to the given line.

According to the postulate, if ℓ and P are the given line and point, then:

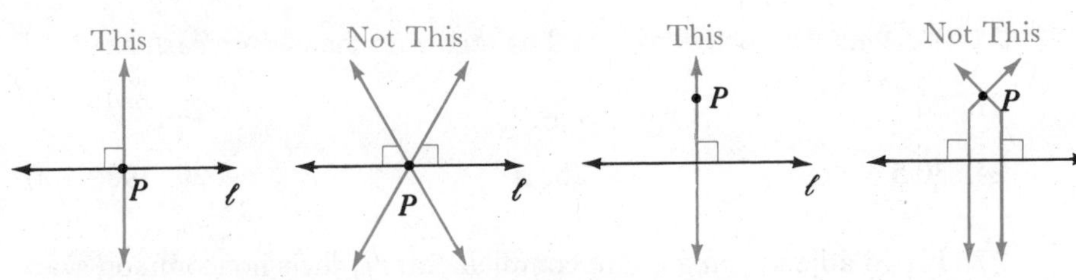

In a plane, the **perpendicular bisector** of a segment is the line that is perpendicular to the segment at its midpoint. Line ℓ is the perpendicular bisector of segment AB.

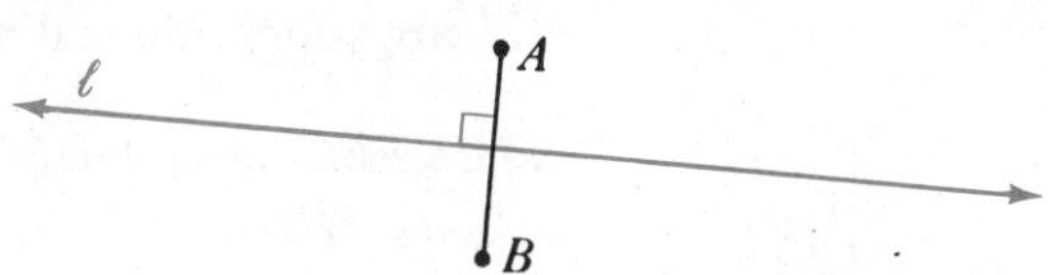

Exercises 2.5

Ⓐ **1–6.** Use acute, obtuse, or right to complete each statement.

1. $\angle MOP$ is a(n) ______ angle.

2. $\angle TOP$ is a(n) ______ angle.

3. $\angle HOP$ is a(n) ______ angle.

T P H O M
Ex. 1–3

4. A(n) ______ angle has a measure of 90.

5. A(n) ______ angle has a measure less than 90.

6. A(n) ______ angle has a measure greater than 90.

7. What is the sum of the measures of two complementary angles?

8. Define *perpendicular lines.*

9. In a plane, how many lines are perpendicular to line ℓ through P?

10. Define *perpendicular bisector.*

Ⓑ **11–16.** $m\angle HCE = 90, m\angle ECL = 25$, $\overleftrightarrow{SL}$ contains C. Name the following.

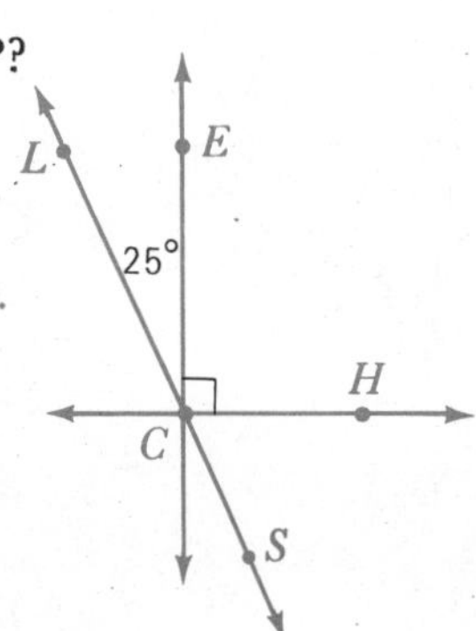

11. two obtuse angles

12. two acute angles

13. two supplementary angles

14. two complementary angles

15. two perpendicular lines

16. two opposite rays

17–20. What type of angle is formed by the hands of a clock at

17. 10:00? **18.** 4:00? **19.** 9:00? **20.** 4:30?

21–26. Find the complement of the angle with the given measure.

21. 80 **22.** 6 **23.** $28\frac{1}{3}$

24. 30.5 **25.** n **26.** $(90 - n)$

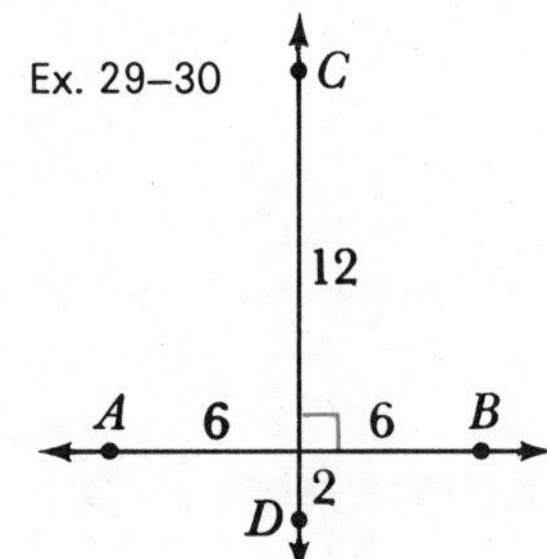

27. If two adjacent angles are complementary, their noncommon sides are (opposite, collinear, perpendicular) rays.

28. $\angle ABC$ and $\angle DBC$ are adjacent complementary angles. Find $m\angle ABD$.

29–30. True or False? $\overleftrightarrow{DC}$ is the perpendicular bisector

29. of $\overline{AB}$. **30.** of $\overleftrightarrow{AB}$.

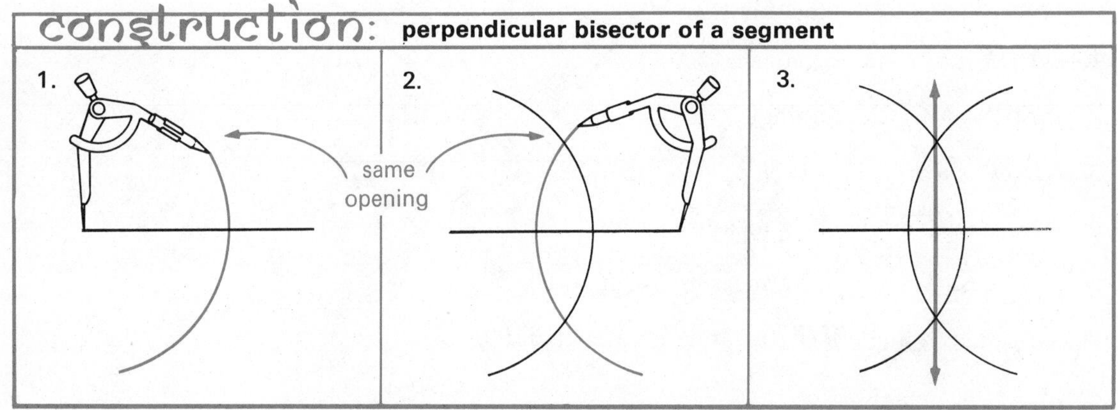

31–34. Draw a segment of the length given. Construct its perpendicular bisector.

31. 6 cm **32.** 12 cm **33.** 8 cm **34.** 70 mm

35–37. Choose one term (acute, obtuse, right) to describe each angle.

35. either of two complementary angles

36. the supplement of an obtuse angle

37. the supplement of a right angle

38. Can an obtuse angle have a complement? Why?

39–44. Find the measure of each angle and its complement.

39. The complement is 10 more than the measure of the angle.

HINT: Let $x =$ the measure of the angle. Then $x + 10 =$ the measure of the complement, and $x + x + 10 = 90$.

40. The complement is 52 less than the measure of the angle.

41. The complement is twice the measure of the angle.

42. The complement is equal to the measure of the angle.

© **43.** The complement is 8 more than 3 times the measure of the angle.

44. The complement is 24 less than twice the measure of the angle.

construction: a perpendicular to a given point on a line

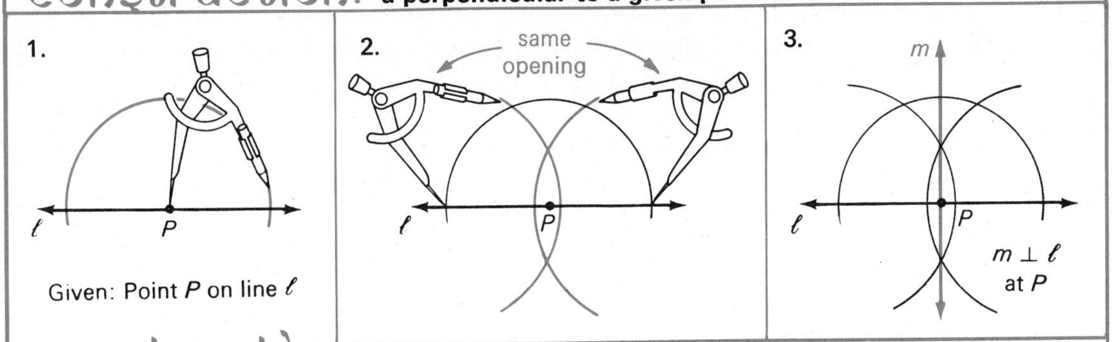

1. Given: Point P on line ℓ

2. same opening

3. $m \perp \ell$ at P

construction: a perpendicular from a given point to a line

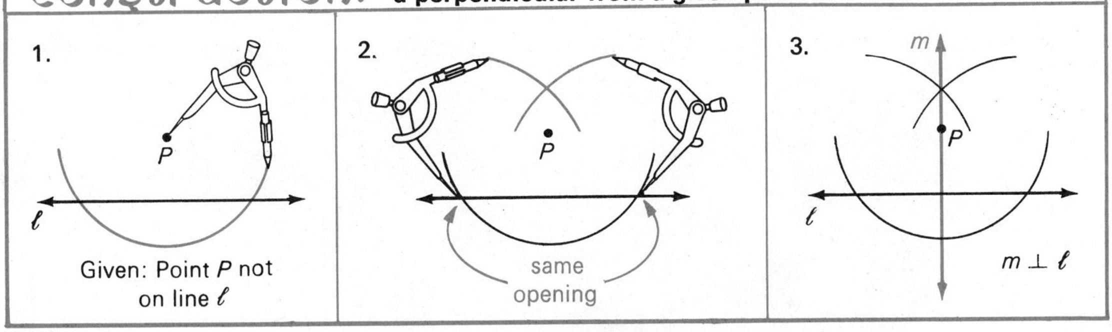

1. Given: Point P not on line ℓ

2. same opening

3. $m \perp \ell$

45–46. Copy. Construct perpendiculars to line ℓ at P and from M.

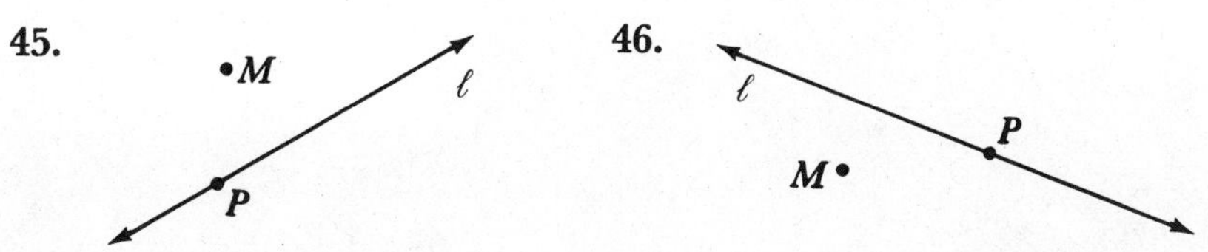

2.6 Congruent Segments and Angles

Angles

Congruent angles are angles that have the same measure.

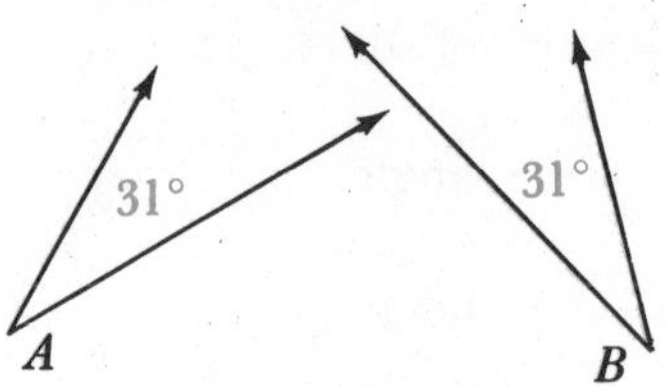

$m\angle A = m\angle B$

$\angle A$ is congruent to $\angle B$

$\angle A \cong \angle B$

Segments

Congruent segments are segments that have the same measure.

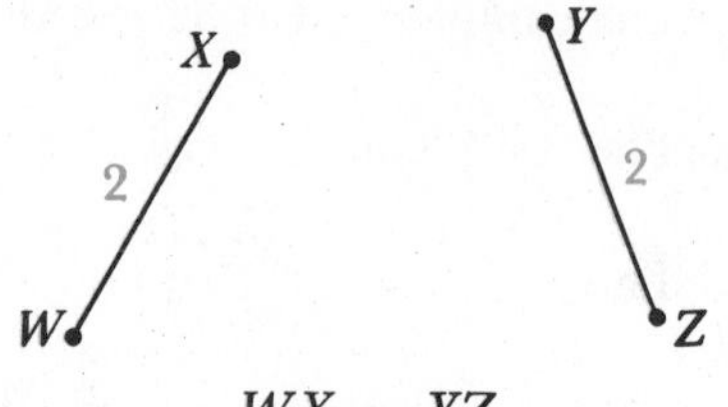

$WX = YZ$

$\overline{WX}$ is congruent to $\overline{YZ}$

$\overline{WX} \cong \overline{YZ}$

$\cong$ means is congruent to

Notice that the geometric figures (segments or angles) are congruent, while their measures, which are numbers, are equal.

$m\angle A = m\angle B$	The top and bottom statements are equivalent. One can be replaced by the other at any time.	$WX = YZ$
$\angle A \cong \angle B$		$\overline{WX} \cong \overline{YZ}$

The properties at the bottom of page 22 can be used to show that similar properties carry over to congruent segments and angles.

Property of Equal Numbers	Property of Congruent Angles	Property of Congruent Segments
$m\angle A = m\angle A$	$\angle A \cong \angle A$	
$XW = XW$		$\overline{XW} \cong \overline{XW}$
If $m\angle A = m\angle B$, then $m\angle B = m\angle A$.	If $\angle A \cong \angle B$, then $\angle B \cong \angle A$.	
If $XW = YZ$, then $YZ = XW$.		If $\overline{XW} \cong \overline{YZ}$, then $\overline{YZ} \cong \overline{XW}$.
If $m\angle A = m\angle B$ and $m\angle B = m\angle C$, then $m\angle A = m\angle C$.	If $\angle A \cong \angle B$ and $\angle B \cong \angle C$, then $\angle A \cong \angle C$.	
If $XW = YZ$ and $YZ = PR$, then $XW = PR$.		If $\overline{XW} \cong \overline{YZ}$ and $\overline{YZ} \cong \overline{PR}$, then $\overline{XW} \cong \overline{PR}$.

These ideas are now stated as theorems.

An angle is congruent to itself.

Congruence of two angles can be stated in either order.

Two angles congruent to the same angle are congruent to each other.

Congruent Angles Theorems

A segment is congruent to itself.

Congruence of two segments can be stated in either order.

Two segments congruent to the same segment are congruent to each other.

Congruent Segments Theorems

If $\angle J$ and $\angle G$ are right angles, then $m\angle J = 90$ and $m\angle G = 90$, making $m\angle J = m\angle G$ and $\angle J \cong \angle G$.

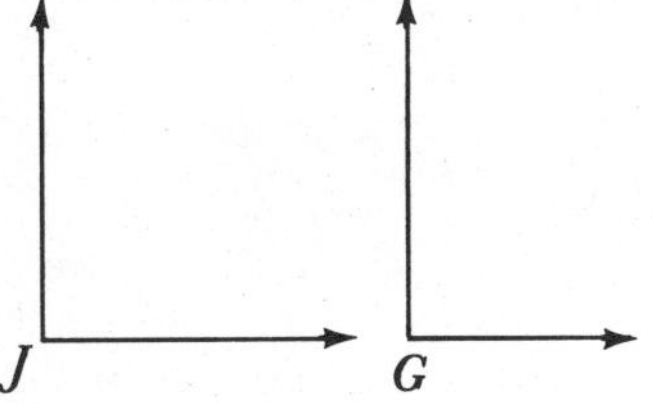

This is why we can state the next theorem.

Any two right angles are congruent.

Theorem

Exercises 2.6

Ⓐ **1.** Define *congruent angles*. **2.** Define *congruent segments*.

3–10. Complete each statement with the best symbol possible.

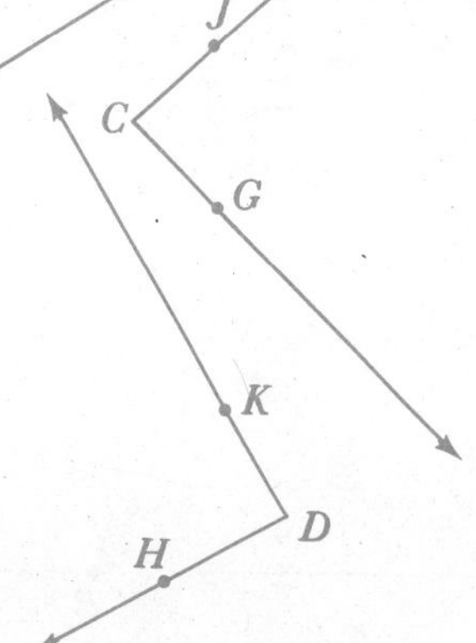

3. $\angle A \cong$ ______ **4.** $\overline{AB} \cong$ ______

5. If $\angle C \cong \angle D$, then $\angle D \cong$ ______.

6. If $\overline{KD} \cong \overline{JC}$, then $\overline{JC} \cong$ ______.

7. If $\angle A \cong \angle C$ and $\angle C \cong \angle D$, then $\angle A \cong$ ______.

8. If $\overline{JC} \cong \overline{HD}$ and $\overline{HD} \cong \overline{BA}$, then $\overline{JC} \cong$ ______.

9. If $\overline{CG} \cong \overline{CJ}$ and $\overline{CJ} \cong \overline{DK}$, then ______ $\cong \overline{DK}$.

10. If $\angle D$ and $\angle C$ are right angles, then $\angle D \cong$ ______.

Ⓑ **11–12.** State these theorems in symbols.

11. Congruence of two angles can be stated in either order.

12. Two segments congruent to the same segment are congruent to each other.

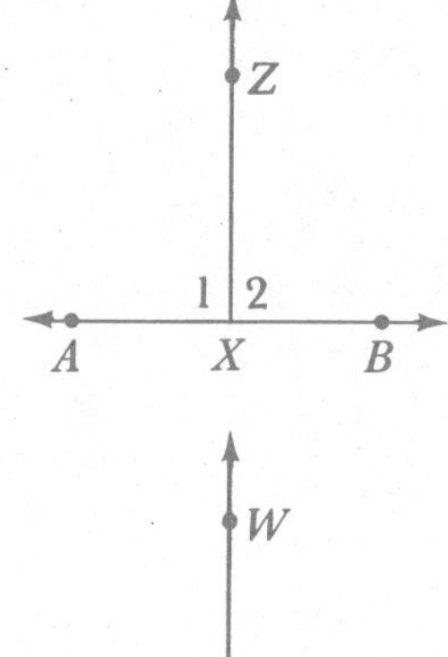

13–16. Complete each statement with the best number or symbol.

13. If $\angle X_1 \cong \angle Y_1$ and $m\angle X_1 = 93$, then $m\angle Y_1 =$ ______.

14. If $AX = 8$ and $CY = 8$, then ______ $\cong$ ______.

15. If $AX = 5$, $CY = 5$, and $\overline{BX} \cong \overline{AX}$, then $\overline{BX} \cong$ ______.

16. If $\angle X_1 \cong \angle Y_1$, $\angle Y_1 \cong \angle X_2$, and $m\angle X_1 = 90$, then $m\angle Y_1 =$ ______ and $m\angle X_2 =$ ______.

17–18. Fill in the blank with $=$ or $\cong$.

17. $\angle Y_1$ ______ $\angle Y_1$

18. XB ______ XB

Ⓒ **19.** The three properties in the Congruent Angles Theorems are called the symmetric, reflexive, and transitive properties. Find out which is which. HINT: It might help to refer to Exercise 57, page 25.

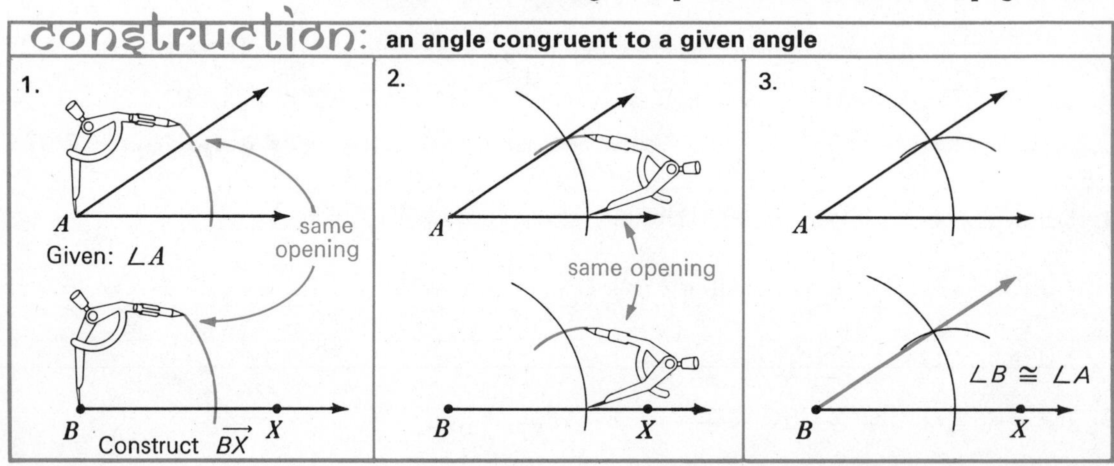

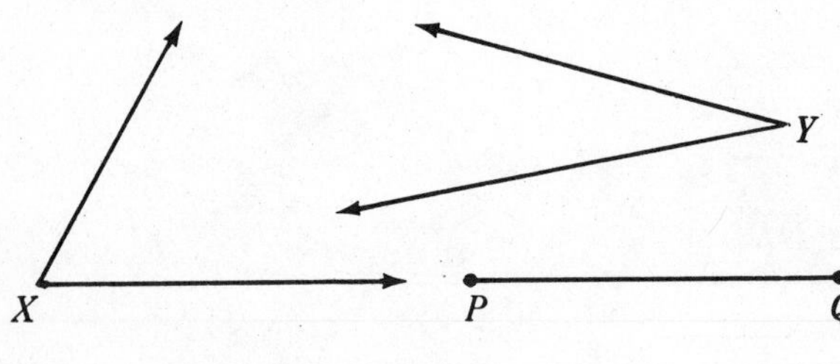

20–23. Use the angles at the left to construct an angle of the given measure.

20. $m\angle X$

21. $m\angle Y$

22. $m\angle X + m\angle Y$

23. $m\angle X - m\angle Y$

24. Construct $\triangle ABC$ with $\angle A \cong \angle X$, $\angle B \cong \angle Y$, and $\overline{AB} \cong \overline{PQ}$

Angle Relationships

$\angle 1 \cong \angle 3$ because they are made to be 150° angles. Angles 1 and 2 as well as angles 3 and 4 are supplementary. Therefore, $\angle 2$ and $\angle 4$ are 30° angles. $\angle 2 \cong \angle 4$

Angles 5 and 7 as well as angles 6 and 8 are complementary angles. If $\angle 5$ and $\angle 8$ are 15° angles, then $\angle 6$ and $\angle 7$ will both be 75° angles, and $\angle 6 \cong \angle 7$.

These relationships suggest the next two theorems.

Artstreet

Supplements of congruent angles are congruent.

Congruent Supplements Theorem

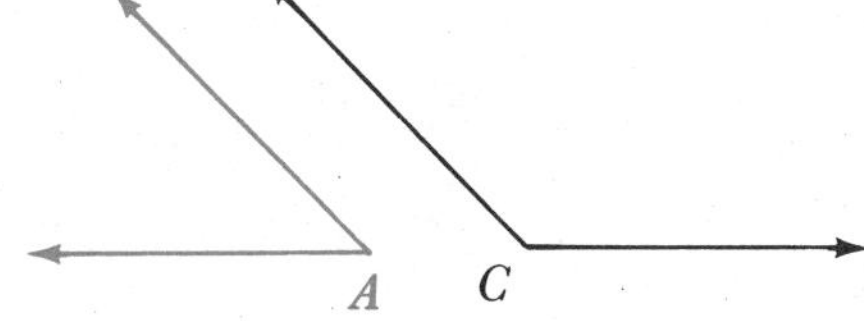

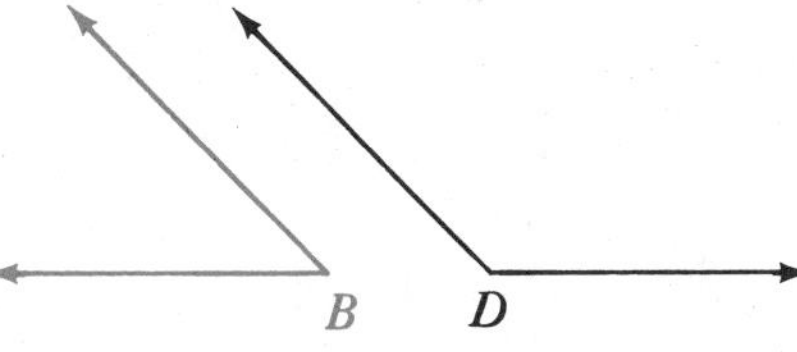

If $\angle A \cong \angle B$, $m\angle A + m\angle C = 180$, and $m\angle B + m\angle D = 180$, then $\angle C \cong \angle D$.

Reasoning:

Since $m\angle A + m\angle C = 180$ and $m\angle B + m\angle D = 180$, ▶ $m\angle A + m\angle C = m\angle B + m\angle D$

Since $\angle A \cong \angle B$, $m\angle A = m\angle B$ and we can substitute $m\angle A$ for $m\angle B$ ▶ $m\angle A + m\angle C = m\angle A + m\angle D$

$$\begin{array}{rcl} m\angle A + m\angle C & = & m\angle A + m\angle D \\ -m\angle A & & -m\angle A \\ \hline \end{array}$$

Subtracting $m\angle A$, we get ▶ $m\angle C = m\angle D$

Since two angles with equal measure are congruent, ▶ $\angle C \cong \angle D$

Since an angle is congruent to itself, the theorem above lets us say that *two angles supplementary to the same angle are congruent.* This will be useful later.

Congruent Complements Theorem

Complements of congruent angles are congruent.

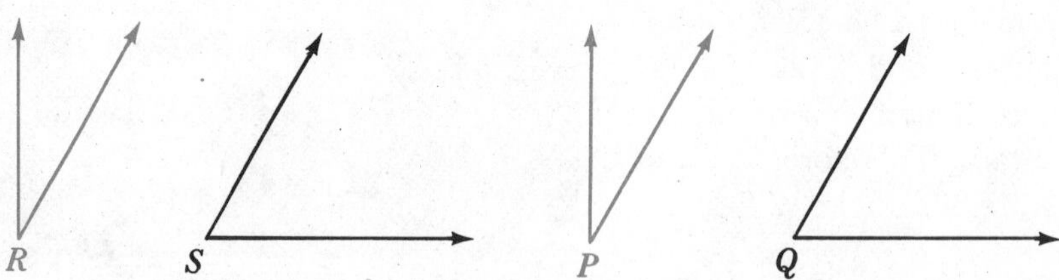

If $\angle R \cong \angle P$, $m\angle R + m\angle S = 90$, and $m\angle P + m\angle Q = 90$, then $\angle S \cong \angle Q$.

Reasoning:

Since $m\angle R + m\angle S = 90$ and $m\angle P + m\angle Q = 90$, ▶ $m\angle R + m\angle S = m\angle P + m\angle Q$

Since $\angle R \cong \angle P$, $m\angle R = m\angle P$ and we can substitute $m\angle R$ for $m\angle P$ ▶ $m\angle R + m\angle S = m\angle R + m\angle Q$

$$\begin{array}{rcl} -m\angle R & & -m\angle R \\ \hline \end{array}$$

Subtracting $m\angle R$, we get ▶ $m\angle S = m\angle Q$

Since two angles with equal measure are congruent, ▶ $\angle S \cong \angle Q$

Since an angle is congruent to itself, the theorem above lets us say that *two angles complementary to the same angle are congruent.*

Theorem

If two angles are congruent and supplementary, then they are right angles.

If $\angle R \cong \angle S$ and $m\angle R + m\angle S = 180$, then $\angle R$ and $\angle S$ are right angles.

Reasoning:

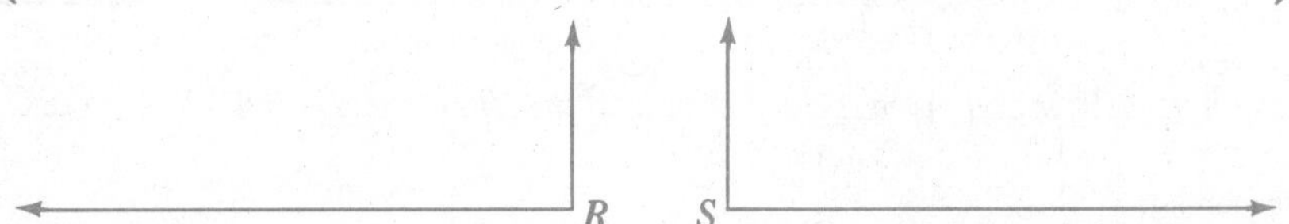

Since $m\angle R = m\angle S$, we can substitute $m\angle R$ for $m\angle S$ in the equation above to obtain $m\angle R + m\angle R = 180$. Simplifying, $2m\angle R = 180$, and $m\angle R = 90$. Therefore, $m\angle S = 90$ and $m\angle R = 90$, and both $\angle R$ and $\angle S$ are right angles.

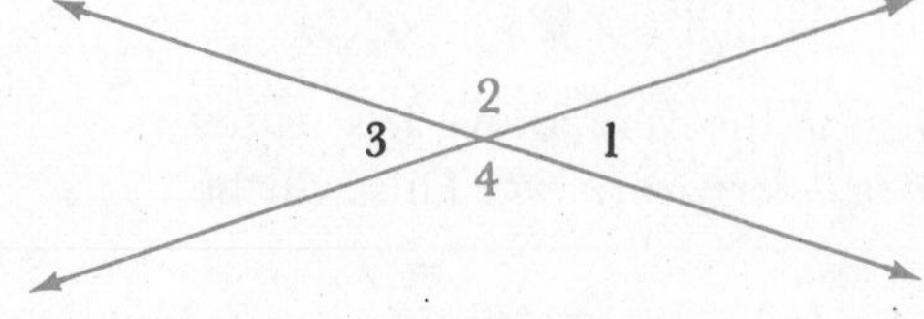

Vertical angles are two nonadjacent angles formed by two intersecting lines. Notice that $\angle 2$ and $\angle 4$ are both supplements of $\angle 1$.

Vertical angles are congruent.

Vertical Angles Theorem

Reasoning:

$\angle 2$ and $\angle 4$ are supplements of $\angle 1$, and $\angle 1$ and $\angle 3$ are supplements of $\angle 2$. Angles supplementary to the same angle are congruent, so $\angle 2 \cong \angle 4$ and $\angle 1 \cong \angle 3$.

Two perpendicular lines meet to form four right angles.

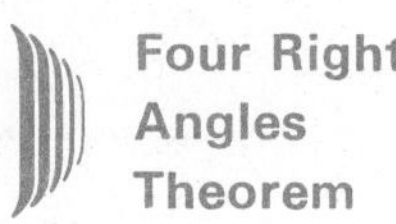

Four Right Angles Theorem

Exercise 41 gives the reasoning for this theorem.

Exercises 2.7

Ⓐ **1–10.** Use the appropriate figures at the right.

3 1
4 2

Ex. 1–2

1. If $\angle 1 \cong \angle 2$, then $\angle 3 \cong \angle$______.

2. $\angle 1$ and ______ as well as $\angle 4$ and ______ are supplementary.

3. $\angle ABC$ and ______ as well as $\angle EBF$ and ______ are complementary.

4. If $\angle CBA \cong \angle FBE$, then $\angle$______ $\cong \angle$______.

5. Find $m\angle DBF$.

6. Name 4 right angles.

7. Name 4 congruent angles.

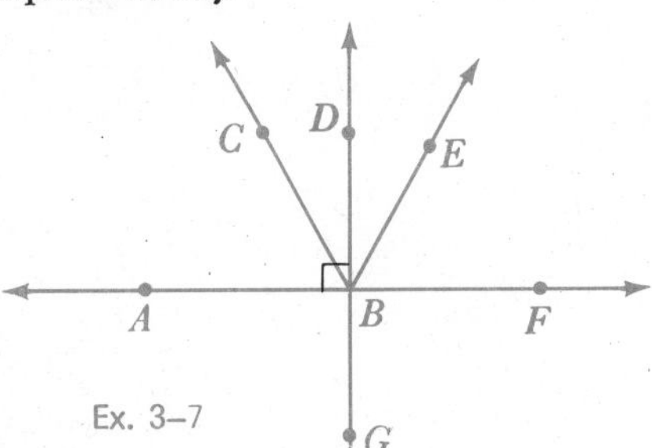

Ex. 3–7

8. $\angle 11$ and $\angle$______ are vertical angles.

9. $\angle 12 \cong$ ______

10. $\angle 13 \cong$ ______

11. Vertical angles are (supplementary, congruent).

12. If two angles are congruent and ______, then they are right angles.

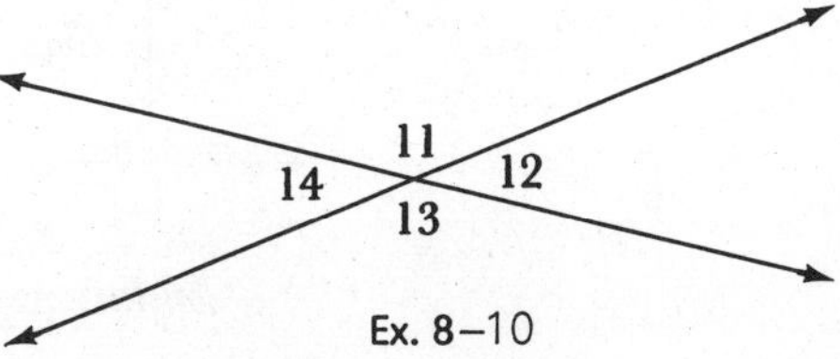

Ex. 8–10

Ⓑ **13–18.** $\angle A_1 \cong \angle B_1$. Lines t and v intersect at point A. Lines s and u intersect at point B. True or False?

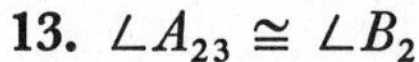

13. $\angle A_{23} \cong \angle B_2$

14. $\angle A_{23} \cong \angle B_4$

15. $\angle A_3 \cong \angle B_2$

16. $\angle A_4 \cong \angle B_3$

17. $\angle A_5 \cong \angle B_2$

18. $\angle A_2 \cong \angle B_3$

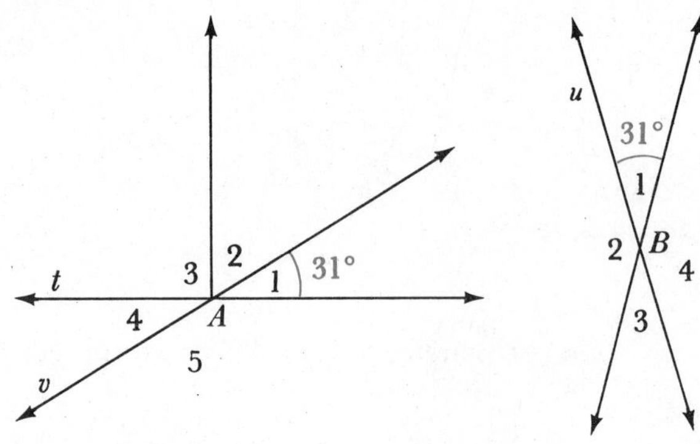

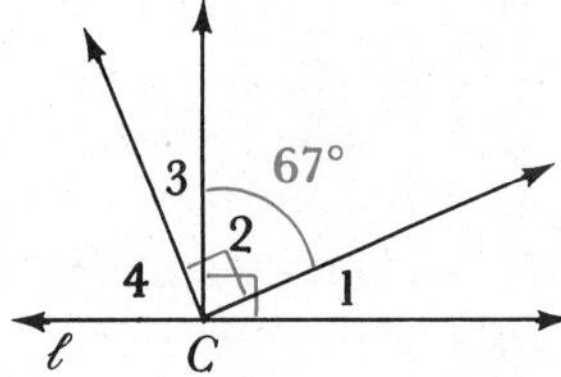

19–28. $\angle C_2 \cong \angle D_1$. Point C is on ℓ. True or False?

19. $\angle C_1 \cong \angle D_2$

20. $\angle C_3 \cong \angle D_1$

21. $\angle C_4 \cong \angle C_2$

22. $\angle C_4 \cong \angle C_1$

23. $\angle C_4 \cong \angle D_2$

24. $\angle C_3 \cong \angle D_2$

25. $\angle C_{34} \cong \angle C_{12}$

26. $\angle D_{12} \cong \angle C_{12}$

27. $\angle C_{23} \cong \angle D_{12}$

28. $\angle C_{23} \cong \angle C_{34}$

29–38. State the theorem that supports each conclusion.

29.

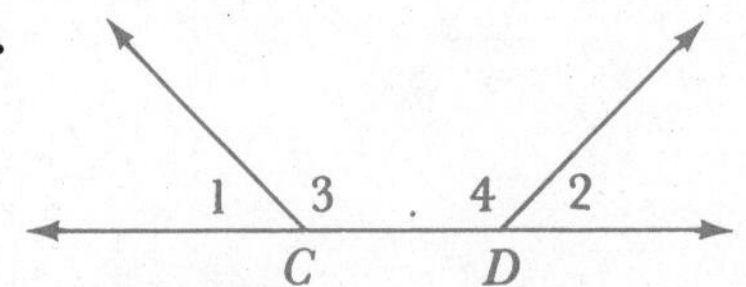

$\overleftrightarrow{CD}$ with $\angle 1 \cong \angle 2$

Conclusion: $\angle 3 \cong \angle 4$

30.

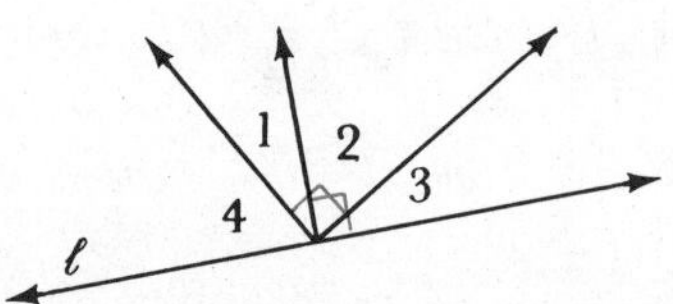

$\angle 1 \cong \angle 3$

Conclusion: $\angle 2 \cong \angle 4$

31.

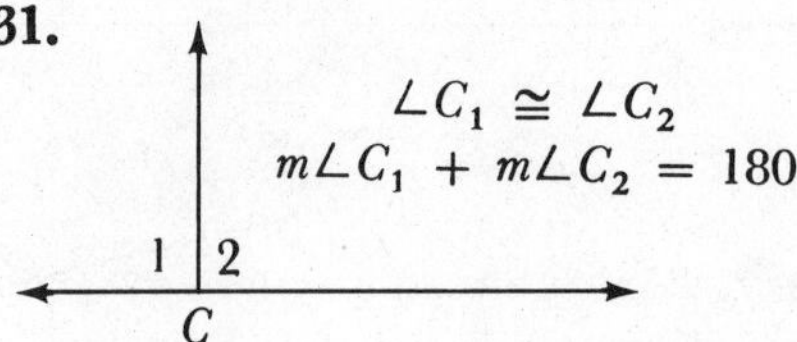

$\angle C_1 \cong \angle C_2$

$m\angle C_1 + m\angle C_2 = 180$

Conclusion: $\angle C_1$ and $\angle C_2$ are right angles.

32.

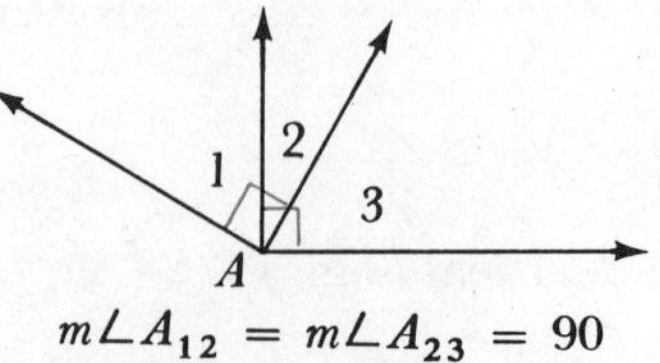

$m\angle A_{12} = m\angle A_{23} = 90$

Conclusion: $\angle 1 \cong \angle 3$

33.

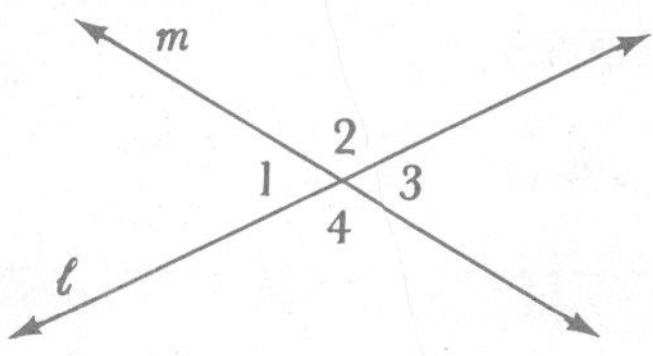

Conclusion: $\angle 1 \cong \angle 3$

34.

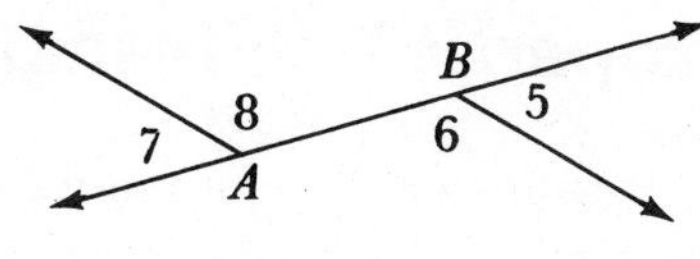

$\overleftrightarrow{AB}$ with $\angle 8 \cong \angle 6$

Conclusion: $\angle 5 \cong \angle 7$

35.

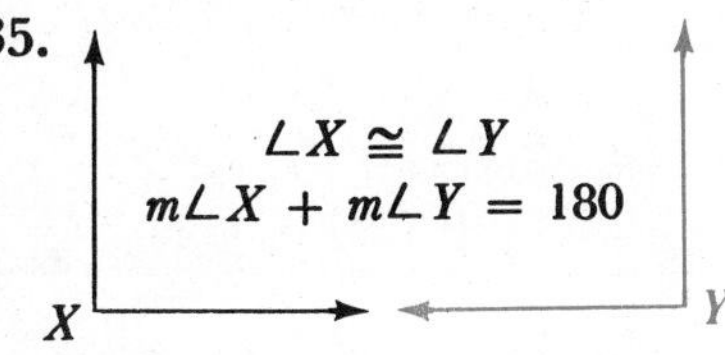

Conclusion: $\angle X$ and $\angle Y$ are right angles.

36.

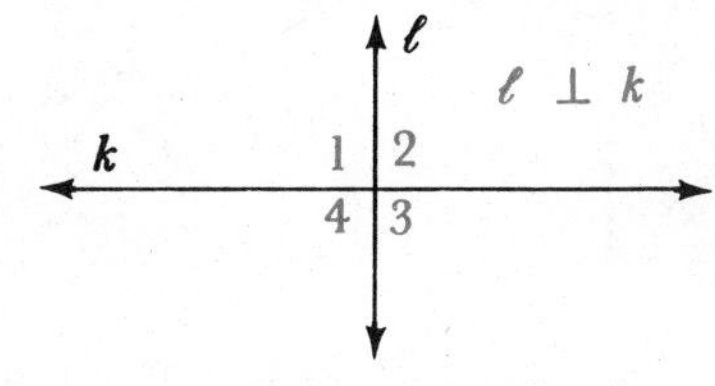

Conclusion: $\angle 1$, $\angle 2$, $\angle 3$, and $\angle 4$ are right angles.

37.

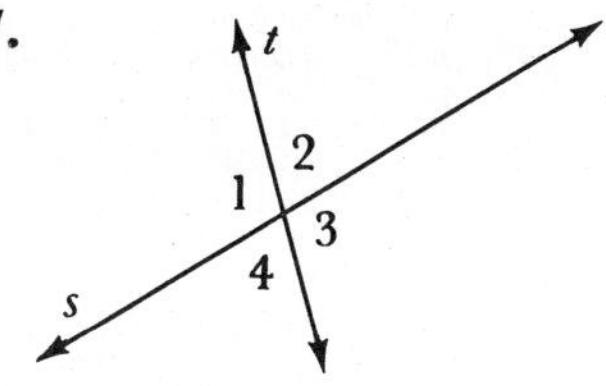

Conclusion: $\angle 2 \cong \angle 4$

38.

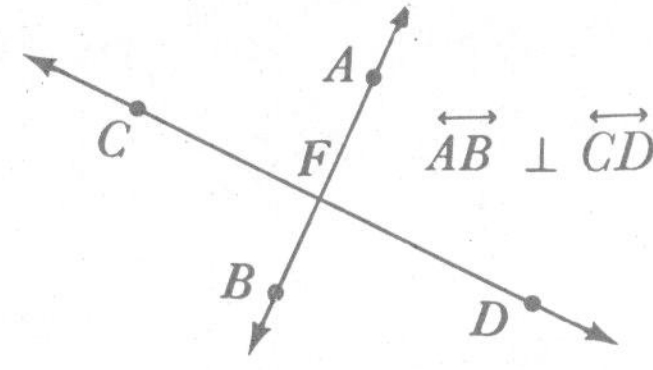

Conclusion: $m\angle AFD = m\angle DFB = m\angle AFC = m\angle BFC = 90$

Ⓒ **39–40.** Solve for the variable.

39.

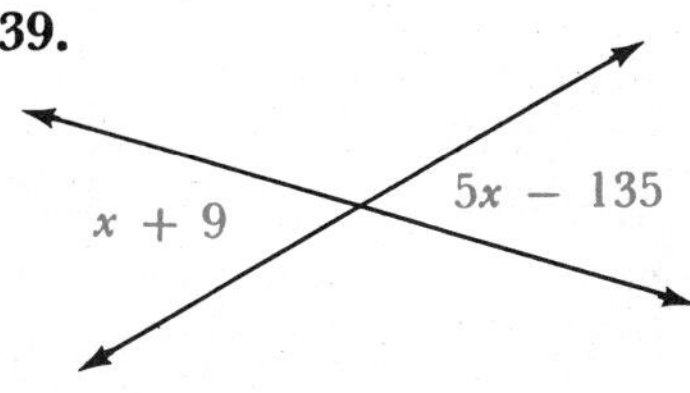

40.

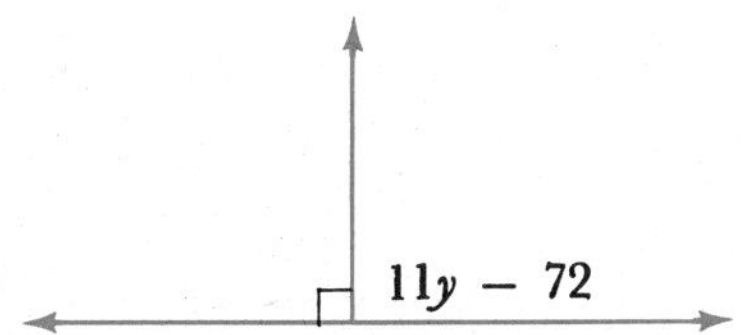

41. Show that the Four Right Angles Theorem, page 69, is true by answering why in steps 2–6.

1. Draw $\ell \perp k$, forming $\angle 1$, $\angle 2$, $\angle 3$, and $\angle 4$.
2. $m\angle 1 = 90$. Why?
3. $m\angle 3 = m\angle 1 = 90$. Why?
4. $m\angle 2 + m\angle 3 = 180$, so $m\angle 2 = 90$. Why?
5. $m\angle 4 = m\angle 2 = 90$. Why?
6. $\angle 1$, $\angle 2$, $\angle 3$, and $\angle 4$ are right angles. Why?

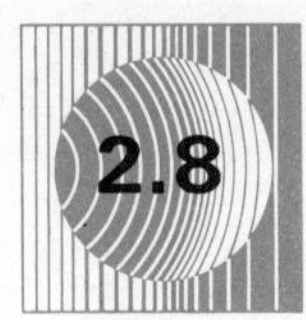

2.8 Some Properties of Transformations

Remember three of the transformations from Chapter 1?

The original and the image look the same. Let's explore why.

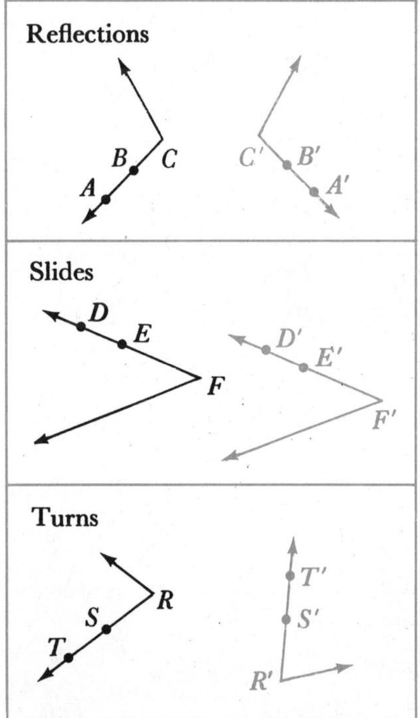

At the left, $\angle C'$ (read "C prime") is the reflection image of $\angle C$, $\angle F'$ is the slide image of $\angle F$, and $\angle R'$ is the turn image of $\angle R$.

Look at the corresponding points of each figure and its image. These drawings suggest that if a point is between two points in the original, then its image is between the images of those two points. Also, if these points are collinear, their images are collinear.

Using a protractor, check that the measure of an angle is the same as the measure of its image. With a ruler, check that the distance between two points is the same as the distance between their images.

We describe these properties of reflections, slides, and turns as follows.

Reflections, slides, and turns preserve

1. betweenness of points
2. collinearity of points
3. distance between points
4. angle measure

Orientation helps describe how triangles or other figures lie in a plane. To find the orientation of $\triangle XYZ$, trace a path from X to Y to Z. Your finger moves in a clockwise direction, making the orientation of $\triangle XYZ$ *clockwise*. The orientation of $\triangle YXZ$ is *counterclockwise*. Consider $\triangle ABC$ and its reflection image $\triangle A'B'C'$.

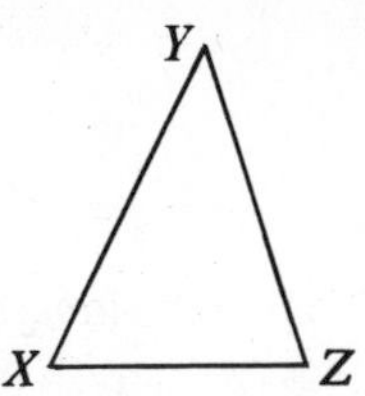

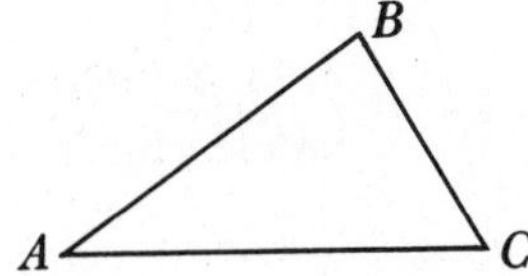

$\triangle ABC$: clockwise orientation

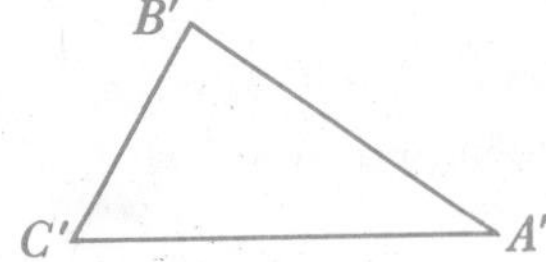

$\triangle A'B'C'$: counterclockwise orientation

Reflections reverse orientation.

Let's look again at a figure and its reflection image.

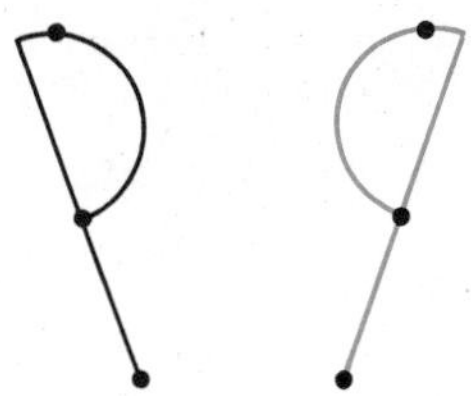

Pick three corresponding points on the original figure and its image.

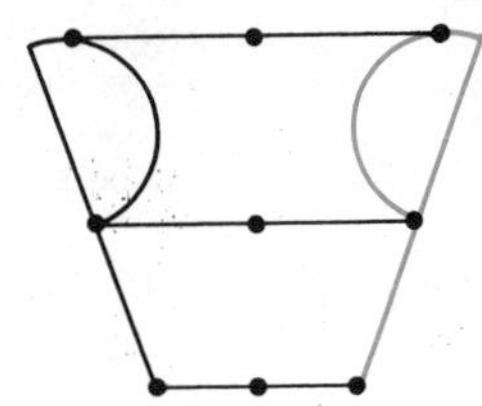

Connect these points. Then find the midpoints of these segments.

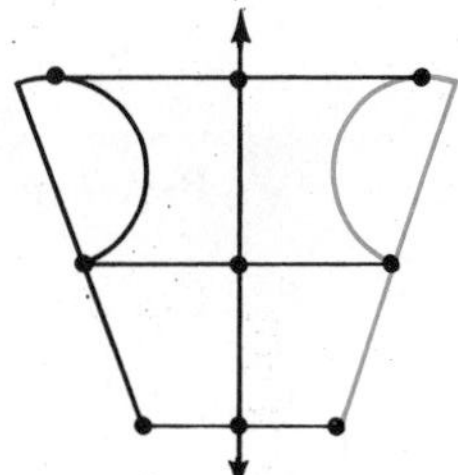

Draw line ℓ through the midpoints.

Line ℓ is called the **reflecting line.** Notice that it is the *perpendicular bisector* of each segment connecting a point to its image.

We can use this relationship to draw the reflection image of a point. Each point when it is reflected over a line has exactly one image.

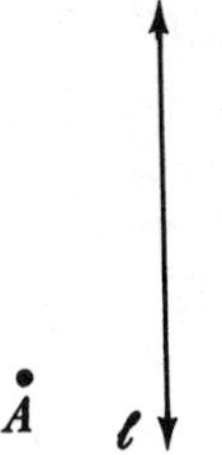

Here is point A and reflecting line ℓ.

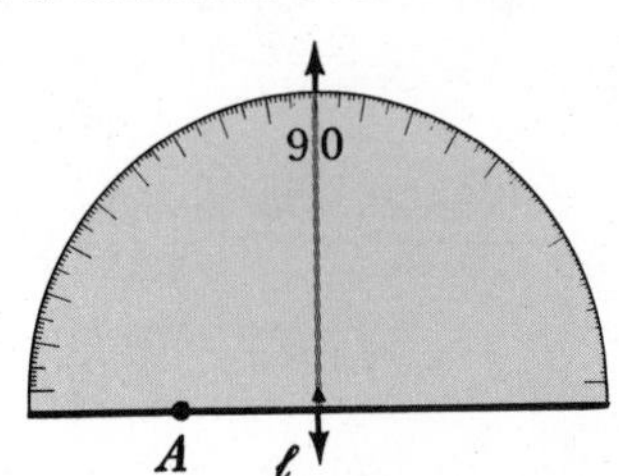

Place your protractor like this one. Draw a segment along the base of the protractor.

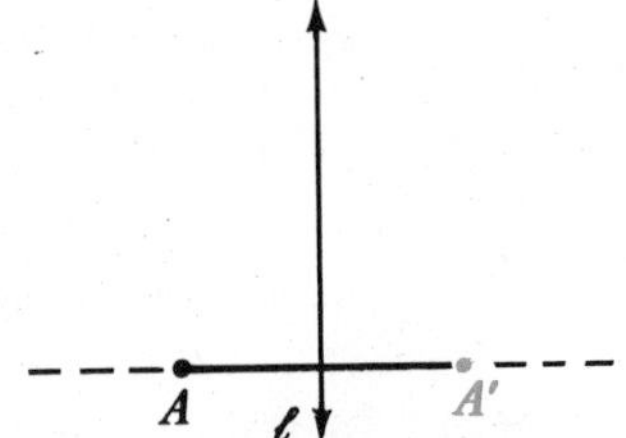

Measure the distance from point A to line ℓ along the segment. Point A' is the same distance away from line ℓ.

You can find the reflection image of a set of points by using this method for finding the reflection image of a point.

To find the image of $\overleftrightarrow{AB}$, find A' and B'.

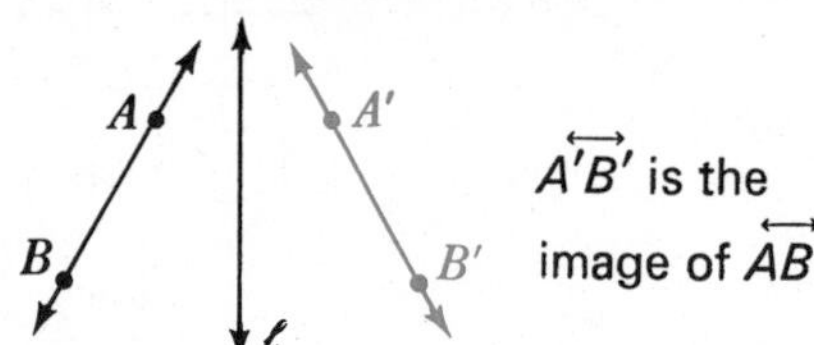

$\overleftrightarrow{A'B'}$ is the image of $\overleftrightarrow{AB}$.

To find the image of $\triangle RST$, find R', S', and T'.

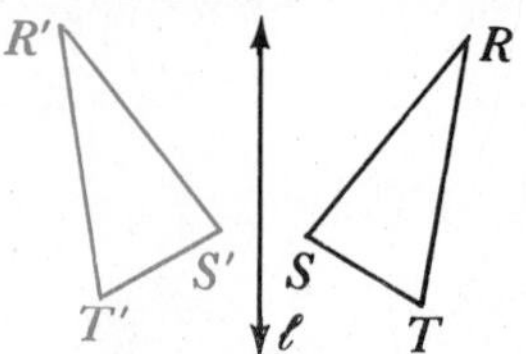

$\triangle R'S'T'$ is the image of $\triangle RST$.

Exercises 2.8

Ⓐ **1–15.** Answer yes or no to tell whether the transformation preserves each property.

property	transformation: Reflection	Slide	Turn
Betweenness	**1.**	**2.**	**3.**
Collinearity	**4.**	**5.**	**6.**
Distance	**7.**	**8.**	**9.**
Angle measure	**10.**	**11.**	**12.**
Orientation	**13.**	**14.**	**15.**

16. The reflection image of point A over line ℓ is A'. Describe the reflecting line.

Ⓑ **17–20.** Write *true* if the statement is always true. Otherwise write *false*.

17. $\overline{A'B'}$ is the reflection image of $\overline{AB}$. If $A'B' = 9$, then $AB = 8$.

18. $\angle C'$ is the slide image of $\angle C$. If $m\angle C = 41$, $m\angle C' = 41$.

19. If G, H, and J are collinear, their reflection and turn images will be collinear.

20. L is between M and N. Only under reflections will L' be between M' and N'.

21–26. What is the orientation of each triangle?

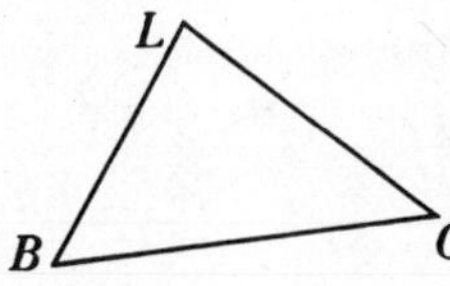

21. $\triangle BLO$

23. $\triangle LOB$

25. $\triangle BOL$

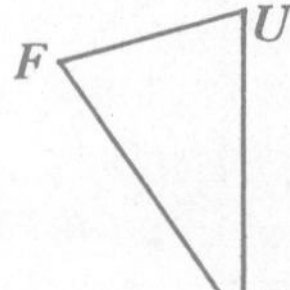

22. $\triangle NUF$

24. $\triangle UNF$

26. $\triangle FUN$

27–30. Copy these drawings. Draw the reflecting line so that the red figure is the image of the black figure.

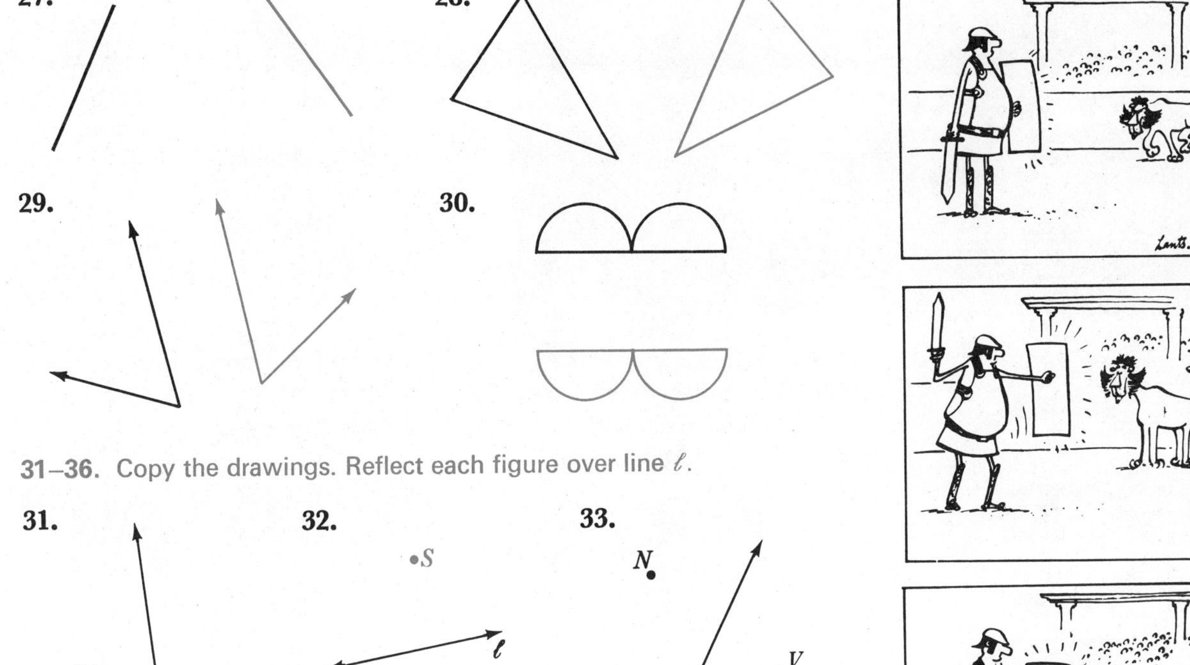

31–36. Copy the drawings. Reflect each figure over line ℓ.

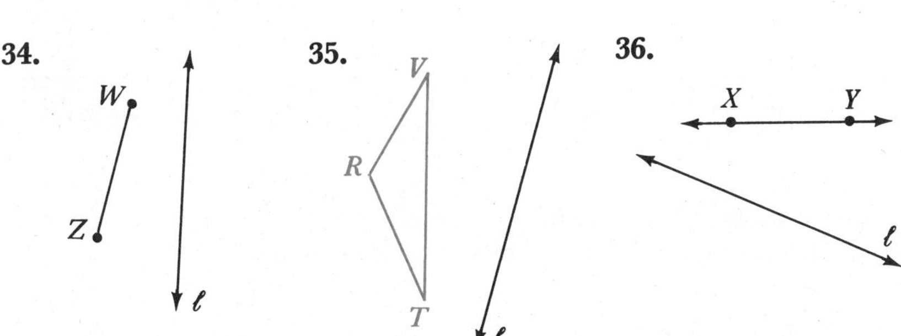

© **37.** Point M is on line ℓ. Draw the reflection image of $\overline{AB}$ over ℓ. What is the reflection image of M?

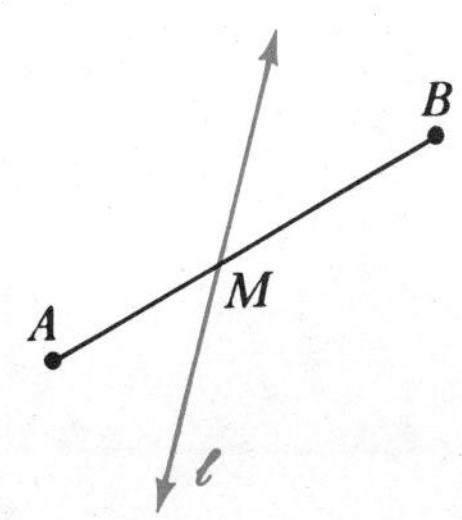

Brent Jones

REFLECTIONS AND MINIATURE GOLF

In miniature golf the object is to use the fewest number of strokes to get the ball into the hole. It is not always possible to aim the ball at the hole. Look at the photo.

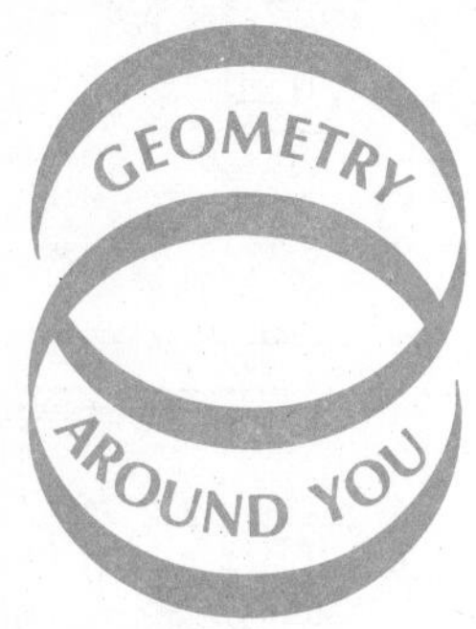

Where should you aim the ball? Knowing about reflections will be helpful. *First*, reflect the hole over the side wall that the ball must bounce off. (When you're actually playing miniature golf, visualize where the reflection image of the hole would be.)

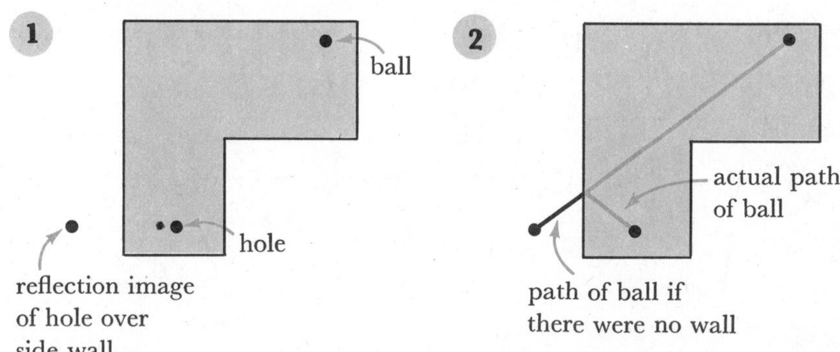

Second, aim for the reflection image of the hole. The ball will bounce off the side and into the hole.

Now look at diagram 2 more closely. Notice the actual path of the ball and the path of the ball if there were no side wall. With the side as the reflecting line, they are reflection images of each other.

Copy each drawing. Draw a path that will get the ball into the hole in 1 stroke.

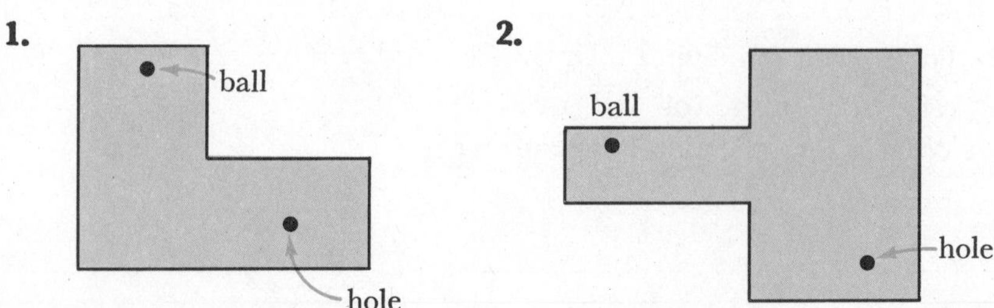

■ Chapter 2 Review ■

1. Define *convex set.* 2.1

2–4. Is each figure a convex set?

2.

3.

4.

5–7. Complete each statement with the best word(s) possible.

5. A plane is separated by a ______ into two ______.

6. Space is separated by a ______ into two ______.

7. A half plane does not contain its ______.

8. Define *angle.* 9. Define *triangle.* 2.2

10–14. Use the figures at the right.

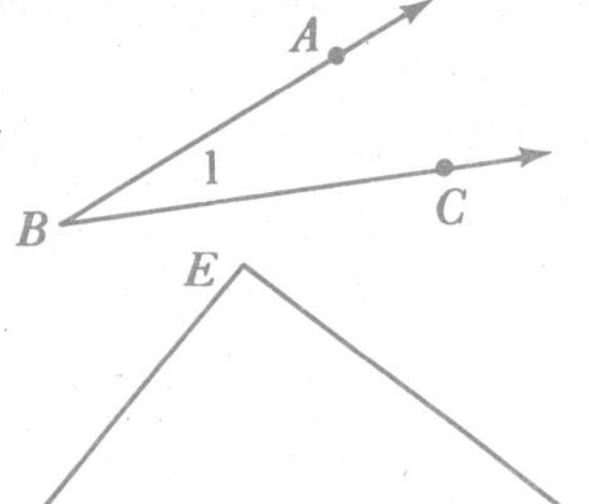

10. State three other names for $\angle 1$.

11. State five other names for $\triangle DEF$.

12. Name the sides of the angle.

13. Name the vertices of the triangle.

14. Which of the following is a convex set?

a. $\angle ABC$ **b.** the interior of $\angle ABC$ **c.** the exterior of $\triangle DEF$

15–16. Measure each angle. 2.3

15. 16.

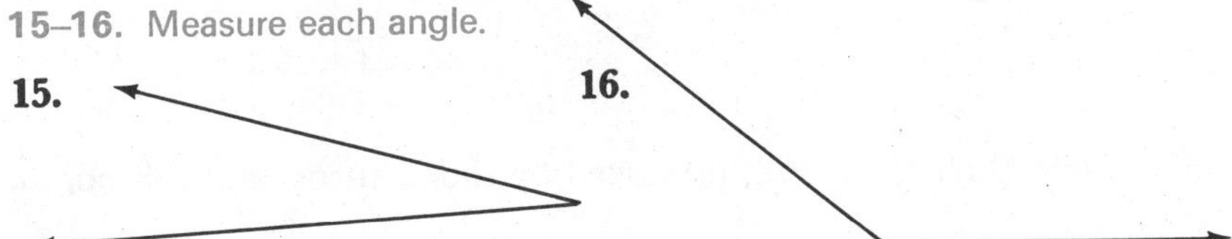

17–18. Point B is on $\overleftrightarrow{EC}$. Find the following:

17. $m\angle ABC$

18. $m\angle ABE$

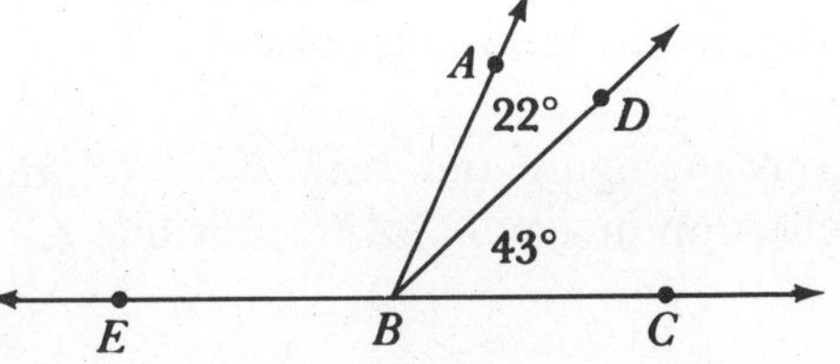

2.4 19–21. $\overrightarrow{AY}$ is the bisector of $\angle XAZ$. $m\angle XAZ = 72$. Find:

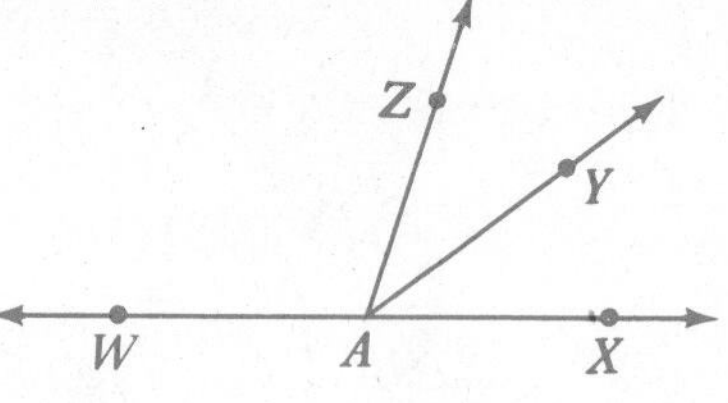

19. $m\angle XAY$

20. $m\angle ZAW$

21. $m\angle YAZ$

22–25. Complete each statement.

22. The sum of the measures of two supplementary angles is ______.

2.5 23. The measure of a right angle is ______.

24. The measure of an acute angle is ______ 90.

25. The measure of an obtuse angle is ______ 90.

26. $m\angle A = 23$ and $m\angle C = 77$. Are $\angle A$ and $\angle C$ complementary? Why?

27. When are two lines *perpendicular*?

28. When is line ℓ the *perpendicular bisector* of $\overline{AB}$?

2.6 29. When are two segments congruent?

30–34. Complete each statement with the best symbol possible.

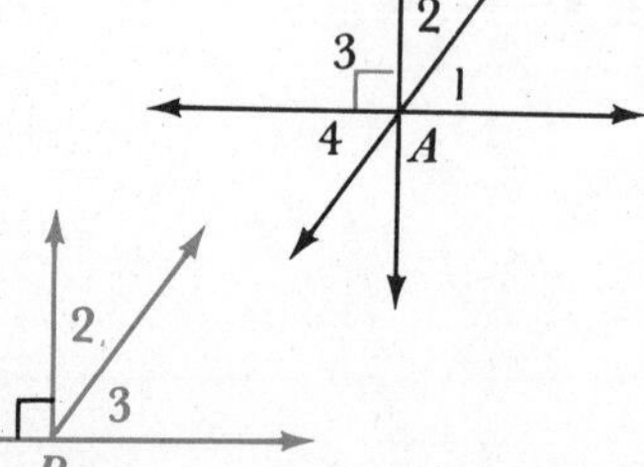

30. $\angle A_2 \cong$ ______

2.7 31. If $\angle A_2 \cong \angle B_2$, then $\angle A_1 \cong$ ______.

32. If $\angle A_1 \cong \angle B_3$, then $\angle B_{21} \cong$ ______.

33. $\angle$______ and $\angle$______ are vertical angles.

34. $\angle A_1 \cong$ ______

2.8 35. Name three properties preserved by slides, turns, and reflections.

36–37. Use the figure at the right.

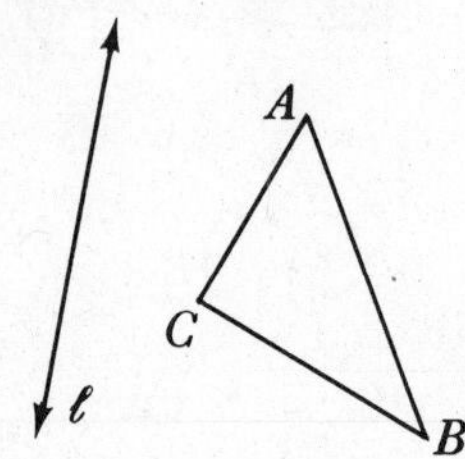

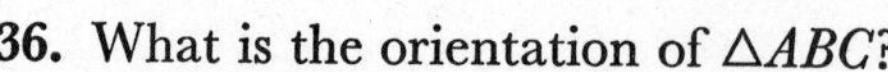

36. What is the orientation of $\triangle ABC$?

37. Copy the figure and draw $\triangle A'B'C'$, the reflection image of $\triangle ABC$ over line ℓ.

Chapter 2 Test

1–5. Write *true* if the statement is always true. Otherwise write *false*.

1. A segment can separate a plane.

2. An angle and its interior form a convex set of points.

3. If $m\angle A = m\angle B$, then $\angle A \cong \angle B$.

4. A line has exactly one perpendicular bisector.

5. In a plane, exactly one line can be drawn perpendicular to $\overleftrightarrow{XY}$ at point X.

6–9. Complete each statement with the best word or number.

6. Complements of ______ angles are congruent.

7. If $\angle A \cong \angle B$ and $\angle A$ and $\angle B$ are supplementary, then $\angle A$ and $\angle B$ are ______ angles.

8. Every angle has a measure between ______ and ______.

9. The supplement of a 25° angle has a measure of ______.

10–17. Use the appropriate figure.

10. Name two complementary angles.

11. Name two vertical angles.

12. Name two angles supplementary to $\angle CAB$.

13. Name a line and a ray that are perpendicular.

Ex. 10–15

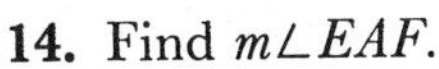

14. Find $m\angle EAF$. **15.** Find $m\angle FAB$.

16. If $m\angle RST = 110$, then $m\angle WST =$ ______.

17. $m\angle RSW =$ ______

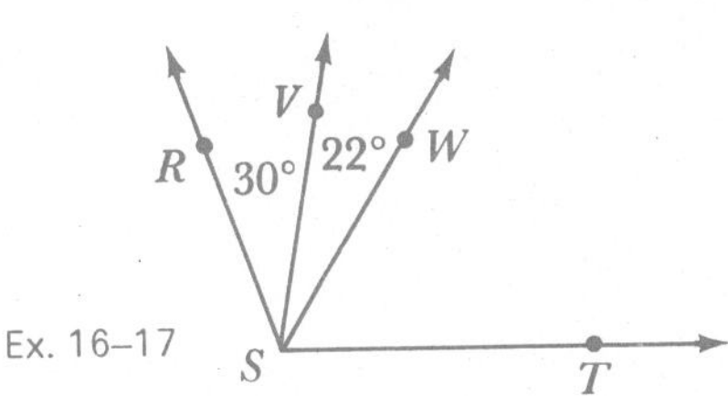

Ex. 16–17

18. Draw an angle whose measure is 161.

19. Is orientation preserved by reflections?

20. Copy this figure. Reflect $\overline{AB}$ over line ℓ.

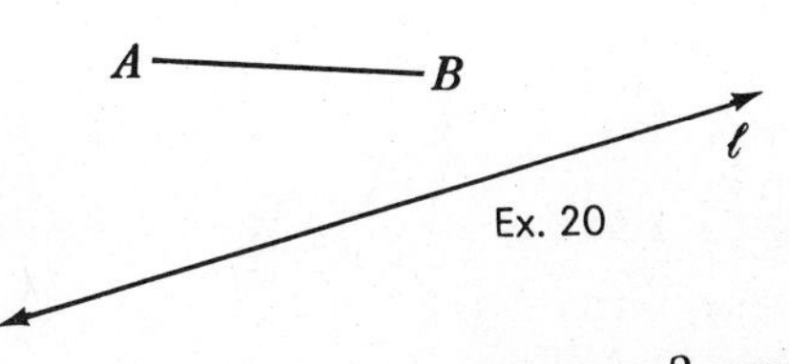

Ex. 20

MINI-CHAPTER: MOD ART

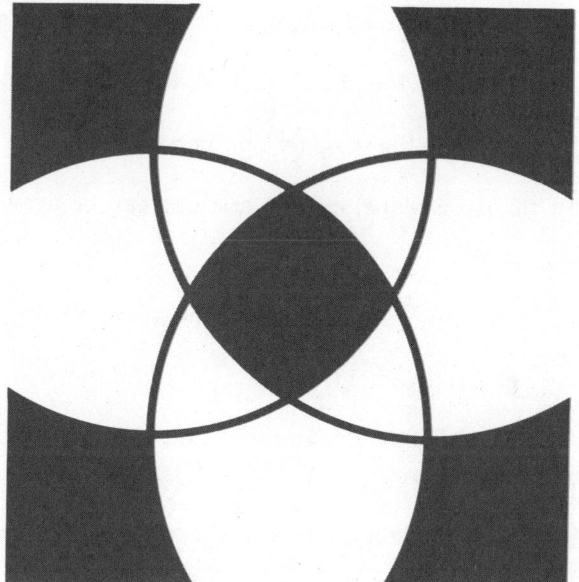

These designs contain geometric figures. Study the designs closely. Can you pick out figures that are images of each other under reflections, slides, or turns?

The designs on the next page are closely related to a mathematical system. They are keyed to an addition table, mod 4.

Mod 4 Addition Table

	0	1	2	3
0	0	1	2	3
1	1	2	3	0
2	2	3	0	1
3	3	0	1	2

To obtain this table, we can think of a clock with 4 numbers on it.

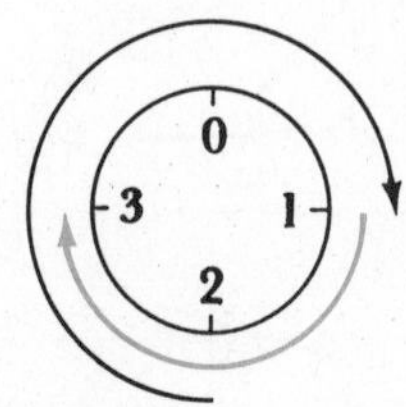

To find 1 + 2

Start at 1

Move clockwise 2 spaces to 3

To find 2 + 3

Start at 2

Move clockwise 3 spaces to 1

To make a design, give each number in the table a pattern.

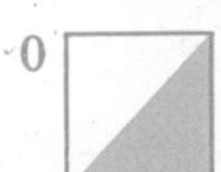

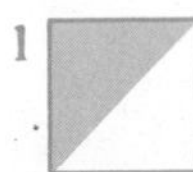

2

Then on grid paper, place the patterns according to the numbers in the table.

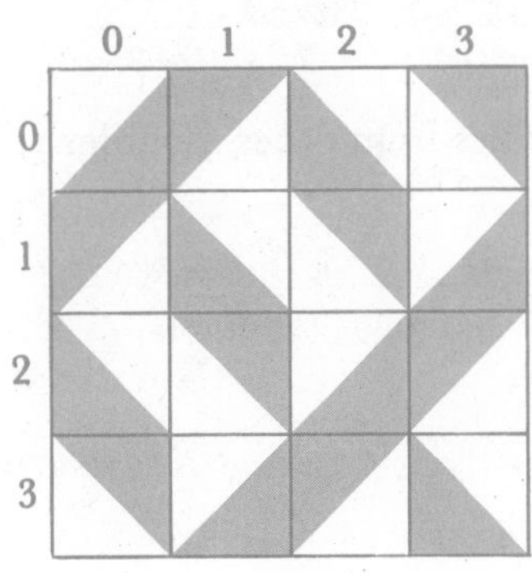

The rows of the design correspond to the rows of the table.

You can use this design, which is 4 squares by 4 squares, to get more elaborate designs. The example below is just one of the many possible designs that are 8 squares by 8 squares.

original design

design reflected over right border

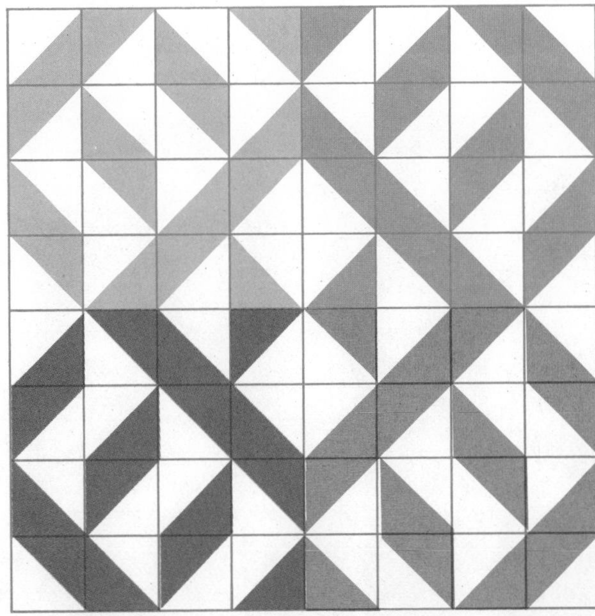

design reflected over bottom border

design reflected over the bottom border and then over the right border

Instead of reflecting, as on page 81, you could use slides, turns, or some combination.

You can make original designs by:

1. using different patterns

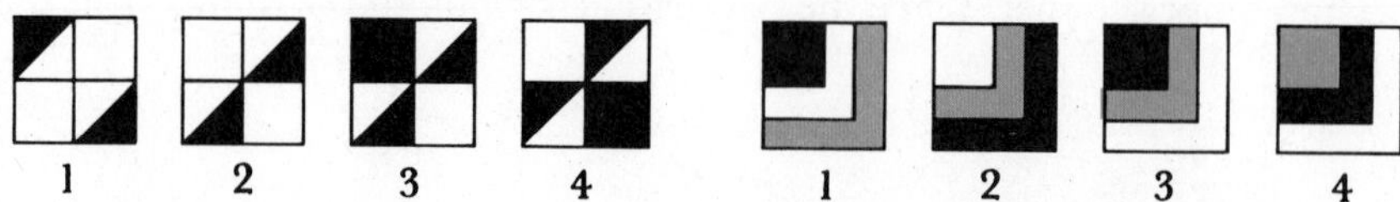

2. using addition or multiplication tables from other modular (clock) arithmetics

	1	2	3	4
1	1	2	3	4
2	2	4	1	3
3	3	1	4	2
4	4	3	2	1

Mod 5 (excluding 0) multiplication table

3. placing the patterns on different grids

kaleidoscope grid

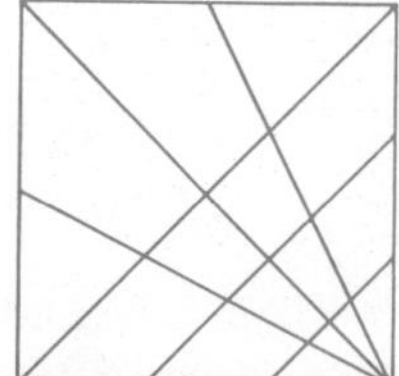

"curve grid"

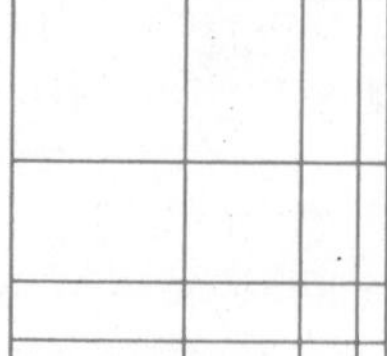

This is the design from page 81 placed on the "curve" grid.

This is the design from page 81 placed on the kaleidoscope grid.

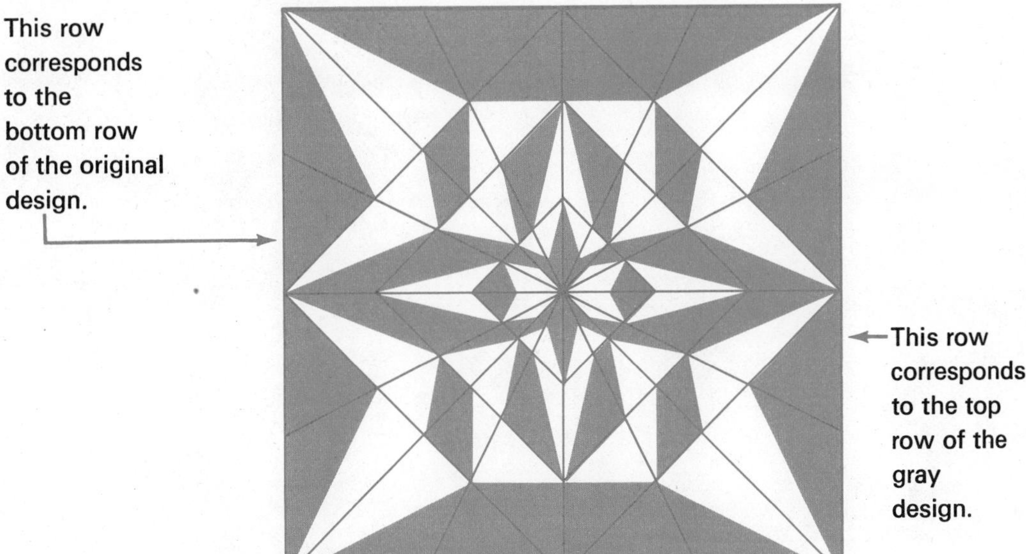
This row corresponds to the bottom row of the original design.
This row corresponds to the top row of the gray design.

Exercises

1. Make a design similar to one on page 80 that has images of figures under reflections, slides, or turns.

2. Choose patterns for 0, 1, 2, and 3. Then use the mod 4 addition table to make a design that is 4 squares by 4 squares.

3. Choose patterns for 1, 2, 3, and 4. Then use the mod 5 (excluding 0) multiplication table to make a design that is 4 squares by 4 squares.

4. Use the design that you made for Exercise 2. Reflect, slide, or turn it to make a poster that is 8 squares by 8 squares.

5. Use the design that you made for Exercise 3. Reflect, slide, or turn it to make a poster that is 8 squares by 8 squares.

6. Make a design using the "curve" grid or the kaleidoscope grid.

7. Make a table for addition in mod 5. Use this table to make a design.

8. Create an original poster. Use a modular arithmetic table. Choose a pattern for each number and a grid. Reflect, slide, or turn the design that you get from the table. Experiment with colors. Most important, use your imagination.

3

Michael James Hruby

Photo Trends

CONGRUENT TRIANGLES

In order to make a triangle that will coincide with another triangle, a carpenter will measure the sides only, not the angles. On the other hand, a surveyor might measure only one side and two angles. Why do both methods work? This chapter will answer that question.

If-Then Statements

Many statements have the form "If . . ., then . . . ." Sometimes the word *then* is omitted (but still understood) in these statements.

If you utter insults, you will also hear them. [Plautus]

If wishes were horses, beggars would ride. [Anonymous]

If you go away on this summer day, then you might as well take the sun away. [from "If You Go Away," English lyrics by Rod McKuen]

"If you were a horse, we could have shot yer!"
© 1977, Universal Press Syndicate.
Unger

If-then statements are very important in geometry. Every if-then statement has two clauses. The clause that follows *if* is the **hypothesis.** The clause that follows *then* is the **conclusion.**

	hypothesis		conclusion
If	B is on $\overline{AC}$,	then	$AB + BC = AC$.
If	$a + c = b + c$,	then	$a = b$.
If	$2x + y = 5$ and $y = 1$,	then	$2x + 1 = 5$.
If	$ab = 0$,	then	$a = 0$ or $b = 0$.

A statement can contain a hypothesis and a conclusion that are not stated explicitly. It is then helpful to change the statement to if-then form. You will have to introduce extra words to do this.

Examples:

1. *Statement:* All squares are rectangles.
If-then form: If a figure is a square, then it is a rectangle.

2. *Statement:* A Volkswagen is a foreign car.
If-then form: If a car is a Volkswagen, then it is a foreign car.

3. *Statement:* No elephant can fly.
If-then form: If an animal is an elephant, then it cannot fly.

Diagrams can be used to picture the preceding if-then statements. These diagrams are called Euler (oil-er) diagrams after a Swiss mathematician named Leonard Euler.

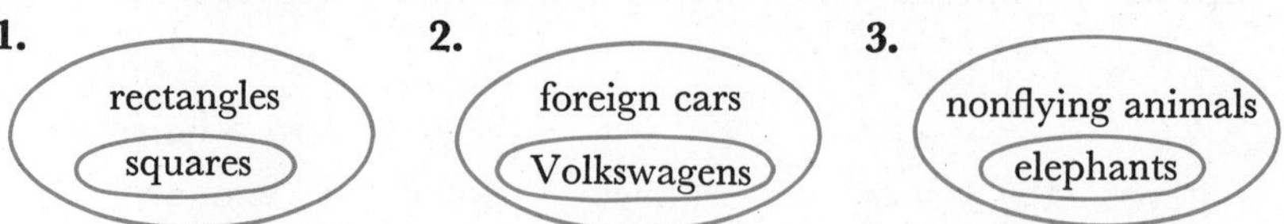

To picture any if-then statement with an Euler diagram, draw two rings, one inside the other. The smaller ring stands for the hypothesis. The larger ring stands for the conclusion. In general,

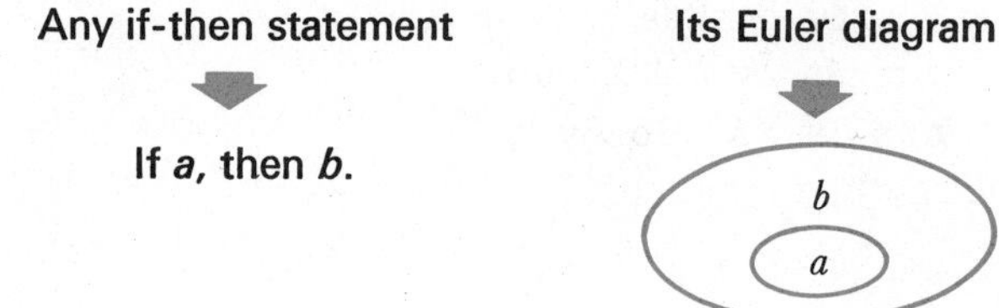

Exercises 3.1

Ⓐ **1.** The clause that follows *if* in an if-then statement is the ______.

2. The clause that follows *then* in an if-then statement is the ______.

3. In an Euler diagram, the smaller ring stands for the ______.

4. In an Euler diagram, the larger ring stands for the ______.

5–6. True or False?

5. In an if-then statement, the word *then* can be omitted.

6. A statement can be changed from some other form to if-then form.

Ⓑ **7–18.** State the hypothesis and conclusion of each statement.

7. If there were two birds sitting on a fence, he would bet you which one would fly first. [Mark Twain]

8. When poverty comes in the door, love flies out the window. [Anonymous]

9. If you brush your teeth with Superwhite, you will be popular.

10. If you keep a thing for seven years, you are sure to find a use for it. [Sir Walter Scott]

11. If $x = 3$, then $x^2 = 9$.

12. If $a \cdot 5 = 0$, then $a = 0$.

13. If $x^2 = 9$, then $x = 3$ or $x = -3$.

14. If $a = b$ and $b = c$, then $a = c$.

15. If $\overline{AB} \cong \overline{CD}$ and $\overline{EF} \cong \overline{CD}$, then $\overline{AB} \cong \overline{EF}$.

16. If A, B, C, and D are four points in order on a line and $AB = CD$, then $AC = BD$.

17. Two angles are complementary if the sum of their measures is 90. HINT: The hypothesis is the clause that follows *if*.

18. An angle is acute if its measure is less than 90.

19–26. Change each statement to if-then form. (The statement may or may not be true!) Remember that you will have to introduce extra words.

19. All birds can fly.

20. All triangles have three sides.

21. No triangle has four sides.

22. No wise man ever wished to be younger. [Jonathan Swift]

23. A salamander is an amphibian.

24. A Datsun is a Japanese car.

25. Every segment has exactly one midpoint.

26. Every Texan is tall.

27–28. Pick the best Euler diagram for each statement.

27. All left-handed people are geniuses.

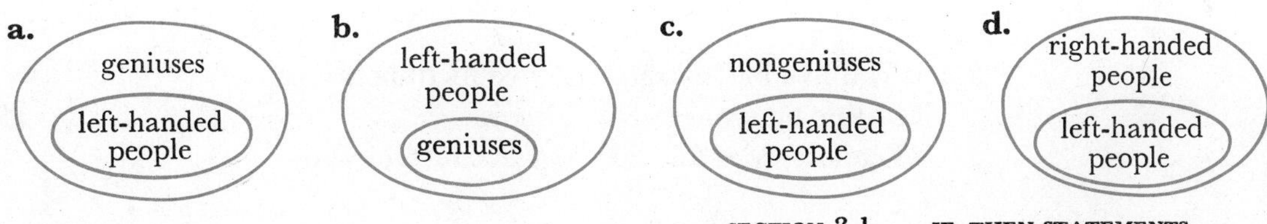

28. No baboon can play a guitar.

a.

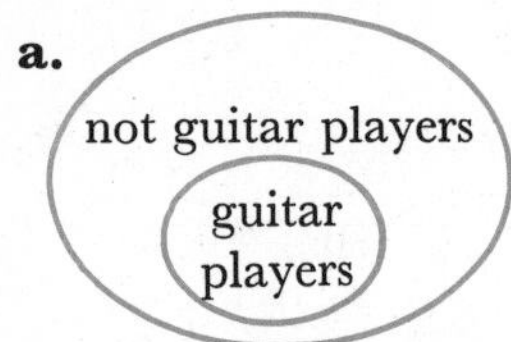

b. **c.** **d.**

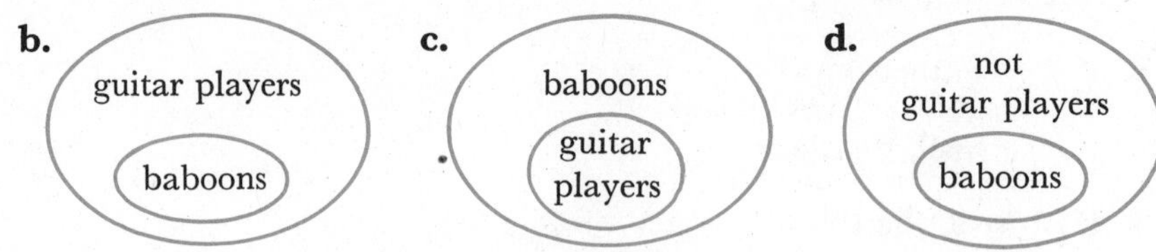

29–32. Draw an Euler diagram to illustrate each statement.

29. If a number is a whole number, it is an integer.

30. All whales are mammals.

31. No planet is a star.

32. Every mogabump is a walapede.

33–34. What if-then statement does each Euler diagram represent?

33.

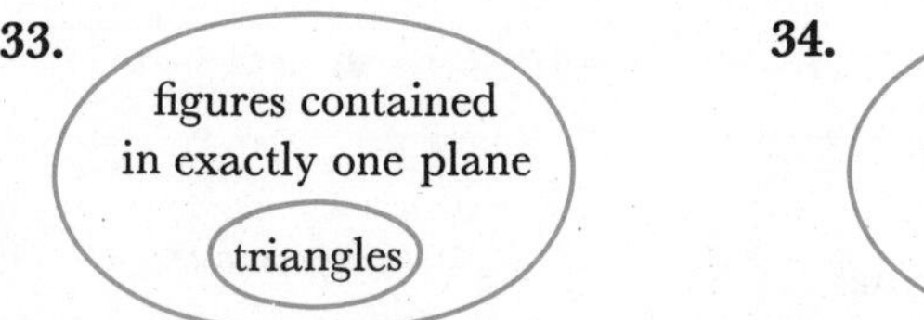

34.

integers

even numbers

Ⓒ **35.** Draw an Euler diagram to illustrate this statement:

All fish can swim.

36. Several if-then statements are listed below. Which of them seem to be true if the diagram you drew in Exercise 35 is correct?

a. If an animal is a fish, it can swim.

b. If an animal is not a fish, it cannot swim.

c. If an animal can swim, it is a fish.

d. If an animal cannot swim, it is not a fish.

37–38. Decide if the following arguments are correct or incorrect. If incorrect, give a reason.

37. If you live in Chicago, you live in Illinois.
Martine does not live in Illinois.
Therefore, Martine does not live in Chicago.

38. If you can vote in Kentucky, you must be 18 or older.
Joe cannot vote in Kentucky.
Therefore, Joe is not yet 18.

39–40. Sometimes two or more if-then statements form a *chain.* Use deductive reasoning to draw a conclusion from each set of statements.

39. If a number is a whole number, then it is an integer.
If a number is an integer, then it is a rational number.
If a number is a rational number, then it is a real number.
0 is a whole number.
Therefore, ________________.

40. If a dog is named Fido, it has fleas.
If a dog has fleas, it scratches.
If a dog scratches, it needs Fly-Away Flea Powder.
My dog is named Fido.
Therefore, ________________.

41–44. The table below lists four other wordings that are commonly used in geometry for if-then statements. Reword each statement in Exercises 11–14 in each of the four ways below.

If-then statement	If a, then b.
other wordings	**a.** b if a. **b.** a only if b. **c.** a is sufficient for b. **d.** b is necessary for a.

Pick a Category

Choose one of the following categories:

Newspapers Magazines Novels Poetry

In your library find five if-then statements used in your chosen category. Give the source of each statement, listing the name of the author and the name of the newspaper, magazine (and article), novel, or poem.

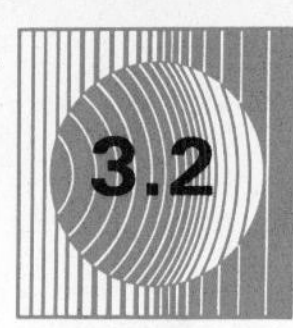

3.2 Proofs

In Chapters 1 and 2, we often used *reasoning* to arrive at a theorem. Actually, we were giving *proofs* of the theorems. A *proof* is just a setting forth of the reasoning that leads from a hypothesis to a conclusion. The proofs in Chapters 1 and 2 were written in paragraph form.

In geometry, we more often use **two-column proofs.** In this method, our reasoning is still the same. But now we write a list of statements and then give a reason for each statement.

The following example illustrates a two-column proof of this statement: If point R is between points P and T, then $PR = PT - RT$.

Example 1:

Given: Point R is between points P and T.

Prove: $PR = PT - RT$

Proof:

STATEMENTS	REASONS
1. R is between P and T.	**1.** Given
2. $PR + RT = PT$	**2.** Definition of between
3. $PR = PT - RT$	**3.** Subtract RT from both sides.

In proving an if-then statement, the hypothesis is labeled as *Given.* The conclusion is labeled *Prove.* A figure is drawn for a proof to show the facts given in the hypothesis. (An accurate, neatly drawn figure can be a big help.) The reason listed for each statement is always one of the following:

Given (facts provided in the hypothesis)
A postulate
A definition
A previously proved theorem

} including those from algebra, as in step 3 above

Example 2:

Given: B is between A and C,
C is between B and D,
$AB = CD$

Prove: $AC = BD$

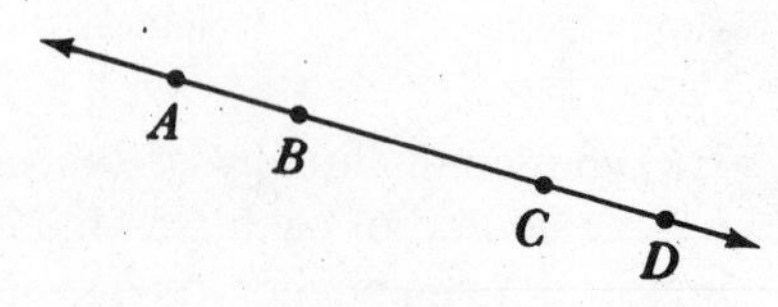

Proof: STATEMENTS	REASONS
1. $AB = CD$	**1.** Given
2. $AB + BC = BC + CD$	**2.** Add BC to both sides.
3. B is between A and C, C is between B and D.	**3.** Given
4. $AB + BC = AC$, $BC + CD = BD$	**4.** Definition of between
5. $AC = BD$	**5.** Substitute from step 4 into step 2 (AC for $AB + BC$ and BD for $BC + CD$).

Exercises 3.2

Ⓐ **1–6.** Complete the following sentences:

1. A ______ is a setting forth of the reasoning that leads from a hypothesis to a conclusion.

2. In proving an if-then statement, the ______ is labeled *Given*, and the ______ is labeled *Prove*.

3. In writing a proof, it is helpful to draw a ______.

4. A two-column proof has one column for ______ and another for ______.

5. What types of reasons can be used in a two-column proof?

6. By the definition of between, if B is between A and C, then $AB +$ ______ $= AC$.

Ⓑ **7–24.** Give the reasons needed to complete each proof.

Given: B is between A and C, $AB = AD$, $DB = BC$

Prove: $AD + DB = AC$

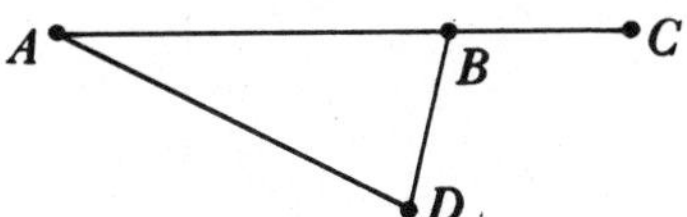

Proof: STATEMENTS	REASONS
1. B is between A and C.	*1.* **7.**
2. $AB + BC = AC$	*2.* **8.**
3. $AB = AD$, $DB = BC$	*3.* **9.**
4. $AD + DB = AC$	*4.* **10.**

Given: B is between A and C,
C is between B and D,
$AC = BD$

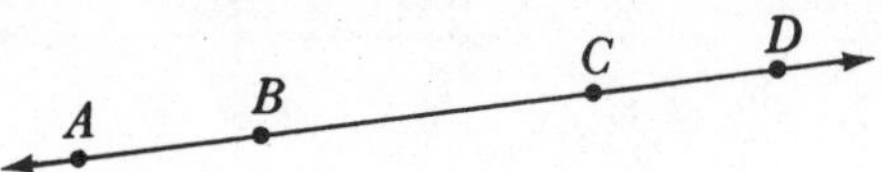

Prove: $AB = CD$

Proof:

STATEMENTS	REASONS
1. $AC = BD$	1. **11.** ____
2. $AC - BC = BD - BC$	2. **12.** ____
3. B is between A and C, C is between B and D.	3. **13.** ____
4. $AB + BC = AC$, $BC + CD = BD$	4. **14.** ____
5. $AB = AC - BC$, $CD = BD - BC$	5. **15.** ____
6. $AB = CD$	6. **16.** ____

Given: $\angle 1$ and $\angle 2$ are vertical angles,
$\angle 1$ and $\angle 2$ are supplementary.

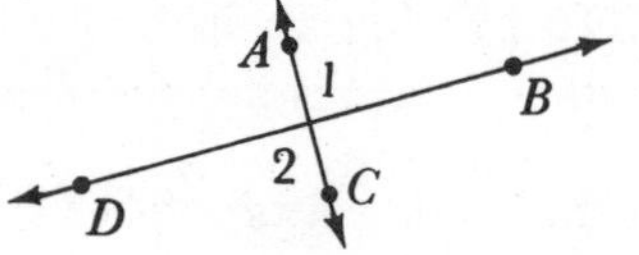

Prove: $\overline{AC} \perp \overline{DB}$

Proof:

STATEMENTS	REASONS
1. $\angle 1$ and $\angle 2$ are vertical angles.	1. **17.** ____
2. $m\angle 1 = m\angle 2$	2. **18.** ____
3. $\angle 1$ and $\angle 2$ are supplementary.	3. **19.** ____
4. $m\angle 1 + m\angle 2 = 180$	4. **20.** ____
5. $m\angle 1 + m\angle 1 = 180$	5. **21.** ____
6. $2m\angle 1 = 180$	6. **22.** ____
7. $m\angle 1 = 90$	7. **23.** ____
8. $\overline{AC} \perp \overline{DB}$	8. **24.** ____

Ⓒ **25.** Give a two-column proof of the following:

Given: Q is between P and R,
$PQ = SQ$, $QR = QT$

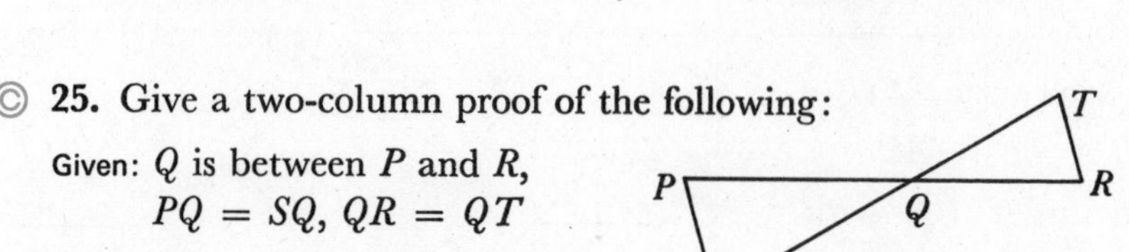

Prove: $SQ + QT = PR$

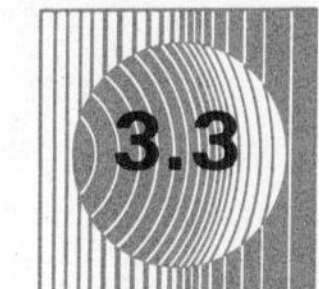

What Are Congruent Triangles?

You see examples of *congruent figures* (figures that have the same size and shape) all around you. Objects that are mass-produced on assembly lines are congruent. And congruent figures are used in construction and designs. In this section, we are concerned with congruent triangles like the two triangles below.

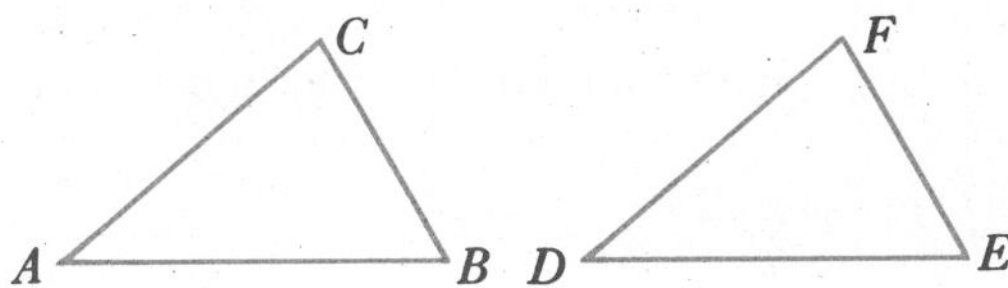

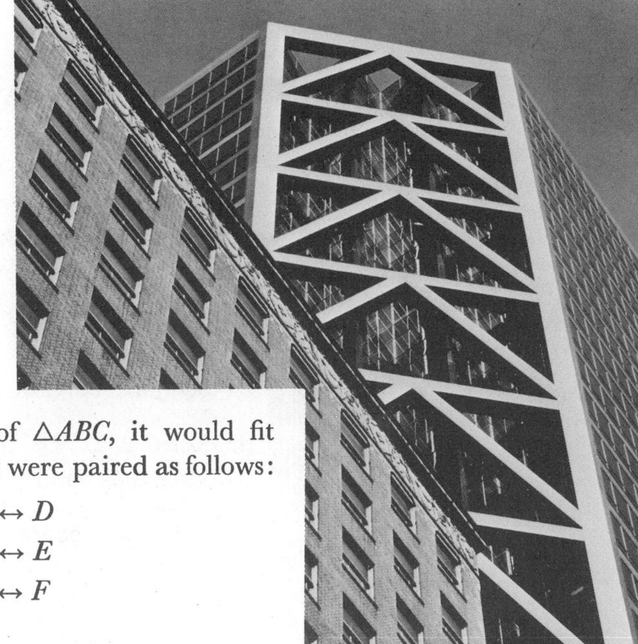

Bill Miller

If $\triangle DEF$ was traced and placed on top of $\triangle ABC$, it would fit exactly. However, it would fit *only* if the vertices were paired as follows:

A paired with D	$A \leftrightarrow D$
B paired with E	$B \leftrightarrow E$
C paired with F	$C \leftrightarrow F$

When the vertices of two triangles are paired in this way, we say there is a one-to-one correspondence between the vertices. A shorter way to write the correspondence above is

$$\triangle ABC \leftrightarrow \triangle DEF$$

There are other correspondences between the vertices of $\triangle ABC$ and $\triangle DEF$. One example is $\triangle ABC \leftrightarrow \triangle EDF$. That is,

$A \leftrightarrow E$ $\quad$ $B \leftrightarrow D$ $\quad$ $C \leftrightarrow F$

In this case, however, the triangles would not fit on top of each other. For example, $\angle A$ and $\angle E$ are not the same size.

Any one-to-one correspondence of two triangles like $\triangle ABC \leftrightarrow \triangle DEF$ leads to six pairs of **corresponding parts.** For example,

$$\triangle ABC \leftrightarrow \triangle DEF$$

corresponding angles	$\angle A$ and $\angle D$	$\overline{AB}$ and $\overline{DE}$	corresponding sides
	$\angle B$ and $\angle E$	$\overline{BC}$ and $\overline{EF}$	
	$\angle C$ and $\angle F$	$\overline{AC}$ and $\overline{DF}$	

Congruent triangles are two triangles that have the six parts of one triangle congruent to the six corresponding parts of the other triangle. For example,

$\triangle ABC \cong \triangle DEF$

means

$\angle A \cong \angle D$	$\overline{AB} \cong \overline{DE}$
$\angle B \cong \angle E$	$\overline{BC} \cong \overline{EF}$
$\angle C \cong \angle F$	$\overline{AC} \cong \overline{DF}$

◀ Read: "Triangle *ABC* is congruent to triangle *DEF*."

Because congruence of triangles is defined in terms of congruent segments and congruent angles, we can state the following theorems. Each follows from the similar theorems about congruent angles and segments on page 65.

Congruent Triangles Theorems

A triangle is congruent to itself.

If $\triangle ABC \cong \triangle DEF$, then $\triangle DEF \cong \angle ABC$. (That is, congruence of two triangles can be stated in either order.)

Two triangles congruent to the same triangle are congruent to each other.

When we draw congruent triangles, we often mark pairs of corresponding parts to show which is congruent to which. For example,

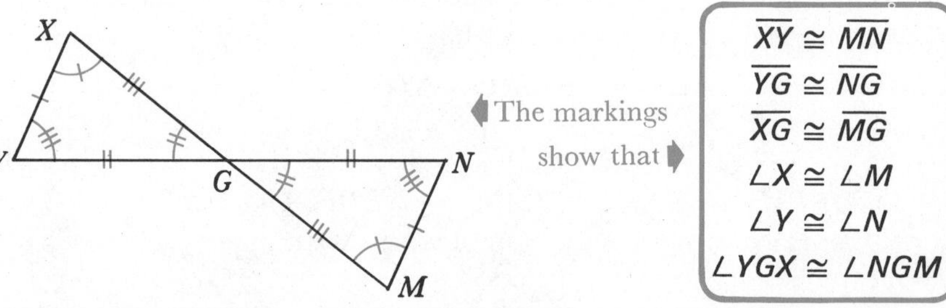

Exercises 3.3

Ⓐ 1–6. For each side or angle, name the corresponding part. $\triangle GHI \cong \triangle JKL$

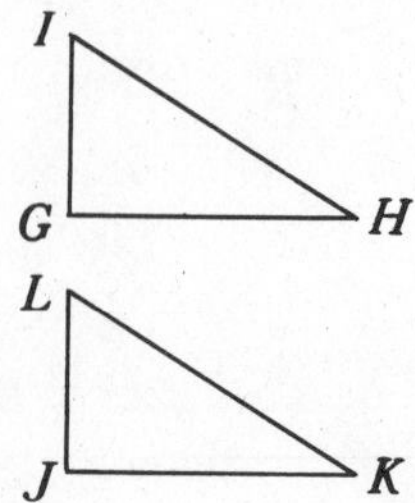

1. $\angle G$
2. $\angle I$
3. $\angle K$
4. $\overline{GI}$
5. $\overline{HI}$
6. $\overline{JK}$

7–12. Complete each statement. $\triangle ABC \cong \triangle DBC$

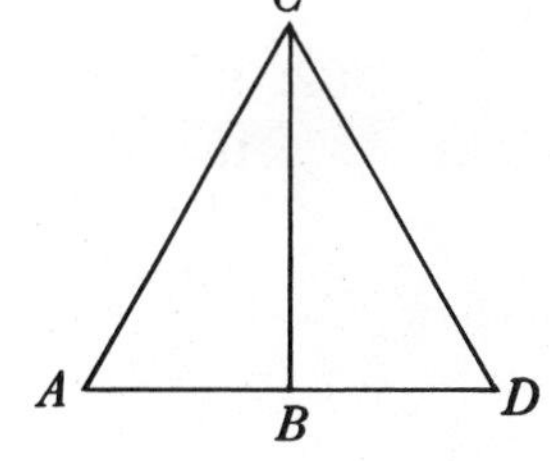

7. $\angle A$ corresponds to ______.

8. $\angle ABC$ corresponds to ______.

9. $\angle BCD$ corresponds to ______.

10. $\overline{AB}$ corresponds to ______.

11. $\overline{DC}$ corresponds to ______.

12. $\overline{BC}$ corresponds to ______. (That is, ______ corresponds to itself.)

13–18. Complete each statement. $\triangle RED \cong \triangle CAP$

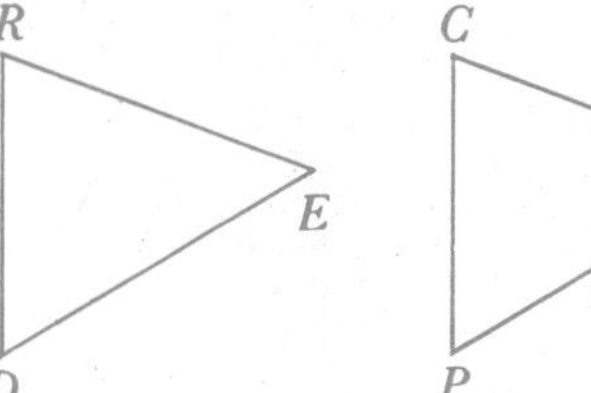

13. $\angle R \cong$ ______

14. $\angle E \cong$ ______

15. $\angle D \cong$ ______

16. $\overline{ED} \cong$ ______

17. $\overline{RE} \cong$ ______

18. $\overline{DR} \cong$ ______

19–24. Complete each statement. $\triangle BUM \cong \triangle RAP$

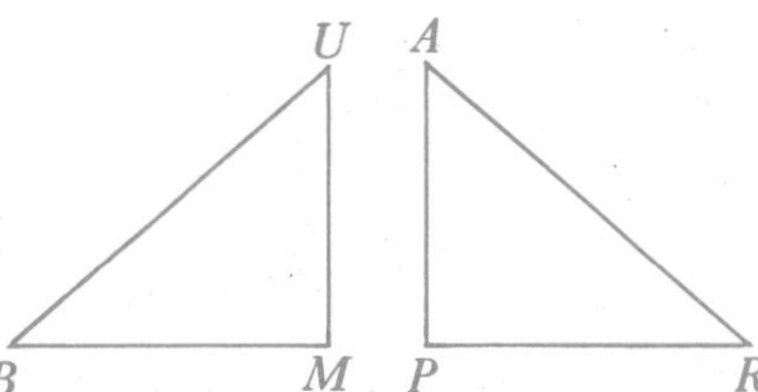

19. $\angle B \cong$ ______

20. $\angle M \cong$ ______

21. $\overline{BU} \cong$ ______

22. $\overline{UM} \cong$ ______

23. ______ $\cong \angle A$

24. ______ $\cong \overline{RP}$

Ⓑ 25–30. In each exercise, the corresponding congruent parts are marked. Complete each statement.

25.

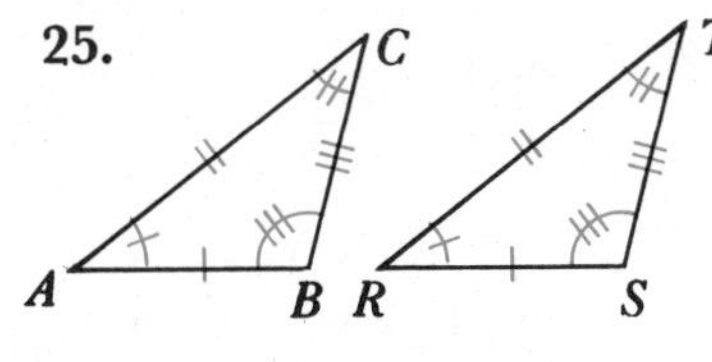

$\triangle ABC \cong$ ______

26.

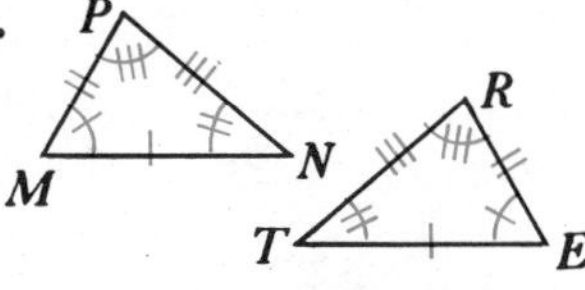

$\triangle PMN \cong$ ______

27.

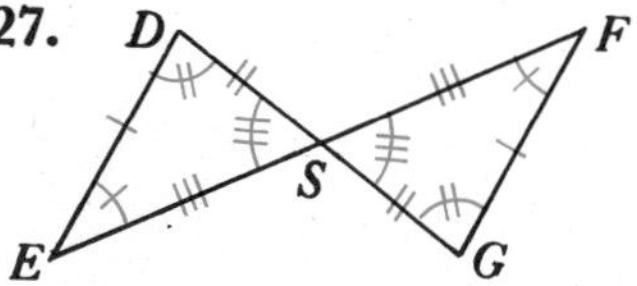

$\triangle SGF \cong$ ______

28.

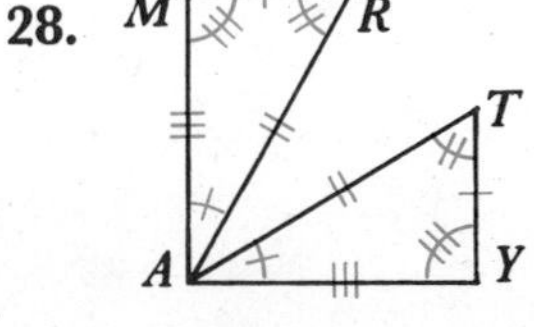

$\triangle ARM \cong$ ______

29.

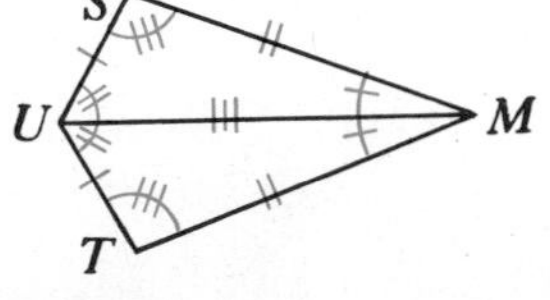

$\triangle SUM \cong$ ______

30.

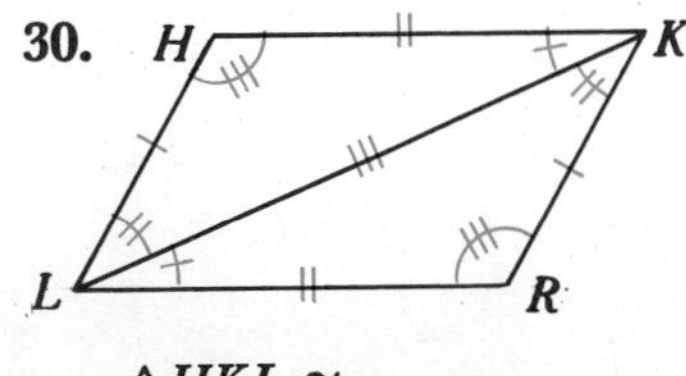

$\triangle HKL \cong$ ______

31. List all six congruence statements concerning angles and sides that follow from $\triangle TOP \cong \triangle CAR$.

32. List all six congruence statements concerning angles and sides that follow from $\triangle PQR \cong \triangle STV$.

33. The congruence statement $\triangle PAL \cong \triangle KUH$ can be stated correctly in five other ways. One way is $\triangle LAP \cong \triangle HUK$. Name the other four ways.

34. Name the congruence statement $\triangle TOL \cong \triangle NES$ correctly in five other ways.

© **35–37.** *Activities:* Use strips of cardboard (about 1 centimeter wide) and metal fasteners to make three models of triangles as follows:

35. Use three strips, making the distances between the fastening holes 14, 10, and 7 centimeters.

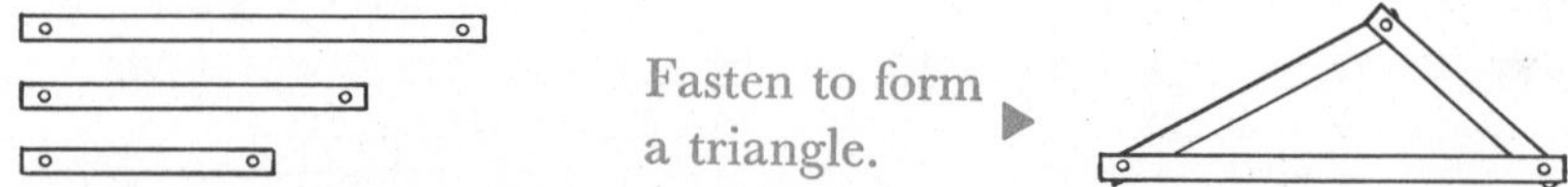
Fasten to form
a triangle.

Compare your model with those of your classmates. Are they congruent?

36. Use two strips, making the distances between the fastening holes 16 and 12 centimeters. Fasten at one vertex and make the angle between the strips 40°.

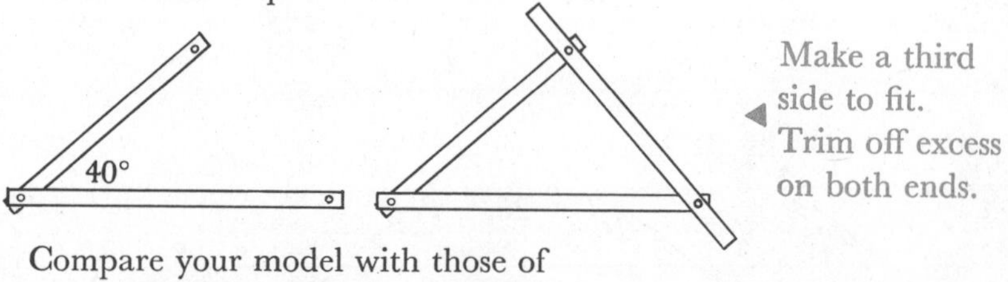
40°
Make a third
side to fit.
Trim off excess
on both ends.

Compare your model with those of your classmates. Are they congruent?

37. Use one strip, making the distance between the holes 20 centimeters. Use two other strips of sufficient lengths to meet after the angles are measured as follows:

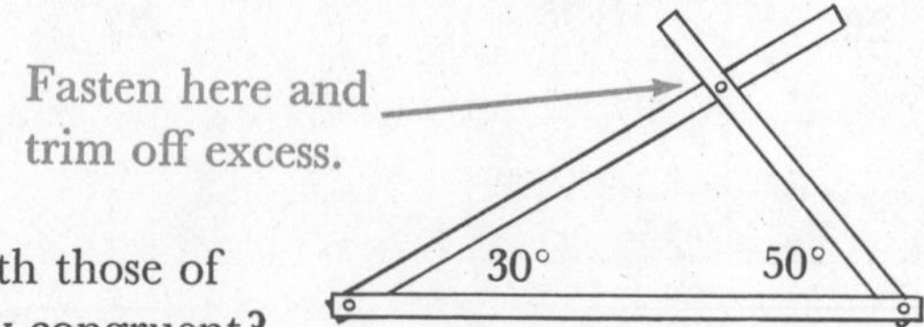
Fasten here and
trim off excess.
30°
50°

Compare your model with those of your classmates. Are they congruent?

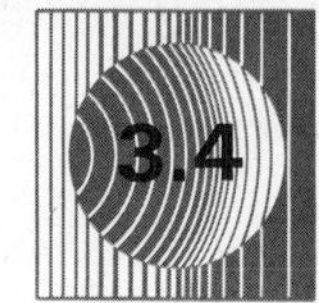

Postulates About Congruent Triangles

When two triangles are congruent, there are six pairs of congruent parts. However, you can tell two triangles are congruent without knowing that all six pairs of corresponding parts are congruent. The following postulates indicate conditions that result in congruent triangles.

SSS Postulate

Side-Side-Side Postulate: If three sides of one triangle are congruent to the corresponding sides of another triangle, the triangles are congruent.

Example 1:

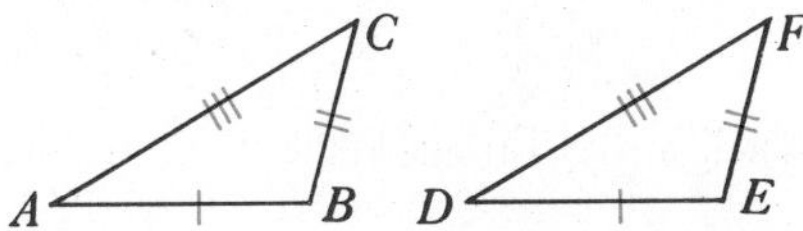

Given: $\overline{AB} \cong \overline{DE}$, $\overline{BC} \cong \overline{EF}$, $\overline{AC} \cong \overline{DF}$

$\triangle ABC \cong \triangle DEF$ by the SSS Postulate.

To state the next two postulates, it will be helpful to use the terms **included angle** and **included side.**

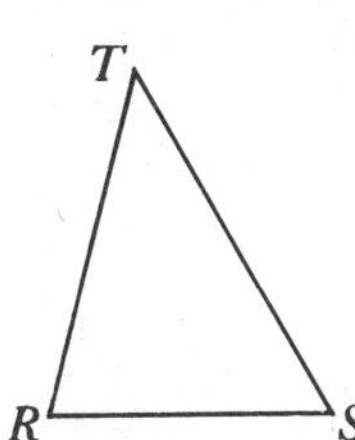

included angles

$\angle R$ is included between $\overline{RT}$ and $\overline{RS}$.
$\angle S$ is included between $\overline{SR}$ and $\overline{ST}$.
$\angle T$ is included between $\overline{TR}$ and $\overline{TS}$.

included sides

$\overline{RS}$ is included between $\angle R$ and $\angle S$.
$\overline{ST}$ is included between $\angle S$ and $\angle T$.
$\overline{RT}$ is included between $\angle R$ and $\angle T$.

SAS Postulate

Side-Angle-Side Postulate: If two sides and the included angle of one triangle are congruent to the corresponding parts of another triangle, the triangles are congruent.

Example 2:

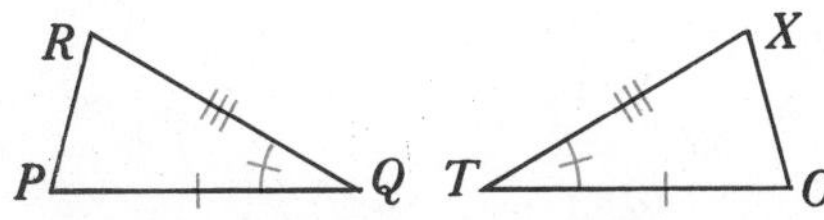

Given: $\overline{PQ} \cong \overline{OT}$, $\overline{QR} \cong \overline{TX}$, $\angle Q \cong \angle T$

$\triangle PQR \cong \triangle OTX$ by the SAS Postulate.

ASA Postulate

Angle-Side-Angle Postulate: If two angles and the included side of one triangle are congruent to the corresponding parts of another triangle, the triangles are congruent.

Example 3:

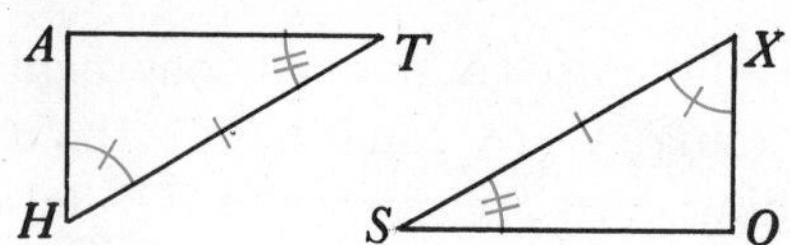

Given: $\angle H \cong \angle X$, $\angle T \cong \angle S$, $\overline{HT} \cong \overline{XS}$

$\triangle HTA \cong \triangle XSO$ by the ASA Postulate.

Two triangles cannot be proved congruent by angle-angle-angle or by side-side-angle. The figures below show why.

AAA

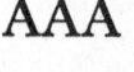

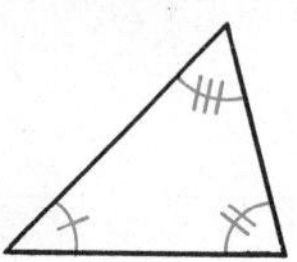

SSA

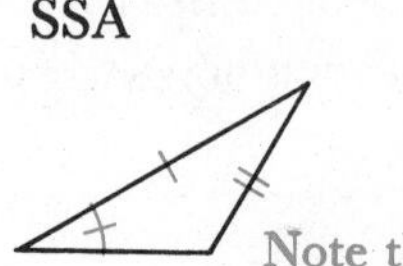

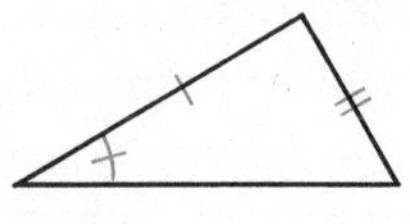

Note that the angle is not included between the sides.

Exercises 3.4

Ⓐ **1–3.** What does each abbreviation stand for?

1. SAS Postulate **2.** ASA Postulate **3.** SSS Postulate

4–6. Which postulate lets us conclude that the triangles are congruent?

4.

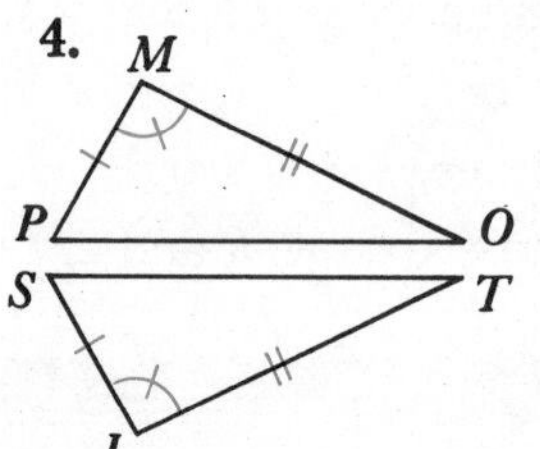

$\triangle MOP \cong \triangle ITS$

5.

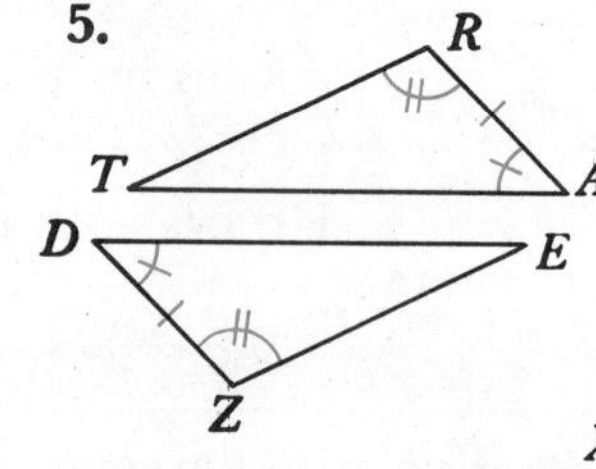

$\triangle RTA \cong \triangle ZED$

6.

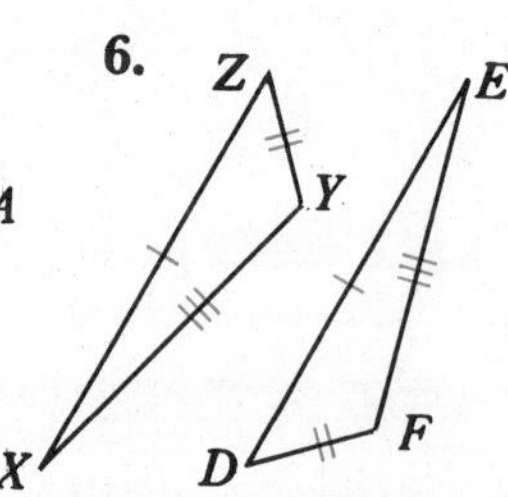

$\triangle XYZ \cong \triangle EFD$

Ⓑ **7–14.** Are the triangles congruent? If so, write a correct congruence statement like $\triangle GFE \cong \triangle KHE$ and give the correct postulate as SSS, SAS, or ASA. If not, write *not congruent.*

7.

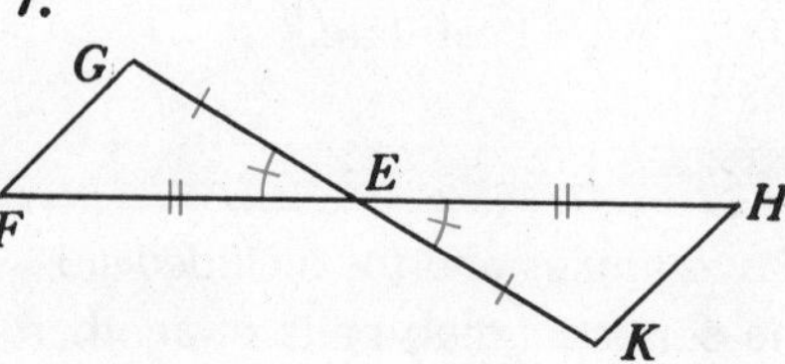

8.

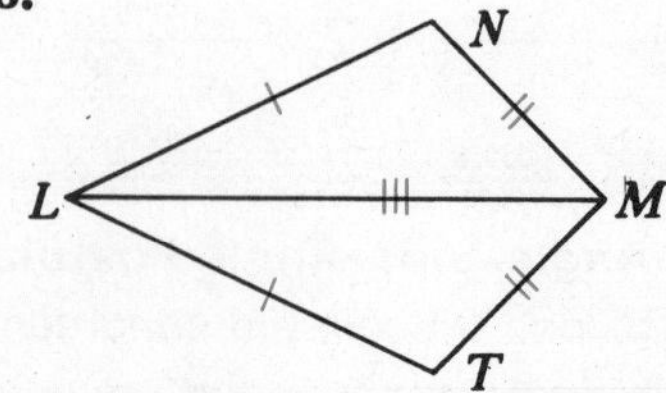

9. 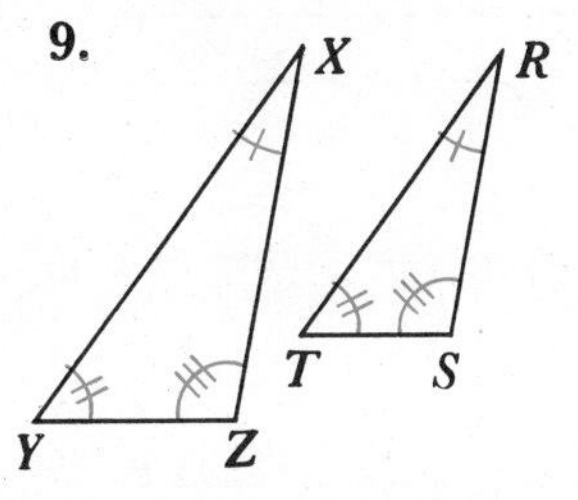

10. 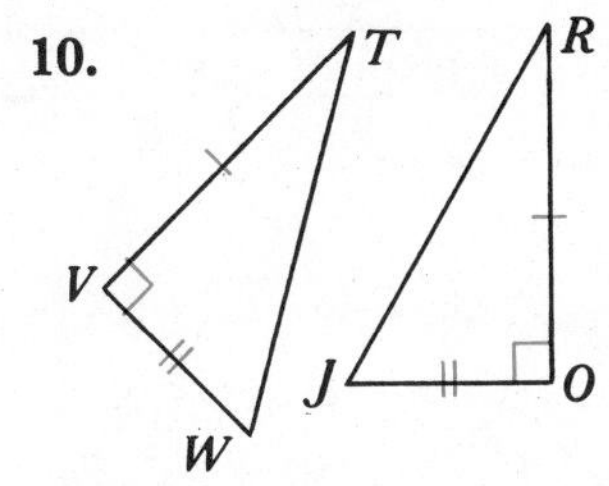

11. 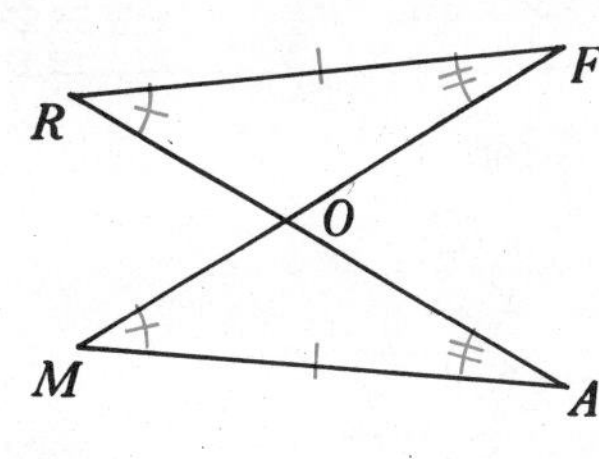

12. 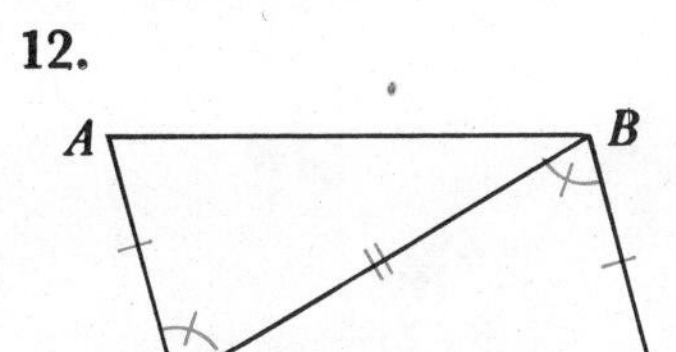

13. 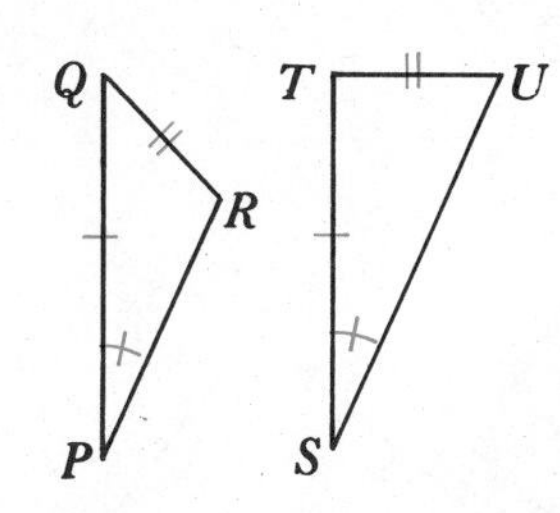

14. 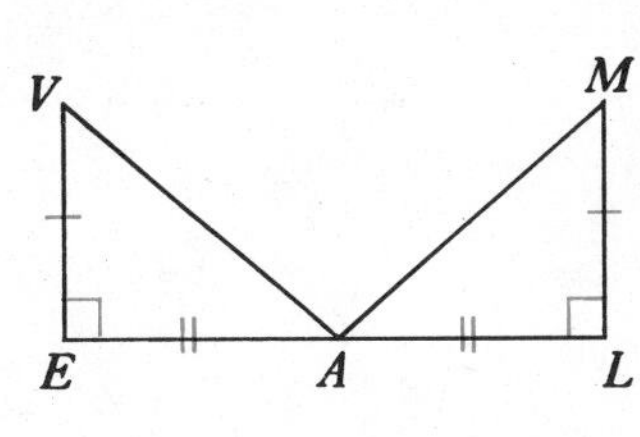

15. Which of Exercises 7–14 illustrates that three angles of one triangle can be congruent to the corresponding angles in another triangle without the triangles being congruent?

16. Which of Exercises 7–14 illustrates that two sides and an angle *not* included between them can be congruent to the corresponding parts of another triangle without the triangles being congruent?

17–20. Name the postulate you would use to prove $\triangle BCD \cong \triangle EFG$.

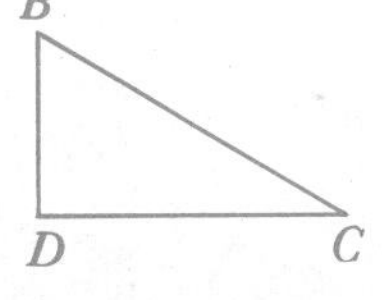

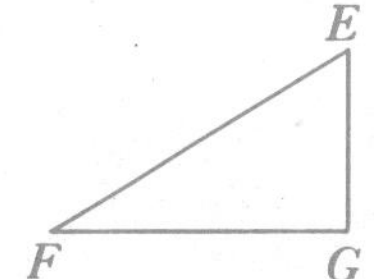

17. Given: $\overline{BD} \cong \overline{EG}$, $\angle B \cong \angle E$, $\overline{BC} \cong \overline{EF}$

18. Given: $\overline{BD} \cong \overline{EG}$, $\overline{BC} \cong \overline{EF}$, $\overline{CD} \cong \overline{FG}$

19. Given: $\angle B \cong \angle E$, $\angle C \cong \angle F$, $\overline{BC} \cong \overline{EF}$

20. Given: $\overline{BD} \perp \overline{DC}$, $\overline{EG} \perp \overline{FG}$, $\angle C \cong \angle F$, $\overline{CD} \cong \overline{FG}$

21–22. Each pair of triangles below has two pairs of corresponding parts marked congruent. What other information would be needed in order to use the given postulate?

21. 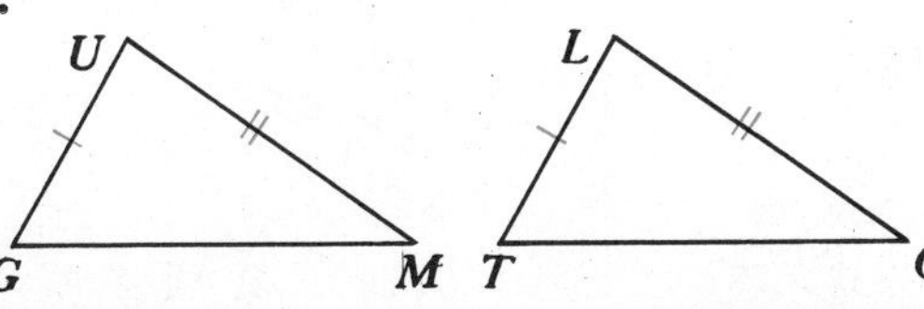

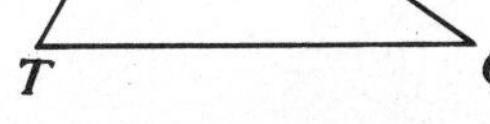

a. SAS Postulate **b.** SSS Postulate

22. 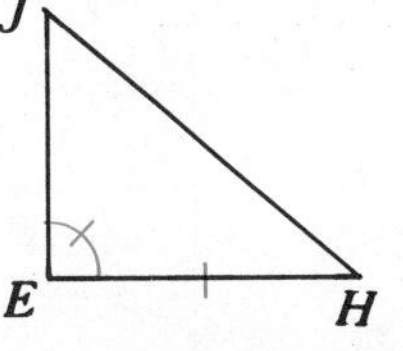

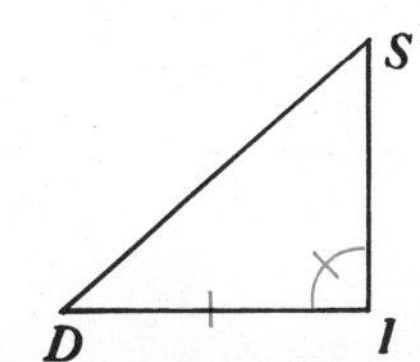

a. ASA Postulate **b.** SAS Postulate

construction: triangle, given three sides

1. Given:

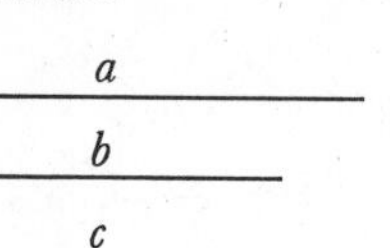

2.

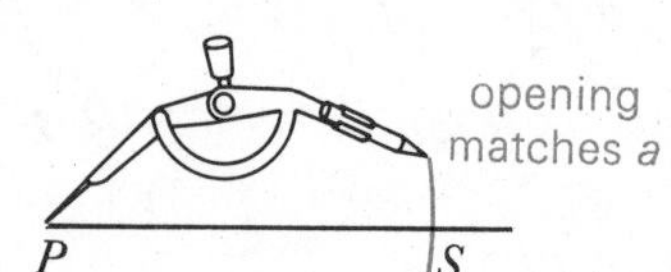

3.

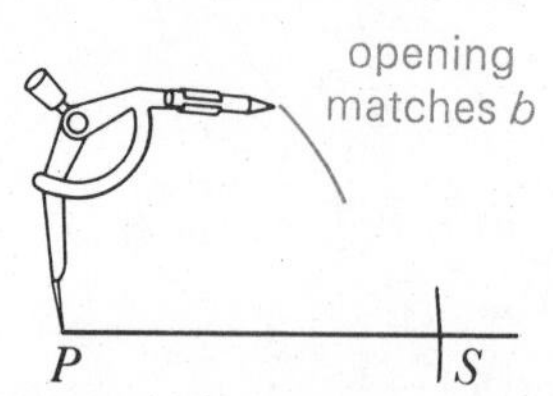

4.

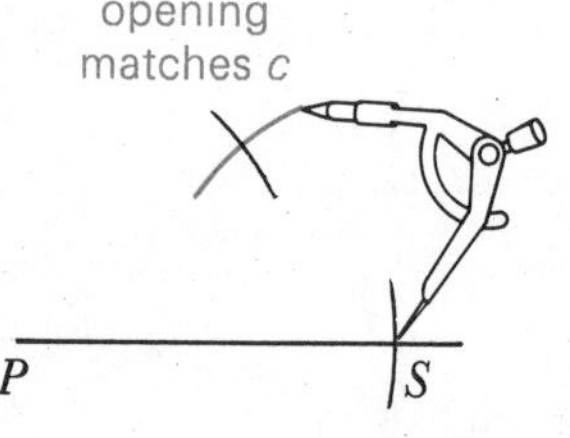

5.

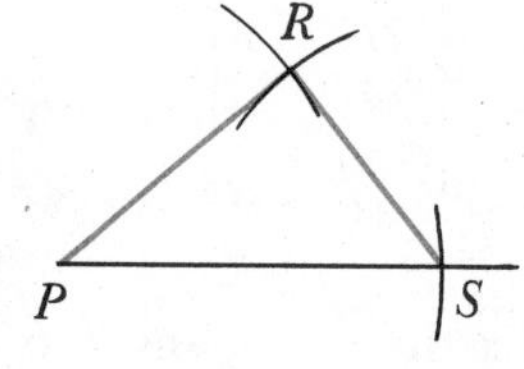

△*PSR* is the desired triangle.

C 23–26. Draw segments having the given lengths. Then construct a triangle having sides congruent to the segments you drew.

23. 5 cm, 6 cm, 8 cm

24. 6 cm, 4 cm, 4 cm

25. 4.5 cm, 3.6 cm, 5.2 cm

26. 5.6 cm, 5.6 cm, 5.6 cm

27. Construct a triangle congruent to $\triangle ABC$.

28. Which postulate guarantees that the triangle you constructed in Exercise 27 is congruent to $\triangle ABC$?

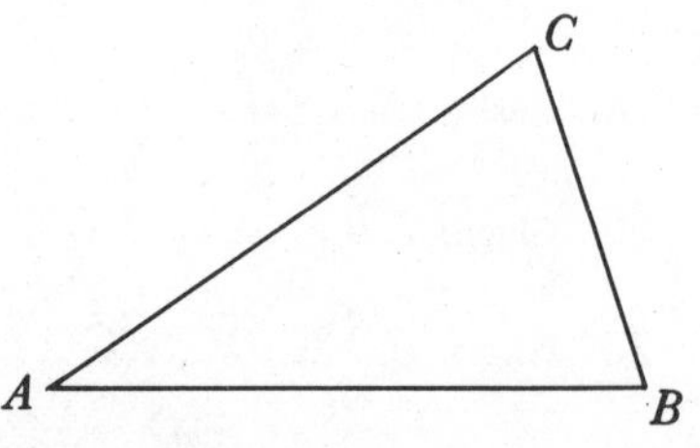

construction: triangle, given two sides and the included angle

1. Given:

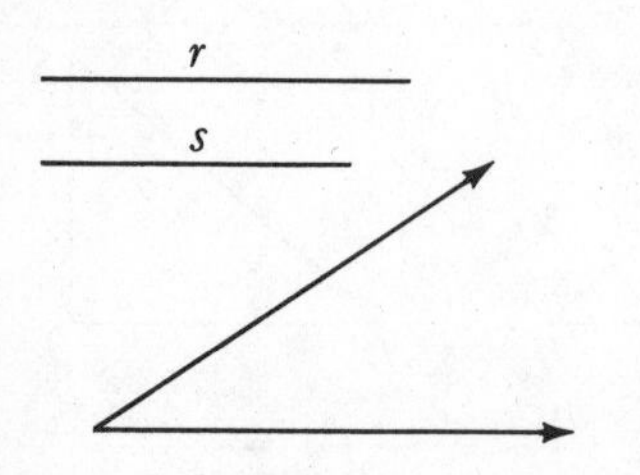

2. Construct an angle congruent to given angle (see page 66.)

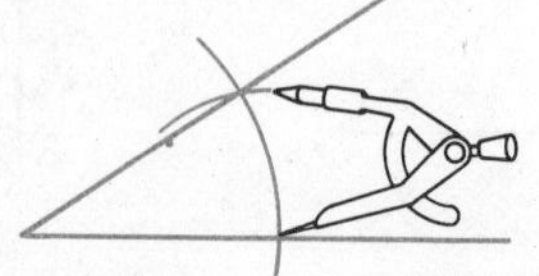

3. Construct the sides that include the angle.

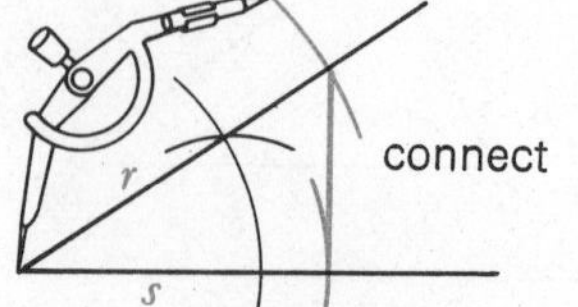

29–30. Construct triangles with the given parts. The angle is included between the sides.

29.

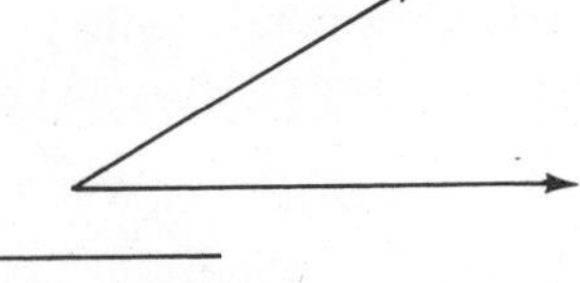

30.

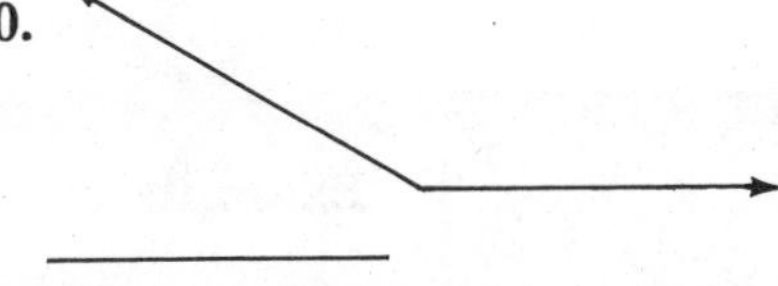

USING CONGRUENT TRIANGLES

GEOMETRY AT WORK

Suppose a carpenter wants to make a pair of congruent triangular braces. The carpenter will cut three pairs of congruent sides and fasten them to form the triangles. Which postulate of Section 3.4 is being used?

A surveyor might lay out a pair of congruent triangles as follows: A pair of congruent segments would be measured off. At corresponding endpoints of the segments, pairs of congruent angles would be measured. Which postulate of Section 3.4 is being used?

Quick Quiz for Sections 3.1 to 3.4

1. State the hypothesis and conclusion of the following: If two angles are right angles, they are congruent.

2. Change this sentence to if-then form: All collies are dogs.

3. Draw an Euler diagram to illustrate the if-then statement in Exercise 2.

4. Name the four types of reasons that can be used in a two-column proof.

5. List six statements about congruent angles and sides that follow from $\triangle TED \cong \triangle BIG$.

6–7. Which postulate tells you that the triangles are congruent?

6.

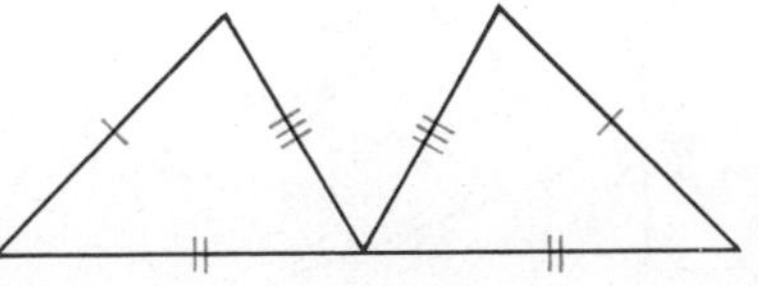

7.

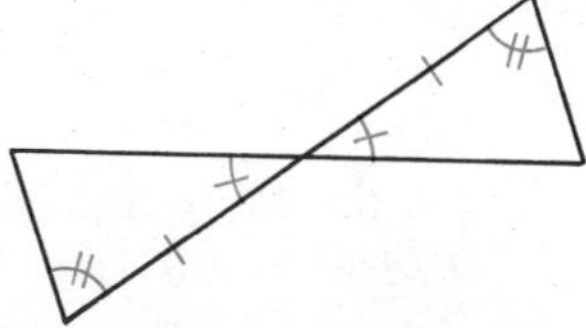

3.5 Proving Triangles Congruent

With the three postulates from Section 3.4, it is possible to prove many triangles congruent.

BELVEDERE by Nat Greenwood. Reproduced through the courtesy of Field Newspaper Syndicate.

Example 1:

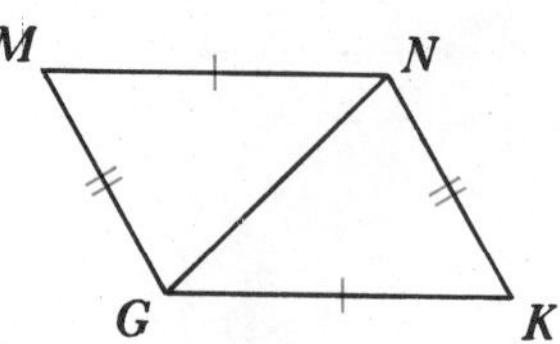

Given: $\overline{MN} \cong \overline{GK}$,
$\overline{MG} \cong \overline{NK}$

Prove: $\triangle MGN \cong \triangle KNG$

Proof:

STATEMENTS	REASONS
1. $\overline{MN} \cong \overline{GK}$, $\overline{MG} \cong \overline{NK}$	1. Given
2. $\overline{GN} \cong \overline{GN}$	2. A segment is congruent to itself.
3. $\triangle MGN \cong \triangle KNG$	3. SSS Postulate

Example 2:

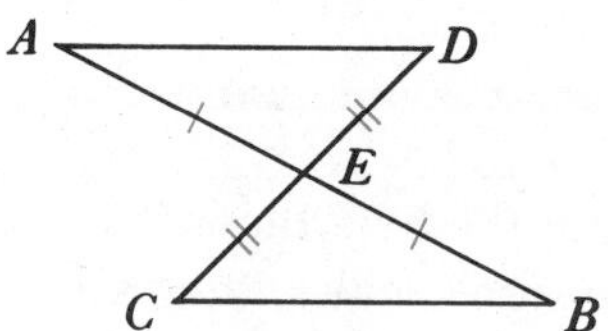

Given: $\overline{AB}$ and $\overline{CD}$ bisect each other at E.

Prove: $\triangle ADE \cong \triangle BCE$

Proof:

STATEMENTS	REASONS
1. $\overline{AB}$ and $\overline{CD}$ bisect each other at E.	1. Given
2. $\overline{AE} \cong \overline{EB}$ and $\overline{CE} \cong \overline{ED}$	2. Definition of bisect
3. $\angle AED$ and $\angle BEC$ are vertical angles.	3. Definition of vertical angles.
4. $\angle AED \cong \angle BEC$	4. Vertical angles are congruent.
5. $\triangle ADE \cong \triangle BCE$	5. SAS Postulate

Example 3:

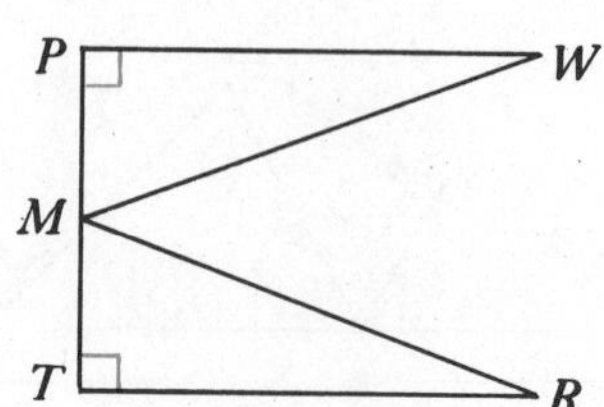

Given: $\overline{MP} \perp \overline{PW}$, $\overline{MT} \perp \overline{TR}$,
M is the midpoint of $\overline{PT}$,
$\angle PMW \cong \angle TMR$

Prove: $\triangle MPW \cong \triangle MTR$

Proof: STATEMENTS	REASONS
1. $\overline{MP} \perp \overline{PW}$, $\overline{MT} \perp \overline{TR}$	1. Given
2. $\angle P$ and $\angle T$ are right angles.	2. Definition of perpendicular
3. $\angle P \cong \angle T$	3. Right angles are congruent.
4. M is the midpoint of $\overline{PT}$.	4. Given
5. $\overline{PM} \cong \overline{MT}$	5. Definition of midpoint
6. $\angle PMW \cong \angle TMR$	6. Given
7. $\triangle MPW \cong \triangle MTR$	7. ASA Postulate

Exercises 3.5

Ⓐ **1.** For Example 3, give the numbers of the steps in which we proved the three parts needed before we could use the ASA Postulate.

2–6. One more fact is needed to prove $\triangle ABC \cong \triangle DFE$ in each case. Tell what fact is needed in order to use the given postulate.

2. $\overline{AB} \cong \overline{DF}$, $\overline{BC} \cong \overline{FE}$, SSS Postulate

3. $\overline{BC} \cong \overline{FE}$, $\overline{AC} \cong \overline{DE}$, SAS Postulate

4. $\overline{AC} \cong \overline{DE}$, $\angle A \cong \angle D$, ASA Postulate

5. $\angle A \cong \angle D$, $\angle B \cong \angle F$, ASA Postulate

6. $\overline{AB} \perp \overline{BC}$, $\overline{DF} \perp \overline{FE}$, $\overline{AB} \cong \overline{DF}$, SAS Postulate

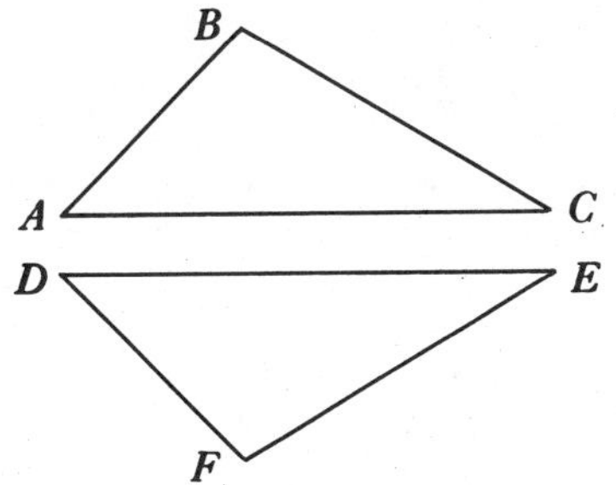

Ⓑ **7–12.** Can the triangles be proved congruent? If so, give the correct postulate as SSS, SAS, or ASA. If not, write *no*.

7.

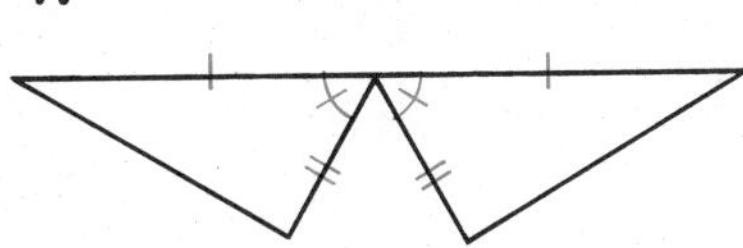

8.

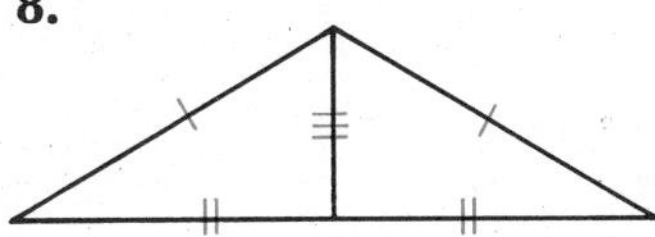

9.

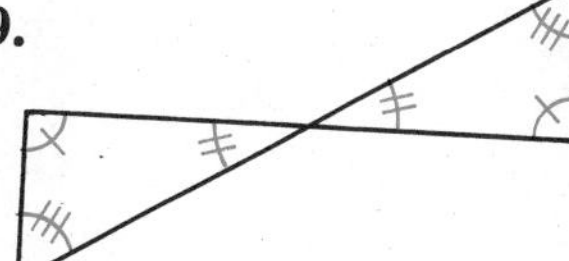

10.

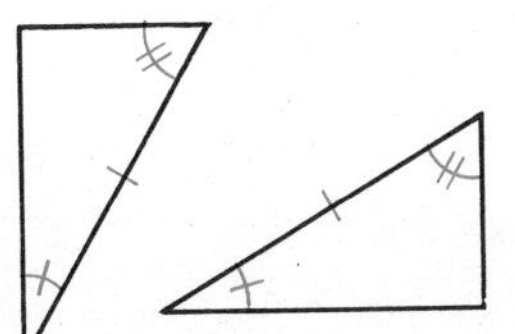

11.

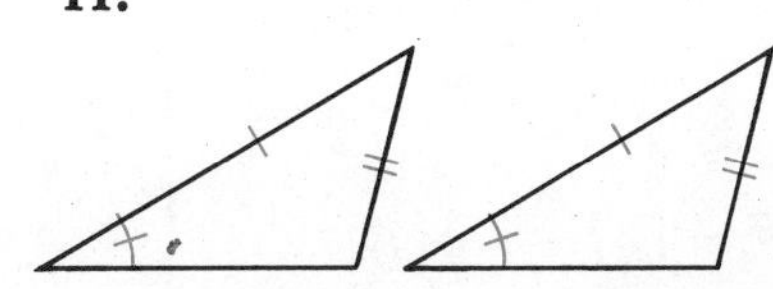

12.

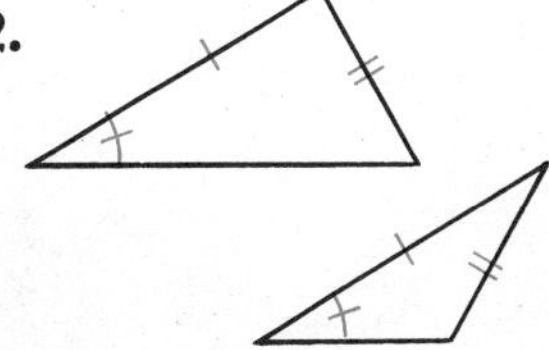

13–32. Give the reasons needed to complete each proof.

Given: E is the midpoint of $\overline{DF}$, $\overline{GD} \cong \overline{HF}$, $\overline{GE} \cong \overline{HE}$

Prove: $\triangle GDE \cong \triangle HFE$

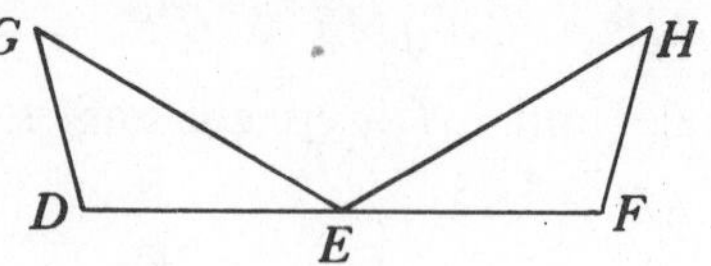

Proof:

STATEMENTS	REASONS
1. E is the midpoint of $\overline{DF}$.	1. **13.**
2. $\overline{DE} \cong \overline{EF}$	2. **14.**
3. $\overline{GD} \cong \overline{HF}$, $\overline{GE} \cong \overline{HE}$	3. **15.**
4. $\triangle GDE \cong \triangle HFE$	4. **16.**

Given: $\angle PMN \cong \angle QMN$, $\angle PNM \cong \angle QNM$

Prove: $\triangle PMN \cong \triangle QMN$

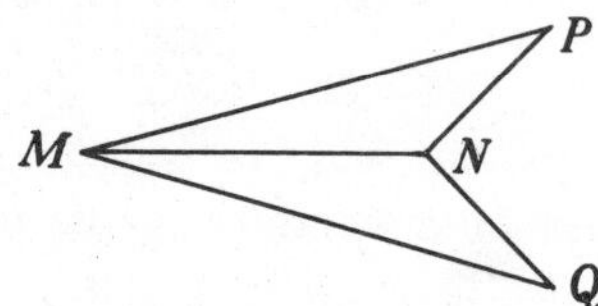

Proof:

STATEMENTS	REASONS
1. $\angle PMN \cong \angle QMN$	1. **17.**
2. $\angle PNM \cong \angle QNM$	2. **18.**
3. $\overline{MN} \cong \overline{MN}$	3. **19.**
4. $\triangle PMN \cong \triangle QMN$	4. **20.**

Given: $\angle 2 \cong \angle 3$, $\overline{DE} \cong \overline{GH}$, $\overline{EF} \cong \overline{GF}$

Prove: $\triangle DEF \cong \triangle HGF$

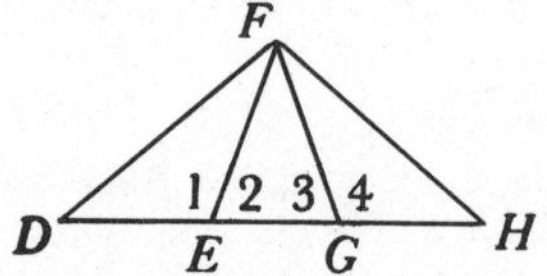

Proof:

STATEMENTS	REASONS
1. $\angle 1$ and $\angle 2$ as well as $\angle 3$ and $\angle 4$ are supplementary.	1. If noncommon sides of adjacent angles are opposite rays, the angles are supplementary.
2. $\angle 2 \cong \angle 3$	2. **21.**
3. $\angle 1 \cong \angle 4$	3. **22.**
4. $\overline{DE} \cong \overline{GH}$, $\overline{EF} \cong \overline{GF}$	4. **23.**
5. $\triangle DEF \cong \triangle HGF$	5. **24.**

Given: $EC = DA$, $\overline{RE} \perp \overline{EA}$,
$\overline{BA} \perp \overline{EA}$, $\overline{RE} \cong \overline{AB}$

Prove: $\triangle RED \cong \triangle BAC$

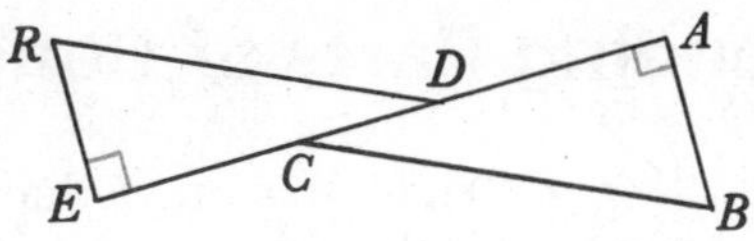

Proof:

STATEMENTS	REASONS
1. $EC = DA$	1. **25.** ____
2. $EC + CD = CD + DA$	2. **26.** ____
3. $ED = EC + CD$, $CA = CD + DA$	3. Definition of between
4. $ED = CA$	4. **27.** ____
5. $\overline{ED} \cong \overline{CA}$	5. **28.** ____
6. $\overline{RE} \perp \overline{EA}$, $\overline{BA} \perp \overline{EA}$	6. Given
7. $\angle E$ and $\angle A$ are right angles.	7. **29.** ____
8. $\angle E \cong \angle A$	8. **30.** ____
9. $\overline{RE} \cong \overline{AB}$	9. **31.** ____
10. $\triangle RED \cong \triangle BAC$	10. **32.** ____

Ⓒ **33–34.** Write a two-column proof for each of the following:

33. Given: $\overline{RW} \perp \overline{TS}$, W is the midpoint of $\overline{TS}$.

Prove: $\triangle RWS \cong \triangle RWT$

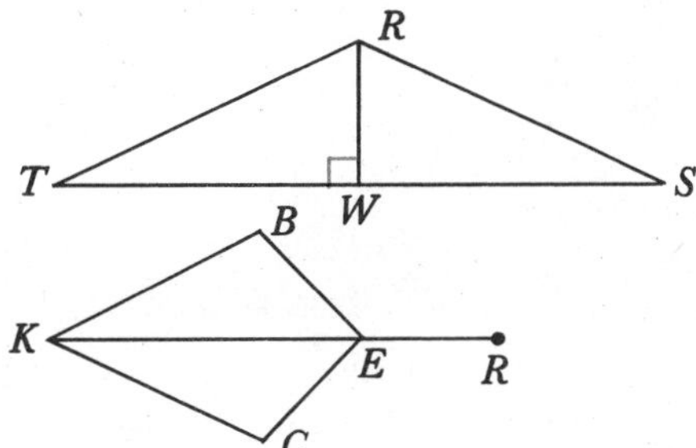

34. Given: $\angle BKE \cong \angle CKE$, $\angle BER \cong \angle CER$

Prove: $\triangle BKE \cong \triangle CKE$

GEOMETRY AT WORK

USING SAS

An artist, drafter, or geometry student often uses the SAS Postulate without even being aware of it. For example,

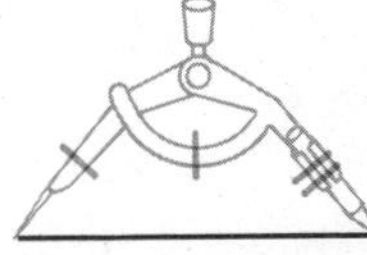

given segment

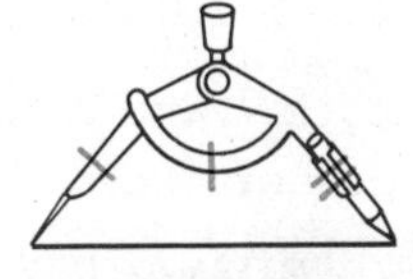

a congruent segment

Note that the legs of the compass need not be congruent to each other.

3.6 Corresponding Parts of Congruent Triangles

Grant Heilman

Often we can prove that two triangles are congruent by SSS, SAS, or ASA. Then we can use the definition of congruent triangles to prove that other parts of these triangles are also congruent. When we use the definition of congruent triangles in this way, we say

Corresponding parts of congruent triangles are congruent. (Abbreviation: Corres. parts of ≅ △s are ≅.)

Example 1:

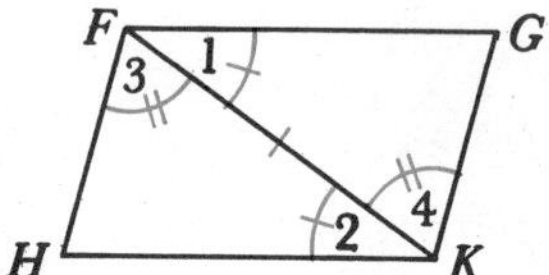

Given: $\angle 1 \cong \angle 2$, $\angle 3 \cong \angle 4$

Prove: $\overline{FH} \cong \overline{KG}$

Proof:

STATEMENTS	REASONS
1. $\angle 1 \cong \angle 2$	1. Given
2. $\angle 3 \cong \angle 4$	2. Given
3. $\overline{FK} \cong \overline{FK}$	3. A segment is congruent to itself.
4. $\triangle FKH \cong \triangle KFG$	4. ASA Postulate
5. $\overline{FH} \cong \overline{KG}$	5. Corres. parts of ≅ △s are ≅.

Example 2:

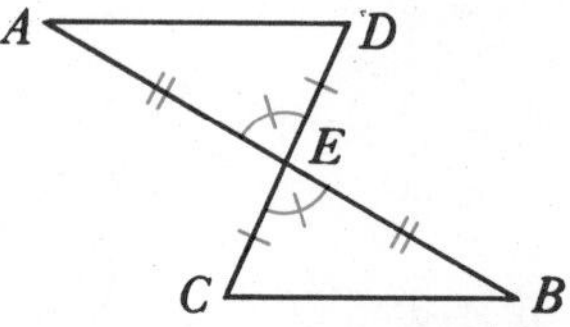

Given: $\overline{AB}$ and $\overline{CD}$ bisect each other at E.

Prove: $\overline{AD} \cong \overline{BC}$

Proof:

STATEMENTS	REASONS
1. $\overline{AB}$ and $\overline{CD}$ bisect at E.	1. Given
2. $\overline{AE} \cong \overline{EB}$ and $\overline{CE} \cong \overline{ED}$	2. Definition of bisect.
3. $\angle AED$ and $\angle BEC$ are vertical angles.	3. Definition of vertical angles
4. $\angle AED \cong \angle BEC$	4. Vertical angles are congruent.
5. $\triangle ADE \cong \triangle BCE$	5. SAS Postulate
6. $\overline{AD} \cong \overline{BC}$	6. Corres. parts of ≅ △s are ≅.

Exercises 3.6

Ⓐ **1–2.** In order to prove $\overline{AB} \cong \overline{CD}$ in each exercise, which two triangles would you first have to prove congruent? By which postulate?

1.

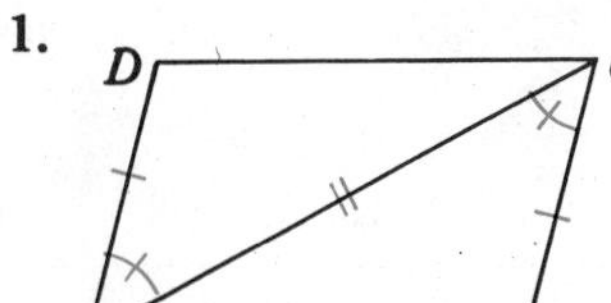

2.

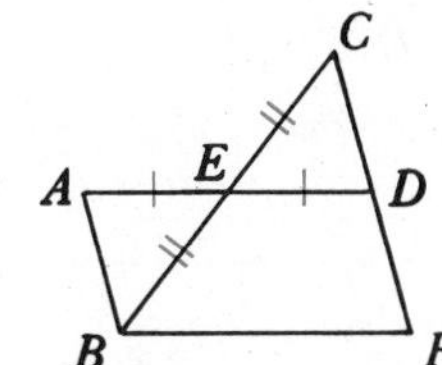

3. After you prove the triangles congruent in Exercise 1, what reason would you give for $\overline{AB} \cong \overline{CD}$?

4. After you prove the triangles congruent in Exercise 2, could you say $\angle A \cong \angle CDE$? For what reason?

Ⓑ **5–24.** Supply the missing reasons in each proof.

Given: $\overline{RE} \cong \overline{WT}$, $\overline{ES} \cong \overline{TM}$, $RM = SW$

Prove: $\angle E \cong \angle T$

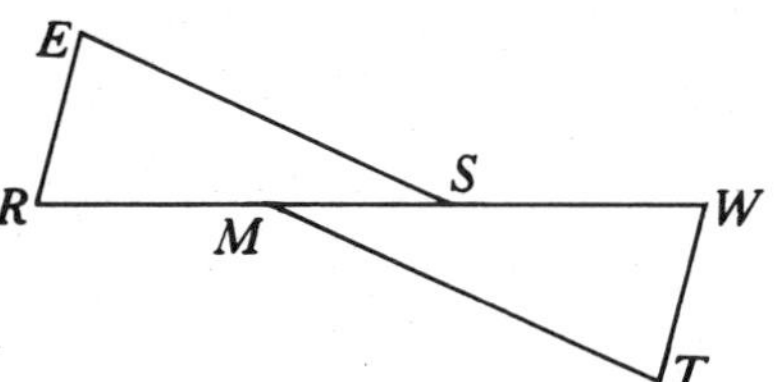

Proof:

STATEMENTS	REASONS
1. $RM = SW$	1. **5.** ______
2. $RM + MS = MS + SW$	2. **6.** ______
3. $RS = RM + MS$, $MW = MS + SW$	3. **7.** ______
4. $RS = MW$	4. **8.** ______
5. $\overline{RS} \cong \overline{MW}$	5. **9.** ______
6. $\overline{RE} \cong \overline{WT}$, $\overline{ES} \cong \overline{TM}$	6. **10.** ______
7. $\triangle RES \cong \triangle WTM$	7. **11.** ______
8. $\angle E \cong \angle T$	8. **12.** ______

Given: $\angle 1 \cong \angle 2$, $\overline{GC} \perp \overline{CB}$, $\overline{AM} \perp \overline{CB}$, $\overline{HB} \perp \overline{CB}$, M is the midpoint of $\overline{CB}$.

Prove: $\overline{GM} \cong \overline{HM}$

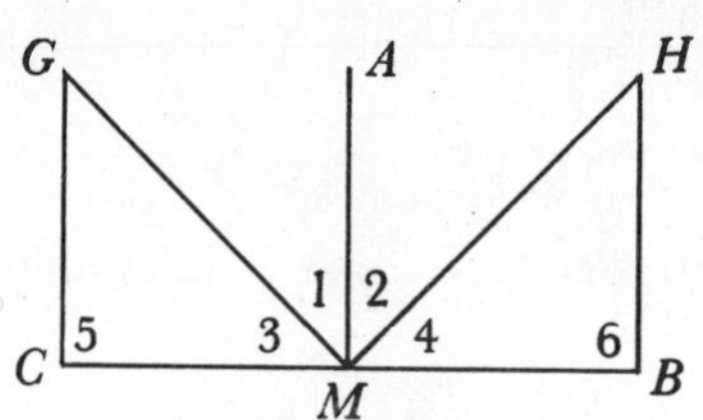

Proof:

STATEMENTS	REASONS
1. $\angle 1 \cong \angle 2$	1. **13.** ____
2. $\overline{AM} \perp \overline{CB}$	2. **14.** ____
3. $\angle M_{13}$ and $\angle M_{24}$ are right angles.	3. **15.** ____
4. $\angle 1$ and $\angle 3$ are complementary, $\angle 2$ and $\angle 4$ are complementary.	4. **16.** ____
5. $\angle 3 \cong \angle 4$	5. **17.** ____
6. $\overline{GC} \perp \overline{CB}$, $\overline{HB} \perp \overline{CB}$	6. **18.** ____
7. $\angle 5$ and $\angle 6$ are right angles.	7. **19.** ____
8. $\angle 5 \cong \angle 6$	8. **20.** ____
9. M is the midpoint of $\overline{CB}$.	9. **21.** ____
10. $\overline{CM} \cong \overline{MB}$	10. **22.** ____
11. $\triangle GCM \cong \triangle HBM$	11. **23.** ____
12. $\overline{GM} \cong \overline{HM}$	12. **24.** ____

Ⓒ **25–28.** Write a two-column proof for each of the following:

25. Given: $\overline{AC} \perp \overline{BD}$, B is the midpoint of $\overline{AC}$.

Prove: $\angle A \cong \angle C$

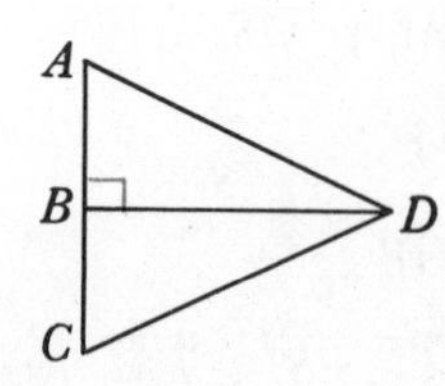

26. Given: G is the midpoint of $\overline{EH}$, $\angle E \cong \angle H$

Prove: $\overline{FG} \cong \overline{KG}$

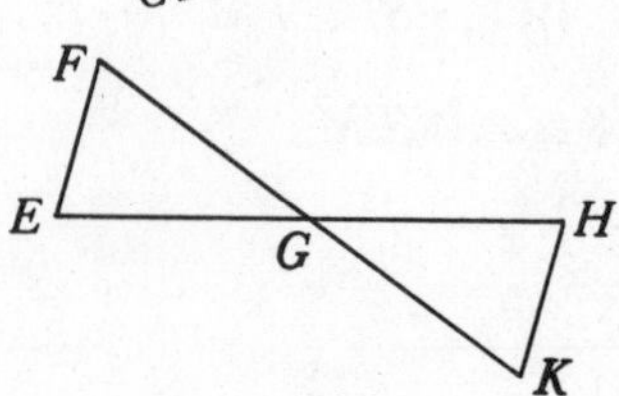

27. Given: $\angle 4 \cong \angle 6$, $\overline{RN} \cong \overline{RQ}$, $\overline{MQ}$ and $\overline{PN}$ intersect at R.

Prove: $\overline{PR} \cong \overline{MR}$

HINT: Prove $\triangle MRN \cong \triangle PRQ$.

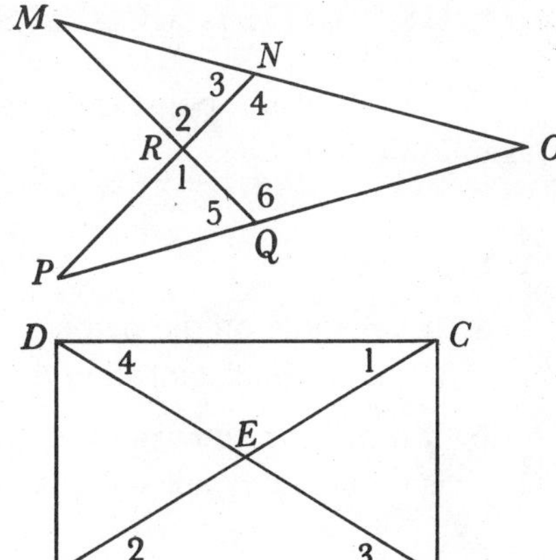

28. Given: $\overline{AB} \cong \overline{CD}$, $\angle 1 \cong \angle 2$, $\angle 3 \cong \angle 4$, $\overline{AC}$ and $\overline{BD}$ intersect at E.

Prove: $\overline{AC}$ and $\overline{BD}$ bisect each other at E.

HINT: Prove $\overline{AE} \cong \overline{CE}$ and $\overline{DE} \cong \overline{BE}$ by proving two triangles congruent.

29. An observer in a lighthouse tower sights down at a boat with an instrument called a clinometer. $\angle SCB$ is measured as 50°. Then the observer sights at a 50° angle toward shore until he locates an object at A that he knows is 120 meters away from B. How far is the boat from B? With what postulate can you justify your answer?

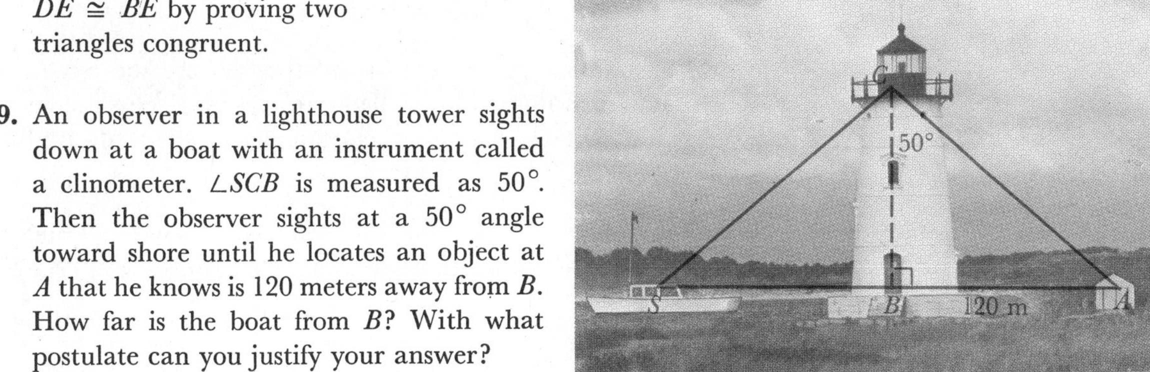

Courtesy American Airlines

30. The distance between two points A and B can sometimes be found as follows: Drive a stake at a convenient point C. Sight along $\overline{AC}$ and measure off to get $\overline{CE} \cong \overline{AC}$. In the same way, sight along $\overline{BC}$ to get $\overline{BC} \cong \overline{CF}$. Why is $\overline{AB} \cong \overline{EF}$?

Ex. 30

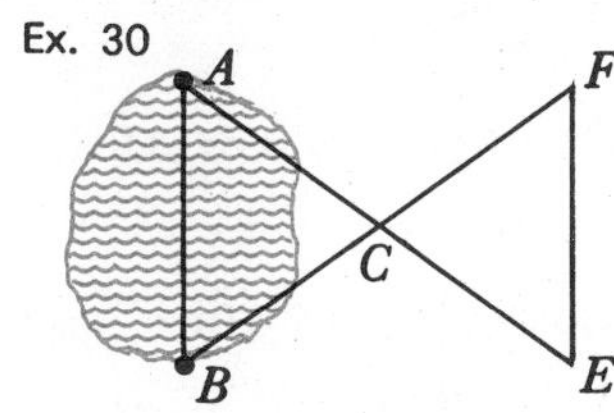

Ex. 31

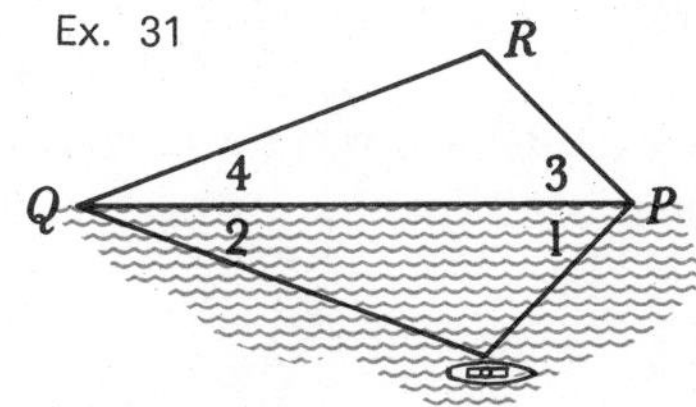

31. An old method that can be used to find the distance from point P to a ship at sea is as follows: Pick a point Q. Measure $\angle 1$ and $\angle 2$. Make $\angle 3 \cong \angle 1$ and $\angle 4 \cong \angle 2$. Why does $\overline{PR}$ give the desired distance?

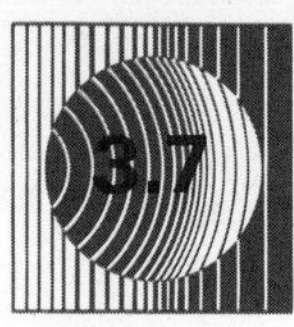

More About Perpendiculars

We can tell if a point is on the perpendicular bisector of a segment as follows:

Perpendicular Bisector Theorem

In a plane,

a. If a point is on the perpendicular bisector of a segment, then the point is equidistant from the endpoints of the segment.

b. If a point is equidistant from the endpoints of a segment, then it is on the perpendicular bisector of the segment.

This theorem is stated in two parts which have the following form:

Part a: If p, then q.

Part b: If q, then p.

Two if-then statements related in this way (where the hypothesis and conclusion are switched) are called **converses.** Each statement is the converse of the other. A true if-then statement does *not* always have a true converse.

Statement: If an angle measures 90, then it is a right angle. (True)
Converse: If an angle is a right angle, then it measures 90. (True)

Statement: If an angle measures more than 90, then it is not a right angle. (True)
Converse: If an angle is not a right angle, then it measures more than 90. (False)

Since a converse may be true or false, proving an if-then statement DOES NOT prove its converse. We will prove part **a** of the Perpendicular Bisector Theorem here. The proof of the converse (part **b**) is covered in Exercises 7–14.

Part a. First we restate part **a** in terms of a figure where $\overline{AB}$ is any segment and line ℓ is its perpendicular bisector.

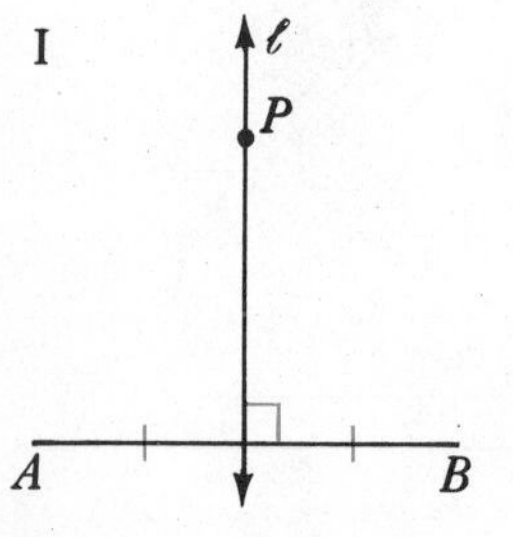

Given: Line ℓ is the perpendicular bisector of $\overline{AB}$, P is a point on ℓ.

Prove: $PA = PB$

[*Plan:* See figure II. Segments PA and PB are corresponding parts of $\triangle PCA$ and $\triangle PCB$. Show that $\triangle PCA \cong \triangle PCB$.]

Proof: STATEMENTS	REASONS
1. Line ℓ intersects $\overline{AB}$ at its midpoint C.	**1.** Definition of perpendicular bisector
2. $\overline{CA} \cong \overline{CB}$	**2.** Definition of midpoint
3. $\overline{PC} \cong \overline{PC}$	**3.** A segment is congruent to itself.
4. $\angle PCA$ and $\angle PCB$ are right angles.	**4.** ℓ is the perpendicular bisector of $\overline{AB}$.
5. $\angle PCA \cong \angle PCB$	**5.** Right angles are congruent.
6. $\triangle PCA \cong \triangle PCB$	**6.** SAS Postulate
7. $PA = PB$	**7.** Corres. parts of $\cong$ $\triangle$s are $\cong$.

NOTE: In the proof above, we picked P not on $\overline{AB}$. So $\triangle PCA$ and $\triangle PCB$ are formed. However, if we pick P on $\overline{AB}$, then P must be the midpoint C, and $PA = PB$ by definition of midpoint.

A **corollary** is a theorem that is closely related to and easily proved from another theorem. The next theorem is therefore a corollary. Its proof is covered in Exercises 15–17.

In a plane, two points that are equidistant from the endpoints of a segment determine the perpendicular bisector of the segment.
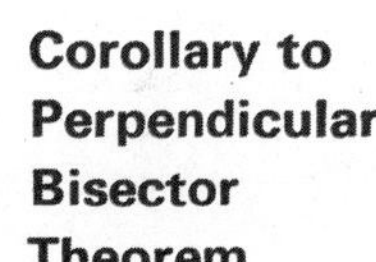

Corollary to Perpendicular Bisector Theorem

Exercises 3.7

Ⓐ **1–4.** Tell whether each if-then statement is true. Then state the converse, and tell if it is true.

1. If $\overleftrightarrow{AB} \perp \overleftrightarrow{AC}$, then $m\angle BAC = 90$.

2. If $m\angle A$ is less than 90, then $\angle A$ is not a right angle.

3. If the corresponding angles of $\triangle ABC$ and $\triangle DEF$ are congruent, then $\triangle ABC \cong \triangle DEF$.

4. If $m\angle A + m\angle B = 90$, then $\angle A$ and $\angle B$ are vertical angles.

5. Line ℓ is the perpendicular bisector of $\overline{AB}$. Find the values of x, y, and z.

6. In the figure below, $EM = 8$, $EN = 8$, $FM = 6$, and $FN = 6$. What can you say about $\overleftrightarrow{EF}$?

Ex. 5

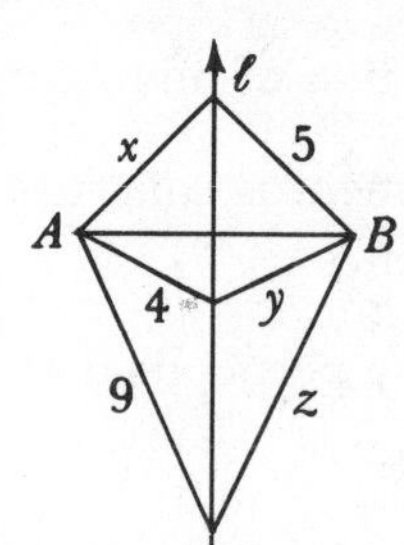

Ex. 6

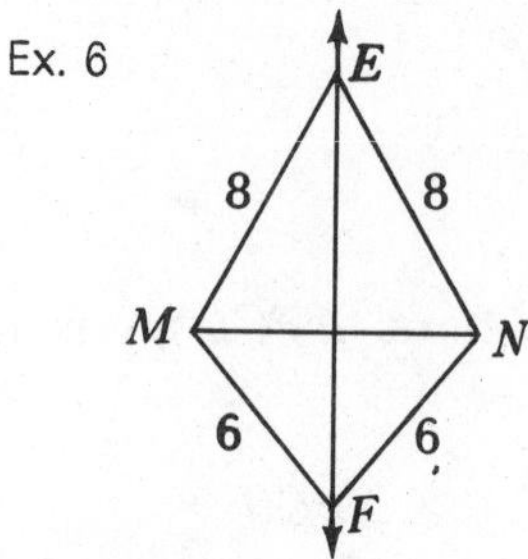

Ⓑ **7–14.** Give a reason for each statement in the following proof. This is a proof for part **b** of the Perpendicular Bisector Theorem.

Given: P is a point not on $\overline{AB}$ and $\overline{PA} \cong \overline{PB}$, C is the midpoint of $\overline{AB}$.

Prove: P is on the perpendicular bisector of $\overline{AB}$.

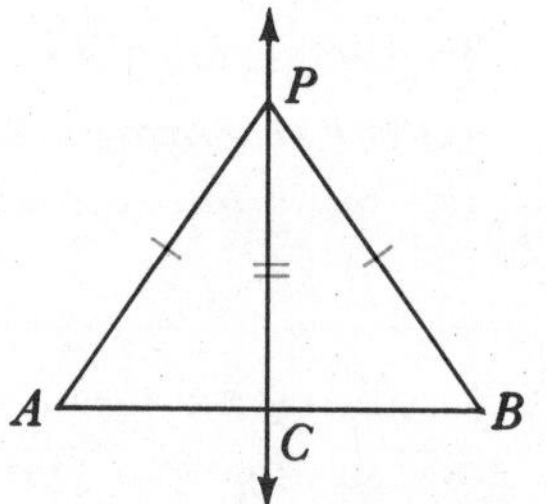

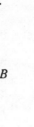

Proof:

STATEMENTS	REASONS
1. $\overline{PC} \cong \overline{PC}$	1. **7.**
2. $\overline{PA} \cong \overline{PB}$, C is the midpoint of $\overline{AB}$.	2. **8.**
3. $\overline{AC} \cong \overline{CB}$	3. **9.**
4. $\triangle ACP \cong \triangle BCP$	4. **10.**
5. $\angle ACP \cong \angle BCP$	5. **11.**
6. $\angle ACP$ and $\angle BCP$ are supplementary.	6. Supplement Postulate (p. 56)
7. $\angle ACP$ and $\angle BCP$ are right angles.	7. **12.**
8. $\overline{PC} \perp \overline{AB}$	8. **13.**
9. $\overleftrightarrow{PC}$ is the perpendicular bisector of $\overline{AB}$.	9. **14.**

15–20. Give a reason for each statement. Exercises 15–17 are a proof of the Corollary to the Perpendicular Bisector Theorem.

Given: P and Q are equidistant from A and B.

Prove: $\overleftrightarrow{PQ}$ is the perpendicular bisector of $\overline{AB}$.

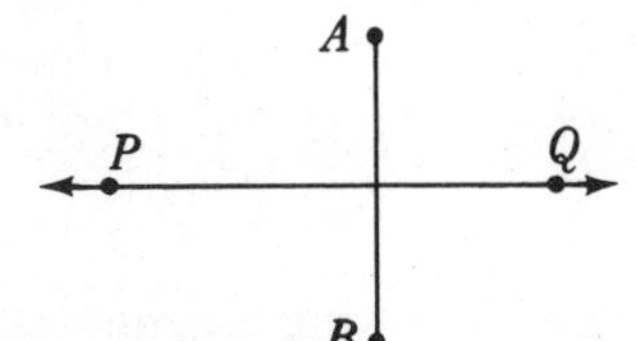

Proof:

STATEMENTS	REASONS
1. P and Q are equidistant from A and B.	1. **15.** ____
2. P and Q are on the perpendicular bisector of $\overline{AB}$.	2. **16.** ____
3. $\overleftrightarrow{PQ}$ is the perpendicular bisector of $\overline{AB}$.	3. **17.** ____

Given: $EG = EK$, $GM = MK$, H is on $\overleftrightarrow{EM}$.

Prove: $GH = KH$

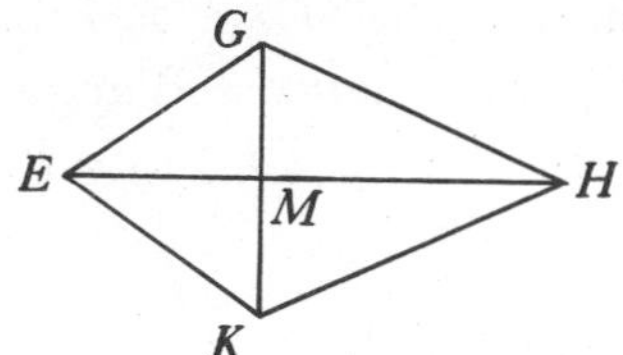

Proof:

STATEMENTS	REASONS
1. $EG = EK$ and $GM = MK$	1. **18.** ____
2. $\overleftrightarrow{EM}$ is the perpendicular bisector of $\overline{GK}$.	2. **19.** ____
3. $GH = HK$	3. **20.** ____

21–22. Construct the perpendicular bisector of each segment below. Refer to the construction on page 62.

21. ______________________ **22.** __________________

Ⓒ **23.** Which theorem or corollary in this section shows why the construction on page 62 works?

24. Give a two-column proof for the following:

Given: Line m is the perpendicular bisector of $\overline{AB}$, $\overrightarrow{AX}$ intersects m at C.

Prove: $AX = CB + CX$

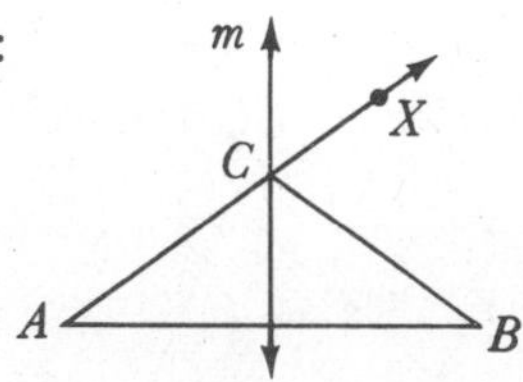

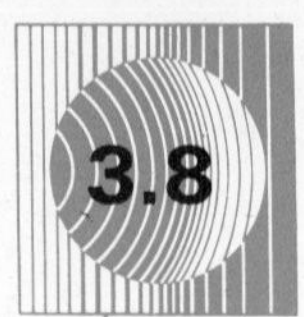

3.8 Transformations and Congruent Triangles

From Section 2.8, you know that reflections, slides, and turns preserve distance and angle measure. These ideas can help in thinking about congruent triangles.

The following example illustrates the SAS Postulate.

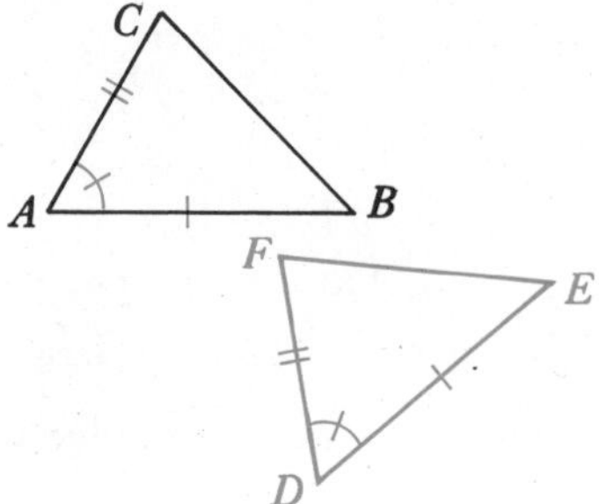

Example: Given $\triangle ABC$ and $\triangle DEF$ with $\overline{AB} \cong \overline{DE}$, $\overline{AC} \cong \overline{DF}$, and $\angle BAC \cong \angle EDF$, show that $\triangle ABC$ can be made to coincide with $\triangle DEF$.

Case 1: $\triangle ABC$ and $\triangle DEF$ have the same orientation.

First slide $\triangle ABC$ so that point A falls on point D. (See figure below.) Since distance and angle measure are preserved under a slide, $\overline{DC'} \cong \overline{AC}$, $\overline{DB'} \cong \overline{AB}$, and $\angle BAC \cong \angle B'DC'$.

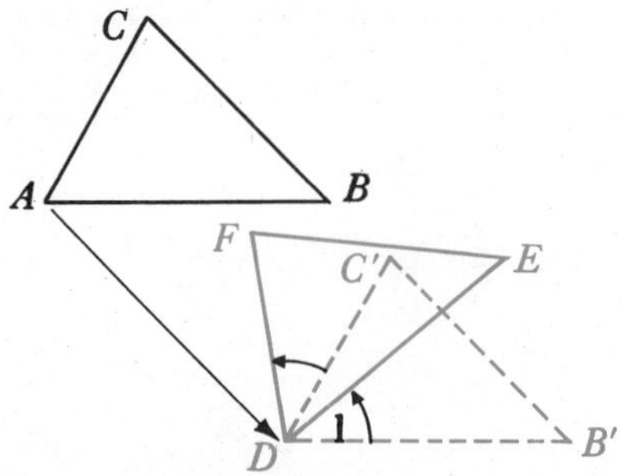

Next turn $\triangle DB'C'$ about D through $\angle 1$. Then $\overline{DB'}$ will coincide with $\overline{DE}$, and $\overline{DC'}$ will coincide with $\overline{DF}$ because angle measure is preserved under a turn. Also B' will coincide with E, and C' will coincide with F because distance is preserved under a turn.

As a result, $\triangle ABC$ coincides with $\triangle DEF$.

Case 2: $\triangle ABC$ and $\triangle DEF$ have opposite orientation.

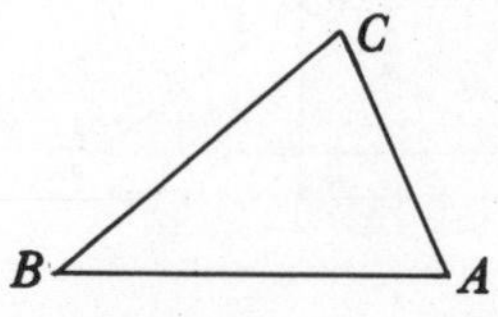

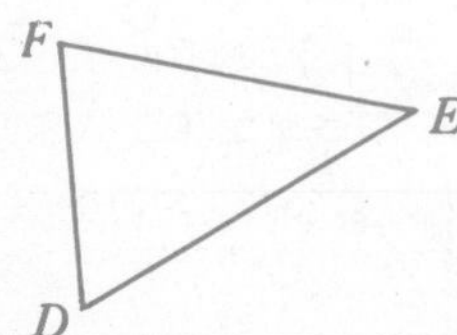

Since $\triangle ABC$ and $\triangle DEF$ have opposite orientation, we can reflect $\triangle ABC$ over any line.

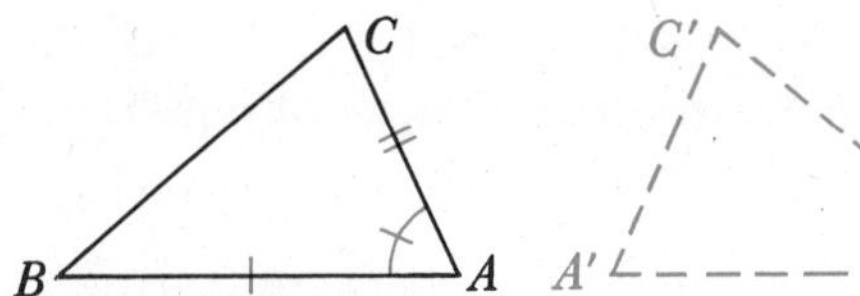

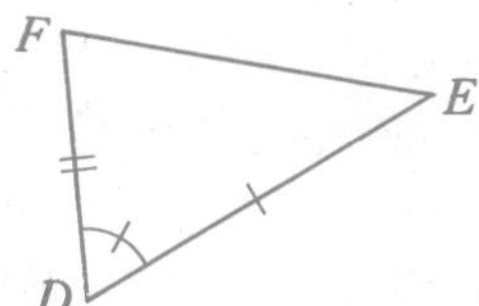

Now $\triangle A'B'C'$ and $\triangle DEF$ have the same orientation. So we can proceed just as we did in Case 1. (We will not repeat the steps here.) As this example shows, two triangles related by SAS are congruent because they can always be made to coincide.

Exercises 3.8

Ⓐ **1–6.** Tell if a slide, a reflection, or a turn is needed to make the two triangles coincide.

1.

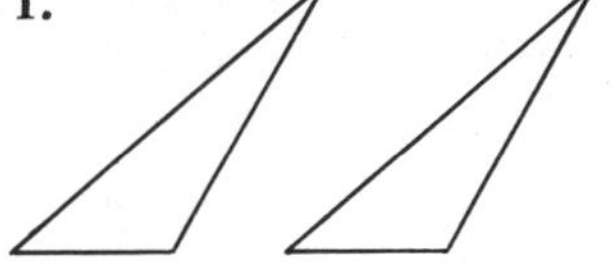

2.

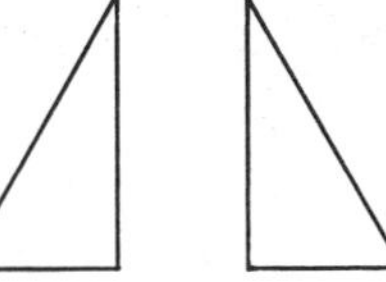

3.

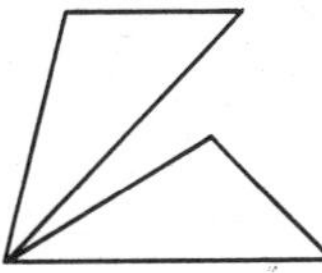

4.

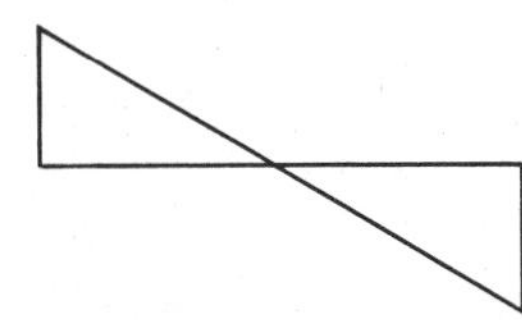

5.

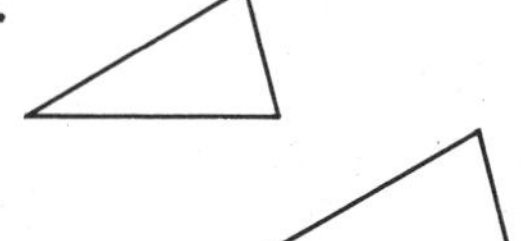

6.

Ⓑ **7–10.** Name two transformations that can be used to make the two triangles coincide in each case.

7.

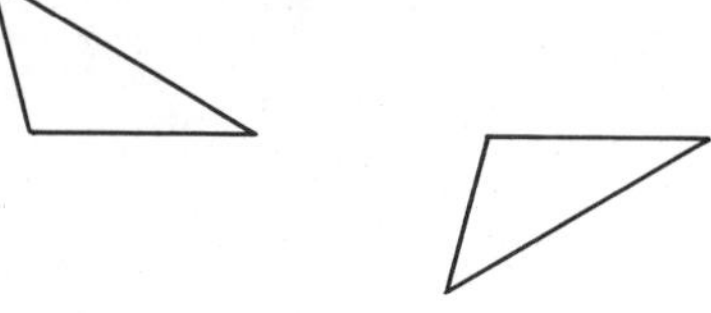

8.

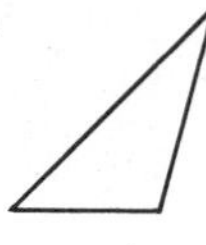

9.

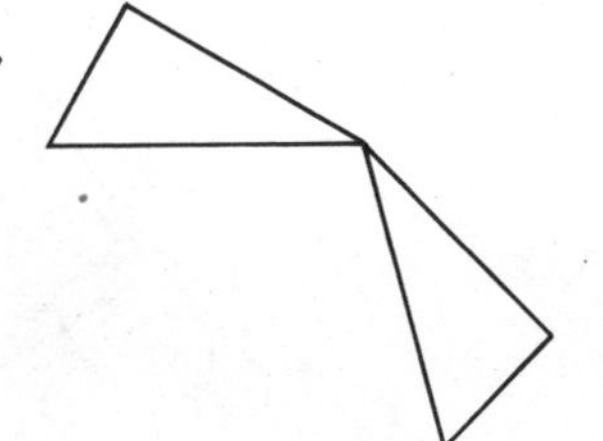

10.

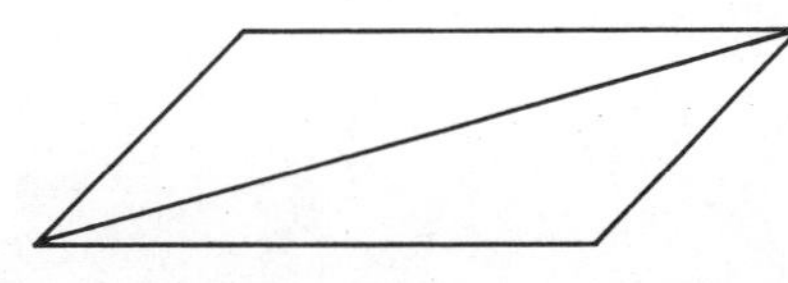

11–18. These exercises illustrate how two triangles that are related by SSS can be made to coincide by transformations.

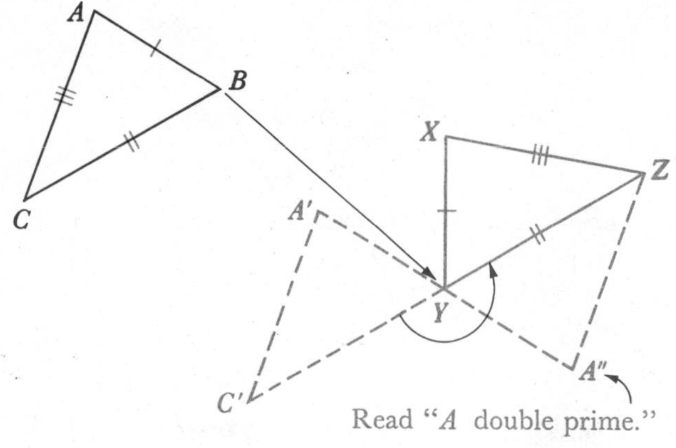

Read "A double prime."

11. Do $\triangle ABC$ and $\triangle XYZ$ have the same or opposite orientation?

12. What is the first transformation (shown by the straight arrow)? Which points are made to coincide?

13. What is the second transformation (shown by the curved arrow)? Which segments are made to coincide?

14. By both transformations, side $\overline{BC}$ is made to coincide with side ______.

15. Compare sides $\overline{A''Y}$ and $\overline{XY}$ as well as sides $\overline{A''Z}$ and $\overline{XZ}$. Is $\overleftrightarrow{YZ}$ the perpendicular bisector of $\overline{A''X}$? Why?

16. If $\triangle A''YZ$ is reflected over $\overleftrightarrow{YZ}$, what will be the image of A''? Why? Will $\triangle A''YZ$ coincide with $\triangle XYZ$?

17. Which three transformations (in order) are used to make $\triangle ABC$ and $\triangle XYZ$ coincide?

18. If two triangles that are related by SSS have the same orientation, which transformation could be done first before repeating the process above?

© **19–20.** Two triangles that are related by ASA can be made to coincide exactly as was done in the example on pages 114–115. Copy, and show with arrows how $\triangle ABC$ can be made to coincide with $\triangle HIJ$.

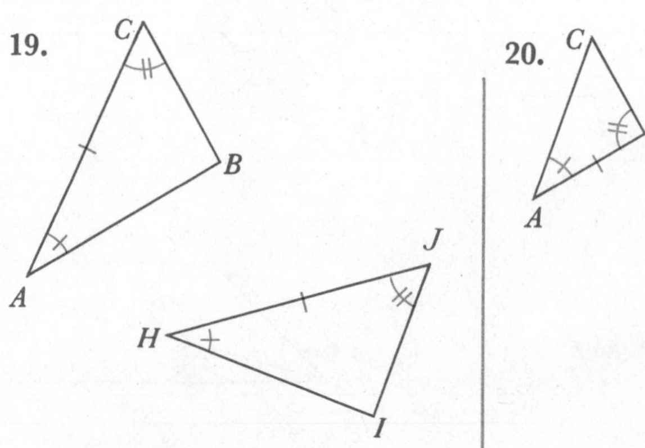

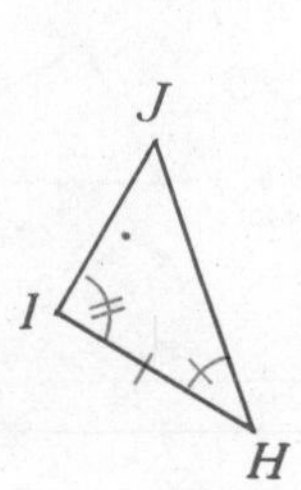

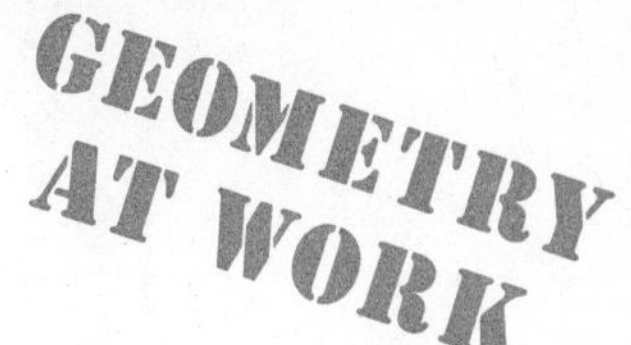

ART AND DESIGN

The art and design occupations include such specialized workers as architects, commercial artists, store-display workers, floral designers, industrial designers, interior designers, landscape architects, and photographers. All these workers are concerned with making products more appealing and useful and with bringing them to the public's attention.

Different art and design careers require different levels of education and training. For example, floral designers learn on the job and may not need a high-school diploma. Architects, on the other hand, need at least five years of college. Regardless of the amount or the kind of training, art and design workers should be creative and be able to communicate ideas through designs and displays. A knowledge of geometry can be a big help.

Look at the famous trademarks and symbols below. For each one, tell at least one use of congruent figures (or parts) or of transformations.

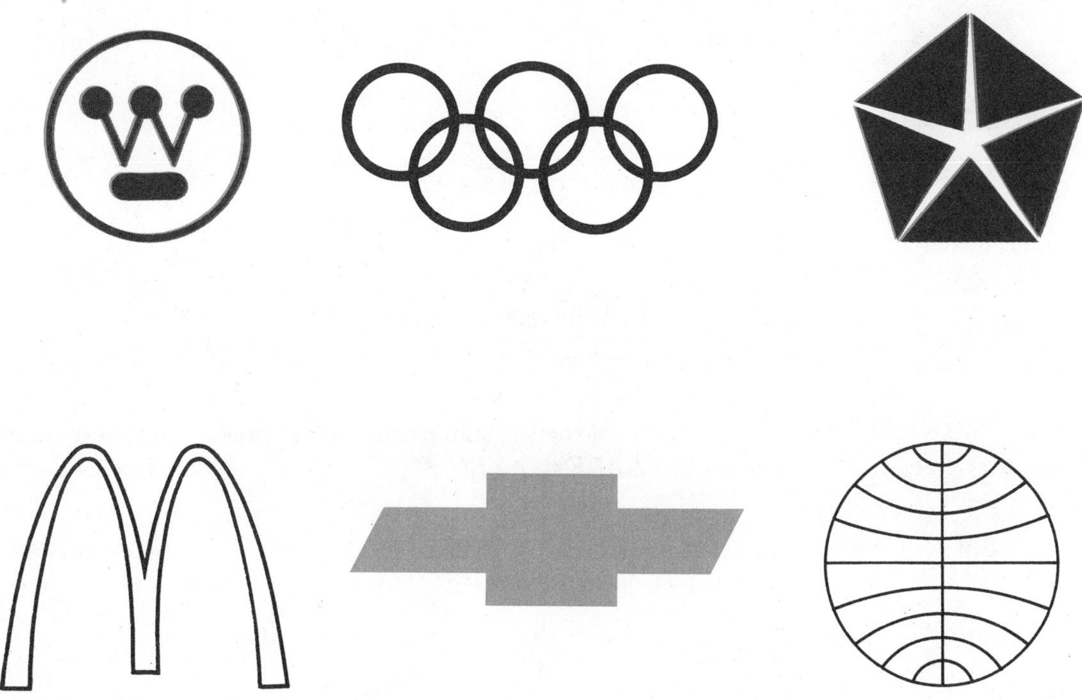

Design a symbol of your own. Let it stand for your school, your town, a club, or a team, or design a new symbol for some famous company or organization.

Chapter 3 Review

3.1

1–2. Name the hypothesis and the conclusion of each statement.

1. If A, B, and C are noncollinear, then $AB + BC > AC$.

2. If $x + y = 5$ and $y = 2$, then $x = 3$.

3–4. Change each statement to if-then form.

3. All giraffes gargle with Listerine.

4. No right angle is an obtuse angle.

5–6. Draw an Euler diagram for each statement in Exercises **3–4.**

3.2

7. Which of the following could not be used as a reason in a two-column proof?

a. Postulate **b.** Definition **c.** Instinct

3.3

8–12. If $\triangle AEG \cong \triangle TSR$, complete each statement.

8. $\angle A \cong$ ______ **9.** $\overline{AE} \cong$ ______

10. $\overline{RS} \cong$ ______ **11.** $\angle T \cong$ ______

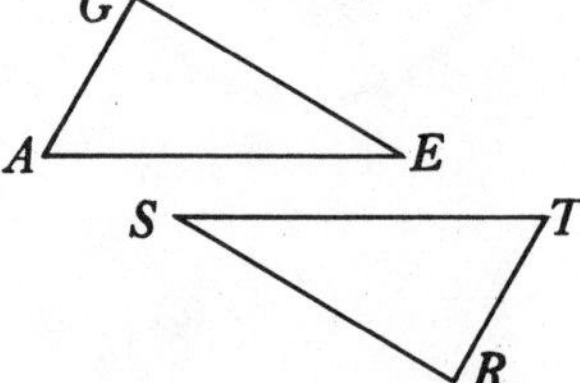

12. In $\triangle AEG$, $\angle A$ is included between ______ and ______.

13. List all six congruence statements about angles and sides that follow from $\triangle ARE \cong \triangle YPU$.

3.4

14–16. Which postulate could be used to show that the given triangles are congruent? Like marks are used to show corresponding congruent parts.

14.

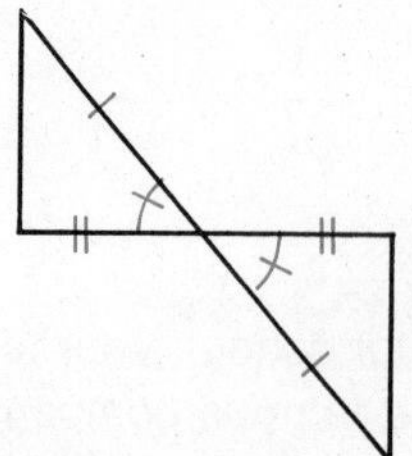

15.

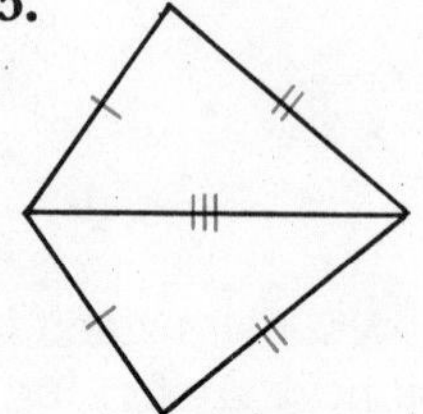

16.

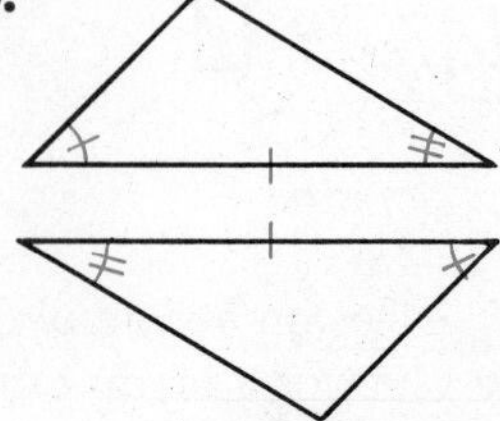

17–23. Give a reason for each statement in the following proofs: **3.5**

Given: $\angle ACD \cong \angle CAB$, $\angle DAC \cong \angle BCA$

Prove: $\triangle ACD \cong \triangle CAB$

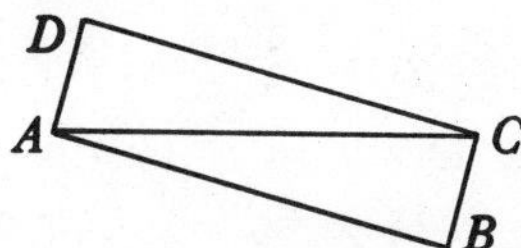

Proof:

STATEMENTS	REASONS
1. $\angle ACD \cong \angle CAB$, $\angle DAC \cong \angle BCA$	1. **17.** ____
2. $\overline{AC} \cong \overline{AC}$	2. **18.** ____
3. $\triangle ACD \cong \triangle CAB$	3. **19.** ____

Given: $\overline{WO} \cong \overline{VO}$, $\overline{WT} \cong \overline{VT}$ **3.6**

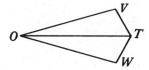

Prove: $\angle W \cong \angle V$

Proof:

STATEMENTS	REASONS
1. $\overline{WO} \cong \overline{VO}$, $\overline{WT} \cong \overline{VT}$	1. **20.** ____
2. $\overline{OT} \cong \overline{OT}$	2. **21.** ____
3. $\triangle OWT \cong \triangle OVT$	3. **22.** ____
4. $\angle W \cong \angle V$	4. **23.** ____

24. Line m is the perpendicular bisector of $\overline{RS}$. Find the values of a and b. **3.7**

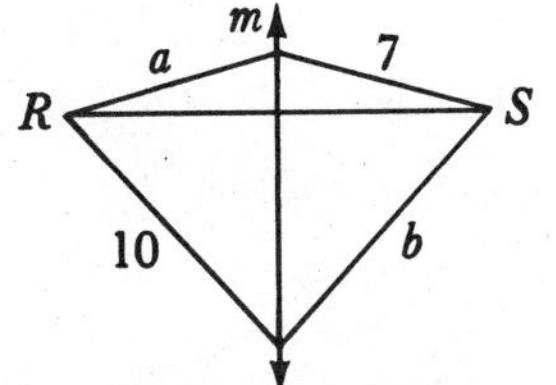

25–26. Tell if a slide, a turn, or a reflection is needed to make the two triangles coincide. **3.8**

25.

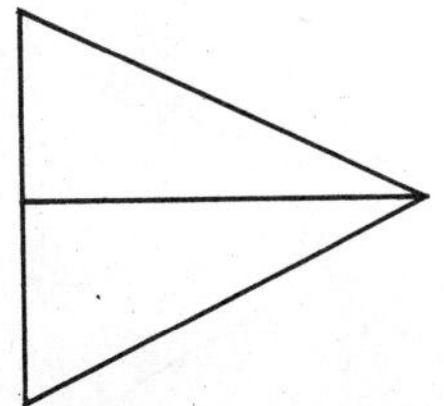

26.

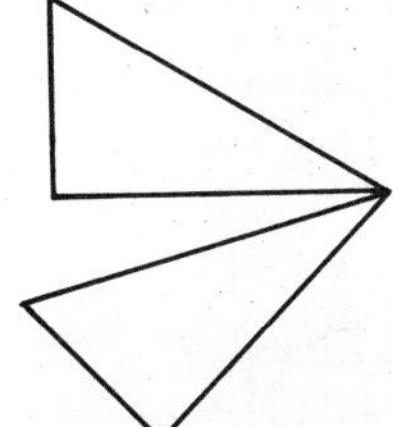

Chapter 3 Test

1. Change the following statement to if-then form: All whole numbers are integers.

2. Draw an Euler diagram for the statement in Exercise 1.

3. If $\triangle TOH \cong \triangle PIL$, complete each statement.

   a. $\angle P \cong$ _____ b. $\overline{TH} \cong$ _____ c. $\angle I \cong$ _____

4–5. Which postulate could be used to show that each pair of triangles is congruent? Like marks are used to show corresponding congruent parts.

4.

5.

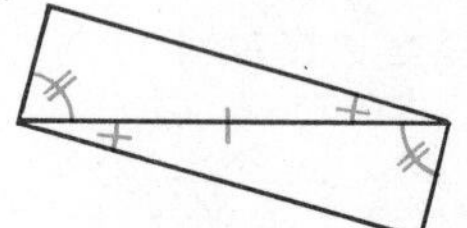

6–13. Give a reason for each statement in the following proof:

Given: B is the midpoint of $\overline{AC}$,
C is the midpoint of $\overline{BD}$,
$\angle A \cong \angle D$, $\angle 1 \cong \angle 2$

Prove: $\overline{EB} \cong \overline{FC}$

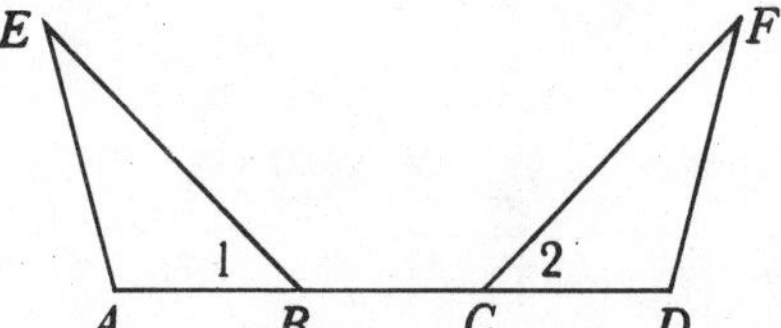

Proof:

STATEMENTS	REASONS
1. B is the midpoint of $\overline{AC}$.	1. **6.** _____
2. $\overline{AB} \cong \overline{BC}$	2. **7.** _____
3. C is the midpoint of $\overline{BD}$.	3. **8.** _____
4. $\overline{BC} \cong \overline{CD}$	4. **9.** _____
5. $\overline{AB} \cong \overline{CD}$	5. **10.** _____
6. $\angle A \cong \angle D$, $\angle 1 \cong \angle 2$	6. **11.** _____
7. $\triangle ABE \cong \triangle DCF$	7. **12.** _____
8. $\overline{EB} \cong \overline{FC}$	8. **13.** _____

14–15. Tell if a slide, a reflection, or a turn is needed to make the two triangles coincide.

14.

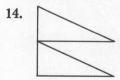

15.

Cumulative Review: Chapters 1–3

Ch. 1

1–6. Refer to the figure to complete each sentence.

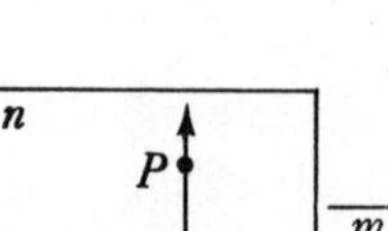

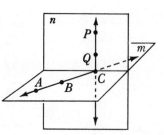

1. A point collinear with A and B is ______.

2. The intersection of $\overleftrightarrow{AB}$ and $\overleftrightarrow{PQ}$ is ______.

3. The ray opposite $\overrightarrow{BA}$ is ______.

4. The intersection of $\overleftrightarrow{QP}$ and plane m is ______.

5. If the coordinates of A and B are 1 and 5, the ______ of $\overline{AB}$ is $|1 - 5|$.

6. If $AB = BC$, then B is the ______ of $\overline{AC}$.

7–10. Match the lettered item to its definition or description.

7. reasoning from examples
8. a statement accepted as true without proof
9. a statement of a hypothesis and its logical conclusion
10. reasoning from postulates and definitions

a. postulate
b. inductive reasoning
c. theorem
d. deductive reasoning

11–14. Refer to the figure for Exercises 1–6. Which postulate or theorem leads to the given conclusion?

11. Every point on $\overleftrightarrow{AB}$ is in m.

12. $\overleftrightarrow{AB}$ and $\overleftrightarrow{PQ}$ determine a plane.

13. There is exactly one point on $\overrightarrow{AB}$ a distance AB from A.

14. There is a point in m not on $\overleftrightarrow{AB}$.

Ch. 2

15. Is the exterior of a triangle a convex set? Why?

16. A plane separates space into two convex sets called ______.

17–20. $\overleftrightarrow{AC}$ intersects $\overleftrightarrow{BD}$ at E.

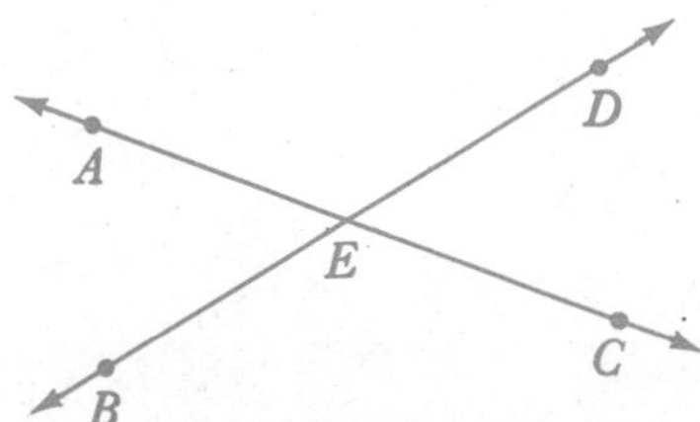

17. Name the vertical angles.

18. Name any congruent angles.

19. Find $m\angle BEC$ with a protractor.

20. Using Exercise 19, find all the obtuse angles.

21–22. Use the figure at the right.

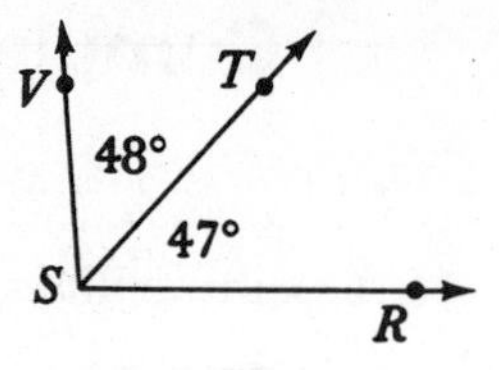

21. Is $\overrightarrow{ST}$ the bisector of $\angle RSV$?

22. Find $m\angle RSV$.

23–25. $\ell \perp m$ at P.

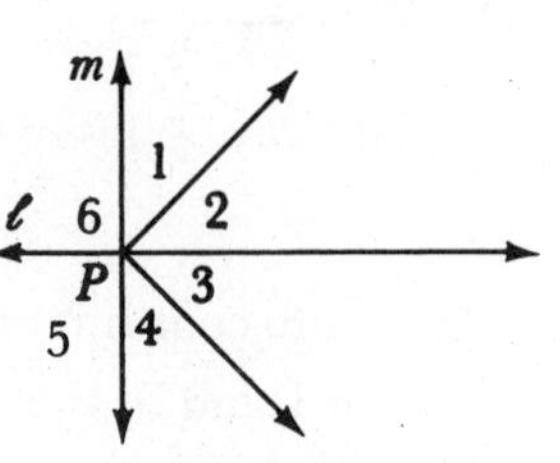

23. Name four right angles.

24. Name the complements of $\angle P_1$ and $\angle P_4$.

25. If $\angle 1 \cong \angle 4$, why is $\angle 2 \cong \angle 3$?

26. If $m\angle X = 73$, find the measures of the complement of $\angle X$ and the supplement of $\angle X$.

Ch. 3

27. Draw an Euler diagram for the following statement: If a figure is a half plane, then it is a convex set.

28. List the six congruence statements about sides and angles that follow from $\triangle ESP \cong \triangle MOT$.

29–30. Which postulate lets us conclude the triangles are congruent?

29.

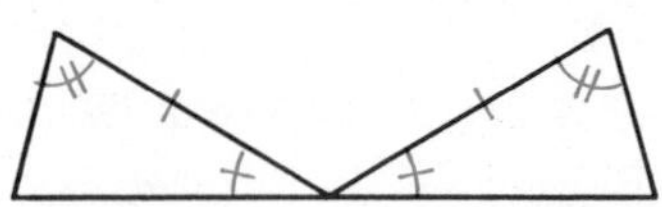

30.

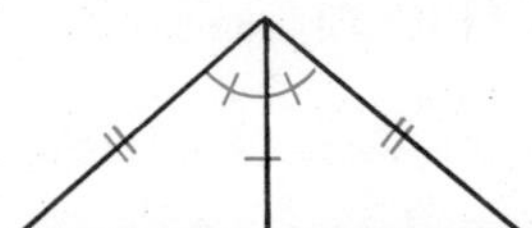

31–34. Give a reason for each statement in the following proof:

Given: $\overline{AD} \cong \overline{DC}$, $\overline{AB} \cong \overline{BC}$

Prove: $\angle A \cong \angle C$

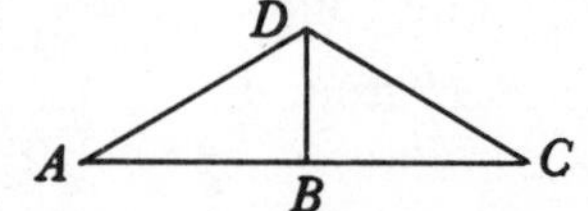

Proof:

STATEMENTS	REASONS
1. $\overline{AD} \cong \overline{DC}$, $\overline{AB} \cong \overline{BC}$	1. **31.** ____
2. $\overline{BD} \cong \overline{BD}$	2. **32.** ____
3. $\triangle ABD \cong \triangle CBD$	3. **33.** ____
4. $\angle A \cong \angle C$	4. **34.** ____

35. In a plane, if points A and B are equidistant from the endpoints of $\overline{CD}$, how is $\overleftrightarrow{AB}$ related to $\overline{CD}$?

Western Pennsylvania Conservancy

PARALLEL LINES IN A PLANE

It may seem obvious that any two lines either meet or do not meet. In geometry, however, their meeting or not meeting has important results, some of which we explore in this chapter. There are actually three ways in which lines in space may be related.

coplanar
intersecting

coplanar
nonintersecting

These lines are **parallel.**

noncoplanar
nonintersecting

These lines are **skew.**

4.1 The Parallel Postulate

This model of parallel lines suggests the next theorem.

Theorem  Two parallel lines determine a plane.

This theorem concerns two parallel lines, so we draw lines ℓ and k to represent *any* two parallel lines. In symbols, $\ell \parallel k$.

Given: $\ell \parallel k$

Prove: Exactly one plane contains both ℓ and k.

Proof:

- By definition of parallel lines, ℓ and k are coplanar, so there is *at least one* plane that contains them both. If there is another plane that contains both ℓ and k, then ℓ and some point P on k are in both planes. (Copying the figure and adding P may help you follow this reasoning.) But, according to the Plane Theorem on page 32, this can't happen. So there is *not more than one* plane that contains both ℓ and k.

- Since there is *at least one* plane but *not more than one* plane that contains both ℓ and k, there is *exactly one* plane that contains ℓ and k.

Look again at this proof.

If there is another plane that contains both ℓ and k,	This assumption is the opposite of what we want to prove.
then ℓ and some point P on k are in both planes.	It leads to this conclusion.
But, according to the Plane Theorem, this can't happen.	The conclusion contradicts a statement already known to be true.
So there is not more than one plane that contains ℓ and k.	So the assumption that led to the conclusion is false. (And its opposite, which we wanted to prove, is true.)

This kind of reasoning is based on the principle below, which is also used in the proof of the next theorem.

Principle of Indirect Reasoning

If assuming statement p is true leads to a contradiction of a true statement, then statement p is false.

In a plane, two lines perpendicular to the same line are parallel.

Theorem

First, draw line n. Then draw ℓ and k to represent *any* two lines perpendicular to n. Finally, restate the theorem in terms of the figure.

Given: Lines ℓ, k, and n are coplanar, $\ell \perp n$, $k \perp n$

Prove: $\ell \parallel k$

Proof:

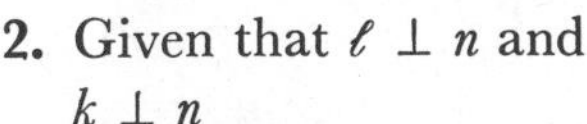

STATEMENTS	REASONS
1. Assume ℓ and k intersect at P. (*It is helpful to draw another figure to show this situation.*)	**1.** For an indirect proof, assume the opposite of what is to be proved.
2. Through point P there are two lines perpendicular to ℓ.	**2.** Given that $\ell \perp n$ and $k \perp n$
3. But through point P there is exactly one line perpendicular to ℓ.	**3.** In any plane containing a given line and point, there is exactly one line through the point perpendicular to the given line.
4. So ℓ and k do not intersect ($\ell \parallel k$).	**4.** Principle of Indirect Reasoning

Again suppose there is a line ℓ and a point P that is not on ℓ. We could use the theorem above to prove that there is *at least one* line through P parallel to ℓ (see Exercises 23–26). But we can't prove that there is *not more than one* such line, so we assume this is the case.

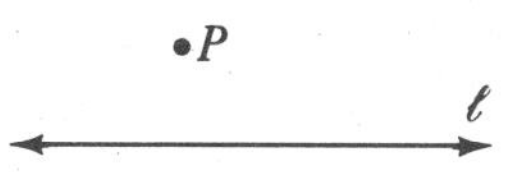

Parallel Postulate

If point P is not on line ℓ, there is exactly one line through P parallel to ℓ.

Exercises 4.1

Ⓐ **1–6.** Which of the words listed would best complete each sentence?

a. coplanar **b.** noncoplanar **c.** intersecting **d.** nonintersecting

1. Coplanar lines may be ______ or ______.

2. Nonintersecting lines may be ______ or ______.

3. Parallel lines are ______ and ______.

4. Skew lines are ______ and ______.

5. Intersecting lines are ______.

6. Noncoplanar lines are ______.

7–14. True or False? A plane is determined by:

7. two intersecting lines
8. two skew lines
9. two parallel lines
10. a line and a point not on it
11. a line and a point on it
12. two points
13. three collinear points
14. three noncollinear points

Ⓑ **15–18.** Match each statement with its restatement in given-prove form.

15. In a plane, two lines parallel to a third line are parallel.

16. In a plane, a line perpendicular to one of two parallel lines is perpendicular to the other.

17. In a plane, a line that intersects one of two parallel lines intersects the other.

18. A line that intersects only one of two parallel lines is skew to the other.

a. Given: $\ell \parallel k$, t intersects ℓ.
Prove: t intersects k.

b. Given: $t \parallel \ell$, $t \parallel k$
Prove: $\ell \parallel k$

c. Given: $\ell \parallel k$, t intersects ℓ, t does not intersect k.
Prove: t and k are skew lines.

d. Given: $\ell \parallel k$, $t \perp \ell$
Prove: $t \perp k$

19–22. Suppose an indirect proof is to be used for the exercise listed. Which assumption—a, b, c, or d—would be made as the first step?

a. t and k are coplanar.
b. $t \parallel k$
c. t and k are not perpendicular.
d. ℓ and k intersect.

19. Exercise 15 **20.** Exercise 16 **21.** Exercise 17 **22.** Exercise 18

23–26. Complete this proof that if P is not on line ℓ, there is at least one line through P parallel to ℓ.

Given: **23.** ______

Prove: There is a line k through P such that $k \parallel \ell$.

Proof:

STATEMENTS	REASONS
1. There is a line n through P such that $n \perp \ell$.	*1.* **24.**
2. There is a line k through P such that $k \perp n$.	*2.* **25.**
3. $k \parallel \ell$	*3.* **26.**

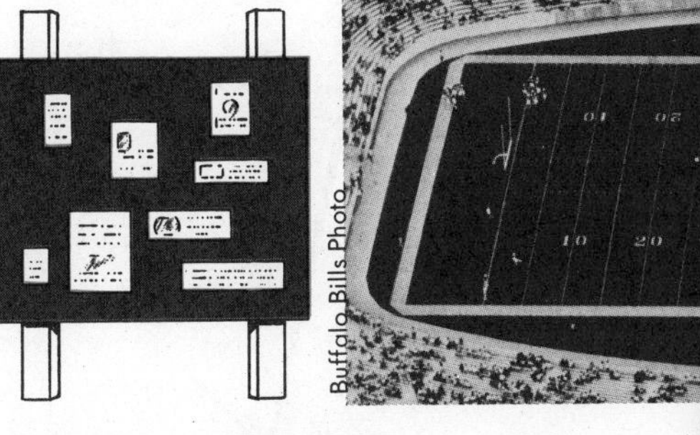

27. Two uprights of a room divider are made parallel using a carpenter's level. Will a solid panel fit flat against both uprights? Why?

28. Each yard line on a football field is laid out perpendicular to the sidelines. Are the yard lines parallel? Why?

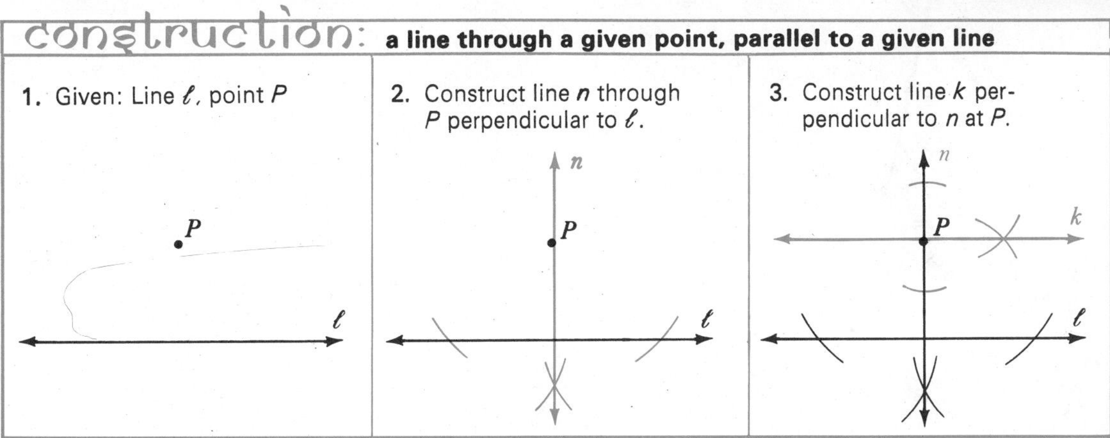

construction: a line through a given point, parallel to a given line
1. Given: Line ℓ, point P
P
ℓ
2. Construct line n through P perpendicular to ℓ.
n
P
ℓ
3. Construct line k perpendicular to n at P.
n
P
k
ℓ

29–32. Copy. Then construct a line through P parallel to $\overleftrightarrow{AB}$.

29.

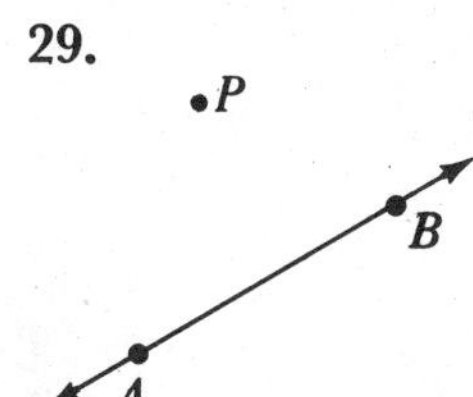

30.

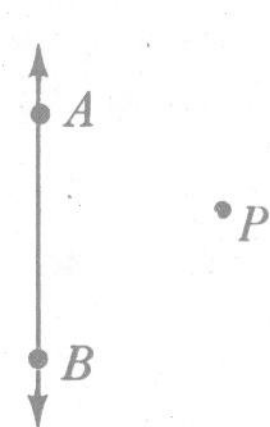

31.

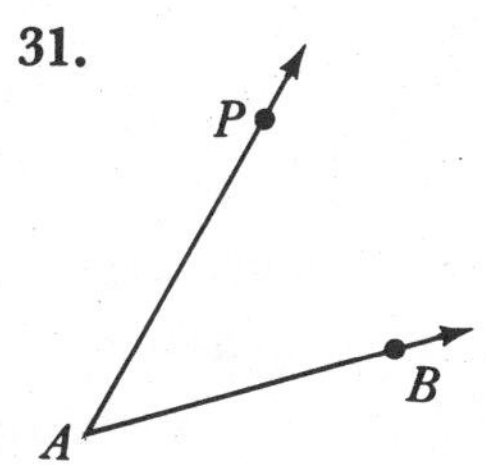

32.

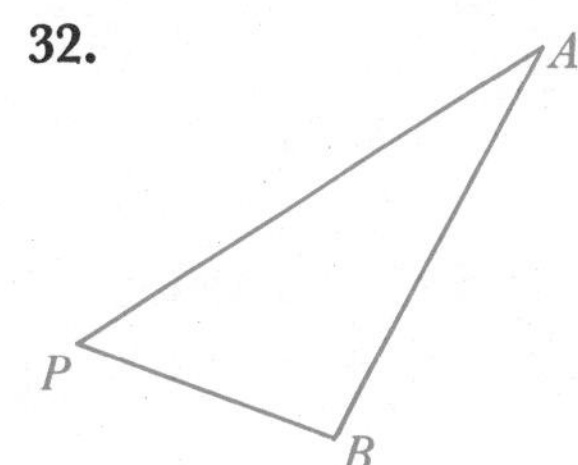

© **33.** In the construction above, what theorem assures that $k \parallel \ell$?

34. Suppose the instruction for step 2 of the construction read: Construct line n so $n \perp \ell$ at any point Q on ℓ. Show how to do step 2. Then write an instruction for step 3 and show how to do it.

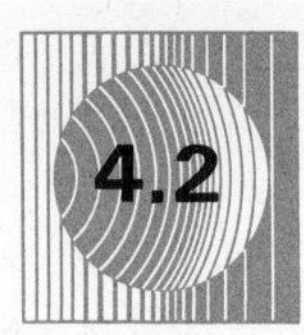

Alternate Interior Angles

A **transversal** is a line that intersects two or more coplanar lines at distinct points. The angles formed by two lines and a transversal are named according to position.

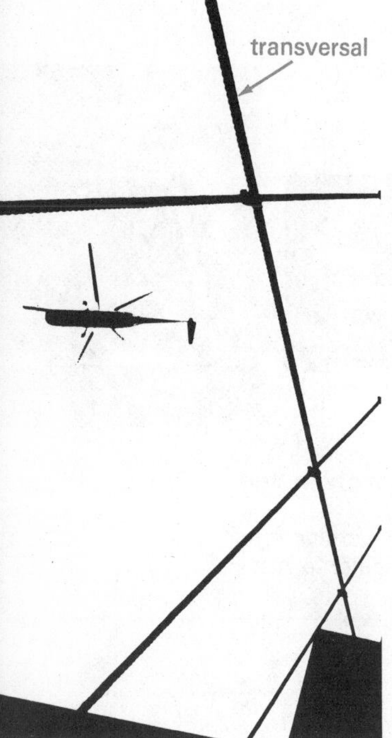

Photo Research International

interior angles: $\angle 3$, $\angle 4$, $\angle 5$, $\angle 6$
exterior angles: $\angle 1$, $\angle 2$, $\angle 7$, $\angle 8$

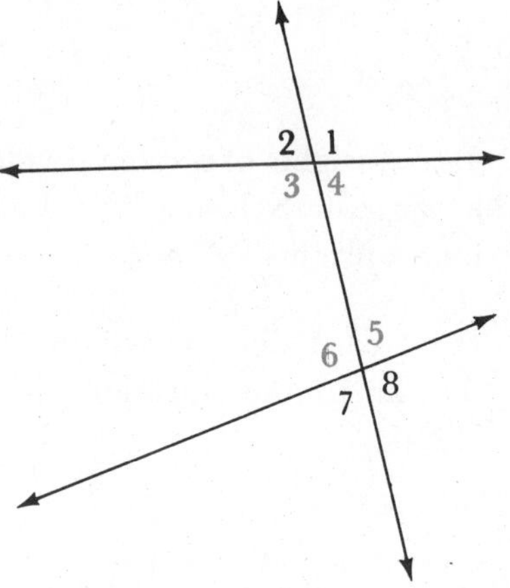

alternate interior angles (2 pairs) $\begin{cases} \angle 3 \text{ and } \angle 5 \\ \angle 4 \text{ and } \angle 6 \end{cases}$

alternate exterior angles (2 pairs) $\begin{cases} \angle 1 \text{ and } \angle 7 \\ \angle 2 \text{ and } \angle 8 \end{cases}$

If one pair of alternate (interior or exterior) angles are congruent, all four such pairs are congruent. For example, let $\angle 3 \cong \angle 5$. Suppose $\angle 3$ and $\angle 5$ have measure 120. Using facts about vertical and supplementary angles, we can find the measures of all eight angles.

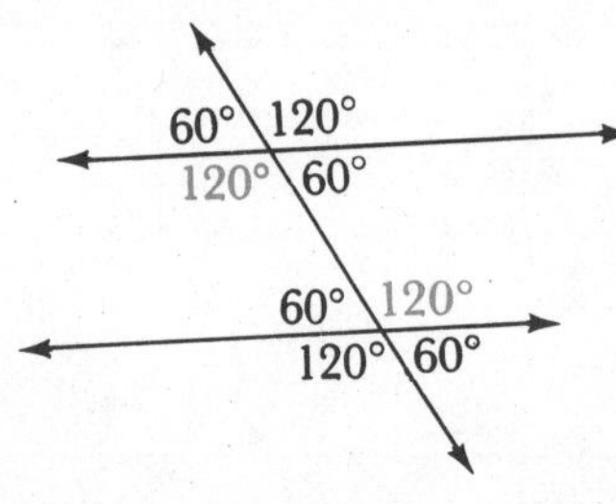

Given	$\angle 3 \cong \angle 5$
We can show	$\angle 4 \cong \angle 6$
	$\angle 1 \cong \angle 7$
	$\angle 2 \cong \angle 8$

So theorems involving alternate interior or exterior angles need to be proved for only one pair of angles.

Alternate Interior Angles Theorem

When a transversal intersects two lines,

a. If alternate interior angles are congruent, the lines are parallel.

b. If the lines are parallel, alternate interior angles are congruent.

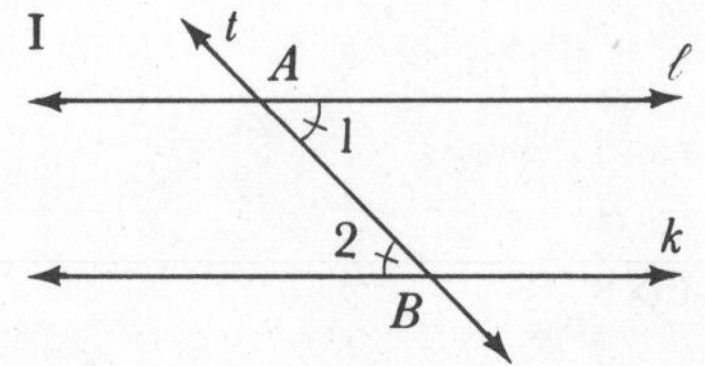

Part a. This part of the theorem concerns two lines, a transversal, and congruent alternate interior angles, as in diagram I.

Given: Lines ℓ and k, transversal t, $\angle 1 \cong \angle 2$
Prove: $\ell \parallel k$

[*Plan:* Make use of the midpoint M of $\overline{AB}$ and a line s through M perpendicular to ℓ, as in diagram II.]

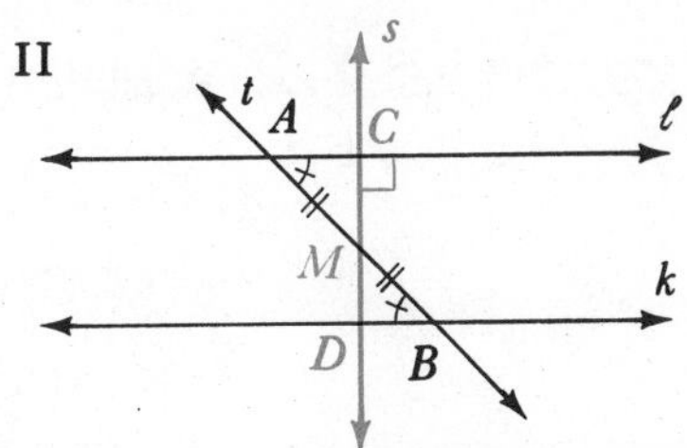

Figures like M and s, added to the given figure, are called **auxiliary** figures. The first two reasons below explain why we can use this point and line.

NOTE: Reasons can be shortened by using abbreviations and symbols.

Proof:

STATEMENTS	REASONS
1. Let M be the midpoint of $\overline{AB}$.	**1.** A segment has exactly 1 midpoint.
2. Let $\overleftrightarrow{MC}$ be perpendicular to ℓ.	**2.** In a plane, there is exactly 1 line through a pt. $\perp$ to a given line.
3. $\overline{MA} \cong \overline{MB}$	**3.** Definition of midpoint
4. $\angle 1 \cong \angle 2$	**4.** Given
5. $\angle AMC \cong \angle BMD$	**5.** Vertical $\angle$s are $\cong$.
6. $\triangle AMC \cong \triangle BMD$	**6.** ASA Postulate
7. $\angle ACM \cong \angle BDM$	**7.** Corres. parts of $\cong$ $\triangle$s are $\cong$.
8. $m\angle ACM = 90$	**8.** Definition of $\perp$
9. $m\angle BDM = 90$	**9.** Definition of $\cong$ $\angle$s
10. $\overleftrightarrow{MC} \perp k$	**10.** Definition of $\perp$
11. $\ell \parallel k$	**11.** In a plane, lines $\perp$ to the same line are $\parallel$. (steps 2 and 10)

Part b. This is the converse of part **a.**

Given: Lines ℓ and k, transversal t, $\ell \parallel k$

Prove: $\angle 1 \cong \angle 2$

[*Plan:* Use auxiliary line n to form congruent alternate interior angles. Show that n is really the same as given line ℓ.]

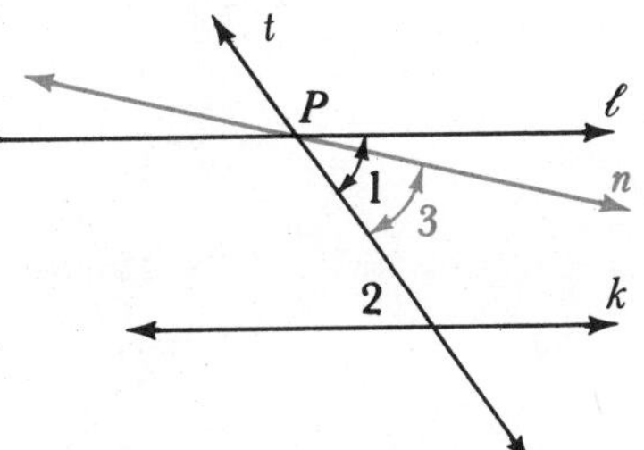

Proof:

STATEMENTS	REASONS
1. Let n go through P so $\angle 3 \cong \angle 2$.	**1.** $\angle$ Construction Post. (p. 53)
2. $n \parallel k$	**2.** Part **a,** just proved
3. $\ell \parallel k$	**3.** Given
4. n and ℓ are the same line.	**4.** Parallel Postulate
5. $\angle 1$ and $\angle 3$ are the same angle.	**5.** $\angle$ Construction Post.
6. $\angle 1 \cong \angle 3$	**6.** An $\angle$ is $\cong$ to itself.
7. $\angle 1 \cong \angle 2$	**7.** $\angle$s $\cong$ to the same $\angle$ are $\cong$. (steps 1 and 6)

Exercises 4.2

Ⓐ **1–10.** Refer to the figure. Name all angles or pairs of angles of each type.

1. exterior **2.** alternate exterior

3. interior **4.** alternate interior

5. vertical **6.** adjacent to $\angle 1$ **7.** supplementary to $\angle 1$

8. adjacent to $\angle 2$ **9.** adjacent to $\angle 5$ **10.** supplementary to $\angle 6$

11–16. Refer to the figure above.

11. If $m\angle 1 = 70$, then $m\angle 3 =$ ______.

12. If $m\angle 6 = 120$, then $m\angle 8 =$ ______.

13. If $m\angle 1 = 70$, then $m\angle 4 = 180 -$ ______ $=$ ______.

14. If $m\angle 6 = 120$, then $m\angle 5 = 180 -$ ______ $=$ ______.

15. If $\ell \parallel n$ and $m\angle 3 = 62$, then $m\angle 5 =$ ______.

16. If $m\angle 4 = 118$ and $m\angle 6 = 118$, then ℓ ______ n.

Ⓑ **17–24.** Refer to the figure above. Use the given information to find the measures of as many angles as possible.

17. $m\angle 2 = 118$, $\ell \parallel n$

18. $m\angle 7 = 53$, $\ell \parallel n$

19. $m\angle 5 = 67$, $\ell \parallel n$

20. $m\angle 2 = 117$, $\ell \parallel n$

21. $m\angle 4 = 112$

22. $m\angle 6 = 123$

23. $m\angle 3 = 75$, $m\angle 8 = 120$

24. $m\angle 5 = 83$, $m\angle 1 = 78$

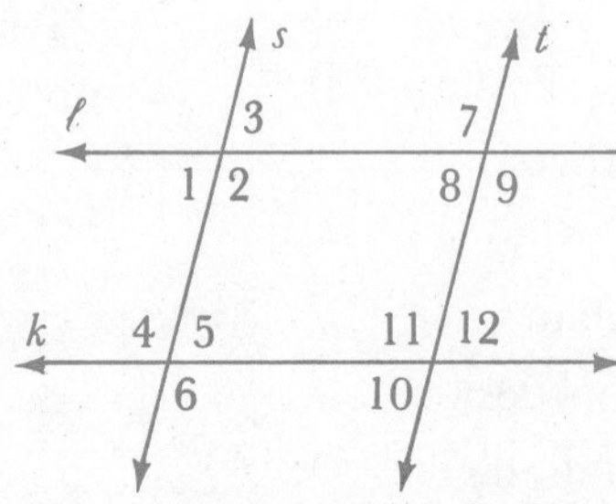

25–30. Refer to the figure at the left.

25. If $\ell \parallel k$, then $\angle 2 \cong$ ______ and $\angle 2 \cong$ ______.

26. If $s \parallel t$, then $\angle 5 \cong$ ______ and $\angle 5 \cong$ ______.

27. If $\angle 2 \cong \angle 7$, then ______ $\parallel$ ______.

28. If $\angle 9 \cong \angle 11$, then ______ $\parallel$ ______.

29. If $\ell \parallel k$ and $t \parallel s$, which angles are congruent to $\angle 4$?

30. If $s \parallel t$ and $k \parallel \ell$, which angles are congruent to $\angle 11$?

31–32. A surveyor is laying out a new highway that will intersect state highways 5 and 7 as shown by the map.

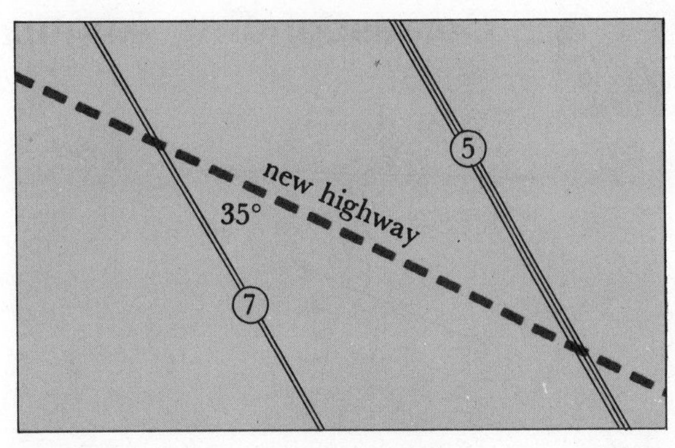

31. If highways 5 and 7 are parallel, what size acute angle should the new highway make with highway 5?

32. If the new highway forms a 140° angle with highway 5, are highways 5 and 7 parallel?

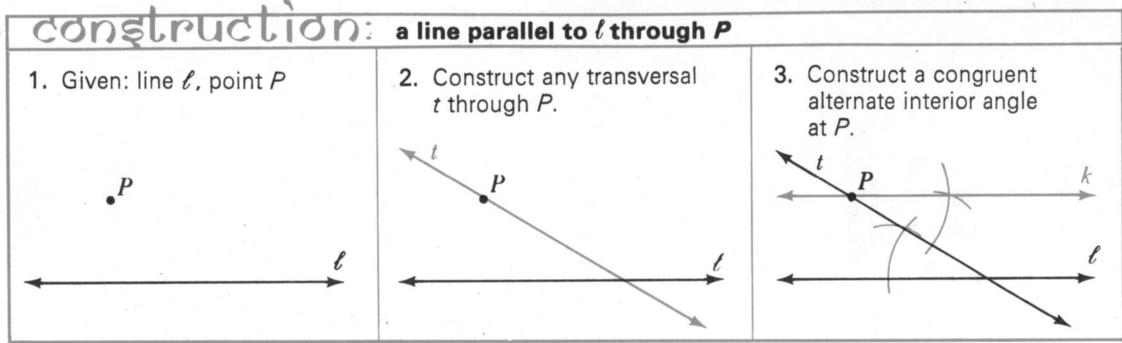

construction: a line parallel to ℓ through P
1. Given: line ℓ, point P
P
ℓ
2. Construct any transversal t through P.
t
P
ℓ
3. Construct a congruent alternate interior angle at P.
t
P
k
ℓ

33. Why is $k \parallel \ell$ in step 3 of the construction above?

34. Since t is any transversal through P, what is the only thing you need to consider in constructing t?

35–38. Copy P, R, n, and s. Then construct the line described.

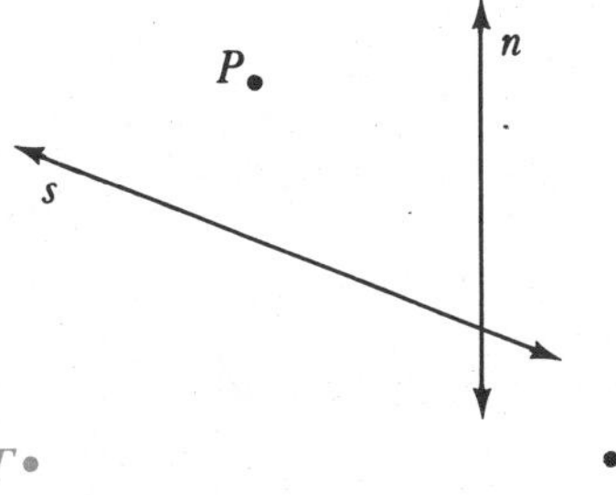

35. through P parallel to n

36. through P parallel to s

37. through R parallel to s

38. through R parallel to n

© **39.** Copy T, V, and r. Using only one transversal, construct lines through T and V parallel to r.

T
r
V

40–41. Refer to the figure.

40. Given: $d \parallel c$, $\angle 2 \cong \angle 4$

Prove: $d \parallel e$

41. Given: $d \parallel e$, $\angle 1 \cong \angle 3$

Prove: $\angle 2 \cong \angle 4$

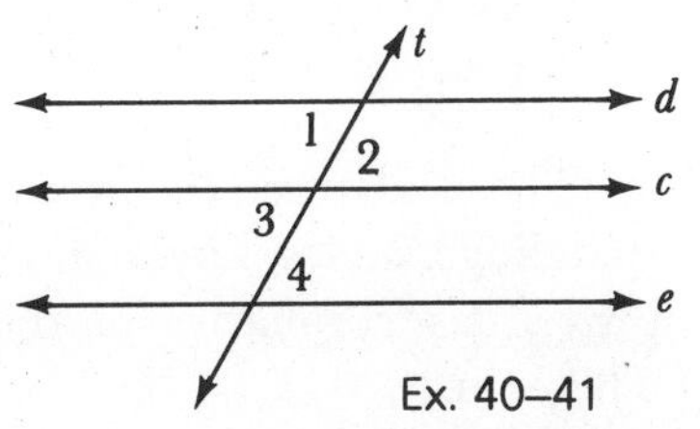

Ex. 40–41

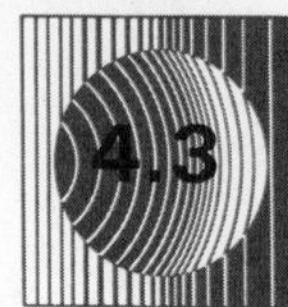

Corresponding Angles

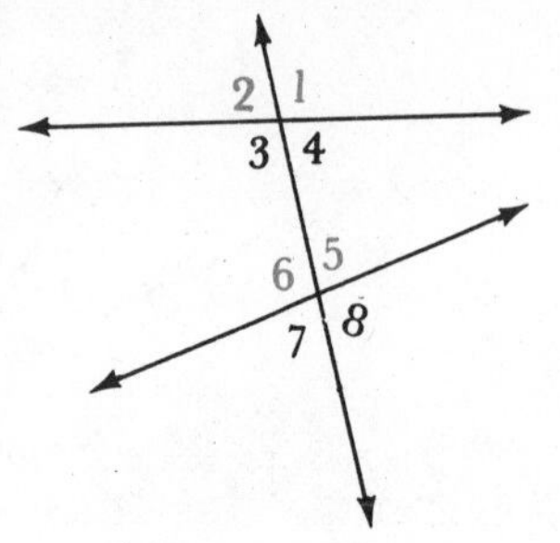

corresponding angles (4 pairs)

∠1 and ∠5	∠3 and ∠7
∠2 and ∠6	∠4 and ∠8

At the left is shown another way to pair the angles formed by two lines and a transversal.

Suppose ∠3 ≅ ∠5.

∠1 ≅ ∠3, since they are vertical angles.

∠1 ≅ ∠5, since they are congruent to the same angle.

So most statements true for alternate interior angles are also true for corresponding angles.

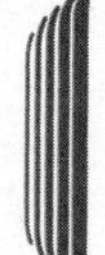

Corresponding Angles Theorem

When a transversal intersects two lines,

a. If corresponding angles are congruent, the lines are parallel.

b. If the lines are parallel, corresponding angles are congruent.

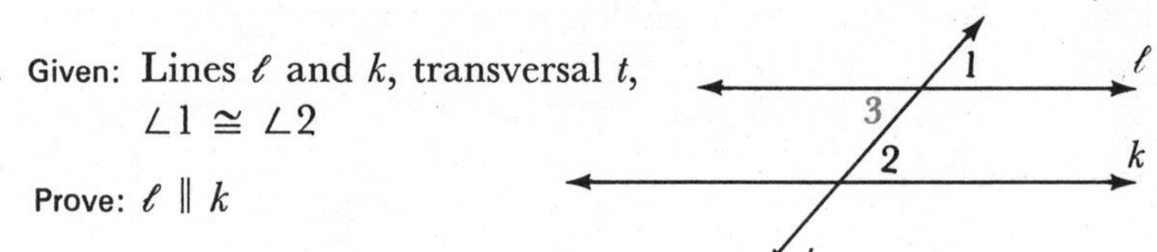

Part a. Given: Lines ℓ and k, transversal t, ∠1 ≅ ∠2

Prove: $\ell \parallel k$

Proof: STATEMENTS	REASONS
1. ∠1 ≅ ∠2	**1.** Given
2. ∠1 ≅ ∠3	**2.** Vertical ∠s are ≅.
3. ∠2 ≅ ∠3	**3.** ∠s ≅ to the same ∠ are ≅.
4. $\ell \parallel k$	**4.** Alternate Interior ∠s Theorem

Part **b** of the Corresponding Angles Theorem is the converse of part **a.** It is proved in Exercise 25.

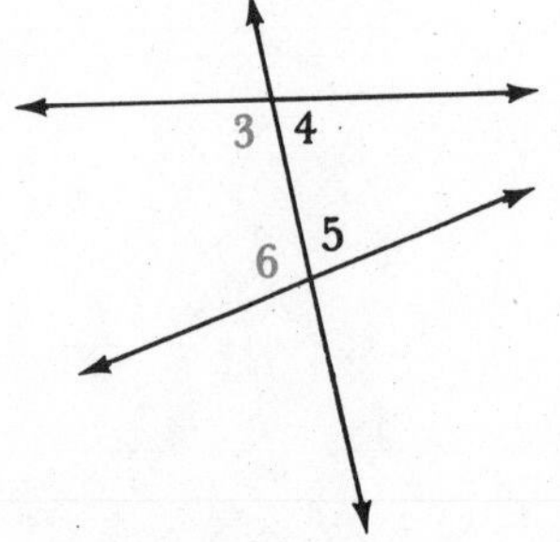

There remains one more way to pair interior angles.

interior angles on the same side of the transversal (2 pairs) { ∠3 and ∠6, ∠4 and ∠5 }

The next three theorems are corollaries of the Corresponding Angles Theorem. They could just as easily be proved as corollaries of the Alternate Interior Angles Theorem.

Theorem

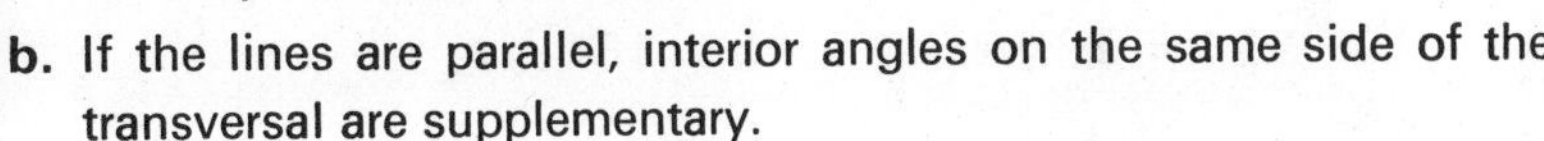

When a transversal intersects two lines,

a. If interior angles on the same side of the transversal are supplementary, the lines are parallel.

b. If the lines are parallel, interior angles on the same side of the transversal are supplementary.

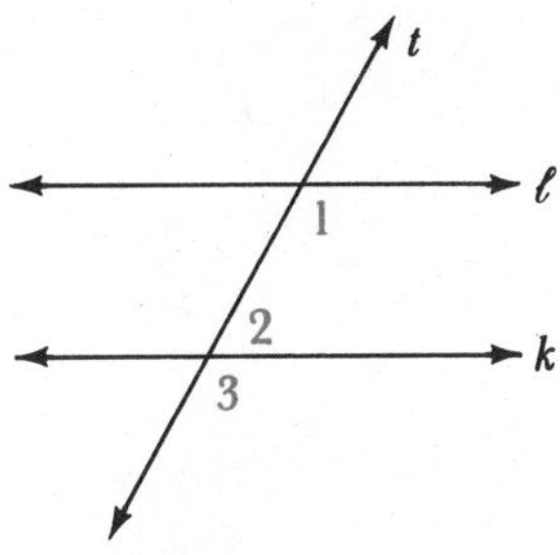

In the figure, $\angle 2$ and $\angle 3$ are supplementary (Supplement Post., p. 56). If $\angle 1$ and $\angle 2$ are also supplementary, then $\angle 1 \cong \angle 3$ (supplements of the same $\angle$). So $\ell \parallel k$, and part **a** is proved.

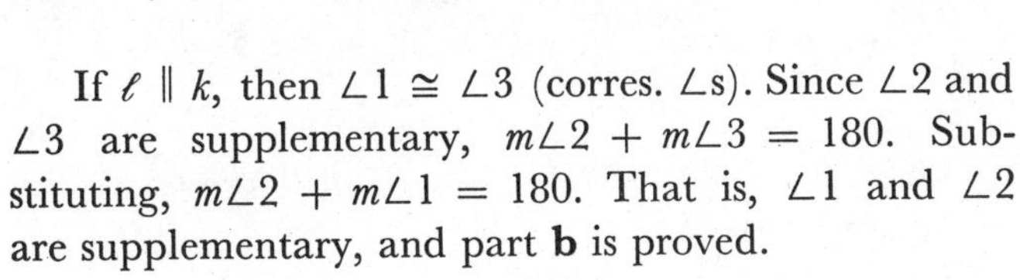

If $\ell \parallel k$, then $\angle 1 \cong \angle 3$ (corres. $\angle$s). Since $\angle 2$ and $\angle 3$ are supplementary, $m\angle 2 + m\angle 3 = 180$. Substituting, $m\angle 2 + m\angle 1 = 180$. That is, $\angle 1$ and $\angle 2$ are supplementary, and part **b** is proved.

Of course, if $\ell \parallel k$ and $\angle 1$ is a right angle, part **b** of the theorem above tells you that $\angle 2$ is also a right angle. That is, if $\ell \parallel k$ and $t \perp \ell$, then $t \perp k$. This proves the theorem below.

Theorem

In a plane, a line perpendicular to one of two parallel lines is perpendicular to the other.

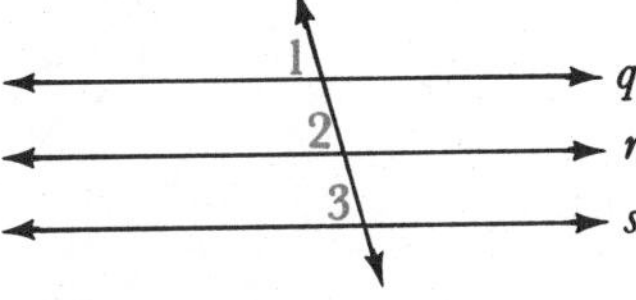

Suppose $q \parallel r$ and $r \parallel s$. Then $\angle 1 \cong \angle 2$ and $\angle 2 \cong \angle 3$. So $\angle 1 \cong \angle 3$ and, as a result, $q \parallel s$. (We can write $q \parallel r \parallel s$.)

Theorem

In a plane, two lines parallel to a third line are parallel.

Exercises 4.3

Ⓐ **1–4.** Refer to the figure.

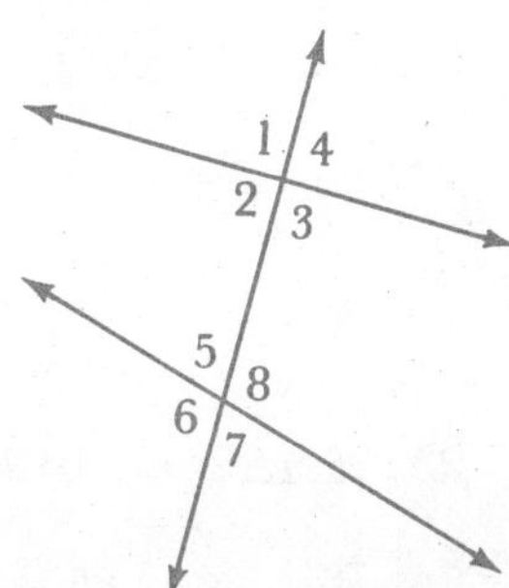

1. $\angle 2$ and ______ are alternate interior angles.

2. $\angle 2$ and ______ are interior angles on the same side of the transversal.

3. $\angle 2$ and ______ are corresponding angles.

4. $\angle 2$ and ______ are vertical angles.

5–6. Refer to the figure.

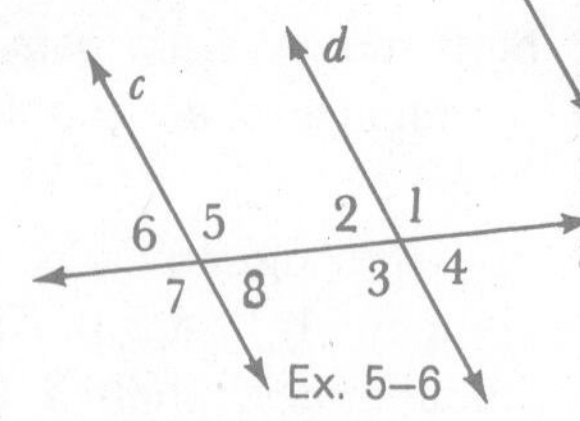

Ex. 5–6

5. Which statements lead to the conclusion that $c \parallel d$?

a. $\angle 3 \cong \angle 5$ **b.** $m\angle 3 + m\angle 5 = 180$

c. $\angle 3 \cong \angle 1$ **d.** $m\angle 3 + m\angle 8 = 180$

e. $\angle 3 \cong \angle 7$ **f.** $c \parallel n,\ d \parallel n$

6. If $c \parallel d$, which statements are true?

a. $\angle 2 \cong \angle 8$ **b.** $\angle 4 \cong \angle 7$ **c.** If $t \perp d$, then $t \perp c$.

d. $\angle 1 \cong \angle 5$ **e.** $\angle 8 \cong \angle 3$ **f.** $m\angle 2 + m\angle 5 = 180$

Ⓑ **7–18.** If $\ell \parallel s$, use the given information to find the measures of as many angles in the figure as possible.

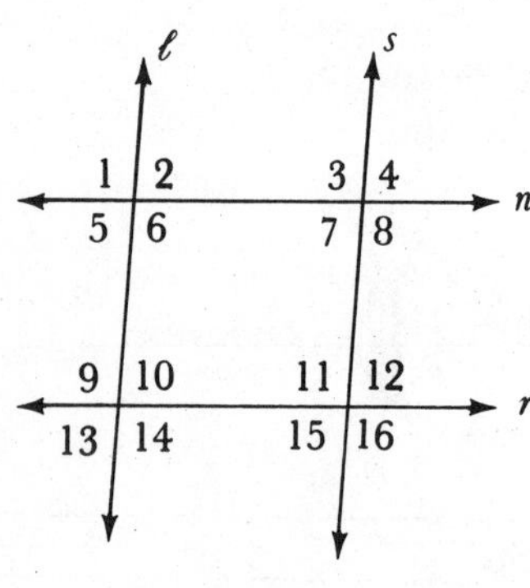

Ex. 7–18

7. $m\angle 2 = 87$

8. $m\angle 16 = 96$

9. $m\angle 11 = 102$

10. $m\angle 5 = 72$

11. $n \parallel r,\ m\angle 7 = 72$

12. $r \parallel n,\ m\angle 4 = 83$

13. $m\angle 10 = 90$

14. $s \perp r$

15. $m\angle 7 + m\angle 11 = 180,\ m\angle 13 = 68$

16. $m\angle 5 + m\angle 9 = 180,\ m\angle 4 = 76$

17. $\ell \perp n$

18. $m\angle 12 = m\angle 16$

19–22. Use the given information to find the measures of all numbered angles in the figure.

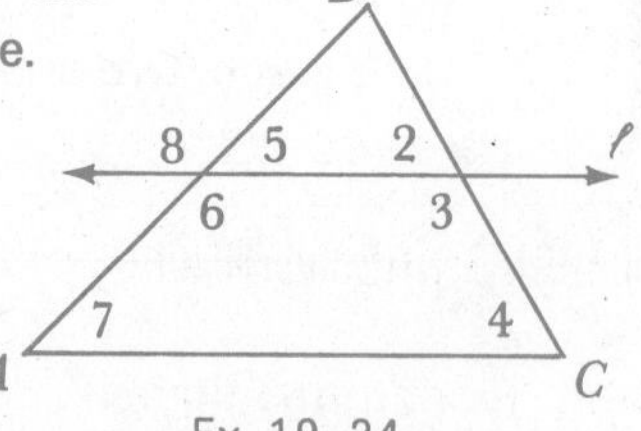

Ex. 19–24

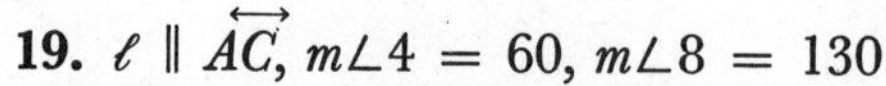

19. $\ell \parallel \overleftrightarrow{AC},\ m\angle 4 = 60,\ m\angle 8 = 130$

20. $\ell \parallel \overleftrightarrow{AC},\ m\angle 2 = 60,\ m\angle 7 = 50$

21. $\angle 2 \cong \angle 4,\ m\angle 2 = 80,\ m\angle 7 = 40$

22. $m\angle 6 + m\angle 7 = 180,\ m\angle 3 = 110,\ m\angle 5 = 60$

23–24. Refer to the figure for Exercises 19–22.

23. If $m\angle 8 = 110$ and $m\angle 7 = 70$, is $\ell \parallel \overleftrightarrow{AC}$?

24. If $m\angle 4 = 85$ and $m\angle 3 = 95$, is $\ell \parallel \overleftrightarrow{AC}$?

25–26. Give a reason for each statement.

25. Given: $\ell \parallel k$

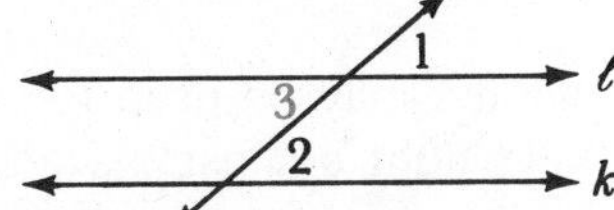

Prove: $\angle 1 \cong \angle 2$

Proof:

STATEMENTS	REASONS
1. $\angle 2 \cong \angle 3$	1. ____
2. $\angle 1 \cong \angle 3$	2. ____
3. $\angle 1 \cong \angle 2$	3. ____

26. Given: $\angle 1$ and $\angle 2$ are supplementary.

Prove: $r \parallel s$

Proof:

STATEMENTS	REASONS
1. $\angle 1$ and $\angle 2$ are supplementary.	1. Given
2. $\angle 2$ and $\angle 3$ are supplementary.	2. ____
3. $\angle 1 \cong \angle 3$	3. ____
4. $r \parallel s$	4. ____

© 27. *Construction:* Copy P and ℓ. Then construct n parallel to ℓ through P by using corresponding angles rather than alternate interior angles.

28–30. Write a two-column proof of the theorem.

28. If a transversal intersects two parallel lines, interior angles on the same side of the transversal are supplementary.

29. In a plane, a line perpendicular to one of two parallel lines is perpendicular to the other.

30. In a plane, two lines parallel to a third line are parallel.

Algebra Review

Review this skill:

- ***solving equations***

Solve.

1. $x = 153 + 21 + 6$
2. $93 + 27 + 60 = y$
3. $125 + 45 + n = 180$
4. $180 = m + 39 + 97$
5. $180 = 67 + p + 88$
6. $x + 124 + 73 = 180$
7. $2a + 58 = 180$
8. $3n = 180$

GEOMETRY AT WORK

PARALLELS IN DRAFTING

In drafting, a T-square may be used to draw parallel lines. The head of the T-square is held tight against the edge of the drawing board as each line is drawn.

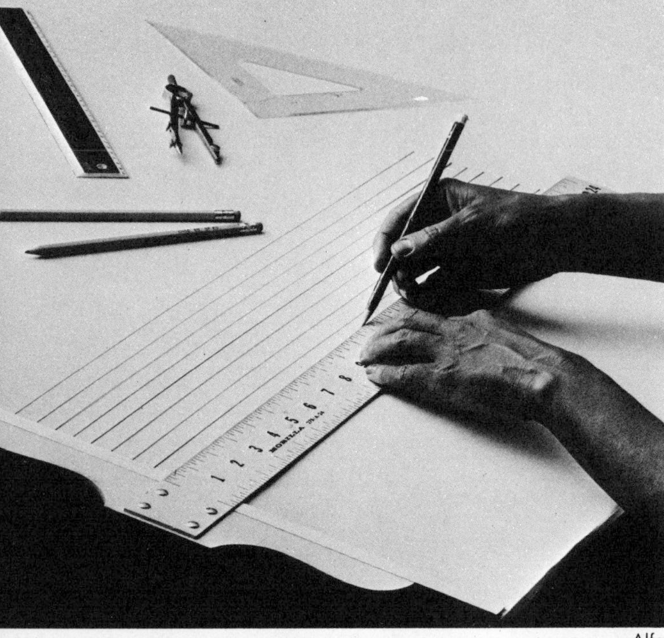

Alfa

1. What theorem assures that the lines drawn by this method are parallel?

Another device used for drawing parallel lines is the triangle. In this method, the T-square is held as described above, and the triangle is held tight against the T-square as each line is drawn.

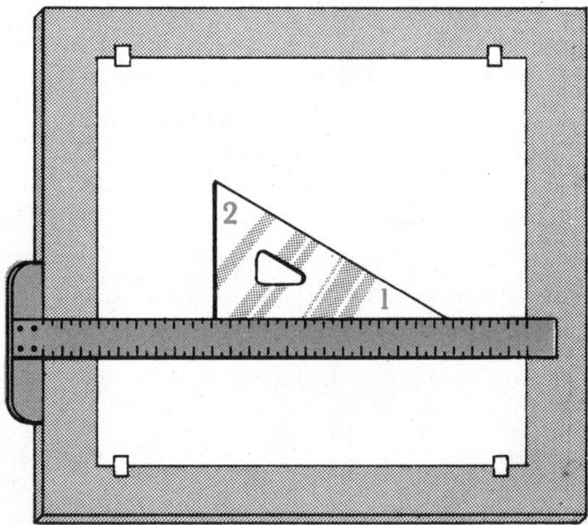

2. Which edge of the triangle is used to guide the pencil if the parallel lines are to be perpendicular to the edge of the T-square?

3. Which edge of the triangle is used to guide the pencil if the parallel lines are to make an acute angle the size of $\angle 1$ with the edge of the T-square?

4. How can the triangle be used so that the parallel lines make an acute angle the size of $\angle 2$ with the edge of the T-square?

A. Devaney, Inc.

The Angle Sum Theorem for Triangles

You can cut a triangle from paper, tear it, and arrange the pieces as shown. This suggests the next theorem.

Angle Sum Theorem for Triangles

The sum of the measures of the angles of a triangle is 180.

Call the angles at C, in the figure at the right, $\angle C_1$, $\angle C_2$, $\angle C_3$, $\angle C_{12}$, and $\angle C_{23}$.

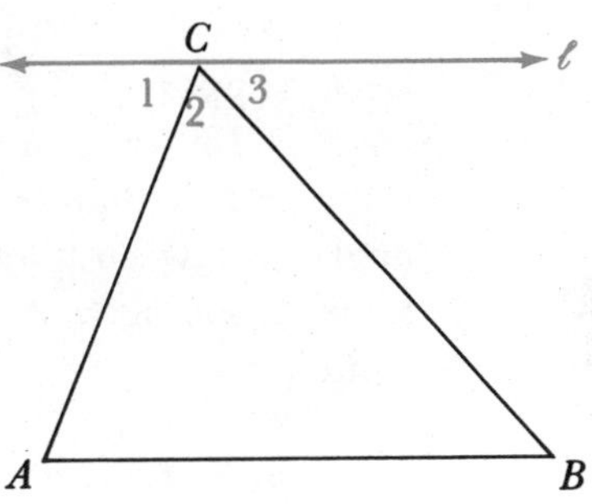

Given: $\triangle ABC$

Prove: $m\angle A + m\angle B + m\angle C_2 = 180$

[*Plan:* Use a line ℓ through C to form three angles whose measures add to 180. Make $\ell \parallel \overleftrightarrow{AB}$ so these angles are congruent to the angles of $\triangle ABC$.]

Proof:

STATEMENTS	REASONS
1. There is a line ℓ through C such that $\ell \parallel \overleftrightarrow{AB}$.	1. Parallel Postulate
2. $m\angle A = m\angle C_1, m\angle B = m\angle C_3$	2. Alt. Interior $\angle$s Theorem
3. $\angle C_1$ and $\angle C_{23}$ are supplements.	3. Supplement Post. (p. 56)
4. $m\angle C_1 + m\angle C_{23} = 180$	4. Definition of supplement
5. $m\angle C_2 + m\angle C_3 = m\angle C_{23}$	5. $\angle$ Addition Post. (p. 53)
6. $m\angle C_1 + m\angle C_2 + m\angle C_3 = 180$	6. Substitution (steps 4 and 5)
7. $m\angle A + m\angle B + m\angle C_2 = 180$	7. Substitution (steps 2 and 6)

The next theorem is a corollary of the Angle Sum Theorem for Triangles. The restatement is below, and the proof is in Exercises 2–6.

Theorem

If two angles of one triangle are congruent to two angles of another, the remaining angles of the triangles are congruent.

Given: $\triangle ABC$, $\triangle DEF$,
$\angle A \cong \angle D$, $\angle B \cong \angle E$

Prove: $\angle C \cong \angle F$

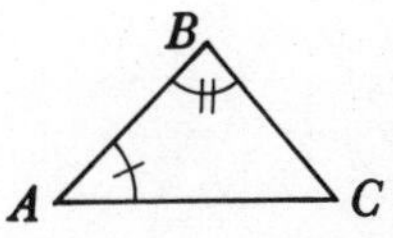

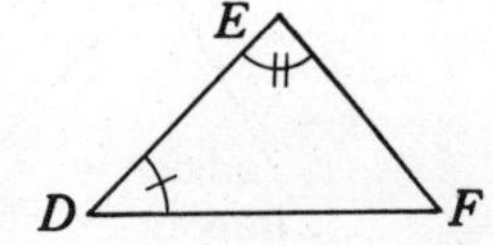

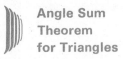

The next three theorems are also corollaries of the Angle Sum Theorem for Triangles.

Theorem If one angle of a triangle is right or obtuse, the other two angles are acute.

An indirect proof of this theorem is given below in paragraph form.

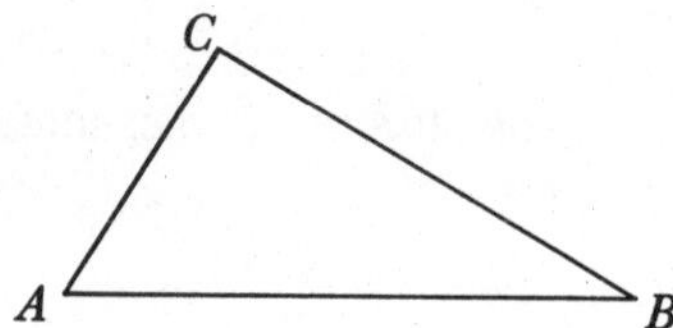

Given: $\triangle ABC$, $\angle C$ is right or obtuse.

Prove: $\angle A$ and $\angle B$ are acute.

Proof: Suppose $\angle B$ is also right or obtuse. Then the sum of $m\angle B$ and $m\angle C$ is 180 or more, and since $m\angle A + m\angle B + m\angle C = 180$, $m\angle A$ is not greater than 0. But this cannot be so, because the measure of any angle is between 0 and 180. So $\angle B$ is not right or obtuse, and by the same reasoning, $\angle A$ is not right or obtuse. That is, $\angle A$ and $\angle B$ are acute.

A **right triangle** is a triangle with one right angle.

Theorem The acute angles of a right triangle are complementary.

Given: $\triangle ABC$, $m\angle C = 90$ (Refer to the figure above.)

Prove: $m\angle A + m\angle B = 90$

Proof:

STATEMENTS	REASONS
1. $m\angle A + m\angle B + m\angle C = 180$	**1.** Why?
2. $m\angle C = 90$	**2.** Given
3. $m\angle A + m\angle B + 90 = 180$	**3.** Why?
4. $m\angle A + m\angle B = 90$	**4.** Add -90 to both sides.

By extending a side of a triangle, we can form an angle adjacent to an angle of the triangle. The noncommon sides of these adjacent angles are opposite rays, so the angles are supplementary. Terms used to refer to the angles are shown below.

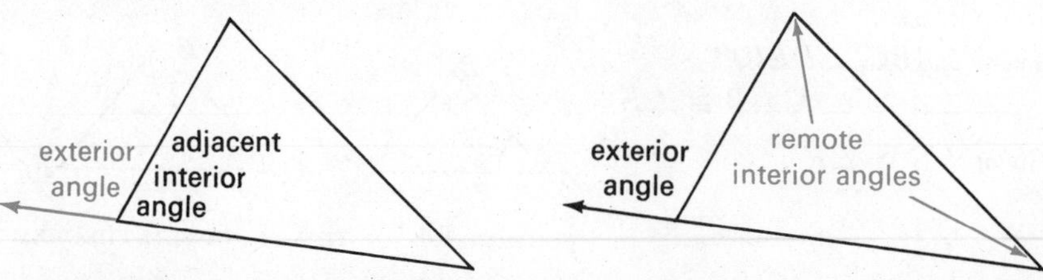

The measure of an exterior angle of a triangle is equal to the sum of the measures of the remote interior angles.

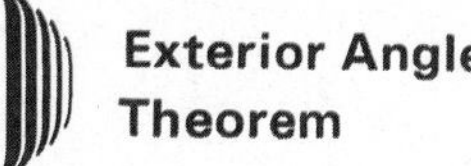

Exterior Angle Theorem

Given: $\triangle ABC$, $\angle 2$ is an exterior angle.

Prove: $m\angle 2 = m\angle B + m\angle C$

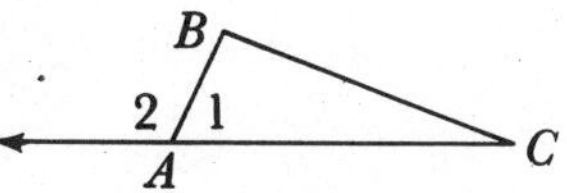

Proof:

STATEMENTS	REASONS
1. $\angle 1$ and $\angle 2$ are supplementary.	1. Supplement Post. (p. 56)
2. $m\angle 1 + m\angle 2 = 180$	2. Definition of supplementary $\angle$s
3. $m\angle 1 + m\angle B + m\angle C = 180$	3. $\angle$ Sum Theorem for $\triangle$s
4. $m\angle 2 = 180 - m\angle 1$, $m\angle B + m\angle C = 180 - m\angle 1$	4. Why?
5. $m\angle 2 = m\angle B + m\angle C$	5. Why?

Exercises 4.4

Ⓐ **1.** Does the experiment with the paper triangle, on page 137, prove the Angle Sum Theorem for Triangles?

2–6. Give a reason for each statement. You may refer to the figure or to preceding steps. (This proves the theorem at the bottom of page 137.)

2. $m\angle A + m\angle B + m\angle C = 180$, $m\angle D + m\angle E + m\angle F = 180$

3. $m\angle A + m\angle B + m\angle C = m\angle D + m\angle E + m\angle F$

4. $m\angle A = m\angle D$, $m\angle B = m\angle E$

5. $m\angle D + m\angle E + m\angle C = m\angle D + m\angle E + m\angle F$

6. $m\angle C = m\angle F$

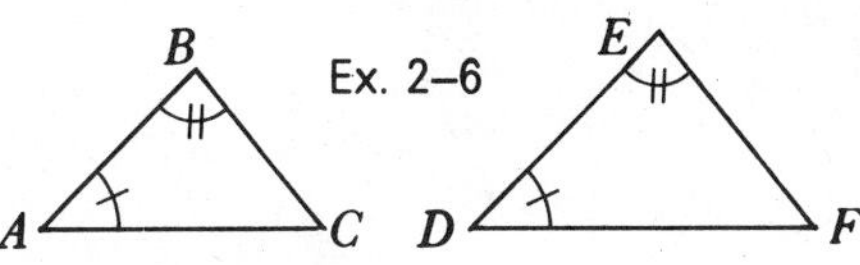

7–8. Give the missing reasons in each proof.

7. The acute angles of a right triangle are complementary. (p. 138)

8. Exterior Angle Theorem (above)

9–12. In the figure, $\overline{MP} \perp \overline{MO}$.

9. If $m\angle 2 = 50$, $m\angle 1 =$ ______.

10. If $m\angle 2 = 30$, $m\angle P =$ ______.

11. If $\angle P \cong \angle 2$, $m\angle P =$ ______.

12. If $m\angle P = 40$, $m\angle 1 =$ ______.

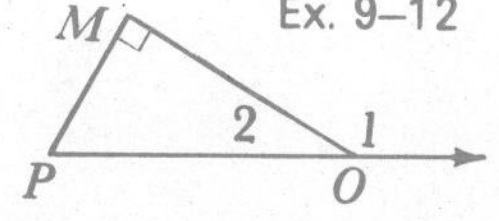

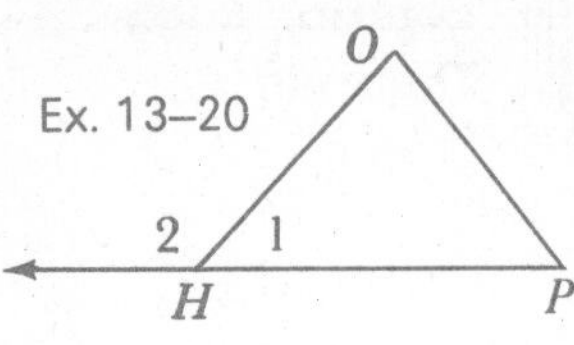

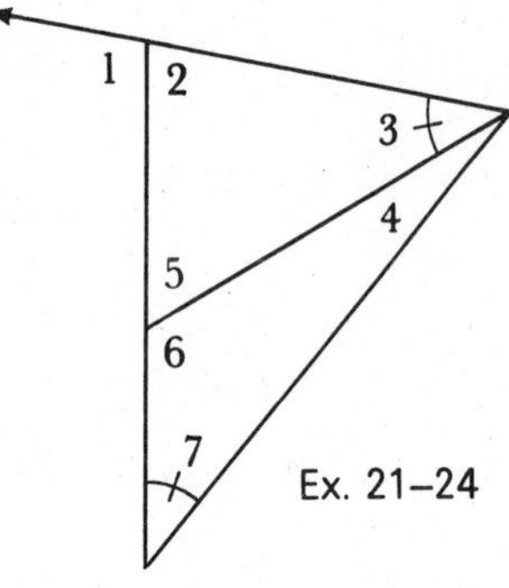

Ⓑ **13–20.** For each angle in the figure, find the measure if it is not given.

13. $m\angle P = 38, m\angle O = 70$ **14.** $m\angle 1 = 46, m\angle P = 38$

15. $m\angle O = 90, m\angle 1 = 55$ **16.** $m\angle O = 90, m\angle 1 = 63$

17. $\angle O \cong \angle P, m\angle 1 = 36$ **18.** $\angle P \cong \angle 1, m\angle O = 90$

19. $m\angle 2 = 127, m\angle P = 45$ **20.** $m\angle 2 = 133, m\angle O = 90$

21–24. Use the given information to find the measure of each numbered angle in the figure. $\angle 3 \cong \angle 7$

21. $m\angle 2 = 60, m\angle 6 = 115$ **22.** $m\angle 4 = 20, m\angle 6 = 120$

23. $m\angle 1 = 108, m\angle 7 = 40$ **24.** $m\angle 3 = 32, m\angle 5 = 54$

Ⓒ **25–26.** *Constructions:* Draw $\overline{MN}$, $\angle A$, and $\angle B$ so that $MN = 5$ cm, $m\angle A = 30$, and $m\angle B = 130$. Then construct the figure described.

25. $\triangle POD$ with $\overline{PO} \cong \overline{MN}$, $\angle O \cong \angle A$, and $130°$ exterior angle at P

26. $\triangle TRS$ with $\overline{TS} \cong \overline{MN}$, $\angle T \cong \angle A$, and $100°$ exterior angle at S

1–4. In the figure, identify all angles or pairs of angles of each type.

1. exterior **2.** alternate interior

3. corresponding **4.** interior on same side of transversal

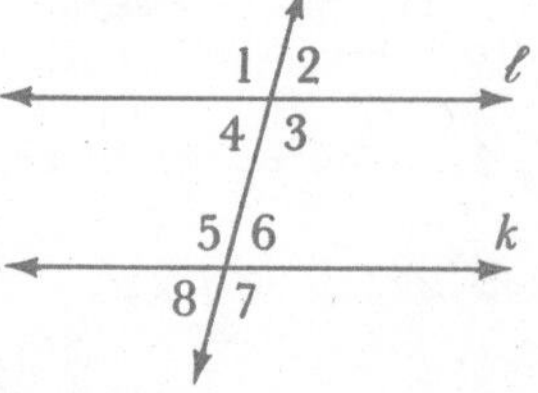

5–8. In the figure for Exercises 1–4, let $\ell \parallel k$.

5. If $m\angle 2 = 55, m\angle 6 =$ ____. **6.** If $m\angle 3 = 112, m\angle 5 =$ ____.

7. $m\angle 4 + m\angle 5 =$ ____. **8.** If $m\angle 6 = 75, m\angle 3 =$ ____.

9–14. True or False? In the figure for Exercises 1–4, $\ell \parallel k$ when

9. $\angle 1 \cong \angle 5$ **10.** $\angle 3 \cong \angle 6$ **11.** $\angle 6 \cong \angle 4$ **12.** $\angle 4 \cong \angle 7$

13. $m\angle 2 + m\angle 3 = 180$ **14.** $m\angle 4 + m\angle 5 = 180$

15. State the Parallel Postulate. **16.** State the Angle Sum Theorem for Triangles.

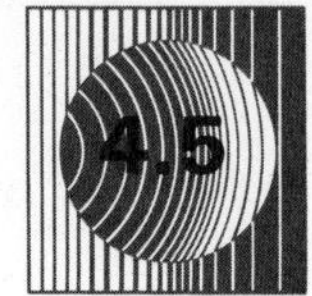

Quadrilaterals: Parallelograms

A, B, C, and *D* are coplanar points (**vertices**), no three of which are collinear. The points are joined by four segments (**sides**) that intersect only at the vertices (two at each vertex). The resulting figure is a **quadrilateral.**

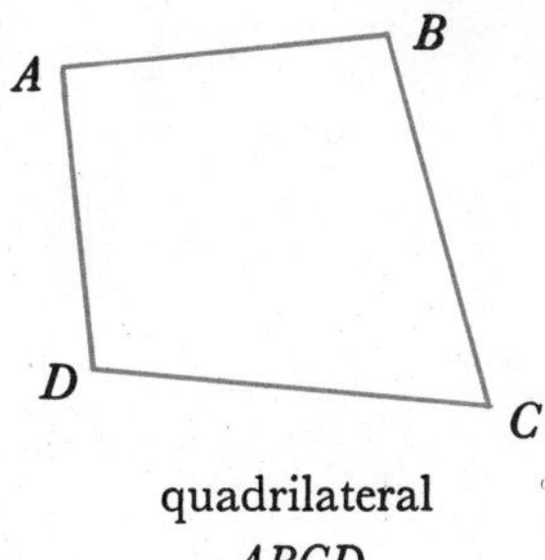

quadrilateral
ABCD

A quadrilateral is named by listing its vertices, starting at any vertex and reading clockwise or counterclockwise. So *ABCD, BCDA, ADCB,* and so forth, name the same figure.

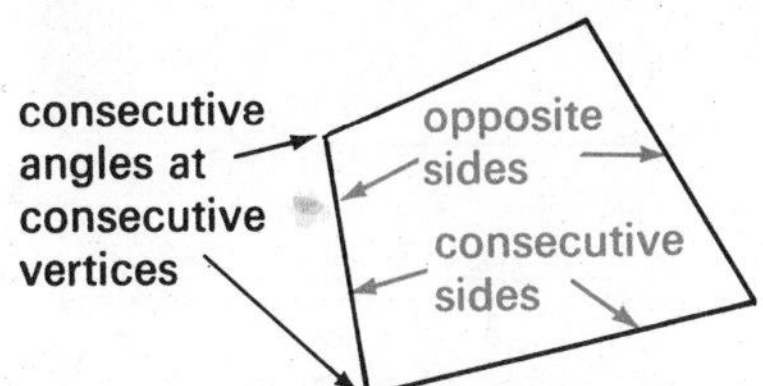

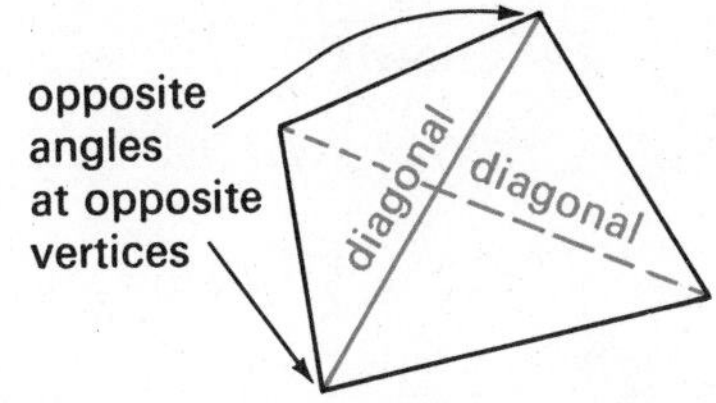

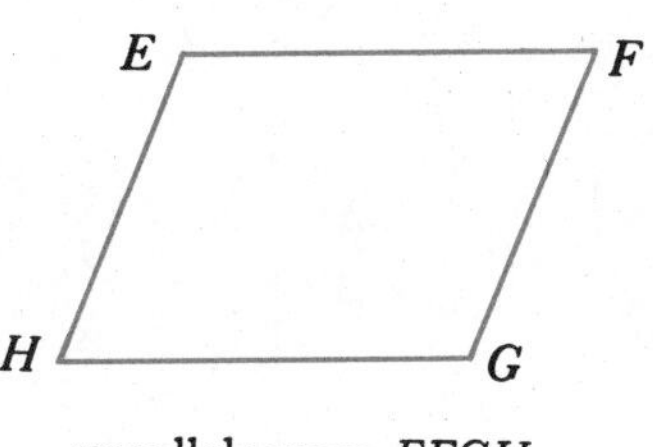

parallelogram *EFGH*
▱*EFGH*

Segments that are contained in parallel lines are also said to be parallel. A quadrilateral with both pairs of opposite sides parallel is a **parallelogram.** The next proof uses both pairs of sides as parallels and uses a diagonal as a transversal.

The sides and either diagonal of a parallelogram form two congruent triangles.

Theorem

Given: ▱$ABCD$, diagonal $\overline{BD}$

Prove: $\triangle ABD \cong \triangle CDB$

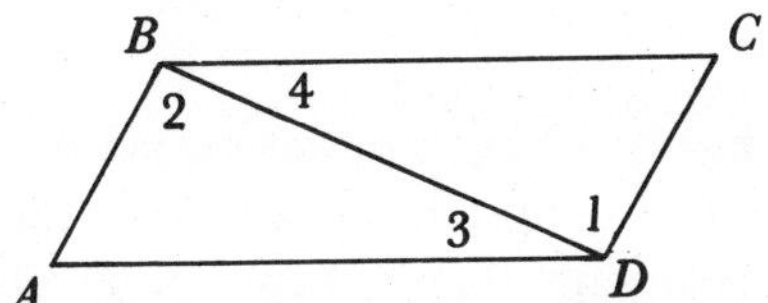

Proof:

STATEMENTS	REASONS
1. $\overleftrightarrow{DC} \parallel \overleftrightarrow{AB}$, $\overleftrightarrow{AD} \parallel \overleftrightarrow{BC}$	**1.** Opp. sides of a ▱ are ∥.
2. $\angle 1 \cong \angle 2$, $\angle 3 \cong \angle 4$	**2.** Alt. Int. ∠s Theorem
3. $\overline{BD} \cong \overline{BD}$	**3.** A segment is ≅ to itself.
4. $\triangle ABD \cong \triangle CDB$	**4.** ASA Postulate

The proof can be repeated using the other diagonal. The next theorem follows directly from the fact that corresponding parts of these congruent triangles are congruent.

Theorem  Opposite sides of a parallelogram are congruent.

Opposite angles of a parallelogram are congruent. 

The next theorem describes another characteristic of parallelograms.

Theorem  The diagonals of a parallelogram bisect each other. 

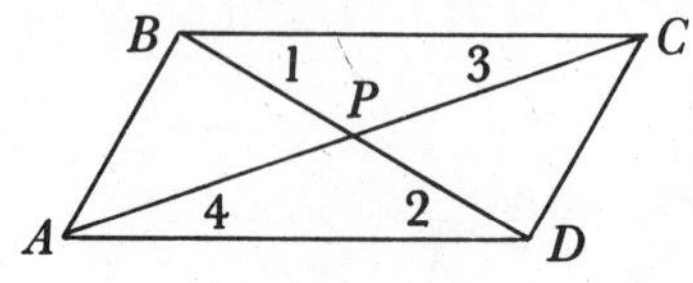

Given: $\square ABCD$, diagonals $\overline{AC}$ and $\overline{BD}$

Prove: $\overline{BP} \cong \overline{PD}$ and $\overline{AP} \cong \overline{PC}$

[*Plan:* Prove $\triangle BPC \cong \triangle DPA$.]

Proof:

STATEMENTS	REASONS
1. $\overline{BC} \cong \overline{AD}$	**1.** Opp. sides of a $\square$ are $\cong$.
2. $\overline{BC} \parallel \overline{AD}$	**2.** Opp. sides of a $\square$ are $\parallel$.
3. Using transversal $\overleftrightarrow{BD}$, $\angle 1 \cong \angle 2$ Using transversal $\overleftrightarrow{AC}$, $\angle 3 \cong \angle 4$	**3.** Alt. Int. $\angle$s Theorem.
4. $\triangle BPC \cong \triangle DPA$	**4.** ASA Postulate
5. $\overline{BP} \cong \overline{PD}$ and $\overline{AP} \cong \overline{PC}$	**5.** Corres. parts of $\cong$ $\triangle$s are $\cong$.

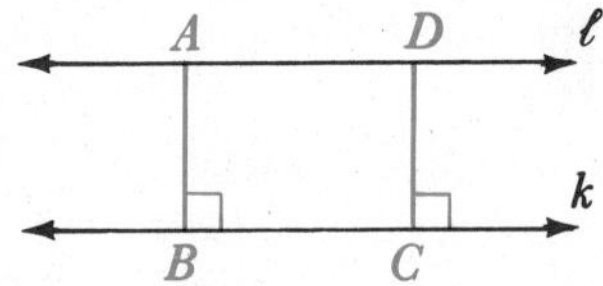

Let ℓ and k be any two parallel lines and let A and D be any two points on ℓ. Then perpendiculars from points A and D to line k are parallel. So $ABCD$ is a parallelogram, and $\overline{AB} \cong \overline{CD}$.

That is, every segment perpendicular to ℓ and k, with endpoints on ℓ and k, is congruent to all other such segments. We call the length of these segments the **distance between two parallel lines** ℓ and k.

Theorem  Two parallel lines are everywhere equidistant. 

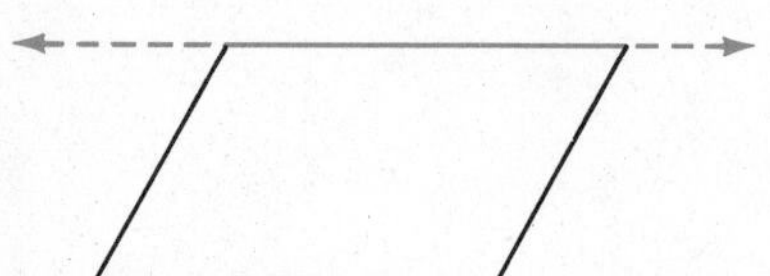

Any side of a parallelogram can be used as a transversal. Then two consecutive angles of the parallelogram are interior angles on the same side of the transversal.

Theorem  Consecutive angles of a parallelogram are supplementary. 

Exercises 4.5

Ⓐ **1–9.** Choose the best example from the list. Refer to the figure.

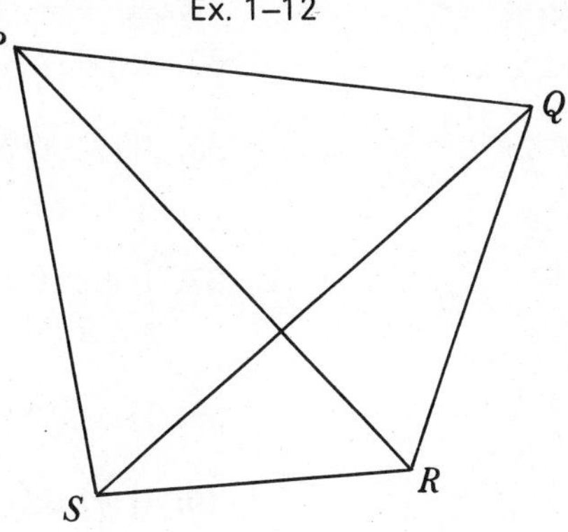

a. $\overline{PS}$, $\overline{SR}$ **b.** $\overline{PS}$, $\overline{QR}$ **c.** $\angle QRS$, $\angle RSP$

d. $\overline{PR}$ **e.** S, Q **f.** P

g. P, S **h.** $\overline{SR}$ **i.** $\angle QRS$, $\angle SPQ$

1. a vertex **2.** a side

3. opposite sides **4.** consecutive sides

5. opposite vertices **6.** consecutive vertices

7. opposite angles **8.** consecutive angles

9. a diagonal

10–12. Refer to the figure above. Name as many transversals as you can for the given lines.

10. $\overleftrightarrow{PQ}$, $\overleftrightarrow{SR}$ **11.** $\overleftrightarrow{PS}$, $\overleftrightarrow{QR}$ **12.** $\overleftrightarrow{SQ}$, $\overleftrightarrow{PR}$

Ⓑ **13–16.** Refer to the figure below. Identify the two parallel lines and the transversal you would use in each case to show that the angles are interior angles on the same side of the transversal. NOTE: This proves that the consecutive angles of a parallelogram are supplementary.

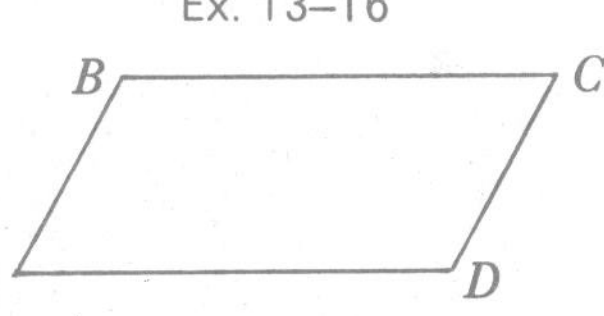

13. $m\angle A + m\angle B = 180$ **14.** $m\angle B + m\angle C = 180$

15. $m\angle C + m\angle D = 180$ **16.** $m\angle D + m\angle A = 180$

17–30. Refer to ▱*MNRS* at the right.

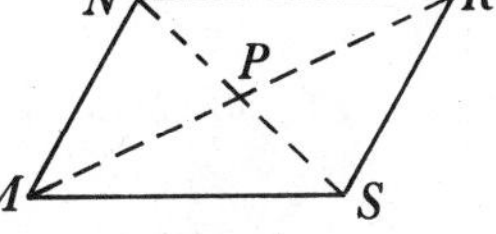

17. $\triangle MNR \cong$ ______ **18.** $\triangle SRN \cong$ ______

19. $\overline{MN} \cong$ ______ **20.** $\overline{NR} \cong$ ______

21. $\overline{PN} \cong$ ______ **22.** $\overline{MP} \cong$ ______

23. $\angle MNR \cong$ ______ **24.** $\angle SRN \cong$ ______

25. If $PM = 3$, then $PR =$ ______. **26.** If $RS = 7$, then ______ $= 7$.

27. If $RN = 10$, then ______ $= 10$. **28.** If $PS = 5$, then $NP =$ ______.

29. If $m\angle PRS = 30$, then ______ $= 30$. **30.** If $m\angle PNR = 26$, then ______ $= 26$.

Ex. 31–40

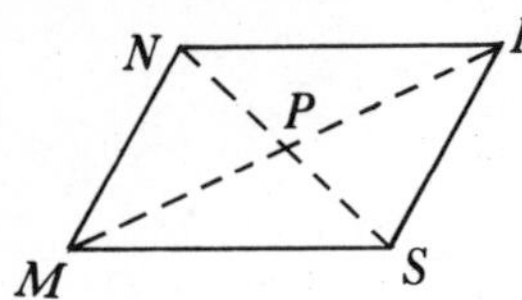

31–40. Refer to ▱$MNRS$ at the left.

31. If $m\angle SMN = 82$, then ______ $= 82$.

32. If $m\angle RPN = 112$, then ______ $= 112$.

33. $m\angle RSM + m\angle SMN =$ ______

34. $m\angle SRN + m\angle MSR =$ ______

35. If $m\angle RPS = 21$, then ______ $= 21$.

36. If $m\angle RSM = 130$, then $m\angle SRN =$ ______.

37. If $m\angle NRS = 75$, then $m\angle RNM =$ ______.

38. If $m\angle RSM = 128$, then ______ $= 128$.

39. If $m\angle RSN = 35$ and $m\angle RNS = 27$, then $m\angle SRN =$ ______.

40. If $m\angle SMN = 63$ and $m\angle MSN = 40$, then $m\angle MNS =$ ______.

construction: a parallelogram given two consecutive sides and an angle

1. Given: two segments and an angle.

A —— B

C —— D

F

2. Construct a congruent angle. On the sides of the angle, construct segments congruent to the given segments.

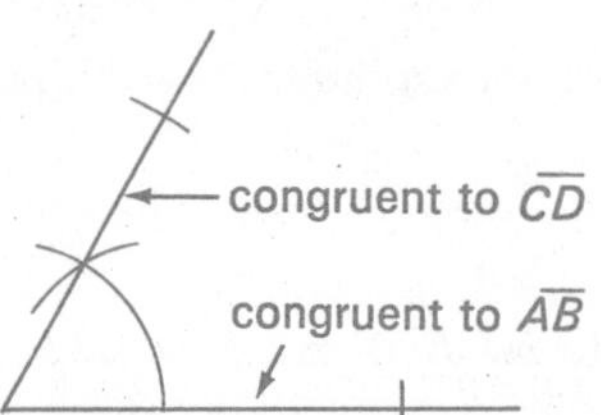

3. At the endpoints, construct intersecting segments congruent to the opposite segments.

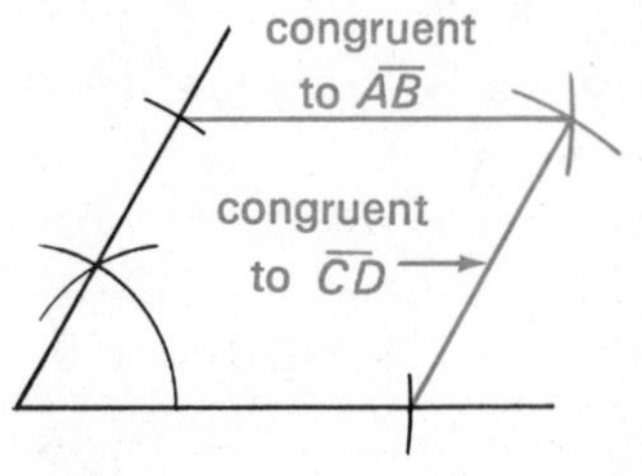

41–44. Draw segments and an angle with the given measures. Then construct a parallelogram with consecutive sides and an angle congruent to the figures you drew.

41. 3 cm, 5 cm, 30°

42. 4 cm, 6 cm, 70°

43. 35 mm, 52 mm, 130°

44. 47 mm, 63 mm, 140°

Ⓒ **45.** *Construction:* Draw segments 3, 4, and 5 cm long. Then construct ▱$TAPS$ with $PA = 5$ cm, $PS = 3$ cm, and $SA = 4$ cm.

46. Write a two-column proof that parallel lines are everywhere equidistant. HINT: Restate the *given* and *prove* in terms of the second figure on page 142.

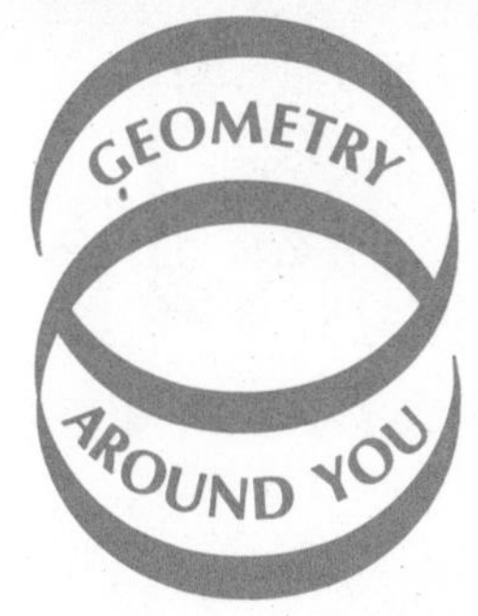

PICTURING PARALLELS

Most of the parallel lines in this chapter have been drawn as if we were looking down on the plane which contains the parallel lines. But in everyday experience, we seldom see models of parallels from this point of view. In these pictures, you know which lines are parallel in the situation shown, even though they are not parallel on the plane of the page.

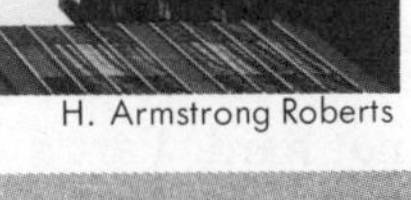

H. Armstrong Roberts

Photo Research International

Herb Slodounik

4.6 More About Quadrilaterals

If a quadrilateral is a parallelogram, the opposite sides of the quadrilateral are congruent.	If the opposite sides of a quadrilateral are congruent, the quadrilateral is a parallelogram.

The two statements above are converses. In fact, the statement on the left says simply that *opposite sides of a parallelogram are congruent*. This was proved in Section 4.5. But can the converse also be proved? Here is one way to look for an answer to that question.

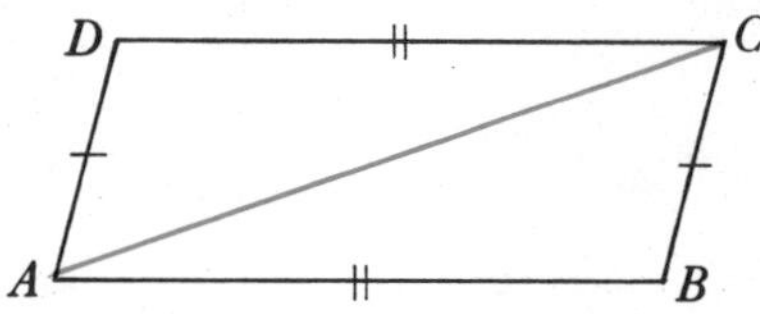

1. Draw quadrilateral $ABCD$.
2. Remembering how useful the diagonal was in earlier proofs, add a diagonal to the figure.
3. Notice that the diagonal forms two congruent triangles, so there are three pairs of congruent angles.
4. To prove $ABCD$ is a parallelogram, prove opposite sides parallel.
5. The opposite sides are parallel if alternate interior (or corresponding) angles are congruent.
6. Are any congruent angles in the triangles (step 3 above) alternate interior angles?

Once the plan for the proof is decided on, writing the proof itself is not hard. Part **a** of the following theorem is proved in Exercises 17–20. Parts **b** and **c** are the subjects of Exercises 21 and 22.

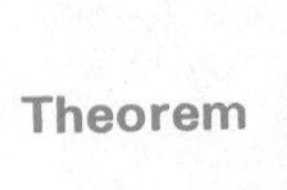

Theorem

If any one of the following conditions is met, a quadrilateral is a parallelogram.

- **a.** Opposite sides are congruent.
- **b.** Two sides are parallel and congruent.
- **c.** The diagonals bisect each other.

Exercises 4.6

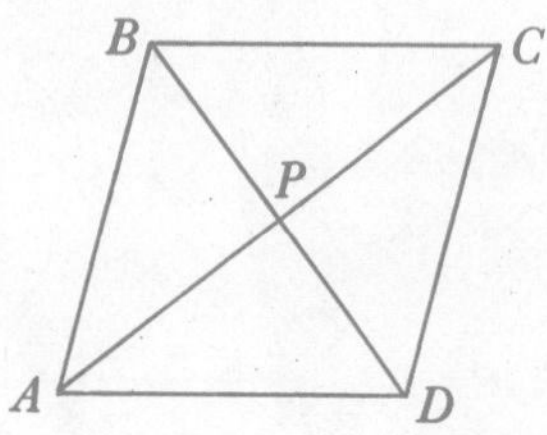

Ⓐ **1–8.** Under the given conditions, is $ABCD$ a parallelogram?

1. $\overline{AB} \cong \overline{CD}, \overline{AD} \cong \overline{BC}$ **2.** $\overline{AB} \cong \overline{CD}, \overline{BC} \parallel \overline{AD}$

3. $\overline{AB} \cong \overline{CD}, \overline{AB} \parallel \overline{CD}$ **4.** $\overline{BP} \cong \overline{PD}, \overline{AP} \cong \overline{PC}$

5. $\overline{AB} \parallel \overline{CD}, \overline{AD} \parallel \overline{BC}$ **6.** $\overline{AB} \cong \overline{BC}, \overline{AD} \cong \overline{DC}$

7. $m\angle DAB + m\angle ABC = 180$, $m\angle BCD + m\angle CDA = 180$

8. $m\angle DAB + m\angle ABC = 180$, $m\angle ABC + m\angle BCD = 180$

Ⓑ **9–14.** Refer to the figure for Exercises 1–8. Why is *ABCD* a parallelogram under the given conditions?

9. $AP = 2$, $PC = 2$, $BP = 1.5$, $PD = 1.5$

10. $AB = 5$, $BC = 5$, $CD = 5$, $DA = 5$

11. $AD = 3$, $BC = 3$, $\angle DAC \cong \angle ACB$

12. $\angle BCA \cong \angle CAD$, $\angle DCA \cong \angle CAB$

13. $AB = 7$, $CD = 7$, $BC = 5$, $AD = 5$

14. $BP = 3$, $PC = 3$, $PD = 3$, $PA = 3$

15–16. State the converse and tell whether it seems to be true.

15. If two angles are consecutive angles of a parallelogram, then they are supplementary.

16. If a figure is a parallelogram, it is a quadrilateral.

17–20. Refer to the figure for Exercises 1–8. Complete the proof.

Given: $\overline{AD} \cong \overline{BC}$, $\overline{AB} \cong \overline{DC}$

Prove: *ABCD* is a parallelogram.

Proof:

STATEMENTS	REASONS
1. Let $\overline{AC}$ be a diagonal of *ABCD*.	1. Definition of diagonal
2. $\overline{AC} \cong \overline{AC}$	2. **17.** ____
3. $\overline{AD} \cong \overline{BC}$, $\overline{AB} \cong \overline{DC}$	3. Given
4. $\triangle ADC \cong \triangle CBA$	4. **18.** ____
5. $\angle CAD \cong \angle ACB$, $\angle ACD \cong \angle CAB$	5. **19.** ____
6. $\overline{AD} \parallel \overline{BC}$, $\overline{AB} \parallel \overline{DC}$	6. **20.** ____
7. *ABCD* is a parallelogram.	7. Definition of ▱

Ⓒ **21–22.** Write a two-column proof.

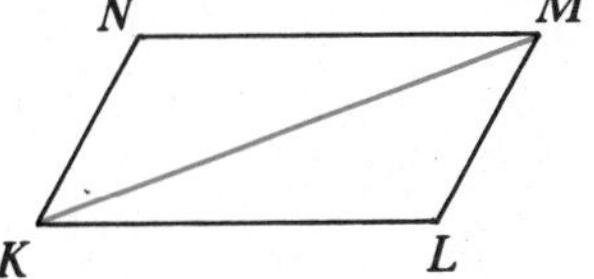

21. Given: $\overline{KN} \cong \overline{ML}$, $\overline{KN} \parallel \overline{ML}$

Prove: *KLMN* is a parallelogram.

[*Plan:* Prove either $\overline{KL} \cong \overline{MN}$ or $\overline{KL} \parallel \overline{MN}$.]

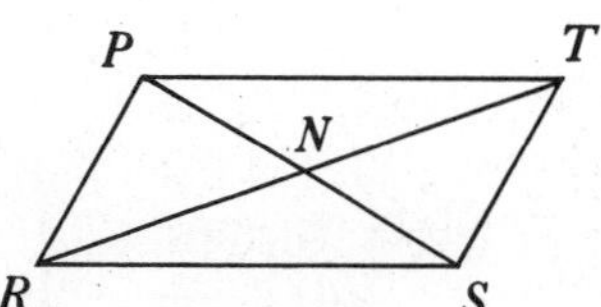

22. Given: $\overline{PS}$ and $\overline{RT}$ bisect each other.

Prove: *PRST* is a parallelogram.

[*Plan:* Use congruent triangles and the definition of ▱ or part **a** or part **b** of the theorem on page 146.]

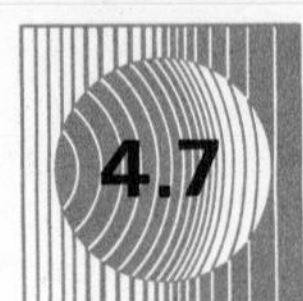

The Triangle Midline Theorem

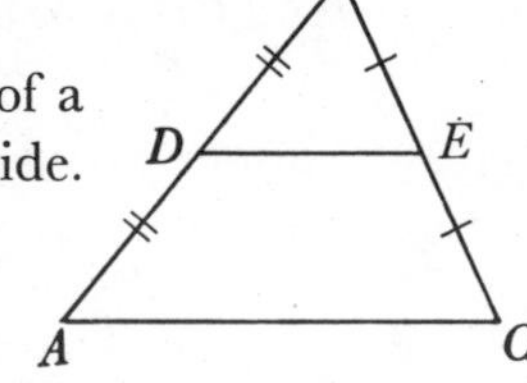

The segment joining the midpoints of two sides of a triangle (called a **midline**) is parallel to the third side.

Given: $\triangle ABC$, $\overline{AD} \cong \overline{DB}$, $\overline{CE} \cong \overline{EB}$
Prove: $\overline{DE} \parallel \overline{AC}$

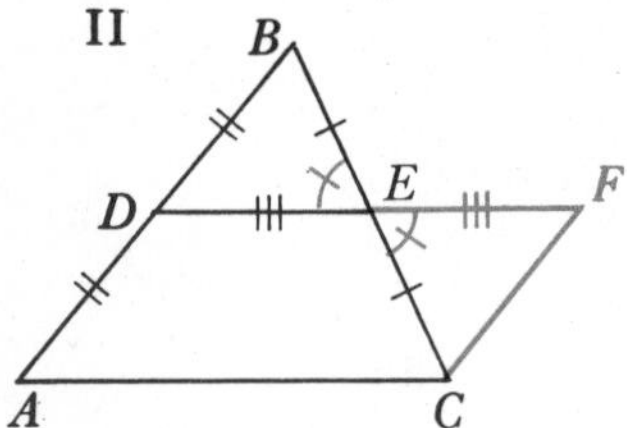

Form a quadrilateral and two (congruent) triangles.

$\overleftrightarrow{DF}$ is a transversal of $\overline{AB}$ and $\overline{FC}$.

Proof:

STATEMENTS	REASONS
1. Let F be on $\overrightarrow{DE}$, $\overline{EF} \cong \overline{DE}$.	1. Point Plotting Thm. (p. 27)
2. Join F and C.	2. 2 pts. determine a line.
3. $\overline{CE} \cong \overline{EB}$	3. Given
4. $\angle BED \cong \angle CEF$	4. Vertical $\angle$s are $\cong$.
5. $\triangle BED \cong \triangle CEF$	5. SAS Postulate
6. $\angle F \cong \angle BDE$, $\overline{FC} \cong \overline{DB}$	6. Corres. parts of $\cong$ $\triangle$s are $\cong$.
7. $\overline{AB} \parallel \overline{FC}$, so $\overline{AD} \parallel \overline{FC}$	7. Alt. Interior $\angle$s Thm.
8. $\overline{AD} \cong \overline{DB}$	8. Given
9. $\overline{AD} \cong \overline{FC}$	9. Segs. $\cong$ to same seg. are $\cong$.
10. $ADFC$ is a ▱.	10. 2 sides are $\parallel$ and $\cong$.
11. $\overline{DF} \parallel \overline{AC}$, so $\overline{DE} \parallel \overline{AC}$	11. Opp. sides of a ▱ are $\parallel$.

Gene Kuechmann

A midline of a triangle is half as long as the third side.

Given: $\triangle ABC$, $AD = DB$, $CE = EB$ (See figures I and II above.)
Prove: $DE = \frac{1}{2}AC$

Proof:

STATEMENTS	REASONS
1. Form ▱ $ADFC$, with $EF = DE$.	1. Steps 1–10 above
2. $DE + EF = DF$	2. Definition of between
3. $DE + DE = DF$, so $2DE = DF$	3. Substitution and addition
4. $DE = \frac{1}{2}DF$	4. Mult. both sides by $\frac{1}{2}$
5. $DF = AC$	5. Opp. sides of a ▱ are $\cong$.
6. $DE = \frac{1}{2}AC$	6. Substitution

The two properties just proved are usually combined in one theorem.

Triangle Midline Theorem

The segment joining the midpoints of two sides of a triangle is parallel to the third side and half as long.

Exercises 4.7

Ⓐ **1–7.** Refer to the figure.

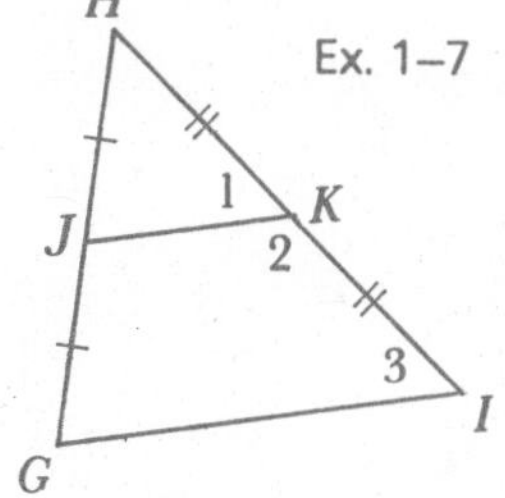

1. $\overline{JK} \parallel$ ______

2. If $GI = 6$, $JK =$ ______.

3. If $JK = 12$, $GI =$ ______.

4. If $m\angle 1 = 42$, $m\angle 3 =$ ______.

5. $m\angle 2 + m\angle 3 =$ ______

6. $\overline{JK}$ is called a ______ of $\triangle GHI$.

7. If B is the midpoint of $\overline{GI}$, name another midline of $\triangle GHI$.

8. How many midlines does any triangle have?

Ⓑ **9–18.** In the figure, M and N are the midpoints of $\overline{PT}$ and $\overline{RT}$.

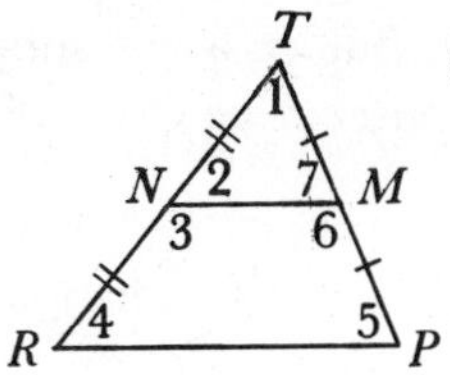

9. If $m\angle 4 = 48$, then $m\angle 2 =$ ______.

10. If $m\angle 6 = 96$, then $m\angle 5 =$ ______.

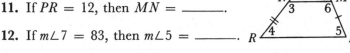

11. If $PR = 12$, then $MN =$ ______.

12. If $m\angle 7 = 83$, then $m\angle 5 =$ ______.

Ex. 9–18

13. If $m\angle 3 = 120$ and $m\angle 7 = 72$, then $m\angle 1 =$ ______.

14. If $MN = 7\frac{1}{2}$, then $PR =$ ______.

15. If $\overline{TR} \cong \overline{TP}$ and $TN = 4$, then $MP =$ ______.

16. If $\overline{TN} \cong \overline{NM}$ and $TN = 4$, then $RP =$ ______.

17. If $\overline{MN} \cong \overline{TN}$ and $RP = 16$, then $TN =$ ______.

18. If $\overline{MP} \cong \overline{NR}$ and $MP = 5$, then $TN =$ ______.

Ⓒ **19–26.** Let $ABCD$ be any quadrilateral, and let E, F, G, and H be midpoints of its sides. $\overline{AC}$ is a diagonal.

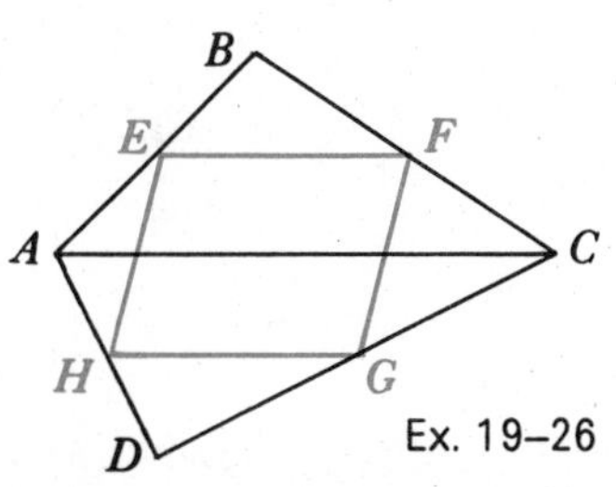

Ex. 19–26

19. Why is $\overline{EF} \parallel \overline{AC}$?

20. Why is $\overline{GH} \parallel \overline{AC}$?

21. Why is $\overline{EF} \parallel \overline{GH}$?

22. $EF = \frac{1}{2}$______

23. $GH = \frac{1}{2}$______

24. Why is $\overline{EF} \cong \overline{GH}$?

25. Since $\overline{EF} \cong \overline{GH}$ and $\overline{EF} \parallel \overline{GH}$, $EFGH$ is a ______.

26. If the midpoints of the sides of any quadrilateral are joined, the segments joining them form a ______. NOTE: This is called Varignon's Theorem, after a French mathematician.

Special Parallelograms

rectangle

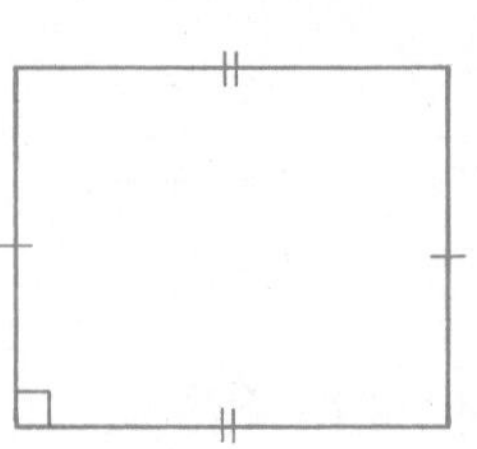

parallelogram with a right angle

rhombus

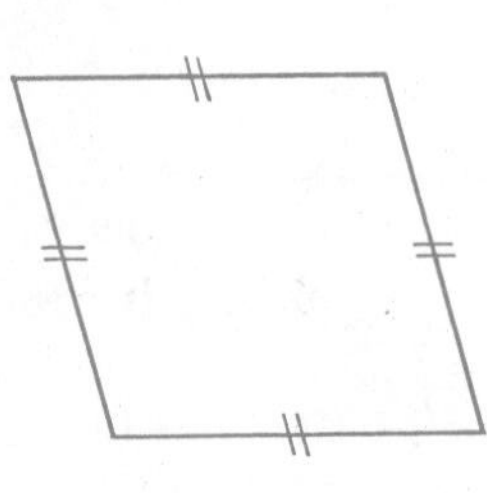

parallelogram with all sides congruent

square

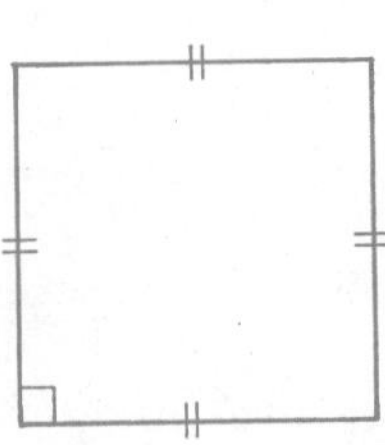

rhombus with a right angle or rectangle with all sides congruent

Since a rectangle is a parallelogram, its consecutive angles are supplementary. But an angle supplementary to a right angle is also a right angle, so consecutive sides of a rectangle are perpendicular. That is,

Theorem  **A rectangle has four right angles.**

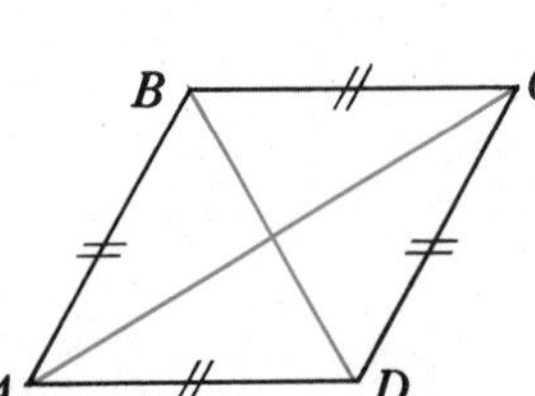

In rhombus $ABCD$, $\overline{AB} \cong \overline{BC}$ and $\overline{AD} \cong \overline{DC}$. That is, B and D are each equidistant from the endpoints of $\overline{AC}$. But in a plane, two points equidistant from the endpoints of a segment determine its perpendicular bisector, so $\overleftrightarrow{BD}$ is the perpendicular bisector of $\overline{AC}$. And, by the same reasoning, $\overleftrightarrow{AC}$ is the perpendicular bisector of $\overline{BD}$.

Theorem  **The diagonals of a rhombus are perpendicular and bisect each other.**

Theorem  **If the diagonals of a parallelogram are perpendicular, the parallelogram is a rhombus.**

Given: $\square MNOP$, $\overline{PN} \perp \overline{MO}$

Prove: $\square MNOP$ is a rhombus.

[*Plan*: Prove $\overline{MN} \cong \overline{NO} \cong \overline{OP} \cong \overline{PM}$ by proving $\triangle MNQ \cong \triangle ONQ \cong \triangle OPQ \cong \triangle MPQ$.] (Exercise 29 calls for the completed proof.)

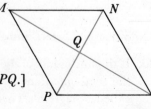

This chart shows how special parallelograms are related. Think of the properties of each figure as carried along to those below it on the chart.

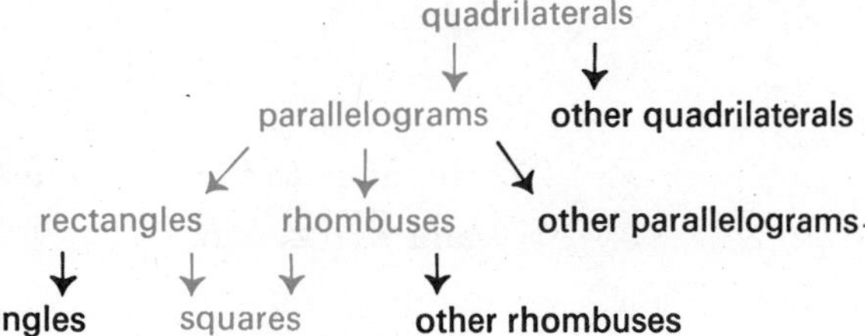

Exercises 4.8

Ⓐ **1–10.** True or False?

1. Every quadrilateral is a parallelogram.

2. Every parallelogram is a rhombus.

3. Every square is a rhombus.

4. Every square is a rectangle.

5. No parallelogram is a square.

6. Every square is a parallelogram.

7. The diagonals of a rhombus are perpendicular and bisect each other.

8. The diagonals of a rectangle are perpendicular.

9. The opposite angles of a rhombus are congruent.

10. If the diagonals of a quadrilateral bisect each other and are perpendicular, the quadrilateral is a rhombus.

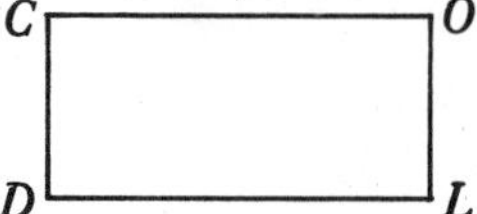

Ⓑ **11–22.** *COLD* is a rectangle, *SUIT* is a rhombus, and *WHEN* is a square.

S U T I

11. $\overline{IS} \perp$ ______

12. $\overline{UT}$ bisects ______.

13. If $m\angle ITS = 130$, find $m\angle TSU$.

14. If $LO = 4$, $CD =$ ______.

15. If $CO = 12$, $LD =$ ______.

16. If $NE = 4$, $WN =$ ______.

17. Find $m\angle D$.

18. If $m\angle TSU = 48$, find $m\angle SUI$.

19. If $WH = 7$, $HE =$ ______.

20. If $ST = 12$, $US =$ ______.

21. If $US = 6$, $IT =$ ______.

22. Find $m\angle N$.

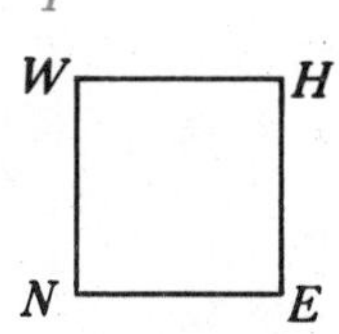

23–26. Why is the conclusion true?

23. *PINK* is a parallelogram,
$\overline{PI} \cong \overline{IN}$
Conclusion: *PINK* is a rhombus.

24. *BONE* is a parallelogram,
$\overline{BN} \perp \overline{OE}$
Conclusion: *BONE* is a rhombus.

25. *SONG* is a rhombus, $m\angle G = 90$
Conclusion: $m\angle S = 90$

26. *ROAM* is a rhombus.
Conclusion: $\overline{AR} \perp \overline{OM}$

27–28. *Constructions:* Draw $\overline{MN}$, $\overline{PD}$, and $\angle A$ so that $MN = 4$ cm, $PD = 3$ cm, and $m\angle A = 50$. Then construct the figure described.

27. rhombus $RHOS$ with $\angle R \cong \angle A$ and $\overline{RH} \cong \overline{MN}$

28. rectangle $RECT$ with $\overline{RE} \cong \overline{MN}$ and $\overline{EC} \cong \overline{PD}$

Ⓒ 29–30. Write a two-column proof.

29. If the diagonals of a parallelogram are perpendicular, the parallelogram is a rhombus.

30. The diagonals of a rhombus bisect the angles.

Given: Rhombus $PDQT$, diagonal $\overline{DT}$

Prove: $\angle 1 \cong \angle 2$, $\angle 3 \cong \angle 4$

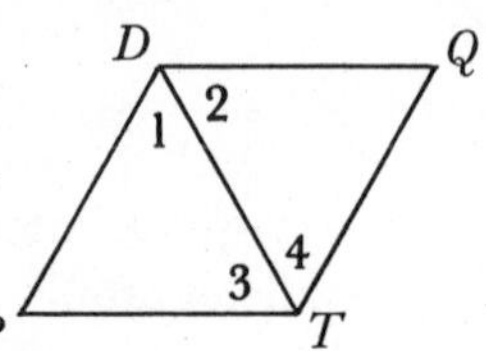

KITES AND ARROWS

Did you know that kites and arrows are geometric figures?

A kite and an arrow both have two pairs of consecutive sides congruent, and no side is common to both pairs. But the diagonals of a kite intersect, while the diagonals of an arrow do not.

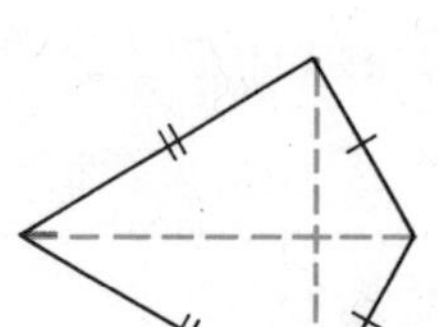
kite

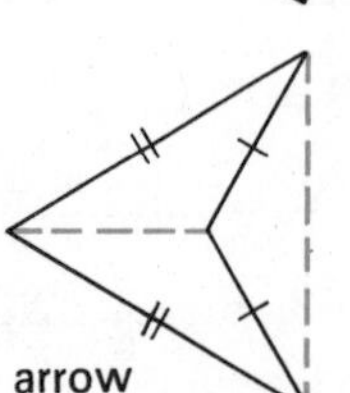
arrow

Here are some questions to explore.

- What is a kite with four congruent sides called?
- Can an arrow have four congruent sides?
- Are any angles congruent in a kite? In an arrow?
- How are the lines containing the diagonals of a kite or an arrow related?

The kite is so named because it is shaped like the simplest form of the flying toy called a kite.

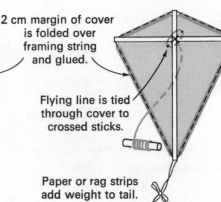

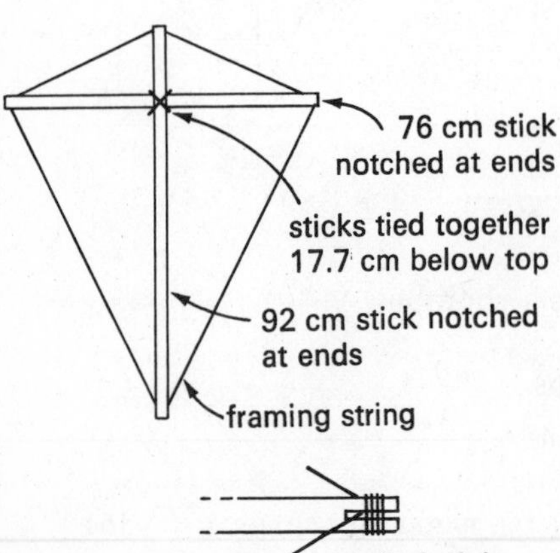

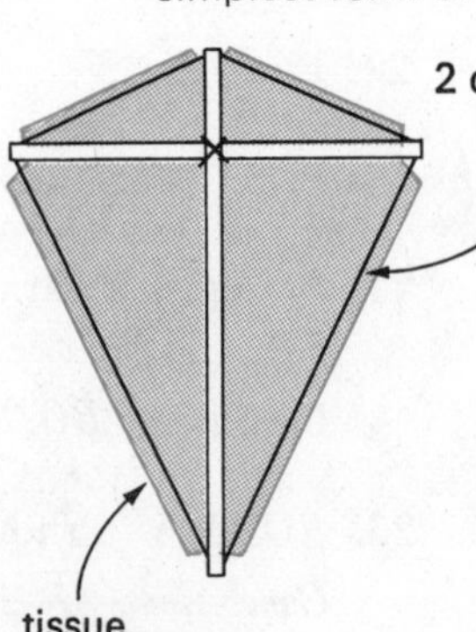

Transversals and Parallel Lines

The edge of the ruler in the photograph represents a transversal of the parallel lines marked on the board. The parallel lines **intercept** segments on the transversal.

If three parallel lines intercept congruent segments on transversal *t*, they intercept congruent segments on every transversal parallel to *t*.

Given: $\ell \parallel k \parallel n$, $s \parallel t$, $\overline{AB} \cong \overline{BC}$
Prove: $\overline{DE} \cong \overline{EF}$

Proof:

STATEMENTS	REASONS
1. *ABED*, *BCFE* are parallelograms.	1. Definition of ▱
2. $\overline{AB} \cong \overline{DE}$, $\overline{BC} \cong \overline{EF}$	2. Opp. sides of a ▱ are ≅.
3. $\overline{AB} \cong \overline{BC}$	3. Given
4. $\overline{DE} \cong \overline{BC}$	4. Segs. ≅ to the same seg. are ≅.
5. $\overline{DE} \cong \overline{EF}$	5. Segs. ≅ to the same seg. are ≅.

We can now prove this more general statement:

If three parallel lines intercept congruent segments on transversal *t*, they intercept congruent segments on all other transversals.

Given: $\ell \parallel k \parallel n$, transversals *r* and *t*,
$\overline{AB} \cong \overline{BC}$
Prove: $\overline{DE} \cong \overline{EF}$

Proof:

STATEMENTS	REASONS
1. There is a line *s* through *E*, so that $s \parallel t$.	1. Parallel Postulate (p. 125)
2. $\ell \parallel k \parallel n$, $\overline{AB} \cong \overline{BC}$	2. Given
3. $\overline{GE} \cong \overline{EH}$	3. Steps 1 and 2 and proof above
4. $\angle DEG \cong \angle FEH$	4. Vertical ∠s are ≅.
5. $\angle DGE \cong \angle FHE$	5. Alt. Interior ∠s Theorem
6. $\triangle DGE \cong \triangle FHE$	6. ASA Postulate
7. $\overline{DE} \cong \overline{EF}$	7. Corres. parts of ≅ △s are ≅.

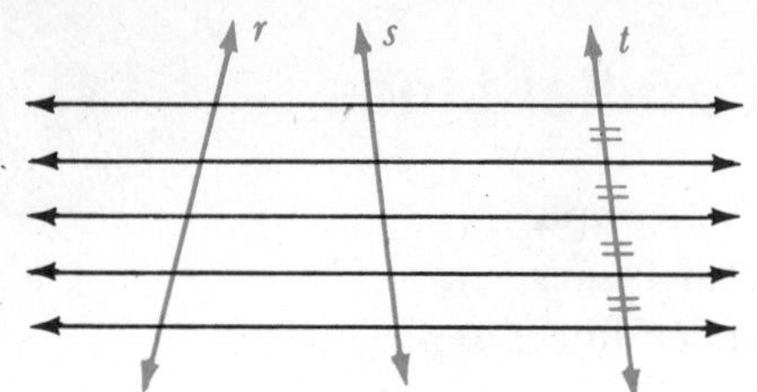

Suppose there are more than three parallel lines. By using the same reasoning as before, over and over again, we can prove that all of the intercepted segments on s (or on r) are congruent to one another.

Intercepted Segment Theorem

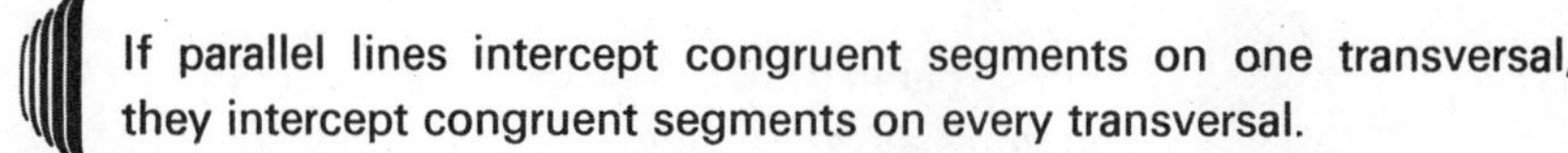
If parallel lines intercept congruent segments on one transversal, they intercept congruent segments on every transversal.

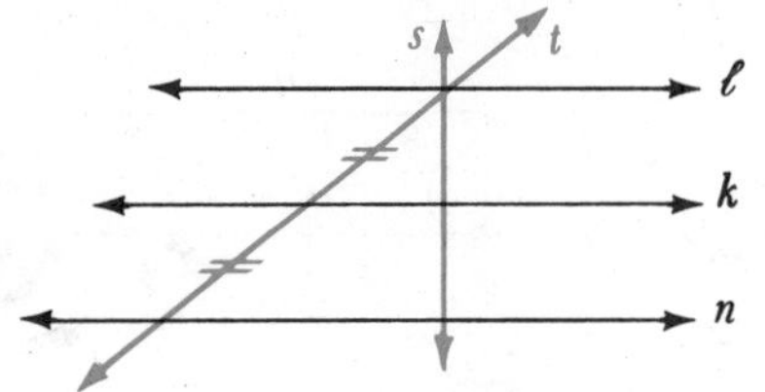

Suppose parallel lines ℓ, k, and n intercept congruent segments on transversal t. By the Intercepted Segment Theorem, the intercepted segments on s are also congruent. Since s, t, and n form a triangle,

Theorem

If a line parallel to one side of a triangle bisects either of the other two sides of the triangle, it bisects both of them.

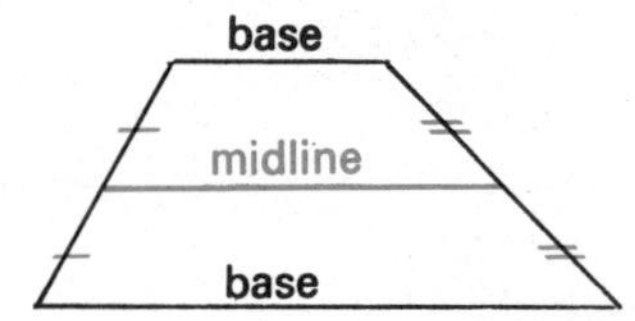

A **trapezoid** is a quadrilateral with exactly *one* pair of parallel sides. The parallel sides are the **bases** of the trapezoid. The **midline** (or **median**) of a trapezoid joins the midpoints of the nonparallel sides (called **legs**).

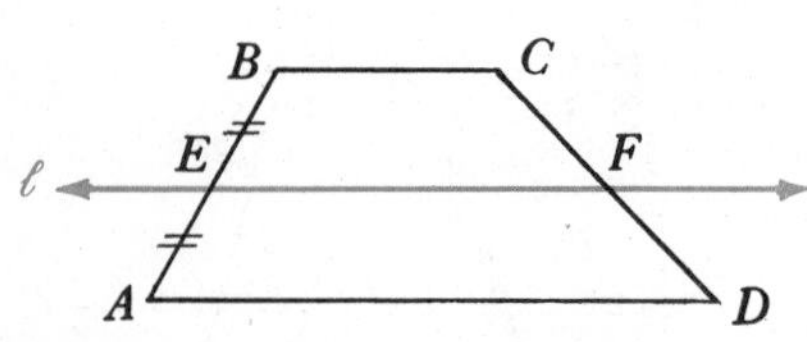

In trapezoid $ABCD$, E is the midpoint of $\overline{AB}$, and ℓ goes through E parallel to $\overline{AD}$ and $\overline{BC}$. Since ℓ, $\overleftrightarrow{AD}$, and $\overleftrightarrow{BC}$ intercept congruent segments on $\overline{AB}$, they intercept congruent segments on $\overline{CD}$. So F is the midpoint of $\overline{CD}$, and $\overline{EF}$ is the midline of trapezoid $ABCD$. There is exactly one midline and exactly one parallel through E, so part **a** of the next theorem is proved.

Trapezoid Midline Theorem

a. The midline of a trapezoid is parallel to the bases.

b. The length of the midline of a trapezoid is one half the sum of the lengths of the bases.

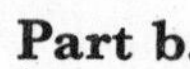
Part b.

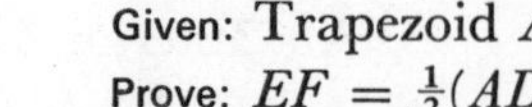
Given: Trapezoid $ABCD$, midline $\overline{EF}$

Prove: $EF = \frac{1}{2}(AD + BC)$

[*Plan:* Draw diagonal $\overline{BD}$ and apply the Triangle Midline Theorem, p. 148, to $\triangle ABD$ and $\triangle BCD$.]

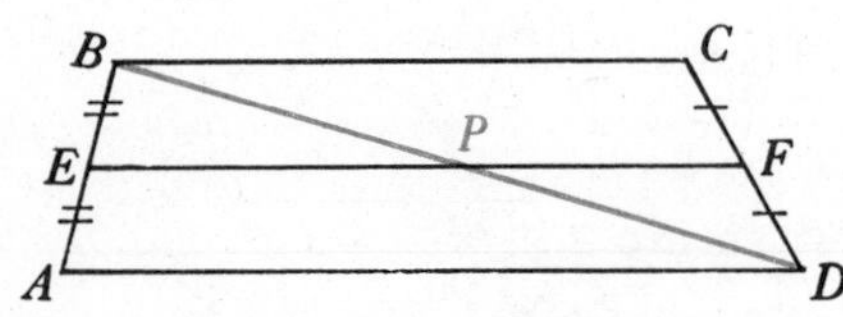

Exercises 4.9

Ⓐ **1–10.** In the given figure, lines a, b, c, and d are parallel.

1. We can write $a \parallel b \parallel c \parallel d$ to indicate ______.

2. The transversals of the parallel lines are ______ and ______.

3. On k, lines a and b intercept ______.

4. On n, lines b and c intercept ______.

5. If $\overline{ST} \cong \overline{TV}$, name congruent segments on n.

6. If b bisects $\overline{SP}$, it also bisects ______.

7. Figure $TNPV$ is a ______.

8. If V and P are midpoints of $\overline{TW}$ and $\overline{NR}$, then $\overline{VP}$ is the ______ of $TNRW$.

Ex. 1–10

9. If $\overline{TN}$ is the midline of $\triangle SVP$, then $TN = \frac{1}{2}$______.

10. If $\overline{VP}$ joins the midpoints of $\overline{TW}$ and $\overline{NR}$, then $VP = \frac{1}{2}$(______).

Ⓑ **11–20.** In the given figure, $\ell \parallel k \parallel n \parallel p$ and $\overline{DE} \cong \overline{EF} \cong \overline{FG}$.

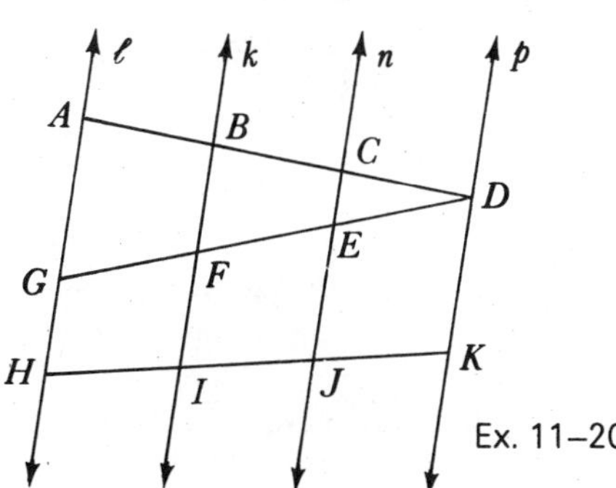

Ex. 11–20

11. If $AB = 4$, then $BC =$ ______.

12. If $CD = 7$, then $AB =$ ______.

13. If $BF = 6$, then $CE =$ ______.

14. If $CE = 4$, then $BF =$ ______.

15. If $AG = 6$ and $CE = 2$, then $BF =$ ______.

16. If $DK = 8$ and $IF = 4$, then $EJ =$ ______.

17. If $IF = 6$, $EJ + GH =$ ______.

18. If $EJ = 12$, $DK + IF =$ ______.

19. If $DK = 8$ and $EJ = 6$, then $IF =$ ______.

20. If $IF = 4$ and $EJ = 10$, then $DK =$ ______.

21–22. The photograph on page 153 shows how a carpenter can use a ruler to mark a board off into five strips of equal width. How should the position of the ruler be changed to mark the board off into

21. six strips of equal width?

22. four strips of equal width?

construction: separate a segment into three congruent segments

1. Given: any segment $\overline{AB}$ 	2. Construct $\overrightarrow{AP}$. Mark off 3 congruent segments on AP starting at A. 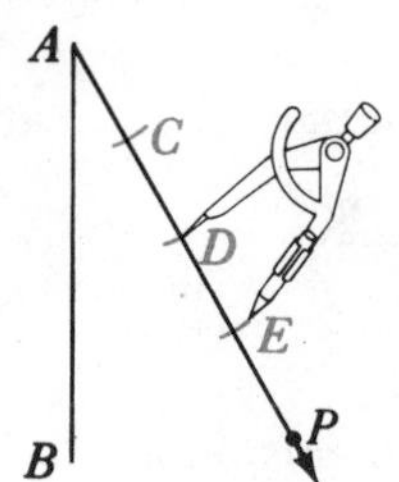	3. Join B and E. Construct parallels to $\overline{BE}$ through C and D. 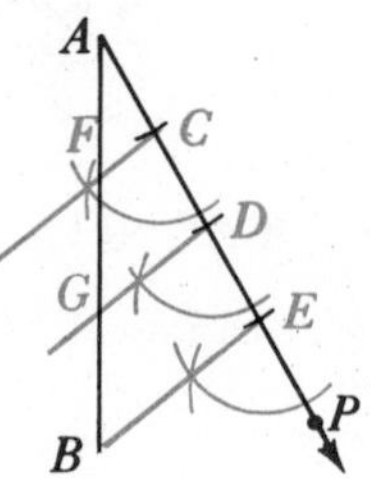

23–26. Refer to the construction above.

23. Why is $\overleftrightarrow{FC} \parallel \overleftrightarrow{GD} \parallel \overleftrightarrow{BE}$?

24. Why is $\overline{AF} \cong \overline{FG} \cong \overline{GB}$?

25. To separate $\overline{AB}$ into 4 congruent segments, what would you do in step 2?

26. How would you separate $\overline{AB}$ into 5 congruent segments?

27–28. Draw $\overline{MN}$ 10 cm long. Use the method above to do each exercise.

27. Separate $\overline{MN}$ into 3 congruent segments.

28. Separate $\overline{MN}$ into 5 congruent segments.

Ⓒ **29.** Cut a strip of unlined paper 6.5 by 27.5 cm. Then use the edge of a sheet of ruled paper to mark off seven strips of equal width each 27.5 cm long. HINT: See Exercises 21–22.

30. Prove that the length of the midline of a trapezoid is one half the sum of the lengths of the bases (see p. 154).

31–36. How does this Euler diagram illustrate each statement?

31. Every rectangle is a parallelogram.

32. Some parallelograms are rhombuses.

33. No trapezoid is a rectangle.

34. Every square is a rectangle.

35. Some rectangles are rhombuses.

36. No parallelogram is a trapezoid.

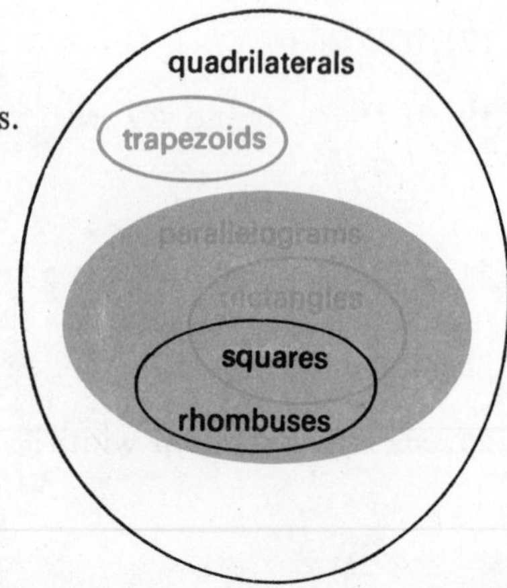

SHUT THE TRAPEZOID!

In the Andes mountains of southeastern Peru lie the ruins of the fortress-city Machu Picchu. This city and others nearby were built by the Incas, natives of the region, probably about five hundred years ago.

One of the surprising things about Machu Picchu is the way trapezoids were used in buildings—including trapezoid-shaped doors and windows.

Photos by David Mangurian

4.10 Transformations: Slides

A slide can be described by using an arrow to show how far each point slides (the **magnitude** of the slide) and in what **direction**.

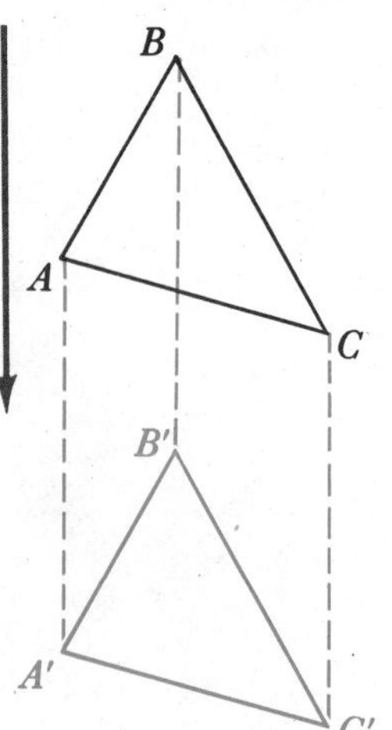

To draw the slide image of $\triangle ABC$:

1. From each vertex, draw a ray with the same direction as the arrow.
2. On each ray, measure off a segment with the same length as the arrow. (The points so located are A', B', and C', the images of A, B, and C.)
3. Join A', B', and C'. ($\triangle A'B'C'$ is the slide image of $\triangle ABC$.)

Since a slide preserves length, $\overline{AB} \cong \overline{A'B'}$. And since each point slides as far as each other point, $\overline{AA'} \cong \overline{BB'}$. Thus, quadrilateral $ABB'A'$ has opposite sides congruent, so it is a parallelogram.

The same reasoning would show that $BCC'B'$ and $ACC'A'$ are also parallelograms, so we can come to the following conclusions:

A line is parallel to its slide image (if they don't coincide). Segments joining points and their slide images are parallel.

You can see from the figure that the next statement is also justified.

Slides preserve orientation.

If you were to draw two parallel lines on a piece of paper and slide, flip, or turn the paper, you would probably decide that all three of these transformations preserve parallelism.

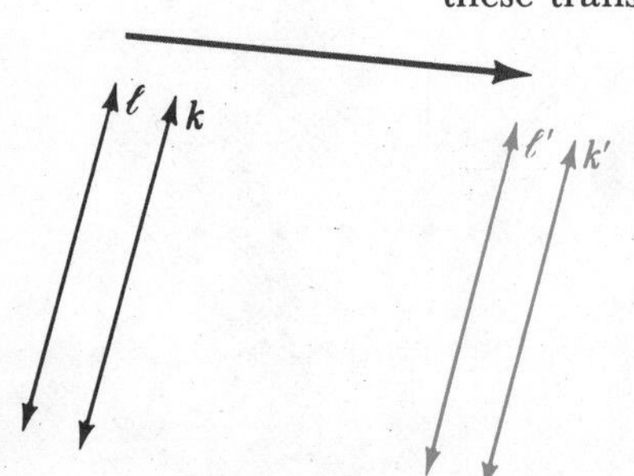

Consider the case in which ℓ and k are parallel and ℓ' and k' are slide images of ℓ and k. Since a line is parallel to its slide image, $\ell \parallel \ell'$ and $k \parallel k'$.

But $\ell \parallel k$, and a line parallel to one of two parallel lines is also parallel to the other. So $\ell' \parallel k$ and, finally, $\ell' \parallel k'$.

Slides preserve parallelism.

Exercises 4.10

Ⓐ **1.** An arrow can show the ______ and the ______ of a slide.

2. When would a line and its slide image coincide?

3–8. True or False?

3. Slides preserve length.

4. Slides reverse orientation.

5. Slides preserve parallelism.

6. Slides change angle measure.

7. A line is perpendicular to its slide image.

8. Slides preserve collinearity.

Ⓑ **9–12.** The arrow in the figure describes a slide. Copy the figure listed and draw the slide image.

9. $\triangle MOE$

10. $\triangle ONA$

11. trapezoid $NAME$

12. $\square LAME$

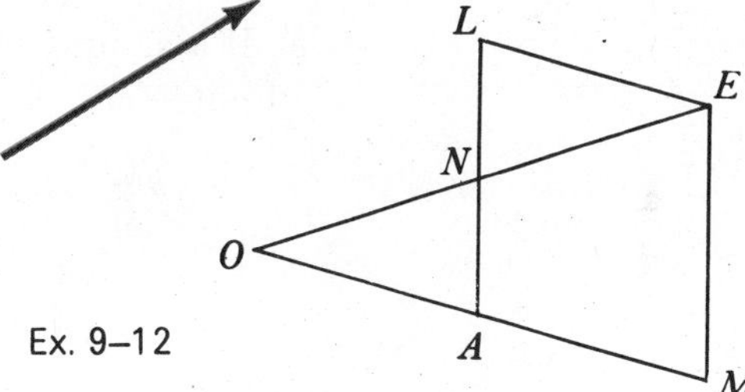

Ex. 9–12

13–14. Copy $\triangle ABC$ and point P. Then draw the slide image of $\triangle ABC$. HINT: First draw an arrow from the given vertex to P.

13. P is the image of B.

14. P is the image of C.

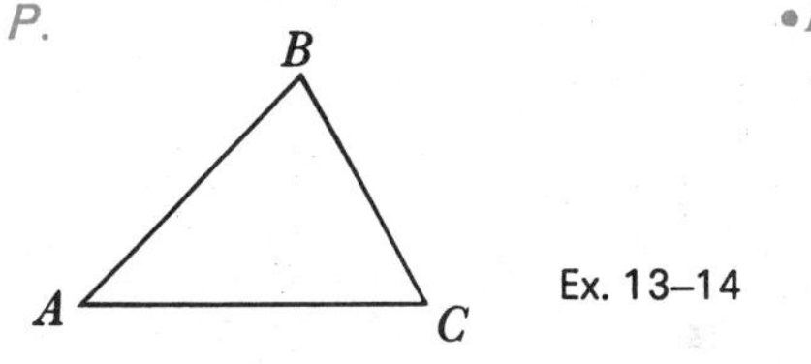

Ex. 13–14

15–18. Copy ℓ and t. Then draw the slide images of ℓ and t if P' is the image of P.

15. Is $\ell \parallel \ell'$? Why?

16. Are any angles at P and P' congruent? Why?

17. What theorem about corresponding angles does this suggest?

18. What theorem about alternate interior angles does this suggest?

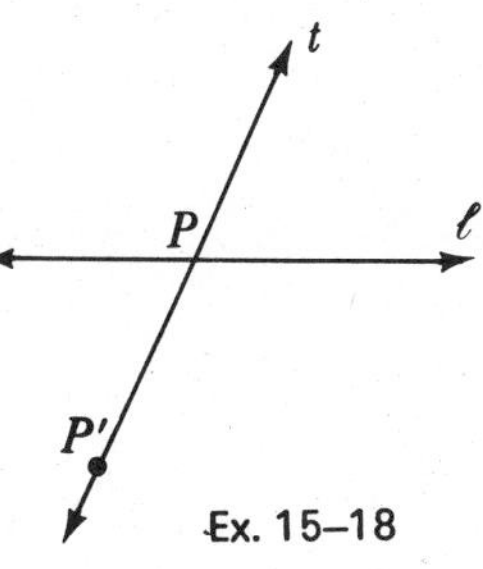

Ex. 15–18

Ⓒ **19–22.** Copy $\triangle ABC$ and point P used for Exercises 13–14.

19. Draw a line ℓ through P. Draw line k so $k \parallel \ell$ and the distance between ℓ and k is 8 cm.

20. Reflect $\triangle ABC$ over ℓ. Label the image $\triangle A'B'C'$.

21. Reflect $\triangle A'B'C'$ over k. Label the image $\triangle A''B''C''$.

22. How do $\triangle ABC$ and $\triangle A''B''C''$ appear to be related?

■ Chapter 4 Review ■

4.1 **1–4.** Correctly complete the sentence in as many ways as possible using

a. coplanar b. noncoplanar c. nonintersecting

1. Two parallel lines are ______.

2. Two skew lines are ______.

3. Two intersecting lines are ______.

4. In a plane, two lines perpendicular to a line ℓ are ______.

5. Point P is not on line k. Can two lines through P both be parallel to k? Why?

6. If assuming statement p is true leads to a contradiction of a true statement, then ______.

4.2 **7–20.** Refer to the figure below.

7. Using ℓ, k, and transversal r, name a pair of alternate interior angles.

8. If $\angle 1 \cong$ ______, then $\ell \parallel k$.

9. If $\ell \parallel k$, then $\angle 10 \cong$ ______.

4.3 **10.** $\angle 5$ and ______ are corresponding angles.

11. If $m\angle 4 + m$ ______ $= 180$, then $\ell \parallel k$.

12. If $\ell \parallel k$, then $m\angle 9 + m$ ______ $= 180$.

13. If $\ell \parallel k$ and $m\angle 9 = 90$, then $m\angle 8 =$ ______.

14. If $\ell \parallel k$ and $t \perp \ell$, then $t \perp$ ______.

15. If $\angle 3 \cong$ ______, then $\ell \parallel k$.

16. If $\ell \parallel k$, $\angle 6 \cong$ ______.

4.4 **17.** $m\angle 2 + m\angle 5 + m\angle 9 =$ ______

18. $m\angle 7 = m\angle 3 + m$ ______

19. If $\angle 9$ is obtuse, $\angle 2$ and $\angle 5$ are ______.

20. If $m\angle 9 = 90$, then $m\angle 5 + m\angle 2 =$ ______.

4.5 **21–28.** Which are always true for ▱$ABCD$? HINT: Draw a diagram.

21. $\overline{AB} \cong \overline{CD}$

22. $\triangle ABC \cong \triangle ADC$

23. $\angle A \cong \angle B$

24. $\angle D \cong \angle B$

25. $\overline{AC} \perp \overline{BD}$

26. $\overline{AC}$ bisects $\overline{BD}$.

27. $m\angle B + m\angle C = 180$

28. $\overline{BD}$ and $\overline{AC}$ bisect each other.

29–32. Which conditions make quadrilateral *MNOP* a parallelogram? **4.6**

29. $\overline{MN} \cong \overline{NO}$, $\overline{NO} \cong \overline{OP}$

30. $\overline{NO} \parallel \overline{PM}$, $\overline{NO} \cong \overline{PM}$

31. $\overline{MO}$ bisects $\overline{NP}$.

32. $MN = OP$, $NO = PM$

33–35. In the figure, *E* is the midpoint of $\overline{AB}$. **4.7**

33. If $AC = 8$, $ED =$ ______.

34. $\angle 3 \cong$ ______

35. $m\angle 2 + m\angle 3 =$ ______

36–40. Give another name for each figure. **4.8**

36. In ▱*MNPR*, $\overline{MN} \perp \overline{NP}$.

37. In ▱*MNPR*, $\overline{MN} \cong \overline{NP}$.

38. In rectangle *TREW*, $\overline{TR} \cong \overline{TW}$.

39. In ▱*GRAM*, $\overline{GA} \perp \overline{RM}$.

40. In rhombus *RHOM*, $m\angle M = 90$.

41. In the figure above, let $\overline{ED} \parallel \overline{AC}$. Why does $AE = EB$? **4.9**

42–44. In the figure, $n \parallel \ell$ and $\overleftrightarrow{AD}$ and $\overleftrightarrow{BC}$ intersect.

42. If $k \parallel n$ and $\overline{FC} \cong \overline{FB}$, then $\overline{AE} \cong$ ______.

43. *ABCD* is a ______.

44. If $AE = ED$ and $BF = FC$, then $\overline{AB} \parallel \overline{DC} \parallel$ ______ and $FE = \frac{1}{2}$______.

45–49. $\triangle P'D'T'$ is the slide image of $\triangle PDT$. **4.10**

45. The slide has ______ *PP′* and the same ______ as $\overrightarrow{PP'}$.

46. $\overline{PD} \parallel$ ______

47. $\overline{DD'} \parallel$ ______ $\parallel$ ______

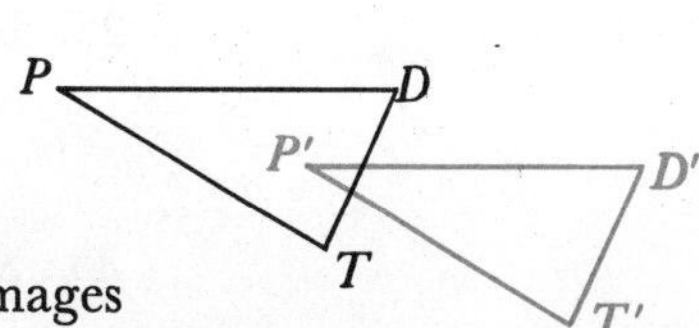

48. $\triangle PDT$ and $\triangle P'D'T'$ have (the same, opposite) orientation.

49. Segments joining the vertices of a triangle and their slide images (are, are not) parallel.

Chapter 4 Test

1. Coplanar nonintersecting lines are (parallel, skew).

2. The first step in (inductive, indirect) reasoning is to assume the opposite of what is to be proved.

3–16. In the figure, $\ell \parallel r$.

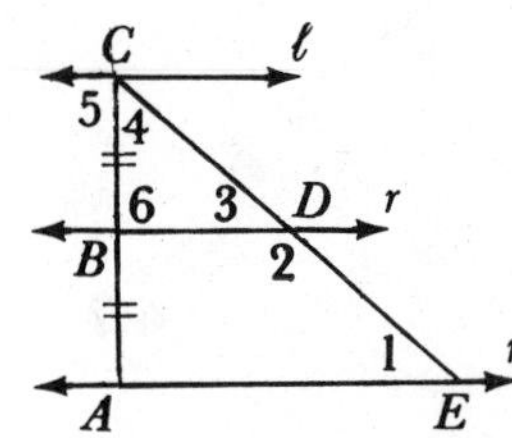

3. $\angle 5$ and $\angle 6$ are (corresponding, alternate interior) angles.

4. In quadrilateral *ABDE*, $\overline{AB}$ is a (diagonal, side).

5. If $\overline{CD} \cong \overline{DE}$, $\overline{BD}$ is the (median, midline) of $\triangle ACE$.

6. If $r \parallel n$, *ABDE* is a (parallelogram, trapezoid).

7. If $m\angle 5 = 87$,
m ______ $= 87$.

8. If $m\angle C_{45} = 130$,
m ______ $= 50$.

9. If $m\angle 1 = 55$ and
m ______ $= 55$, $r \parallel n$.

10. If $n \perp \overline{CA}$ and $m\angle 6 = 90$,
r ______ n.

11. If $m\angle 2 = 140$ and
$m\angle 4 = 50$, $m\angle 6 =$ ______.

12. If $m\angle 1 = 50$ and
m ______ $= 130$, $r \parallel n$.

13. If $r \parallel n$ and $DE = 6$,
______ $= 6$.

14. If $m\angle 6 = 90$,
$m\angle 3 + m\angle 4 =$ ______.

15. If $r \parallel n$ and $BD = 4$,
$AE =$ ______.

16. If $CD = 3$ and ______ $= 3$,
$r \parallel n$.

17–24. Complete the statement in as many ways as possible using

a. parallelogram **b.** rhombus **c.** rectangle **d.** square

17. If *ABCD* is a ______,
$\triangle ABC \cong \triangle CDA$.

18. If $\overline{AB} \parallel \overline{CD}$ and $\overline{AB} \cong \overline{CD}$,
ABCD is a ______.

19. If *ABCD* is a ______,
$\overline{AB} \cong \overline{BC}$.

20. If *ABCD* is a ______,
$\angle A \cong \angle B$.

21. In ▱*ABCD*, if $\overline{AB} \perp \overline{CB}$,
ABCD is a ______.

22. If $\overline{AC}$ and $\overline{BD}$ bisect each other, *ABCD* is a ______.

23. If *ABCD* is a ______,
$m\angle A + m\angle B = 180$.

24. If $\overline{AC}$ and $\overline{BD}$ bisect and
$\overline{AC} \perp \overline{BD}$, *ABCD* is a ______.

25. Slides (do, do not) preserve parallelism.

NARROW
BRIDGE

5 POLYGONS

Different types of traffic signs have different shapes. But the outline of each sign is roughly a *polygon*.

You have already worked with two important kinds of polygons — triangles and quadrilaterals. In this chapter, we introduce other kinds of polygons and continue the study of triangles and quadrilaterals.

STOP

5.1 What Are Polygons?

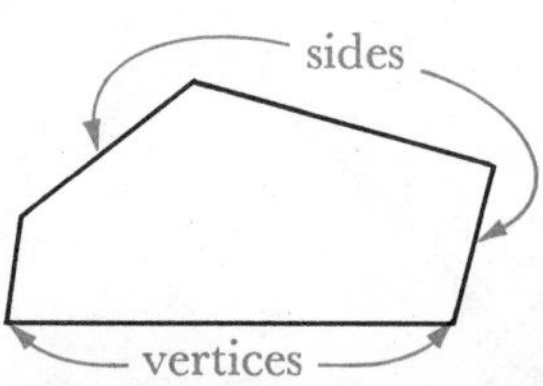

A **polygon** is a figure formed by joining three or more coplanar segments (called *sides*) at their endpoints (called *vertices*). The sides intersect at the vertices only, with each side intersecting exactly one other side at each vertex. Also, two sides with a common vertex are *not* collinear.

Polygons

Not Polygons

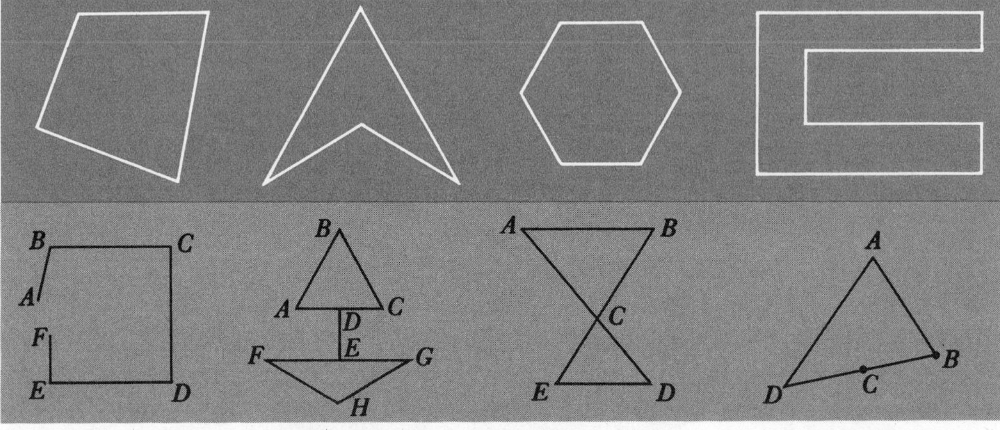

Sides $\overline{AB}$ and $\overline{EF}$ do not intersect another side at each of their endpoints.	Side $\overline{DE}$ does not intersect sides $\overline{AC}$ and $\overline{FG}$ at their endpoints.	Side $\overline{AC}$ intersects more than one side at vertex C.	Sides $\overline{CD}$ and $\overline{CB}$ are collinear. (Though $ABCD$ is not a four-sided polygon, ABD is a three-sided one.)

Notice	Comments
polygon *ABCDEF* or polygon *CBAFED*	Name a polygon by naming its vertices in order.
The *diagonals* that can be drawn from vertex A are $\overline{AC}$, $\overline{AD}$, and $\overline{AE}$.	**Diagonals** are segments with nonconsecutive vertices as endpoints.
The *interior* of this polygon is a *convex* set.	A polygon separates the plane into two parts, its **interior** and its **exterior**.
ABCDEF is a *convex polygon*.	A polygon is **convex** when its interior is a convex set.

Every triangle is a convex polygon, but polygons with more than three sides may or may not be convex.

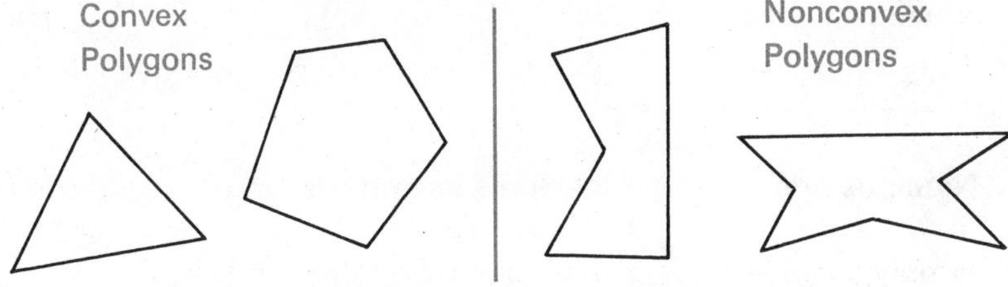

Types of Polygons

Name	Number of sides
triangle	3
quadrilateral	4
pentagon	5
hexagon	6
heptagon	7
octagon	8
nonagon	9
decagon	10
12-gon	12
28-gon	28
n-gon	n

Figures

triangle quadrilateral pentagon hexagon

heptagon octagon decagon 12-gon

Any polygon may be called an n-gon (where n is the number of sides). Common names for some polygons are listed above.

Exercises 5.1

Ⓐ **1–2.** Complete each statement with the best words possible.

1. A polygon is a figure formed by joining three or more ______ segments (called ______) at their endpoints (called ______).

2. The sides intersect at the ______ only. Each side intersects exactly ______ other side(s) at each vertex.

3–5. Is the given figure a polygon?

3.

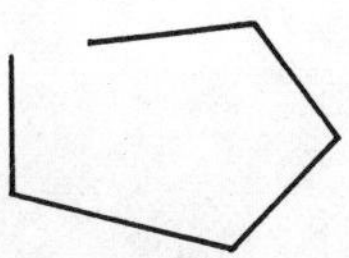

4.

5.

6. When is a polygon convex?

Ⓑ **7–10.** Use the polygon at the right.

7. Name its sides.

8. Name its vertices.

9. Is polygon *AMECIN* a name for this polygon? Why?

10. Name the diagonals that can be drawn from vertex *E*.

11–18. How many sides does each polygon have?

11. pentagon **12.** hexagon **13.** heptagon **14.** octagon

15. nonagon **16.** decagon **17.** 36-gon **18.** *n*-gon

19–22. Draw each type of polygon.

19. convex pentagon **20.** convex decagon

21. nonconvex hexagon **22.** nonconvex heptagon

23–26. For each convex polygon, draw all possible diagonals.

23. quadrilateral **24.** pentagon

25. hexagon **26.** heptagon

Ⓒ **27.** Without drawing, find how many diagonals are in these convex polygons: an octagon, a nonagon, and a 12-gon. HINT: Make a table of your answers for Exercises 23–26.

28. Identify the polygon that is the shape of each traffic sign on page 163.

29. Identify the polygons in each photo.

Rohn Engh/Van Cleve Photography

Van Cleve/Van Cleve Photography

Perimeter

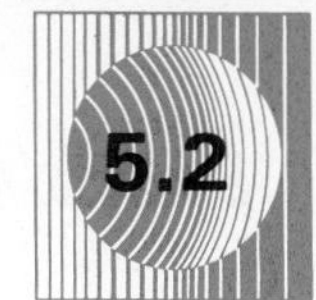

The **perimeter** of a polygon is the sum of the lengths of its sides. To find the perimeter P of polygon $ABCDE$, we add the lengths of the sides.

$$P = AB + BC + CD + DE + EA$$

$$P = 6 + 3 + 2 + 5\tfrac{1}{2} + 4 = 20\tfrac{1}{2}$$

The perimeter P of $ABCDE$ is $20\frac{1}{2}$.

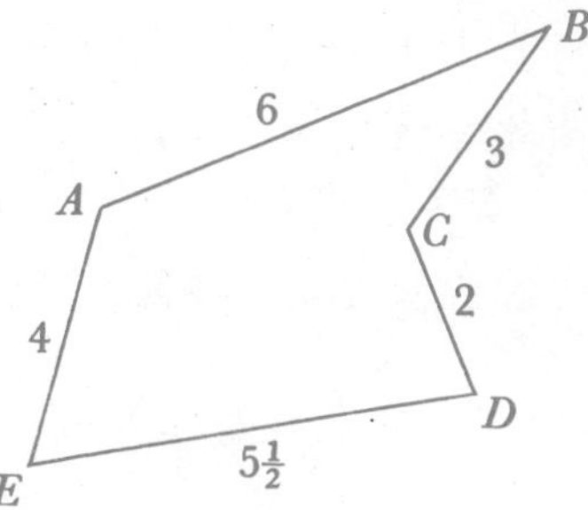

Consider $\square JKMN$ with $JK = MN$ and $KM = NJ$. For one pair of sides $JK = MN = b_1$, and for the other pair of sides $KM = NJ = b_2$.

M b_1 N
b_2 b_2
K b_1 J

$$P = JK + KM + MN + NJ$$

$$P = b_1 + b_2 + b_1 + b_2$$

$$P = 2b_1 + 2b_2$$

$$\boxed{P = 2(b_1 + b_2)}$$

Use the formula above to find the perimeter of any parallelogram.

Rectangle $RSTV$ is also a parallelogram. Suppose that b_1 is the length of $RSTV$ and b_2 is the width. To find the perimeter of a rectangle, we use this formula:

$$P = 2(b_1 + b_2)$$

Substituting $b_1 = \ell$ and $b_2 = w$ $\quad \boxed{P = 2(\ell + w)}$

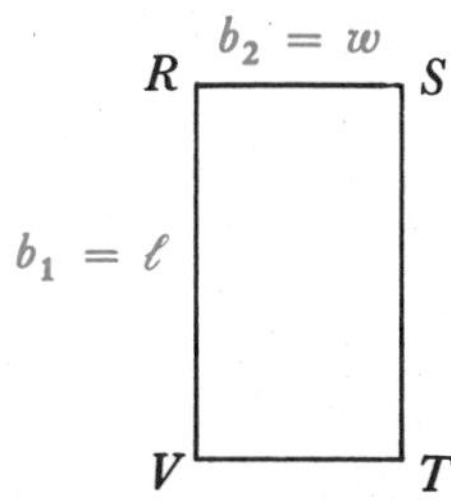

A **regular polygon** is a convex polygon that is *equiangular* (all angles congruent) and *equilateral* (all sides congruent).

square

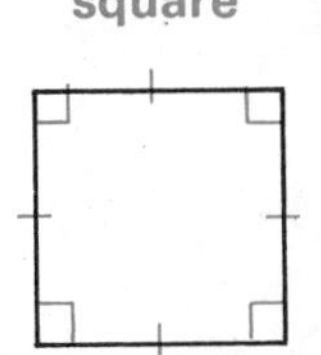

regular polygon

rectangle

equiangular polygon

rhombus

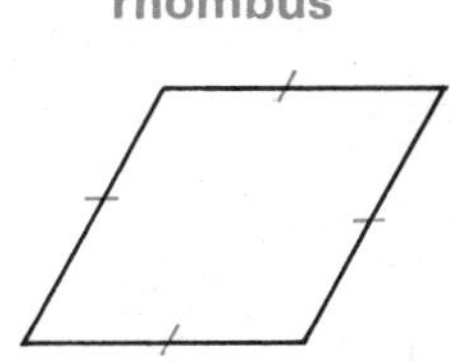

equilateral polygon

Consider any regular polygon with n sides. Each side has the same length s. To find the perimeter, multiply the length of one side by the number of sides.

$$\boxed{P = ns}$$

Exercises 5.2

Ⓐ **1.** Define *perimeter* of a polygon.

2–4. Identify each variable in the following formulas:

2. $P = 2(b_1 + b_2)$ **3.** $P = 2(\ell + w)$ **4.** $P = ns$

5. Define *regular polygon.* **6.** Define *equilateral polygon.*

Ⓑ **7–10.** Find the perimeter of each of the following:

7.

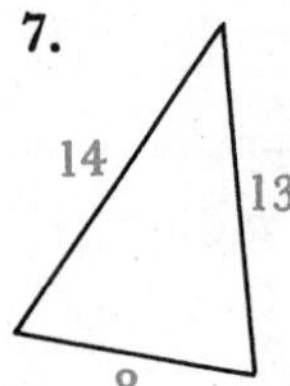

8.

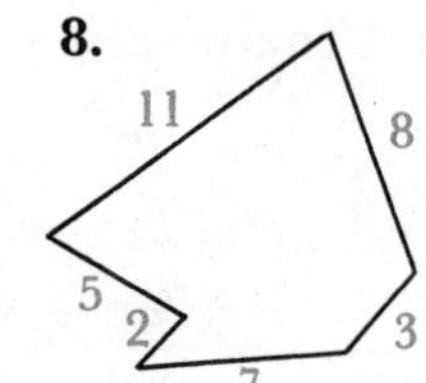

9.

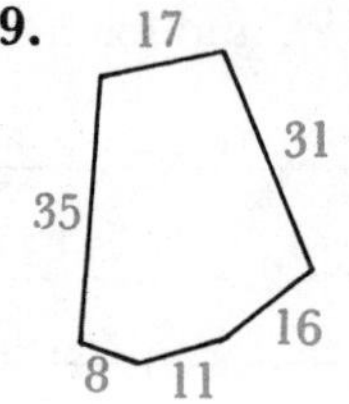

10.

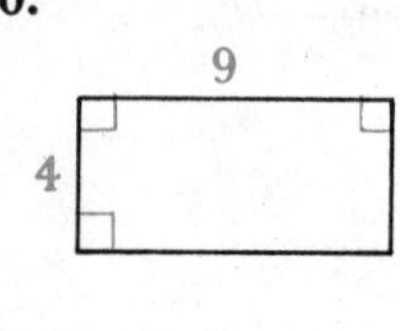

11–14. Find the perimeter of each parallelogram with sides of the given lengths.

11. 12 cm, 6 cm **12.** 8 m, 7.3 m

13. 2.1 km, 3 km **14.** 13 km, 8 km

15–18. Use the given information to find the perimeter of each rectangle.

15. $\ell = 18$ m, $w = 2$ m **16.** $\ell = 5.2$ cm, $w = 7.9$ cm

17. $\ell = x$, $w = 4x$ **18.** $\ell = 5$, $w = 7 + 2y$

19–20. Measure the sides and angles of each figure. Is it a regular polygon? Why or why not?

19.

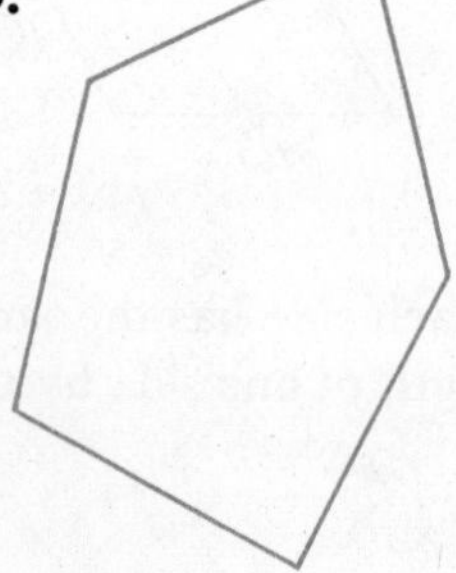

20.

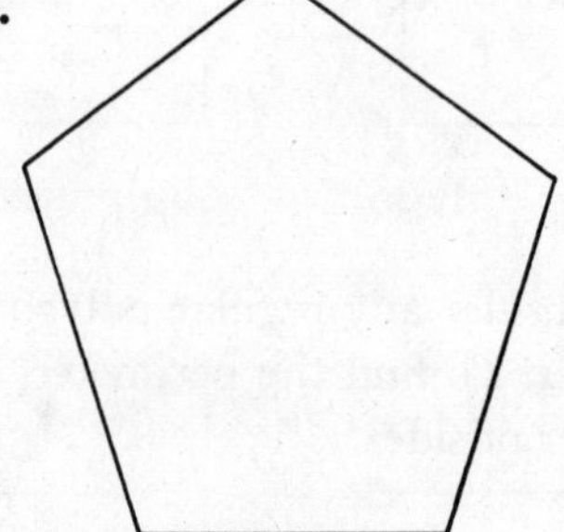

21–24. Use the given information to find the perimeter of each regular polygon (s = length of a side).

21. hexagon, $s = 4$ cm

22. decagon, $s = 2.6$ m

23. pentagon, $s = 7 + 8x$

24. nonagon, $s = 4w$

© **25.** How many meters of fencing are needed for this tennis-court area?

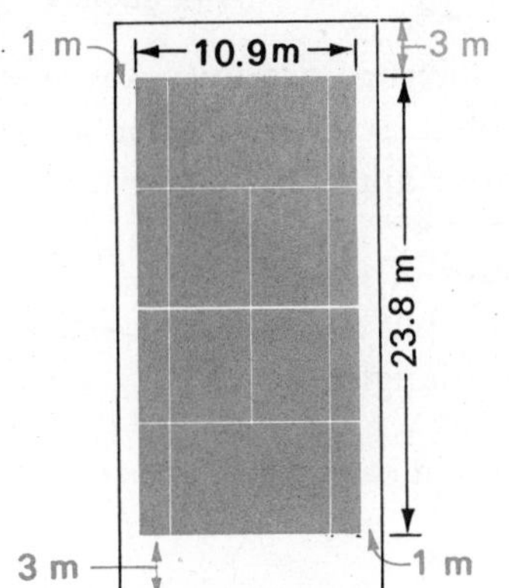

26. What is the perimeter of the Mescalero Apache Indian Reservation in Arizona, shown below?

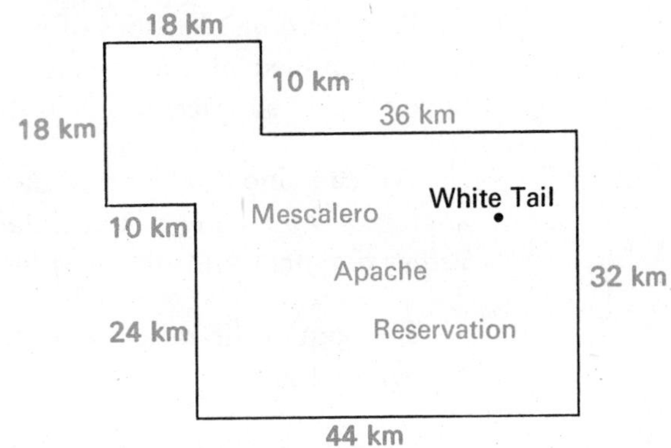

27. Find the perimeter of a rhombus with sides of the given length.

a. 5 m **b.** 12 cm **c.** r

28. Using your answer to Exercise 27, state a formula for the perimeter of a rhombus.

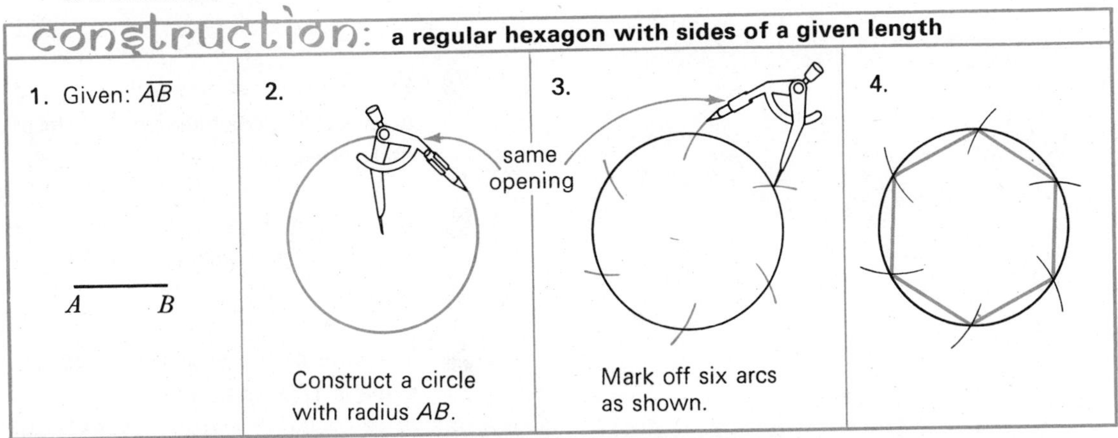

construction: a regular hexagon with sides of a given length
1. Given: $\overline{AB}$
A B
2.
same
opening
Construct a circle
with radius AB.
3.
Mark off six arcs
as shown.
4.

29–30. Construct a regular hexagon with sides of the given length.

29. ______________________

30. ______________

Angles of Convex Polygons

For any convex polygon, each pair of consecutive sides determines an **angle** of the polygon. These angles are also called **interior angles.**

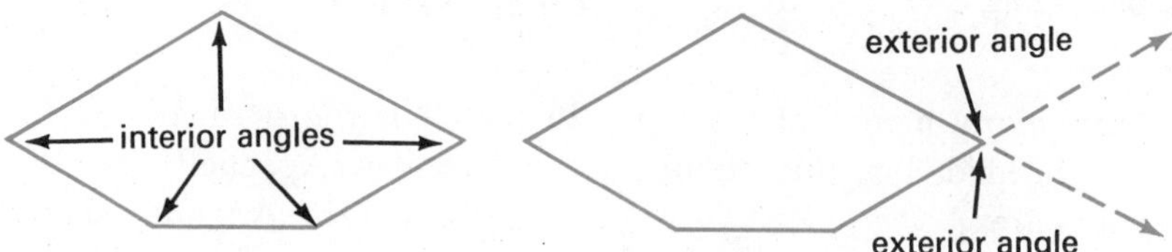

By extending the sides of a convex polygon, two **exterior angles** are determined at each vertex. Each of these two exterior angles is adjacent and supplementary to the interior angle at that vertex.

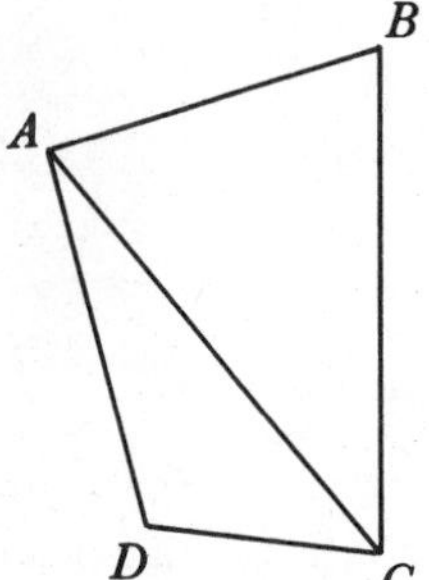

We can find the sum of the measures of the angles of any convex quadrilateral as follows. Either diagonal and the sides form two triangles.

The sum of the measures of the angles in each triangle is 180.

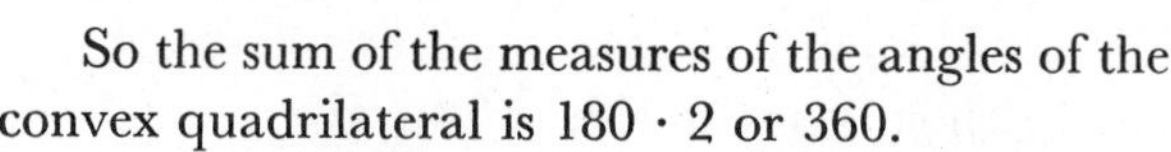

So the sum of the measures of the angles of the convex quadrilateral is $180 \cdot 2$ or 360.

Using a similar procedure, you can find the sum of the measures of the interior angles of any convex polygon. (For convenience, in the rest of this section we'll shorten *sum of the measures of the angles* to *sum of the angles.*)

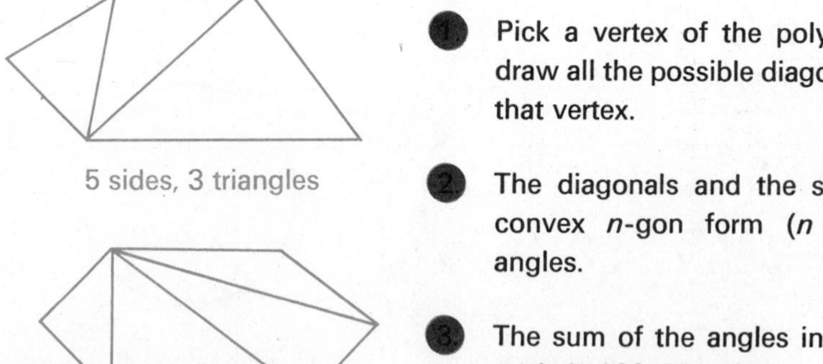

5 sides, 3 triangles

6 sides, 4 triangles

1. Pick a vertex of the polygon, and draw all the possible diagonals from that vertex.
2. The diagonals and the sides of a convex n-gon form $(n - 2)$ triangles.
3. The sum of the angles in each triangle is 180. Therefore,

sum of interior angles of a convex polygon with n sides $= 180 \cdot (n - 2)$

Remember that $(n - 2)$ is the number of triangles.

Once you know the sum of the interior angles of a convex polygon, you can find the sum of the exterior angles, *one* at each vertex. The sum of the interior angle and one exterior angle at each vertex is 180. So the sum of the interior angles and exterior angles (one at each vertex) of a polygon is 180 times the number of vertices (or sides). We find the sum of the exterior angles as follows:

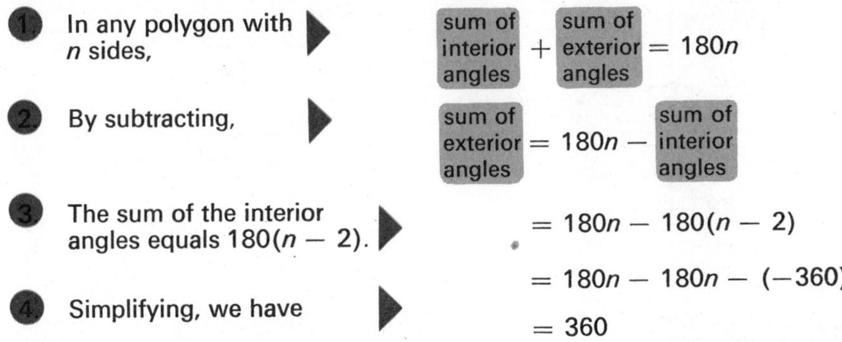

1. In any polygon with n sides,
sum of interior angles + sum of exterior angles = 180n
2. By subtracting,
sum of exterior angles = 180n − sum of interior angles
3. The sum of the interior angles equals 180(n − 2).
= 180n − 180(n − 2)
= 180n − 180n − (−360)
4. Simplifying, we have
= 360

In a regular polygon, all the interior angles are congruent. The exterior angles are also congruent, since supplements of congruent angles are congruent. Therefore, for regular polygons, we can write formulas for finding the measure of *each* interior or exterior angle.

$$\text{Measure of each interior angle of a regular } n\text{-gon} = \frac{180(n-2)}{n}$$

$180(n - 2)$ ← sum of all interior angles; n ← number of congruent angles

$$\text{Measure of each exterior angle of a regular } n\text{-gon} = \frac{360}{n}$$

360 ← sum of all exterior angles; n ← number of congruent angles

Exercises 5.3

Ⓐ **1–2.** Answer questions **a–d** for each polygon.

1.

A

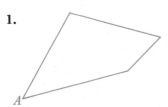

2.

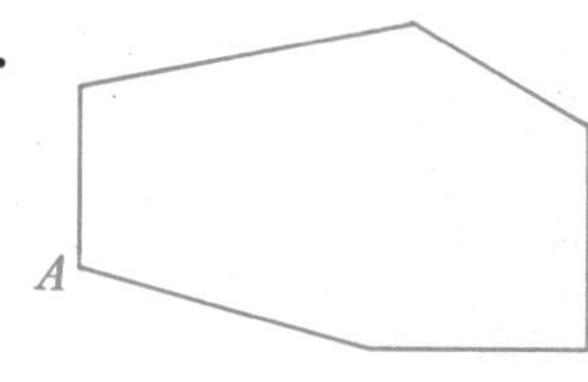

a. How many diagonals can be drawn from point *A*?

b. How many triangles are formed?

c. What is the sum of the interior angles?

d. What is the sum of the exterior angles, one at each vertex?

Ⓑ **3–16.** Copy and complete the table.

	Convex polygon	Number of sides	Number of triangles	Sum of interior angles	Sum of exterior angles
3.	triangle				
4.		4			
5.	pentagon				
6.			4		
7.		7			
8.			6		
9.	nonagon				
10.	10-gon				
11.		12			
12.			15		
13.				3240	
14.				3600	
15.				6120	
16.				9000	

17–18. Four of the angle measures in a convex pentagon are given. Find the measure of the fifth angle.

17. 70, 120, 80, 92

18. 150, 148, 93, 76

19–20. Five of the angle measures in a convex hexagon are given. Find the measure of the sixth angle.

19. 150, 148, 137, 81, 76

20. 43, 78, 148, 160, 151

21–22. For these polygons, measure the angles. Find the sum of (a) the interior angles and (b) the exterior angles, one at each vertex.

21.

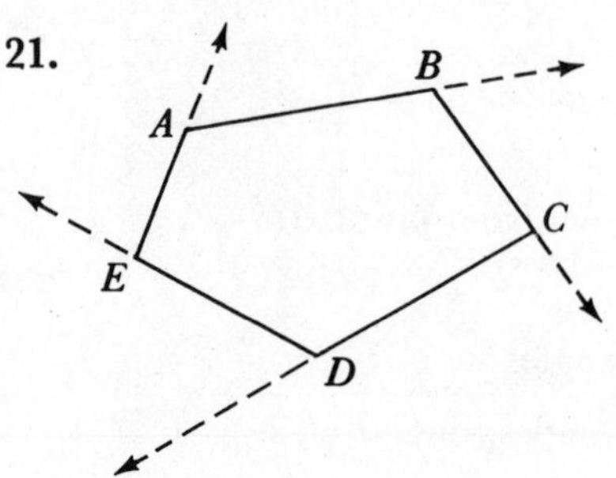

22.

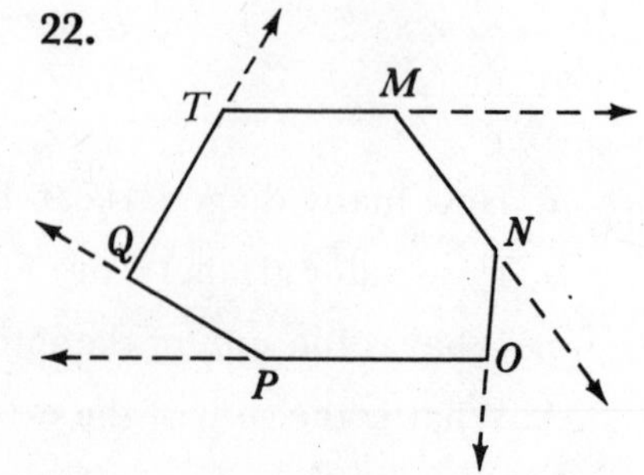

23–36. Copy and complete the table.

	Regular polygon	Number of sides	Measure of each interior angle	Measure of each exterior angle
23.		3		
24.		4		
25.	pentagon			
26.	hexagon			
27.		7		
28.		8		
29.	nonagon			
30.		10		
31.	50-gon			
32.	100-gon			
33.			150	
34.			168	
35.				20
36.				8

37–40. Draw each regular polygon. HINT: Use a protractor to draw interior angles of the proper measure.

37. pentagon: side 6 cm

38. hexagon: side 4 cm

39. octagon: side 45 mm

40. pentagon: side 5 cm

Ⓒ **41.** *Construct:* a regular quadrilateral with a side of length 2 cm

42. *Construct:* a regular octagon with a side of length 2 cm

HINT:

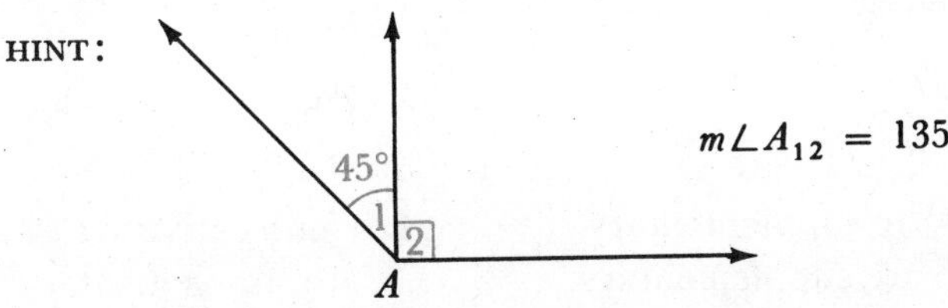

$m\angle A_{12} = 135$

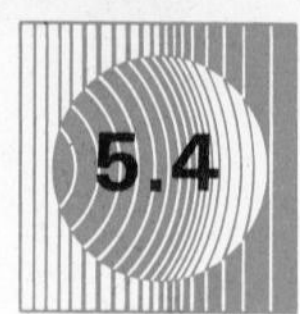

5.4 Congruent Polygons

Harrison

Congruent polygons are two polygons that have all parts (sides and angles) of one polygon congruent to the corresponding parts of the other. As with congruent triangles, there is a one-to-one correspondence between the vertices of congruent polygons.

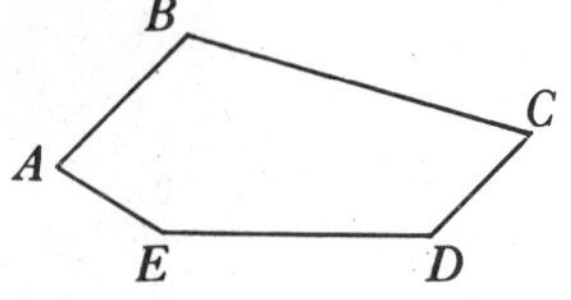

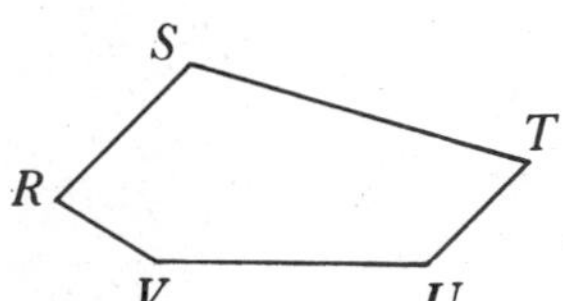

corresponding angles → | ← corresponding sides

$ABCDE \cong RSTUV$	
$\angle A$ and $\angle R$	$\overline{AB}$ and $\overline{RS}$
$\angle B$ and $\angle S$	$\overline{BC}$ and $\overline{ST}$
$\angle C$ and $\angle T$	$\overline{CD}$ and $\overline{TU}$
$\angle D$ and $\angle U$	$\overline{DE}$ and $\overline{UV}$
$\angle E$ and $\angle V$	$\overline{AE}$ and $\overline{RV}$

For certain special polygons we can tell whether they are congruent without knowing that all corresponding parts are congruent.

SAS Theorem for Parallelograms

Side-Angle-Side Theorem for Parallelograms: If two consecutive sides and the angle they determine of one parallelogram are congruent to the corresponding parts of another parallelogram, then the parallelograms are congruent.

Given: $\overline{AD} \cong \overline{WZ}$, $\overline{DC} \cong \overline{ZY}$, $\angle D \cong \angle Z$

Prove: $\square ABCD \cong \square WXYZ$

[*Plan:* Use properties of parallelograms and parallel lines to show that all corresponding sides and angles are congruent.]

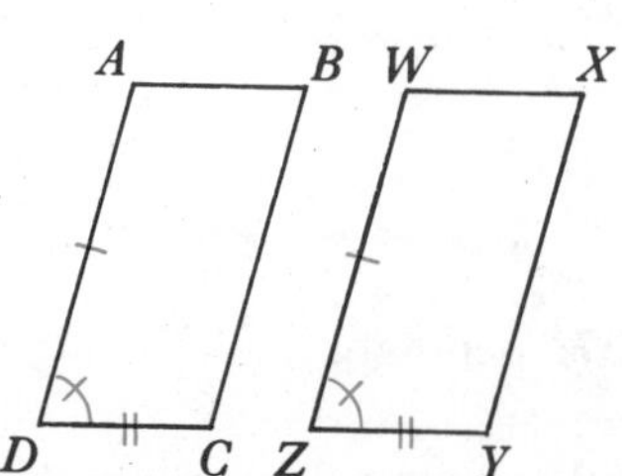

Proof:

STATEMENTS	REASONS
1. $\overline{AD} \cong \overline{WZ}$, $\overline{DC} \cong \overline{ZY}$, $\angle D \cong \angle Z$	1. Given
2. $\overline{AD} \cong \overline{BC}$, $\overline{DC} \cong \overline{AB}$, $\overline{WZ} \cong \overline{XY}$, $\overline{ZY} \cong \overline{WX}$	2. Opposite sides of a $\square$ are $\cong$.
3. $\overline{BC} \cong \overline{WZ}$, $\overline{AB} \cong \overline{ZY}$, $\overline{BC} \cong \overline{XY}$, $\overline{AB} \cong \overline{WX}$	3. Segments $\cong$ to the same segment are $\cong$.
4. $\angle A$ and $\angle D$ are supplementary, $\angle W$ and $\angle Z$ are supplementary.	4. Consecutive $\angle$s of a $\square$ are supplementary.

5. $\angle A \cong \angle W$	5. Two angles supp. to $\cong$ $\angle$s are $\cong$.
6. $\angle D \cong \angle B$, $\angle A \cong \angle C$, $\angle Z \cong \angle X$, $\angle W \cong \angle Y$	6. Opp. $\angle$s of a ▱ are $\cong$.
7. $\angle B \cong \angle Z$, $\angle C \cong \angle W$ $\angle B \cong \angle X$, $\angle C \cong \angle Y$	7. $\angle$s $\cong$ to the same angle are $\cong$.
8. ▱$ABCD \cong$ ▱$WXYZ$	8. Definition of congruent polygons

Exercises 5.4

Ⓐ **1.** Define *congruent polygons.*

2–3. Name the corresponding parts of the congruent polygons.

2.

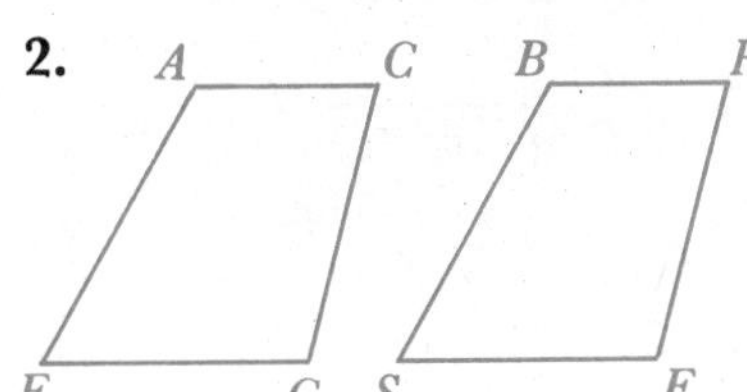

3.

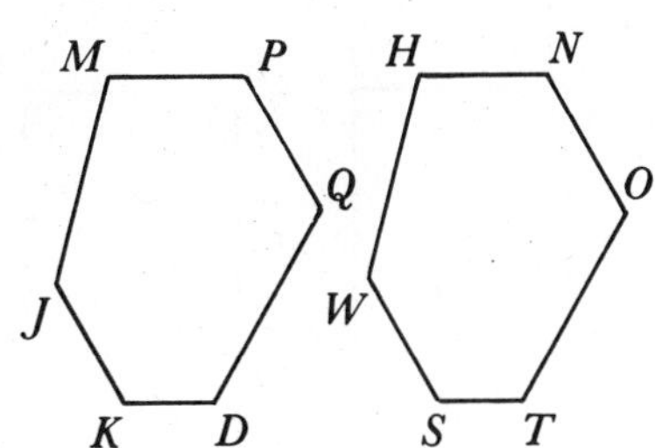

4–6. Corresponding congruent parts are marked.
Is each pair of parallelograms congruent? Why?

4.

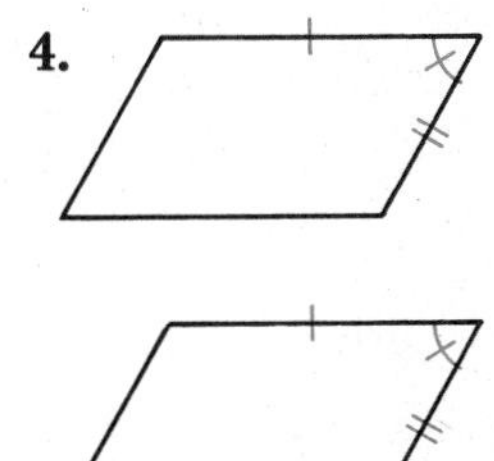

5.

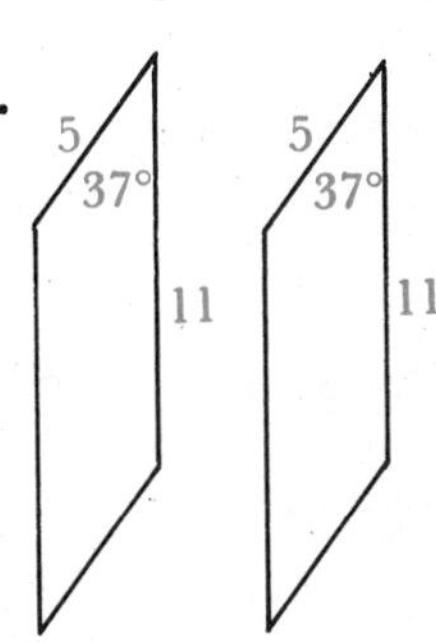

6.

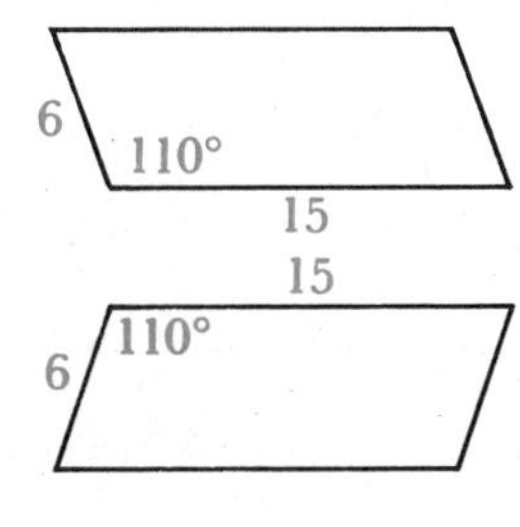

Ⓑ **7–14.** *RELYZA* $\cong$ *MOSNPD*, find:

7. MO **8.** LE **9.** RA

10. YZ **11.** $m\angle O$ **12.** $m\angle A$

13. $m\angle Y$ **14.** $m\angle Z$

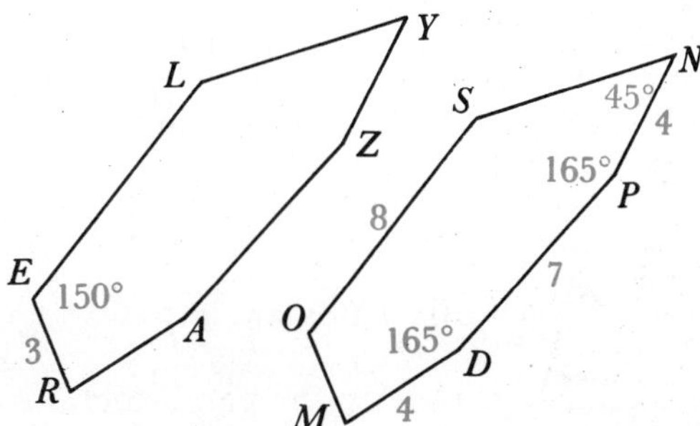

15. Given: $\square ABCD$, $\square EFGH$,
$\angle A \cong \angle E$, $\overline{AB} \cong \overline{EF}$, $\overline{BC} \cong \overline{FG}$

Prove: $\square ABCD \cong \square EFGH$

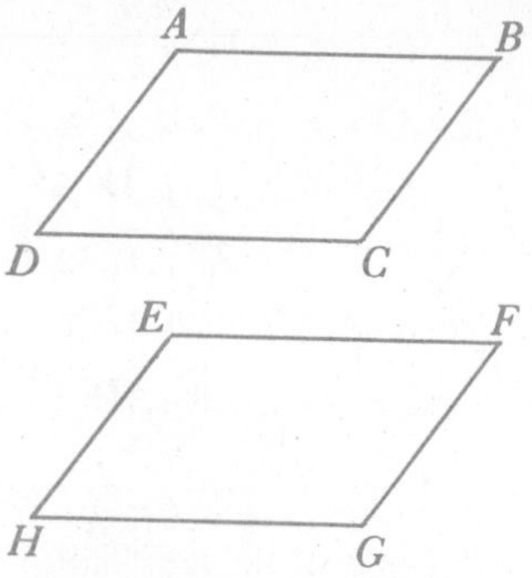

16. Given: $\square ABCD$, $\square EFGH$,
$\overline{BC} \cong \overline{FG}$, $\overline{EF} \cong \overline{DC}$, $\angle A \cong \angle E$

Prove: $\square ABCD \cong \square EFGH$

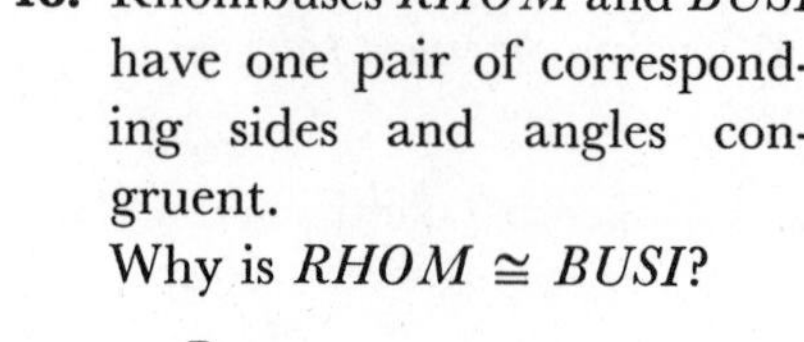

© 17. Rectangles *MEZO* and *BDAF* have two pairs of corresponding consecutive sides congruent. Why is $MEZO \cong BDAF$?

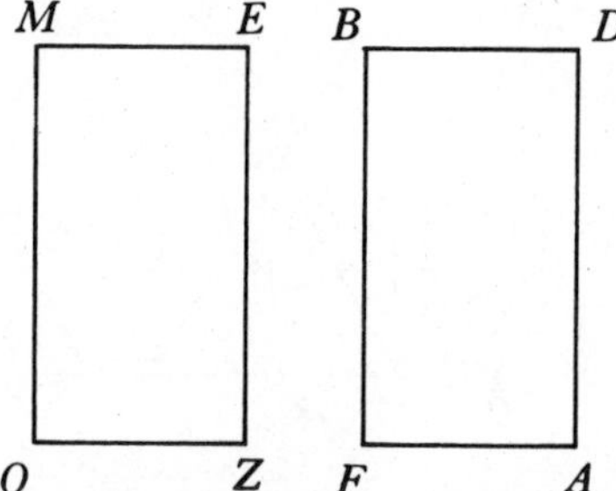

18. Rhombuses *RHOM* and *BUSI* have one pair of corresponding sides and angles congruent. Why is $RHOM \cong BUSI$?

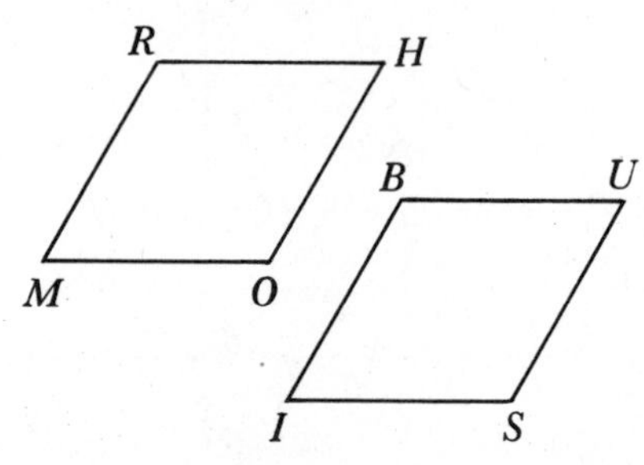

Quick Quiz for Sections 5.1 to 5.4

1–3. Define these terms.

1. *polygon* 2. *convex polygon* 3. *equilateral polygon*

4–9. Find the following:

4. perimeter of a regular hexagon with a side of length 3
5. perimeter of a parallelogram with sides of lengths 5 and 7
6. sum of the interior angles of a convex hexagon
7. sum of the exterior angles, one at each vertex, of a convex heptagon
8. measure of each interior angle of a regular octagon
9. measure of each exterior angle of a regular 12-gon

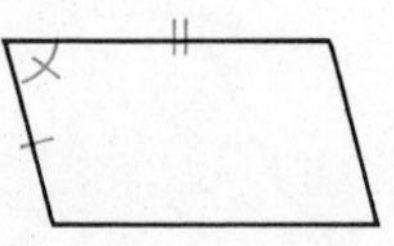

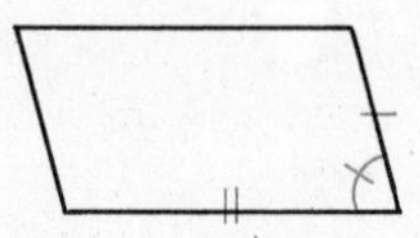

10. When are any two regular hexagons congruent polygons?
11. Are the parallelograms at the left congruent? Why?

PRACTICAL POLYGONS

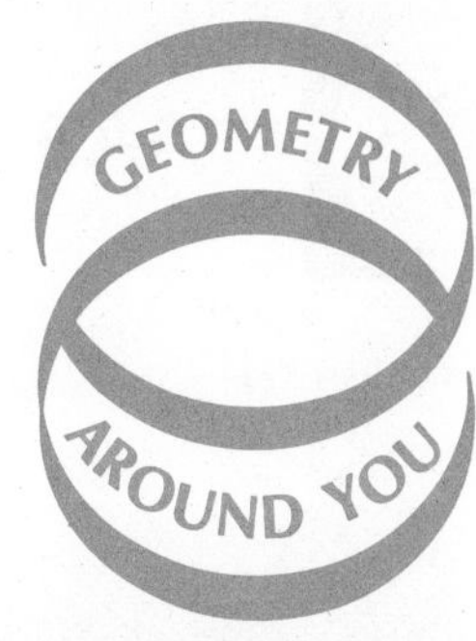

The congruent polygons shown here are used in industry, buildings, and designs.

Authenticated News International

Marimekko

Courtesy Burroughs Wellcome Company

5.5 AAS Theorem

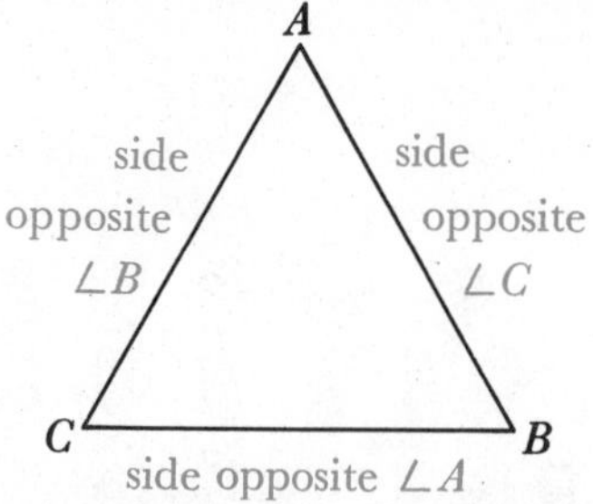

We now return to the study of congruent triangles that was begun in Chapter 3.

In any triangle, each side is **opposite** one of the angles.

AAS Theorem

Angle-Angle-Side Theorem: In a triangle, if two angles and the side opposite one of them are congruent to the corresponding parts of another triangle, then the triangles are congruent.

Given: $\overline{AB} \cong \overline{DE}$, $\angle C \cong \angle F$, $\angle A \cong \angle D$

Prove: $\triangle ABC \cong \triangle DEF$

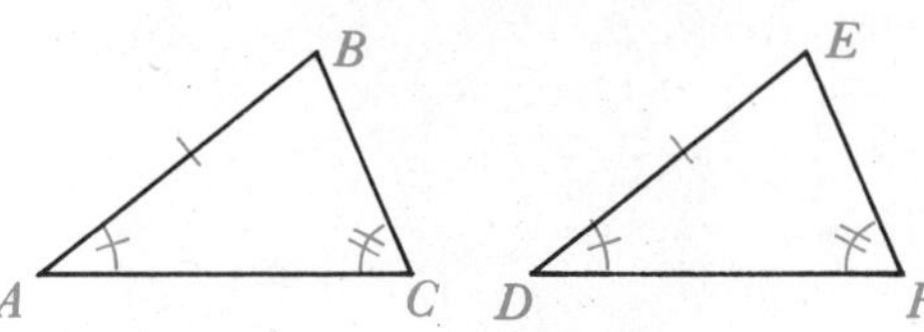

Proof:

STATEMENTS	REASONS
1. $\angle C \cong \angle F$, $\angle A \cong \angle D$	1. Given
2. $\angle B \cong \angle E$	2. If two angles of a △ are ≅ to two ∠s of another △, the remaining ∠s are ≅.
3. $\overline{AB} \cong \overline{DE}$	3. Given
4. $\triangle ABC \cong \triangle DEF$	4. ASA Postulate

Exercises 5.5

Ⓐ **1–4.** Corresponding congruent parts are marked. Tell which postulate (from Chapter 3) or theorem (AAS) can be used to prove the triangles congruent.

1.

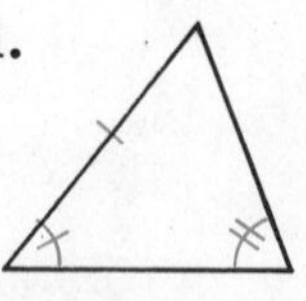

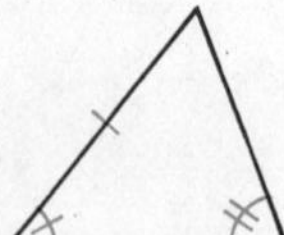

2.

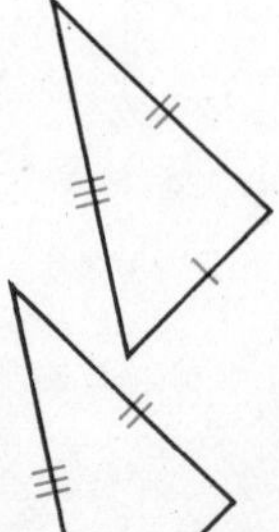

3.

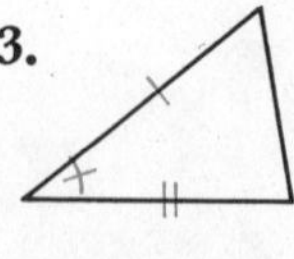

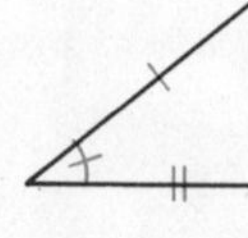

4.

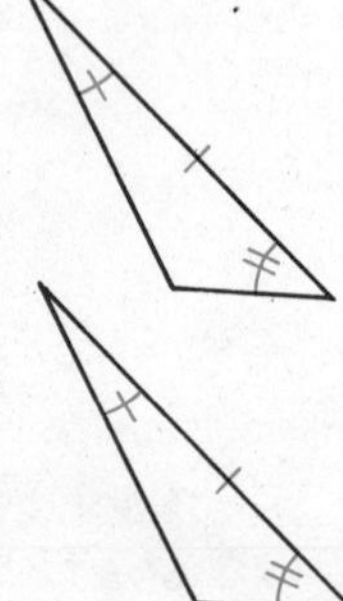

Ⓑ **5–10.** Using the given information, which postulate or theorem can be used to prove $\triangle NAR \cong \triangle NAI$? Remember $\overline{AN} \cong \overline{AN}$.

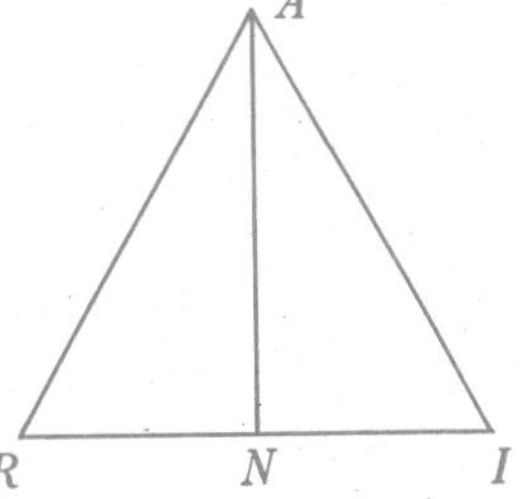

5. $\angle RNA$, $\angle INA$ right angles, $\angle R \cong \angle I$

6. $\angle RNA \cong \angle INA$, $\overrightarrow{AN}$ the bisector of $\angle RAI$

7. $\angle RNA \cong \angle INA$, $\overline{NR} \cong \overline{NI}$

8. $\overline{RA} \cong \overline{IA}$, $\overline{RN} \cong \overline{IN}$

9. $\angle R \cong \angle I$, $\overrightarrow{AN}$ the bisector of $\angle RAI$

10. $\overline{AR} \cong \overline{AI}$, $m\angle RAN = m\angle IAN$

11–20. Give a reason for each statement.

Given: $\overline{AE}$ bisects $\overline{ST}$ at K. $\angle E \cong \angle A$

Prove: $\triangle SKE \cong \triangle TKA$

Proof:

STATEMENTS	REASONS
1. $\overline{AE}$ bisects $\overline{ST}$ at K.	1. **11.**
2. $\overline{SK} \cong \overline{KT}$	2. **12.**
3. $\angle SKE \cong \angle TKA$	3. **13.**
4. $\angle E \cong \angle A$	4. **14.**
5. $\triangle SKE \cong \triangle TKA$	5. **15.**

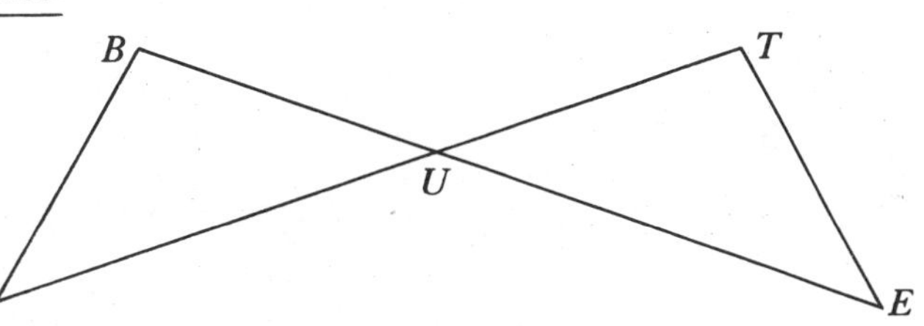

Given: $\overline{BU} \cong \overline{TU}$, $\angle BRU \cong \angle TEU$, $\overline{BE}$ and $\overline{TR}$ intersect at U.

Prove: $\overline{UR} \cong \overline{UE}$

Proof:

STATEMENTS	REASONS
1. $\overline{BU} \cong \overline{TU}$	1. **16.**
2. $\angle BRU \cong \angle TEU$	2. **17.**
3. $\angle BUR \cong \angle TUE$	3. **18.**
4. $\triangle BUR \cong \triangle TUE$	4. **19.**
5. $\overline{UR} \cong \overline{UE}$	5. **20.**

Ⓒ **21.** Given: $\angle D \cong \angle E$, $\angle DIM \cong \angle EIM$

Prove: $\overline{DM} \cong \overline{EM}$

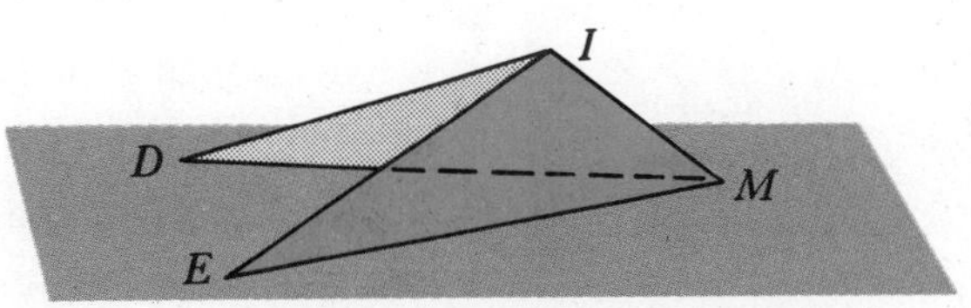

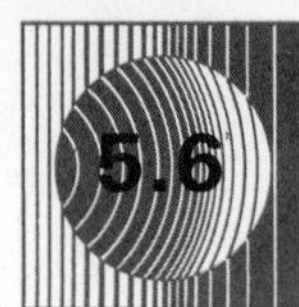

Isosceles Triangles and Trapezoids

Some triangles are given special names because of their sides or angles.

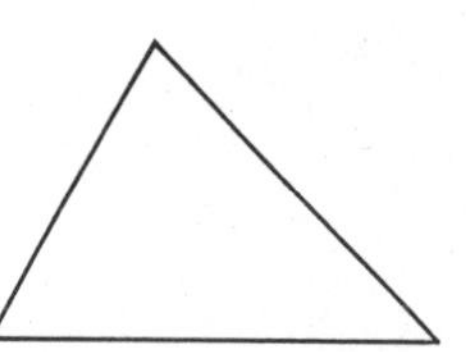
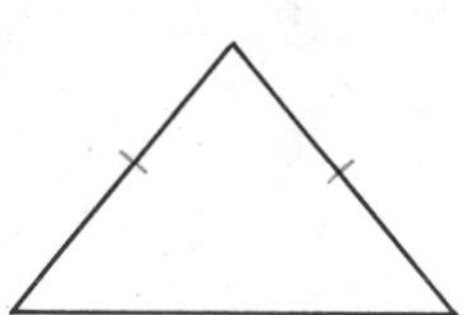
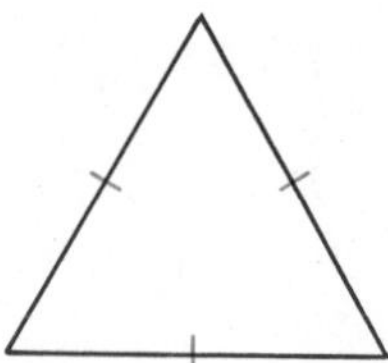

Triangles named according to their sides	**scalene triangle:** no congruent sides	**isosceles triangle:** at least two congruent sides	**equilateral triangle:** three congruent sides

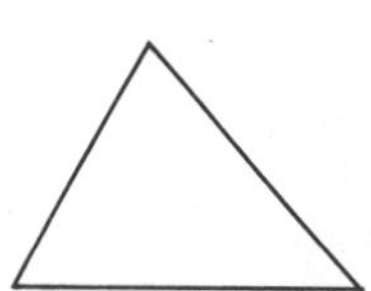
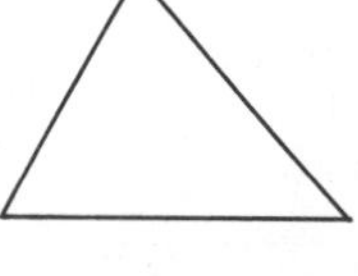
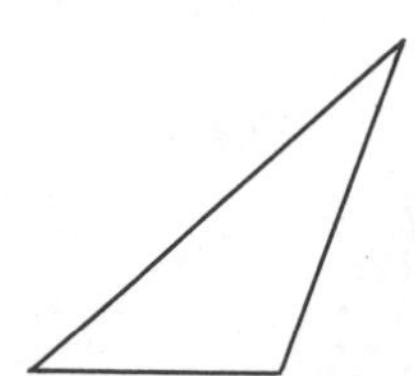
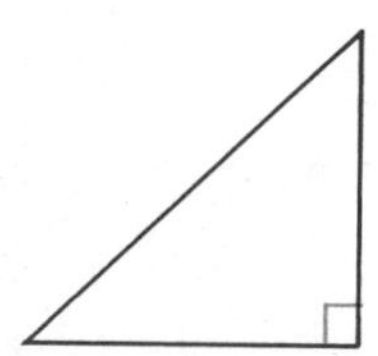
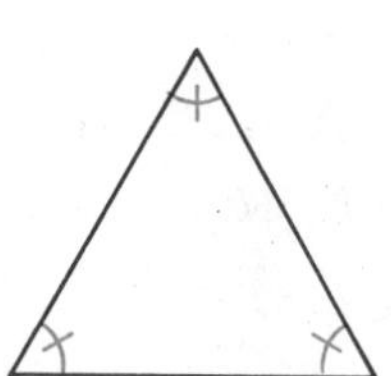

Triangles named according to their angles	**acute triangle:** three acute angles	**obtuse triangle:** exactly one obtuse angle	**right triangle:** exactly one right angle	**equiangular triangle:** three congruent angles

An **isosceles trapezoid** is a trapezoid whose nonparallel sides are congruent. The parts of isosceles triangles and isosceles trapezoids have similar names.

Isosceles triangle

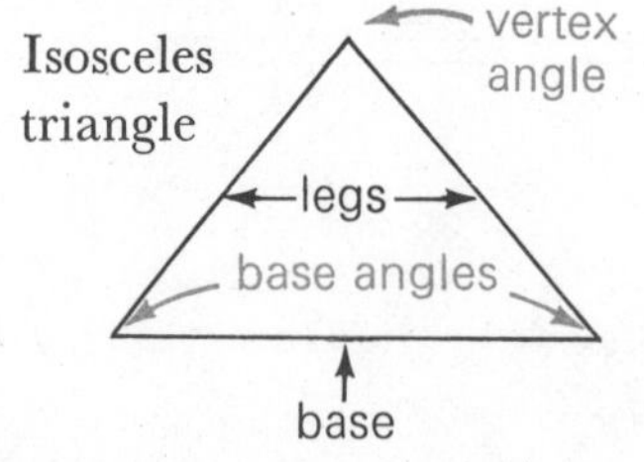

Isosceles trapezoid

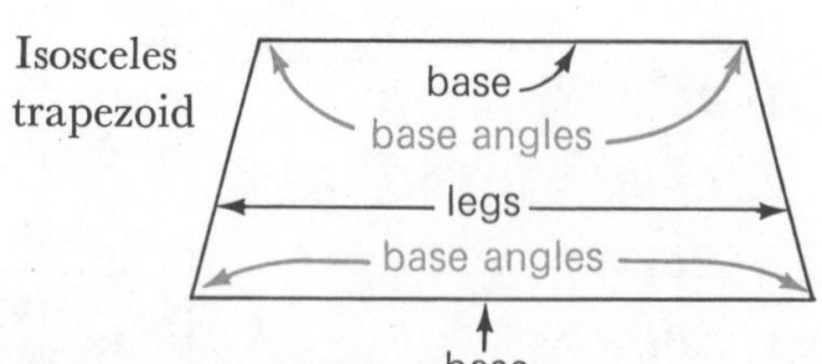

Isosceles Triangle Theorem

a. If two sides of a triangle are congruent, the angles opposite those sides are congruent.

b. If two angles of a triangle are congruent, the sides opposite those angles are congruent.

Part **a** of this theorem is often stated as follows: *Base angles of an isosceles triangle are congruent.* The proof of part **a** follows. Part **b** (the converse of part **a**) is proved in Exercises 31–36.

Given: $\overline{AC} \cong \overline{BC}$

Prove: $\angle A \cong \angle B$

[*Plan:* Use the bisector of $\angle ACB$ as an auxiliary ray. Prove $\triangle ACM \cong \triangle BCM$.]

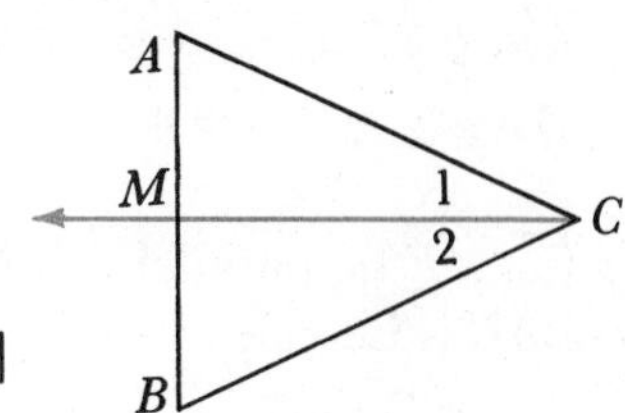

Proof:

STATEMENTS	REASONS
1. Let $\overrightarrow{CM}$ be the bisector of $\angle ACB$.	**1.** Every angle has a bisector.
2. $\angle 1 \cong \angle 2$	**2.** Definition of angle bisector
3. $\overline{AC} \cong \overline{BC}$	**3.** Given
4. $\overline{MC} \cong \overline{MC}$	**4.** A segment is $\cong$ to itself.
5. $\triangle ACM \cong \triangle BCM$	**5.** SAS Postulate
6. $\angle A \cong \angle B$	**6.** Corres. parts of $\cong$ $\triangle$s are $\cong$.

The next theorem is a corollary of the Isosceles Triangle Theorem.

a. If a triangle is equilateral, it is equiangular.
b. If a triangle is equiangular, it is equilateral.

Equilateral Triangle Theorem

Part a.

Given: $\overline{RS} \cong \overline{TS} \cong \overline{TR}$

Prove: $\angle T \cong \angle R \cong \angle S$

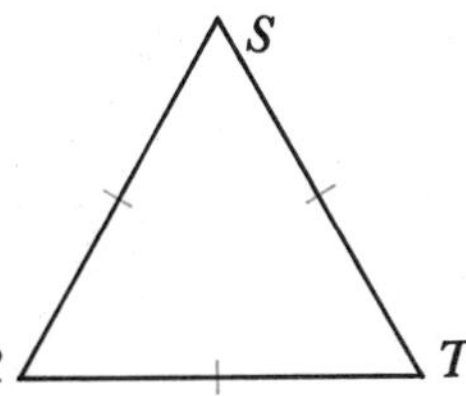

Proof:

STATEMENTS	REASONS
1. $\overline{RS} \cong \overline{TS}$, $\overline{TS} \cong \overline{TR}$	**1.** Given
2. $\angle T \cong \angle R$, $\angle R \cong \angle S$	**2.** Isosceles Triangle Theorem
3. $\angle T \cong \angle R \cong \angle S$	**3.** $\angle$s $\cong$ to the same $\angle$ are $\cong$.

Part **b**, above, is proved in Exercises 37–38.

a. If the nonparallel sides of a trapezoid are congruent, both pairs of base angles are congruent.
b. If either pair of base angles of a trapezoid are congruent, the nonparallel sides are congruent.

Isosceles Trapezoid Theorem

The proof of part **a** follows. Part **b** is proved in Exercises 39–48.

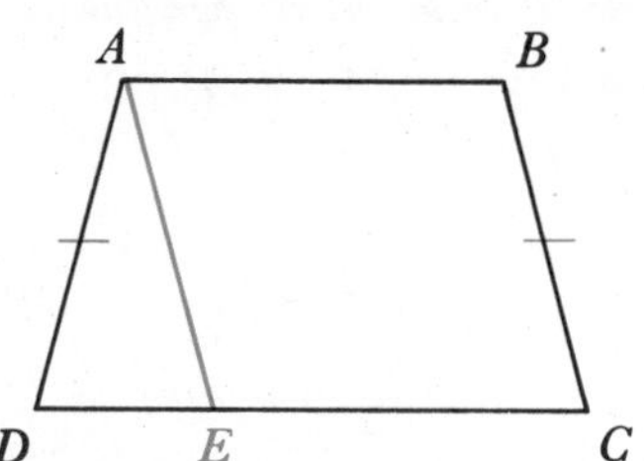

Given: Trapezoid $ABCD$ with $\overline{AB} \parallel \overline{DC}$, $\overline{AD} \cong \overline{BC}$

Prove: $\angle D \cong \angle C$, $\angle DAB \cong \angle B$

[*Plan:* Let $\overline{AE}$ be parallel to $\overline{BC}$. Show that $\triangle DAE$ is isosceles.]

Proof:

STATEMENTS	REASONS
1. Let $\overline{AE}$ be parallel to $\overline{BC}$.	**1.** Parallel Postulate (p. 125)
2. $\overline{AB} \parallel \overline{DC}$	**2.** Given
3. $ABCE$ is a parallelogram.	**3.** Definition of parallelogram
4. $\overline{BC} \cong \overline{AE}$	**4.** Opposite sides of a ▱ are ≅.
5. $\overline{AD} \cong \overline{BC}$	**5.** Given
6. $\overline{AD} \cong \overline{AE}$	**6.** Segments ≅ to the same seg. are ≅.
7. $\angle D \cong \angle AED$	**7.** Isosceles Triangle Theorem
8. $\angle AED \cong \angle C$	**8.** Since $\overleftrightarrow{BC} \parallel \overleftrightarrow{AE}$, corres. ∠s are ≅. ($\overleftrightarrow{CD}$ is a transversal of $\overleftrightarrow{BC}$ and $\overleftrightarrow{AE}$.)
9. $\angle D \cong \angle C$	**9.** ∠s ≅ to same ∠ are ≅.
10. $\angle DAB$ and $\angle D$ are supplementary, $\angle B$ and $\angle C$ are supplementary.	**10.** Since $\overleftrightarrow{AB} \parallel \overleftrightarrow{DC}$, interior ∠s on same side of transversal are supp.
11. $\angle DAB \cong \angle B$	**11.** Supplements of ≅ ∠s are ≅.

Exercises 5.6

Ⓐ **1–8.** Describe each of the following special polygons:

1. equilateral triangle

2. equiangular triangle

3. scalene triangle

4. right triangle

5. obtuse triangle

6. isosceles triangle

7. acute triangle

8. isosceles trapezoid

9–10. Use the figure.

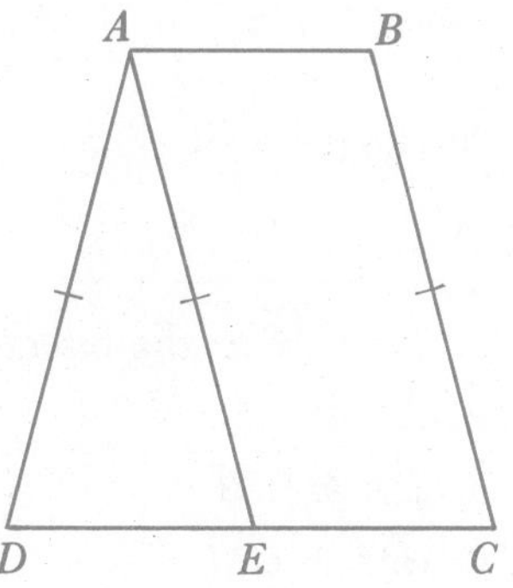

9. For isosceles $\triangle DAE$, name the

a. legs **b.** base angles

c. base **d.** vertex angle

10. For isosceles trapezoid *ABCD* name the

a. legs **b.** bases

c. base angles (both pairs)

11–16. Using $\triangle HES$ and the given information, name any other segments or angles that will be congruent.

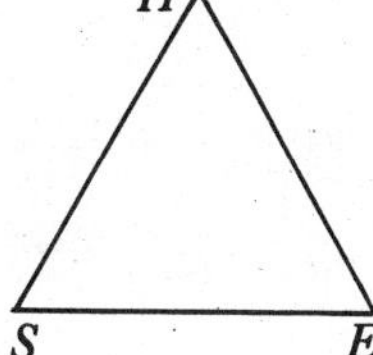

11. $\overline{HE} \cong \overline{HS}$ **12.** $\overline{HS} \cong \overline{ES}$

13. $\overline{HS} \cong \overline{SE} \cong \overline{EH}$ **14.** $\angle H \cong \angle S$

15. $\angle H \cong \angle E$ **16.** $\angle H \cong \angle E \cong \angle S$

Ⓑ **17–24.** Draw these triangles if possible. If it is impossible to draw the triangle, write *impossible* on your paper.

17. isosceles right triangle **18.** right scalene triangle

19. obtuse equilateral triangle **20.** obtuse isosceles triangle

21. right equilateral triangle **22.** obtuse scalene triangle

23. acute scalene triangle **24.** acute isosceles triangle

25–30. *ODEC* is an isosceles trapezoid. Use the given information to find the measures of as many segments and angles as possible.

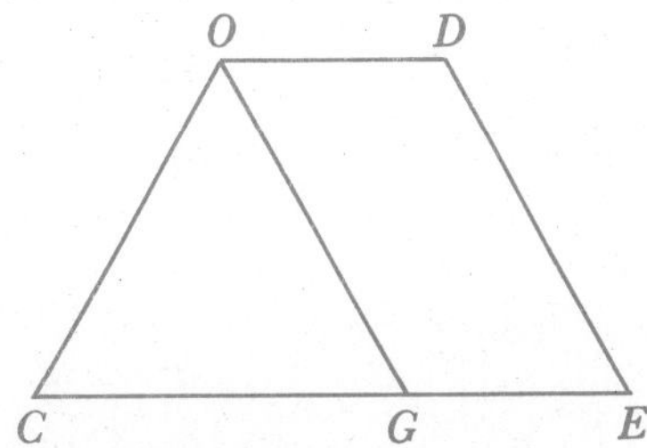

25. $\triangle COG$ is isosceles. $CO = GO = 12$, $m\angle COG = 50$

26. $\triangle OGC$ is equiangular. $OC = 4$

27. $\triangle GOC$ is equilateral. $OC = 8$, *ODEG* is a rhombus.

28. $\triangle COG$ is isosceles. $OC = CG = 3$, $m\angle CGO = 70$

29. $\triangle COG$ is isosceles. $OC = CG = 5$, $m\angle CGO = 74$

30. $\triangle OGC$ is isosceles. $OC = CG = 20$, $m\angle OGC = 52$

31–48. Give a reason for each statement.

Given: $\angle A \cong \angle B$

Prove: $\overline{AC} \cong \overline{BC}$

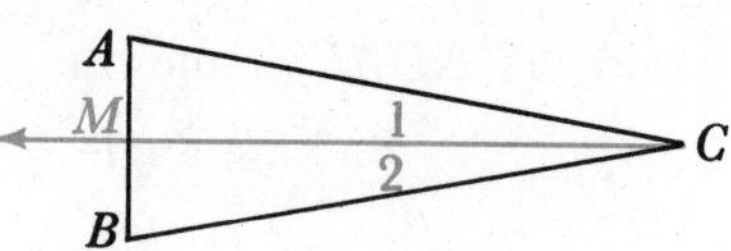

Proof:

STATEMENTS	REASONS
1. Let $\overrightarrow{CM}$ be the bisector of $\angle ACB$.	1. **31.**
2. $\angle 1 \cong \angle 2$	2. **32.**
3. $\angle A \cong \angle B$	3. **33.**
4. $\overline{CM} \cong \overline{CM}$	4. **34.**
5. $\triangle ACM \cong \triangle BCM$	5. **35.**
6. $\overline{AC} \cong \overline{BC}$	6. **36.**

Given: $\angle T \cong \angle R \cong \angle S$

Prove: $\overline{RS} \cong \overline{TS} \cong \overline{TR}$

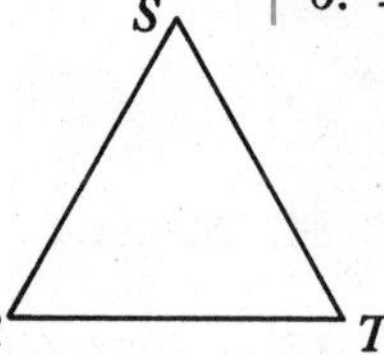

Proof:

STATEMENTS	REASONS
1. $\angle T \cong \angle R$, $\angle R \cong \angle S$	1. Given
2. $\overline{RS} \cong \overline{TS}$, $\overline{TS} \cong \overline{TR}$	2. **37.**
3. $\overline{RS} \cong \overline{TS} \cong \overline{TR}$	3. **38.**

© Given: Trapezoid $ABCD$ with $\overline{AB} \parallel \overline{DC}$, $\angle DAB \cong \angle B$

Prove: $\overline{AD} \cong \overline{BC}$

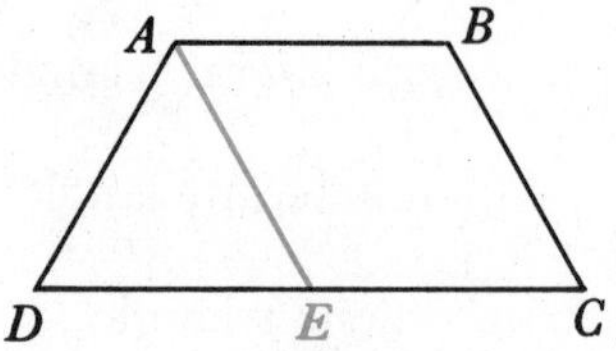

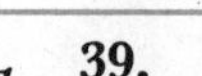

Proof:

STATEMENTS	REASONS
1. $\overline{AB} \parallel \overline{DC}$, $\angle DAB \cong \angle B$	1. **39.**
2. $\angle C$ and $\angle B$, $\angle D$ and $\angle DAB$ are supp.	2. **40.**
3. $\angle C \cong \angle D$	3. **41.**
4. Let $\overline{AE}$ be parallel to $\overline{BC}$.	4. **42.**
5. $ABCE$ is a parallelogram.	5. **43.**
6. $\overline{AE} \cong \overline{BC}$	6. **44.**
7. $\angle AED \cong \angle C$	7. **45.**
8. $\angle AED \cong \angle D$	8. **46.**
9. $\overline{AD} \cong \overline{AE}$	9. **47.**
10. $\overline{AD} \cong \overline{BC}$	10. **48.**

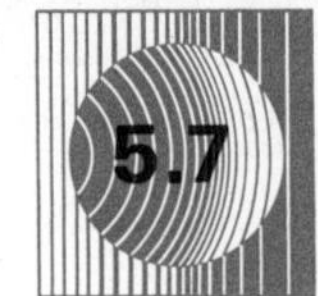

Congruent Right Triangles

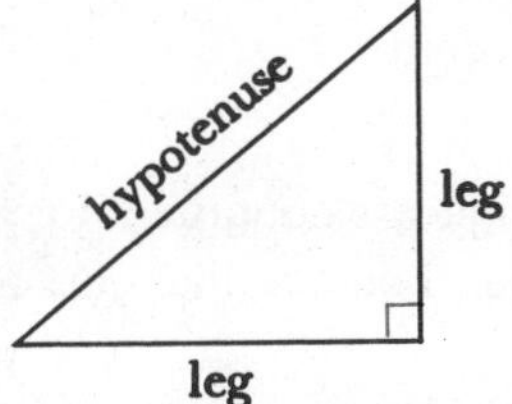

In a right triangle, the side opposite the right angle is called the **hypotenuse.** The sides opposite the acute angles are called **legs.**

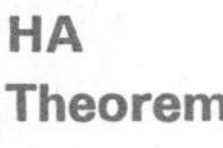

Hypotenuse–Acute-Angle Theorem: If the hypotenuse and an acute angle of one right triangle are congruent to the corresponding parts of another right triangle, then the triangles are congruent.

Given: $\overline{AC} \cong \overline{XZ}$, $\angle C \cong \angle Z$,
$\angle B$ and $\angle Y$ are right angles.

Prove: $\triangle ABC \cong \triangle XYZ$

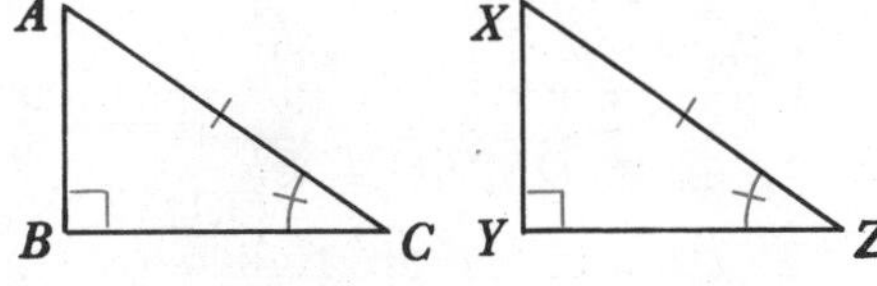

Proof:

STATEMENTS	REASONS
1. $\overline{AC} \cong \overline{XZ}$, $\angle C \cong \angle Z$	1. Given
2. $\angle B$ and $\angle Y$ are right angles.	2. Given
3. $\angle B \cong \angle Y$	3. Any two right $\angle$s are $\cong$.
4. $\triangle ABC \cong \triangle XYZ$	4. AAS Theorem

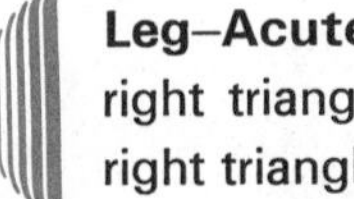

Leg–Acute-Angle Theorem: If a leg and an acute angle of one right triangle are congruent to the corresponding parts of another right triangle, then the triangles are congruent.

Case 1: The given leg is opposite the given acute angle.

Given: $\angle A \cong \angle D$, $\overline{BC} \cong \overline{EF}$, $\angle B$ and $\angle E$ are right angles.

Prove: $\triangle ABC \cong \triangle DEF$

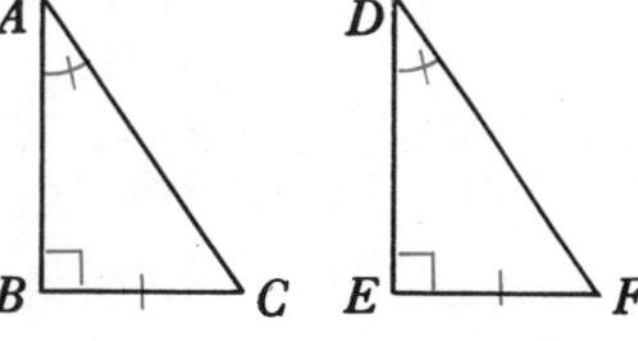

Proof:

STATEMENTS	REASONS
1. $\angle A \cong \angle D$, $\overline{BC} \cong \overline{EF}$	1. Given
2. $\angle B$ and $\angle E$ are right angles.	2. Given
3. $\angle B \cong \angle E$	3. Any two right $\angle$s are $\cong$.
4. $\triangle ABC \cong \triangle DEF$	4. AAS Theorem

Case 2: The given leg is *not* opposite the given acute angle.
Case 2 is proved in Exercises 13–15.

Other theorems for proving right triangles congruent are the Leg-Leg Theorem and the Hypotenuse-Leg Theorem.

LL Theorem

Leg-Leg Theorem: If two legs of one right triangle are congruent to the corresponding parts of another right triangle, then the triangles are congruent.

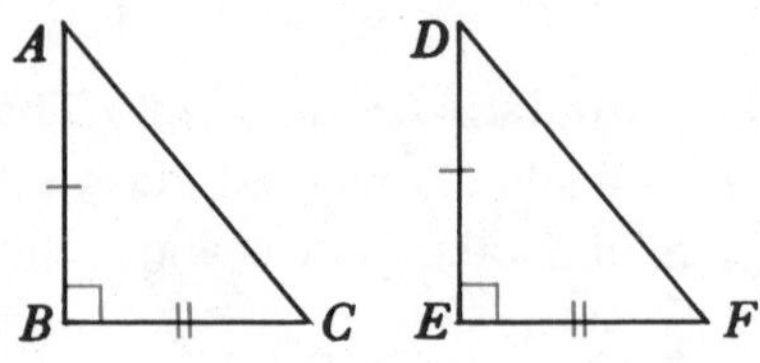

Given: $\overline{AB} \cong \overline{DE}$, $\overline{BC} \cong \overline{EF}$,
$\angle B$ and $\angle E$ are right angles.

Prove: $\triangle ABC \cong \triangle DEF$

Proof: STATEMENTS	REASONS
1. $\overline{AB} \cong \overline{DE}$, $\overline{BC} \cong \overline{EF}$	1. Given
2. $\angle B$ and $\angle E$ are right angles.	2. Given
3. $\angle B \cong \angle E$	3. Any two right $\angle$s are $\cong$.
4. $\triangle ABC \cong \triangle DEF$	4. SAS Postulate

HL Theorem

Hypotenuse-Leg Theorem: If the hypotenuse and a leg of one right triangle are congruent to the corresponding parts of another right triangle, then the triangles are congruent.

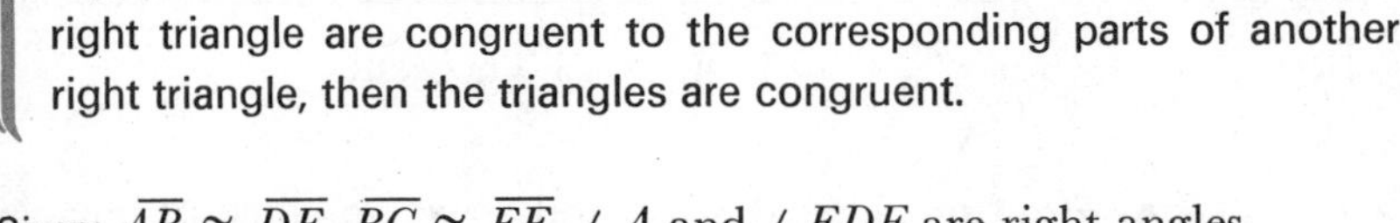

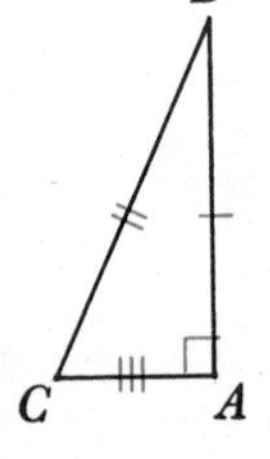

Given: $\overline{AB} \cong \overline{DE}$, $\overline{BC} \cong \overline{EF}$, $\angle A$ and $\angle EDF$ are right angles.

Prove: $\triangle ABC \cong \triangle DEF$

[*Plan:* Use auxiliary segment DG on the ray opposite $\overrightarrow{DF}$ and congruent to $\overline{AC}$. Then prove $\triangle DEG \cong \triangle ABC$. Next prove $\triangle DEG \cong \triangle DEF$.]

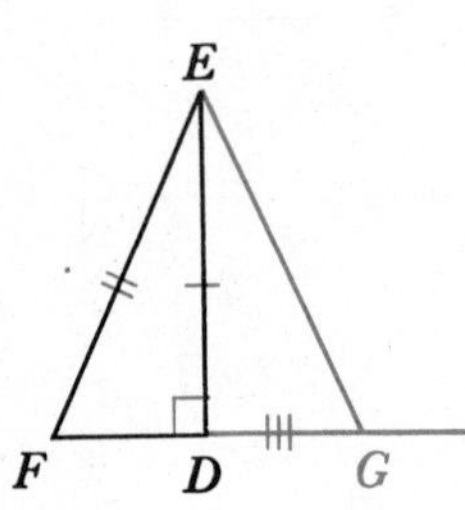

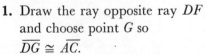

Proof: STATEMENTS	REASONS
1. Draw the ray opposite ray DF and choose point G so $\overline{DG} \cong \overline{AC}$.	1. Point Plotting Theorem (p. 27)
2. $\overline{AB} \cong \overline{DE}$, $\angle A$ and $\angle EDF$ are right $\angle$s.	2. Given
3. $\overleftrightarrow{DE} \perp \overleftrightarrow{FG}$ at D	3. Definition of $\perp$ lines
4. $\angle EDG$ is a right angle.	4. $\perp$ lines form 4 right angles.
5. $\triangle DEG$, $\triangle DEF$, $\triangle ABC$ are right $\triangle$s.	5. Definition of a right $\triangle$

6. $\triangle ABC \cong \triangle DEG$	**6.** LL Theorem
7. $\overline{BC} \cong \overline{EG}$	**7.** Corres. parts of $\cong$ $\triangle$s are $\cong$.
8. $\overline{BC} \cong \overline{EF}$	**8.** Given
9. $\overline{EG} \cong \overline{EF}$	**9.** Segments $\cong$ to the same segment are $\cong$.
10. $\angle G \cong \angle F$	**10.** Isosceles Triangle Theorem
11. $\triangle DEG \cong \triangle DEF$	**11.** HA Theorem
12. $\triangle ABC \cong \triangle DEF$	**12.** $\triangle$s $\cong$ to the same $\triangle$ are $\cong$.

Exercises 5.7

Ⓐ **1–6.** Corresponding congruent parts and right angles are indicated. What theorem from this section can be used to prove the triangles congruent?

1.

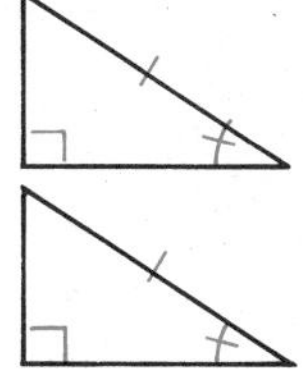

2.

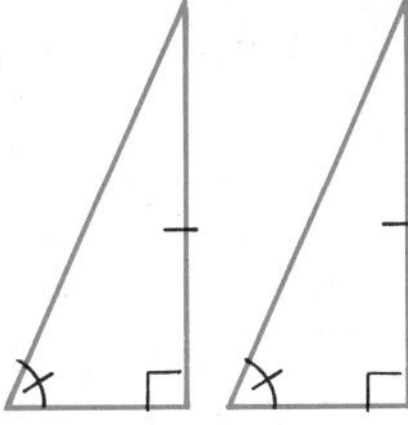

3.

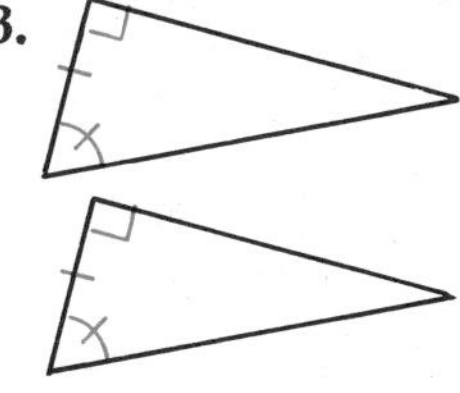

4.

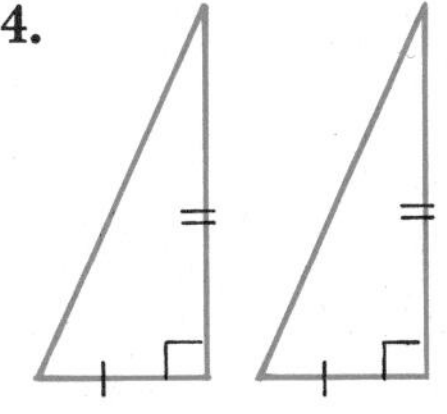

5.

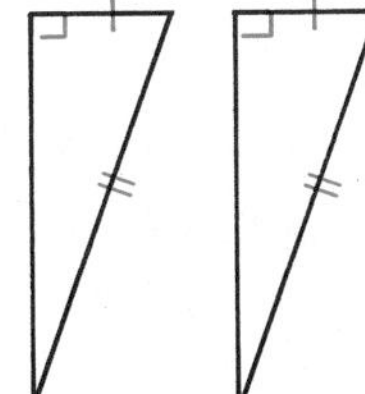

6.

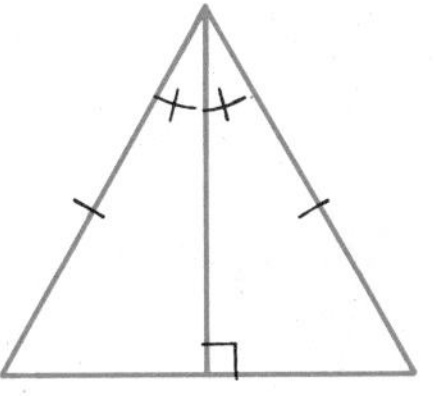

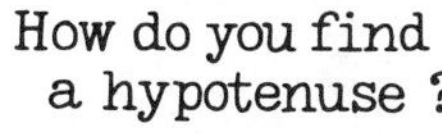

How do you find
a hypotenuse ?

Ⓑ **7–12.** With the given information, what theorem from this section can be used to prove $\triangle NAS \cong \triangle NAT$? Remember $\overline{AN} \cong \overline{AN}$.

7. $\angle 3$ and $\angle 4$ are right $\angle$s, $\angle 1 \cong \angle 2$

8. $\angle 3$ and $\angle 4$ are right $\angle$s, $\angle S \cong \angle T$

9. $\angle 3$ and $\angle 4$ are right $\angle$s, $\overline{SA} \cong \overline{TA}$

10. $m\angle 3 = 90$, $m\angle 4 = 90$, $\angle S \cong \angle T$, $\overline{AS} \cong \overline{AT}$

11. $\overleftrightarrow{AN}$ the perpendicular bisector of $\overline{ST}$

12. $\overline{AN} \perp \overline{ST}$, $AS = AT$

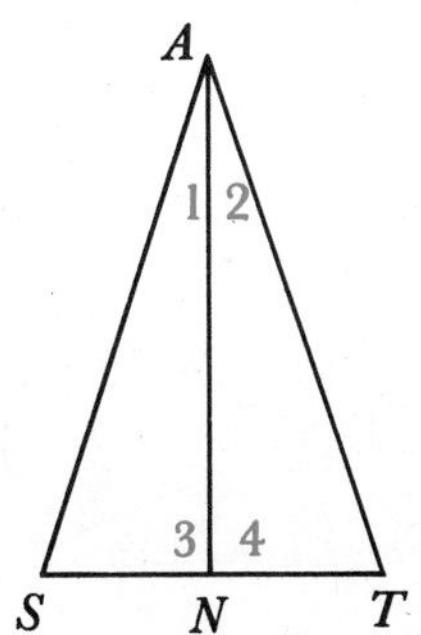

Look for tracks
around the water
hole !

13–20. Give a reason for each statement.

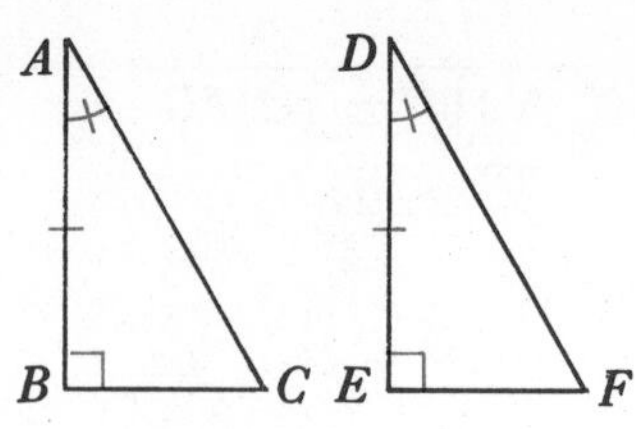

Given: $\angle A \cong \angle D$, $\overline{AB} \cong \overline{DE}$,
$\angle B$ and $\angle E$ are right $\angle$s.

Prove: $\triangle ABC \cong \triangle DEF$

Proof:

STATEMENTS	REASONS
1. $\angle A \cong \angle D$, $\overline{AB} \cong \overline{DE}$	*1.* **13.**
2. $\angle B$ and $\angle E$ are right $\angle$s.	*2.* **14.**
3. $\angle B \cong \angle E$	*3.* **15.**
4. $\triangle ABC \cong \triangle DEF$	*4.* ASA Post.

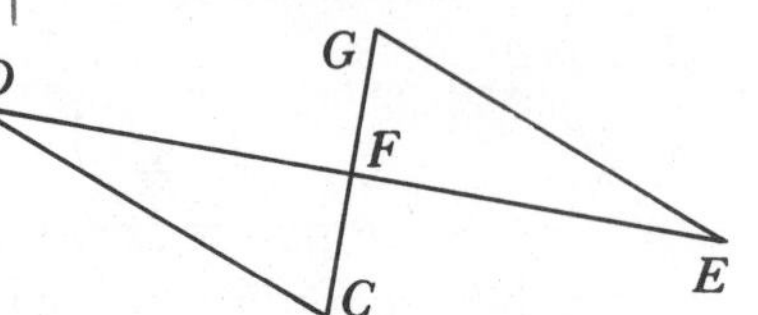

Given: $\overleftrightarrow{GC}$ the $\perp$ bisector of $\overline{DE}$,
$\overline{GE} \cong \overline{CD}$

Prove: $\triangle GFE \cong \triangle CFD$

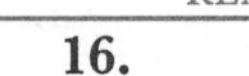

Proof:

STATEMENTS	REASONS
1. $\overleftrightarrow{GC}$ the $\perp$ bisector of $\overline{DE}$, $\overline{GE} \cong \overline{CD}$	*1.* **16.**
2. $\overline{DF} \cong \overline{EF}$	*2.* **17.**
3. $\angle CFD$ and $\angle GFE$ are right $\angle$s.	*3.* **18.**
4. $\triangle CFD$ and $\triangle GFE$ are right $\triangle$s.	*4.* **19.**
5. $\triangle GFE \cong \triangle CFD$	*5.* **20.**

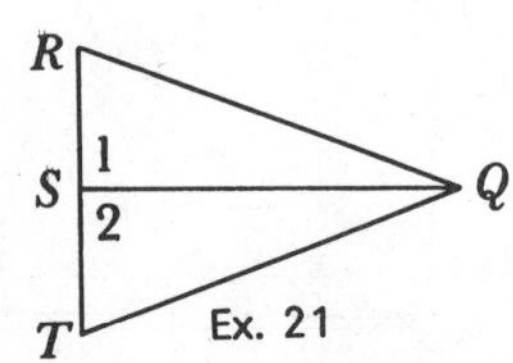

Ex. 21

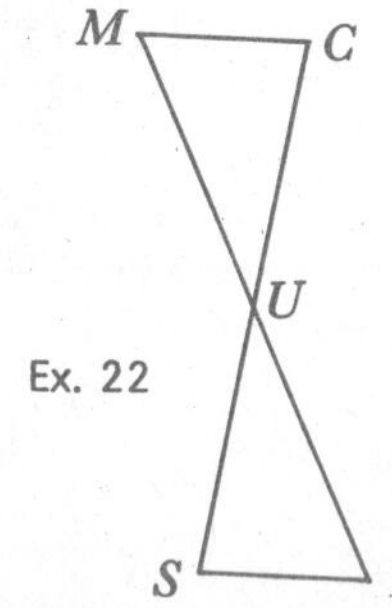

Ex. 22

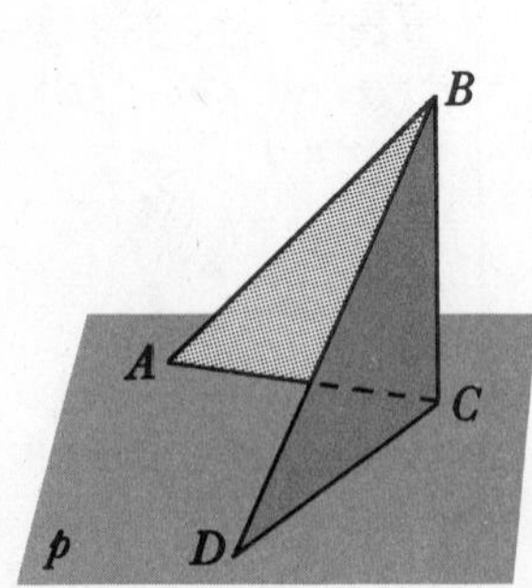

Ex. 23

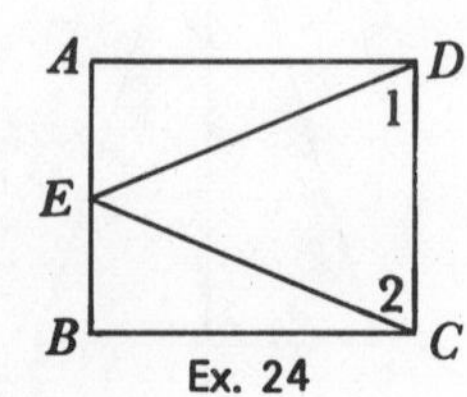

Ex. 24

21. Given: $\angle 1$ and $\angle 2$ are right $\angle$s,
$RS = 5$, $ST = 5$

Prove: $\triangle RSQ \cong \triangle TSQ$

22. Given: $\angle C$ and $\angle S$ are right $\angle$s,
$\overline{MC} \cong \overline{IS}$

Prove: $\triangle MCU \cong \triangle ISU$

© **23.** Given: $\overline{AC} \cong \overline{DC}$,
$\angle BCA$ and $\angle BCD$ are right $\angle$s.

Prove: $\overline{AB} \cong \overline{DB}$

24. Given: Rectangle $ABCD$, $\angle 1 \cong \angle 2$,
E the midpoint of $\overline{AB}$

Prove: $\triangle EAD \cong \triangle EBC$

Triangle Congruence Summarized

Triangles can be proved congruent by

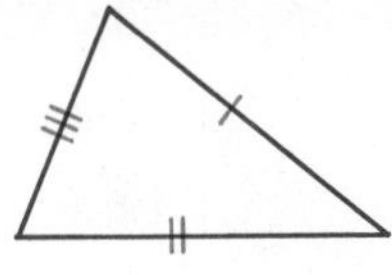
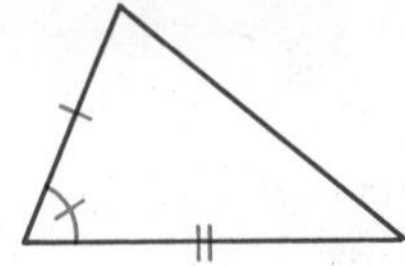
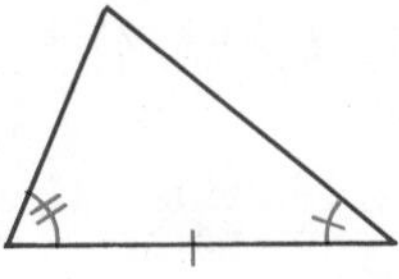
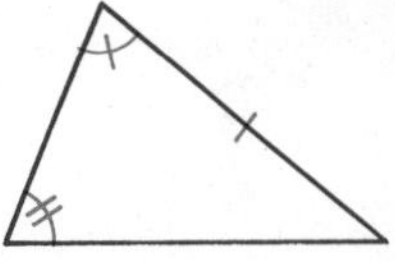
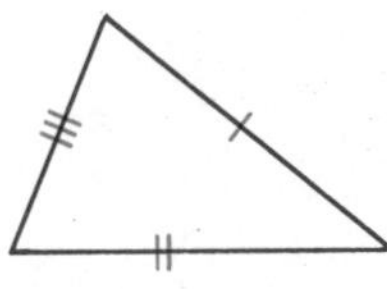
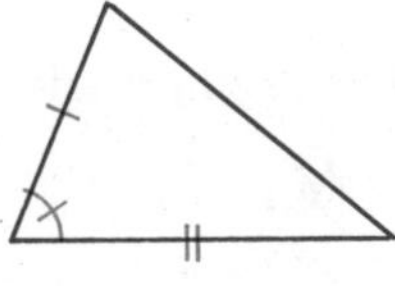
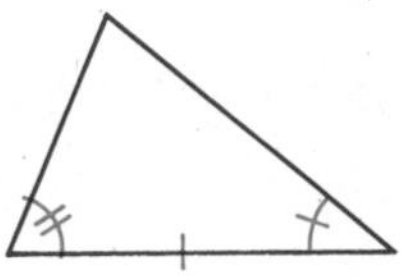
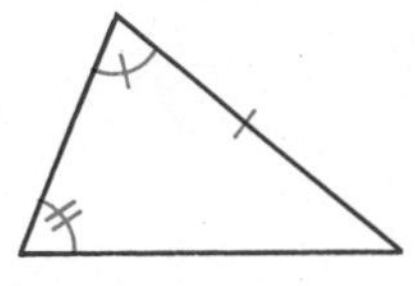

Side-Side-Side | Side-Angle-Side | Angle-Side-Angle | Angle-Angle-Side

Right triangles can be proved congruent by

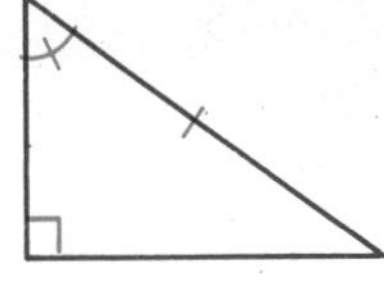
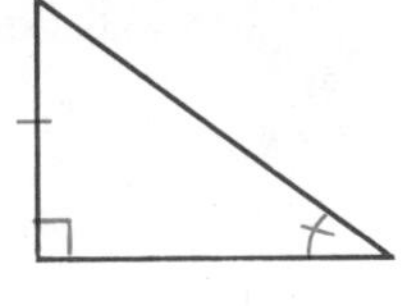
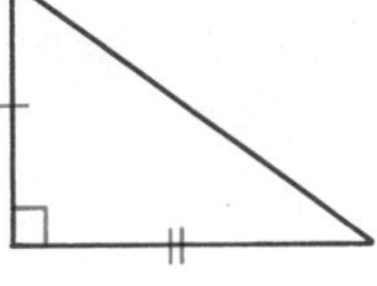
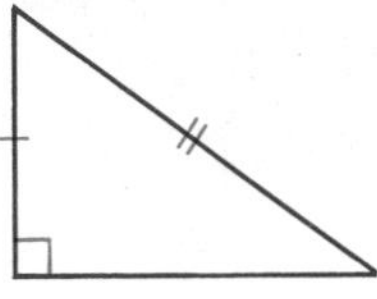
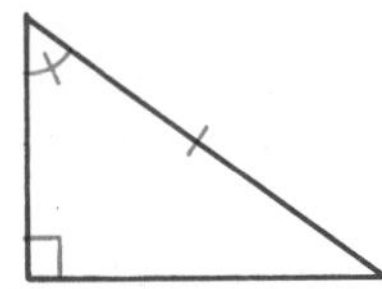
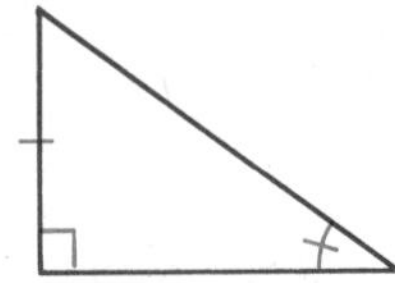
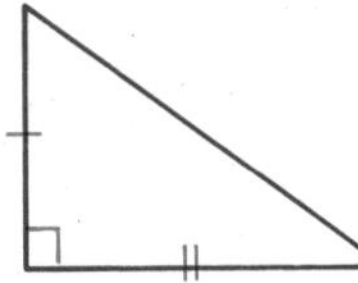
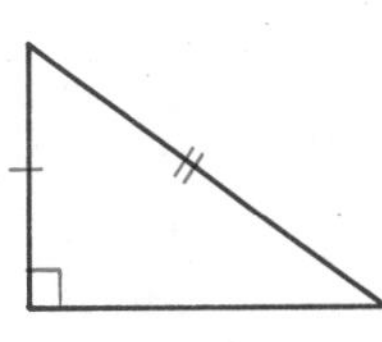

Hypotenuse–Acute-Angle | Leg–Acute-Angle | Leg-Leg | Hypotenuse-Leg

Triangles **cannot** be proved congruent by

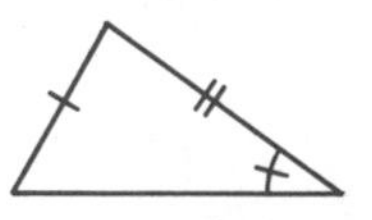
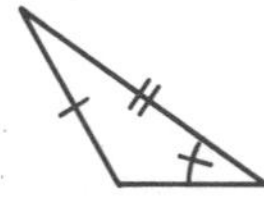

Side-Side-Angle

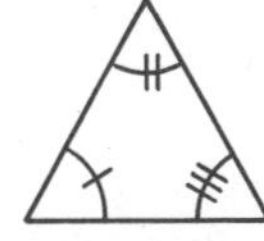

Angle-Angle-Angle

Exercises 5.8

Ⓐ **1–4.** Corresponding congruent parts are marked. What theorem or postulate lets you state that the triangles are congruent?

1.

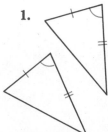

2.

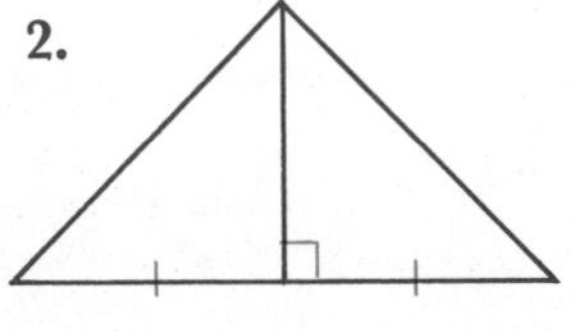

3.

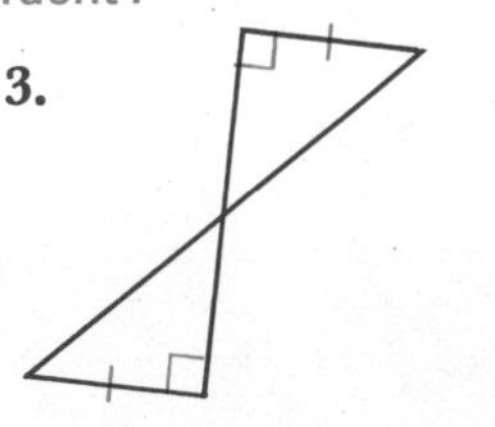

4.

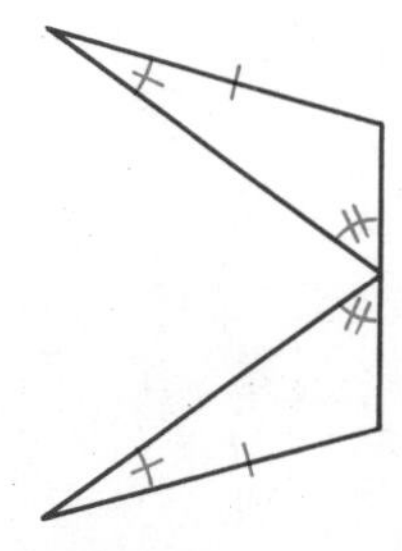

5–10. Using the given information, what theorem or postulate can be used to prove $\triangle ABC \cong \triangle ADC$?

5. $\overline{AB} \cong \overline{AD}$, $\overline{BC} \cong \overline{DC}$

6. $\angle B$ and $\angle D$ are right angles, $AB = AD$

7. $\overrightarrow{CA}$ bisects $\angle C$, $\overrightarrow{AC}$ bisects $\angle A$.

8. $\overrightarrow{AC}$ bisects $\angle A$, $\overline{AD} \cong \overline{AB}$

9. $\overline{BC} \cong \overline{DC}$, $\angle B$ and $\angle D$ are right angles.

10. $\overrightarrow{CA}$ bisects $\angle C$, $\overline{BC} \cong \overline{DC}$

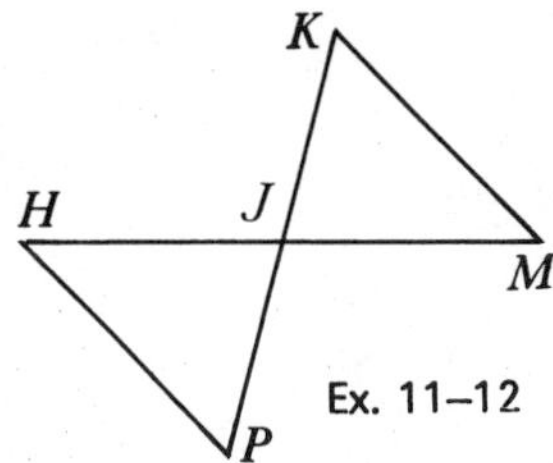

Ex. 11–12

Ⓑ **11.** Given: $\overline{HP} \cong \overline{MK}$, $\angle P \cong \angle K$

Prove: $\triangle PJH \cong \triangle KJM$

12. Given: Point J the midpoint of $\overline{KP}$ and $\overline{HM}$

Prove: $\triangle PJH \cong \triangle KJM$

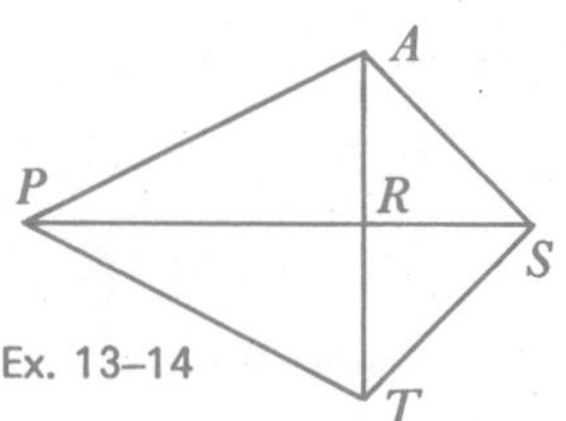

Ex. 13–14

13. Given: $\overleftrightarrow{PS}$ the $\perp$ bisector of $\overline{AT}$

Prove: $\triangle PRA \cong \triangle PRT$

14. Given: $m\angle PRT = 90$, $\overline{PA} \cong \overline{PT}$, $m\angle PRA = 90$

Prove: $\overline{AR} \cong \overline{TR}$

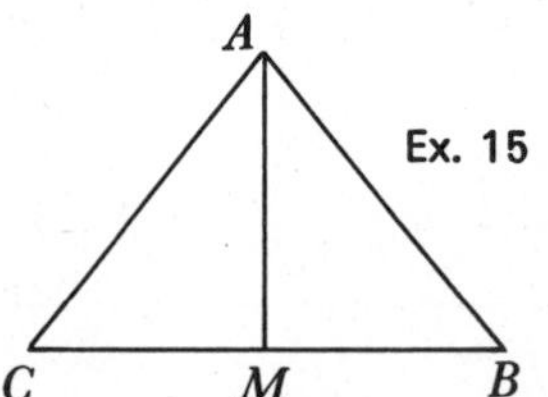

Ex. 15

Ⓒ **15.** Given: $\overleftrightarrow{AM}$ the $\perp$ bisector of $\overline{BC}$

Prove: $\triangle ABC$ isosceles

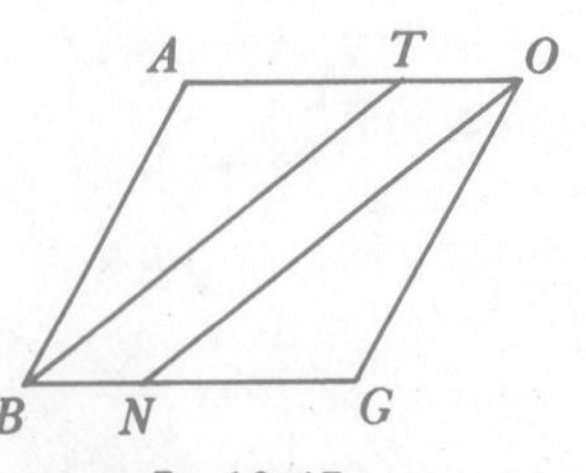

Ex. 16–17

16. Given: $\square BTON$, $\angle ABT \cong \angle GON$

Prove: $\triangle ABT \cong \triangle GON$

17. Given: Rhombus $AOGB$, $\overline{BT} \parallel \overline{NO}$

Prove: $\triangle ATB \cong \triangle GNO$

18. Given: Regular hexagon $ABCDEF$

Prove: $ACDF$ is a rectangle.

Overlapping Triangles

If you look closely, you will see a vase and the silhouette of two faces.

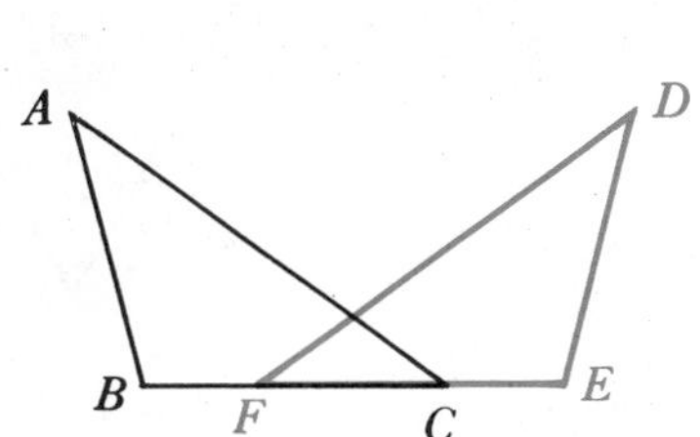

By looking closely at figure I, you will see two congruent triangles that overlap. **Overlapping triangles** are triangles whose interiors have points in common.

If we redraw the figure so that the triangles no longer overlap, it is easier to see which parts correspond. See figure II.

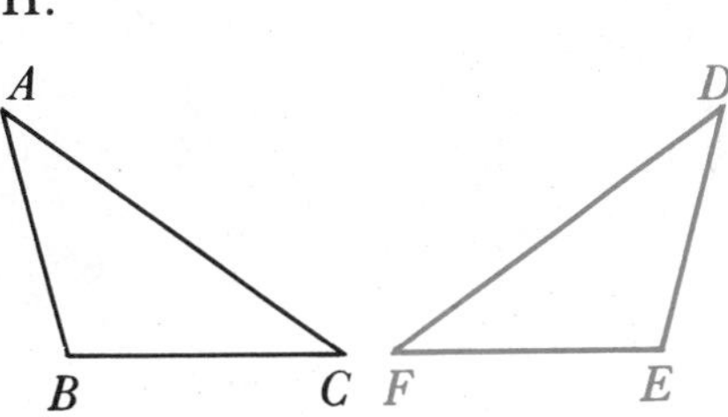

$\overline{AB} \cong \overline{DE}$ $\quad \angle A \cong \angle D$
$\overline{BC} \cong \overline{EF}$ $\quad \angle B \cong \angle E$
$\overline{CA} \cong \overline{FD}$ $\quad \angle C \cong \angle F$

If we draw in the diagonals of an isosceles trapezoid, overlapping triangles *ADC* and *BCD* are formed. See figure III. These triangles can be used in proving the next theorem. Part **a** is proved in Exercises 13–17.

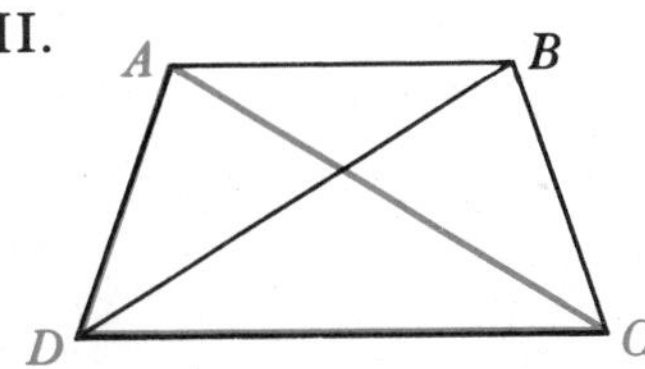

a. If a trapezoid is isosceles, its diagonals are congruent.
b. If a trapezoid has congruent diagonals, it is isosceles.

Theorem

Exercises 5.9

Ⓐ **1–8.** Tell **(a)** if the triangles overlap or not and **(b)** if they appear to be congruent.

1. $\triangle MAW$, $\triangle MON$
2. $\triangle MAW$, $\triangle NAW$
3. $\triangle POW$, $\triangle PAN$

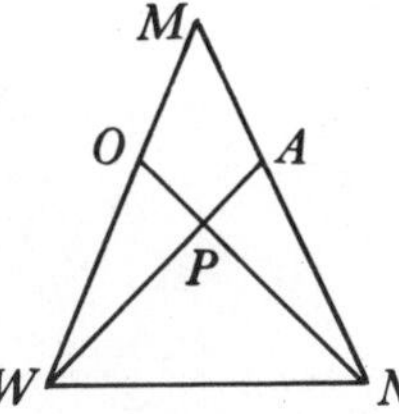

4. $\triangle MEI$, $\triangle OEV$
5. $\triangle VEI$, $\triangle VEO$
6. $\triangle MIV$, $\triangle OVI$

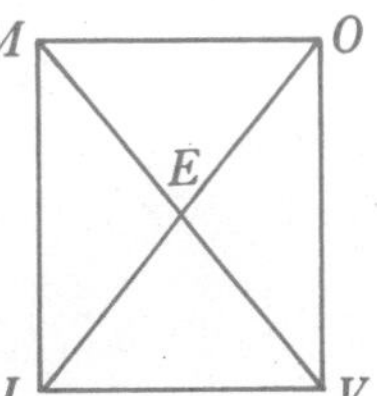

Ⓑ **7–8.** The blue triangle and the black triangle are congruent. Redraw them so that they do not overlap, then name the corresponding congruent parts, and complete the statement $\triangle$______ $\cong$ $\triangle$______.

7.

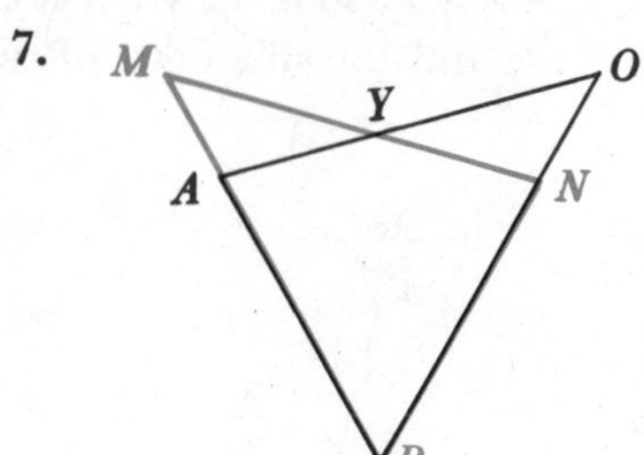

8.

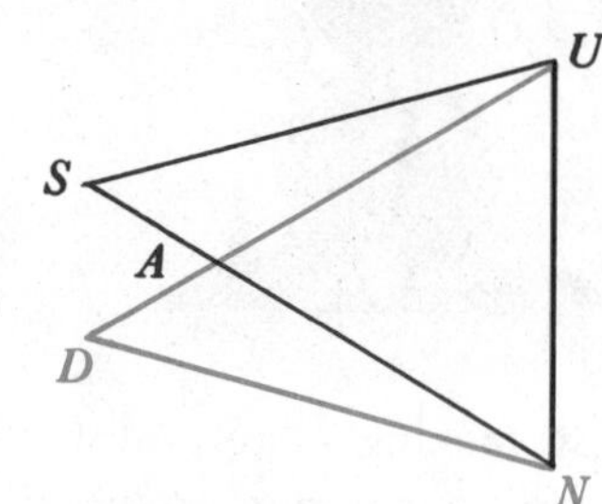

9–12. What theorem or postulate lets you conclude that $\triangle GOT \cong \triangle TEG$? HINT: What segment is a side of both triangles?

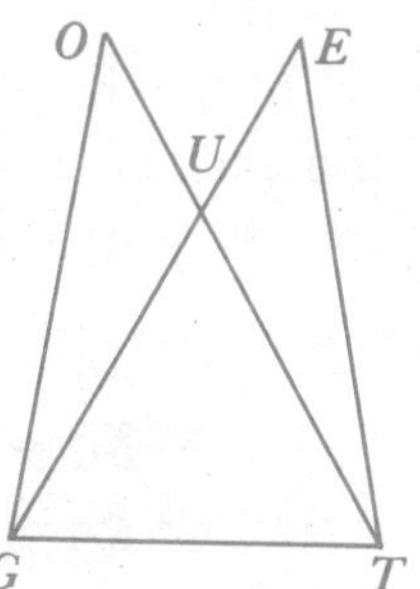

9. $\overline{GO} \cong \overline{TE}$, $\overline{OT} \cong \overline{EG}$

10. $\angle UGT \cong \angle UTG$, $\angle O \cong \angle E$

11. $\overline{OG} \cong \overline{ET}$, $\angle OGT \cong \angle ETG$

12. $\angle OGT$ and $\angle ETG$ are right angles, $\angle O \cong \angle E$

13–22. Give a reason for each statement.

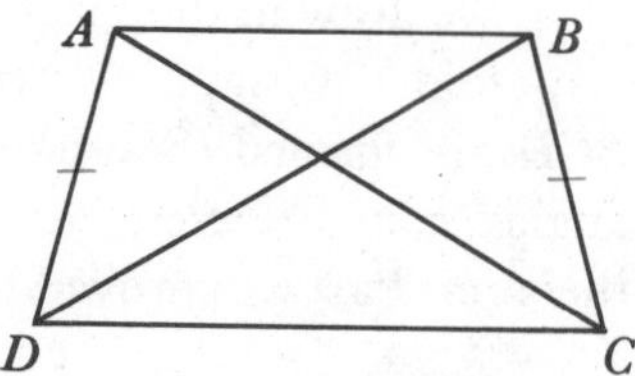

Given: Isosceles trapezoid $ABCD$ with $\overline{AD} \cong \overline{BC}$

Prove: $\overline{BD} \cong \overline{AC}$

Proof:

STATEMENTS	REASONS
1. $\overline{AD} \cong \overline{BC}$	1. **13.** ____
2. $\angle ADC \cong \angle BCD$	2. **14.** ____
3. $\overline{DC} \cong \overline{DC}$	3. **15.** ____
4. $\triangle ADC \cong \triangle BCD$	4. **16.** ____
5. $\overline{BD} \cong \overline{AC}$	5. **17.** ____

Given: $HGDC$ a rectangle, $\overline{CF} \cong \overline{DA}$

Prove: $\triangle ADG \cong \triangle FCH$

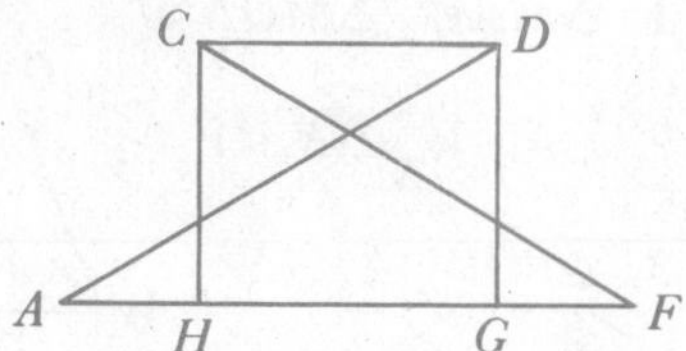

Proof:

STATEMENTS	REASONS
1. $HGDC$ a rectangle, $\overline{CF} \cong \overline{DA}$	1. **18.** ____
2. $\overline{CH} \cong \overline{DG}$	2. **19.** ____
3. $\angle CHF$ and $\angle DGA$ are right $\angle$s.	3. **20.** ____
4. $\triangle ADG$ and $\triangle FCH$ are right $\triangle$s.	4. **21.** ____
5. $\triangle ADG \cong \triangle FCH$	5. **22.** ____

23. Given: $\overline{GE} \cong \overline{GA}$, $\angle RGA \cong \angle TGE$

Prove: $\triangle RGA \cong \triangle TGE$

Ex. 23–24

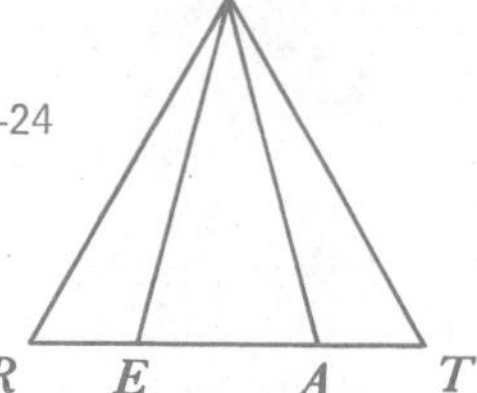

24. Given: $\angle R \cong \angle T$, $\overline{RA} \cong \overline{TE}$

Prove: $\triangle RGA \cong \triangle TGE$

© **25.** Given: $\overline{SC} \cong \overline{EC}$, $\overline{NC} \cong \overline{DC}$, $\angle 1 \cong \angle 2$

Prove: $\overline{SU} \cong \overline{EA}$

Ex. 25–26

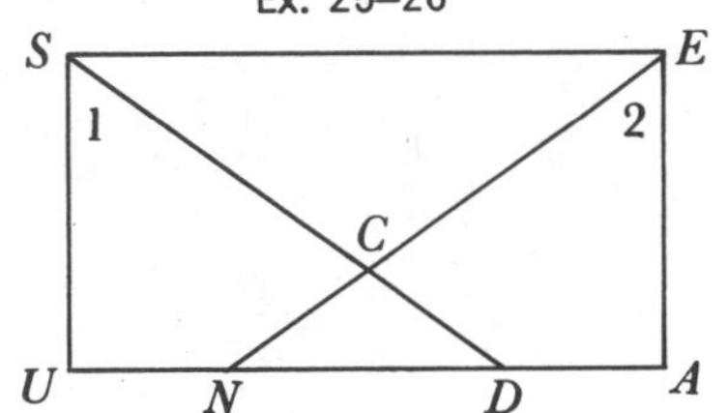

26. Given: $\angle U$ and $\angle A$ are right $\angle$s, $\overline{SU} \cong \overline{EA}$, $\angle 1 \cong \angle 2$

Prove: $\overline{NC} \cong \overline{DC}$

27. Prove part **b** of the theorem on page 191. [*Plan:* In the figure for Exercises 13–17, draw $\overline{AF} \perp \overline{DC}$ at F and $\overline{BE} \perp \overline{DC}$ at E. Prove $\triangle AFC \cong \triangle BED$. Then prove $\triangle ADC \cong \triangle BCD$.]

TRIANGLES IN BUILDINGS

William Means

Carpenters build supports in the shape of triangles for roofs of buildings. The photo shows one way of building the framework for a roof. Pick out where the carpenter used isosceles triangles and right triangles.

The framework is built in the shape of triangles because triangles are rigid figures. Triangular supports change shape only when a side breaks. Quadrilateral supports can change shape when boards become loose at their joints.

5.10 Transformations: Line Symmetry

If a figure can be folded into two "congruent halves" (same size and shape) so that one half coincides with the other half, the figure has line, or reflection, symmetry. A figure that has **line symmetry** can be reflected over a line so that the original figure is its own image. The reflecting line is called a symmetry line of the figure.

These figures have line symmetry. They are called line symmetric figures. Notice that a figure may be line symmetric to more than one line.

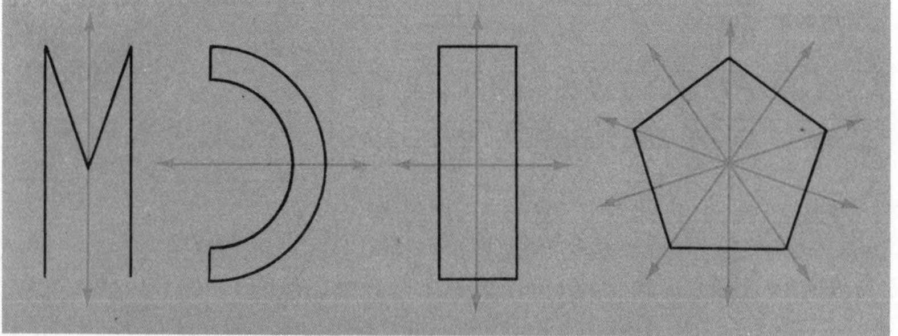

These figures do not have line symmetry.

Some polygons have line symmetry, while others do not. Are regular polygons line symmetric? Exercises 5–16 will help you answer that question.

Exercises 5.10

Ⓐ **1.** What is a line symmetric figure?

2–4. Name the symmetry lines, if any, for each figure.

2.

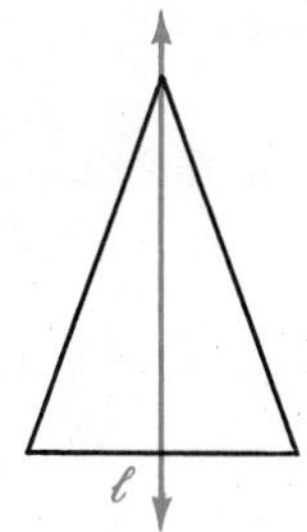

3.

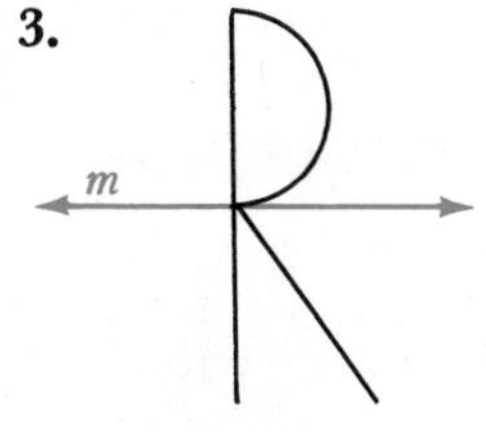

4.

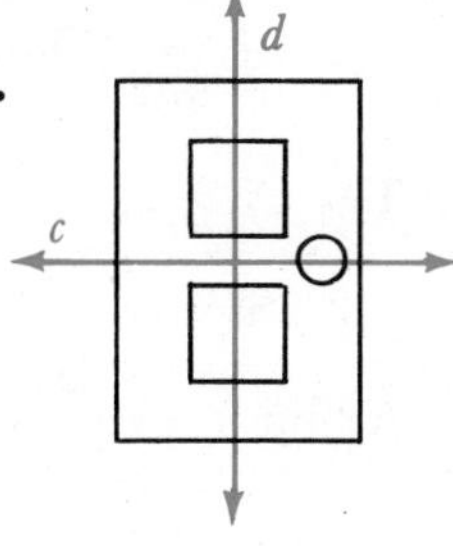

Ⓑ **5–16.** Copy each figure. Draw all symmetry lines.

5.

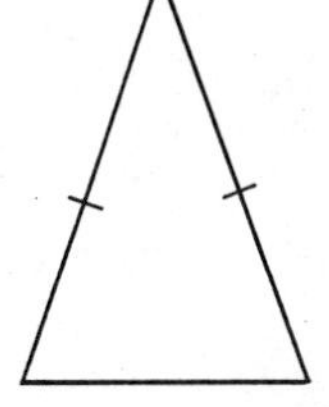

6.

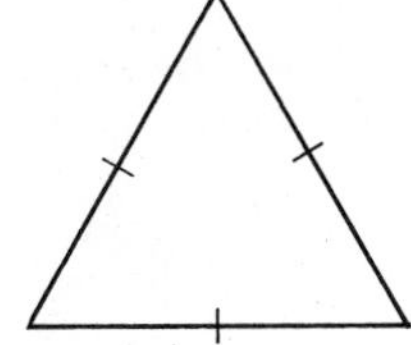

7.

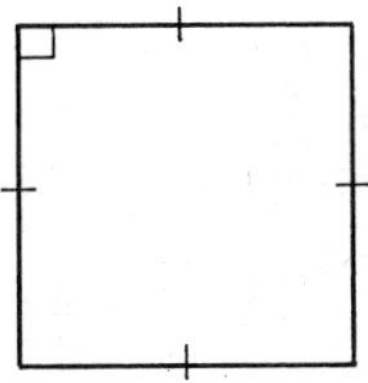

8.

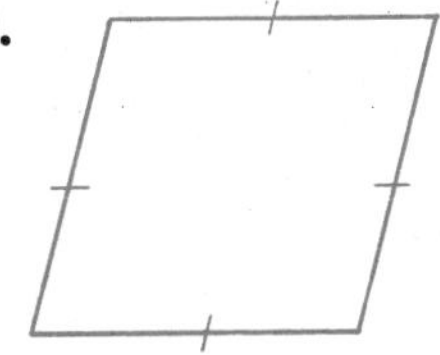

9.

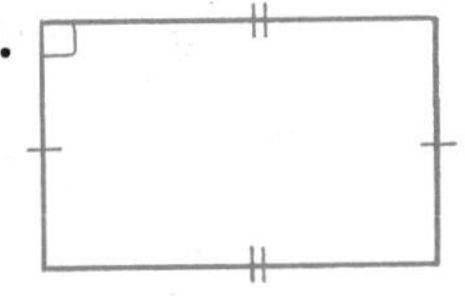

10.

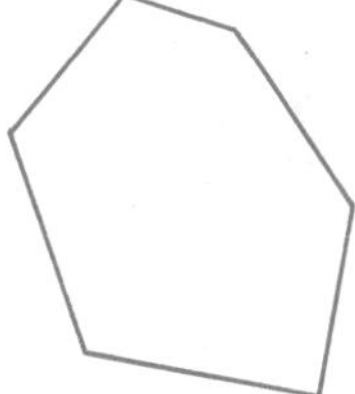

11.

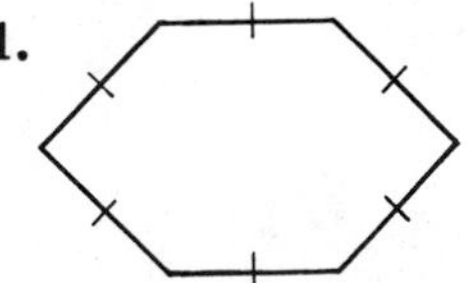

12.

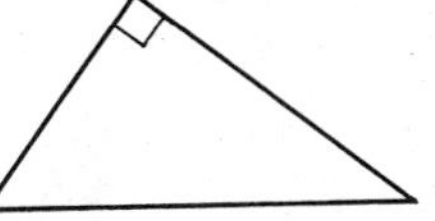

13.

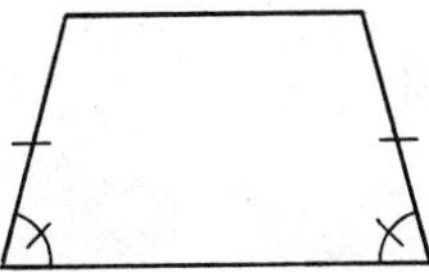

14.

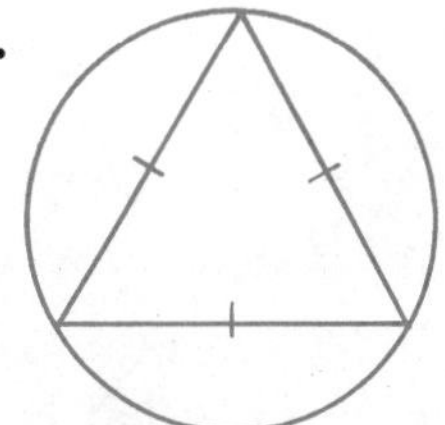

15.

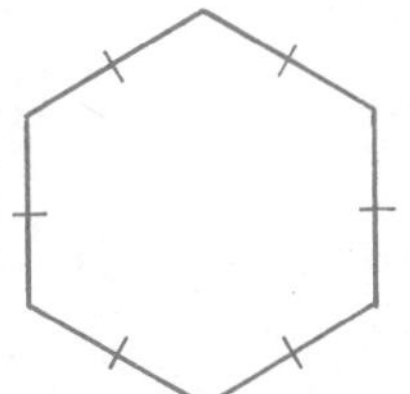

16.

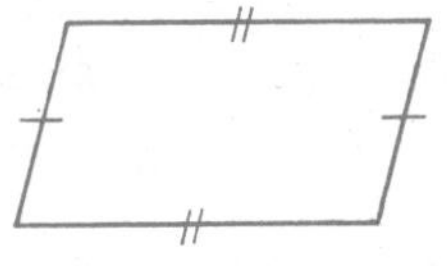

17–22. True or False? Draw a figure to explain your answer.

17. The symmetry line of an isosceles triangle bisects the vertex angle.

18. The diagonal of a rectangle is on a symmetry line for the rectangle.

19. The bisector of an angle is on a symmetry line for the angle.

20. A line has exactly one symmetry line.

21. A symmetry line of an equilateral triangle bisects a side.

22. The perpendicular bisector of a segment is a symmetry line for the segment.

23–28. How many symmetry lines does each polygon have? HINT: Your answers to Exercises 5–16 will be helpful.

23. isosceles triangle

24. equilateral triangle

25. square

26. regular octagon

© **27.** regular 20-gon

28. regular *n*-gon

29–30. Many designs used in floor tiles, fabrics, and rugs are line symmetric. Is each design line symmetric?

29.

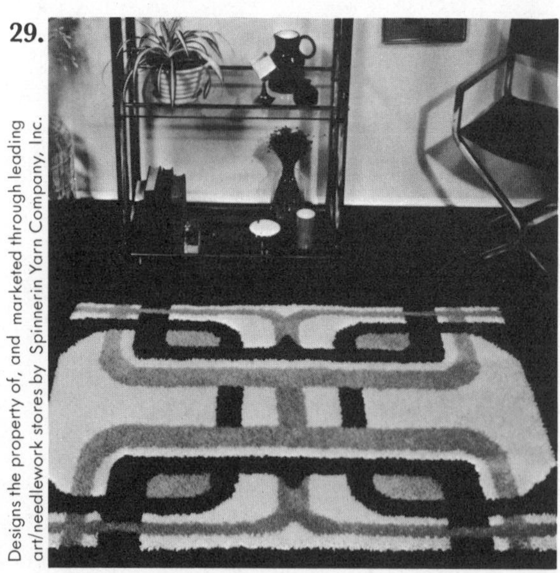

Designs the property of, and marketed through leading art/needlework stores by Spinnerin Yarn Company, Inc.

30.

31. Some words are line symmetric. WOW and DID are examples. Where are the symmetry lines? Name two more words that have a symmetry line.

Chapter 5 Review

1. Define *polygon*. **2.** Define *convex polygon*. **5.1**

3–5. Use the figure at the right.

A 8.5 B 3 C 5 D 8.7 E 9

3. Use the letters in the figure to give two names for the polygon.

4. What type of convex polygon is this?

5. Find the perimeter. **5.2**

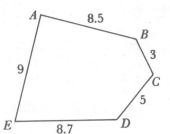

6. Find the perimeter of a regular hexagon with side of length 3.

7. Find the perimeter of a rectangle if $\ell = 4$ and $w = 7\frac{1}{2}$.

8. Find the sum of the exterior angles, one at each vertex, of a 300-gon. **5.3**

9. Find the sum of the interior angles of a 42-gon.

10. Find the measure of each interior angle of a regular 22-gon.

11. Find the measure of each exterior angle of a regular 30-gon.

12–15. *ABCD* ≅ *EFGH*, *ABCD* a parallelogram, find: **5.4**

A B 6 37° 143° D C E F H 9 G

12. *AB* **13.** *GF*

14. $m\angle H$ **15.** $m\angle E$

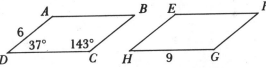

16. Is $\triangle RST \cong \triangle WXY$ by the AAS Theorem? Why? **5.5**

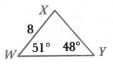

S 8 R 48° 51° T X 8 W 51° 48° Y

17–20. Identify each triangle with the most specific name possible. **5.6**

17.

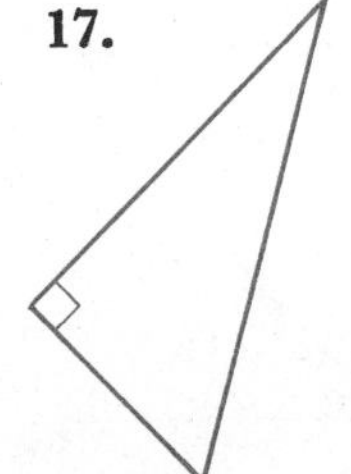

18.

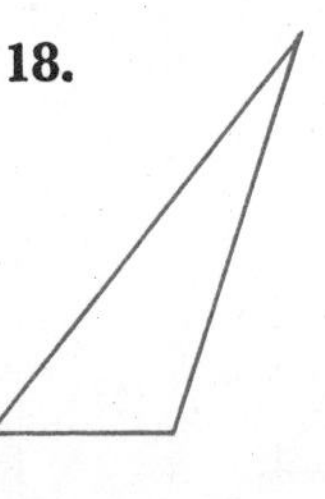

19.

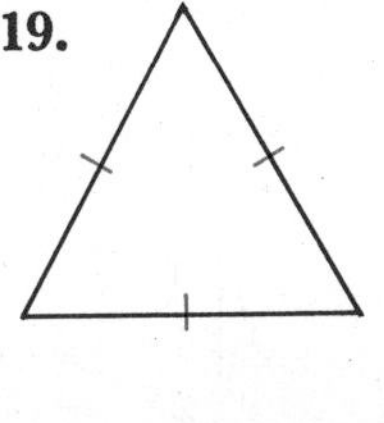

20.

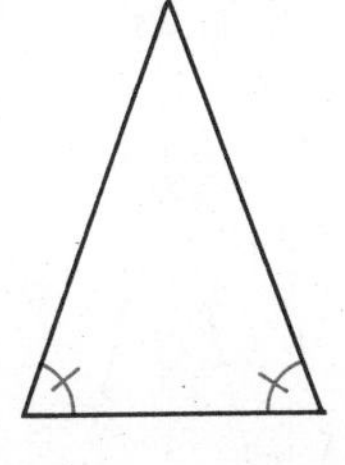

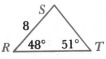

21. Given: $\angle T \cong \angle S$

Prove: $\overline{AT} \cong \overline{AS}$

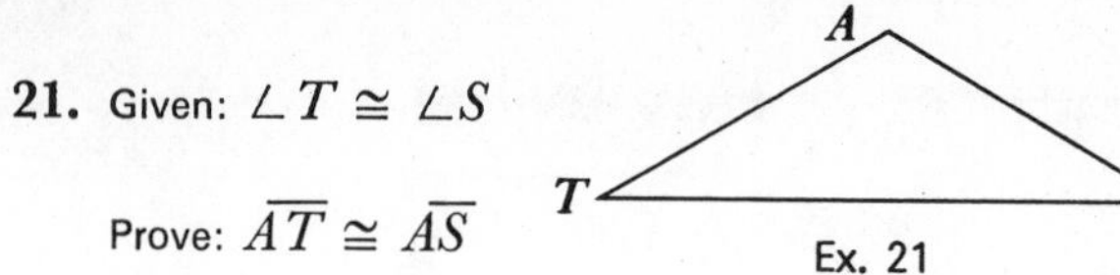

Ex. 21

5.7 22. Given: $\overline{RI} \perp \overline{RE}$, $\overline{RI} \perp \overline{WI}$, $\overline{EV} \cong \overline{WV}$

Prove: $\triangle REV \cong \triangle IWV$

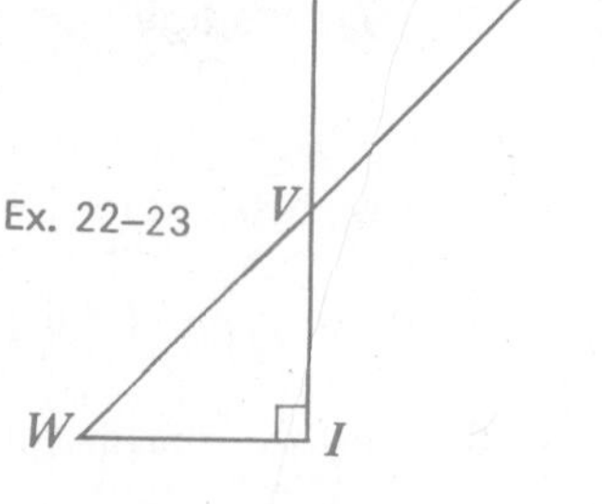

Ex. 22–23

23. Given: $\angle R$ and $\angle I$ are right $\angle$s, $\overline{RV} \cong \overline{VI}$

Prove: $\triangle VER \cong \triangle VWI$

5.8 24. Name 8 postulates or theorems used to prove triangles congruent.

5.9 25. Name the corresponding parts of the overlapping triangles, $\triangle RTS \cong \triangle WTU$.

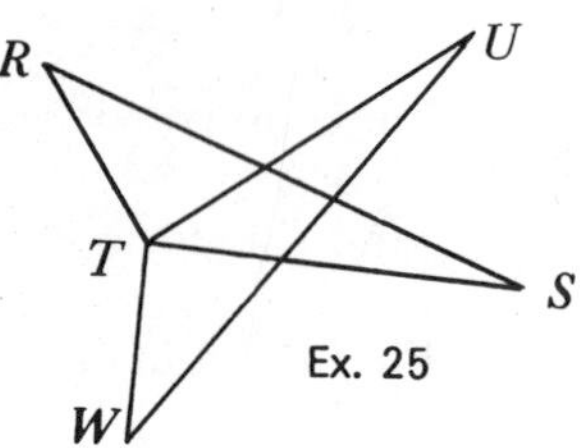

Ex. 25

26–30. Give a reason for each statement.

Given: $\overline{AX} \cong \overline{CX}$, $\overline{CB} \cong \overline{AD}$

Prove: $\triangle ACB \cong \triangle CAD$

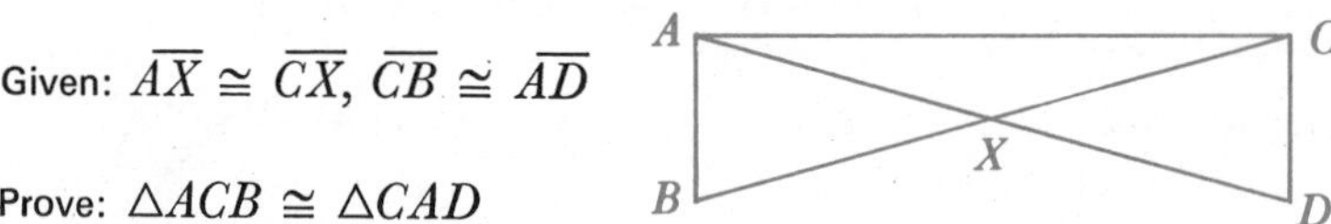

Proof:

STATEMENTS	REASONS
1. $\overline{AX} \cong \overline{CX}$	1. 26.
2. $\angle XCA \cong \angle XAC$	2. 27.
3. $\overline{AC} \cong \overline{AC}$	3. 28.
4. $\overline{CB} \cong \overline{AD}$	4. 29.
5. $\triangle ACB \cong \triangle CAD$	5. 30.

5.10 31–33. Is the red line a symmetry line for the figure?

31. 32. 33.

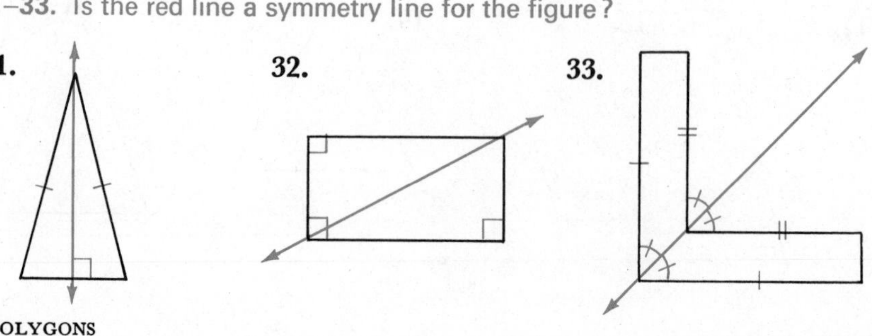

Chapter 5 Test

1. Define *congruent polygons*.

2. Define *regular polygon*.

3. Draw a nonconvex polygon.

4. Why is the figure at right not a polygon?

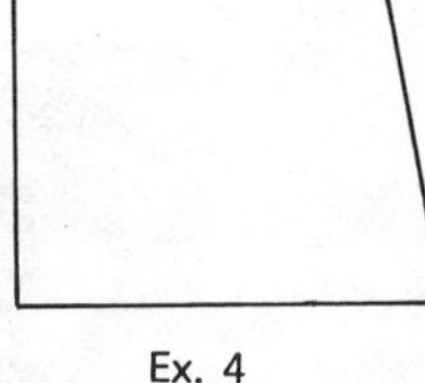

Ex. 4

5. Can a scalene triangle have an obtuse angle?

6. Is an equiangular triangle always isosceles?

7. For a convex 20-gon find the sum of (**a**) the interior angles and (**b**) the exterior angles, one at each vertex.

8. For a regular 36-gon find the measure of each (**a**) interior angle and (**b**) exterior angle.

9. Find the perimeter of a parallelogram with sides of lengths 5 and 3.2.

10–11. State a reason for each conclusion.

10. *Given:* $\square ABCD$, $\square FEHG$, $\overline{EH} \cong \overline{BC}$, $\overline{EF} \cong \overline{AB}$, $\angle B \cong \angle E$

    Conclusion: $ABCD \cong FEHG$

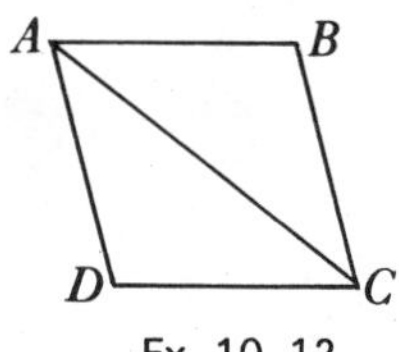

Ex. 10–12

11. *Given:* $\angle E \cong \angle B$, $\angle EFH \cong \angle BAC$, $\overline{AC} \cong \overline{HF}$

    Conclusion: $\triangle EFH \cong \triangle BAC$

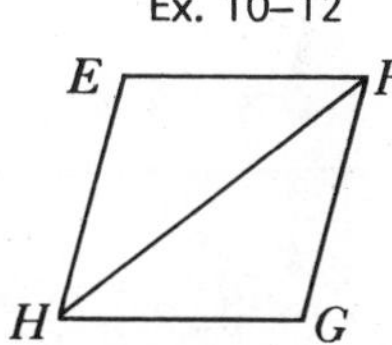

12. Given: $ABCD$ a rhombus

    Prove: $\triangle ADC$ isosceles

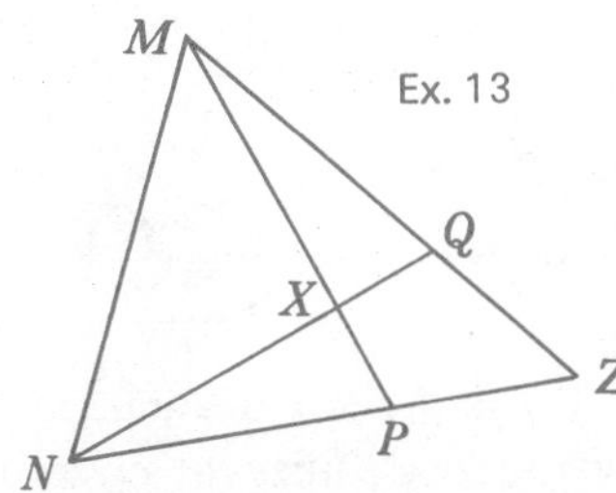

Ex. 13

13. Given: $\overline{MZ} \cong \overline{NZ}$, $\overline{MQ} \cong \overline{NP}$

    Prove: $\triangle MQN \cong \triangle NPM$

14. Draw a square and all of its symmetry lines.

MINI-CHAPTER: REPEATING DESIGNS

The floor tiles cover the floor with a repeating design.

The wallpaper covers the wall with a repeating design.

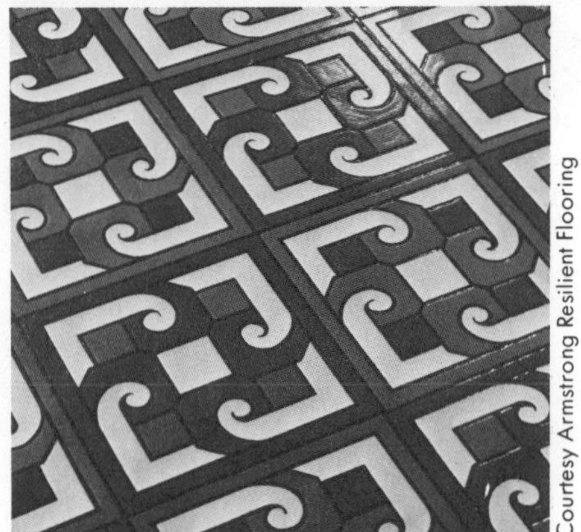

Courtesy Armstrong Resilient Flooring

Marimekko

Consider the floor or wall as part of a plane. The entire plane can be covered with the repeating design of wallpaper, floor tile, or polygons, as shown below. Covering a plane with a repeating design is called **tessellating** the plane.

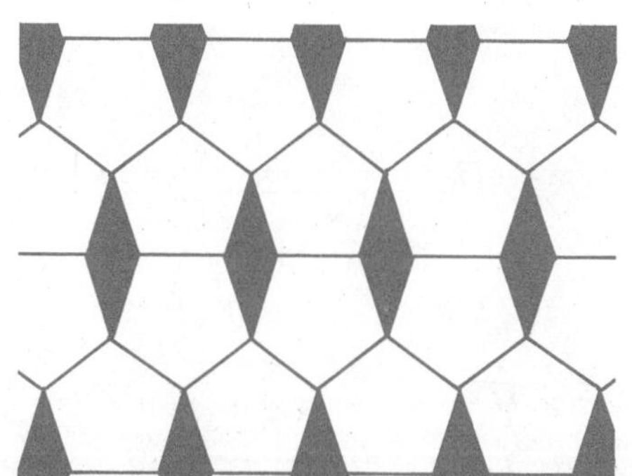

Photri

About 700 years ago, repeating designs were used to decorate the Alhambra, a palace in Spain. Moorish artists used tiles to make their designs. A Moorish design is pictured at the left.

These designs influenced a modern Dutch artist, M. C. Escher. He saw the possibility of covering a surface with a repeating design of animals or people. Here are some examples of Escher's work.

M. C. Escher, Escher Foundation, Haags Gemeentemuseum, The Hague

Notice that each of these designs, if repeated, will cover a plane. Escher constructed his designs from regular polygons. In the first figure he used an equilateral triangle, in the second a square, and in the third a regular hexagon.

You can make designs that tessellate the plane from both regular and nonregular polygons.

Example 1:

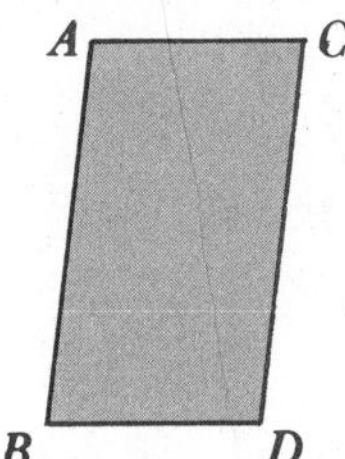

Since parallelograms will tessellate the plane, we can use them to make a repeating design.

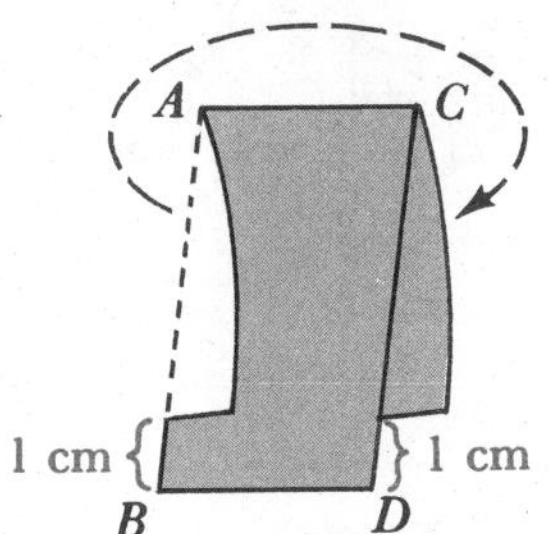

Cut a pattern from side $\overline{AB}$ and slide it to side $\overline{DC}$ or vice versa.

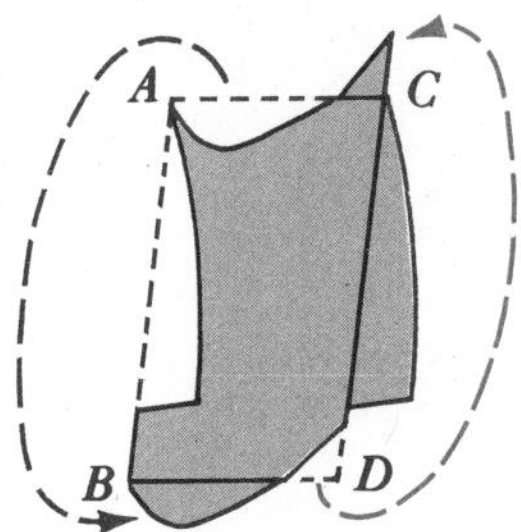

Cut a pattern from side $\overline{AC}$ and slide it to side $\overline{BD}$ or vice versa. Or as in this case, do both.

The last shape above can usually be made to look like something interesting by adding some lines and shading. In this case, we can make it look like a sailboat.

Then the sailboat pattern can be used to make a repeating design. Trace the outline of the pattern, slide it, trace again, and so on. Then add the necessary lines and shading.

Notice that we can slide any figure onto any other figure in the design.

Example 2:

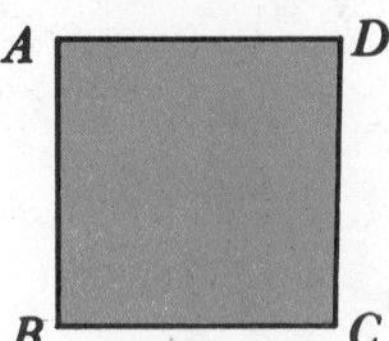

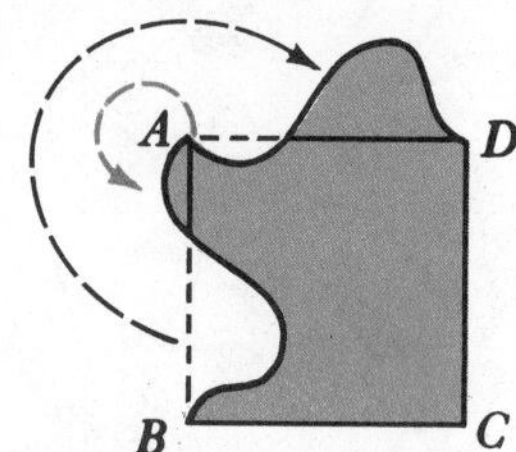

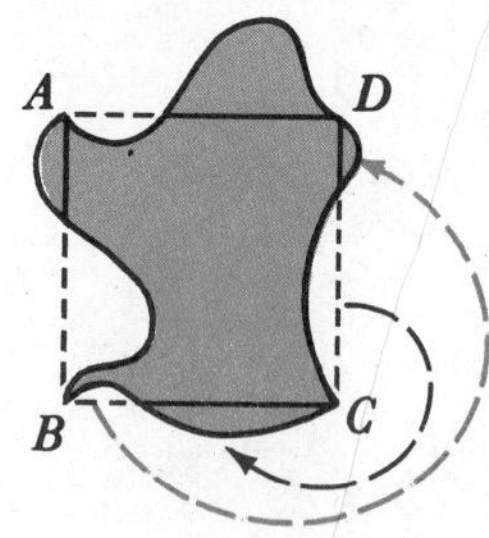

To make a figure that will tessellate the plane from square *ABCD*, pair sides $\overline{AB}$ and $\overline{AD}$ with common vertex *A*, and sides $\overline{CB}$ and $\overline{CD}$ with common vertex *C*.

Cut a shape from side $\overline{AD}$. Turn it onto side $\overline{AB}$ or vice versa. Place the shape so that it is the same distance from *A*.

Cut a shape from side $\overline{CD}$. Turn it onto side $\overline{CB}$ or vice versa. Place the shape so that it is the same distance from *C*.

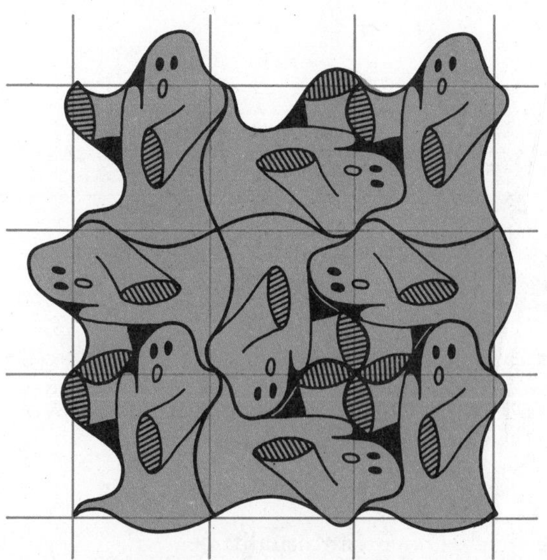

At certain points in this design, one figure can be turned onto another. For example, the four figures in the upper left can be turned to coincide with one another.

Example 3:

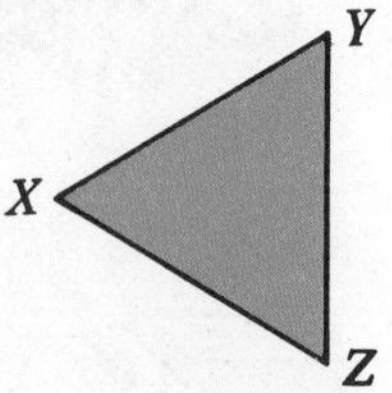

Using equilateral triangle *XYZ*, we can make one of Escher's figures that tessellate a plane.

Cut a shape from side $\overline{XY}$, flip it over, and add it to side $\overline{XZ}$ so that any point on the shape will be the same distance from point X as it was from point Y.

Construct M, the midpoint of $\overline{YZ}$.

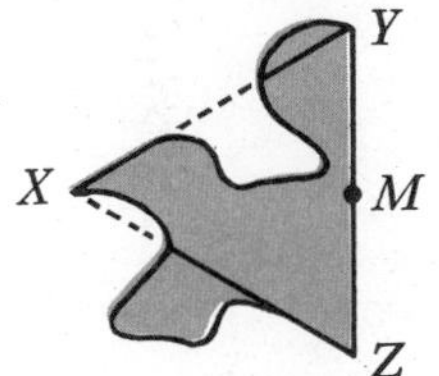

Cut a shape from $\overline{YM}$, flip it, and add it to $\overline{MZ}$ so that a point is the same distance from M as it was from Y.

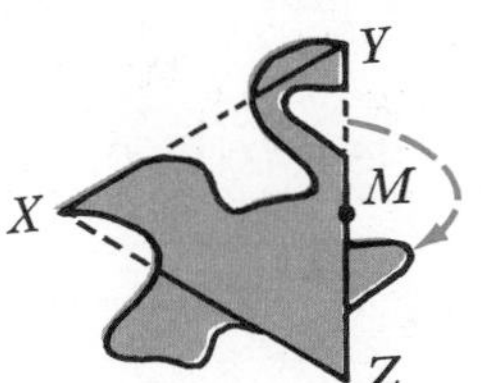

Cut a shape from $\overline{MZ}$, flip it, and add it to $\overline{YM}$ so that a point is the same distance from Y as it was from M.

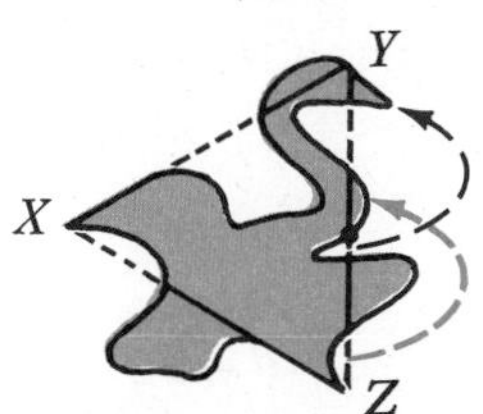

Notice that we can slide any white or gray swan onto any swan of the same color. We can also reflect and then slide any white or gray swan onto any swan of the other color.

M. C. Escher, Escher Foundation, Haags Gemeentemuseum, The Hague

Now try to tessellate the plane. First use polygons in a repeating pattern. Then draw your own repeating design. Use any method shown in the three examples.

6 MORE ABOUT PROOFS

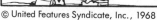

Reasoning is very important in writing proofs. But reasoning is used in other places besides geometry. Even Charlie Brown uses reasoning to decide that he cannot talk to the little red-haired girl.

Now that you have worked with proofs, we can take a more detailed look at the ideas involved.

True and False If-Then Statements

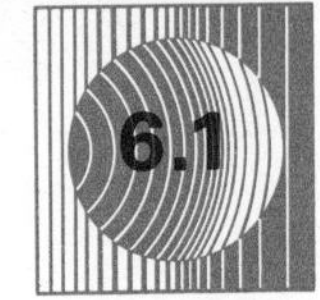

We use if-then statements frequently in everyday life, as well as in mathematics. Obviously, not every if-then statement is true.

hypothesis — conclusion

If you have a white beard, your name is Santa Claus.

A. Devaney, Inc.

Authenticated News International

The sentence is true for the man on the left, but not for the man on the right. In Uncle Sam's case, the hypothesis is true (he has a white beard), but the conclusion is false. Since a case exists for which the hypothesis is true and the conclusion is false, we say the if-then statement is false.

An if-then statement is false if an example can be found for which the hypothesis is true and the conclusion is false.

Such an example is called a **counterexample.** Only one counterexample is needed to prove that an if-then statement is false. (The statement might be true in some cases, but it must be true in *all* cases before we say it is true.)

Example 1: Find a counterexample to show that the following if-then statement is false:

If $x^2 = 16$, then $x = 4$.

Counterexample: $x = -4$ (The hypothesis $x^2 = 16$ is true, but the conclusion $x = 4$ is false.)

To show that an if-then statement is true, we usually prove it as a theorem. First, however, we have to accept some if-then statements as being true without proof. These are our postulates.

We can't prove theorems without having some postulates. If we try to do that, our reasoning will take us in circles. This is similar to circular definitions. If we try to define terms without first accepting some undefined terms, our definitions would circle back to the term we are trying to define.

Example 2: What if-then statement is proved by the following two-column proof?

Given: $4x = 20$

Prove: $x = 5$

Proof:

STATEMENTS	REASONS
1. $4x = 20$	1. Given
2. $\frac{1}{4}(4x) = \frac{1}{4}(20)$	2. Multiplication Property of =
3. $\frac{1}{4}(4x) = 5$	3. Substitution of 5 for $\frac{1}{4}(20)$
4. $(\frac{1}{4} \cdot 4)x = 5$	4. Associative Property of Mult.
5. $1x = 5$	5. Inverse Prop. of Mult.
6. $x = 5$	6. Identity Prop. of Mult.

This proves If $4x = 20$, then $x = 5$.

In Example 2, you might be tempted to say that we have proved $x = 5$. You would be wrong! We proved *If* $4x = 20$, *then* $x = 5$. In any proof we are proving that an if-then statement is true.

An if-then statement is **true** if when the hypothesis is true, the conclusion is true.

When we prove a general if-then statement (such as the Angle-Angle-Side Theorem on page 178), we usually restate it in given-prove form. We draw a figure and introduce appropriate labels. Remember that every theorem can be restated in if-then form, even if it is not stated that way to begin with.

Exercises 6.1

Ⓐ **1.** An if-then statement is false when the hypothesis is true and the conclusion is (true, false).

2. An example that makes the hypothesis true and the conclusion false in an if-then statement is called a ______.

3. An if-then statement is true if whenever the hypothesis is true, the conclusion is (true, false).

4. When we use a two-column proof to prove an if-then statement, we label the (hypothesis, conclusion) as *Given*.

Ⓑ 5–16. Find a counterexample to show that each if-then statement is false. Use the real numbers as the replacement set in Exercises 9–12.

5. If a man lives in Kansas City, he lives in Kansas.

6. If a woman lives in Missouri, she lives in St. Louis.

Authenticated News International

7. If an animal can fly, it is a bird.

8. If an animal is a bird, it can fly.

9. If $x^2 = 25$, then $x = -5$.

10. If $x > 3$, then $x = 4$ or $x > 4$.

11. If $ab = 0$, then $a = 0$.

12. If x is nonnegative, then $x > 0$.

13. If two angles are complementary, the angles are not congruent.

14. If two angles are supplementary, one is acute and the other is obtuse.

15. If two angles have the same vertex, the angles are adjacent.

16. If three angles of one triangle are congruent to the corresponding angles of another triangle, the triangles are congruent.

17–20. Restate each theorem in if-then form.

17. Vertical angles are congruent.

18. Alternate interior angles formed by a transversal and two parallel lines are congruent.

19. In a plane, two lines that are perpendicular to the same line are parallel.

20. The diagonals of a rectangle are congruent.

21–24. Which theorem in Exercises 17–20 is restated in given-prove form in each exercise below? (You do *not* need to prove the theorem.)

21. Given: Coplanar lines a, b, and c; $a \perp c$; $b \perp c$

Prove: $a \parallel b$

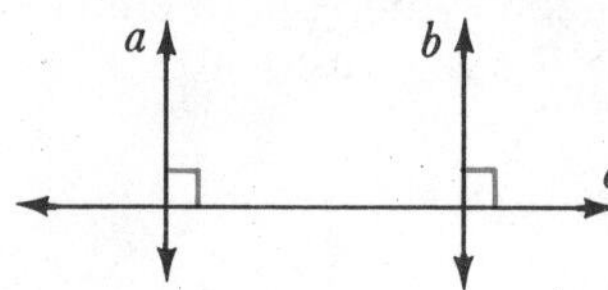

22. Given: Intersecting lines a and b

Prove: $\angle 1 \cong \angle 2$

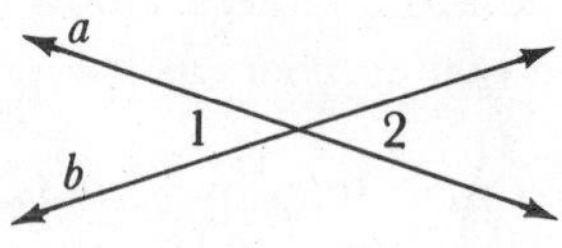

23. Given: $c \parallel d$, transversal t

Prove: $\angle 1 \cong \angle 2$

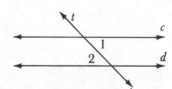

24. Given: Rectangle $ABCD$ with diagonals $\overline{AC}$ and $\overline{BD}$

Prove: $\overline{AC} \cong \overline{BD}$

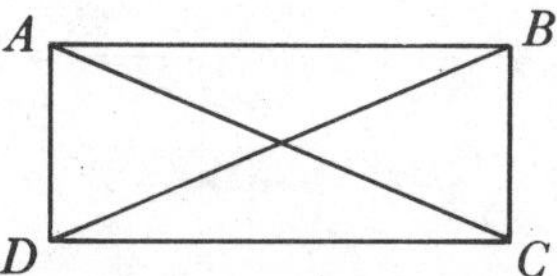

© **25–28.** Refer to Exercises 25–28 on pages 108 and 109. Write the if-then statement that is proved in each exercise.

29–34. The if-then statement *If X, then Y* can be expressed in other ways such as the following:

Y if *X*.	*X* is sufficient for *Y*.
X only if *Y*.	*Y* is necessary for *X*.
X implies *Y*.	*Y* follows from *X*.

Express each statement below in if-then form.

29. Fudge is good only if it has walnuts in it.

30. Today is Monday implies tomorrow is Tuesday.

31. Two angles are supplementary if the sum of their measures is 180.

32. Two lines being in the same plane is necessary for the lines to be parallel or intersecting.

33. $x = 4$ follows from $2x - 1 = 7$.

34. $x^2 = 16$ is sufficient for $x = 4$ or $x = -4$.

If-and-Only-If Statements

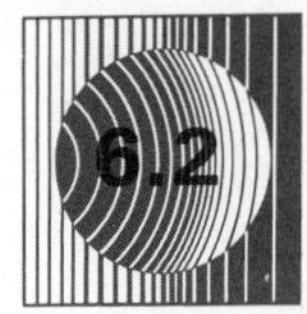

H. Armstrong Roberts

If an animal is a giraffe, it has a long neck.

If an animal has a long neck, it is a giraffe.

Grant Heilman

Recall that two if-then statements related as above (the hypothesis and the conclusion are interchanged) are **converses.** An if-then statement can be true while its converse is false.

In some cases, however, both the if-then statement and its converse are true. In that case, the two sentences can be replaced by one true sentence that employs **if and only if**.

If an angle is acute, its measure is less than 90.

These two true statements can be replaced by one true statement.

If its measure is less than 90, an angle is acute.

An angle is acute *if and only if* its measure is less than 90.

In general,

both true: If X, then Y. / If Y, then X. — is equivalent to — X if and only if Y.

Example: Replace the following true statements with one true statement:

If $a + c = b + c$, then $a = b$.
If $a = b$, then $a + c = b + c$.

$a + c = b + c$ if and only if $a = b$.

Sometimes theorems are stated in *if-and-only-if* form. If so, the proof consists of two parts. Consider the following theorem:

Angle Bisector Theorem

A point is on the bisector of an angle if and only if the point is *equidistant* from the sides of the angle.

NOTE: We take *equidistant* to mean the point is in the interior of the angle and the perpendicular segments from the point to both sides are congruent.

The two statements to be proved are

a. If a point is on the bisector of an angle, it is equidistant from the sides of the angle.

b. If a point is equidistant from the sides of an angle, it is on the bisector of the angle.

Part a.

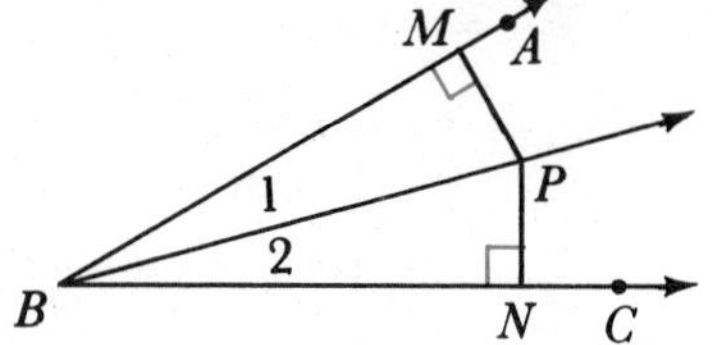

Given: Point P is on the bisector of $\angle ABC$.

Prove: $\overline{PM} \cong \overline{PN}$

Proof:

STATEMENTS	REASONS
1. $\angle 1 \cong \angle 2$	1. Definition of angle bisector
2. $\overline{PM} \perp \overline{MB}$, $\overline{PN} \perp \overline{NB}$	2. Perp. Line Post. (p. 60)
3. $\angle BMP$ and $\angle BNP$ are rt. $\angle$s.	3. Definition of perpendicular
4. $\triangle BMP$ and $\triangle BNP$ are rt. $\triangle$s.	4. Definition of right triangle
5. $\overline{BP} \cong \overline{BP}$	5. A segment is $\cong$ to itself.
6. $\triangle BMP \cong \triangle BNP$	6. HA Theorem
7. $\overline{PM} \cong \overline{PN}$	7. Corres. parts of $\cong$ $\triangle$s are $\cong$.

The proof of part **b** is left as an exercise.

Exercises 6.2

Ⓐ **1.** When you interchange the hypothesis and the conclusion of an if-then statement, the resulting sentence is called the ______.

2. When an if-then statement and its converse are both true, we can restate them as one true ______ statement.

3. True or False? If an if-then statement is true, its converse is also true.

4. What is the converse of *If* $3x = 9$, *then* $x = 3$?

Ⓑ **5–16.** Write *true* or *false* for each statement. Then write the converse of each statement and tell if it is true or false.

5. If a family lives in Hawaii, the family lives on an island.

6. If a flower has thorns, it is a rose.

7. If a car is a foreign car, it is a Fiat.

8. If a cat's name is Morris, it is finicky.

9. If $a^2 > 0$, then $a > 0$.

10. If $x^2 = 64$, then $x = 8$.

11. If two angles are vertical angles, the angles are congruent.

12. If two triangles are congruent, the corresponding sides and angles are congruent.

13. If two lines are parallel, the alternate interior angles formed by the two lines and a transversal are congruent.

14. If two angles are congruent, the angles are right angles.

15. If x is an integer, x is a real number.

16. If $a^2 - b^2 = 0$, then $a = b$.

17–20. Rewrite each pair of statements by using *if and only if*.

17. If $a = b$, then $a - b = 0$.
If $a - b = 0$, then $a = b$.

18. If $\triangle ABC$ is equilateral, then $\triangle ABC$ is equiangular.
If $\triangle ABC$ is equiangular, then $\triangle ABC$ is equilateral.

19. If an angle is a right angle, then its measure is 90.
If its measure is 90, then an angle is a right angle.

20. If the nonparallel sides of a trapezoid are congruent, both pairs of base angles are congruent.
If both pairs of base angles of a trapezoid are congruent, the nonparallel sides are congruent.

21–24. Rewrite each theorem in if-and-only-if form.

21. Perpendicular Bisector Theorem (p. 110)

22. Alternate Interior Angles Theorem (p. 128)

23. Corresponding Angles Theorem (p. 132)

24. Isosceles Triangle Theorem (p. 180)

25–28. Determine if statements X and Y can be connected by *if and only if* to form a true statement. If not possible, write *no*. If possible, write the statement.

	X	Y
25.	Two angles are adjacent.	Two angles share a vertex.
26.	$a - c = b - c$	$a = b$
27.	The sum of the measures of two angles is 90.	Two angles are complementary.
28.	Two lines are perpendicular.	The lines form a right angle.

29–32. Write the two if-then statements that can be formed from each if-and-only-if statement.

29. $\dfrac{x^2 - y^2}{x - y} = x + y$ if and only if $x \neq y$.

30. An if-then statement is false if and only if the hypothesis is true and the conclusion is false.

31. An angle is an obtuse angle if and only if its measure is greater than 90.

32. Two lines in the same plane are parallel if and only if the lines do not intersect.

© **33.** Prove part **b** of the Angle Bisector Theorem, using the restatement and the figure below.

Given: $\overline{PM} \perp \overline{MB}$, $\overline{PN} \perp \overline{NB}$, $\overline{PM} \cong \overline{PN}$

Prove: Point P is on the bisector of $\angle ABC$.

[*Plan:* Prove $\triangle BMP \cong \triangle BNP$ by the HL Theorem.]

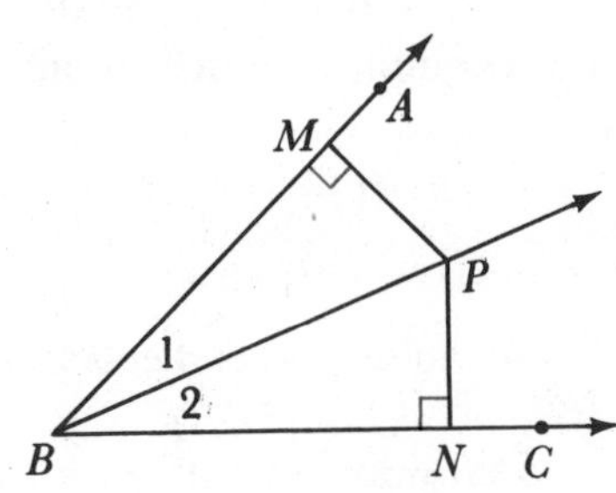

34–37. Every if-then statement has two other related statements besides the converse. These are called the **inverse** and the **contrapositive.**

Given statement: If X, then Y.

Inverse: If not X, then not Y.

Contrapositive: If not Y, then not X.

Write the inverse and the contrapositive of each statement in Exercises 11–14. Then write *true* or *false* for each.

38. When an if-then statement is true, is its inverse necessarily true?

39. When an if-then statement is true, does its contrapositive seem to be true?

40. True or False? For a given if-then statement, the contrapositive of the converse is the inverse.

41. True or False? For a given if-then statement, the converse of the inverse is the contrapositive.

42. Some other ways of stating X if and only if Y are as follows:

X is necessary and sufficient for Y.
Y is necessary and sufficient for X.
If X, then Y, and conversely.
If Y, then X, and conversely.

Rewrite the statement in Exercise 31 in each form above.

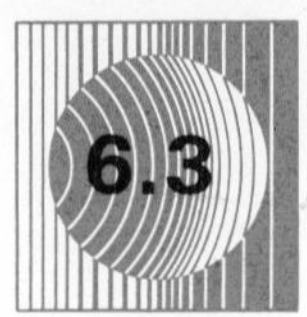

6.3 Good Definitions

A good definition should be stated in such a way that it is reversible. For example, the definition

A *regular polygon* is an equilateral and equiangular convex polygon

can be reversed as

An equilateral and equiangular convex polygon is a *regular polygon*.

Definitions should be reversible, because in geometry we consider all definitions to be equivalent to if-and-only-if statements, which are reversible.

X if and only if *Y*  *Y* if and only if *X*.

We often state definitions in if-and-only-if form to make sure that they are reversible. For example,

A polygon is a *regular polygon* if and only if it is an equilateral and equiangular convex polygon.

Exercises 6.3

Ⓐ **1.** In geometry, all definitions are equivalent to ______ statements, which are reversible.

2. *X* if and only if *Y* means the same as (*X* and *Y*, *Y* if *X*, *Y* if and only if *X*).

3–10. Are the following definitions reversible?

3. A cow is an animal with four legs.

4. A banjo is a stringed musical instrument.

5. The midpoint of a segment is the point that is between the endpoints and equidistant from them.

6. A triangle is a 3-sided polygon.

7. A rectangle is a 4-sided polygon.

8. Alabama is a southern state.

9. A right angle is an angle whose measure is 90.

10. Adjacent angles are two angles with a common side.

Ⓑ **11–18.** Complete each definition.

11. Points are collinear if and only if ______. (p. 14)

12. A figure is a segment DE if and only if ______. (p. 15)

13. Two rays are opposite rays if and only if ______. (p. 15)

14. A statement is a postulate if and only if ______. (p. 11)

15. A ray AZ is the bisector of $\angle BAC$ if and only if ______. (p. 56)

16. Two angles are supplementary if and only if ______. (p. 56)

17. In a plane, a line is the perpendicular bisector of a segment if and only if ______. (p. 61)

18. Angles are congruent angles if and only if ______. (p. 64)

19–28. Restate the definition of each term in if-and-only-if form.

19. coplanar points (p. 14)
20. angle (p. 48)
21. acute angle (p. 60)
22. complementary angles (p. 60)
23. perpendicular lines (p. 60)
24. congruent triangles (p. 94)
25. isosceles triangle (p. 180)
26. obtuse triangle (p. 180)
27. transversal (p. 128)
28. right triangle (p. 180)

Ⓒ **29–30.** Write *yes* or *no* to tell if the "definition" can be used as a reason for the given conclusion.

Definition: If the measure of an angle is less than 90, it is acute.

29. *Given:* $m\angle A < 90$

Conclusion: $\angle A$ is acute.

30. *Given:* $\angle A$ is acute.

Conclusion: $m\angle A < 90$

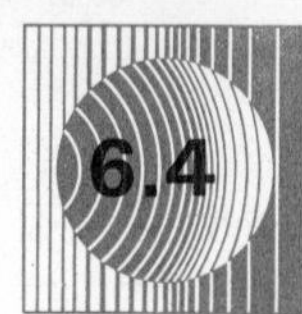

6.4 Patterns of Reasoning

Courtesy General Motors Corporation

If a car is a Cadillac, it is an American car.

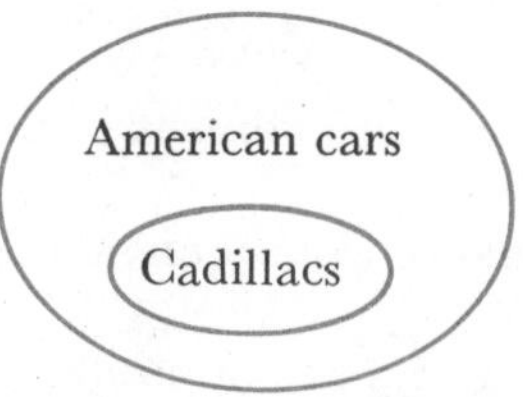

Look at the Euler diagram and consider each argument below.

TRUE	A Seville is a Cadillac. So a Seville is an American car.	A Toyota is not an American car. So a Toyota is not a Cadillac.
FALSE	A Volare is an American car. So a Volare is a Cadillac.	A Corvette is not a Cadillac. So a Corvette is not an American car.

Each argument above is based on the original if-then statement and one other statement. If we let X stand for the hypothesis and Y for the conclusion, the patterns of reasoning can be shown as follows:

VALID ARGUMENTS	**Affirming the Hypothesis** If X, then Y. X. So Y.	When these are true, this is true.	**Denying the Conclusion** If X, then Y. Not Y. So not X.
FAULTY ARGUMENTS	**Affirming the Conclusion** If X, then Y. Y. So X.	When these are true, this might be false.	**Denying the Hypothesis** If X, then Y. Not X. So not Y.

Examples: Decide if each argument is valid or faulty. Then name the pattern of reasoning that is illustrated.

1. If two angles are vertical angles, the angles are congruent.
$\angle A$ and $\angle B$ are vertical angles.
So $\angle A$ and $\angle B$ are congruent.

The argument is valid. It illustrates Affirming the Hypothesis.

2. If a cat eats Tasty Tuna Cat Food, it will be healthy and happy.
Minerva does not eat Tasty Tuna Cat Food.
So Minerva will not be healthy and happy.

The argument is faulty. It illustrates Denying the Hypothesis.

3. If a woman wears Blinky-Winky Eyelashes, she will be beautiful.
Ms. Hollywood Starr is beautiful.
So Ms. Hollywood Starr wears Blinky-Winky Eyelashes.

The argument is faulty. It illustrates Affirming the Conclusion.

Most advertisers are too clever to make their advertising as clearly false as in Examples 2 and 3. Nevertheless, some of them hope you will use faulty reasoning when you see their advertisements. Suppose you see an advertisement like the following:

The advertiser hopes you will use the following faulty pattern of reasoning (Denying the Hypothesis):

If a man uses Slicko Hair Cream, he will attract beautiful women.
The man on the right doesn't use Slicko.
So the man on the right will not attract beautiful women.

Exercises 6.4

Ⓐ 1. Which patterns of reasoning below are valid?

a. Affirming the Hypothesis b. Denying the Hypothesis

c. Denying the Conclusion d. Affirming the Conclusion

2. Which patterns of reasoning in Exercise 1 are faulty?

3–6. Which pattern of reasoning in Exercise 1 is illustrated?

3. If X, then Y.
Not X.
So not Y.

4. If X, then Y.
Not Y.
So not X.

5. If X, then Y.
X.
So Y.

6. If X, then Y.
Y.
So X.

Ⓑ 7–10. Write *valid* or *faulty* for each argument. Then name the pattern of reasoning that is used.

Courtesy Qantas Airways Limited

7. If a person lives in Quebec, he or she lives in Canada.
Pierre lives in Quebec.
So Pierre lives in Canada.

8. If today is Friday, tomorrow is Saturday.
Tomorrow is not Saturday.
So today is not Friday.

9. If you are from Australia, you have seen a koala.
Ann is not from Australia.
So Ann has not seen a koala.

10. If it rains in Spain, it falls mainly on the plain.
The rain is falling mainly on the plain.
So it is raining in Spain.

11–22. Make a valid conclusion from each pair of statements if possible. If not possible, write *no conclusion possible*.

11. If $x = \sqrt{2}$, then $x^2 = 2$.
$x^2 \neq 2$

12. If a number is rational, the number is real.
$\frac{2}{3}$ is rational.

13. If a person lives in Boise, he or she lives in Idaho.
Connie lives in Idaho.

14. If you live in Puerto Rico, you live on an island.
Juan doesn't live on an island.

15. If two angles are congruent, their measures are equal.
$\angle A \cong \angle B$

16. If an angle is acute, its measure is less than 90.
$m\angle A$ is less than 90.

17. In $\triangle ABC$ if $\overline{AC} \cong \overline{AB}$, then $\angle B \cong \angle C$.
$\overline{AC}$ is not $\cong$ to $\overline{AB}$.

18. If $\triangle ABC \cong \triangle DEF$, then $\angle A \cong \angle D$.
$\angle A$ is not $\cong$ to $\angle D$.

19. If alternate interior angles 1 and 2 are congruent, lines ℓ and k are parallel.
ℓ and k are not parallel.

20. If lines r and s are parallel, corresponding angles 3 and 4 are congruent.
r and s are not parallel.

21. No pigs can fly.
Porky is a pig.

22. All fish can swim.
Flipper cannot swim.

© 23–25. The following pairs of statements come from a book called *Symbolic Logic* by Lewis Carroll. Carroll is better known as the author of *Alice in Wonderland,* but he was also a mathematician. See if you can draw a conclusion from each pair of statements. You may find it helpful to change the statements to if-then form.

23. All well-fed canaries sing loud.
No canary is melancholy if it sings loud.

24. All my sisters have colds.
No one can sing who has a cold.

25. No lobsters are unreasonable.
No reasonable creatures expect impossibilities.

1–2. Find a counterexample to show that each statement is false.

1. If x^2 is positive, then x is positive.

2. If an angle is acute, its measure is less than 45.

3–4. Write the converse of each statement in Exercises 1–2. Then tell if the converse is true or false.

5. Can statements A and B be connected by *if and only if* to form a true statement? (Assume $c \neq 0$).

A: If $a = b$, then $ac = bc$. B: If $ac = bc$, then $a = b$.

6. Restate the following definition in if-and-only-if form:
An obtuse angle is an angle whose measure is greater than 90.

7. Is the pattern of reasoning at the right valid?

If X, then Y.
Not Y.
So not X.

REASONING AT WORK

OFFICE OCCUPATIONS

Office workers do a wide range of jobs. Many clerical employees work with objects and often do detailed and repetitive tasks. On the other hand, most professional office employees work with ideas. To do their jobs, they need good judgment and the ability to use valid reasoning.

Office workers might deal with any of the following topics. See if you can use reasoning to answer each question.

1. ***Labor Contract:*** *Employees who have earned 1–4 days of paid vacation may request an additional number of days without pay for a total of no more than 5 days. Employees who have earned 6–9 days of paid vacation may request an additional number of days without pay for a total of no more than 10 days.*
   An employee has earned 3 days of paid vacation. How many days of total vacation can he or she take? How many of these days will be unpaid?

2. ***Insurance Policy:*** *If a total of \$200 of eligible expenses is incurred collectively by the covered members of a family during the calendar year, the deductible requirement will be waived for all covered members of the family for the rest of the year.*
   A certain family has had \$457 in eligible expenses during the calendar year till now. If further expenses are incurred, will the deductible have to be paid again?

3. ***Income Tax:*** *If interest is \$400 or less, do not complete this part. But enter amount of interest received on Form 1040, line 11.*
   A person received \$178 in interest. What amount should be entered on Form 1040, line 11?

Frank Kuechmann

Indirect Proofs

Most of the proofs in this book have been *direct proofs*. Another type of proof is the **indirect proof.** Theorems that are difficult to prove with a direct proof can sometimes be proved easily with an indirect proof.

Let's talk about an example of indirect proof from everyday life. This type of indirect argument is heard often on TV detective shows.

Example 1:

Defending attorney: If my clients had committed the crime, they had to be at the scene of the crime. According to witnesses, the crime occurred at 3:10 A.M. We have a witness who saw the defendants at an all-night diner at 3:20 A.M. The diner is 17 miles from the scene of the crime. Therefore, my clients are not guilty.

A brief outline of the attorney's indirect argument is as follows:

1. The clients are either guilty or not guilty.
2. To prove they are *not* guilty, I will assume they are guilty and show that this leads to a contradiction of a known fact.
3. When I assume they are guilty, this means they had to be at the scene of the crime. But we have a witness who saw them at another place at about the time the crime was committed.
4. Therefore, my clients are not guilty.

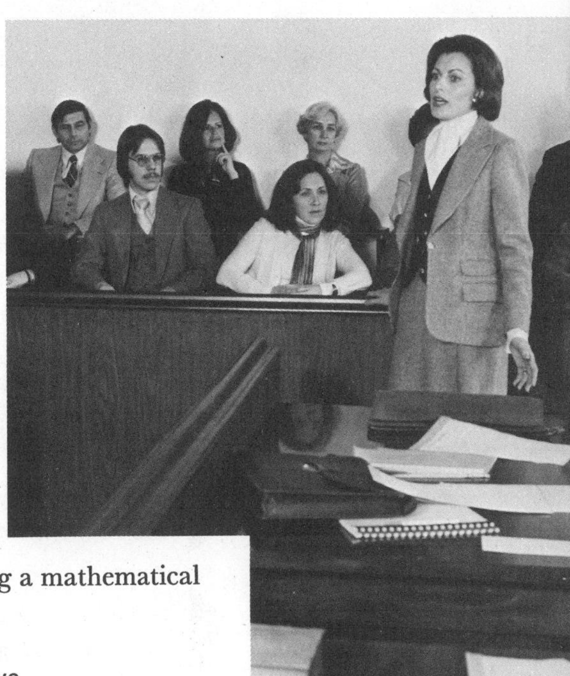

H. Armstrong Roberts

This same type of argument can be used in proving a mathematical theorem by an indirect proof:

1. Assume the opposite of the fact you want to prove.
2. Show that this leads to a contradiction of a known fact.
3. So you know that your original assumption is false and that the fact you want to prove must be true.

We have already used indirect proofs earlier, and we introduced the Principle of Indirect Reasoning at that time.

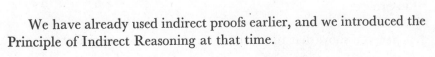

Principle of Indirect Reasoning

> If assuming statement p is true leads to a contradiction of a true statement, then statement p is false.

Notice how the Principle of Indirect Reasoning is used in the following proof. (NOTE: $\ncong$ means "is not congruent to.")

Example 2:

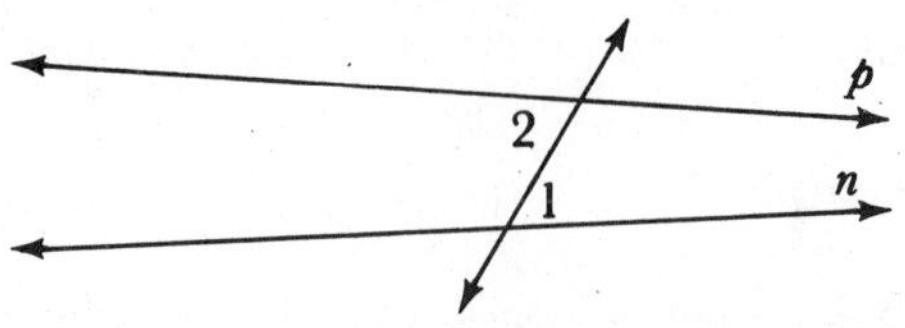

Given: $\angle 1 \ncong \angle 2$

Prove: p is not parallel to n.

Proof:

STATEMENTS	REASONS
1. Assume $p \parallel n$.	**1.** Assumption for indirect proof
2. $\angle 1 \cong \angle 2$	**2.** If a transversal intersects two $\parallel$ lines, the alternate interior $\angle$s are $\cong$.
3. But, $\angle 1 \ncong \angle 2$.	**3.** Given
4. Therefore, p is not parallel to n.	**4.** Principle of Indirect Reasoning

Notice how step 3 denies the conclusion in step 2. So in step 4 we can conclude the opposite of the hypothesis in step 1.

The proofs of the next two theorems will be left as exercises. Restatements are given in Exercises 28 and 29.

Theorem

In a plane, if two lines intersect and there is a line perpendicular to each of them, the perpendiculars to the intersecting lines also intersect.

Theorem

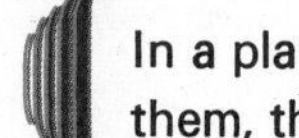

In a plane, if two lines intersect and there is a line parallel to each of them, the parallels to the intersecting lines also intersect.

Exercises 6.5

Ⓐ **1.** In an indirect proof, you assume the ______ of the fact you want to prove.

2. Then you show that this leads to a ______ of a known fact.

3–10. Give the opposite of each statement.

3. $m\angle A = m\angle B$ **4.** $\angle C \cong \angle D$ **5.** $\ell \perp k$

6. $y = 4$ **7.** n is odd. **8.** $x^2 \neq 2$

9. $\overline{AB} \ncong \overline{CD}$ **10.** ℓ is not parallel to p.

Ⓑ **11–24.** Give the missing reasons.

Given: $\overline{AC} \ncong \overline{BC}$

Prove: $\angle A \ncong \angle B$

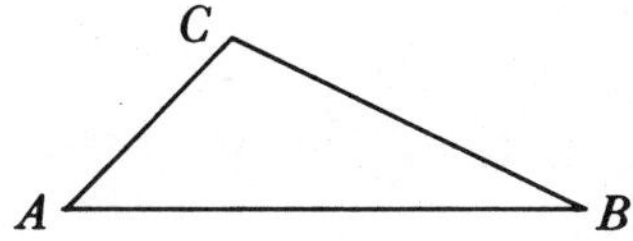

Proof:

STATEMENTS	REASONS
1. Assume $\angle A \cong \angle B$.	1. **11.** ___
2. Then $\overline{AC} \cong \overline{BC}$	2. **12.** ___
3. But, $\overline{AC} \ncong \overline{BC}$	3. **13.** ___
4. Therefore, $\angle A \ncong \angle B$.	4. **14.** ___

Given: $\overline{DF} \ncong \overline{EF}$, $\overline{FG} \perp \overline{DE}$

Prove: G is not the midpoint of $\overline{DE}$.

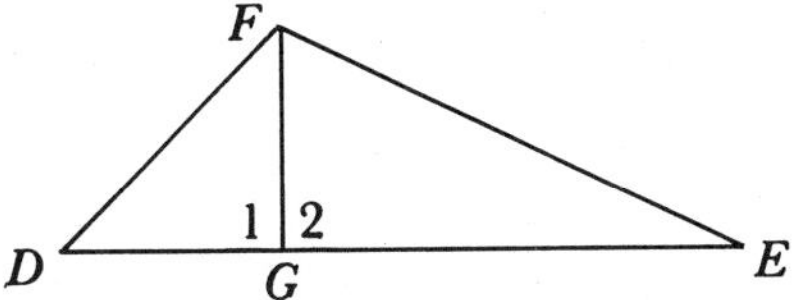

Proof:

STATEMENTS	REASONS
1. Assume G is the midpoint of $\overline{DE}$.	1. **15.** ___
2. Then $\overline{DG} \cong \overline{GE}$.	2. **16.** ___
3. $\overline{FG} \perp \overline{DE}$	3. **17.** ___
4. $\angle 1$ and $\angle 2$ are right angles.	4. **18.** ___
5. $\triangle DGF$ and $\triangle EGF$ are right $\triangle$s.	5. **19.** ___
6. $\overline{FG} \cong \overline{FG}$	6. **20.** ___
7. $\triangle DGF \cong \triangle EGF$	7. **21.** ___
8. $\overline{DF} \cong \overline{EF}$	8. **22.** ___
9. But, $\overline{DF} \ncong \overline{EF}$.	9. **23.** ___
10. Therefore, G is not the midpoint of $\overline{DE}$.	10. **24.** ___

Ⓒ **25–29.** Give an indirect proof of each of the following:

25. Given: $a \parallel c$, $\angle 2 \ncong \angle 3$

Prove: b is not parallel to a.

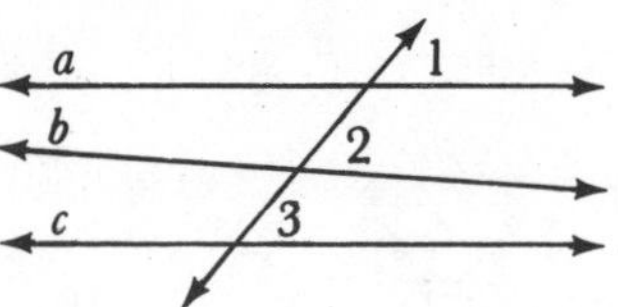

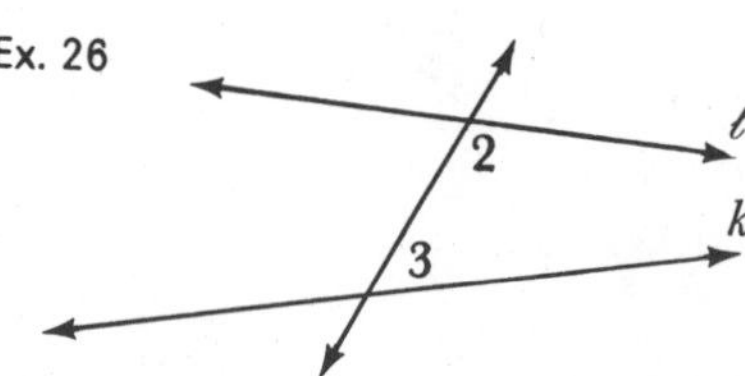

26. Given: $m\angle 2 + m\angle 3 \neq 180$

Prove: ℓ is not parallel to k.

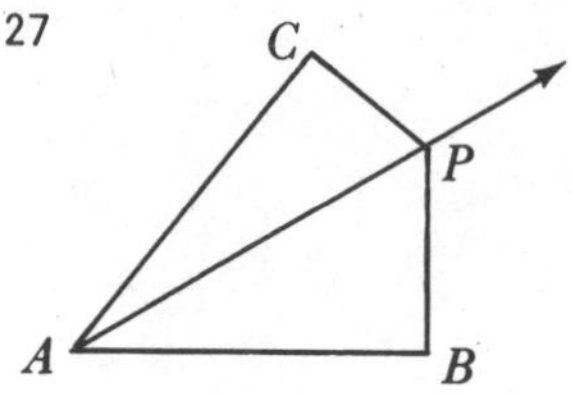

27. Given: $\overline{AC} \cong \overline{AB}$, $\overline{CP} \ncong \overline{PB}$

Prove: $\overrightarrow{AP}$ is not the bisector of $\angle CAB$.

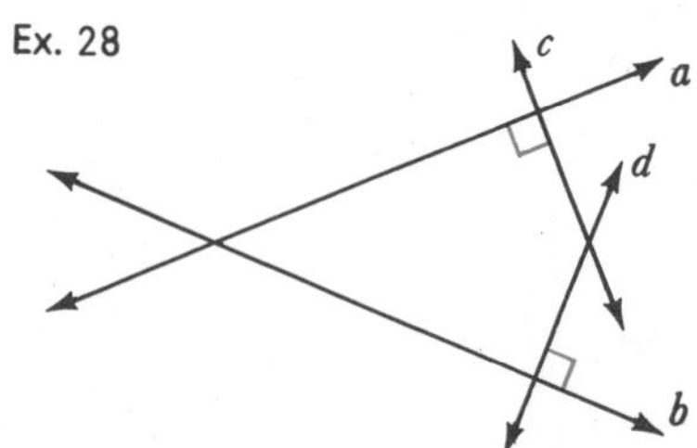

28. Given: a and b are intersecting lines, $c \perp a$, $d \perp b$

Prove: c intersects d.

HINT: Assume $c \parallel d$.

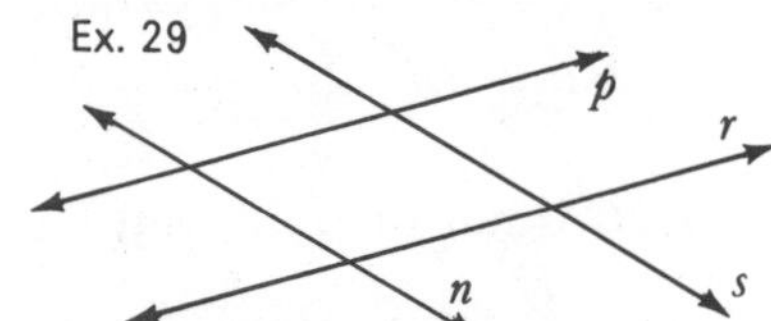

29. Given: p and n are intersecting lines, $r \parallel p$, $s \parallel n$

Prove: r intersects s.

Algebra Review

Review these skills:

- *using <, =, and >*
- *solving inequalities*

1–9. Which symbol, <, =, or >, should replace each ▨ ?

1. $0 \cdot 5$ ▨ 5 **2.** 2^3 ▨ 8 **3.** $|-3|$ ▨ 0

4. $\frac{3}{4}$ ▨ $\frac{5}{6}$ **5.** $\frac{1}{8}$ ▨ 0.125 **6.** 10^3 ▨ 999

7–18. Solve.

7. $x + 2 < 3$ **8.** $y - 7 > 10$ **9.** $7y < 49$

10. $4a > 36$ **11.** $\frac{x}{2} > 8$ **12.** $\frac{b}{5} < 2$

13. $3r > 2$ **14.** $5x - 2 < 23$ **15.** $6x + 3 > 15$

16. $\frac{a}{3} + 2 < 1$ **17.** $-x < 2$ **18.** $-3y > 15$

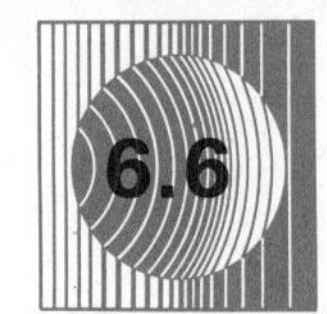

Is There Only One Proof?

There is usually more than one way to prove the same theorem. In this section, we consider some different proofs for theorems proved earlier. First, we introduce two new terms.

A **median** of a triangle is a segment from a vertex to the midpoint of the opposite side.

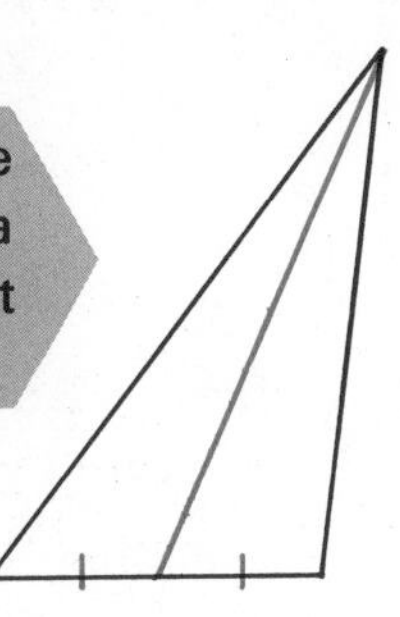

An **altitude** of a triangle is a segment from a vertex perpendicular to the line containing the opposite side.

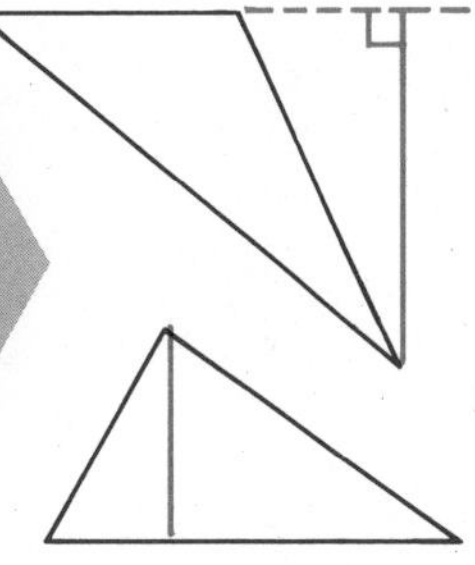

Every triangle has three medians and three altitudes, and every triangle has three bisectors of its angles. Also, in the plane of a given triangle there are three perpendicular bisectors of the sides.

In Section 5.6 we proved both parts of the Isosceles Triangle Theorem (p. 180) by using the bisector of the vertex angle as an auxiliary figure. Now we give another proof of part **a,** using the median to the base. (In Exercises 9–13, another proof of part **b** is given, using the altitude to the base.)

Given: $\overline{AC} \cong \overline{BC}$

Prove: $\angle A \cong \angle B$

[*Plan:* Use the median to side $\overline{AB}$ as an auxiliary segment. Prove $\triangle ACM \cong \triangle BCM$ by SSS.]

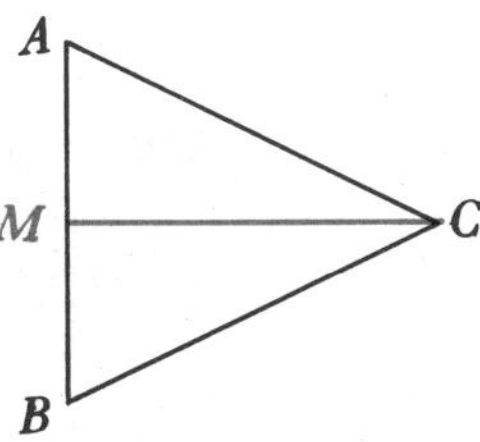

Proof:

STATEMENTS	REASONS
1. Let M be the midpoint of $\overline{AB}$.	**1.** Every segment has exactly one midpoint.
2. $\overline{CM}$ is a median.	**2.** Definition of a median.
3. $\overline{CM} \cong \overline{CM}$	**3.** A segment is $\cong$ to itself.
4. $\overline{MA} \cong \overline{MB}$	**4.** Definition of midpoint
5. $\overline{AC} \cong \overline{BC}$	**5.** Given
6. $\triangle ACM \cong \triangle BCM$	**6.** SSS Postulate
7. $\angle A \cong \angle B$	**7.** Corres. parts of $\cong$ $\triangle$s are $\cong$.

In using an auxiliary figure, we must be careful not to put too many conditions on it. Otherwise, we might "prove" something absurd. For example, we could "prove" *any triangle is isosceles* as follows:

Given: $\triangle ABC$

Prove: $\overline{AB} \cong \overline{AC}$

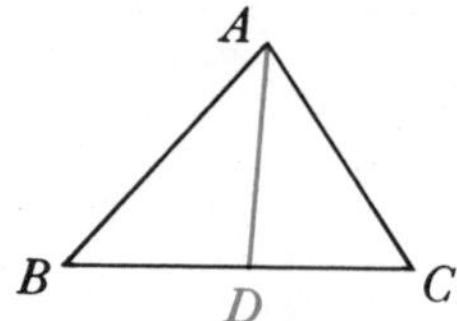

Proof:

STATEMENTS	REASONS
1. Let $\overline{AD}$ be the median and the altitude from A to $\overline{BC}$.	**1.** Every triangle has a median and an altitude from each vertex.
2. $\overline{BD} \cong \overline{DC}$	**2.** Definition of median
3. $\overline{AD} \perp \overline{BC}$	**3.** Definition of altitude
4. $\angle ADB$ and $\angle ADC$ are rt. $\angle$s.	**4.** Definition of perpendicular
5. $\triangle ADB$ and $\triangle ADC$ are rt. $\triangle$s.	**5.** Definition of rt. $\triangle$
6. $\overline{AD} \cong \overline{AD}$	**6.** A segment is $\cong$ to itself.
7. $\triangle ADB \cong \triangle ADC$	**7.** LL Theorem
8. $\overline{AB} \cong \overline{AC}$	**8.** Corres. parts of $\cong$ $\triangle$s are $\cong$.

The error above is that we stated $\overline{AD}$ can be *both* a median and an altitude. This can be true only if $\triangle ABC$ is isosceles.

Exercises 6.6

Ⓐ **1–5.** Refer to $\triangle ABC$ and $\triangle SET$ to name the following:

1. altitude to $\overline{AC}$

2. altitude to $\overleftrightarrow{AB}$

3. altitude to $\overline{ET}$

4. median to $\overline{ET}$

5. altitude to $\overline{SE}$

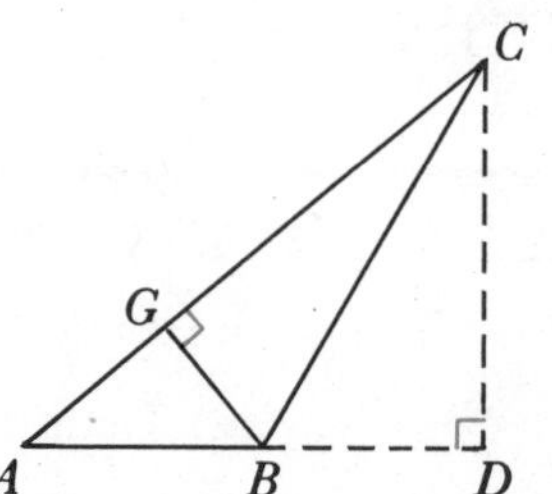

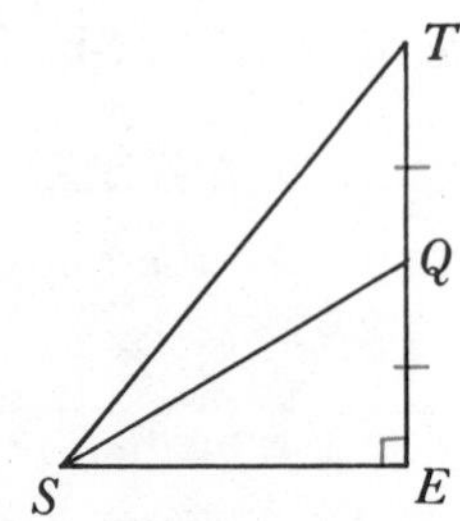

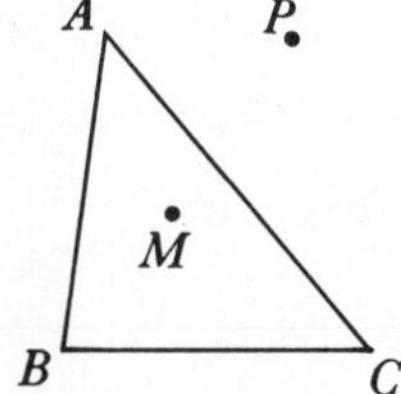

6–8. Can an auxiliary figure meet the conditions described? Refer to the figure at left.

6. $\overline{BD}$ is the median to $\overline{AC}$.

7. $\overleftrightarrow{BP}$ is the $\perp$ bis. of $\overline{AC}$.

8. $\overline{AM}$ is the altitude from A to $\overline{BC}$.

Ⓑ **9–22.** Give the missing reasons.

Given: $\angle A \cong \angle B$

Prove: $\overline{AC} \cong \overline{BC}$

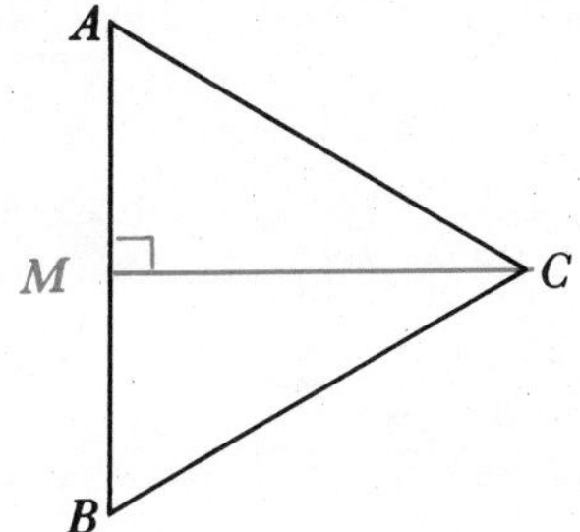

[*Plan:* Use the altitude to side $\overline{AB}$ as an auxiliary segment. Prove $\triangle ACM \cong \triangle BCM$ by LA.]

Proof:

STATEMENTS	REASONS
1. Let $\overline{CM}$ be $\perp$ to $\overline{AB}$.	*1.* Perp. Line Post. (p. 60)
2. $\angle CMB$ and $\angle CMA$ are right $\angle$s.	*2.* Def. of perpendicular
3. $\triangle ACM$ and $\triangle BCM$ are right $\triangle$s.	*3.* **9.** ____
4. $\angle A \cong \angle B$	*4.* **10.** ____
5. $\overline{MC} \cong \overline{MC}$	*5.* **11.** ____
6. $\triangle ACM \cong \triangle BCM$	*6.* **12.** ____
7. $\overline{AC} \cong \overline{BC}$	*7.* **13.** ____

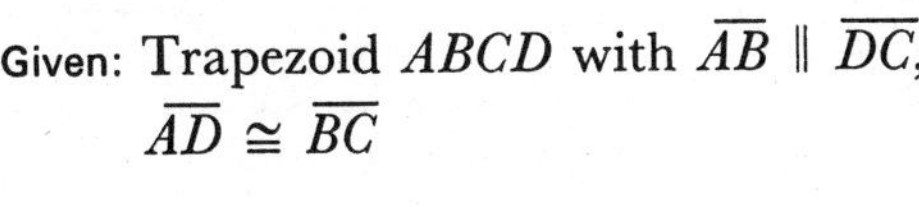

Given: Trapezoid $ABCD$ with $\overline{AB} \parallel \overline{DC}$, $\overline{AD} \cong \overline{BC}$

Prove: $\angle D \cong \angle C$, $\angle DAB \cong \angle CBA$

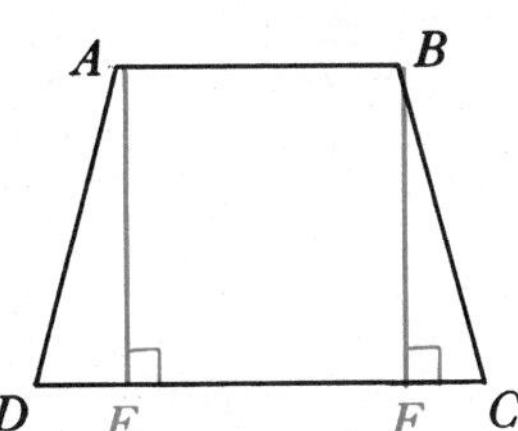

NOTE: This is another proof of part **a** of the Isosceles Trapezoid Theorem, page 181.

[*Plan:* Let $\overline{AE}$ and $\overline{BF}$ be $\perp$ to $\overline{DC}$. Show $\triangle AED \cong \triangle BFC$ by HL.]

Proof:

STATEMENTS	REASONS
1. Let $\overline{AE} \perp \overline{DC}$ and $\overline{BF} \perp \overline{DC}$.	*1.* **14.** ____
2. $\angle AED$ and $\angle BFC$ are rt. $\angle$s.	*2.* **15.** ____
3. $\triangle AED$ and $\triangle BFC$ are rt. $\triangle$s.	*3.* **16.** ____
4. $\overline{AD} \cong \overline{BC}$, $\overline{AB} \parallel \overline{DC}$	*4.* **17.** ____
5. $\overline{AE} \cong \overline{BF}$	*5.* **18.** ____
6. $\triangle AED \cong \triangle BFC$	*6.* **19.** ____
7. $\angle D \cong \angle C$	*7.* **20.** ____
8. $\angle DAB$ and $\angle D$ are supp., as are $\angle CBA$ and $\angle C$.	*8.* **21.** ____
9. $\angle DAB \cong \angle CBA$	*9.* **22.** ____

23–24. Use the plan given to write a proof.

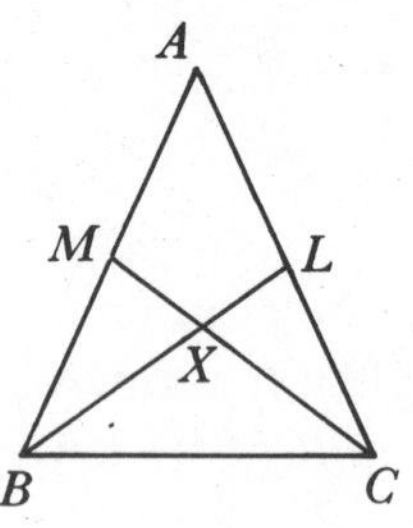

Given: $\triangle ABC$ with $\overline{AB} \cong \overline{AC}$,
$\overline{CM}$ is the median to $\overline{AB}$,
$\overline{BL}$ is the median to $\overline{AC}$.

Prove: $\overline{CM} \cong \overline{BL}$

23. [*Plan:* Show $\triangle BCL \cong \triangle CBM$.]

24. [*Plan:* Show $\triangle BLA \cong \triangle CMA$.]

Ⓒ **25.** Given: Trapezoid $ABCD$ with $\overline{AB} \parallel \overline{DC}$,
$\angle DAB \cong \angle CBA$

Prove: $\overline{AD} \cong \overline{BC}$

[*Plan:* Show $\triangle ADE \cong \triangle BCF$ by LA.]

NOTE: This is another proof of part **b** of the Isosceles Trapezoid Theorem, page 181.

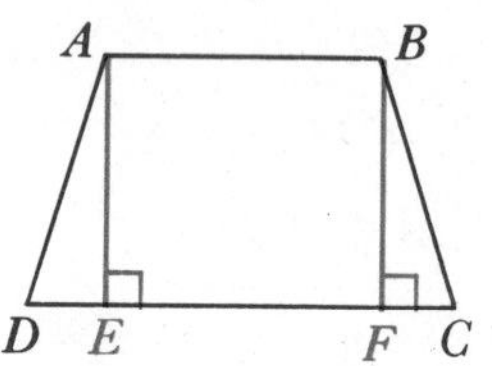

construction: median and altitude of a triangle

Median		Altitude Case I	Altitude Case II
1. Given: $\triangle ABC$	2.	Given: $\triangle ABC$	Given: $\triangle ABC$
B, A, C	B, A, X, C	B, A, C	B, A, C
Construct the perpendicular bisector of $\overline{AC}$.	X is the midpoint of $\overline{AC}$. $\overline{BX}$ is the median to side $\overline{AC}$.	Construct a segment from point B perpendicular to segment AC.	If necessary, extend $\overline{AC}$ and construct a segment from point B perpendicular to $\overleftrightarrow{AC}$.

26–29. Use $\triangle DEF$ shown at the left.

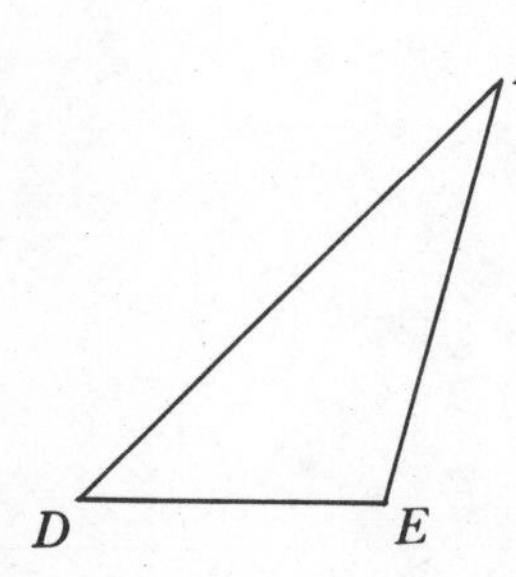

26. Copy $\triangle DEF$ and construct its medians.

27. Copy $\triangle DEF$ and construct its altitudes.

28. Copy $\triangle DEF$ and construct the perpendicular bisectors of its sides.

29. Copy $\triangle DEF$ and construct the bisectors of its angles.

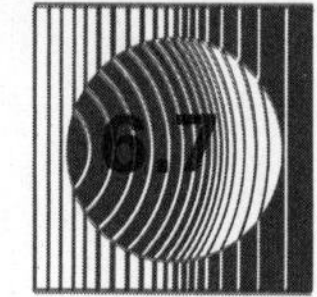

Some Concurrence Theorems

We can prove that the perpendicular bisectors of the sides of a triangle intersect at the same point. We say the perpendicular bisectors are *concurrent*. Two or more lines are **concurrent** if and only if there is a single point at which they all intersect.

We can also prove that the lines containing the altitudes of a triangle are concurrent, as are the angle bisectors and the medians.

The perpendicular bisectors of the sides of a triangle are concurrent at a point that is equidistant from the vertices of the triangle.

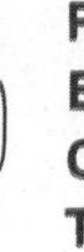

Perpendicular Bisector Concurrence Theorem

Given: $\triangle ABC$ with ℓ_1, ℓ_2, and ℓ_3 the $\perp$ bisectors of $\overline{AB}$, $\overline{AC}$, and $\overline{CB}$

Prove: ℓ_1, ℓ_2, and ℓ_3 are concurrent at P, and P is equidistant from A, B, and C.

[*Plan:* Let P be the pt. where two of the $\perp$ bis. intersect. Show that the pt. is equidistant from the endpts. of the third side and is therefore on its $\perp$ bis.]

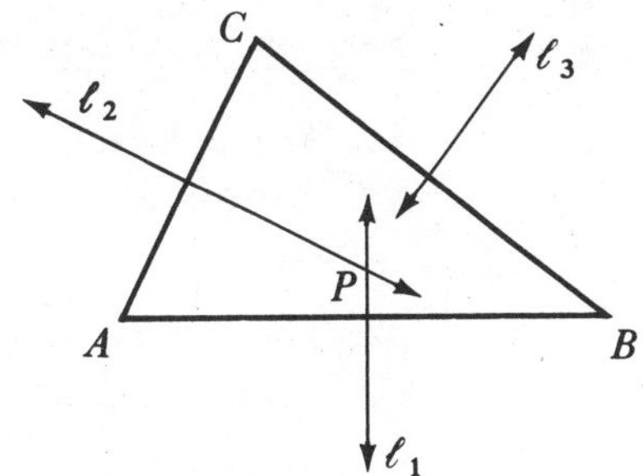

Proof:

STATEMENTS	REASONS
1. Let P be the point where ℓ_1 and ℓ_2 intersect.	**1.** Perpendiculars to intersecting lines also intersect.
2. $PA = PB$, $PA = PC$	**2.** A pt. on the $\perp$ bis. of a seg. is equidistant from the endpts. (P is on ℓ_1 and on ℓ_2.)
3. $PB = PC$	**3.** Substitution
4. P is on the perpendicular bisector of $\overline{BC}$. (P is on ℓ_3.)	**4.** A pt. equidistant from the endpts. of a seg. is on the $\perp$ bis. ($PB = PC$)
5. ℓ_1, ℓ_2, and ℓ_3 are concurrent at P.	**5.** P is on ℓ_1, ℓ_2, and ℓ_3.
6. P is equidistant from A, B, and C.	**6.** $PA = PB = PC$

Altitude Concurrence Theorem

The lines containing the altitudes of a triangle are concurrent.

Given: $\triangle ABC$, ℓ_1 contains the altitude from B to $\overline{AC}$, ℓ_2 contains the altitude from C to $\overline{AB}$, ℓ_3 contains the altitude from A to $\overline{BC}$.

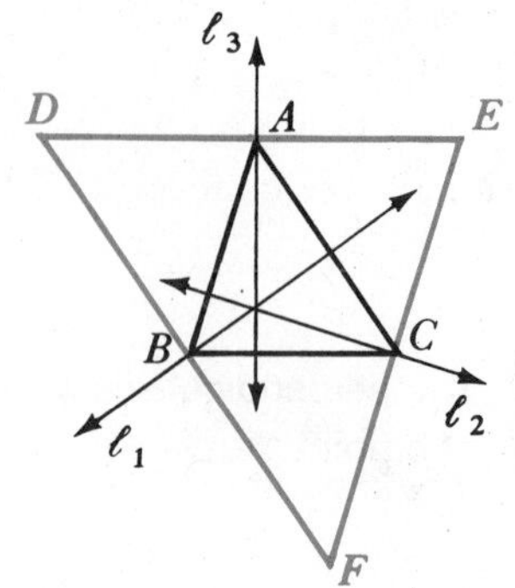

Prove: ℓ_1, ℓ_2, and ℓ_3 are concurrent.

[*Plan:* Form $\triangle DEF$ by drawing a line through each vertex of $\triangle ABC$ and parallel to the opposite side. Show that the lines containing the altitudes of $\triangle ABC$ are the $\perp$ bisectors of the sides of $\triangle DEF$.]

Proof:

STATEMENTS	REASONS
1. Through each vertex of $\triangle ABC$, there is a line $\parallel$ to the opp. side.	**1.** Parallel Postulate
2. These three lines determine a triangle, $\triangle DEF$.	**2.** Parallels to intersecting lines also intersect.
3. *ACBD* is a parallelogram. *ACFB* is a parallelogram.	**3.** The opposite sides are parallel.
4. $AC = DB$, $AC = BF$	**4.** Opp. sides of a ▱ are $\cong$.
5. $DB = BF$	**5.** Substitution
6. $\ell_1 \perp DF$	**6.** In a plane, a line $\perp$ to one of two parallel lines is $\perp$ to the other.
7. ℓ_1 is the $\perp$ bis. of $\overline{DF}$.	**7.** $DB = BF$, $\ell_1 \perp \overline{DF}$
8. Likewise, ℓ_2 and ℓ_3 are the $\perp$ bis. of $\overline{FE}$ and $\overline{DE}$.	**8.** Reasoning similar to steps 3–7
9. The $\perp$ bis. of the sides of $\triangle DEF$ are concurrent.	**9.** Perpendicular Bisector Concurrence Theorem
10. The lines containing the altitudes of $\triangle ABC$ are concurrent.	**10.** The lines containing the alt. of $\triangle ABC$ are the $\perp$ bis. of the sides of $\triangle DEF$.

The proofs of the next two theorems are covered in the exercises.

The bisectors of the angles of a triangle are concurrent.

Angle Bisector Concurrence Theorem

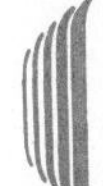

The medians of a triangle are concurrent. The point of concurrence is two thirds the distance from each vertex to the midpoint of the opposite side.

Median Concurrence Theorem

Exercises 6.7

Ⓐ **1–4.** Which concurrence theorem is illustrated by each figure?

1.

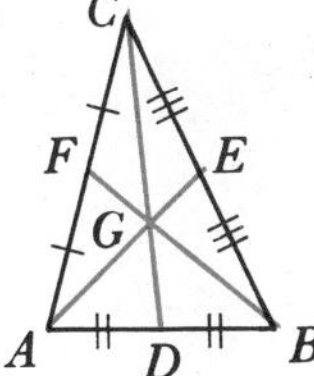

2.

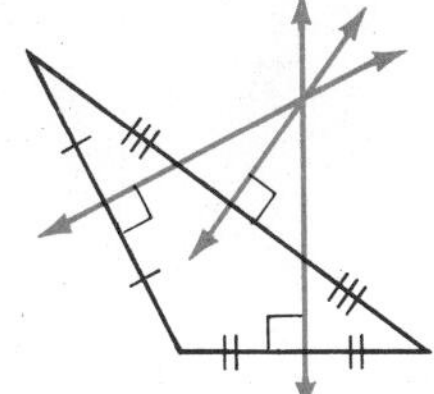

3.

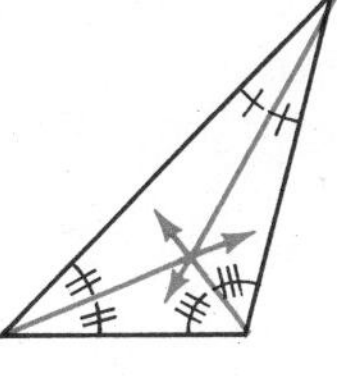

4.

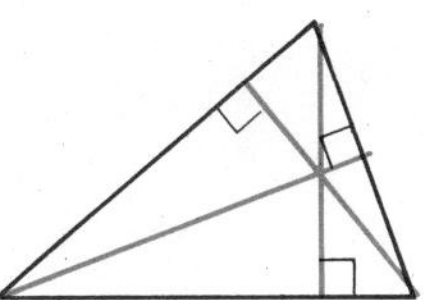

5. In $\triangle ABC$ above, $AE = 6$. Find AG.

6. In $\triangle ABC$ above, $DG = 3$. Find GC.

Ⓑ **7–20.** Give the missing reasons.

Given: $\triangle ABC$ with angle bisectors b_1, b_2, and b_3; b_1 and b_2 intersect at P.

Prove: b_1, b_2, and b_3 are concurrent.

[*Plan:* Show that P is equidistant from the sides of $\angle C$ and is therefore on the bisector of $\angle C$.]

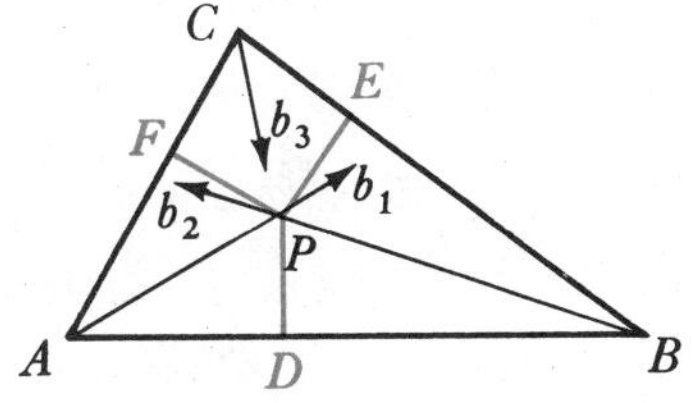

Proof:

STATEMENTS	REASONS
1. b_1 and b_2 intersect at P.	1. Given
2. Let $\overline{PD}$, $\overline{PE}$, and $\overline{PF}$ be the perpendiculars from P to $\overline{AB}$, $\overline{BC}$, and $\overline{AC}$.	2. **7.**
3. $PF = PD$, $PD = PE$	3. **8.**
4. $PF = PE$	4. **9.**
5. P is on the bisector of $\angle C$.	5. **10.**
6. b_1, b_2, and b_3 are concurrent.	6. **11.**

Given: $\triangle ABC$, medians $\overline{BE}$ and $\overline{CF}$ intersect at P, $\overrightarrow{AP}$ intersects $\overline{BC}$ at D.

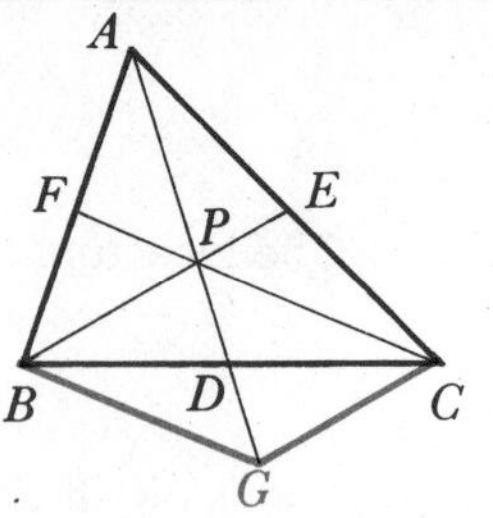

Prove: The medians of $\triangle ABC$ are concurrent.

[*Plan:* Draw a ray from A through P and extend it to G so that $AP = PG$. Show $BPCG$ is a parallelogram.]

Proof: STATEMENTS	REASONS
1. Medians $\overline{BE}$ and $\overline{CF}$ intersect at P, $\overrightarrow{AP}$ intersects $\overline{BC}$ at D.	*1.* Given
2. Let G be the point of $\overrightarrow{AP}$ beyond P from A, such that $AP = PG$.	*2.* **12.** ____
3. P is the midpoint of $\overline{AG}$.	*3.* **13.** ____
4. Draw $\overline{BG}$ and $\overline{CG}$.	*4.* **14.** ____
5. F is the midpoint of $\overline{AB}$, E is the midpoint of $\overline{AC}$.	*5.* **15.** ____
6. $\overleftrightarrow{FP} \parallel \overline{BG}$	*6.* **16.** ____
7. Likewise, $\overleftrightarrow{PE} \parallel \overline{GC}$.	*7.* **17.** ____
8. $BPCG$ is a parallelogram.	*8.* **18.** ____
9. D is the midpoint of $\overline{BC}$.	*9.* **19.** ____
10. $\overline{AD}$ is a median to $\overline{BC}$.	*10.* **20.** ____
11. The medians $\overline{CF}$, $\overline{BE}$, and $\overline{AD}$ are concurrent.	*11.* P is on $\overline{CF}$, $\overline{BE}$, and $\overline{AD}$.

© **21.** Prove that the medians of a triangle are concurrent at a point that is two thirds the distance from each vertex to the midpoint of the opposite side. (Use the figure for Exercises 12–20 and prove $BP = \frac{2}{3}BE$. HINT: $PE = \frac{1}{2}GC$)

22. *Activity:* The point of concurrence of the medians of a triangle is called the **centroid** (center of mass). Draw a triangle on cardboard or stiff paper and carefully construct the medians to find their point of intersection. Then cut out the triangle and suspend it with string from its centroid. Suspend another triangle by an interior point that is not the centroid. What happens in each case?

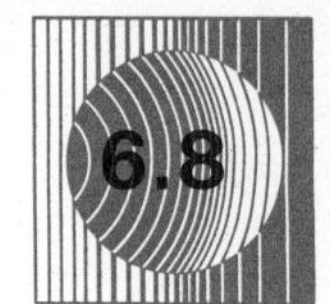

Transformations and Proofs

We have used transformations in earlier chapters to explore various properties of figures. In this section, we show how transformations can also be used in proofs. First, we would have to accept some postulates about transformations. For example, let's accept these postulates.

Postulate: Reflections preserve collinearity.

Postulate: Reflections preserve distance.

Then we can prove

Theorem: Reflections preserve betweenness.

Given: A', B', and C' are the reflection images of A, B, and C over line ℓ; B is between A and C.

Prove: B' is between A' and C'.

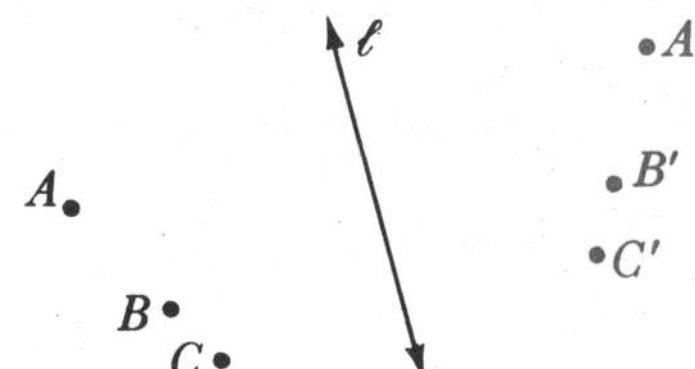

Proof:

STATEMENTS	REASONS
1. B is between A and C.	1. Given
2. A, B, and C are collinear, $AB + BC = AC$.	2. Definition of between
3. A', B', and C' are collinear.	3. Reflections preserve collinearity.
4. $A'B' = AB$, $B'C' = BC$, $A'C' = AC$	4. Reflections preserve distance.
5. $A'B' + B'C' = AB + B'C'$	5. Add $B'C'$ to both sides of $A'B' = AB$.
6. $A'B' + B'C' = AB + BC$ $= AC$ $= A'C'$	6. Substitution (from steps 2 and 4, BC for $B'C'$, AC for $AB + BC$, and $A'C'$ for AC)
7. B' is between A' and C'.	7. Definition of between

Exercises 6.8

Ⓐ 1. Transformations (can, cannot) be used in proofs.

2. We postulated that reflections preserve ______ and ______ to prove that reflections preserve betweenness.

3. In going from step 5 to step 6 in the proof on page 233, we first substituted ______ for $B'C'$.

4. Then we substituted AC for ______, then ______ for AC.

Ⓑ **5–12.** Give the missing reasons.

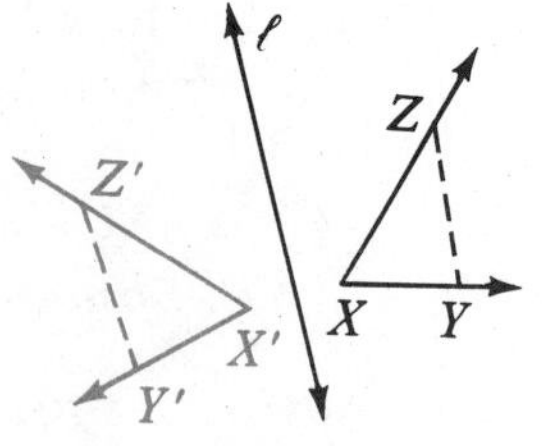

Theorem: Reflections preserve angle measure.

Given: X', Y', and Z' are the reflection images of X, Y, and Z over line ℓ.

Prove: $m\angle X' = m\angle X$

Proof:

STATEMENTS	REASONS
1. Draw $\overline{Y'Z'}$ and $\overline{YZ}$.	1. Two points determine a line.
2. $X'Y' = XY$, $X'Z' = XZ$, $Y'Z' = YZ$	2. **5.** ______
3. $\overline{X'Y'} \cong \overline{XY}$, $\overline{X'Z'} \cong \overline{XZ}$, $\overline{Y'Z'} \cong \overline{YZ}$	3. **6.** ______
4. $\triangle X'Y'Z' \cong \triangle XYZ$	4. **7.** ______
5. $\angle X' \cong \angle X$	5. **8.** ______
6. $m\angle X' = m\angle X$	6. **9.** ______

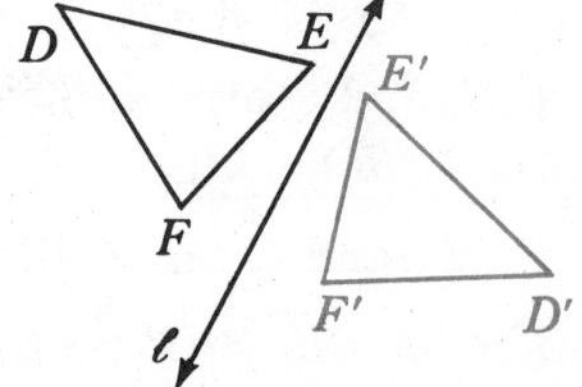

Theorem: A triangle and its reflection image are congruent.

Given: $\triangle D'E'F'$ is the reflection image of $\triangle DEF$ over line ℓ.

Prove: $\triangle D'E'F' \cong \triangle DEF$

Proof:

STATEMENTS	REASONS
1. $D'E' = DE$, $E'F' = EF$, $F'D' = FD$	1. **10.** ______
2. $\overline{D'E'} \cong \overline{DE}$, $\overline{E'F'} \cong \overline{EF}$, $\overline{F'D'} \cong \overline{FD}$	2. **11.** ______
3. $\triangle D'E'F' \cong \triangle DEF$	3. **12.** ______

Ⓒ **13.** Prove this theorem: Reflections preserve parallelism.

Given: r' and n' are the reflection images of r and n over ℓ, $r \parallel n$

Prove: $r' \parallel n'$

[*Plan:* Use an auxiliary line k perpendicular to r.]

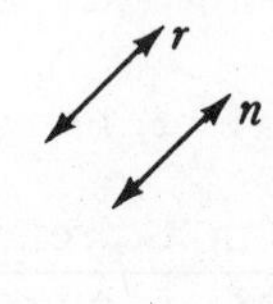

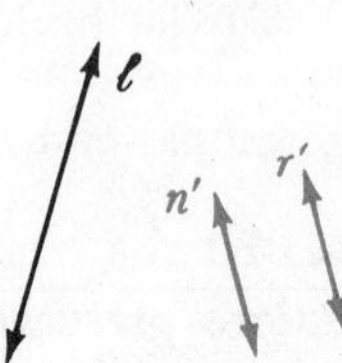

■ Chapter 6 Review ■

1. An if-then statement is false when the hypothesis is true and the conclusion is ______. **6.1**

2–3. Find a counterexample to show that each statement is false.

2. If the product of two numbers is positive, the numbers are positive.

3. If two angles are supplementary, the angles are not congruent.

4–5. Write *true* or *false* for each statement. Then write the converse and tell if it is true or false. **6.2**

4. If a triangle has two congruent sides, it has two congruent angles.

5. If a number is a rational number, it is a real number.

6. What two true if-then statements can be formed from the following?

$$x^2 = 36 \text{ if and only if } x = 6 \text{ or } x = -6.$$

7. Can statements X and Y be connected by *if and only if* to form a true statement?

   X: Two lines are parallel.
   Y: The two lines form congruent alternate interior angles with a transversal.

8. Restate the following definition in if-and-only-if form: **6.3**

   A median of a triangle is a segment from a vertex to the midpoint of the opposite side.

9–10. Write *valid* or *faulty* for each argument. Then name the pattern of reasoning that is used. **6.4**

9. If a dog eats Briskies, the dog will not be hungry.
   Spot is not hungry.
   So Spot eats Briskies.

10. If two angles are vertical angles, the angles are congruent.
    $\angle A$ and $\angle B$ are not congruent.
    So $\angle A$ and $\angle B$ are not vertical angles.

6.5 **11–17.** Give a reason for each step in this indirect proof.

Given: $\triangle ABC$ with $\overline{AB} \cong \overline{BC}$,
$\angle 1 \ncong \angle 2$

Prove: $\overline{AD} \ncong \overline{DC}$

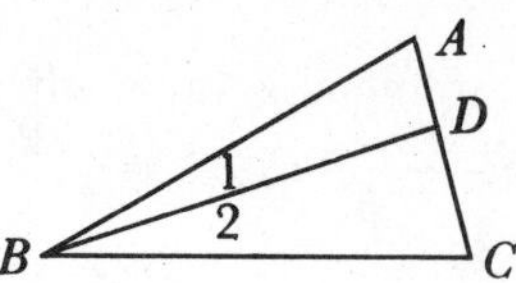

Proof:

STATEMENTS	REASONS
1. Assume $\overline{AD} \cong \overline{DC}$.	*1.* **11.**
2. $\overline{AB} \cong \overline{BC}$	*2.* **12.**
3. $\overline{BD} \cong \overline{BD}$	*3.* **13.**
4. $\triangle ADB \cong \triangle CDB$	*4.* **14.**
5. $\angle 1 \cong \angle 2$	*5.* **15.**
6. But, $\angle 1 \ncong \angle 2$.	*6.* **16.**
7. So, $\overline{AD} \ncong \overline{DC}$.	*7.* **17.**

6.6 **18–19.** Use the plan given to write a proof.

Given: $\triangle TEG$ with $\overline{TG} \cong \overline{EG}$.
$\overline{TL}$ is the altitude from T to $\overline{GE}$,
$\overline{ER}$ is the altitude from E to $\overline{GT}$.

Prove: $\overline{ER} \cong \overline{TL}$

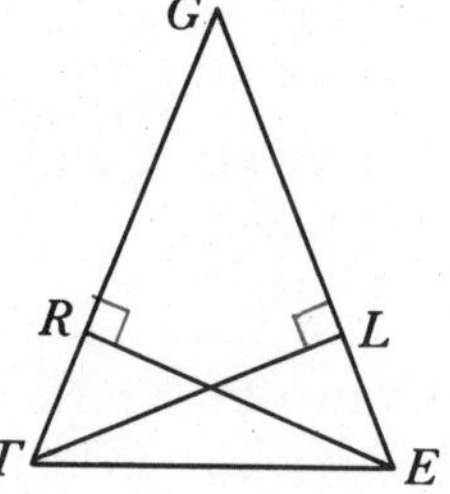

18. [*Plan:* Show $\triangle ETL \cong \triangle TER$.]

19. [*Plan:* Show $\triangle TLG \cong \triangle ERG$.]

6.7 **20.** Two or more lines are ______ if and only if there is a single point at which they all intersect.

21–22. Which concurrence theorem is illustrated by each diagram?

21.

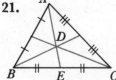

22.

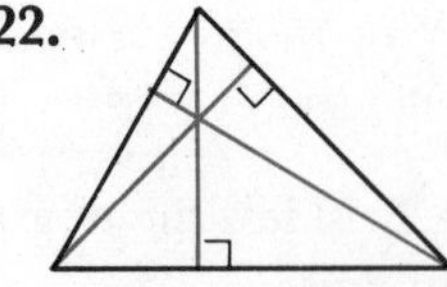

23. In $\triangle ABC$ above, how long is AD if $AE = 9$?

6.8 **24.** What postulates did we assume in order to prove that reflections preserve betweenness?

Chapter 6 Test

1–2. Find a counterexample to show that each statement is false.

1. If $x \geq 0$, then $-x < 0$.

2. If two angles have a common side, the angles are adjacent.

3–4. Write *true* or *false* for each statement. Then write the converse and tell if it is true or false.

3. If you live in Florida, the weather is usually warm.

4. If a triangle has three congruent angles, it has three congruent sides.

5. What two true statements can be made from the following?

$$x = 2 \text{ if and only if } x^3 = 8.$$

6. Restate the following definition in if-and-only-if form:

An altitude of a triangle is a segment from a vertex perpendicular to the line containing the opposite side.

7–8. Write *valid* or *faulty* for each argument. Then name the pattern of reasoning that is used.

7. If M is the midpoint of $\overline{AB}$,
then $AM = MB$.
$AM = MB$
So M is the midpoint of $\overline{AB}$.

8. If a horse wins the Derby,
it can run fast.
Lightning cannot run fast.
So Lightning cannot win the Derby.

9–12. Give a reason for each step in this indirect proof.

Given: c is not parallel to d.

Prove: $\angle 1 \not\cong \angle 2$

Proof:

STATEMENTS	REASONS
1. Assume $\angle 1 \cong \angle 2$.	*1.* **9.**
2. Then $c \parallel d$.	*2.* **10.**
3. But, c is not parallel to d.	*3.* **11.**
4. So, $\angle 1 \not\cong \angle 2$.	*4.* **12.**

13. Draw a sketch to illustrate the Altitude Concurrence Theorem.

14. True or False? Proofs about transformations are based on postulates.

7

GEOMETRIC INEQUALITIES

In geometry, as in life, it can be just as important to notice how things differ as it is to notice how they are alike. In this chapter we apply the ideas of *smaller than, larger than, less than,* and *greater than* to geometric figures.

Properties of Inequality

The meanings of *is less than* and *is greater than* were given on page 7 by using the number line. But these terms can also be defined without using the number line. Let a and b stand for any real numbers.

$a > b$ if and only if $a = b + c$ for some positive number c.

$a < b$ if and only if $a + c = b$ for some positive number c.

Two numbers are unequal if and only if there is a positive number that can be added to one number to get the other number.

Example 1:

a. $5 > 3$, since $5 = 3 + 2$. (2: positive)   **b.** $6\frac{1}{2} < 7$, since $6\frac{1}{2} + \frac{1}{2} = 7$. ($\frac{1}{2}$: positive)

c. If $x + 4 = 6$, $x < 6$.   **d.** $-3 + n = 2$ for $n = 5$, so $-3 < 2$.

Three order properties of real numbers are also listed on page 7.

Let a, b, and c stand for any real numbers.	**Examples:**
$a < b$, $a = b$, or $a > b$ ◀ Exactly one of these is true.	• $3 < 2$, $3 = 2$, or $3 > 2$ • $\frac{1}{2} < 0.5$, $\frac{1}{2} = 0.5$, or $\frac{1}{2} > 0.5$
If $a < b$ and $b < c$, then $a < c$.	$2 < 5$ and $5 < 6$, so $2 < 6$
If $a < b$, then $b > a$.	$4 < 7$, so $7 > 4$

The properties below are used to simplify (or *solve*) statements of inequality. Though stated here for $>$, they are also true for $<$.

	$a > b$	◀ Given an inequality, you can:
Addition Property	$a + c > b + c$	◀ add the same number to both sides
Subtraction Property	$a - c > b - c$	◀ subtract the same number from both sides
Multiplication Property	If $c > 0$, $ac > bc$.	◀ multiply both sides by the same **positive** number
Division Property	If $c > 0$, $\frac{a}{c} > \frac{b}{c}$.	◀ divide both sides by the same **positive** number

Example 2:

a.
$$x - 3 > 4$$
$$x - 3 + 3 > 4 + 3$$
$$x > 7$$

b.
$$n + 2 > 5$$
$$n + 2 - 2 > 5 - 2$$
$$n > 3$$

c.
$$\frac{1}{2}r < 5$$
$$2 \cdot \frac{1}{2}r < 2 \cdot 5$$
$$r < 10$$

Because $a < b$, $a = b$, or $a > b$ for any real numbers a and b, a statement that one or more of these is *not* true tells us which possibilities may be true. For example,

This statement	is equivalent to this statement.
a is not less than *b*.	*a* is greater than or equal to *b*.
a is not greater than or equal to *b*.	*a* is less than *b*.
a is not equal to *b*.	*a* is less than or greater than *b*.

Exercises 7.1

Ⓐ **1–6.** Which symbol, > or <, should replace the ▨?

1. If $n + 2 = 5$, n ▨ 5.

2. If $0 = s + 3$, s ▨ 0.

3. Since $-2 + 4 = 2$, -2 ▨ 2.

4. Since $\frac{5}{8} = \frac{1}{4} + \frac{3}{8}$, $\frac{1}{4}$ ▨ $\frac{5}{8}$.

5. If $a - 8 > 7$, then a ▨ 15.

6. If $14 < \frac{1}{2}d$, then 28 ▨ d.

7. If x is not greater than 12, then x is ______ 12 or x is ______ 12.

8. If n is greater than or equal to 3, then n is not ______ 3.

Ⓑ **9–16.** Use the definitions of > and < to state four inequalities for each equation. (*Example:* $7 = 3 + 4$: $7 > 3$, $3 < 7$, $7 > 4$, $4 < 7$)

9. $12 = 9 + 3$

10. $5 + 10 = 15$

11. $50 + 130 = 180$

12. $90 = 30 + 60$

13. $23 = x + 7$

14. $19 = y + 6$

15. $5 + 9 = n$

16. $6 + 13 = c$

17–20. Use the definitions of > and < to state an equation for each inequality.

17. $14 > 3$

18. $28 > 5$

19. $60 < 90$

20. $45 < 75$

21–28. Write an equivalent statement.

21. m is greater than 12.

22. 4 is less than r.

23. n is not less than 3.

24. x is not equal to 15.

25. t is not greater than 9.

26. a is equal to 4.

27. 5 is less than or equal to s.

28. v is not less than or equal to 23.

29–44. Solve.

29. $n + 4 > 9$ **30.** $d + 7 < 16$ **31.** $s - 5 < 6$ **32.** $m - 3 > 15$

33. $4x < 20$ **34.** $7n > 28$ **35.** $m - 8 > 2$ **36.** $r - 15 < 4$

37. $\frac{t}{3} < 5$ **38.** $\frac{r}{4} > 6$ **39.** $3 > \frac{1}{2}p$ **40.** $10 < \frac{1}{7}y$

41. $\frac{1}{5}p < -2$ **42.** $\frac{1}{3}n > -5$ **43.** $\frac{2}{5}x < 6$ **44.** $\frac{3}{4}n > 9$

© **45.** $\frac{3}{5}x + 2 < 14$ **46.** $\frac{5}{6}n - 2 > 8$ **47.** $-5 < \frac{4}{7}r$ **48.** $\frac{7}{8}t - 2 > 3$

49–52. Give an example of each property of inequality listed.

49. If $a > b$ and $c < 0$, then $ac < bc$.

50. If $a > b$ and $c = 0$, then $ac = bc$.

51. If $a > b$, then $c - a < c - b$.

52. If $a > b$ and $c > d$, then $a + c > b + d$.

Putting It Another Way

The three sentences on each line below all say the same thing. Using the numbers and segments as clues, can you rewrite the sentences in English?

A•————•B

C•————•D

Swahili	Spanish	Swedish
15 ni sawa na 9 + 6.	15 es igual a 9 + 6.	15 är den samma 9 + 6.
9 si sawa na 7.	9 no es igual a 7.	9 är inte den samma 7.
9 ni kubwa kuliko 7.	9 es mayor que 7.	9 är mera än 7.
7 ni dogo kuliko 9.	7 es menor que 9.	7 är mindre än 9.
$\overline{AB}$ ni refu kuliko $\overline{CD}$.	$\overline{AB}$ es más largo que $\overline{CD}$.	$\overline{AB}$ är längare än $\overline{CD}$.
$\overline{CD}$ ni fupi kuliko $\overline{AB}$.	$\overline{CD}$ es más corto que $\overline{AB}$.	$\overline{CD}$ är kortare än $\overline{AB}$.

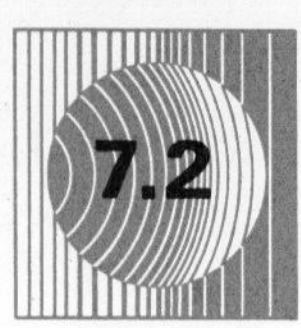

7.2 Comparing Geometric Figures

Since lengths of segments are real numbers, segments can be compared. That is, one segment can be described as *shorter than*, *congruent to*, or *longer than* another. Measures of angles are also real numbers, so angles can be compared. The chart below summarizes how equal measures and congruent figures, and unequal measures and noncongruent figures, are related.

Measures	Figures
$AB = CD$	$\overline{AB} \cong \overline{CD}$
$AB < CD$	$\overline{AB}$ is shorter than $\overline{CD}$.
$AB > CD$	$\overline{AB}$ is longer than $\overline{CD}$.

Measures	Figures
$m\angle A = m\angle B$	$\angle A \cong \angle B$
$m\angle A < m\angle B$	$\angle A$ is smaller than $\angle B$.
$m\angle A > m\angle B$	$\angle A$ is larger than $\angle B$.

When B is between A and C, $AC = AB + BC$. Because both AB and BC are positive numbers, this one equation leads to four inequalities by using the definitions of $>$ and $<$ on page 239.

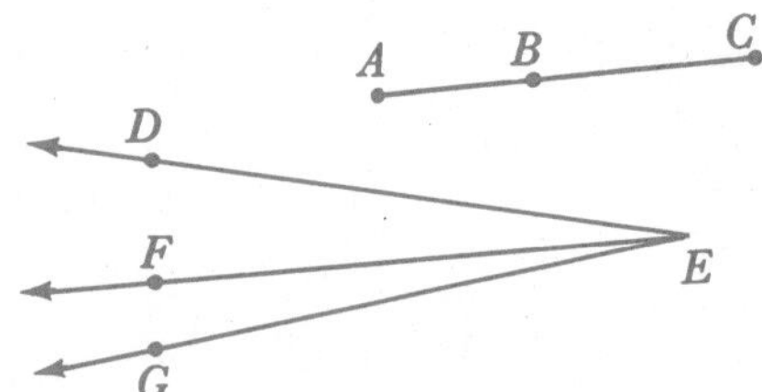

$$AC = AB + BC \quad \left[\begin{array}{ll} AC > AB & AB < AC \\ AC > BC & BC < AC \end{array}\right.$$

The Angle Addition Postulate also results in four inequalities.

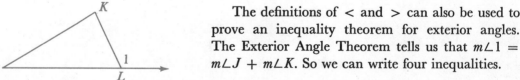

$$m\angle DEG = m\angle DEF + m\angle FEG \quad \left[\begin{array}{ll} m\angle DEG > m\angle DEF & m\angle DEF < m\angle DEG \\ m\angle DEG > m\angle FEG & m\angle FEG < m\angle DEG \end{array}\right.$$

The definitions of $<$ and $>$ can also be used to prove an inequality theorem for exterior angles. The Exterior Angle Theorem tells us that $m\angle 1 = m\angle J + m\angle K$. So we can write four inequalities.

$$m\angle 1 = m\angle J + m\angle K \quad \left[\begin{array}{ll} m\angle 1 > m\angle J & m\angle J < m\angle 1 \\ m\angle 1 > m\angle K & m\angle K < m\angle 1 \end{array}\right.$$

Then this theorem follows.

Exterior Angle Inequality Theorem

An exterior angle of a triangle is larger than either remote interior angle.

Exercises 7.2

Ⓐ **1.** If $MN < PD$, then $\overline{MN}$ _____ $\overline{PD}$.

2. If $m\angle R > m\angle S$, then $\angle R$ _____ $\angle S$.

3. Since $GH < MN$, $GH = MN$, or $GH > MN$, it follows that $\overline{GH}$ _____ $\overline{MN}$, $\overline{GH}$ _____ $\overline{MN}$, or $\overline{GH}$ _____ $\overline{MN}$.

4. How many inequalities does the equation $RS + 3 = RT$ lead to?

5–22. Refer to the figures to decide which symbol, $<$, $=$, or $>$, should replace the ▨.

5. GS ▨ GK **6.** $m\angle 1$ ▨ $m\angle RPT$

7. $m\angle D$ ▨ $m\angle 3$ **8.** $KS + SG$ ▨ KG

Ⓑ **9.** $GS + EF$ ▨ $GK + EF$ **10.** $EF + GK$ ▨ $EF + SK$

11. $GK - EF$ ▨ $GS - EF$ **12.** $GK - SK$ ▨ $GS - SK$

13. $GK - SK$ ▨ GS **14.** $GK - GS$ ▨ SK

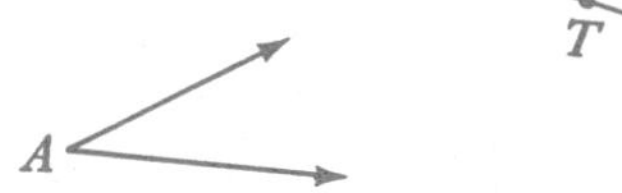

15. $m\angle 2 + m\angle A$ ▨ $m\angle RPT + m\angle A$

16. $m\angle RPT - m\angle 1$ ▨ $m\angle 2 - m\angle 1$

17. $3m\angle RPT$ ▨ $3m\angle 2$ **18.** $\frac{1}{2}m\angle 1$ ▨ $\frac{1}{2}m\angle RPT$

19. $m\angle 3 + m\angle 4$ ▨ 180 **20.** $m\angle N + m\angle D$ ▨ $m\angle 3$

21. If $\overline{MN} \perp \overline{ND}$, $m\angle D$ ▨ 90. **22.** If $m\angle N = 90$, $m\angle 3$ ▨ 90.

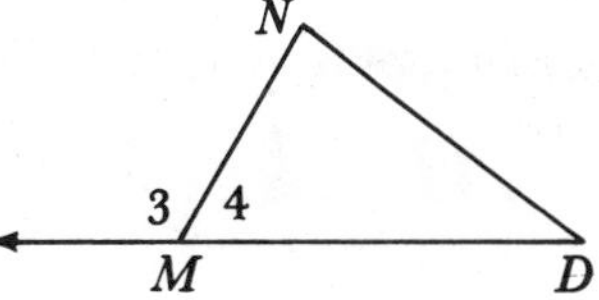

23–24. What theorem, along with the definition of $<$, leads to the statement?

23. In $\triangle ABC$, $m\angle A + m\angle B < 180$.

24. If $\overline{DE}$ is a midline of $\triangle MNP$ and $\overline{DE} \parallel \overline{MN}$, then $DE < MN$.

Ⓒ **25–26.** Prove the theorem.

25. If N and P are between R and S, then $NP < RS$.

26. If A and B are in the interior of $\angle DEF$, then $m\angle AEB < m\angle DEF$.

27–32. A conclusion that has not been proved is a **conjecture.** Though not every conjecture is true, theorems usually begin as conjectures. You may want to work with models or drawings to make the conjectures asked for in these exercises.

27. $AB + BC = AC$ if and only if B is between A and C on $\overline{AC}$. Where is B if $AB + BC > AC$? Can $AB + BC < AC$?

28. What conjectures can you make from these situations?

a. $m\angle AIB + m\angle BIC > m\angle AIC$ **b.** $m\angle AIB + m\angle BIC < m\angle AIC$

29. Two sides of a triangle are congruent if and only if the angles opposite those sides are congruent. In $\triangle DEF$, $EF > DE$. What conjecture can you make about the angles opposite $\overline{EF}$ and $\overline{DE}$?

30. In $\triangle DEF$, $m\angle F \not< m\angle E$. What conjecture can you make about the sides opposite $\angle F$ and $\angle E$?

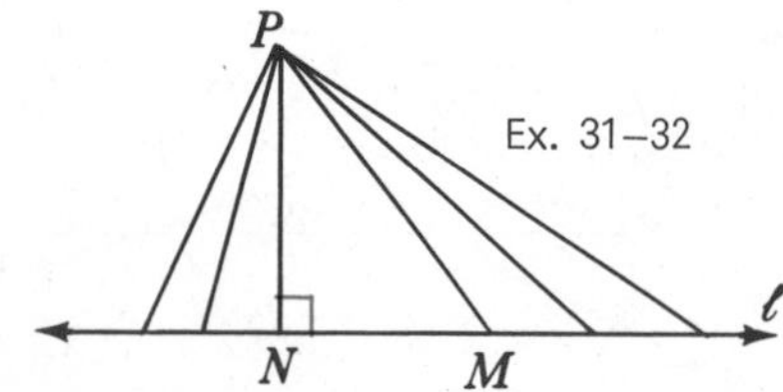

Ex. 31–32

31. What conjecture can you make about the shortest segment from P to ℓ in the figure?

32. In $\triangle MNP$, $\angle N$ is a right angle. What conjectures can you make comparing the sides of $\triangle MNP$?

Algebra Review

Review these skills:

- *multiplying monomials*
- *multiplying a monomial and a binomial*
- *multiplying binomials*

Find each product.

1. $3 \cdot 6n$	**2.** $\frac{1}{2} \cdot 4x$	**3.** $\frac{2}{3} \cdot 5r$
4. $-8 \cdot 3c$	**5.** $-7(-9f)$	**6.** $6(-5h)$
7. $(4p)^2$	**8.** $(\frac{1}{2}h)^2$	**9.** $(\frac{3}{5}t)^2$
10. $(-\frac{2}{3}v)^2$	**11.** $6(s + 4)$	**12.** $(a + 9)b$
13. $\frac{1}{3}(3q + 1)$	**14.** $-2(p + \frac{3}{4})$	**15.** $-9(d - \frac{2}{3})$
16. $(r + 5)(r + 2)$	**17.** $(n + \frac{2}{3})(3n + 6)$	**18.** $(b - 4)(b - 2)$
19. $(d + 3)(d - 3)$	**20.** $(x + 3)^2$	**21.** $(m - 5)^2$
22. $(s - \frac{1}{2})(s + \frac{1}{2})$	**23.** $(2y + 1)^2$	**24.** $(3n - \frac{1}{2})^2$

GEOMETRY AROUND YOU

GEOMETRIC GEOGRAPHY

Have you ever heard of Equality, Illinois, or Converse, Louisiana? There are many place-names that are made up partly or entirely of terms used in mathematics. Some that involve geometry terms are listed here. Identify the terms from the descriptions and figures in 1–14, below. Then decode each place-name by replacing the number with the corresponding term.

1. in a drawing, represents a point
2. postulate, or axiom
3. joins opposite vertices of a square
4. rectangular rhombus
5. geometric figure with no dimensions
6. part of a circle

7. 

8. 

9. 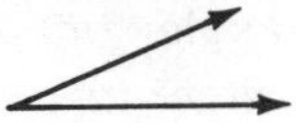

10. 

11. 

12. 

13. 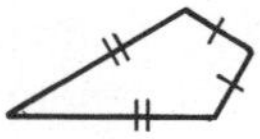

14. 

Newtown __4__, Pa.
State __11__, Miss.
__9__ Inlet, Minn.
__1__ Lake, Alaska
__4__ Butte, Mont.
Rocky __5__, Wyo.
__10__ Pines, Minn.
Central __4__, N.Y.
__6__ Dome Peak, Nev.
__5__ Washington, Fla.
Social __10__, Ga.
Central __5__, Oreg.
Crest__11__, Kans.
Dead Horse __5__, Utah
__7__ River, Alaska

__6__ola, Ind.
Dela__8__, Va.
__7__, N.Dak.
__3__, Iowa
__12__, Idaho
__13__, Ga.
__10__, Mont.
__2__, Ill.
Ex__11__, Iowa
Two__1__, Mont.
__5__s, W.Va.
__6__o, Idaho
__14__, Mo.
__7__ City, Ga.
La __14__, Ky.

__7__ __14__, Mich.
Rich __4__, N.C.
Brook__11__, Mass.
Peri__1__, Ariz.
__10__ Back, Tex.
__11__boro, Md.
__4__ Lake, Maine
__14__ __5__, La.
__10__ville, Ohio
__6__ata, Calif.
__14__ __11__, Mich.
__11__ville, Ala.
__14__ Hill, Ark.
__14__dale, R.I.
Shady __5__, Okla.

Inequalities in a Triangle

On a trail over the top of a hill, you expect the climb up the long side of the hill to be easier than the climb up the short side. This illustrates a theorem relating sides and angles of a triangle.

Simmerman/Van Cleve Photogr

First, we prove this statement:

If two sides of a triangle are not congruent, the angle opposite the longer side is larger than the angle opposite the shorter side.

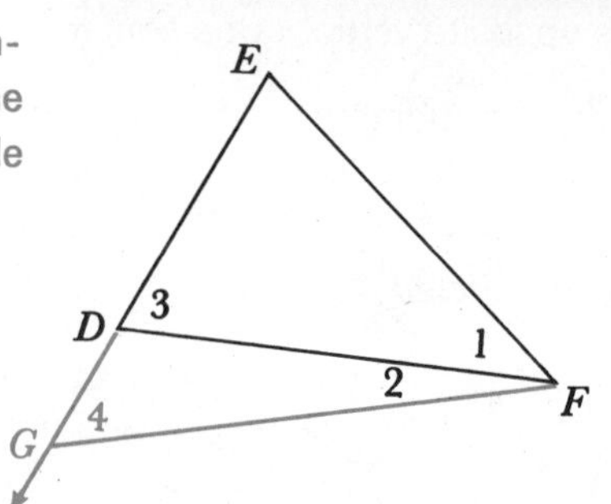

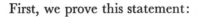

Given: $\triangle DEF$, $EF > DE$

Prove: $m\angle 3 > m\angle 1$

Proof:

STATEMENTS	REASONS
1. Let G be on $\overrightarrow{ED}$ and $EG = EF$.	1. Point Plotting Theorem (p. 27)
2. $m\angle 4 = m\angle EFG$	2. Base $\angle$s of an isos. $\triangle$ are $\cong$.
3. $m\angle 3 > m\angle 4$	3. Exterior $\angle$ Inequality Thm. (p. 242)
4. $m\angle 3 > m\angle EFG$	4. Substitution
5. $EF > DE$	5. Given
6. $EG > DE$	6. Substitution (steps 1 and 5)
7. $m\angle EFG = m\angle 1 + m\angle 2$	7. $\angle$ Addition Post. (p. 53)
8. $m\angle EFG > m\angle 1$	8. Definition of $>$
9. $m\angle 3 > m\angle 1$	9. If $a > b$ and $b > c$, then $a > c$. (steps 4 and 8)

An indirect proof is used for the converse of the statement above.

If two angles of a triangle are not congruent, the side opposite the larger angle is longer than the side opposite the smaller angle.

Given: $\triangle DEF$, $m\angle 3 > m\angle 1$

(See the figure on page 246.)

Prove: $EF > DE$

Proof:

STATEMENTS	REASONS
1. Assume EF is not greater than DE.	**1.** For an indirect proof, assume the opposite of what is to be proved.
2. $EF < DE$ or $EF = DE$.	**2.** $a < b$, $a = b$, or $a > b$.
3. $m\angle 3 < m\angle 1$ or $m\angle 3 = m\angle 1$.	**3.** Larger $\angle$ is opp. longer side of $\triangle$, or base $\angle$s of an isos. $\triangle$ are $\cong$.
4. But, $m\angle 3 > m\angle 1$.	**4.** Given
5. So, $EF > DE$.	**5.** Principle of Indirect Reasoning

Since the two statements just proved are converses, we can combine them in one theorem by using *if and only if.*

In any triangle, one angle is larger than another if and only if the side opposite the first angle is longer than the side opposite the second angle.

Theorem

I

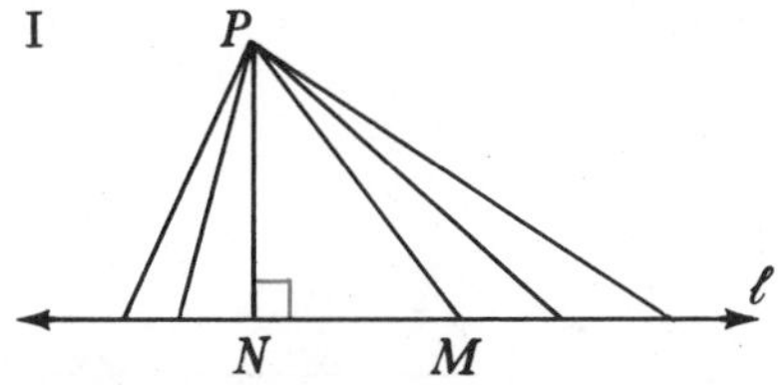

II

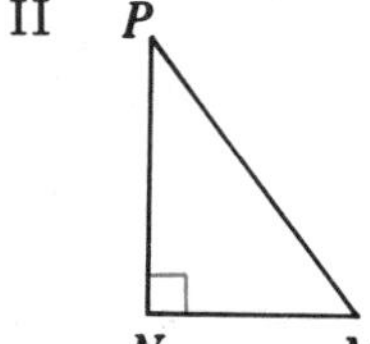

Which segment from P to ℓ seems to be the shortest?

Which side of the right triangle appears to be the longest?

The answers to these two questions give us the theorems below. The proofs appear in Exercises 27–32.

The shortest segment from a point to a line is the segment perpendicular to the line.

Theorem

The hypotenuse of a right triangle is longer than either leg.

Theorem

The first of these two theorems leads us to define **the distance from a point to a line** as the length of the perpendicular segment from the point to the line.

Exercises 7.3

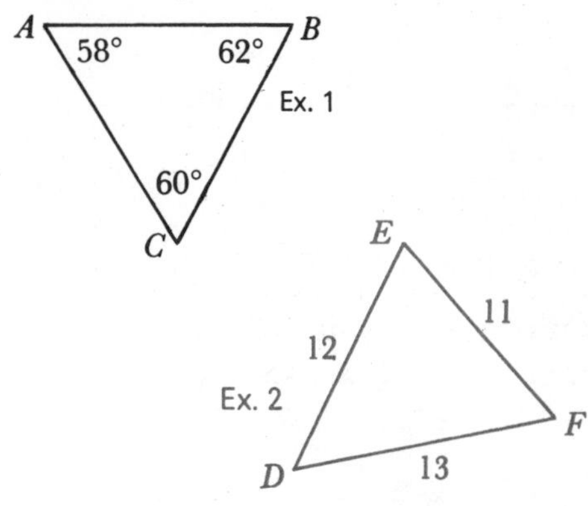

Ex. 1

Ex. 2

Ⓐ **1.** Which side of $\triangle ABC$ is the longest? The shortest?

2. Which angle of $\triangle DEF$ is the largest? The smallest?

3. In a triangle, the ______ angle is always opposite the longest side.

4. You must show that assuming $a < b$ or $a = b$ leads to a contradiction of a true statement to prove that ______ by an indirect proof.

5. Assuming that c is less than or equal to d is equivalent to assuming that c ______ d.

6. Neither leg of a right triangle can be longer than ______.

7. The distance from point P to line ℓ is the length of ______.

8. If $\overline{RD}$ is the shortest segment from R to $\overleftrightarrow{DB}$, then $\overline{RD}$ ______ $\overleftrightarrow{DB}$.

Ⓑ **9–18.** Which symbol, $<$, $=$, or $>$, should replace the ●?

9. If $m\angle G = 70$ and $m\angle J = 40$, GH ● HJ.

10. If $m\angle H = 85$ and $m\angle G = 60$, HJ ● JG.

11. If $m\angle H = 80$ and $m\angle J = 45$, HJ ● HG.

12. If $m\angle J = 40$ and $m\angle G = 60$, HJ ● GJ.

H

G J

Ex. 9–18

13. If $m\angle H = 90$, GJ ● GH.

14. If $\overline{HG} \perp \overline{HJ}$, GJ ● HJ.

15. If $GH = 3$ and $HJ = 5$, $m\angle G$ ● $m\angle J$.

16. If $GJ = 7$ and $HJ = 6$, $m\angle H$ ● $m\angle G$.

17. If $\angle H$ is obtuse, HG ● GJ.

18. If $\angle H$ is obtuse, HJ ● GJ.

19–24. Refer to the figure to find each distance.

19. from A to L

20. from N to E

21. from L to $\overleftrightarrow{AN}$

22. from N to $\overleftrightarrow{LA}$

23. from A to $\overleftrightarrow{LN}$

24. from L to N

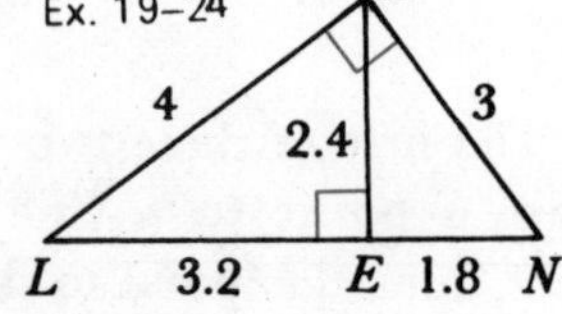

Ex. 19–24

25. What is the longest segment in the figure?

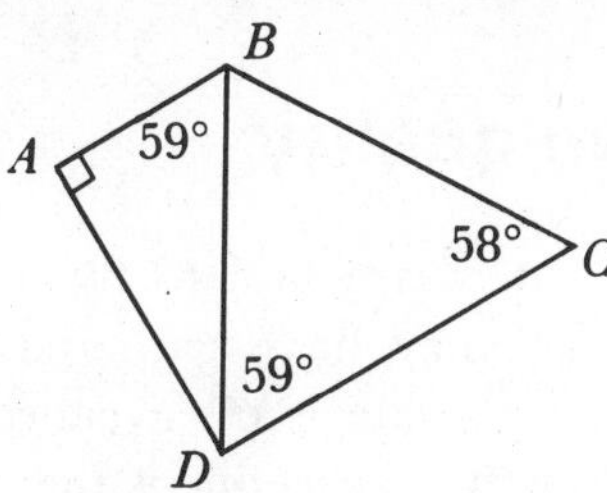

26. What is the shortest segment in the figure?

27–30. Copy figure I on page 247. Then copy and complete this proof that the shortest segment from a point to a line is the segment perpendicular to the line.

Given: $\overline{PN} \perp \ell$, M is any point on ℓ other than N.

Prove: $PN < PM$

Proof:

STATEMENTS	REASONS
1. $m\angle PNM = 90$	1. Given that $\overline{PN} \perp \ell$
2. $\triangle PNM$ is a right triangle.	2. **27.** ____
3. $m\angle NMP < 90$	3. **28.** ____
4. $m\angle NMP < m\angle PNM$	4. **29.** ____
5. $PN < PM$	5. **30.** ____

31–32. Copy figure II on page 247. Then copy and complete this proof that the hypotenuse of a right triangle is longer than either leg.

Given: $\angle N$ is the right angle in $\triangle MNP$.

Prove: $PN < PM$, $MN < PM$

Proof:

STATEMENTS	REASONS
1. $\overline{PN} \perp \overleftrightarrow{MN}$, $\overline{MN} \perp \overleftrightarrow{PN}$	1. **31.** ____
2. $PN < PM$, $MN < PM$	2. **32.** ____

© **33.** Prove that in an acute or an obtuse triangle, an altitude to any side is shorter than either of the other two sides.

Given: $\triangle CAT$, altitude $\overline{AF}$

Prove: $AF < AC$, $AF < AT$

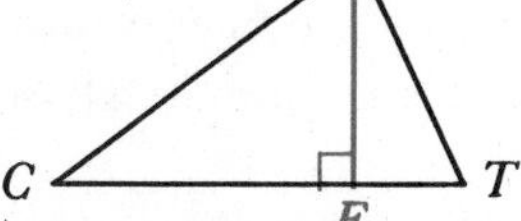

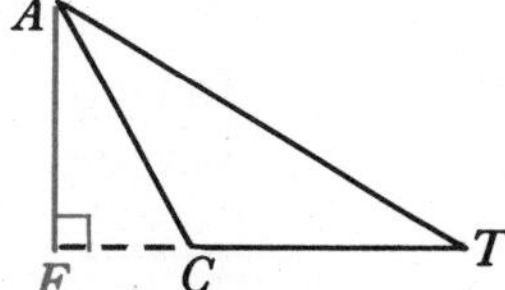

34. Prove that in a right triangle, an altitude to any side is not longer than either of the other two sides. HINT: Consider two cases—the altitude to the hypotenuse and an altitude to either leg.

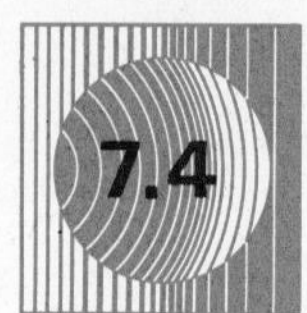

7.4 The Triangle Inequality

Bees are said to fly back to the hive in a straight line after they have gathered a load of nectar. So a straight, direct route is often called a *beeline.* In fact, we can prove that such a beeline is the shortest route to the hive from the last flower visited by the bee.

First, we compare the distance from the flower (F) to the hive (H) with the distance from the flower to a second point (S) and then to the hive.

Larsen/Van Cleve Photography

Given: $\triangle FSH$

Prove: $FS + SH > FH$

Proof:

STATEMENTS	REASONS
1. Let P be on $\overrightarrow{HS}$, S be between H and P, and $PS = FS$.	1. Point Plotting Theorem (p. 27)
2. $m\angle P = m\angle 2$	2. Base $\angle$s of an isos. $\triangle$ are $\cong$.
3. $m\angle HFP = m\angle 1 + m\angle 2$	3. $\angle$ Addition Post. (p. 53)
4. $m\angle HFP > m\angle 2$	4. Definition of $>$
5. $m\angle HFP > m\angle P$	5. Substitution (steps 2 and 4)
6. In $\triangle FPH$, $PH > FH$.	6. Longer side of $\triangle$ is opp. larger $\angle$.
7. $PH = PS + SH$	7. Def. of between (step 1)
8. $PH = FS + SH$	8. Substitution (steps 1 and 7)
9. $FS + SH > FH$	9. Substitution (steps 6 and 8)

What we have just proved can be stated in terms of any triangle.

Triangle Inequality Theorem

The sum of the lengths of any two sides of a triangle is greater than the length of the third side.

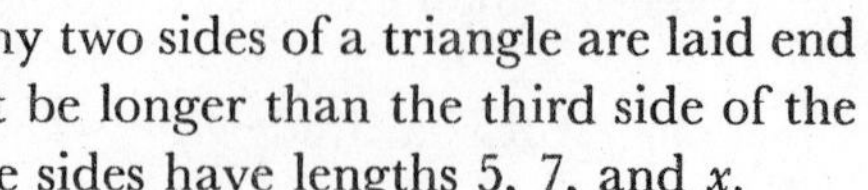

According to this theorem, if any two sides of a triangle are laid end to end, the resulting segment must be longer than the third side of the triangle. Consider a triangle whose sides have lengths 5, 7, and x.

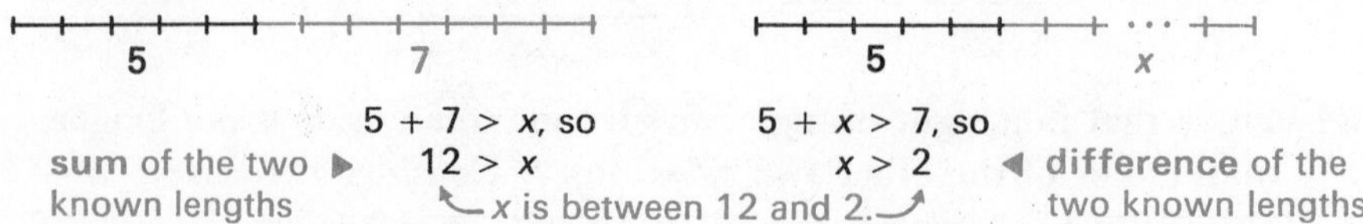

$5 + 7 > x$, so $12 > x$ ◀ **sum** of the two known lengths

$5 + x > 7$, so $x > 2$ ◀ **difference** of the two known lengths

x is between 12 and 2.

Suppose the bee doesn't make a beeline from the flower at F to the hive at H. The bee might take the path formed by the line segments from F to A to B to C to H (call this path $F\text{-}A\text{-}B\text{-}C\text{-}H$). The length of this path is $FA + AB + BC + CH$. But, since $FB < FA + AB$ by the Triangle Inequality, $F\text{-}B\text{-}C\text{-}H$ is shorter. Similar reasoning shows that $F\text{-}C\text{-}H$ is shorter than $F\text{-}B\text{-}C\text{-}H$ and, finally, that $F\text{-}H$ is shorter than $F\text{-}C\text{-}H$. Since the length of $F\text{-}H$ is FH, we have this theorem.

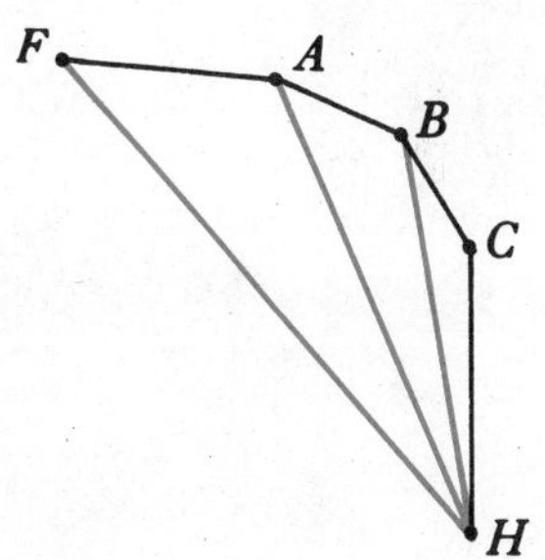

The shortest path between two points is the segment joining them.

Theorem

Exercises 7.4

Ⓐ **1.** Can a triangle have sides 3, 5, and 9 units long?

2. Can a triangle have sides 3, 5, and 6 units long?

3. If $\triangle MNP$ has sides 3, 7, and x units long, then $x <$ ______.

4. If $\triangle MNP$ has sides 3, 7, and x units long, then $x >$ ______.

Ⓑ **5–16.** Can the given numbers be the lengths of the sides of a triangle?

5. 8, 7, 10 **6.** 6, 9, 4 **7.** 9, 4, 5 **8.** 6, 12, 5

9. 7, 7, 9 **10.** 7, 15, 8 **11.** 4, 10, 6 **12.** 5, 5, 2

13. 4, 6, $2\frac{1}{2}$ **14.** 7, 4, $2\frac{1}{2}$ **15.** 8, $4\frac{2}{3}$, 3 **16.** $3\frac{1}{3}$, 5, 3

17–24. $\triangle ABC$ has sides of the given lengths. x is between what numbers?

17. 10, 13, x **18.** 11, 15, x **19.** 11, 5, x **20.** 3, 12, x

21. $2\frac{1}{2}$, 5, x **22.** 4, $5\frac{1}{2}$, x **23.** $7\frac{1}{2}$, $9\frac{1}{2}$, x **24.** $3\frac{1}{2}$, $6\frac{1}{2}$, x

25–28. Refer to the given segments. Can a triangle be formed using the three listed? If the answer is *yes*, construct the triangle.

25. a, b, c **26.** b, c, d

27. a, c, d **28.** a, b, d

a. ______________________ b. __________

c. ____________ d. ____________

Ⓒ **29–30.** Use the Triangle Inequality Theorem to prove that

29. $RS + ST + TU > RU$ in the figure.

30. A diagonal of a square is less than twice as long as a side.

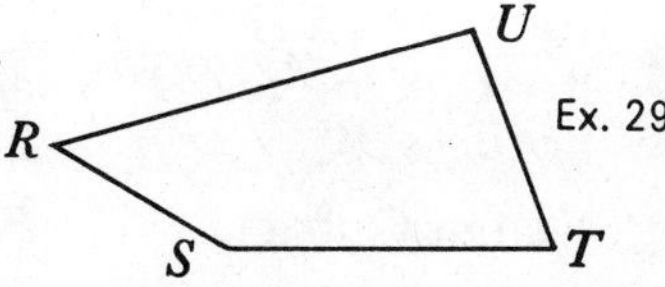

Ex. 29

7.5 Noncongruent Triangles

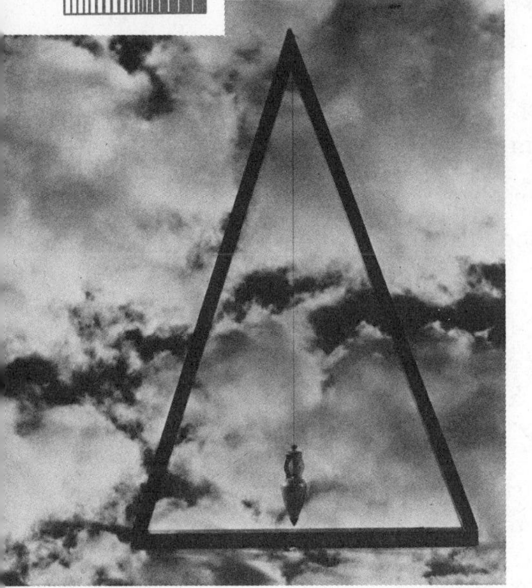

Frank Kuechmann

Suppose a pendulum hangs in a triangular frame, as shown in the photograph. When the weight is on the perpendicular bisector of the base of the frame, it is equidistant from the endpoints of the base. But when the weight swings to one side, its distance from either endpoint is related to the angles at the vertex of the frame.

The proof of the next theorem does not depend on the fact that the weight (point P) is in the interior of $\angle ACB$.

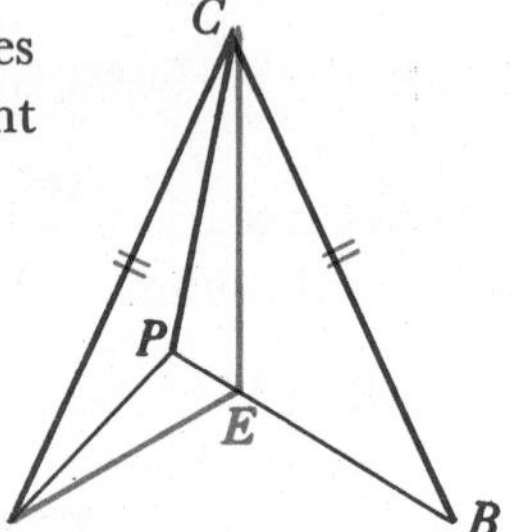

Given: $\overline{AC} \cong \overline{BC}$, P is any point for which $m\angle PCA < m\angle PCB$.

Prove: $PA < PB$

Proof:

STATEMENTS	REASONS
1. Let $\overrightarrow{CE}$ bisect $\angle ACB$ and intersect $\overline{PB}$ at E.	1. Every $\angle$ has exactly 1 bisector.
2. $\angle ACE \cong \angle BCE$	2. Definition of $\angle$ bisector
3. $\overline{AC} \cong \overline{BC}$	3. Given
4. $\overline{CE} \cong \overline{CE}$	4. A segment is $\cong$ to itself.
5. $\triangle ACE \cong \triangle BCE$	5. SAS Postulate
6. $EA = EB$	6. Corres. parts of $\cong$ $\triangle$s are $\cong$.
7. $PA < PE + EA$	7. $\triangle$ Inequality Theorem
8. $PA < PE + EB$	8. Substitution (steps 6 and 7)
9. $PE + EB = PB$	9. Definition of between
10. $PA < PB$	10. Substitution (steps 8 and 9)

This theorem is stated below in symbols rather than in words.

Pendulum Theorem

If $\overline{AC} \cong \overline{BC}$ and P is any point for which $m\angle PCA < m\angle PCB$, then P is closer to A than to B; that is, $PA < PB$.

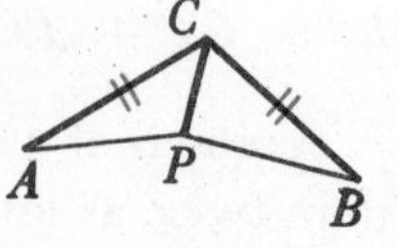

A derrick (named after a seventeenth-century English hangman) is used to lift and move heavy loads.

Notice that the mast, boom, and boom lines form a triangle. When the length of the boom lines is changed, the angle formed by the mast and the boom also changes. The relationship between this angle and the length of the lines is expressed by the next theorem.

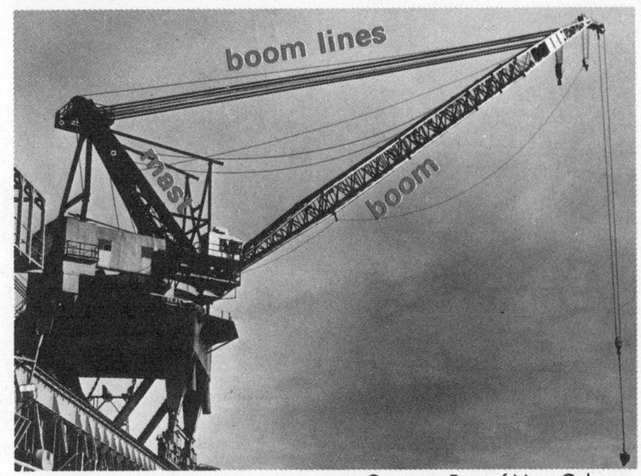

Courtesy Port of New Orleans

Hangman Theorem

If two noncongruent triangles have two sides of one congruent to two sides of the other,

a. The triangle with the smaller included angle has the shorter third side.

b. The triangle with the shorter third side has the smaller included angle.

Part **a** is proved here, while part **b,** the converse, is proved in Exercises 31–38.

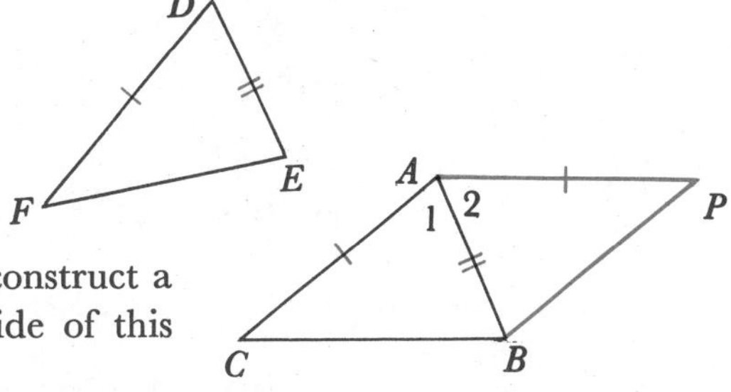

Given: $\overline{AC} \cong \overline{DF}$, $\overline{AB} \cong \overline{DE}$, $m\angle D < m\angle 1$

Prove: $EF < BC$

[*Plan:* On one of the congruent sides of $\triangle ABC$, construct a triangle congruent to $\triangle DEF$. Prove the third side of this triangle is shorter than the third side of $\triangle ABC$.]

Proof:

STATEMENTS	REASONS
1. Let $m\angle 2 = m\angle D$, so $\angle 2 \cong \angle D$.	**1.** $\angle$ Construction Post. (p. 53)
2. Let $AP = DF$, so $\overline{AP} \cong \overline{DF}$.	**2.** Point Plotting Theorem (p. 27)
3. $\overline{AB} \cong \overline{DE}$	**3.** Given
4. $\triangle ABP \cong \triangle DEF$	**4.** SAS Postulate
5. $\overline{AC} \cong \overline{DF}$, so $AC = DF$.	**5.** Given
6. $AC = AP$	**6.** Substitution (steps 2 and 5)
7. $m\angle D < m\angle 1$	**7.** Given
8. $m\angle 2 < m\angle 1$	**8.** Substitution (steps 1 and 7)
9. $BP < BC$	**9.** Pendulum Theorem (steps 6 and 8)
10. $BP = EF$	**10.** Corres. parts of $\cong$ $\triangle$s are $\cong$. (step 4)
11. $EF < BC$	**11.** Substitution (steps 9 and 10)

Exercises 7.5

Ⓐ **1–24.** Refer to the figures. Which symbol, $<, =,$ or $>$, should replace the ▨?

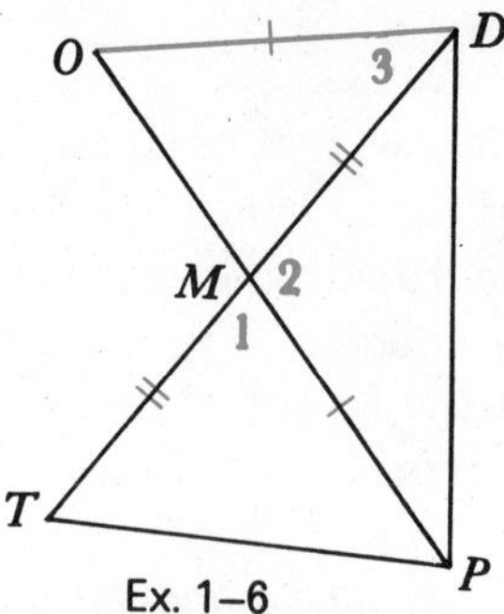

Ex. 1–6

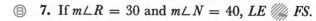

1. MD ▨ MT 2. MP ▨ MP

3. If $PT < PD$, then $m\angle 1$ ▨ $m\angle 2$.

4. If $m\angle 1 < m\angle 2$, then PT ▨ PD.

5. $m\angle 2$ ▨ $m\angle 3$ 6. MO ▨ PD

Ⓑ 7. If $m\angle R = 30$ and $m\angle N = 40$, LE ▨ FS.

8. If $m\angle N = 50$ and $m\angle R = 40$, FS ▨ LE.

9. If $EL = 5$ and $FS = 4$, $m\angle N$ ▨ $m\angle R$.

10. If $SF = 8$ and $LE = 9$, $m\angle N$ ▨ $m\angle R$.

11. If $LE = 10$ and $FS = 10$, $m\angle N$ ▨ $m\angle R$.

12. If $m\angle R = 35$ and $m\angle N = 35$, LE ▨ FS.

Ex. 7–16

13. If $FS < LE$, then $m\angle R$ ▨ $m\angle N$.

14. If $EL < FS$, then $m\angle N$ ▨ $m\angle R$.

15. If $m\angle N > m\angle R$, then LE ▨ FS.

16. If $m\angle R > m\angle N$, then EL ▨ FS.

17. If $AB = 5$ and $BC = 7$, then $m\angle 1$ ▨ $m\angle 2$.

18. If $BC = 9$ and $AB = 12$, then $m\angle 1$ ▨ $m\angle 2$.

19. If $AB = 5$ and $BC = 7$, then $m\angle C$ ▨ $m\angle A$.

20. If $BC = 9$ and $AB = 12$, then $m\angle C$ ▨ $m\angle A$.

21. If $m\angle 1 = 95$, then AB ▨ BC.

22. If $m\angle 1 = 75$, then BC ▨ AB.

23. If $m\angle 1 = 75$, $m\angle C$ ▨ $m\angle A$.

24. If $m\angle 1 = 95$, $m\angle A$ ▨ $m\angle C$.

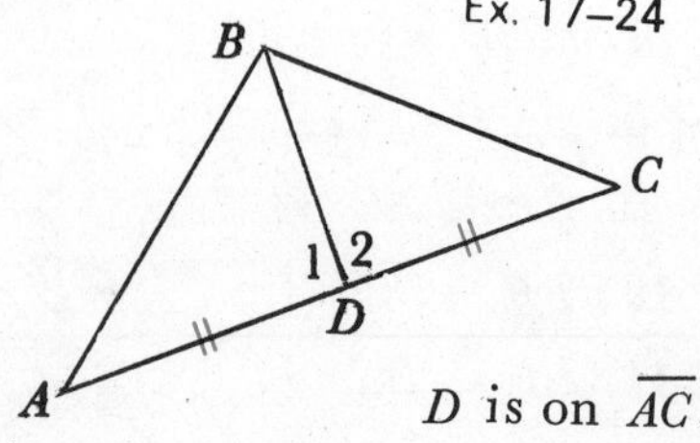

Ex. 17–24

D is on $\overline{AC}$.

25–30. Suppose two noncongruent triangles have two sides of one congruent to two sides of the other.

25. Can one angle of one triangle be congruent to one angle of the other triangle?

26. Can two angles of one triangle be congruent to two angles of the other triangle?

27. Can the third sides be congruent?

28. Can the triangles be isosceles?

29. Can the triangles be right triangles?

30. Can the triangles be equilateral?

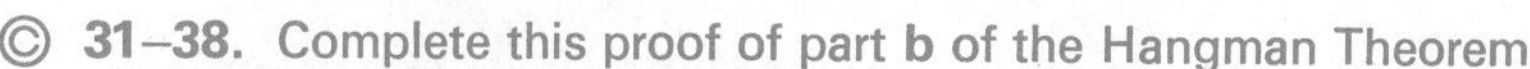

© **31–38.** Complete this proof of part **b** of the Hangman Theorem.

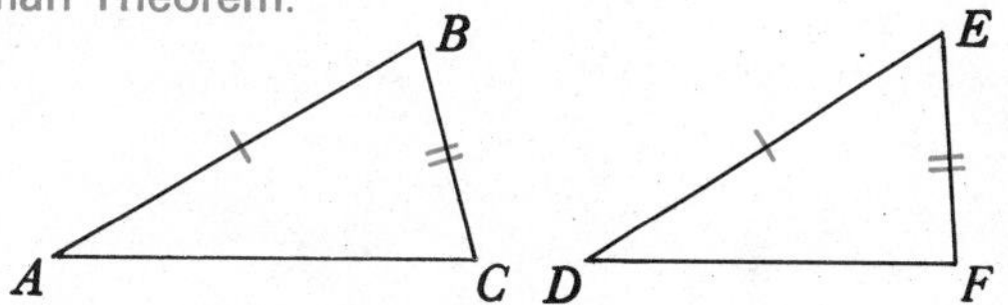

Given: $\triangle ABC$ and $\triangle DEF$ are not congruent, $\overline{AB} \cong \overline{DE}$, $\overline{BC} \cong \overline{EF}$, $DF < AC$

Prove: $m\angle E < m\angle B$

Proof:

STATEMENTS	REASONS
1. Assume $m\angle E$ is not less than $m\angle B$.	*1.* **31.** ____
2. First, assume $m\angle E = m\angle B$.	*2.* $a < b$, $a = b$, or $a > b$.
3. $\overline{AB} \cong \overline{DE}$, $\overline{BC} \cong \overline{EF}$	*3.* **32.** ____
4. $\triangle ABC \cong \triangle DEF$	*4.* **33.** ____
5. But, $\triangle ABC$, $\triangle DEF$ are not congruent.	*5.* **34.** ____
6. So, $m\angle E \neq m\angle B$.	*6.* **35.** ____
7. Now assume $m\angle E > m\angle B$.	*7.* $a < b$, $a = b$, or $a > b$.
8. $DF > AC$	*8.* **36.** ____
9. But, $DF < AC$.	*9.* **37.** ____
10. So, $m\angle E$ is not greater than $m\angle B$.	*10.* **38.** ____
11. Thus, $m\angle E < m\angle B$.	*11.* $a < b$, $a = b$, or $a > b$. (steps 6 and 10)

39. Why does the second compass mark off the longer segment?

40. Why does the first roof have a larger angle at the top?

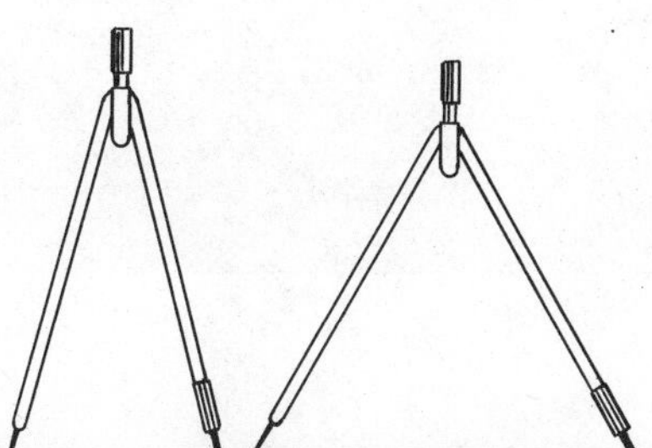

Courtesy American Airlines

THE SHORTEST PATH FROM HERE TO THERE

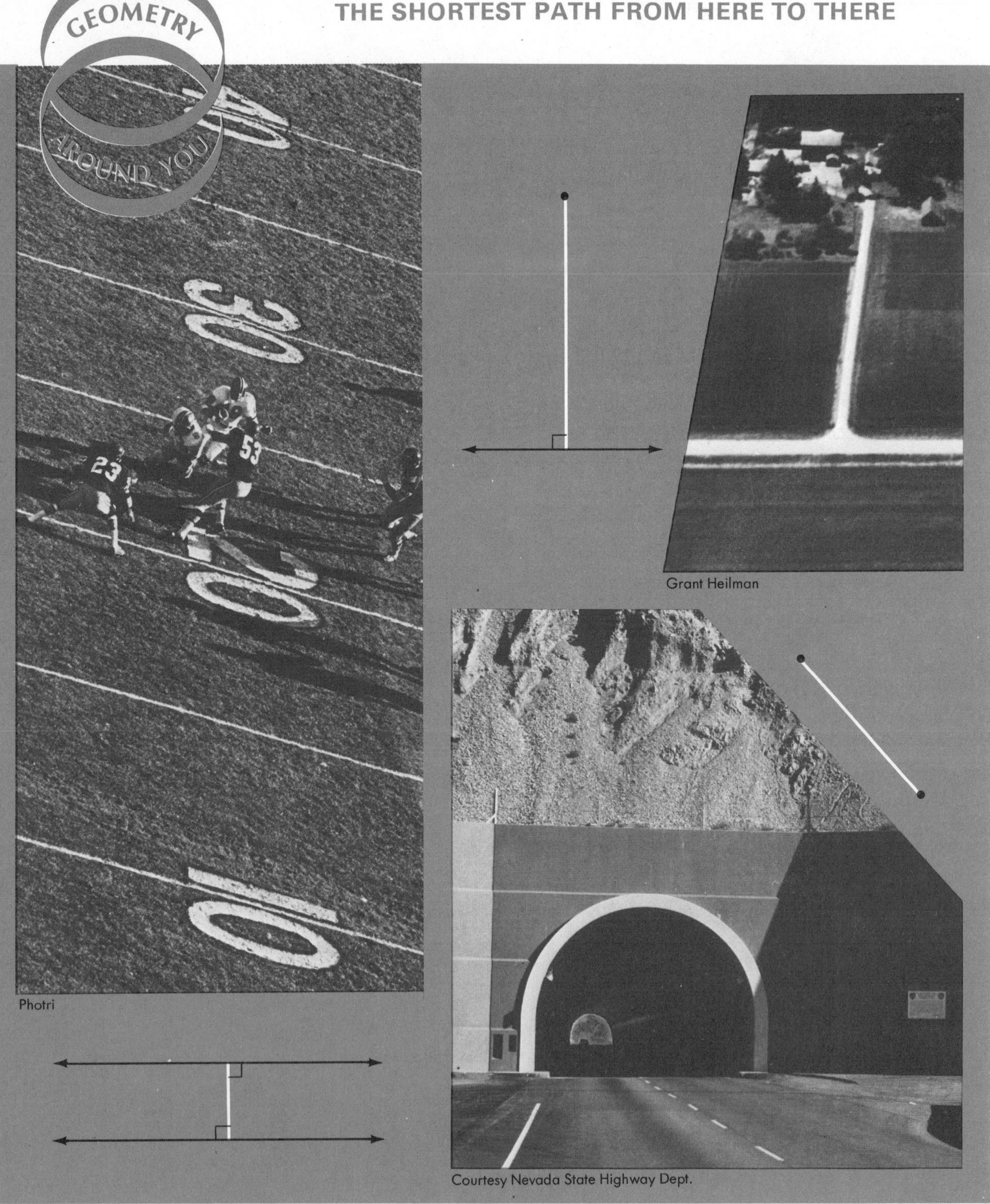

Photri

Grant Heilman

Courtesy Nevada State Highway Dept.

Transformations: Shortest Paths

Suppose that on a flat surface a ball starts rolling from point B. It bounces off wall s at P and stops rolling at point E. At first, the ball is rolling toward E', the reflection image of E over s. But after it hits the wall, its path is the reflection over s of the path it would take if it could go through the wall.

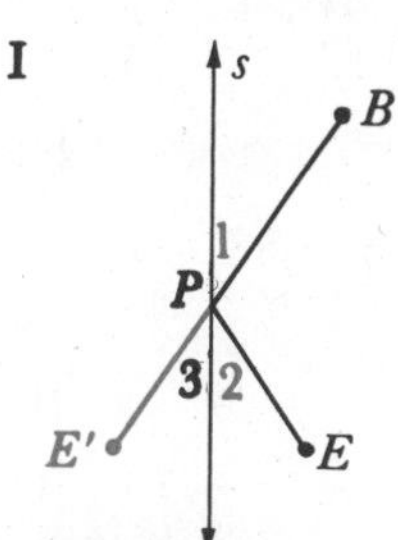

We can prove two things about the path of this ball.

1. **It leaves the wall at the same angle at which it approaches the wall ($\angle 1 \cong \angle 2$).**
2. **It is the shortest path from B to s to E.**

Camerique

It is easy to show that $\angle 1 \cong \angle 2$ (see figure I).

Since reflections preserve angle measure,	$\angle 2 \cong \angle 3$
But $\angle 1$ and $\angle 3$ are vertical angles, so	$\angle 1 \cong \angle 3$
Since $\angle 1$ and $\angle 2$ are both congruent to $\angle 3$,	$\angle 1 \cong \angle 2$

Now consider any other path from B to s to E. In figure II this path touches s at R.

By the Triangle Inequality,	$BR + RE' > BE'$
By the definition of between,	$BE' = BP + PE'$
Substituting,	$BR + RE' > BP + PE'$
Since reflections preserve distance,	$RE = RE'$ and $PE = PE'$
Substituting again,	$BR + RE > BP + PE$

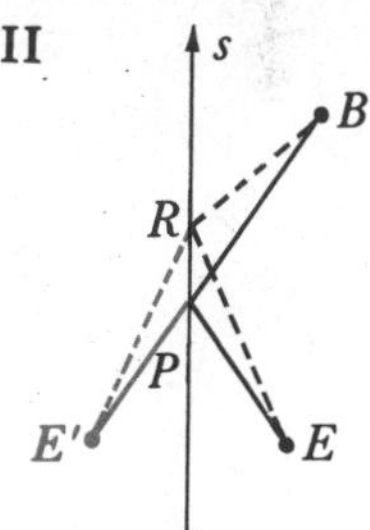

So the shortest path from B to s to E touches the wall where $\overline{BE'}$ intersects s.

In a game of pool, you might want the ball to bounce off two sides of the table before stopping at E. In that case, first reflect E over either side of the table to get E', and then reflect E' over the other side of the table to get E''. Aim at E'' as shown in figure III.

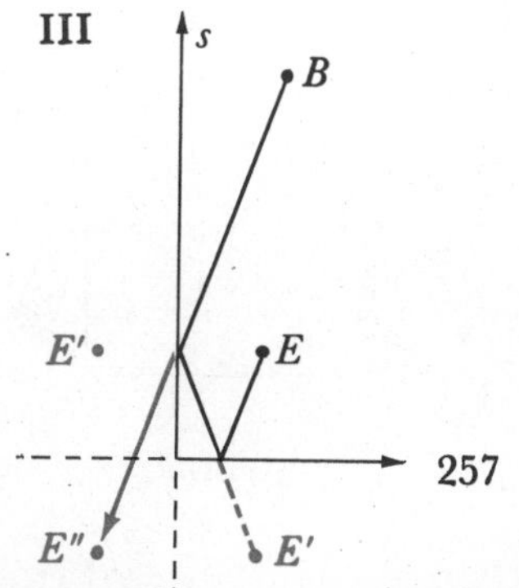

Exercises 7.6

Ⓐ 1. To roll a ball along the shortest path from point B to wall s to point E, at what imaginary point should you aim?

2. A ball is rolled in a path perpendicular to a wall. Describe its path after it hits the wall.

3. If a rolling ball must touch two walls before stopping, how many images must be found?

4. If a rolling ball must touch n walls before stopping, how many images do you think must be found?

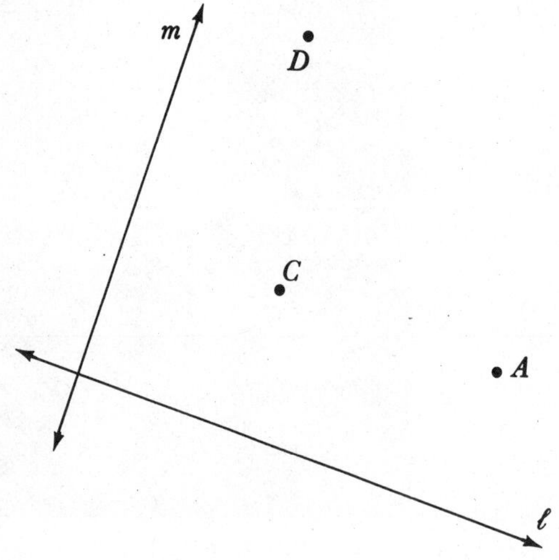

Ⓑ 5–8. Copy the figure.

5. Draw the shortest path from A to ℓ to D. Then draw the shortest path from D to ℓ to A. Are the paths different?

6. Draw the shortest path from C to ℓ to A. Then draw the shortest path from A to ℓ to C. Are the paths different?

7. Draw the shortest path from A to D touching ℓ and m at distinct points.

8. Draw the shortest path from C to A touching m and ℓ at distinct points.

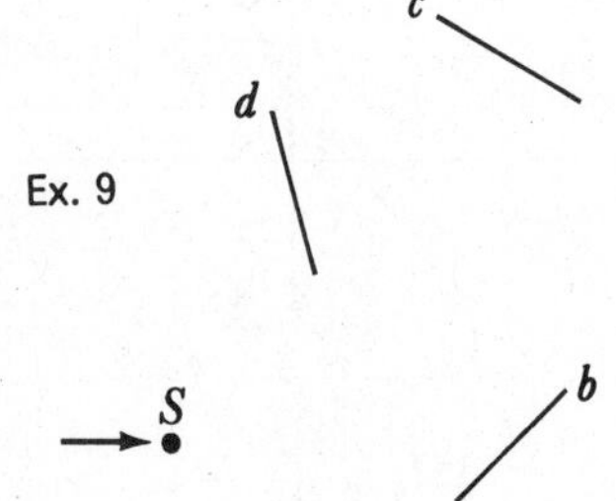

Ex. 9

Ex. 10

Ⓒ 9–10. Light and sound waves bounce off surfaces in the same way a ball does. Use this fact to answer these questions.

9. Light enters a camera at S and is reflected from surfaces at b, c, and d (in that order) before reaching the viewfinder where the photographer sees it. Copy the figure and draw the path of the light.

10. Copy the figure and draw the path of a sound wave that bounces off each side of the room exactly once before it returns to the speaker at P.

11. The congruent angles made by the wall and the ball's path are known as the **angle of incidence** and the **angle of reflection.** Do library research to find out which is which.

■ Chapter 7 Review ■

1–4. Which symbol, $<$, $=$, or $>$, should replace the ◍? **7.1**

1. If n ◍ 9, $n + c = 9$ for some positive number c.

2. If $x = -3 + 7$, then x ◍ -3.

3. If s ◍ 5, s is not less than or equal to 5.

4. If t is not equal to 3, t ◍ 3 or t ◍ 3.

5–8. Solve.

5. $p + 6 < 8$ **6.** $2y > 7$ **7.** $x - 8 < 3$ **8.** $\frac{1}{3}r > 8$

9–16. Which symbol, $<$, $=$, or $>$, should replace the ◍? **7.2**

9. If $\overline{MN}$ is shorter than $\overline{PD}$, then MN ◍ PD.

10. If $\angle 3$ is larger than $\angle 1$, then $m\angle 1$ ◍ $m\angle 3$.

11. If $\triangle ABC$ has a $60°$ exterior angle at A, then $m\angle B$ ◍ 60.

12. If $RS = RT + TS$, then RS ◍ TS.

13. In $\triangle RST$, if $RS > ST$, then $m\angle T$ ◍ $m\angle R$.

14. In $\triangle XVW$, if $m\angle W > m\angle V$, then XW ◍ XV. **7.3**

15. If $\overline{DT} \perp \ell$ at T and $\overline{DS}$ intersects ℓ at S, DT ◍ DS.

16. If $\overline{SM} \perp \overline{MR}$, then SR ◍ SM and MR ◍ SR.

17–20. Can the given numbers be lengths of the sides of a triangle? **7.4**

17. 3, 7, 11 **18.** 9, 7, 3 **19.** 5, 9, 5 **20.** 2, 7, 5

21–23. Which symbol, $<$, $=$, or $>$, should replace the ◍? **7.5**

21. If P were located so that $m\angle CAP$ ◍ $m\angle DAP$, P would be closer to C than to D.

22. If $BC > DE$, then $m\angle 1$ ◍ $m\angle 3$.

23. If $m\angle 3 > m\angle 1$, then BC ◍ DE.

Ex. 21–23

24. Copy S, T, and ℓ. Draw the shortest path from S to ℓ to T. **7.6**

Ex. 24

Chapter 7 Test

1–4. Which symbol, $<$, $=$, or $>$, should replace the ▨ ?

1. A positive number can be added to x to get y if x ▨ y.

2. If n is not less than or equal to 8, n ▨ 8.

3. If AB ▨ PQ, then $\overline{AB}$ is longer than $\overline{PQ}$.

4. If $\angle S$ is larger than $\angle T$, then $m\angle T$ ▨ $m\angle S$.

5. If $\overline{GH} \perp \ell$ at H, then GH is the ______ from G to ℓ.

6. In $\triangle ABC$, $AB + BC > AC$ according to the ______.

7. Solve: **a.** $x - 13 < 2$ **b.** $\frac{3}{5}t > 36$

8. Can $\triangle DEF$ have sides with the given lengths?

a. 13, 5, 7 **b.** 8, 7, 14

9–21. Refer to the figures. Which symbol, $<$, $=$, or $>$, should replace the ▨ ?

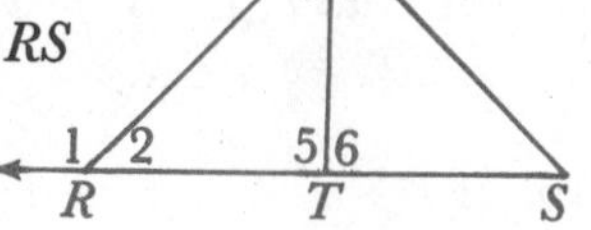

9. $m\angle S$ ▨ $m\angle 1$ **10.** $m\angle 6$ ▨ $m\angle 3$

11. $RT + TS$ ▨ RS **12.** $RV + VS$ ▨ RS

13. If $VT > TS$, then $m\angle 4$ ▨ $m\angle S$.

14. If $m\angle S < m\angle 2$, then VS ▨ VR.

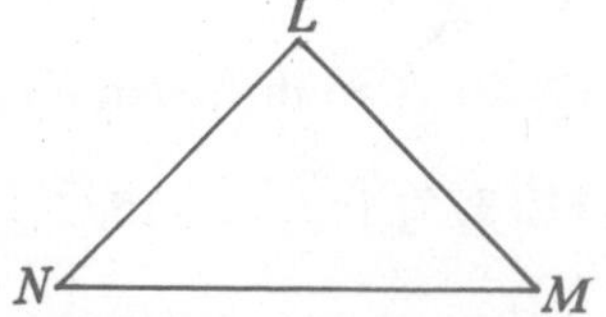

15. If $\overline{VR} \perp \overline{VS}$, then VR ▨ RS.

16. If $RV = SV$ and $m\angle 3$ ▨ $m\angle 4$, then T is closer to S than to R.

17. If $\overline{RT} \cong \overline{TS}$ and $m\angle 5 < m\angle 6$, then RV ▨ SV.

18. If $\overline{RS} \cong \overline{MN}$, $\overline{VR} \cong \overline{LM}$, and $m\angle M < m\angle 2$, then VS ▨ LN.

19. If $\overline{RS} \cong \overline{MN}$, $\overline{VR} \cong \overline{LM}$, and $LN > VS$, then $m\angle 2$ ▨ $m\angle M$.

20. If $m\angle 5 < 90$, $m\angle 4$ ▨ 90. **21.** If $m\angle RVS < 95$, $m\angle 3$ ▨ 95.

22. Refer to the figure. Which point is on the path of the ball?

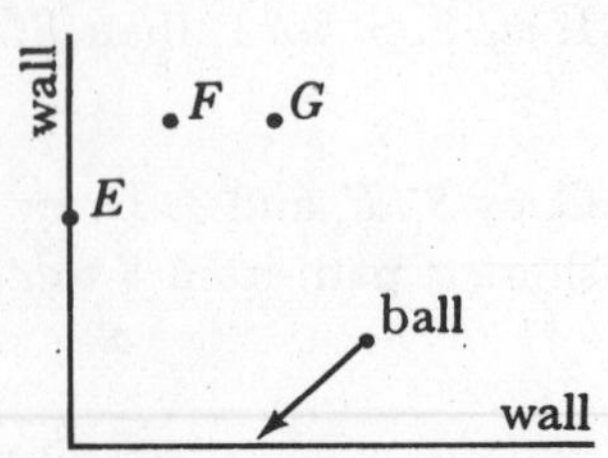

Cumulative Review: Chapters 1–7

1–4. What postulate or theorem leads to the conclusion about the figure? **Ch. 1**

Ex. 1–4

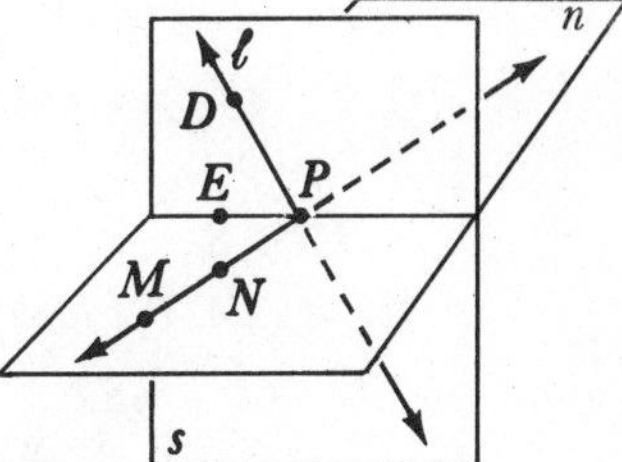

1. Every point on ℓ is in s.
2. N and ℓ determine a plane.
3. s and n intersect at $\overleftrightarrow{PE}$.
4. There is a point in s not on ℓ.

5. A ______ is accepted as true without proof.
6. ______ reasoning is based on examples.
7. A ______ states a hypothesis and its logical conclusion.
8. ______ reasoning is based on postulates and definitions.
9. If the coordinates of A and B are 3 and 7, AB = ______.

10–15. Refer to the figure for Exercises 1–4.

10. Points M, N, and ______ are collinear.
11. $\overleftrightarrow{MN}$ and line ℓ intersect at ______.
12. $\overrightarrow{NP}$ and ______ are opposite rays.
13. Line ℓ intersects plane n at ______.
14. $\overleftrightarrow{MN}$ and plane s intersect at ______.
15. If N is the ______ of $\overline{MP}$, then $MN = NP$.

16. Is a half plane a convex set? **Ch. 2**

17. In a plane, how many lines through a given point are perpendicular to a given line?

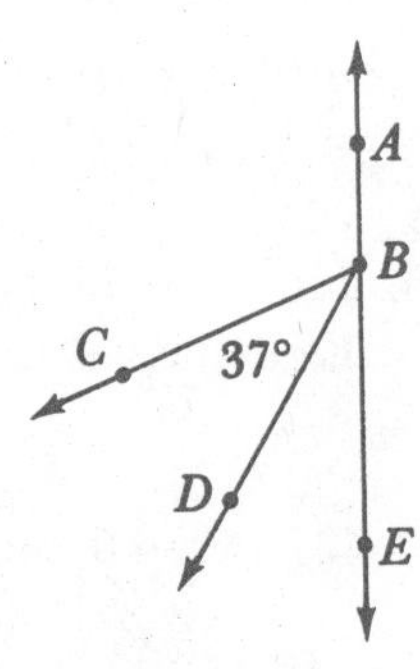

18–22. Refer to the figure. B is on $\overleftrightarrow{AE}$.

18. Name a point in the interior of $\angle ABD$.
19. Name 2 angles adjacent to $\angle CBD$.
20. If $\overrightarrow{BD}$ is the bisector of $\angle CBE$, find $m\angle DBE$.
21. If $m\angle ABD = 151$, find (**a**) $m\angle ABC$ and (**b**) $m\angle DBE$.
22. If $m\angle ABD = 153$, name (**a**) all acute angles, (**b**) all obtuse angles, and (**c**) all right angles.

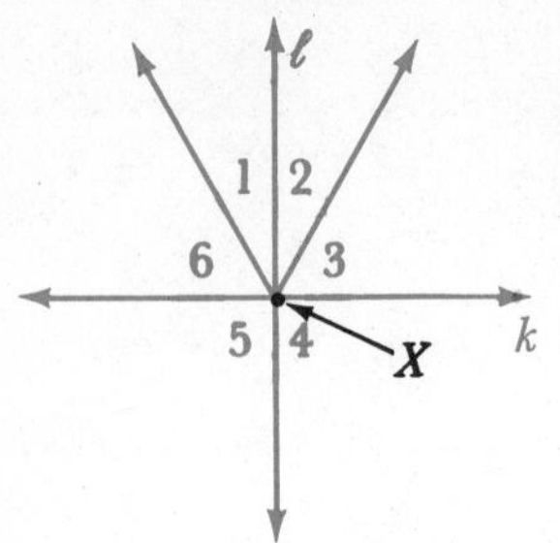

23–26. $\ell \perp k$. What theorem leads to the conclusion about the figure?

23. $\angle X_{16}$, $\angle X_{23}$, $\angle 4$, and $\angle 5$ are right angles.

24. $\angle 4 \cong \angle 5$

25. If $\angle 1 \cong \angle 2$, then $\angle 6 \cong \angle 3$.

26. If $\angle 1 \cong \angle 2$, then $\angle X_{56} \cong \angle_{34}$.

Ch. 3

27. Give the hypothesis and the conclusion of the following statement: If two angles are complementary, the sum of their measures is 90.

28. Change the following statement to if-then form: All rational numbers are real numbers.

29. Draw an Euler diagram for the statement in Exercise 28.

30. If $\triangle TIP \cong \triangle LUM$, complete each statement.

a. $\overline{IP} \cong$ _____ **b.** $\angle P \cong$ _____ **c.** $\overline{TP} \cong$ _____

31–34. Give a reason for each statement.

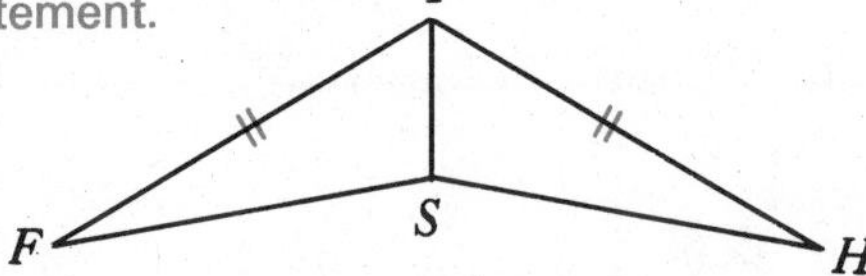

Given: $\overline{FI} \cong \overline{IH}$, $\angle FIS \cong \angle HIS$

Prove: $\overline{FS} \cong \overline{HS}$

Proof: STATEMENTS	REASONS
1. $\overline{FI} \cong \overline{IH}$, $\angle FIS \cong \angle HIS$	1. **31.**
2. $\overline{SI} \cong \overline{SI}$	2. **32.**
3. $\triangle FIS \cong \triangle HIS$	3. **33.**
4. $\overline{FS} \cong \overline{HS}$	4. **34.**

35. Line ℓ is the perpendicular bisector of $\overline{MN}$. Find the values of x and y.

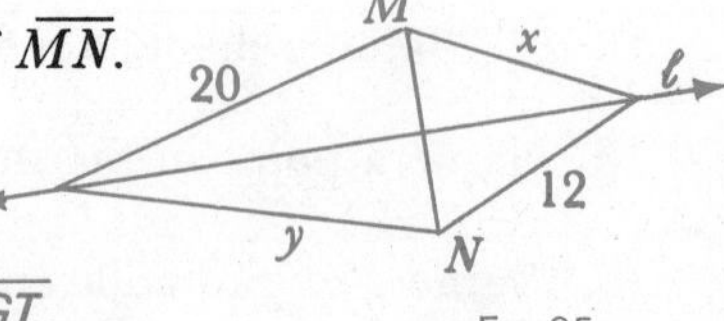

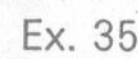

Ch. 4

36–48. In the figure, $\overline{TR} \parallel \overline{IM}$ and A is on $\overline{GT}$.

36. $\angle 2$ and _____ are corresponding angles.

37. $\angle 5$ and _____ are alternate interior angles.

38. $\angle 1$ and _____ are supplementary.

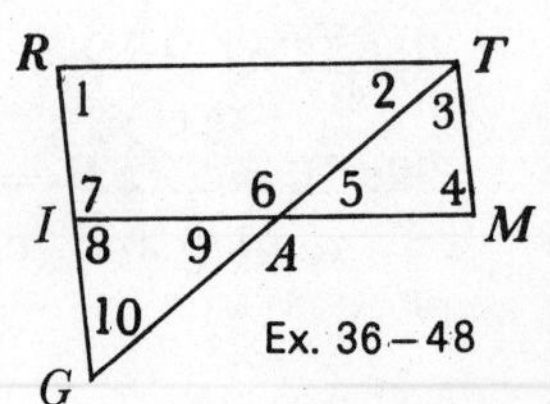

Ex. 36–48

39. If $\overline{IR} \perp \overline{RT}$, $\overline{IR} \perp$ ______.

40. If $\overline{TR} \cong \overline{IM}$, $TRIM$ is a ______.

41. $TRIA$ is a ______.

42. If $RI = IG$, then $TA =$ ______.

43. If $\angle 3 \cong$ ______, $\overline{TM} \parallel \overline{RG}$.

44. $m\angle 2 + m\angle 6 =$ ______

45. $m\angle 1 + m\angle 2 + m\angle 10 =$ ______

46. $m\angle 6 = m\angle 4 + m$ ______

47. How many lines through G are parallel to $\overleftrightarrow{RT}$?

48. $IA = \frac{1}{2}RT$ if $\overline{IA}$ is a ______ of $\triangle RGT$.

49. Given: $\overline{PO} \parallel \overline{HS}$, $\overline{PO} \cong \overline{HS}$, $\overline{PS} \perp \overline{HO}$

Prove: $POSH$ is a rhombus.

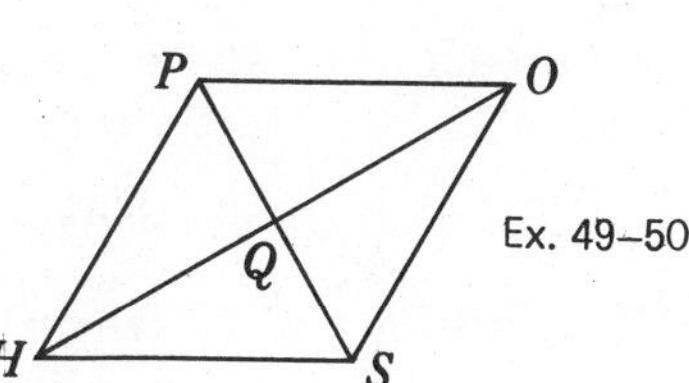

Ex. 49–50

50. Given: Rhombus $POSH$

Prove: $\angle OPQ$ is acute.

51. Is this figure a polygon? Why? **Ch. 5**

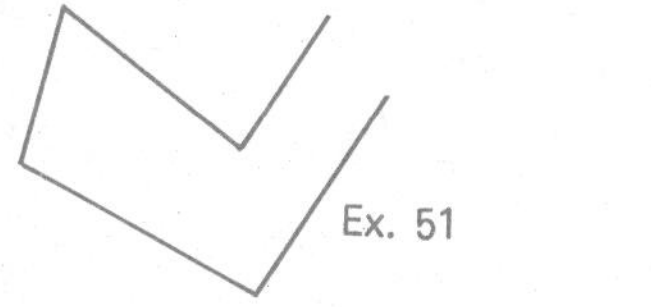
Ex. 51

52–56. *ABCDEFGH* is a regular octagon.

52. Find the sum of its interior angles.

53. Find the sum of its exterior angles, one at each vertex.

54. Find the measure of each interior angle.

55. Find the measure of each exterior angle.

56. If $AB = 6$, find the perimeter of the octagon.

57–60. Using the given information, what postulate or theorem can be used to prove $\triangle XBC \cong \triangle XBA$?

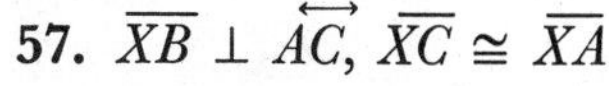
57. $\overline{XB} \perp \overleftrightarrow{AC}$, $\overline{XC} \cong \overline{XA}$

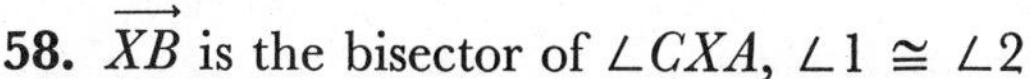
58. $\overrightarrow{XB}$ is the bisector of $\angle CXA$, $\angle 1 \cong \angle 2$

59. $\angle XBC$ and $\angle XBA$ are right angles, $\angle 1 \cong \angle 2$

60. $\triangle XDA \cong \triangle XEC$, $\overline{CB} \cong \overline{BA}$

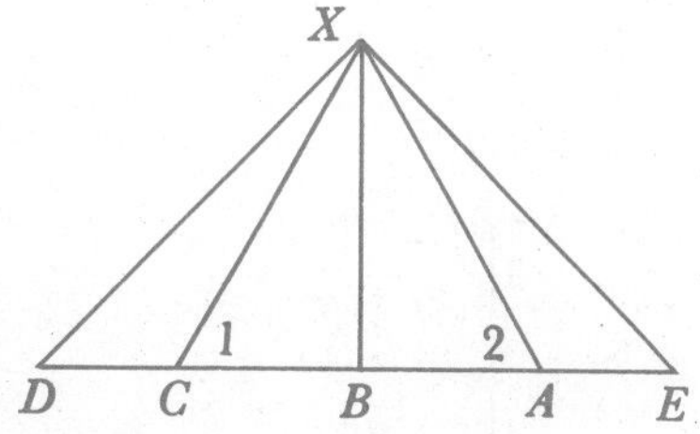

Ch. 6

61. Give a counterexample to show the following statement is false: If two angles are supplementary, both angles are right angles.

62. Write the converse of the statement in Exercise 61. Is it true?

63. Can the statements below be connected by *if and only if* to form a true statement?

    Two triangles are equiangular. Two triangles are equilateral.

64. In an indirect proof, you assume the _____ of the fact you want to prove.

65. Draw a sketch to illustrate the Median Concurrence Theorem.

66–67. Use the given plan to write a proof.

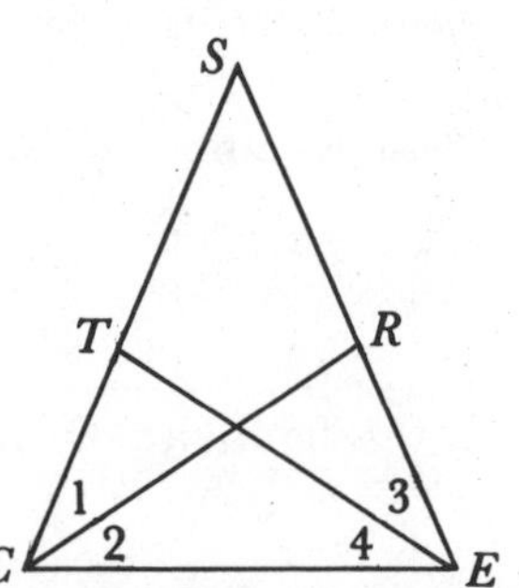

Given: $\triangle CES$ with $\overrightarrow{CR}$ and $\overrightarrow{ET}$ the bisectors of $\angle C$ and $\angle E$, $\overline{CS} \cong \overline{ES}$

Prove: $\overline{CR} \cong \overline{ET}$

66. [*Plan:* Show $\triangle CRS \cong \triangle ETS$.]

67. [*Plan:* Show $\triangle CET \cong \triangle ECR$.]

Ch. 7

68. If _____ can be added to c to get d, then $c < d$.

69. If $\overline{PD}$ is _____ than $\overline{RS}$, then $RS > PD$.

70. If $m\angle A > m\angle B$, then $\angle A$ _____ $\angle B$.

71. Solve: **a.** $t - 14 > 2$ **b.** $\frac{2}{3}n < 5$

72–80. Which symbol, <, =, or >, should replace the ▒?

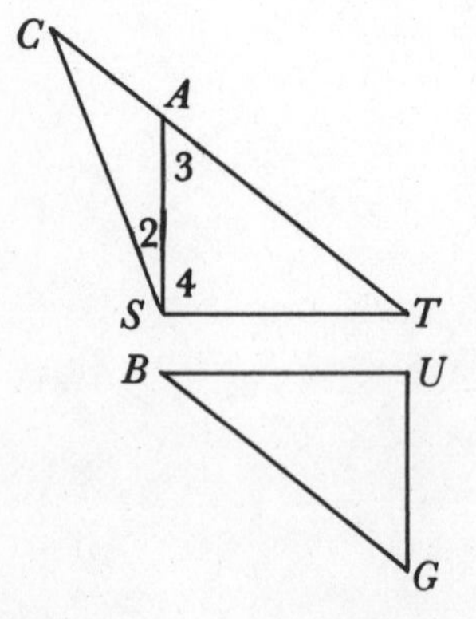

72. $m\angle 3$ ▒ $m\angle C$

73. $m\angle 4$ ▒ $m\angle CST$

74. $CA + AT$ ▒ CT

75. If $m\angle 4 = 90$, ST ▒ AT.

76. $CS + ST$ ▒ CT

77. If $ST > AS$, $m\angle 3$ ▒ $m\angle T$.

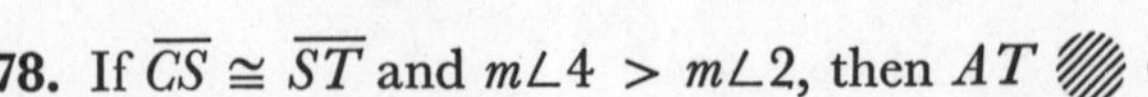

78. If $\overline{CS} \cong \overline{ST}$ and $m\angle 4 > m\angle 2$, then AT ▒ CA.

79. If $\overline{UG} \cong \overline{SA}$, $\overline{BU} \cong \overline{ST}$, and $m\angle 4 > m\angle U$, then AT ▒ BG.

80. If $\overline{AT} \cong \overline{BG}$, $\overline{BU} \cong \overline{AS}$, and $ST > GU$, then $m\angle 3$ ▒ $m\angle B$.

PERPENDICULAR LINES AND PLANES 8

Franco/Van Cleve Photography

Which supports of the rings structure seem to be perpendicular to the plane of the floor?

8.1 When Are a Line and a Plane Perpendicular?

You can easily make the models below.

Model of vertical line and horizontal plane	Model of nonvertical line and horizontal plane

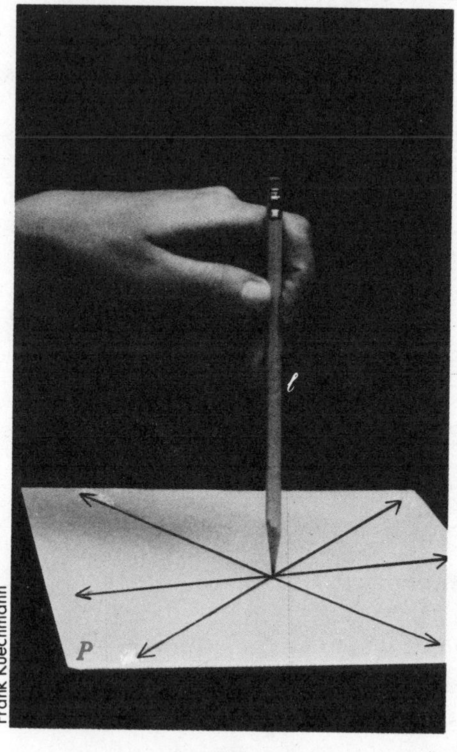

Line ℓ appears to be perpendicular to plane *P* and to *every* line in *P* that passes through the intersection of ℓ and *P*.

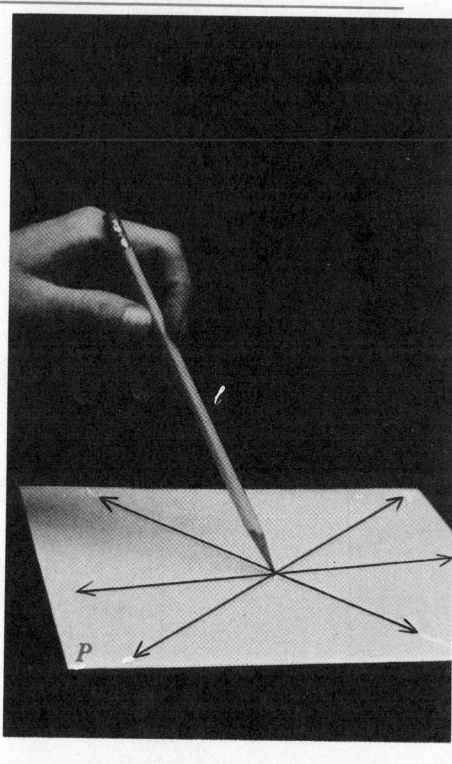

Line ℓ does not appear to be perpendicular to plane *P* or to every line in *P* that passes through the intersection of ℓ and *P*. (But ℓ could be perpendicular to one of these lines. Try it.)

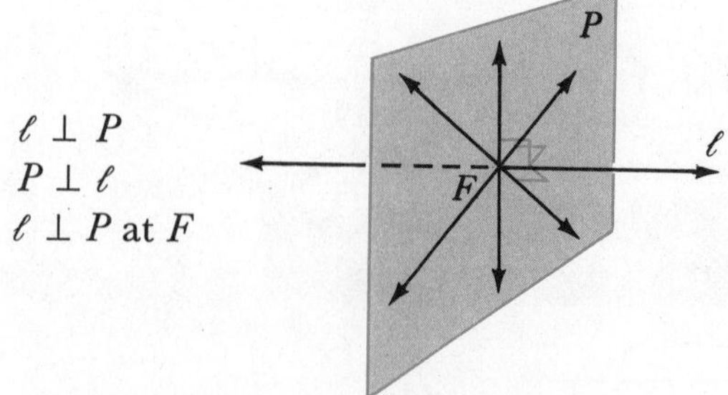

These models lead us to define *perpendicular* for a line and a plane as follows: Line ℓ and plane *P* are **perpendicular** if and only if they intersect and ℓ is perpendicular to every line in *P* that contains the point of intersection. The point of intersection is called the **foot** of the perpendicular.

Earlier, we drew perpendicular lines in a plane to intersect at right angles. See figure I. Now, when we draw perpendicular lines in space, we might *not* draw them to intersect at right angles. See figure II. This is because we are drawing 3-dimensional figures on a 2-dimensional surface.

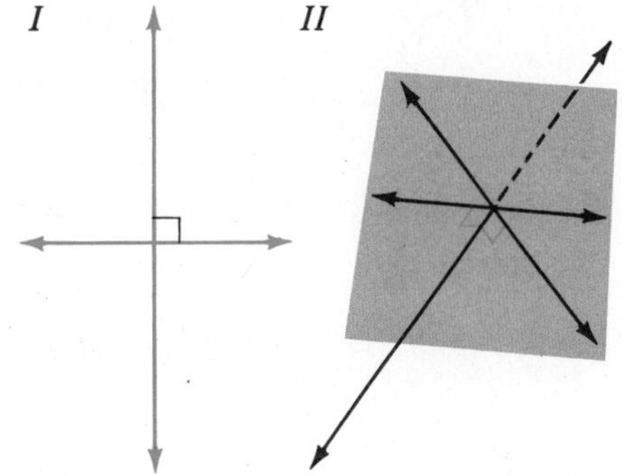

Keep this in mind, and you should have no trouble with the figures in the book or with drawing your own figures. But if you do have trouble, make a simple model like those on page 266.

Exercises 8.1

Ⓐ **1–4.** Refer to the figure.

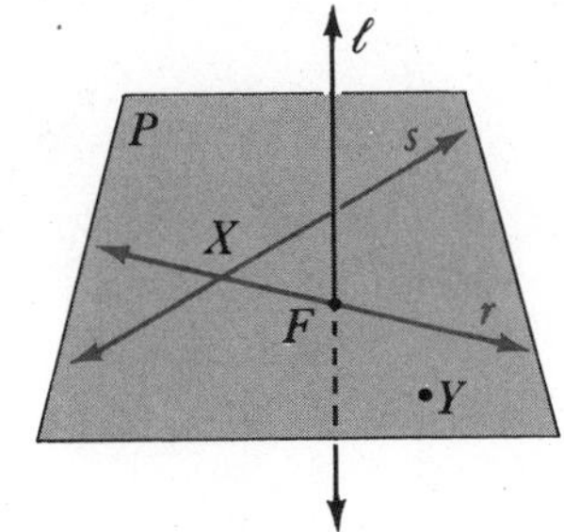

$\ell \perp P$ at F.

P contains lines r and s and point Y.

ℓ intersects r at F.

1. Is $\ell \perp r$?

2. Name the foot of the perpendicular ℓ.

3. Is $\ell \perp s$?

4. Is $\ell \perp \overleftrightarrow{XY}$? To $\overleftrightarrow{XF}$?

5–8. Refer to the figure.

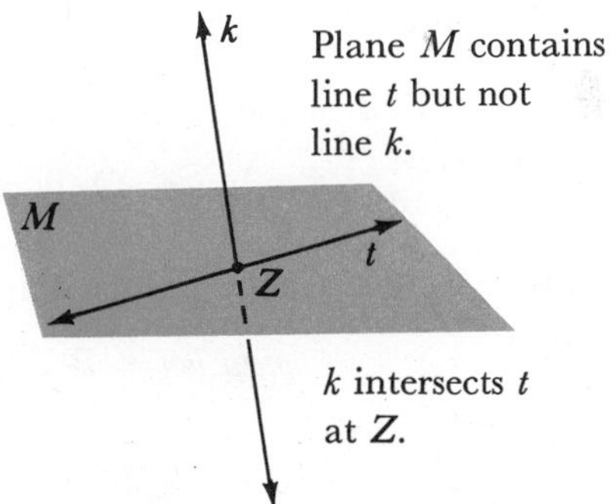

Plane M contains line t but not line k.

k intersects t at Z.

5. Can k be perpendicular to t but not to M?

6. Can k be perpendicular to M but not to t?

7. If $k \perp M$ at Z, what line in M must k be perpendicular to?

8. If k is perpendicular to every line in M containing Z, is $k \perp M$? Why?

9–10. $\overleftrightarrow{AX} \perp p$; p contains W, X, Y, and Z. Use the figure to

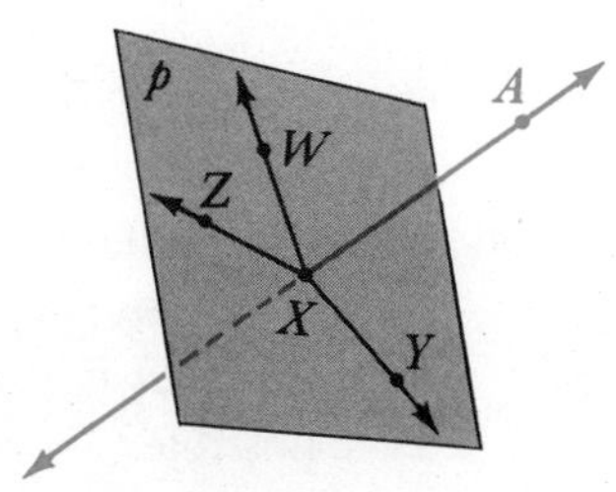

9. Name all pairs of perpendicular lines.

10. Name all right angles.

Ⓑ **11–18.** Plane t contains points B, C, and D. Also, $\overleftrightarrow{AB} \perp t$. Is each statement true or not necessarily true?

11. $\overleftrightarrow{CB} \perp \overleftrightarrow{AB}$ **12.** $\overleftrightarrow{CB} \perp \overleftrightarrow{BD}$

13. $\overleftrightarrow{CD} \perp \overleftrightarrow{AC}$ **14.** $\overleftrightarrow{AD} \perp \overleftrightarrow{CD}$

15. $m\angle CBA = 90$ **16.** $m\angle ABD = 90$

17. $m\angle ADC = 90$ **18.** $m\angle CBD = 90$

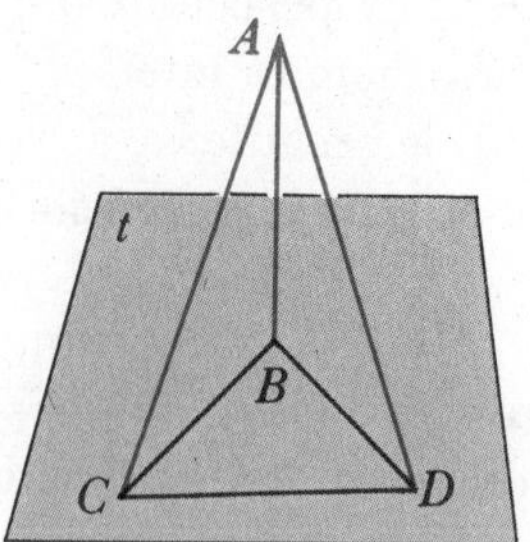

19–20. Refer to the figure.

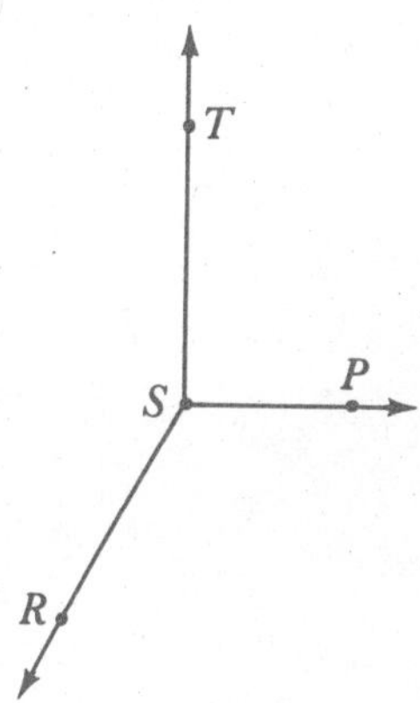

19. If $\overleftrightarrow{PS}$ is perpendicular to the plane containing points R, S, and T, which angles must be right angles?

20. If $\overleftrightarrow{RS}$ is perpendicular to the plane containing points S, T, and P, which angles must be right angles?

21. Sketch a plane perpendicular to a vertical line.

22. Sketch a plane perpendicular to a horizontal line.

23–24. *Review:* Draw a figure and state the reason for each conclusion.

23. *Given:* Lines ℓ and k both contain point P.

Conclusion: Only one plane contains lines ℓ and k.

24. *Given:* Points A and B are in plane r.

Conclusion: $\overleftrightarrow{AB}$ is in plane r.

Ex. 25

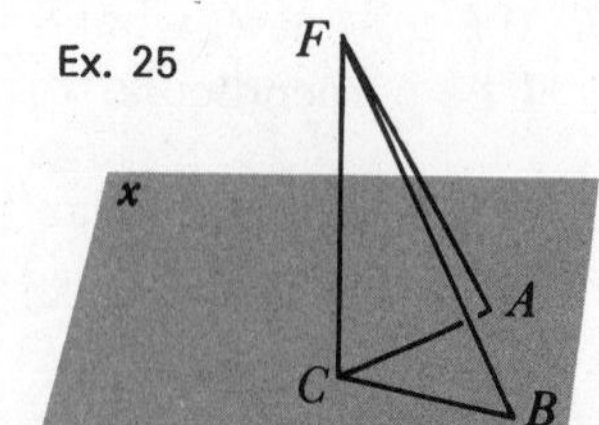

Ⓒ **25.** Given: Plane x contains A, B, and C;
$\overleftrightarrow{FC} \perp x$; $\overline{FA} \cong \overline{FB}$

Prove: $\overline{CA} \cong \overline{CB}$

26. Using a model like the one on page 266, draw two intersecting lines on the paper. Try to hold the pencil at the point of intersection so the pencil is perpendicular to both lines but not to the plane. Is it possible?

GEOM FUNNY

Choose a term from the list to answer the question or to complete the statement.

a. congruent	b. converse	c. geometry	d. hexagon
e. hypotenuse	f. isosceles	g. measure	h. polygon
i. rhombus	j. unit		

1. What did the acorn say when it grew up?
2. What did the girl who received a wool scarf from her boyfriend say?
3. What did the people say when their parrot flew away?
4. What did the witch say after getting rid of the magic spell?
5. What is "mister" in French?
6. What did the bus driver say when asked why the bus hadn't stopped at Main Street?
7. What did the warden call the poetry on the jail-cell wall?
8. About the plant growing in the prison yard, the warden said, "A ________________."
9. Explaining verb tenses, the teacher said, "I see the leaves, ______, I have seen the leaves."
10. When asked if the tall coffee urn was being used, the cook replied, "________________."

Can you make up some of your own?

ANSWERS: 1. c 2. j 3. h 4. d 5. g 6. i 7. b 8. a 9. f 10. e

Algebra Review

Factor to remove the greatest common monomial factor.

1. $4a + 4b$
2. $6r + 12s$
3. $12m - 18n$
4. $ca - cb$
5. $abc - abd$
6. $x^2 - xy$
7. $2x^2 + 2xy$
8. $\pi r^2 + \pi rs$
9. $2\pi r^2 + 2\pi rh$
10. $\frac{1}{2}b_1h + \frac{1}{2}b_2h$
11. $\frac{1}{3}B_1r + \frac{1}{3}B_2r + \frac{1}{3}B_3r$

Review this skill:

- ***factoring out a common monomial factor***

8.2 The Basic Theorem for Perpendiculars

In Section 8.1 we defined a line ℓ to be perpendicular to a plane P if and only if they intersect and ℓ is perpendicular to all lines in P containing the point of intersection. This definition would be awkward to use in proving a plane and a line perpendicular. We now prove the Basic Theorem for Perpendiculars, which will be much easier to use.

Basic Theorem for Perpendiculars

If a line is perpendicular to each of two intersecting lines at their point of intersection, then it is perpendicular to the plane containing them.

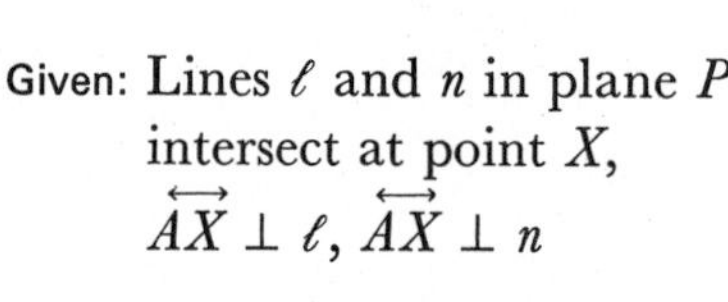

Given: Lines ℓ and n in plane P intersect at point X, $\overleftrightarrow{AX} \perp \ell$, $\overleftrightarrow{AX} \perp n$

Prove: $\overleftrightarrow{AX} \perp P$

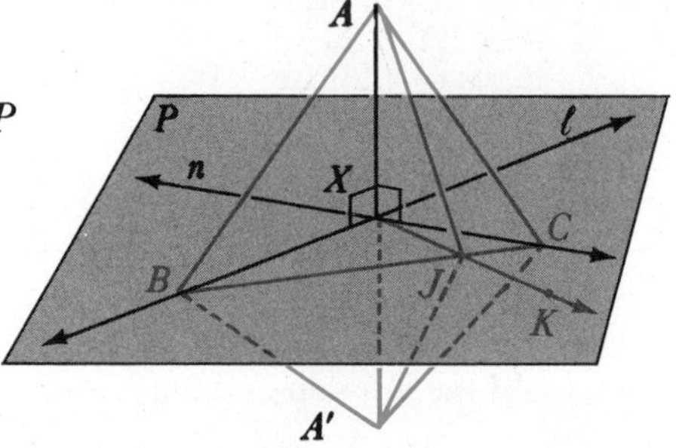

[*Plan:* Show $\overleftrightarrow{AX} \perp \overleftrightarrow{XK}$ ($\overleftrightarrow{XK}$ is any line in P containing X). To do this, draw $\overline{XA'} \cong \overline{XA}$ and prove $\triangle ABC \cong \triangle A'BC$. Next prove $\triangle ABJ \cong \triangle A'BJ$. Then $JA = JA'$, so $\overleftrightarrow{XJ}$ is a $\perp$ bisector of $\overline{AA'}$. Since J is on $\overleftrightarrow{XK}$, $\overleftrightarrow{AX} \perp \overleftrightarrow{XK}$.]

Proof:

STATEMENTS	REASONS
1. Lines ℓ and n in plane P intersect at X, $\overleftrightarrow{AX} \perp \ell$, $\overleftrightarrow{AX} \perp n$.	**1.** Given
2. Choose any point K in P (not on ℓ or n) and draw $\overleftrightarrow{XK}$ in P.	**2.** Two points determine a line, and if two points are in a plane, the line they determine is in that plane.
3. Choose any points B on ℓ and C on n so B and C are on opposite sides of $\overleftrightarrow{XK}$. Then draw $\overleftrightarrow{BC}$ intersecting $\overleftrightarrow{XK}$ at J.	**3.** Plane Separation Postulate (p. 45) since B and C are in opposite half planes with edge $\overleftrightarrow{XK}$.
4. Choose A' on $\overleftrightarrow{AX}$ so $AX = A'X$.	**4.** Point Plotting Thm. (p. 27)
5. Draw $\overline{AB}$, $\overline{AC}$, $\overline{AJ}$, $\overline{A'B}$, $\overline{A'C}$, and $\overline{A'J}$.	**5.** Two pts. determine a line.

6. $\overleftrightarrow{XB}$ is a $\perp$ bisector of $\overline{AA'}$, $\overleftrightarrow{XC}$ is a $\perp$ bisector of $\overline{AA'}$.	6. Def. of $\perp$ bisector
7. $\overline{BA} \cong \overline{BA'}$, $\overline{CA} \cong \overline{CA'}$	7. A pt. on a $\perp$ bisector of a seg. is equidistant from the endpoints of the seg.
8. $\overline{BC} \cong \overline{BC}$	8. A segment is $\cong$ to itself.
9. $\triangle ABC \cong \triangle A'BC$	9. SSS Postulate
10. $\angle ABC \cong \angle A'BC$	10. Corres. parts of $\cong$ $\triangle$s are $\cong$.
11. $\overline{BJ} \cong \overline{BJ}$	11. A segment is $\cong$ to itself.
12. $\triangle ABJ \cong \triangle A'BJ$	12. SAS Postulate
13. $\overline{JA} \cong \overline{JA'}$	13. Corres. parts of $\cong$ $\triangle$s are $\cong$.
14. $\overleftrightarrow{XJ}$ is a $\perp$ bisector of $\overline{AA'}$.	14. Two pts. equidistant from the endpoints of a seg. determine a $\perp$ bisector (steps 4 and 13).
15. $\overleftrightarrow{AX} \perp \overleftrightarrow{XJ}$, so $\overleftrightarrow{AX} \perp \overleftrightarrow{XK}$.	15. Def. of $\perp$ bisector
16. $\overleftrightarrow{AX} \perp P$	16. $\overleftrightarrow{AX}$ is perpendicular to *any* line in plane P containing X.

Exercises 8.2

Ⓐ 1. If $\overleftrightarrow{XC} \perp \overleftrightarrow{AC}$ and $\overleftrightarrow{XC} \perp \overleftrightarrow{DC}$, is $\overleftrightarrow{XC} \perp r$? Why?

Ex. 1

$\overleftrightarrow{AC}$ and $\overleftrightarrow{DC}$ are in r.

2. State the Basic Theorem for Perpendiculars.

Ⓑ 3–6. *WXYZ* is a square. $\overleftrightarrow{AX} \perp \overline{XW}$

3. Name all perpendicular segments. (*Example:* $\overline{XW} \perp \overline{WZ}$)

4. Name all planes that can be determined by the lines in the figure. (*Example:* the plane containing X, W, Y, and Z)

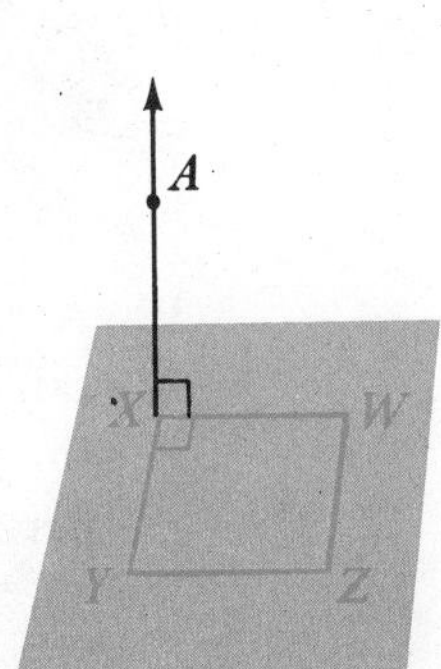

5. Is $\overleftrightarrow{AX}$ perpendicular to the plane containing X, W, Y, and Z?

6. Is $\overleftrightarrow{XW}$ perpendicular to the plane containing A, X, and Y?

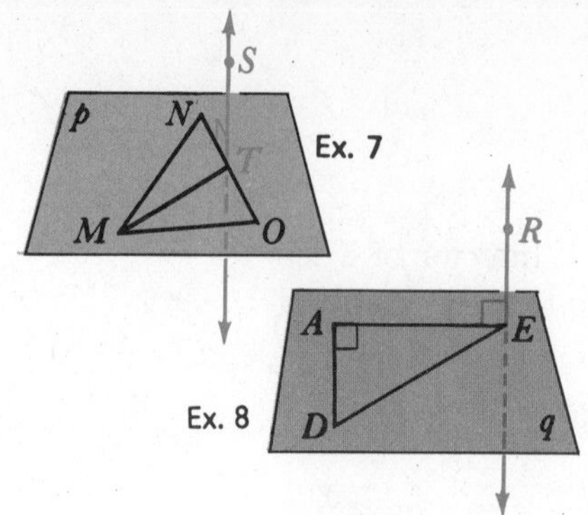

7. $\triangle MNO$ is isosceles, $MN = MO$, $NT = OT$, and $\overleftrightarrow{ST} \perp \overline{NO}$ at T. S is not in plane p. Are any segments perpendicular to planes? Why?

8. $\angle DAE$ is a right angle, and $\overleftrightarrow{RE} \perp \overline{AE}$. Point R is not in plane q. Are any segments perpendicular to planes? Why?

9–16.

plane	a	b	c
contains points	R, S, E, Y	S, E, T, M	E, Y, P, M

$\overleftrightarrow{EY} \perp \overleftrightarrow{EM}$, $\overleftrightarrow{EM} \perp \overleftrightarrow{ES}$, $\overleftrightarrow{ES} \perp \overleftrightarrow{EY}$. True or False?

9. $a \perp \overleftrightarrow{EM}$

10. $c \perp \overleftrightarrow{ES}$

11. $b \perp \overleftrightarrow{ES}$

12. $b \perp \overleftrightarrow{EY}$

13. $\overleftrightarrow{EY} \perp \overleftrightarrow{ET}$

14. $\overleftrightarrow{ES} \perp \overleftrightarrow{EP}$

15. $\overleftrightarrow{ET} \perp \overleftrightarrow{EM}$

16. $\overleftrightarrow{EM} \perp \overleftrightarrow{ER}$

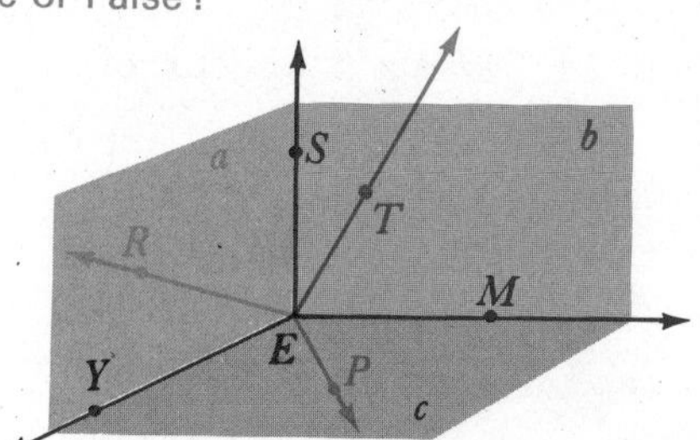

Ex. 17

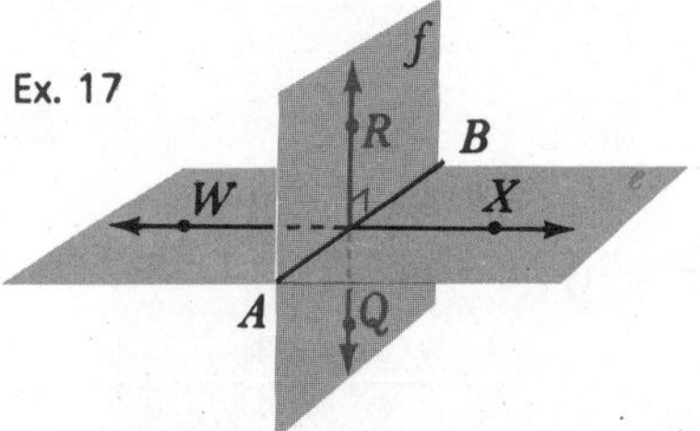

© 17. Given: Planes e and f intersect at $\overleftrightarrow{AB}$, $\overleftrightarrow{RQ}$ is in f, $\overleftrightarrow{WX}$ is in e, $\overleftrightarrow{RQ} \perp \overleftrightarrow{AB}$; $\overleftrightarrow{WX} \perp f$

Prove: $\overleftrightarrow{RQ} \perp e$

Ex. 18

18. Given: $m\angle NGP = 90$; plane r contains P, G, and A; $\overline{NA} \cong \overline{NP}$; $\overline{PG} \cong \overline{AG}$

Prove: $\overleftrightarrow{NG} \perp r$

19. A table leg is attached to a tabletop with two right-angle brackets as shown. Is the leg perpendicular to the top? Why?

Frank Kuechmann

Theorems on Perpendicular Lines and Planes

The Perpendicular Line Postulate (page 60) states that in any plane containing a given line and point, there is exactly one line through the point perpendicular to the given line. The next two postulates deal with perpendicular lines and planes in space in a similar manner.

Perpendicular Line and Plane Postulates

a. Through a given point, there is exactly one plane perpendicular to a given line.

b. Through a given point, there is exactly one line perpendicular to a given plane.

Only plane p is perpendicular to $\overleftrightarrow{AB}$ at X. The only plane containing Y and perpendicular to $\overleftrightarrow{AB}$ is q.

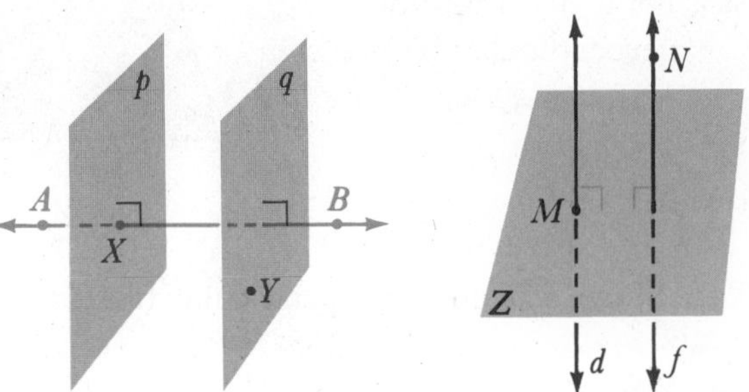

Only line d is perpendicular to Z at M. The only line containing N and perpendicular to Z is f.

Theorem

If a line and a plane are perpendicular, they intersect at a point, and the plane contains every line perpendicular to the given line at that point.

Given: $\ell \perp E$ at P, $j \perp \ell$ at P, $k \perp \ell$ at P

Prove: Plane E contains lines j and k.

Proof:

STATEMENTS	REASONS
1. $\ell \perp E$ at P, $j \perp \ell$ at P, $k \perp \ell$ at P	1. Given
2. ℓ is perpendicular to the plane determined by j and k. Call this plane F.	2. If a line is $\perp$ to each of 2 intersecting lines, it is $\perp$ to the plane they determine.
3. E and F are the same plane.	3. Through a given pt., there is exactly one plane $\perp$ to a given line.
4. E contains j and k.	4. j and k are in F, and $F = E$.

Recall that the perpendicular bisector of a segment is perpendicular to the segment at its midpoint. The **perpendicular bisecting plane** of a segment is the plane perpendicular to the segment at its midpoint.

Perpendicular Bisecting Plane Theorem

A point is in the perpendicular bisecting plane of a segment if and only if it is equidistant from the endpoints of the segment.

NOTE: Because of the if-and-only-if statement, there are two parts to this theorem.

Part a.

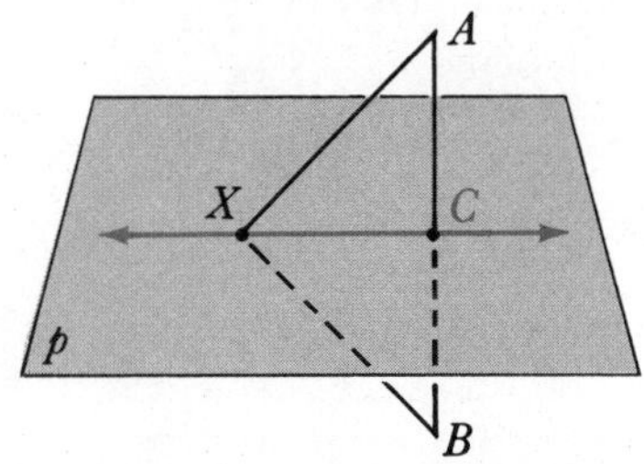

Given: Point X is in p, the perpendicular bisecting plane of $\overline{AB}$.

Prove: $XA = XB$

[*Plan:* Show X is on a perpendicular bisector of $\overline{AB}$.]

Proof:

STATEMENTS	REASONS
1. Point X is in p, the perpendicular bisecting plane of $\overline{AB}$.	**1.** Given
2. Let C be the midpoint of $\overline{AB}$.	**2.** Every segment has a midpoint.
3. $\overleftrightarrow{XC}$ is in p.	**3.** If 2 pts. are in a plane, the line they determine is in that plane.
4. $\overleftrightarrow{AB} \perp \overleftrightarrow{XC}$	**4.** If a line is $\perp$ to a plane, it is $\perp$ to every line in the plane through its foot.
5. In the plane determined by X and $\overleftrightarrow{AB}$, $\overleftrightarrow{XC}$ is the $\perp$ bisector of $\overline{AB}$.	**5.** Def. of $\perp$ bisector
6. $XA = XB$	**6.** If a pt. is on the $\perp$ bisector of a seg., it is equidistant from the endpoints of the segment.

You'll be asked to complete the proof of part **b** in Exercises 21–27.

Exercises 8.3

Ⓐ **1–4.** $\overleftrightarrow{AB} \perp p$ at B, and E is in p.

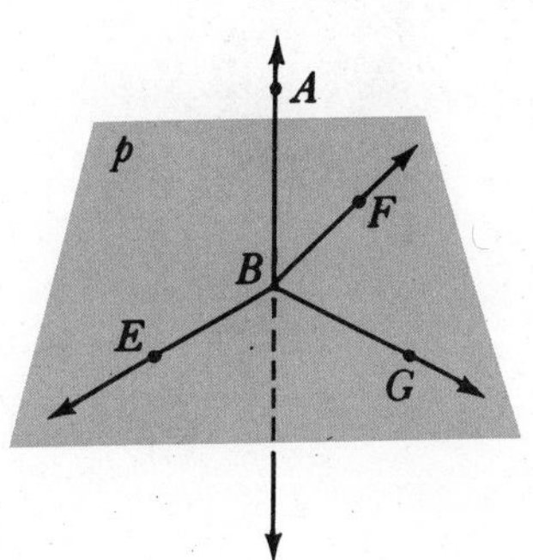

1. How many planes are perpendicular to $\overleftrightarrow{AB}$ at A?

2. How many lines are perpendicular to p at E?

3. If $\overleftrightarrow{AB} \perp \overleftrightarrow{BF}$, is $\overleftrightarrow{BF}$ in p?

4. If $\overleftrightarrow{AB} \perp \overleftrightarrow{GB}$, is G in p?

5–8. Plane e is the perpendicular bisecting plane of $\overline{PR}$. Points A, B, C, and D are in e. Complete each statement.

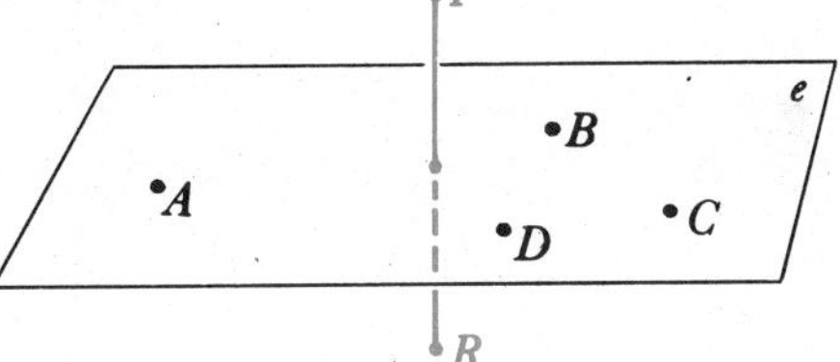

5. $AP =$ ______ **6.** $PC =$ ______

7. $RC =$ ______ **8.** $DR =$ ______

Ⓑ **9–12.** Planes a and b intersect at $\overleftrightarrow{RS}$; $\overleftrightarrow{XY} \perp b$; Y and Z are in b; and W, Y, and X are in a.

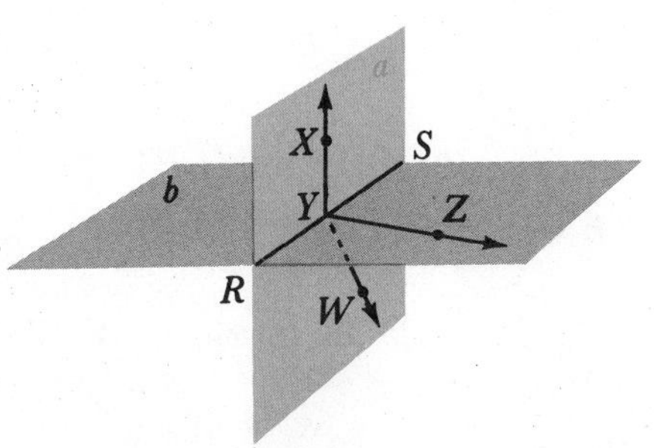

9. Is $\overleftrightarrow{XY} \perp \overleftrightarrow{YZ}$?

10. Is $\overleftrightarrow{XY} \perp \overleftrightarrow{YW}$?

11. Is $\overleftrightarrow{RS} \perp \overleftrightarrow{YZ}$?

12. Is $\overleftrightarrow{RS} \perp \overleftrightarrow{XY}$?

13–16. $\overleftrightarrow{AB} \perp$ plane p at A. Plane p contains G.

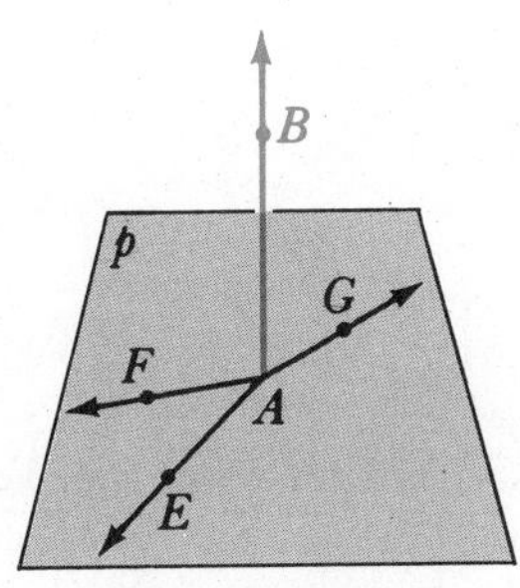

13. If $\overleftrightarrow{AF} \perp \overleftrightarrow{AB}$, does p contain F? Why?

14. If point E is not in p, is $\overleftrightarrow{AE} \perp \overleftrightarrow{AB}$?

15. Could $\overleftrightarrow{BF}$ be perpendicular to plane p? Why?

16. Plane q contains points G, A, and E. If $\overleftrightarrow{AB} \perp q$ at A, is E in plane p? Why?

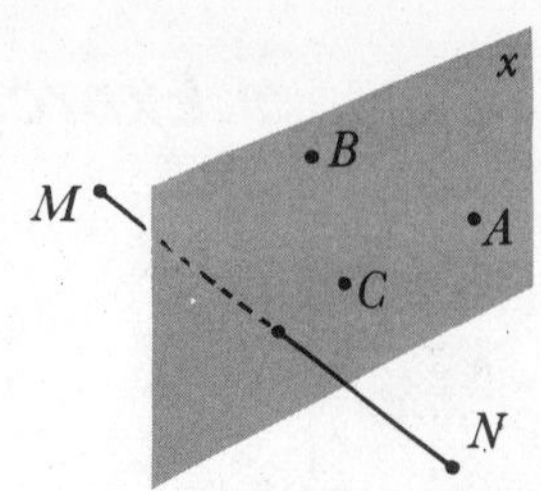

17–20. x is the perpendicular bisecting plane of $\overline{MN}$. A, B, and C are in x. Are these statements always true?

17. $AN = MA$

18. $\overline{MN} \perp \overline{AC}$

19. $\overline{MN} \perp \overline{BC}$

20. $MA = CN$

21–27. Give a reason for each statement.

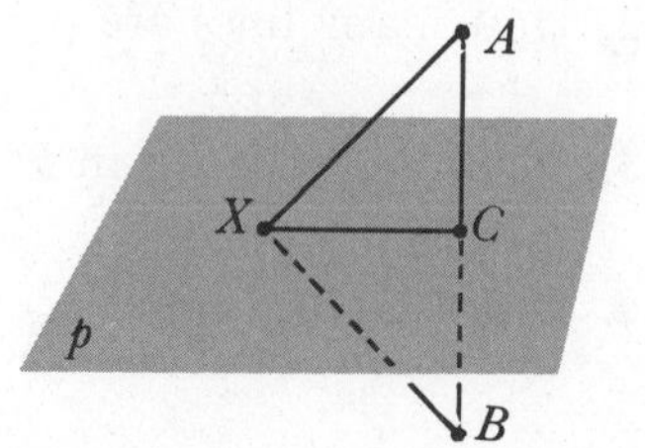

Given: $XA = XB$

Prove: Point X is in p, the perpendicular bisecting plane of $\overline{AB}$.

Proof:

STATEMENTS	REASONS
1. $XA = XB$	1. **21.** ____
2. In the plane determined by X, A, and B, X is on the $\perp$ bisector of $\overline{AB}$.	2. **22.** ____
3. Let C be the midpoint of $\overline{AB}$.	3. **23.** ____
4. $\overleftrightarrow{XC} \perp \overline{AB}$	4. **24.** ____
5. Let p be the perpendicular bisecting plane of $\overline{AB}$.	5. **25.** ____
6. p contains $\overleftrightarrow{XC}$.	6. **26.** ____
7. X is in p, the perpendicular bisecting plane of $\overline{AB}$.	7. **27.** ____

•A

X
• •Z

•Y •W

B•

Ex. 28

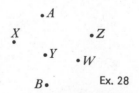

© **28.** Given: A, W, X, Y, Z, and B are not all coplanar, $AW = BW$, $AX = BX$, $AY = BY$, $AZ = BZ$

Prove: W, X, Y, and Z are coplanar.

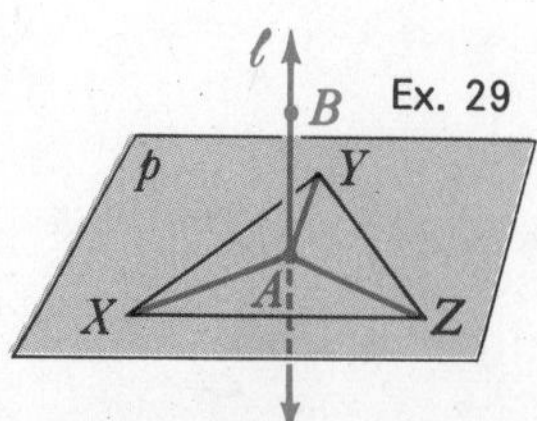

Ex. 29

29. Plane p contains $\triangle XYZ$. Line $\ell \perp p$ at A, and $\overline{AX} \cong \overline{AY} \cong \overline{AZ}$. B is any point on ℓ. Prove that $\overline{BX} \cong \overline{BY} \cong \overline{BZ}$.

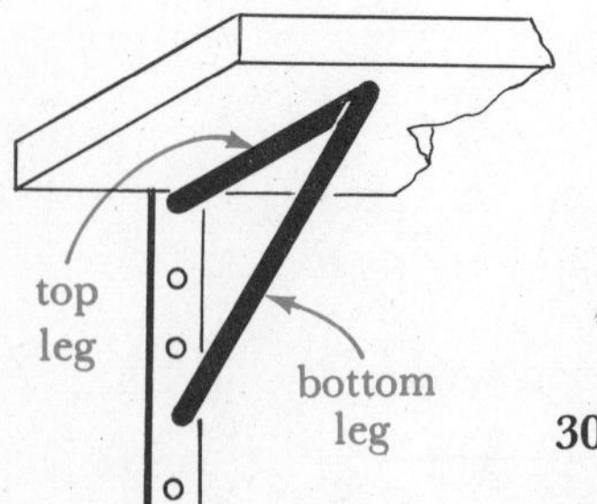

30. A shelf bracket is made as shown. The top leg is perpendicular to the wall. Can the bottom leg be perpendicular to the wall?

GEOMETRY AT WORK

BUILDING THINGS "PLUMB" RIGHT

The plumb line, spirit level, and try square are carpenters' tools. They are used to make things horizontal (level) or vertical (plumb) and to make things perpendicular to each other.

The plumb line consists of a weight (bob) attached to a piece of heavy string. When the weight is hung from the string and the string stops swaying, the plumb line is vertical, or plumb.

Frank Kuechmann

spirit level

The spirit level is a piece of wood or metal containing two or three tubes of liquid. The tubes have markings, and when the bubble in a tube is exactly between the markings, the spirit level is horizontal or vertical.

try square

A try square is shown at left. Each edge is perpendicular to the edge it touches.

1. If the floor is level, how could you use a try square to make sure the uprights of the shelf unit are plumb and the shelf is level?

2. If the floor is not level, how could you use a plumb line and a try square to make sure the shelves are level?

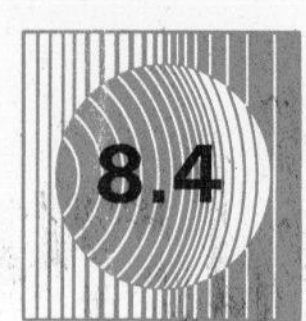

8.4 More About Perpendicular Lines and Planes

The next two theorems round out the important ideas about perpendicular lines and planes.

Theorem Two lines perpendicular to the same plane are coplanar. (In Chapter 13, we prove that these lines are parallel.)

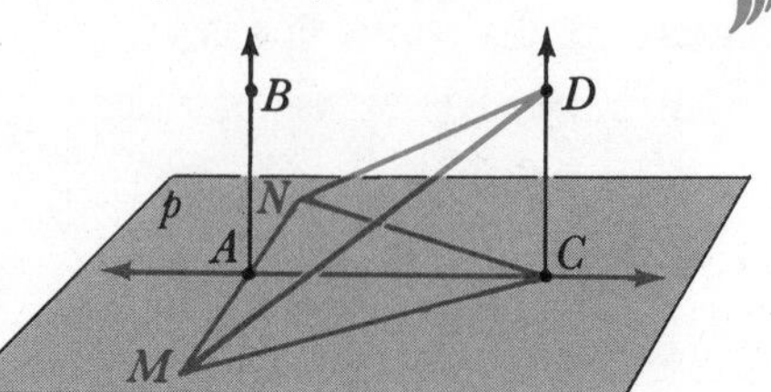

Given: $\overleftrightarrow{AB} \perp p$ at A, $\overleftrightarrow{CD} \perp p$ at C

Prove: $\overleftrightarrow{AB}$ and $\overleftrightarrow{CD}$ are coplanar.

[*Plan:* Use auxiliary segment $\overline{MN}$ where $MA = NA$. Show that $\overleftrightarrow{AB}$ and $\overleftrightarrow{AC}$ are in plane t, the perpendicular bisecting plane of $\overline{MN}$. Then show that D is also in t, so $\overleftrightarrow{AB}$ and $\overleftrightarrow{CD}$ are coplanar.]

Proof:

STATEMENTS	REASONS
1. $\overleftrightarrow{AB} \perp p$ at A, $\overleftrightarrow{CD} \perp p$ at C.	1. Given
2. $\overleftrightarrow{AC}$ is in plane p.	2. If 2 pts. are in a plane, so is the line containing them.
3. In plane p, let $\overline{MN}$ be $\perp$ to $\overleftrightarrow{AC}$ at A and let $MA = NA$.	3. Perp. Line Post. (p. 60) and the Point Plotting Thm. (p. 27)
4. $\overleftrightarrow{AB} \perp \overline{MN}$ at A.	4. A line $\perp$ to a plane is $\perp$ to every line in the plane through its foot.
5. $\overleftrightarrow{AB}$ and $\overleftrightarrow{AC}$ determine a plane (call it t), and $\overline{MN} \perp t$ at A.	5. Two intersecting lines determine a plane, and $\overline{MN}$ is $\perp$ to $\overleftrightarrow{AB}$ and $\overleftrightarrow{AC}$ at A.
6. Plane t (determined by $\overleftrightarrow{AB}$ and $\overleftrightarrow{AC}$) is the $\perp$ bisecting plane of $\overline{MN}$.	6. Def. of $\perp$ bisecting plane
(Now we show that point D is in t, so $\overleftrightarrow{CD}$ is in t.)	
7. $\overleftrightarrow{CD} \perp \overleftrightarrow{CN}$, $\overleftrightarrow{CD} \perp \overleftrightarrow{CM}$	7. If a line is $\perp$ to a plane, it is $\perp$ to every line in the plane through its foot.
8. $\overline{CN} \cong \overline{CM}$	8. Perp. Bisecting Plane Theorem

Courtesy American Airlines

9. $\overline{CD} \cong \overline{CD}$	9. A segment is $\cong$ to itself.
10. $\angle DCN$ and $\angle DCM$ are rt. $\angle$s, $\triangle DCN$ and $\triangle DCM$ are rt. $\triangle$s.	10. Def. of $\perp$ lines and rt. $\triangle$s
11. $\triangle DCN \cong \triangle DCM$	11. LL Theorem
12. $\overline{DN} \cong \overline{DM}$	12. Corres. parts of $\cong$ $\triangle$s are $\cong$.
13. D is in t, the $\perp$ bisecting plane of $\overline{MN}$.	13. Perp. Bisecting Plane Theorem
14. $\overleftrightarrow{CD}$ is in t.	14. If 2 pts. are in a plane, so is the line containing them.
15. $\overleftrightarrow{CD}$ and $\overleftrightarrow{AB}$ are coplanar.	15. Steps 5 and 14

Poles that are perpendicular to the ground are often braced with support wires as shown in the photo. Which is shorter, the pole or the wire? The next theorem proves the answer.

Theorem

The shortest segment to a plane from a point not in the plane is the perpendicular segment.

Given: $\overline{AB} \perp p$ at B,
C is any point in p other than B.

Prove: $AB < AC$

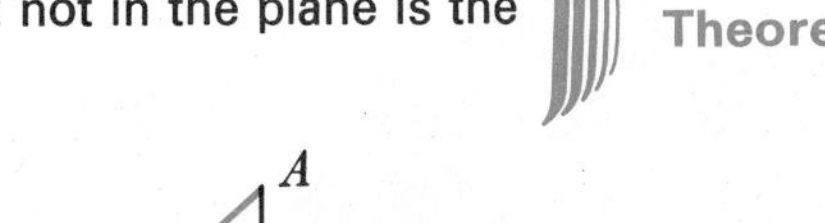

Proof:

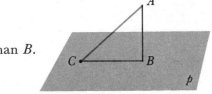

STATEMENTS	REASONS
1. $\overline{AB} \perp p$ at B.	1. Given
2. $\overleftrightarrow{CB}$ is in plane p.	2. If 2 pts. are in a plane, so is the line containing them.
3. $\overline{AB} \perp \overline{CB}$	3. Def. of a $\perp$ line and plane.
4. $\angle ABC$ is a right $\angle$, $\triangle ABC$ is a right $\triangle$.	4. Def. of $\perp$ lines and right $\triangle$s
5. $m\angle ACB < 90$	5. The other $\angle$s of a rt. $\triangle$ are acute.
6. $AB < AC$	6. In a $\triangle$, the side opp. the smaller of 2 $\angle$s is shorter.

Now we can define **the distance from a point to a plane** as the length of the segment perpendicular to the plane from the point.

Exercises 8.4

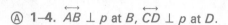

Ⓐ **1–4.** $\overleftrightarrow{AB} \perp p$ at B, $\overleftrightarrow{CD} \perp p$ at D.

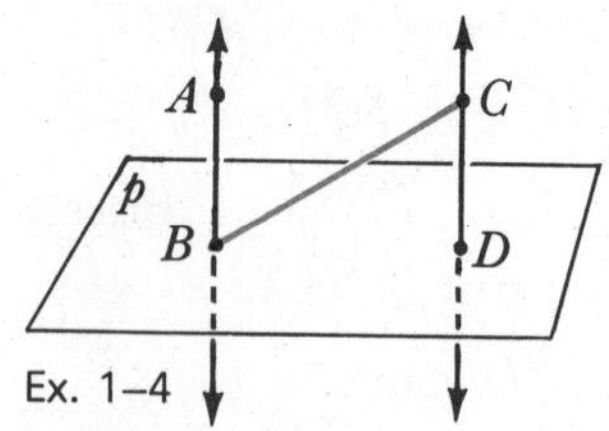

Ex. 1–4

1. Are $\overleftrightarrow{AB}$ and $\overleftrightarrow{CD}$ coplanar?

2. Is $CB < CD$?

3. Name the shortest segment from C to plane p.

4. Define the distance from point A to plane p.

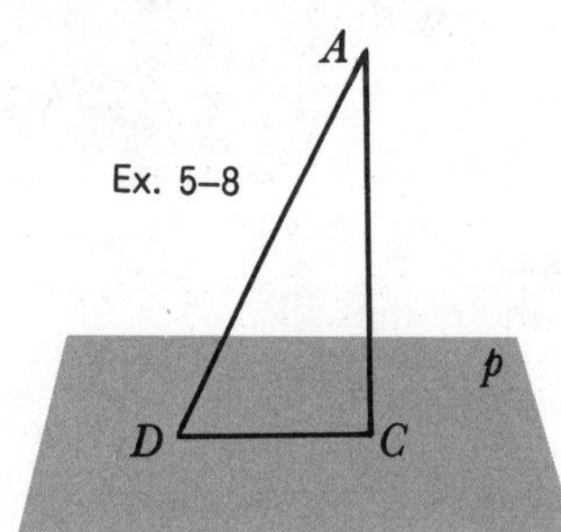

Ex. 5–8

Ⓑ **5–8.** Points D and C are in plane p. $\overline{AC} \perp p$.

5. Can $m\angle ADC > 90$? Why?

6. Can $AD = 7$ and $AC = 9$?

7. If the distance from A to plane p is 12, find AC.

8. If $AC = 5.8$, find the distance from A to plane p.

9. Given: Lines ℓ and k are in plane p, $\overleftrightarrow{WZ} \perp k$, $\overleftrightarrow{WZ} \perp \ell$, $\overline{XY}$ is the shortest segment from Y to plane p.
Prove: $\overline{XY}$ and $\overline{WZ}$ are coplanar.

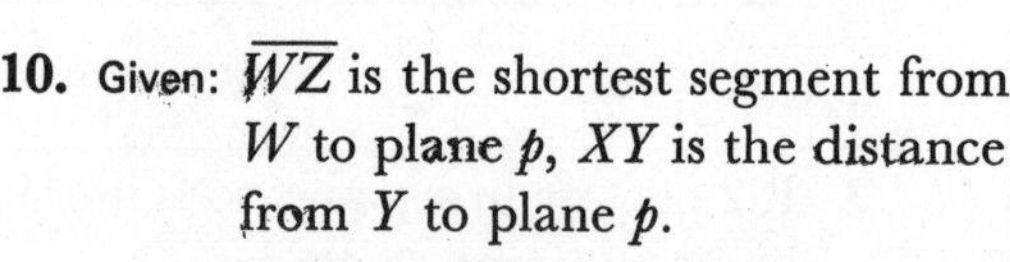

10. Given: $\overline{WZ}$ is the shortest segment from W to plane p, XY is the distance from Y to plane p.
Prove: $\overline{WZ}$ and $\overline{XY}$ are coplanar.

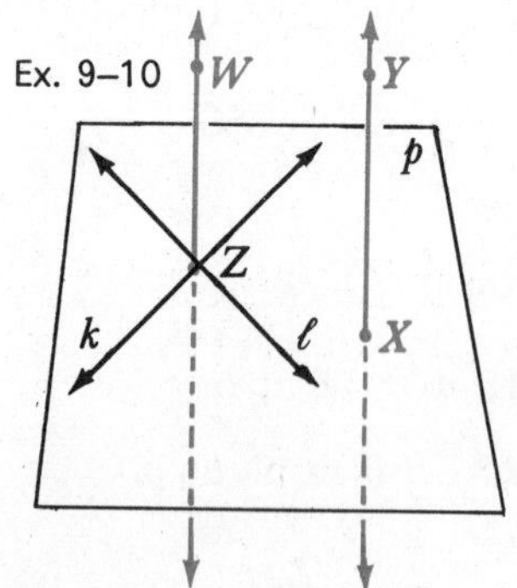

Ex. 9–10

Ⓒ **11.** Two posts are anchored perpendicular to the ground, which is flat. Will a sign fit flat against both posts? Why?

12. Which is longer, the 2×4 or its brace?

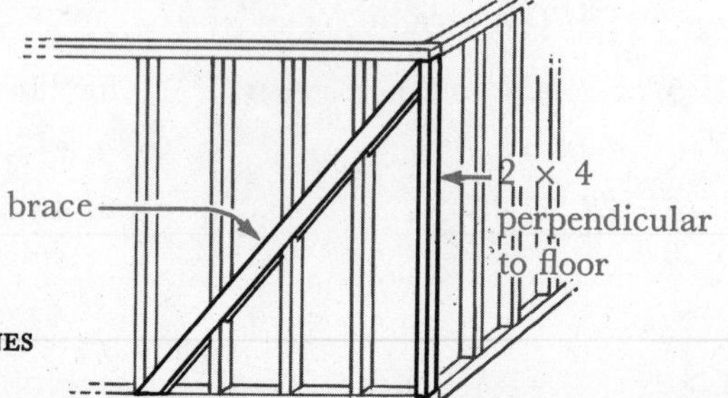

Transformations: Reflections in Space

8.5

We use mirror images as models for reflections in space. In the photo a point and its image are connected by a segment. The mirror appears to be the perpendicular bisecting plane of that segment. We define reflections in space in a manner similar to the definition of reflections in a plane.

Frank Kuechmann

Reflections in a Plane

The reflection image of point A over *reflecting line* ℓ is A'. Line ℓ is the perpendicular bisector of $\overline{AA'}$, and points A and A' are the same distance from line ℓ.

The reflection image of point B is B.

Reflections in Space

The **reflection image** of point C over *reflecting plane* p is point C'. Plane p is the perpendicular bisecting plane of $\overline{CC'}$, and points C and C' are the same distance from plane p.

The reflection image of point D is D.

The images of points A, B, C, and E over reflecting plane p are points A', B', C', and E'.

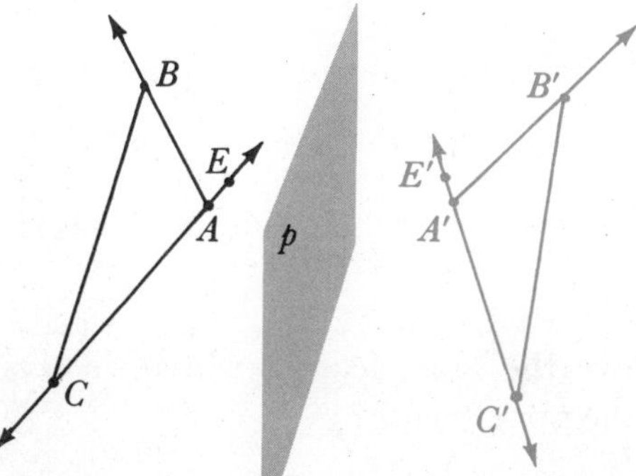

B′
E′
A′
C′

Notice that

1. $m\angle CAB = m\angle C'A'B'$
2. A is between C and E.
   A' is between C' and E'.
3. A, C, and E are collinear.
   A', C', and E' are collinear.
4. $AB = A'B'$
5. A, B, C, and E are coplanar.
   A', B', C', and E' are coplanar.

Reflections in space preserve

1. betweenness of points
2. collinearity of points
3. distance between points
4. angle measure
5. coplanarity of points

In the figures on page 281 consider triangles ABC and $A'B'C'$. The orientation of $\triangle ABC$ is counterclockwise, while the orientation of $\triangle A'B'C'$ is clockwise. This leads to the following conclusion:

Reflections in space reverse orientation.

Exercises 8.5

Ⓐ **1–4.** Plane p is the reflecting plane. Point E is in p. From the drawing tell which point is the reflection image of

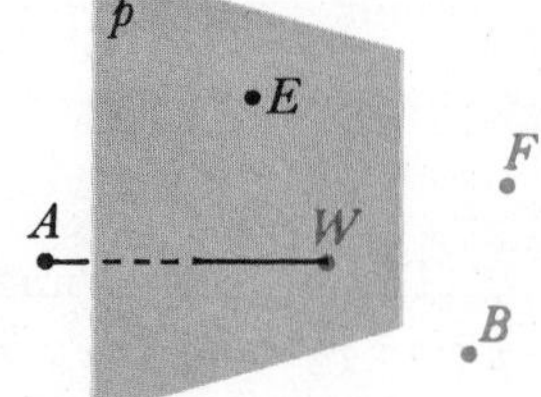

1. A **2.** Z

3. B **4.** E

5. Describe reflecting line ℓ if A' is the image of A over ℓ.

6. Describe reflecting plane p if A' is the image of A over p.

7. Name 5 properties preserved by reflections in space.

8. Name 1 property not preserved by reflections in space.

Ⓑ **9.** Sketch a point and a plane. Then sketch the image of the point when reflected over the plane.

10. Sketch a line and a plane. Then sketch the image of the line when reflected over the plane.

11. If a line and a plane are perpendicular, will their reflection images in space be perpendicular?

12. If 3 noncoplanar segments have the same length, will their reflection images in space have the same length?

13–14. Use the photos. Can a reflecting plane be placed so that each half is the image of the other?

Camerique

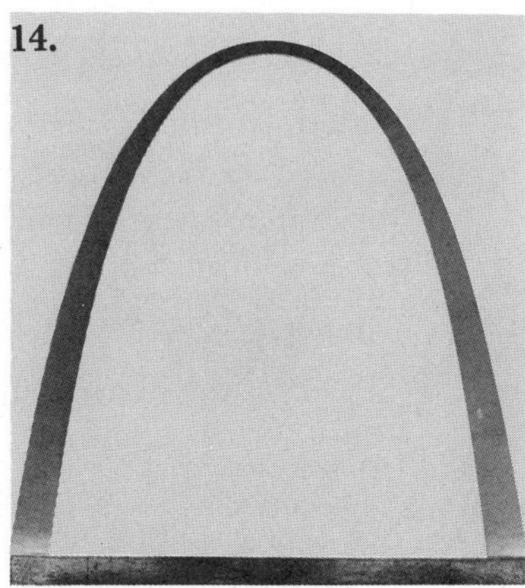

Courtesy Union Pacific Railroad

© **15.** Make a model of a segment or a triangle and its reflection image in space. HINT: You may find pipe cleaners, wire, string, and a shoe box helpful.

GEOMETRIC CHEMISTRY

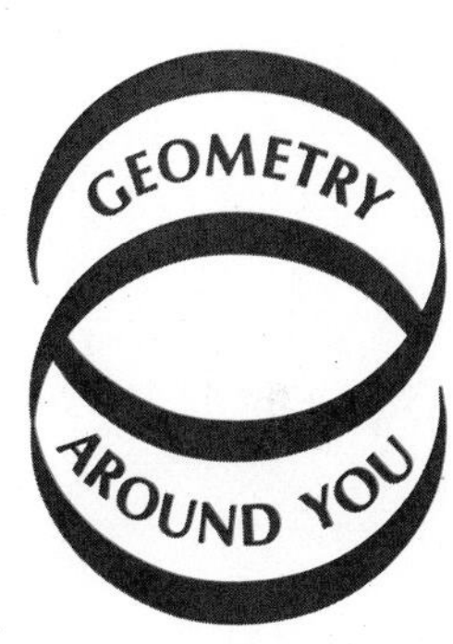

You probably know that each molecule of a compound is made up of the same atoms. But did you know that the molecules of two different compounds can also contain the same atoms? Such compounds are called *isomers*. The molecules of isomers differ in their geometry—the way the atoms are arranged.

For example, lactic acid exists in two forms: *d*-lactic acid is produced by muscles when they work, while *l*-lactic acid is found in sour milk. The molecules can be pictured as follows.

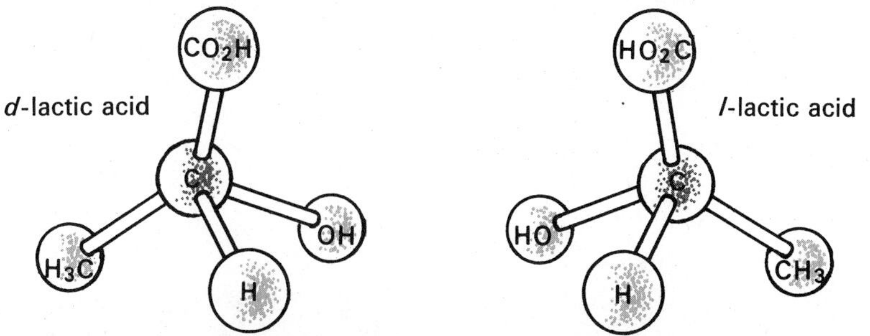

The atoms in each molecule are the same, but the molecular geometry is different. In this case, one molecule is the reflection image of the other over a plane.

Chapter 8 Review

8.1 **1.** By the definition of a perpendicular line and plane, when is a line ℓ perpendicular to a plane p?

8.2 **2–3.** *ABCD* is a rectangle in plane *p*, $\overrightarrow{BF} \perp \overline{AB}$, and $\overrightarrow{BF} \perp \overline{BC}$. Give a reason for each statement.

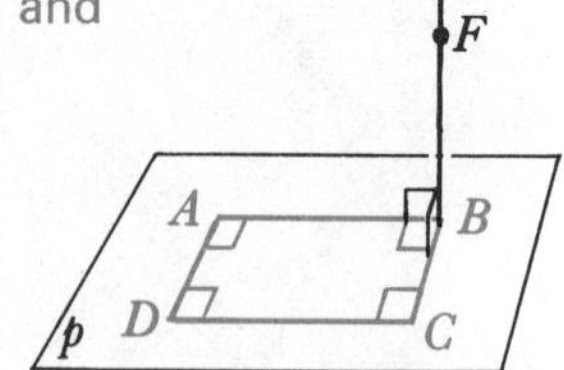

2. $\overrightarrow{BF} \perp$ plane p

3. $\overline{AB} \perp$ the plane containing F, B, and C.

8.3 **4–10.** $\overleftrightarrow{EF} \perp q$ at *F*; *H* and *J* are in *q*; planes *p* and *q* intersect at $\overleftrightarrow{KL}$; *E*, *F*, and *G* are in *p*.

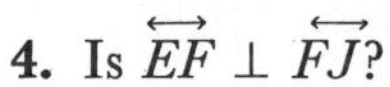

4. Is $\overleftrightarrow{EF} \perp \overleftrightarrow{FJ}$?

5. Is $\overleftrightarrow{FH} \perp \overleftrightarrow{FG}$?

6. Is $\overleftrightarrow{EF} \perp \overleftrightarrow{KL}$?

7. Is $\overleftrightarrow{GF} \perp$ plane q?

8. Find $m\angle EFJ$.

9. Find $m\angle HFE$.

10. How many planes are perpendicular to $\overleftrightarrow{GF}$ at G?

11–13. Plane *n* is the perpendicular bisecting plane of $\overline{RS}$. Plane *n* contains points *A*, *B*, and *C*.

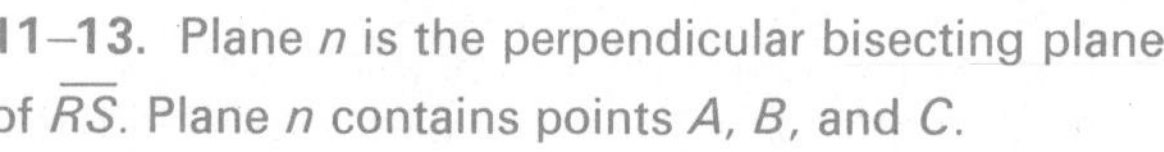

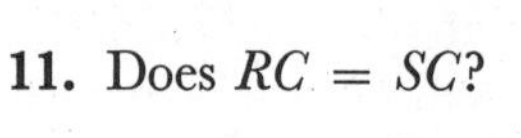

11. Does $RC = SC$?

12. Is $\overleftrightarrow{BC}$ a perpendicular bisector of $\overline{RS}$?

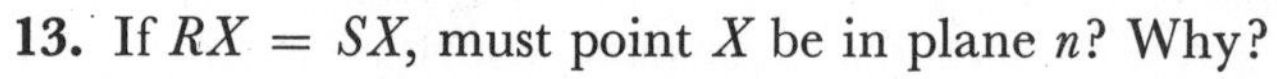

13. If $RX = SX$, must point X be in plane n? Why?

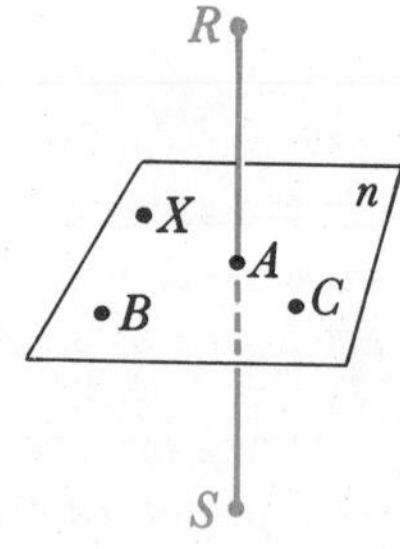

8.4 **14–16.** $\overleftrightarrow{XY} \perp p$ at *Y*, $\overleftrightarrow{ZW} \perp p$ at *Z*.

14. Are $\overleftrightarrow{XY}$ and $\overleftrightarrow{ZW}$ coplanar?

15. Name the shortest segment to p from W.

16. Define the distance from W to plane p.

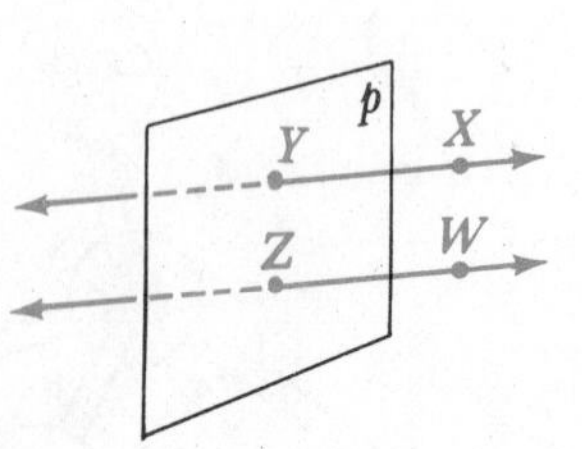

8.5 **17–18.** *A′* is the image of *A* over reflecting plane *p*.

17. Describe plane p.

18. If the distance from A to p is 8, find the distance from A' to p.

Chapter 8 Test

1–3. Complete each statement.

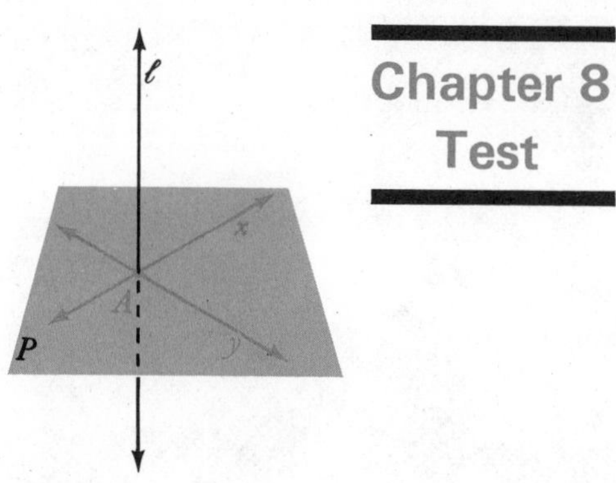

1. If $\ell \perp P$ at A, then ℓ is perpendicular to ______ lines in P ______ A.

2. If lines x and y are in P, $\ell \perp x$, and $\ell \perp y$, then ______ $\perp$ ______.

3. If ℓ intersects P at A, then there will always be ______ line(s) in P perpendicular to ℓ.

4–6. True or False?

4. All the points in space equidistant from points A and B are coplanar.

5. Two distinct lines perpendicular to the same plane are coplanar.

6. Two planes can be perpendicular to a given line at a given point.

7–8. $\overleftrightarrow{AD} \perp p$ at D, $\overleftrightarrow{BC} \perp p$ at C.

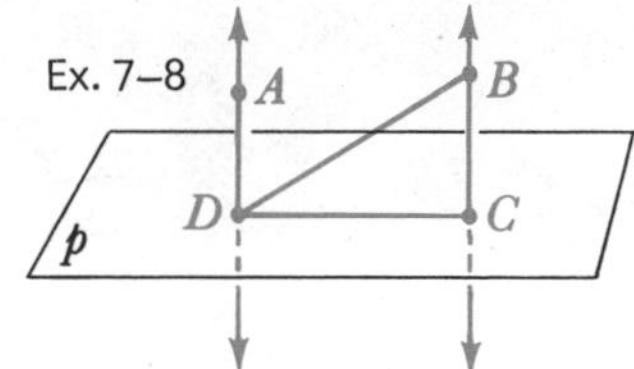

7. How many planes contain points A, B, C, and D?

8. Which is greater, BC or BD?

9–12. Complete this proof.

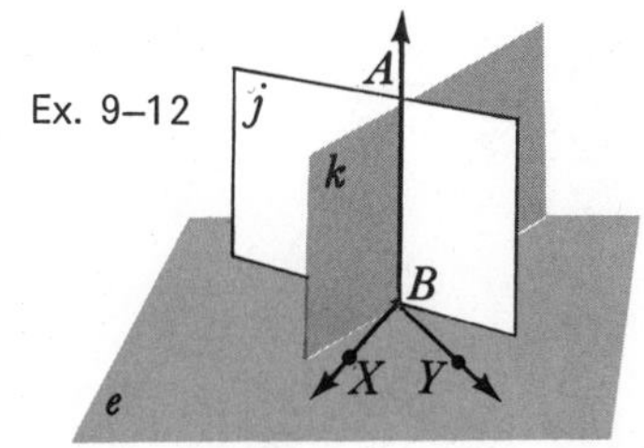

Given: Plane e contains X, Y, and B; $\overleftrightarrow{XB} \perp j$; $\overleftrightarrow{YB} \perp k$; j and k intersect at $\overleftrightarrow{AB}$.

Prove: $\overleftrightarrow{AB} \perp e$

Proof:

STATEMENTS	REASONS
1. $j \perp \overleftrightarrow{XB}$, $k \perp \overleftrightarrow{YB}$	1. **9.**
2. $\overleftrightarrow{XB} \perp \overleftrightarrow{AB}$	2. **10.**
3. $\overleftrightarrow{YB} \perp \overleftrightarrow{AB}$	3. **11.**
4. $\overleftrightarrow{AB} \perp$ plane e	4. **12.**

13. If the distance from A to plane p is 8, and the distance from C to p is 8, can C be the image of A over reflecting plane p?

14. If two lines are perpendicular, will their reflection images in space be perpendicular?

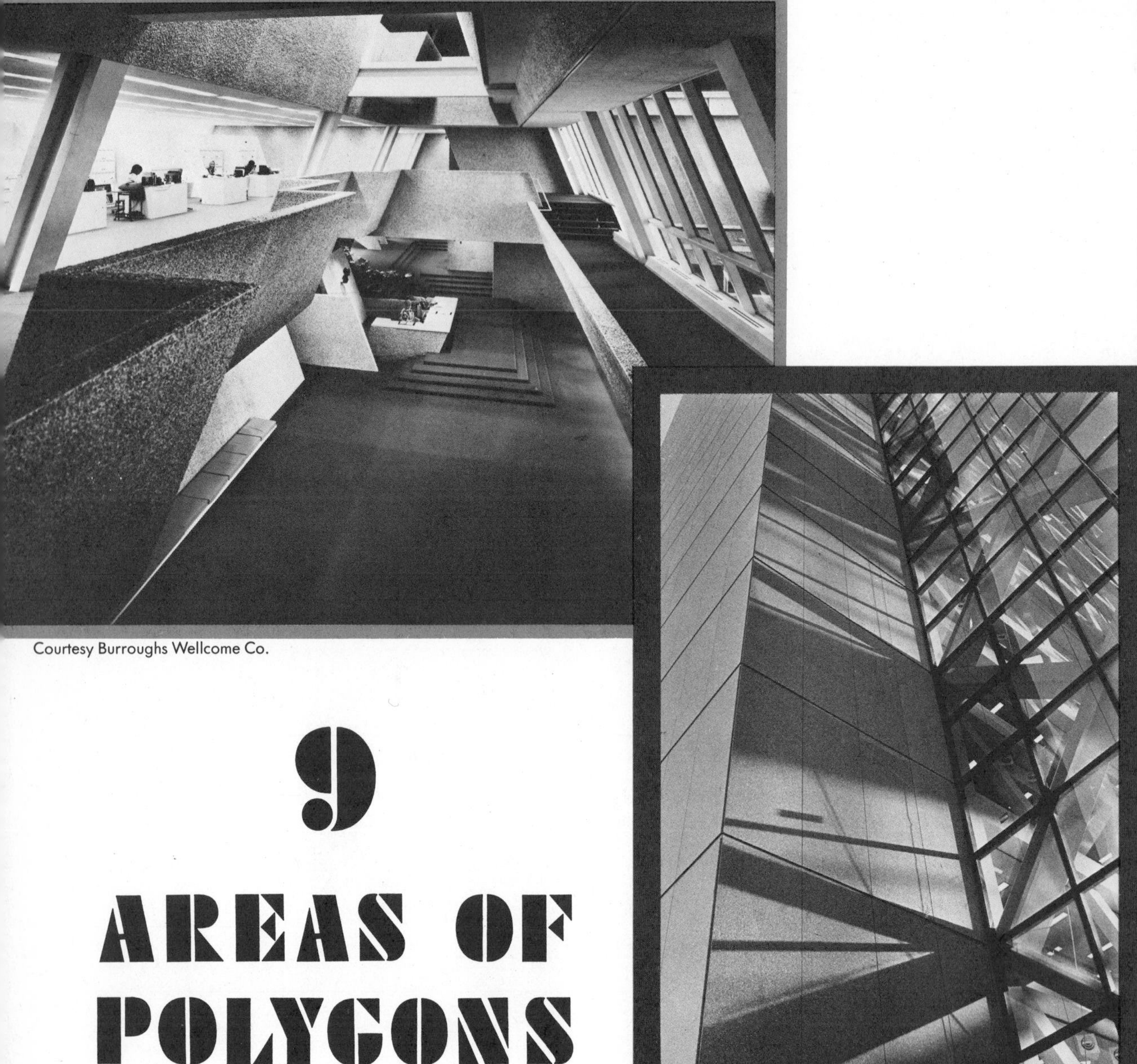

Courtesy Burroughs Wellcome Co.

Bill Miller

9 AREAS OF POLYGONS

The topic of this chapter is one of the most useful in geometry. Since you have worked with area formulas in earlier courses, much of the material will be familiar. We will review area formulas, use them in solving problems, and show how they can be proved. Also, we will prove the Pythagorean Theorem—probably the best known theorem in geometry and all of mathematics.

Areas of Rectangles

A **polygonal region** consists of a polygon and its interior. Some examples are shown below.

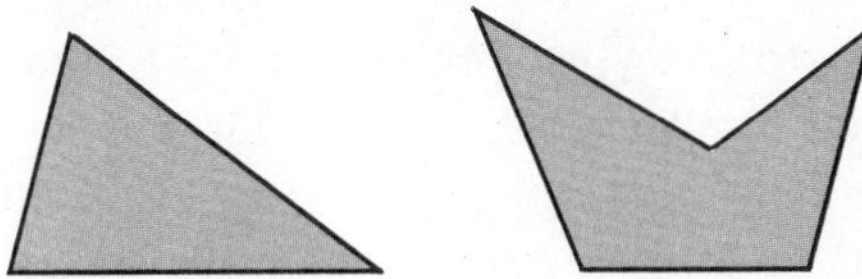

Camerique

Earlier, you saw that for every pair of points there is a unique number, called the *distance* between them. Also, for every angle there is a unique number, called its *degree measure*. Similarly,

Area Postulate

For every polygonal region there is a unique positive real number, called the **area** of the region.

Since congruent triangles have the same size and shape, the following postulate is suggested:

Area Postulate for Congruent Triangles

If two triangles are congruent, then the triangular regions determined by them have the same area.

Another postulate about area is suggested by the following figures:

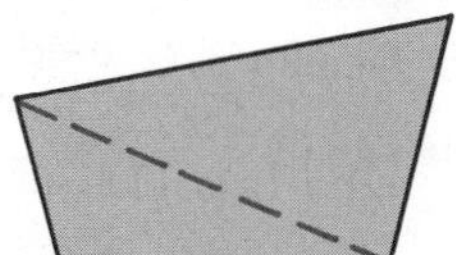

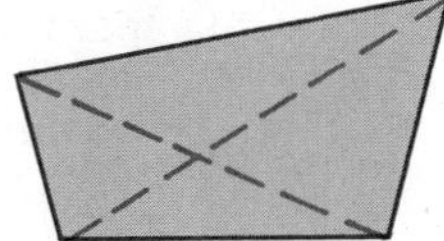

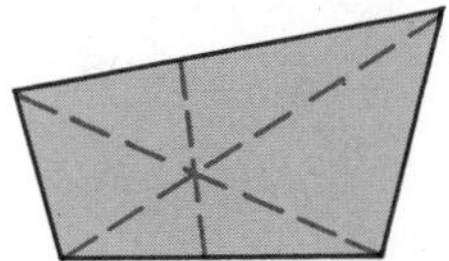

Area Addition Postulate

A polygonal region can be separated into nonoverlapping regions, the sum of whose areas is equal to the area of the given region.

1 unit of length   1 square unit of area

To measure the area of a polygonal region, we must have a unit of area. The most convenient unit is the square unit. If we measure distance in centimeters, we measure area in square centimeters, and so on.

NOTE: For convenience, we often refer to the area of a polygon rather than the area of a polygonal region. Just remember that area always refers to a region, even if not exactly stated that way.

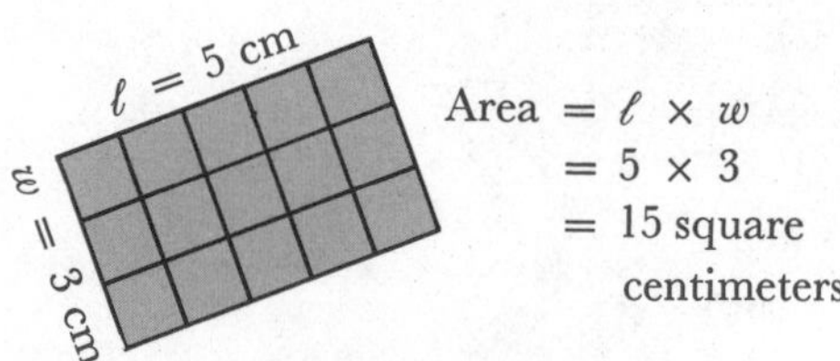

Suppose a rectangle has consecutive sides that are 5 centimeters (cm) and 3 centimeters long. The measure of the longer side is its length; the measure of the shorter side is its width. The figure at the left suggests that the area is length times width. We state this as a postulate.

Area Postulate for a Rectangle

The area (A) of a rectangle is the product of its length (ℓ) and its width (w).

$$A = \ell w$$

Example 1: Find the area of a rectangle with the given length and width.

a. 7 m and 5 m

$A = \ell w$

$A = 7 \cdot 5$

$A = 35 \text{ m}^2$

b. 32 mm and 3 cm

$A = \ell w$

$A = 32 \cdot 30$

$A = 960 \text{ mm}^2$

Since length and width must be in the same units, change 3 cm to 30 mm.

NOTE: m^2 means square meters, cm^2 means square centimeters, and so on.

Example 2: A rectangle has a width of 16 and an area of 400. Find the length.

$$A = \ell w$$
$$400 = \ell \cdot 16$$
$$25 = \ell$$

If no units are listed as here, assume that the same unit has been used for length and width, and the proper square unit has been used for area.

Since a square is a rectangle, the following theorem results:

Area Theorem for a Square

The area (A) of a square is the square of the length (s) of a side.

$$A = s^2$$

Exercises 9.1

Ⓐ 1. What is the formula for the area of a rectangle? What does each letter stand for?

2. What is the formula for the area of a square? What does each letter stand for?

3–6. If the length and width of a rectangle are in the given unit, in what unit would the area be?

3. centimeter (cm) 4. kilometer (km) 5. millimeter (mm) 6. meter (m)

7. If two triangles are congruent, which postulate tells you they have the same area?

8. If two triangles have the same area, are they necessarily congruent?

9–10. Area A = 20, and Area B = 8.

9. Which postulate tells you that the area of the figure shaded in green is 28?

10. Is the area 28 if the rectangles overlap as in the given figure?

Ex. 9

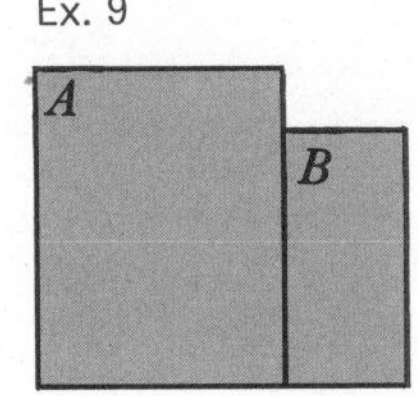

Ex. 10

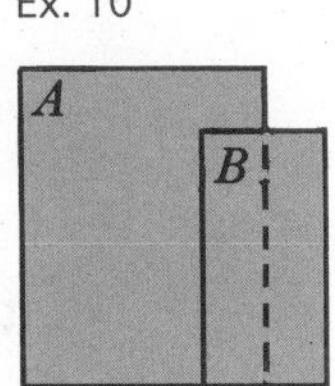

11. In Example 1b, could the area be found by changing 32 mm to 3.2 cm and leaving 3 cm unchanged? What would the area be?

12. If a rectangle has length 30 cm and width 0.2 m, what is its area in cm^2? In m^2?

Ⓑ 13–28. Find the area of each rectangle (or square).

13. $\ell = 19$ m, $w = 13$ m

14. $\ell = 28$ cm, $w = 22$ cm

15. $\ell = 4.5$ km, $w = 2.5$ km

16. $\ell = 7.5$ m, $w = 2.25$ m

17. $\ell = 6$ cm, $w = 33$ mm (Find A in mm^2.)

18. $\ell = 2$ m, $w = 120$ cm (Find A in cm^2.)

19. $\ell = 6$ cm, $w = 33$ mm (Find A in cm^2.)

20. $\ell = 2$ m, $w = 120$ cm (Find A in m^2.)

21. $\ell = 23$ mm, $w = 1.5$ cm

22. $\ell = 6.2$ m, $w = 415$ cm

23. square with $s = 2.3$ m

24. square with $s = 1.8$ cm

25. square with $s = 1\frac{1}{3}$

26. square with $s = 6\frac{1}{2}$

27. square with $s = 1.52$

28. square with $s = 3.4$

29–34. Find the missing length or width of each rectangle.

29. $A = 228$, $\ell = 19$

30. $A = 3066$, $w = 42$

31. $A = 100$, $w = 2.5$

32. $A = 19.04$, $\ell = 5.6$

33. $A = \frac{1}{8}$, $\ell = \frac{1}{2}$

34. $A = 6\frac{1}{4}$, $w = 2$

35. What happens to the area of a rectangle when

a. the length is doubled?
b. the width is doubled?
c. both the length and width are doubled?

36. What happens to the area of a square when

a. the side is doubled?
b. the side is tripled?
c. the side is halved?

37. How many square centimeters are in a square meter?

38. How many square meters are in a square kilometer?

39. How many square meters of paneling are needed to panel a wall that is 3.5 meters high by 5.2 meters wide?

40. How many square-centimeter tiles are needed to tile a tabletop that is 31 cm by 48 cm?

41. How many square meters of artificial turf are needed to cover a soccer field that is 101 m by 64 m?

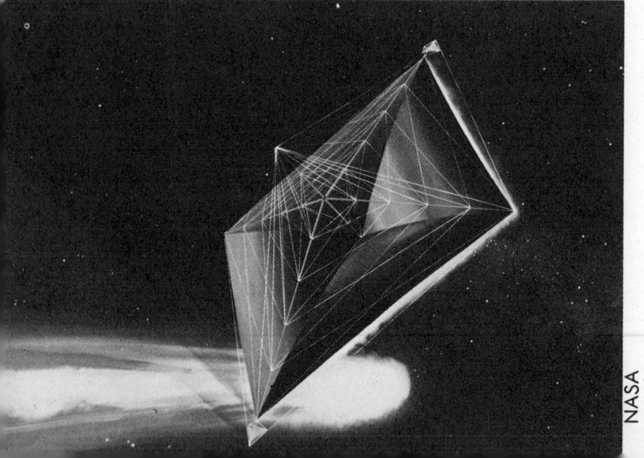
NASA

42. The National Aeronautics and Space Administration is studying plans to launch an unmanned spacecraft to meet with Halley's Comet when it next approaches the sun in 1986. A giant square sail, 800 meters on a side, would be used to propel the spacecraft by means of sunlight. What would be the area of the sail?

43–48. Find the area of each shaded region. All angles are right angles.

43.

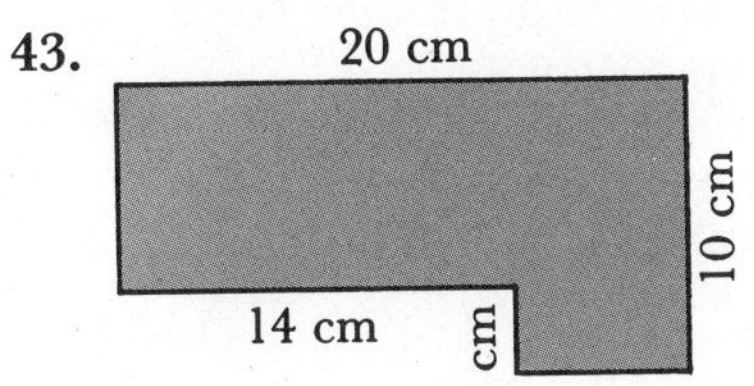

44.

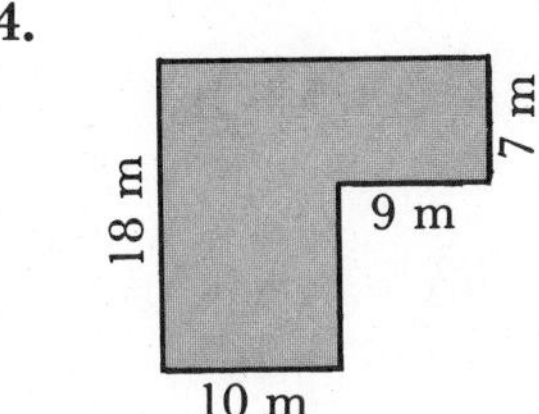

45.

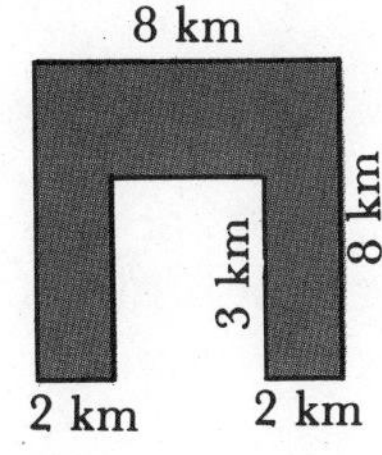

46.

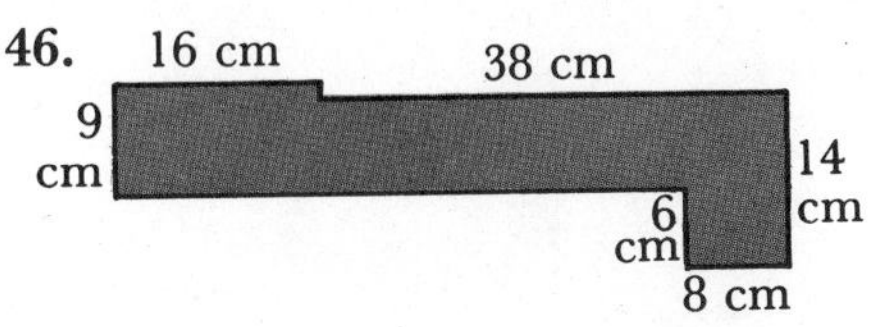

47.

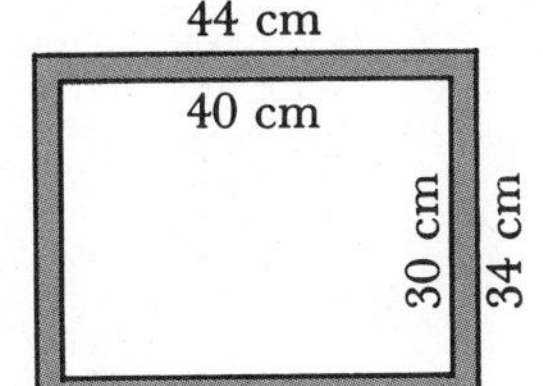

48.

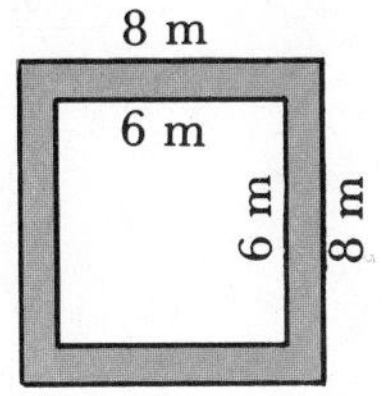

49. Given: Parallelogram $ABCD$ with diagonal $\overline{AC}$

Prove: Area $\triangle ABC = \frac{1}{2}$ area $ABCD$

Ex. 49

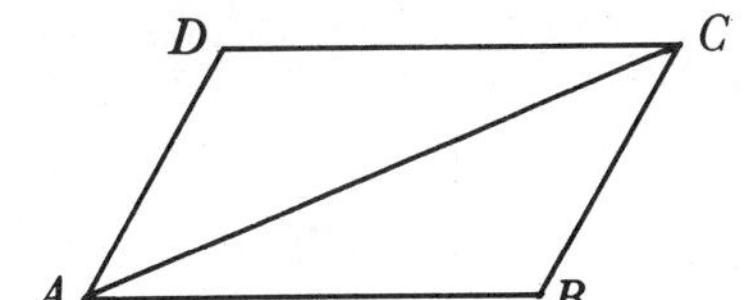

50. Given: Rhombus $SOFA$ with diagonals $\overline{SF}$ and $\overline{AO}$ intersecting at R

Prove: Area $\triangle ARF = \frac{1}{4}$ area $SOFA$

Ex. 50

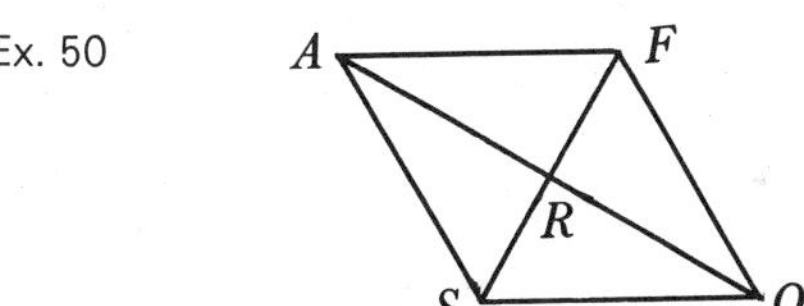

© 51. A housing for an industrial machine is shaped as shown at the right. How many square meters of sheet metal are needed for the surface of the housing? (There is no bottom.)

Ex. 51

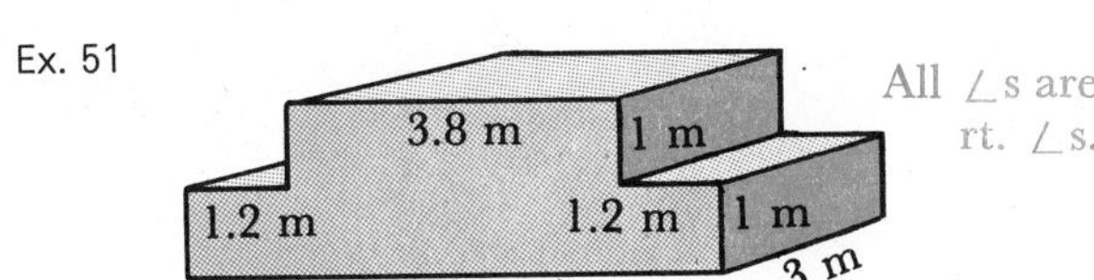

52. The floor plan of a living-dining area is shown at the right. The walls and the ceiling are to be painted. If the height of the ceiling is 2.5 meters, how many square meters of surface must be painted? (Ignore the fact that doors and windows will not be painted.)

Ex. 52

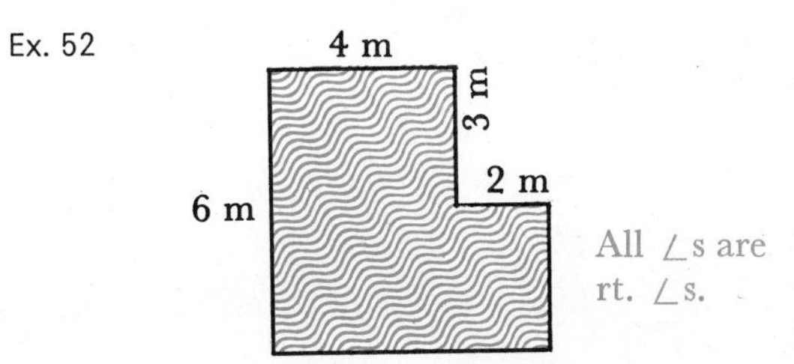

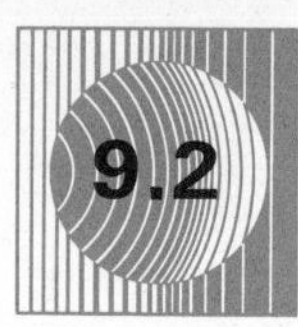

9.2 Areas of Triangles and Parallelograms

The Area Postulate for a Rectangle is useful in finding the areas of other figures such as right triangles and parallelograms.

Area Theorem for a Right Triangle

The area (A) of a right triangle is one half the product of the lengths (b and h) of its legs.

$$A = \tfrac{1}{2}bh$$

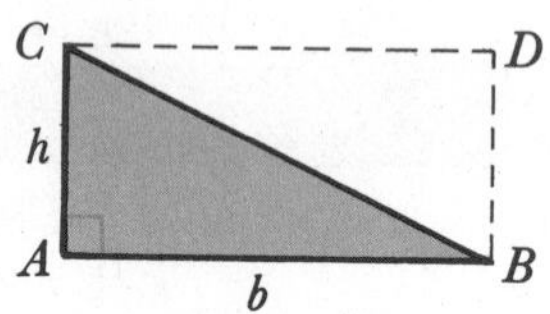

Given: Right $\triangle ABC$ with legs of lengths b and h, $m\angle A = 90$

Prove: Area $\triangle ABC = \frac{1}{2}bh$

Sketch of Proof: Draw a line through C parallel to $\overline{AB}$ and a line through B parallel to $\overline{AC}$. Let D be their point of intersection.

Now we have rectangle ($\square$) $ABDC$. Also, we know $\triangle ABC \cong \triangle DCB$. (Why?) So we can reason as follows:

area $\square ABDC = bh$	Area Post. for a $\square$
area $\triangle ABC$ + area $\triangle DCB = bh$	Area Addition Post.
area $\triangle ABC$ + area $\triangle ABC = bh$	Area Post. for $\cong$ $\triangle$s (Substitute area $\triangle ABC$ for area $\triangle DCB$.)
2 area $\triangle ABC = bh$	Addition
area $\triangle ABC = \frac{1}{2}bh$	Multiply both sides by $\frac{1}{2}$.

Any side of a parallelogram may be called its *base*. Then the *corresponding height* is the distance from the base to the opposite side.

Area Theorem for a Parallelogram

The area (A) of a parallelogram is the length (b) of its base times the corresponding height (h).

$$A = bh$$

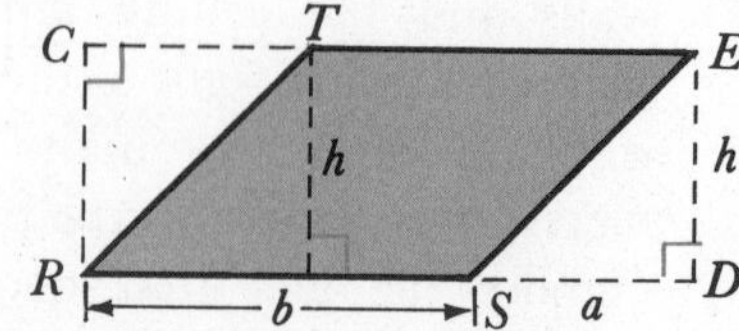

Given: Parallelogram $RSET$ with base of length b and height h

Prove: Area $RSET = bh$

Sketch of Proof: Extend $\overline{RS}$ and draw the perpendicular from E to this extended line. Let D be the point of intersection. Likewise, extend $\overline{ET}$ and draw the perpendicular from R to the extended line. Let C be the point of intersection. Now we have a rectangle $RDEC$. Also, by the HL Theorem we can prove $\triangle RTC \cong \triangle ESD$. So we can reason as follows:

Statement	Reason
$\text{area } \square RDEC = (b + a)h$	Area Post. for a $\square$
$\text{area } \triangle RTC + \text{area } \square RSET + \text{area } \triangle ESD = (b + a)h$	Area Addition Post.
$\text{area } \triangle ESD + \text{area } \square RSET + \text{area } \triangle ESD = (b + a)h$	Area Post. for $\cong$ $\triangle$s
$\frac{1}{2}ah + \text{area } \square RSET + \frac{1}{2}ah = (b + a)h$	Area Thm. for a Rt. $\triangle$
$\text{area } \square RSET + ah = bh + ah$	Use algebra.
$\text{area } \square RSET = bh$	

Any side of a triangle may be called its *base*. Then the length of the altitude to that base is the *corresponding height*.

Area Theorem for a Triangle

The area (A) of a triangle is one half times the length of its base times the corresponding height.

$$A = \frac{1}{2}bh$$

Given: $\triangle ABC$ with base of length b and height h

Prove: Area $\triangle ABC = \frac{1}{2}bh$

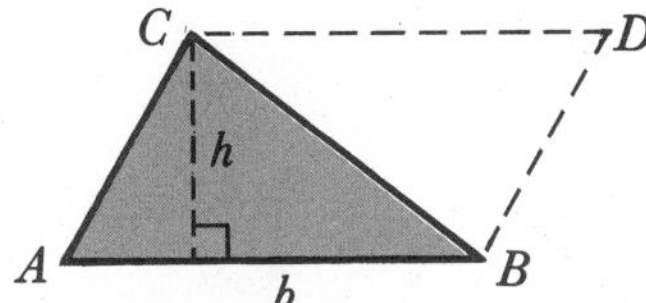

Sketch of Proof: Through C draw a line parallel to $\overline{AB}$. Through B draw a line parallel to $\overline{AC}$. Let D be the point where these two lines intersect. Then $ABDC$ is a parallelogram. So area $\square ABDC = bh$. Since $\overline{BC}$ is a diagonal of $\square ABDC$, $\triangle ABC \cong \triangle DCB$. So area $\triangle ABC = \frac{1}{2}$ area $ABDC$, or area $\triangle ABC = \frac{1}{2}bh$.

In finding the area of a triangle, any side can be the base. Of course, you must know the length of the altitude to that side before you can find the area. The altitude to a given side can (**a**) be in the interior of the triangle, (**b**) coincide with another side, or (**c**) be in the exterior of the triangle.

(a)

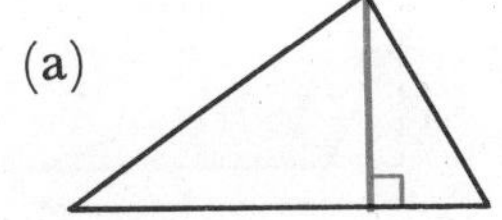

(b)

(c)

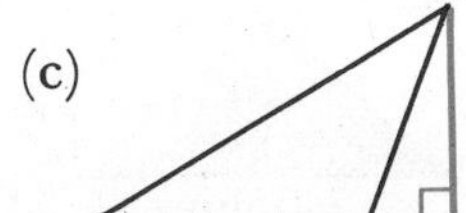

Examples: Find the area of each figure.

1. Find the area of a triangle where $b = 12$ m and $h = 5$ m.

$$A = \frac{1}{2}bh$$
$$A = \frac{1}{2} \cdot 12 \cdot 5$$
$$A = 30 \text{ m}^2$$

2. Find the area of a parallelogram where $b = 3.2$ cm and $h = 40$ mm.

$$A = bh$$
$$A = (3.2)(4) \quad \blacktriangleleft 40 \text{ mm} = 4 \text{ cm}$$
$$A = 12.8 \text{ cm}^2$$

Exercises 9.2

Ⓐ **1–2.** Give the formula for the area of each figure and tell what each letter stands for.

1. a parallelogram

2. a triangle

3–8. For the given base, what is the corresponding height?

Ex. 3–5

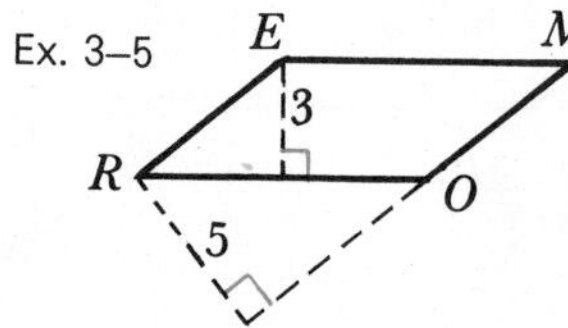

Ex. 6–8

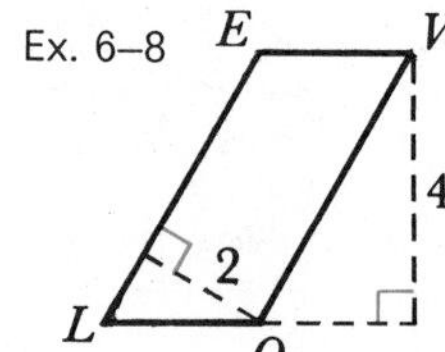

3. $\overline{RO}$ **4.** $\overline{OM}$

5. $\overline{RE}$ **6.** $\overline{LO}$

7. $\overline{LE}$ **8.** $\overline{OV}$

9–14. For each triangle, name the altitude to the given side.

Ex. 9–11

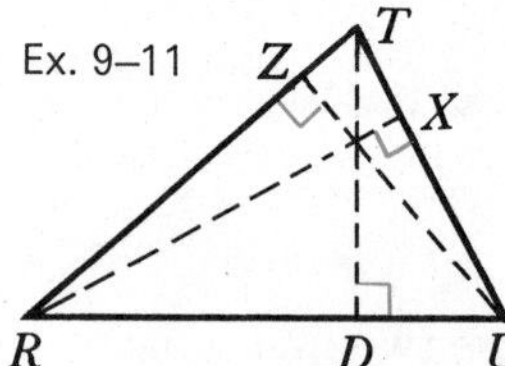

Ex. 12–14

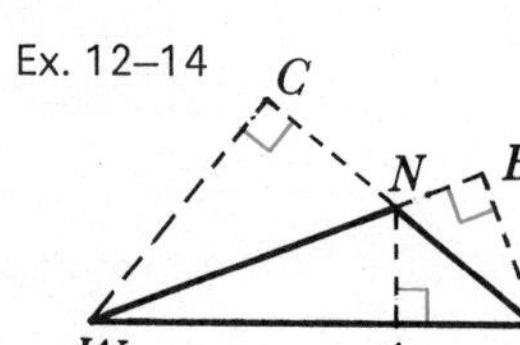

9. $\overline{RU}$ **10.** $\overline{UT}$

11. $\overline{RT}$ **12.** $\overline{WN}$

13. $\overline{WO}$ **14.** $\overline{ON}$

Ⓑ **15–18.** Find the area of each parallelogram.

15.

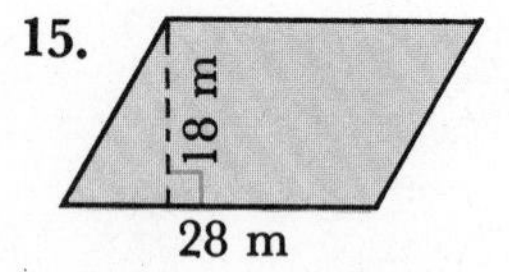

16.

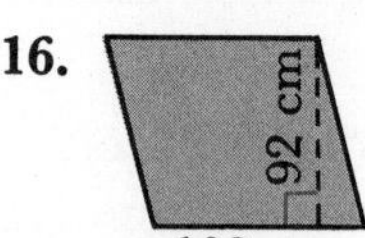

17.

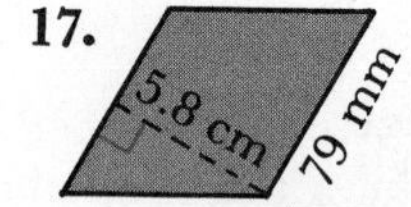

18.

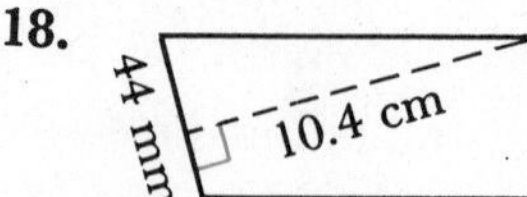

19–22. Find the area of each triangle.

19.

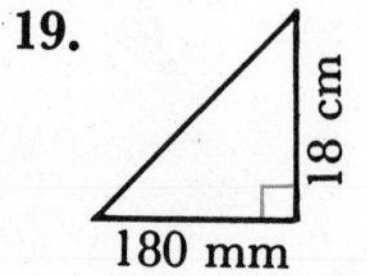

20.

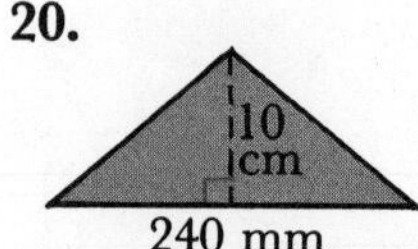

21.

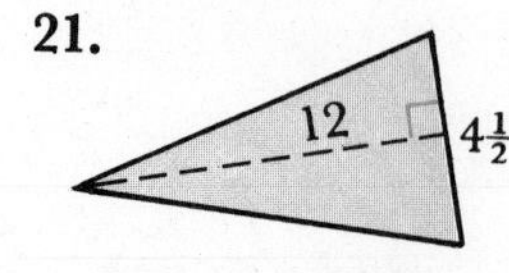

22.

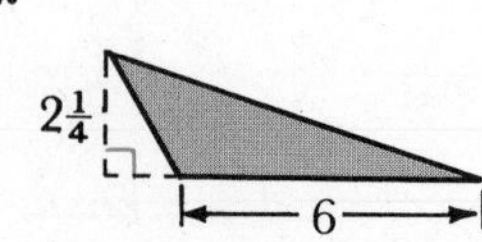

23–30. Find the area of each triangle.

23. $b = 3\frac{2}{3}$, $h = 1\frac{1}{2}$

24. $b = 2\frac{1}{6}$, $h = 3$

25. $b = 5$, $h = 2\frac{2}{5}$

26. $b = 6\frac{1}{4}$, $h = 3\frac{1}{2}$

27. $b = 3.8$, $h = 2.4$

28. $b = 1.5$, $h = 9.4$

29. $b = 1.66$, $h = 3.42$

30. $b = 8.12$, $h = 5.63$

31–38. Find the area of each parallelogram.

31. $b = 8$, $h = 3\frac{1}{2}$

32. $b = 10$, $h = 2\frac{3}{4}$

33. $b = 2\frac{1}{3}$, $h = 2\frac{1}{3}$

34. $b = 6\frac{1}{4}$, $h = 3\frac{1}{2}$

35. $b = 4.3$, $h = 6.3$

36. $b = 1.9$, $h = 3.8$

37. $b = 1.25$, $h = 3.48$

38. $b = 7.29$, $h = 3.57$

39–40. In $\triangle ABC$, $\overline{CD}$ is the altitude to $\overline{AB}$, and $\overline{AE}$ is the altitude to $\overline{BC}$.

39. If $AB = 12$, $CD = 8$, $AE = 9$, find BC.

40. If $AB = 15$, $AE = 11$, $BC = 21$, find CD.

Ⓒ **41.** For the figure at the top of page 292, prove $ABDC$ is a rectangle.

42. For the figure at the bottom of page 292, prove $RDEC$ is a rectangle.

43. How many square meters of tent material are needed to make a tent like that at the right? (There is no floor, so two triangles and two rectangles are involved. Neglect the material needed for hems and seams.)

Ex. 43

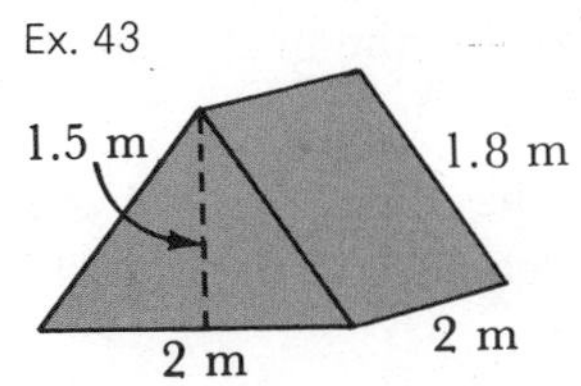

44. A steel storage shed has dimensions as shown in the figure. How many square meters of sheet metal are needed to cover the ends, the sides, and the roof? (Neglect the amount cut out for windows and doors.)

Ex. 44

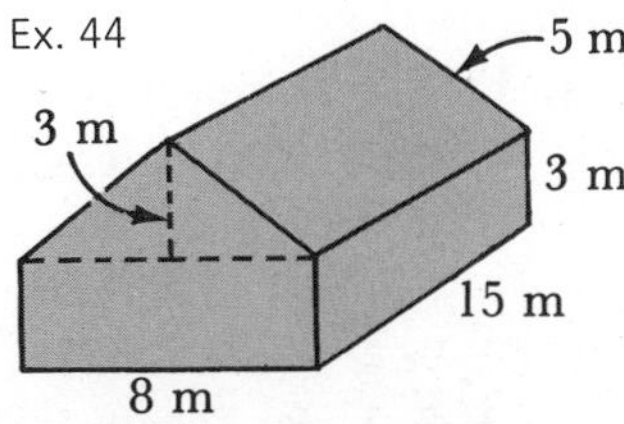

H. Armstrong Roberts

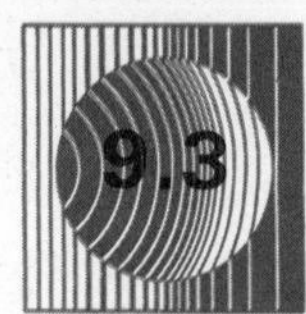

9.3 Areas of Trapezoids and Rhombuses

Remember that a trapezoid has two parallel sides called *bases* and two nonparallel sides. The distance between the parallel sides is called the *height* of the trapezoid.

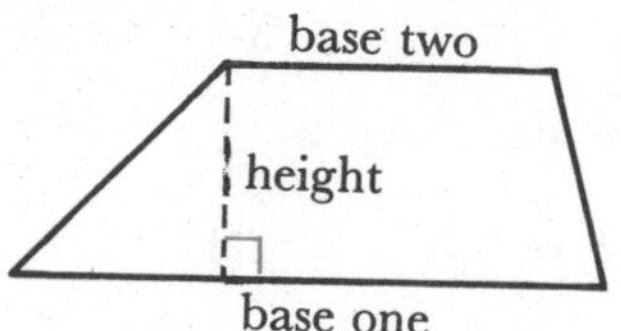

Area Theorem for a Trapezoid

The area (A) of a trapezoid is one half times the height (h) times the sum of the lengths (b_1 and b_2) of its bases.

$$A = \frac{1}{2}h(b_1 + b_2)$$

Given: Trapezoid $ABCD$ with bases of lengths b_1 and b_2, and height h

Prove: Area $ABCD = \frac{1}{2}h(b_1 + b_2)$

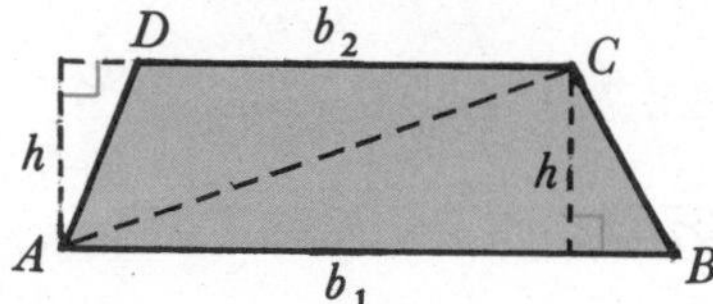

Sketch of Proof: Draw auxiliary segment AC so that $\triangle ABC$ and $\triangle ACD$ are formed. By the Area Addition Postulate, the area of $ABCD$ equals the sum of the areas of $\triangle ABC$ and $\triangle ACD$.

We know area $\triangle ABC = \frac{1}{2}b_1h$ and area $\triangle ACD = \frac{1}{2}b_2h$. (Both triangles have the same height h.) So area $ABCD = \frac{1}{2}b_1h + \frac{1}{2}b_2h$.

Then area $ABCD = \frac{1}{2}h(b_1 + b_2)$.

Another quadrilateral that we sometimes use is the rhombus. The proof of the next theorem is asked for in Exercise 30.

Area Theorem for a Rhombus

The area (A) of a rhombus is one half times the product of the lengths (d_1 and d_2) of its diagonals.

$$A = \frac{1}{2}d_1d_2$$

Examples:

1. Find the area of a trapezoid having bases of lengths 14 and 20 and height 8.

   $A = \frac{1}{2}h(b_1 + b_2)$
   $A = \frac{1}{2} \cdot 8 \cdot (14 + 20)$
   $A = 136$

2. Find the area of a rhombus with diagonals of lengths 4 and $2\frac{1}{2}$.

   $A = \frac{1}{2}d_1d_2$
   $A = \frac{1}{2} \cdot 4 \cdot 2\frac{1}{2}$
   $A = 5$

Exercises 9.3

Ⓐ **1.** What is the formula for the area of a trapezoid? What does each letter stand for?

2. What is the formula for the area of a rhombus? What does each letter stand for?

3–6. For the given trapezoid, is the length of a base or the height listed?

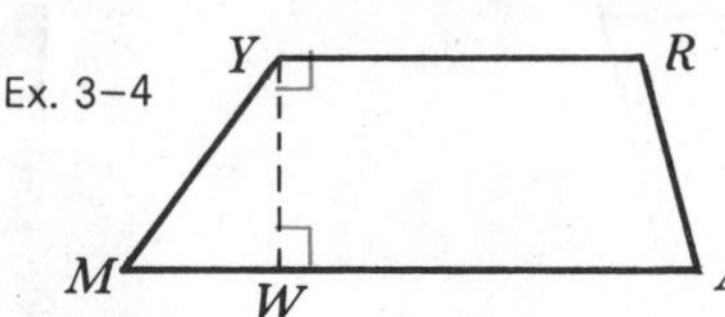

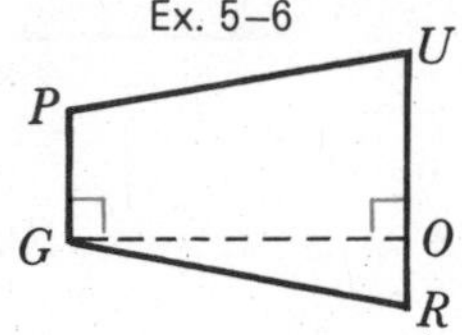

3. MA **4.** YW **5.** OG **6.** UR

7. Can a trapezoid also be a rhombus?

8. Can a parallelogram also be a rhombus?

9–10. Refer to the figure where $DAVE$ is a rhombus.

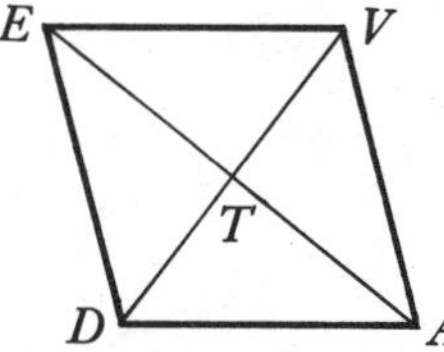

9. What is $m\angle ETV$? $m\angle ATV$?

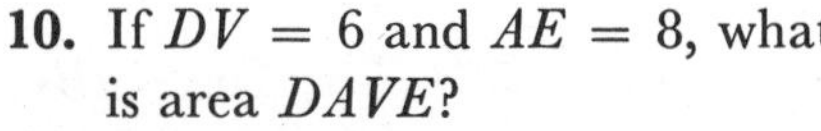

10. If $DV = 6$ and $AE = 8$, what is area $DAVE$?

Ⓑ **11–16.** Find the area of each trapezoid.

11.

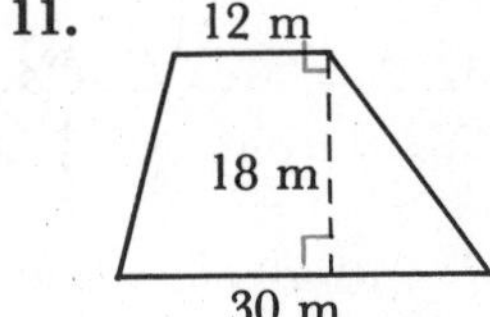

12.

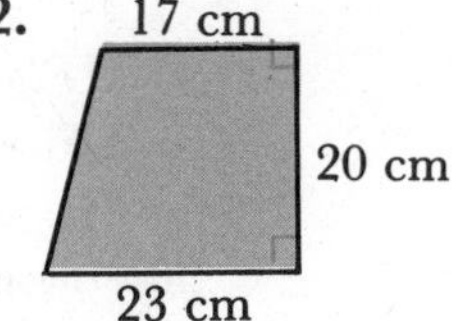

13.

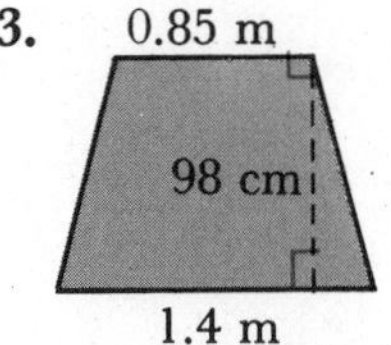

14.

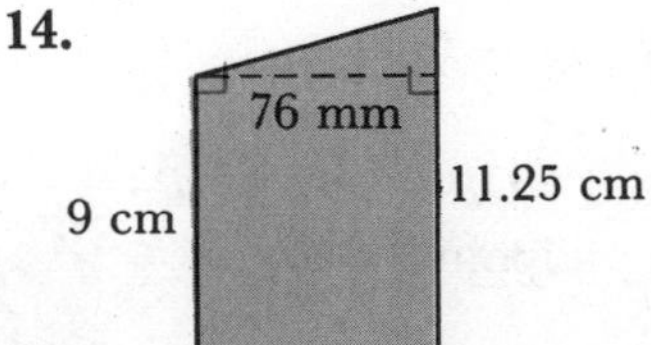

15.

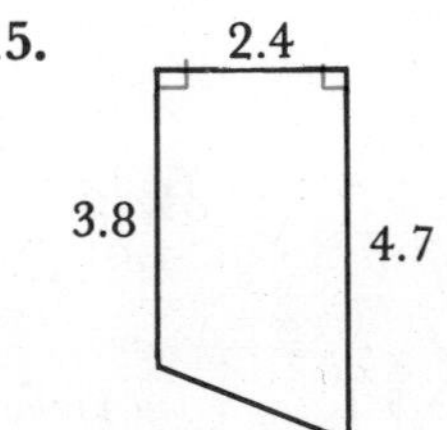

16.

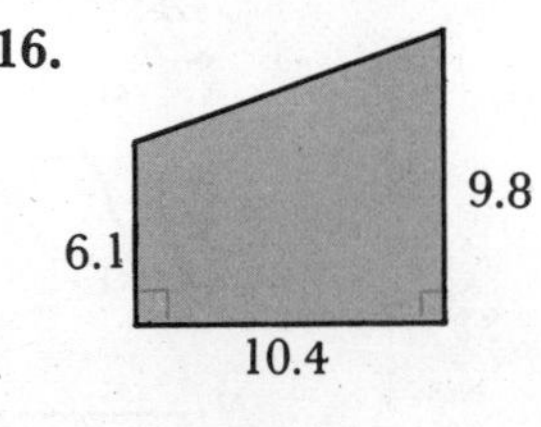

17–20. Find the area of each rhombus.

17.

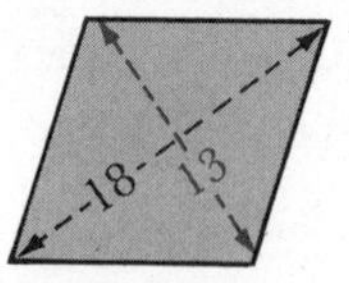

18.

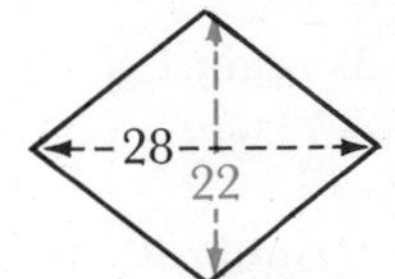

19.

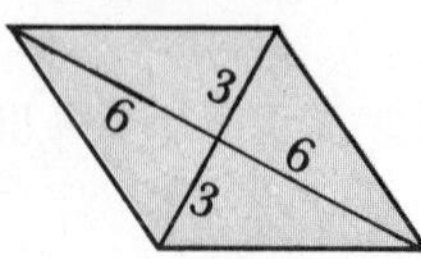

20.

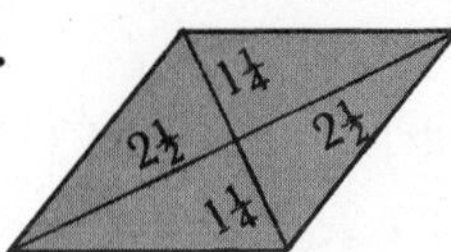

21–24. Find the area of each trapezoid.

21. $h = 21.2$, $b_1 = 18.3$, $b_2 = 15.8$

22. $h = 5.25$, $b_1 = 3.83$, $b_2 = 5.14$

23. $h = 3\frac{1}{4}$, $b_1 = 4\frac{1}{2}$, $b_2 = 3\frac{1}{4}$

24. $h = 9\frac{1}{2}$, $b_1 = 10\frac{1}{4}$, $b_2 = 12\frac{1}{4}$

25–28. Find the area of each rhombus.

25. $d_1 = 4\frac{1}{4}$, $d_2 = 3\frac{1}{2}$

26. $d_1 = 1\frac{1}{8}$, $d_2 = 1\frac{3}{8}$

27. $d_1 = 5.6$, $d_2 = 8.3$

28. $d_1 = 10.6$, $d_2 = 12.4$

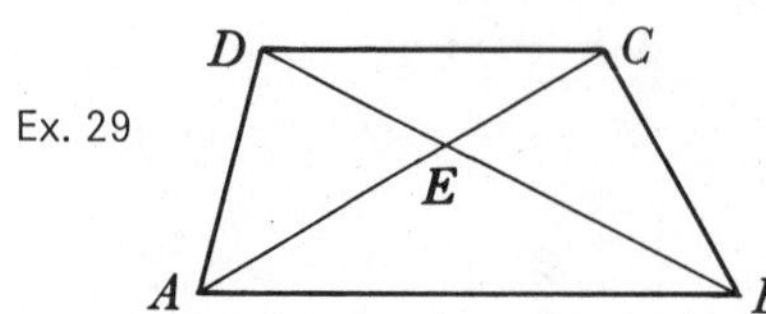

Ex. 29

29. Given: Trapezoid $ABCD$ with bases $\overline{AB}$ and $\overline{CD}$, diagonals $\overline{AC}$ and $\overline{BD}$ intersect at E.

Prove: Area $\triangle ADE$ = area $\triangle BCE$

[*Plan:* Prove area $\triangle ADB$ = area $\triangle BCA$. Then subtract area $\triangle AEB$ from both.]

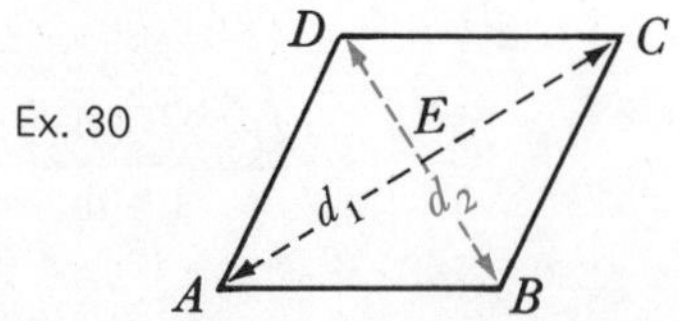

Ex. 30

30. Given: Rhombus $ABCD$ with diagonals of lengths d_1 and d_2

Prove: Area $ABCD = \frac{1}{2}d_1d_2$

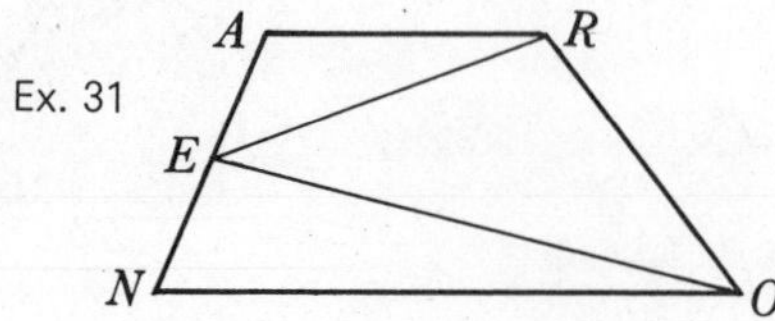

Ex. 31

Ⓒ **31.** Given: Trapezoid $NORA$, $\overline{NO} \parallel \overline{AR}$, E is the midpoint of AN.

Prove: Area $\triangle EOR = \frac{1}{2}$ area $NORA$

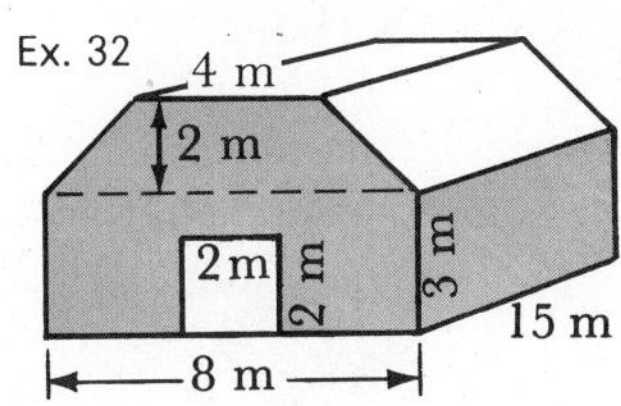

32. The sides and ends of a barn are to be painted. How many square meters of surface need to be covered? See the figure at the left. The door will not be painted.

33. The cross section of a swimming pool is shown at the right. If the sides and bottom are to be painted, find the surface area to be covered. (The pool is 18 feet wide.)

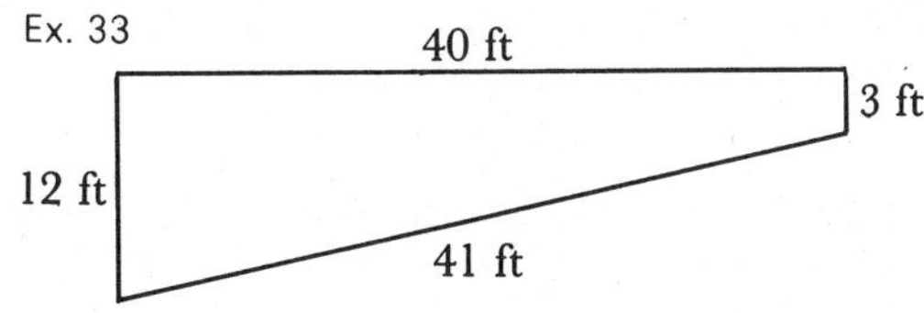

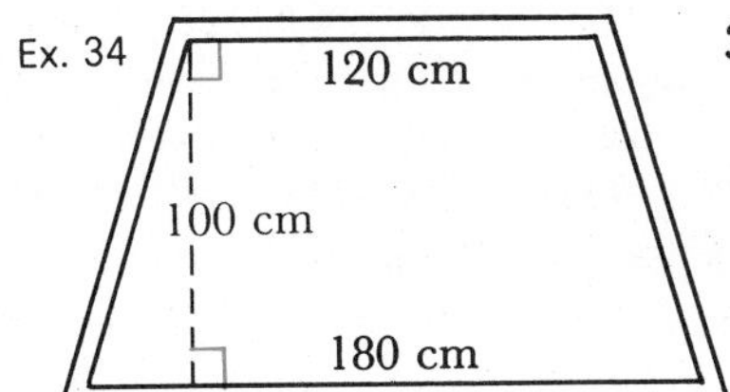

34. A glazier is cutting glass to fit a window shaped like that at the left. The glass is cut from a rectangular sheet of plate glass that is 180 cm by 120 cm. How much glass will be wasted?

35. A surveyor needs to find the area of a plot shaped like *ABCDEF*. A north-south line is determined through *A*, and east-west lines are determined through *C*, *B*, *D*, *A*, *E*, and *F*. Measurements are then made along these lines. Find the area of *ABCDEF*.

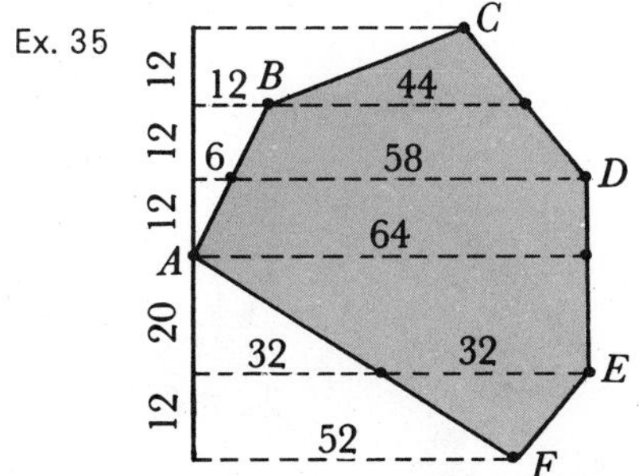

Find the area of each figure.

1. a rectangle with length 9 and width $6\frac{1}{2}$

2. a triangle with base of length 6.8 and height 8

3. a trapezoid with bases of lengths 17 and 21 and height 22

4. a rhombus with diagonals of lengths 14 and 21

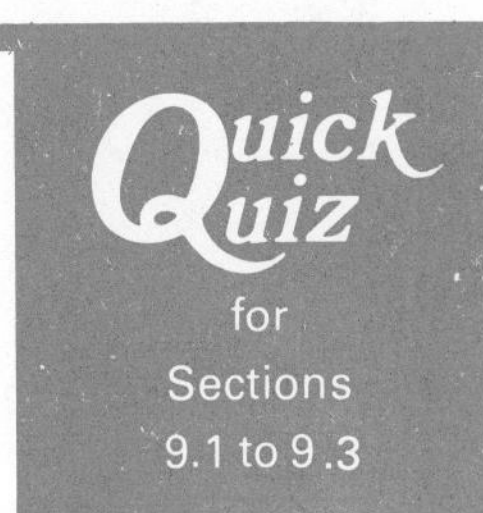

GEOMETRY AT WORK

SCIENTIFIC AND TECHNICAL JOBS

About $2\frac{1}{2}$ million people in the United States have scientific or technical jobs. These include various kinds of engineers, scientists, and technicians, as well as drafters and surveyors. The training needed by these workers ranges from college degrees for some scientists to on-the-job training for some technicians.

High-school graduates with courses in science and mathematics are more likely to get scientific and technical jobs.

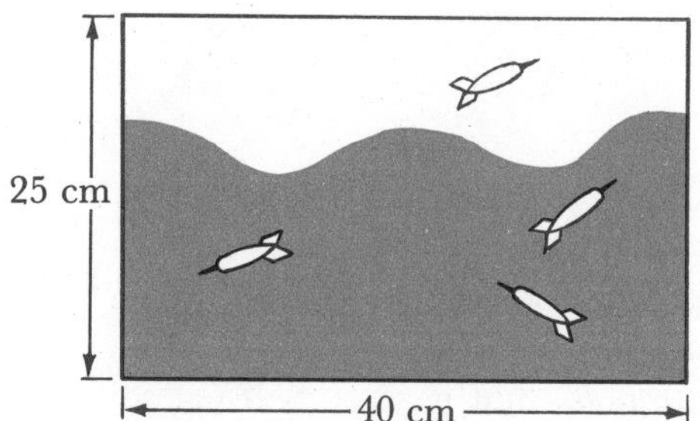

Scientific and technical workers might sometimes use an experiment to find the area of an irregular region like the green region at the left. You can estimate the area of such a region by throwing darts. (A scientific worker wouldn't use darts but might simulate such an experiment with a computer.) Suppose there are 75 hits in the green region out of a total of 100 hits in the rectangular region. The area of the rectangular region is $25 \cdot 40 = 1000$ square centimeters. Solving the proportion below approximates the area of the green region.

$$\frac{75}{100} = \frac{x}{1000}$$

Photri

Square Roots and Radicals

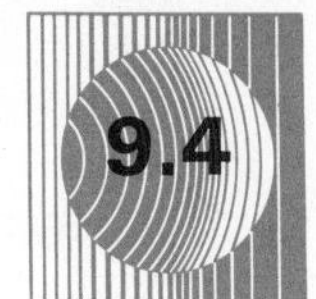

In the next section, we discuss the Pythagorean Theorem. Since square roots are important in using this theorem, we will review the basic ideas about square roots now.

> For real numbers r and x, r is a square root of x if and only if $r^2 = x$.

Example 1: Find the square roots of 36.

Since $6^2 = 36$, 6 is a square root of 36. We write $\sqrt{36} = 6$. Also $(-6)^2 = 36$. So -6 is a square root of 36. We write $-\sqrt{36} = -6$.

You may remember that $\sqrt{36}$ is called a *radical*. The word *radical* comes from a Latin word meaning "root." The sign $\sqrt{}$ is thought to be a form of the letter *r*. In this section we are dealing only with square roots. But radicals can be used for other roots such as $\sqrt[3]{8}$ or $\sqrt[5]{10}$.

Two theorems from algebra are very important in working with radicals.

> If a and b are nonnegative real numbers,
>
> $\sqrt{ab} = \sqrt{a} \cdot \sqrt{b}$ and $\sqrt{\frac{a}{b}} = \frac{\sqrt{a}}{\sqrt{b}}$. $(b \neq 0)$

Example 2: Change each radical expression to *simplest form.*

a. $\sqrt{32}$ **b.** $\sqrt{\frac{7}{9}}$ **c.** $\frac{\sqrt{3}}{\sqrt{2}}$

a. $\sqrt{32} = \sqrt{16} \cdot \sqrt{2} = 4\sqrt{2}$

b. $\sqrt{\frac{7}{9}} = \frac{\sqrt{7}}{\sqrt{9}} = \frac{\sqrt{7}}{3}$

c. $\frac{\sqrt{3}}{\sqrt{2}} = \frac{\sqrt{3}}{\sqrt{2}} \cdot \frac{\sqrt{2}}{\sqrt{2}} = \frac{\sqrt{6}}{2}$

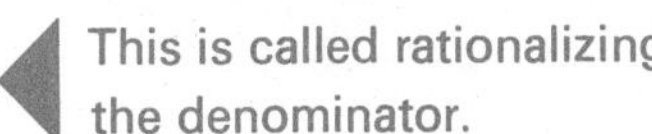

This is called rationalizing the denominator.

These examples show that a radical expression is *not* in simplest form if

a. the number under the square-root sign contains a perfect-square factor.

b. the number under the square-root sign is a fraction.

c. a radical appears in the denominator.

Sometimes it is helpful to change a fraction so that its denominator is a perfect square before the radical is simplified.

Example 3: $\sqrt{\frac{1}{8}} = \sqrt{\frac{2}{16}} = \dfrac{\sqrt{2}}{\sqrt{16}} = \dfrac{\sqrt{2}}{4}$

It should be clear that not all square roots are integers. For example, $\sqrt{14}$ is between 3 and 4 since $3^2 = 9$ and $4^2 = 16$. Approximations to the square roots of integers from 1 to 150 are given in a table on page 562. For integers larger than 150, you can still use the table in some cases, as in the following example:

Example 4: Find $\sqrt{300}$ to the nearest tenth.

$\sqrt{300} = \sqrt{100} \cdot \sqrt{3} = 10\sqrt{3}$

From the table, $\sqrt{3} \approx 1.732$. ($\approx$ means "is approximately equal to.") So $\sqrt{300} = 10\sqrt{3} \approx 10(1.732)$ or 17.32.

To the nearest tenth, $\sqrt{300} \approx 17.3$.

Exercises 9.4

Ⓐ **1.** How many square roots does each positive real number have?

2. Which square roots are not integers?

a. $\sqrt{4}$ **b.** $\sqrt{6}$ **c.** $\sqrt{25}$ **d.** $\sqrt{50}$ **e.** $\sqrt{100}$

3. Which expressions are not in simplest form?

a. $\sqrt{50}$ **b.** $\sqrt{\frac{2}{3}}$ **c.** $\dfrac{\sqrt{2}}{\sqrt{3}}$ **d.** $\sqrt{17}$ **e.** $\dfrac{\sqrt{2}}{3}$

4. Name the largest perfect-square factor of the number under each square-root sign.

a. $\sqrt{12}$ **b.** $\sqrt{75}$ **c.** $\sqrt{48}$ **d.** $\sqrt{200}$ **e.** $\sqrt{72}$

Ⓑ **5–14.** Use the table on page 562 to find each positive square root.

5. $\sqrt{17}$ **6.** $\sqrt{23}$ **7.** $\sqrt{40}$ **8.** $\sqrt{61}$ **9.** $\sqrt{35}$

10. $\sqrt{78}$ **11.** $\sqrt{99}$ **12.** $\sqrt{75}$ **13.** $\sqrt{32}$ **14.** $\sqrt{92}$

15–44. Simplify. Do not use the table on page 562.

15. $\sqrt{16}$ **16.** $\sqrt{36}$ **17.** $\sqrt{64}$ **18.** $\sqrt{100}$ **19.** $\sqrt{81}$

20. $\sqrt{49}$ **21.** $\sqrt{\frac{1}{25}}$ **22.** $\sqrt{\frac{4}{9}}$ **23.** $\sqrt{\frac{25}{49}}$ **24.** $\sqrt{\frac{1}{100}}$

25. $\sqrt{18}$ **26.** $\sqrt{50}$ **27.** $\sqrt{32}$ **28.** $\sqrt{72}$ **29.** $\sqrt{200}$

30. $\sqrt{98}$ **31.** $\sqrt{125}$ **32.** $\sqrt{54}$ **33.** $\sqrt{48}$ **34.** $\sqrt{108}$

35. $\sqrt{\frac{3}{4}}$ **36.** $\sqrt{\frac{5}{16}}$ **37.** $\sqrt{\frac{3}{25}}$ **38.** $\sqrt{\frac{2}{49}}$ **39.** $\frac{\sqrt{2}}{\sqrt{6}}$

40. $\frac{\sqrt{3}}{\sqrt{5}}$ **41.** $\frac{1}{\sqrt{3}}$ **42.** $\frac{\sqrt{3}}{\sqrt{8}}$ **43.** $\sqrt{\frac{1}{5}}$ **44.** $\sqrt{\frac{2}{7}}$

45–48. Find a decimal approximation to the nearest tenth. Refer to the table on page 562. (First simplify each radical.)

45. $\sqrt{180}$ **46.** $\sqrt{162}$ **47.** $\sqrt{192}$ **48.** $\sqrt{200}$

Ⓒ **49.** Make a list of the squares of integers from 11 to 20. Memorize them. Then find these square roots.

$\sqrt{196}$ $\sqrt{144}$ $\sqrt{225}$ $\sqrt{324}$ $\sqrt{121}$

$\sqrt{169}$ $\sqrt{256}$ $\sqrt{361}$ $\sqrt{289}$ $\sqrt{400}$

50. A tile setter has 500 square tiles to use for constructing the largest square patio possible. If only whole tiles are to be used, how many tiles will be left after the patio is constructed?

51. A builder is told that the floor of a building must be square with area 324 m^2. What must the floor dimensions be?

Review this skill:

- *solving quadratic equations*

Solve each quadratic equation. Find answers in simplified radical form when the results are not rational.

1. $6^2 + b^2 = 10^2$

2. $10^2 + 5^2 = x^2$ ← **Example:** $125 = x^2$, $x = \pm 5\sqrt{5}$

3. $a^2 + 12^2 = 15^2$

4. $13^2 = x^2 + 5^2$

5. $15^2 + 20^2 = x^2$

6. $9^2 + x^2 = 41^2$

7. $3^2 + 9^2 = z^2$

8. $7^2 + b^2 = (7\sqrt{2})^2$

Pythagorean Theorem and Its Converse

The Pythagorean Theorem is probably the most famous theorem in mathematics. The theorem takes its name from the Greek mathematician named Pythagoras. It is not known whether Pythagoras or one of his followers was the first to prove the theorem. The following proof is just one of over 200 ways that have been used to prove the theorem.

Pythagorean Theorem

In a right triangle, the square of the length of its hypotenuse is equal to the sum of the squares of the lengths of its legs.

Given: Right $\triangle ABC$ with hypotenuse of length c and legs of lengths a and b

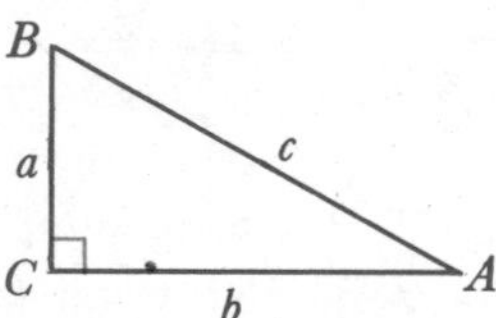

Prove: $c^2 = a^2 + b^2$

Sketch of proof: First, take a square with sides of length $a + b$. In the square draw four right triangles with legs of lengths a and b.

1. By the LL Theorem, each right triangle is congruent to the given $\triangle ABC$. Therefore, each triangle has a hypotenuse of length c.

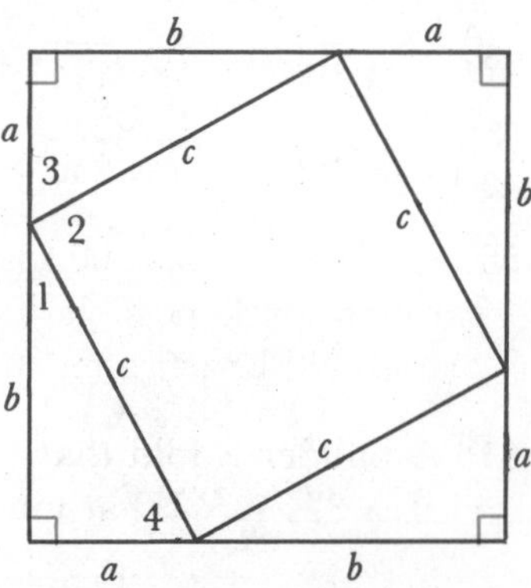

2. Now we must prove that the quadrilateral formed by the four hypotenuses is a square. In the figure,

$$m\angle 1 + m\angle 2 + m\angle 3 = 180$$

Also, $m\angle 4 = m\angle 3$.

So, $m\angle 1 + m\angle 2 + m\angle 4 = 180$.

Since $m\angle 1 + m\angle 4 = 90$ (Why?),

$$m\angle 2 = 90.$$

Likewise, the other angles of the quadrilateral are right angles.

3. By the Area Addition Postulate, the area of the large square is equal to the area of the small square, plus the sum of the areas of the four congruent triangles. This gives

$$(a + b)^2 = c^2 + 4 \cdot \tfrac{1}{2}ab$$

Therefore, $a^2 + 2ab + b^2 = c^2 + 2ab$

and $a^2 + b^2 = c^2$

The converse of the Pythagorean Theorem is also true.

If the square of the length of one side of a triangle is equal to the sum of the squares of the lengths of the other two sides, then the triangle is a right triangle, with the right angle opposite the longest side.

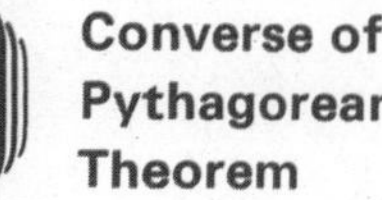

Converse of Pythagorean Theorem

Given: $\triangle ABC$ with $c^2 = a^2 + b^2$

Prove: $\triangle ABC$ is a right triangle.

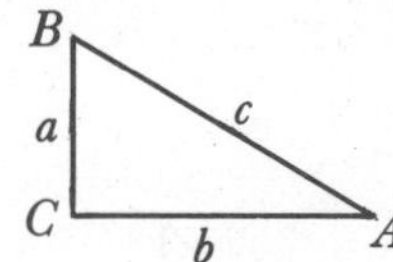

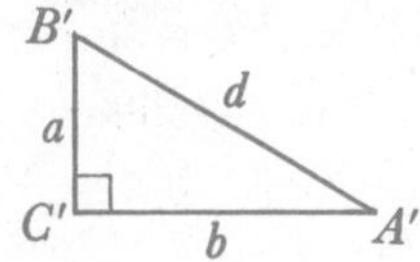

Proof: Let $A'B'C'$ be a right triangle with legs of length a and b and hypotenuse of length d. Then $d^2 = a^2 + b^2$ by the Pythagorean Theorem. Since $c^2 = a^2 + b^2$, then $c^2 = d^2$ or $c = d$. (Actually, $c = \pm d$, but the length of a side of a triangle cannot be negative.) By the SSS Postulate, $\triangle ABC \cong \triangle A'B'C'$. Therefore, $\angle C \cong \angle C'$. Since $\angle C'$ is a right angle, so is $\angle C$.

Examples:

1. Find the length of the hypotenuse of a right triangle having legs of lengths 9 and 12.

$c^2 = 9^2 + 12^2$

$c^2 = 81 + 144 = 225$

$c = 15$

NOTE: This quadratic equation has two roots. But we disregard the negative root since we are finding the length of a side of a triangle.

2. In right $\triangle ABC$, find the length a of one leg if the hypotenuse has length $c = 8$ and the other leg has length $b = 4$.

$8^2 = a^2 + 4^2$

$64 = a^2 + 16$

$48 = a^2$

$\sqrt{48} = a$

$\sqrt{16} \cdot \sqrt{3} = a$

$4\sqrt{3} = a$

3. Can the following be lengths of the sides of a right triangle?

6, 8, 11

$11^2 \stackrel{?}{=} 6^2 + 8^2$

$121 \stackrel{?}{=} 36 + 64$

$121 \neq 100$

No, these could not be the lengths of the sides of a right triangle.

Exercises 9.5

Ⓐ **1.** Can the Pythagorean Theorem be applied to any triangle?

2. If the sides of a right triangle have lengths x, y, and z with z the greatest length, what equation must be true?

3–6. State an equation that can be used to find the missing length for each triangle.

3.
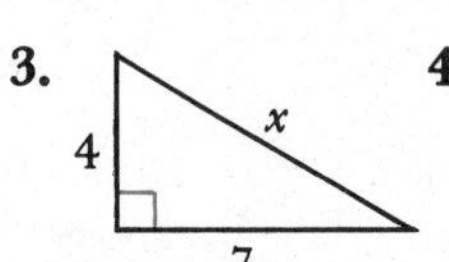

4.
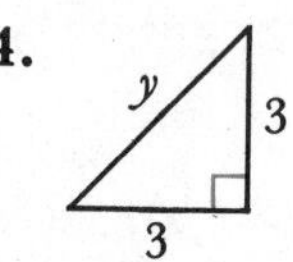

5.
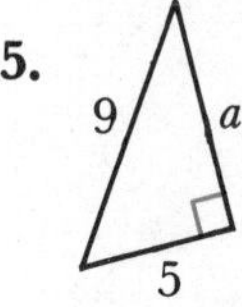

6.
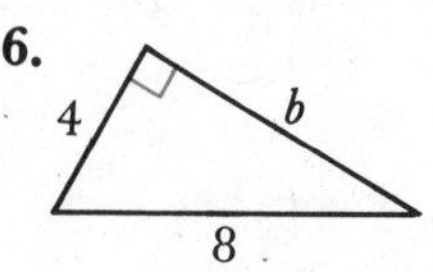

7–10. The lengths of three sides of a triangle are given. Can the triangle be a right triangle?

7. 3, 4, 5 **8.** 4, 5, 6 **9.** 6, 8, 10 **10.** 3, 3, 5

Ⓑ **11–18.** For right $\triangle ABC$, the lengths of two of the three sides are given. Find the length of the third side. Leave answers in simplified radical form where answers are not rational.

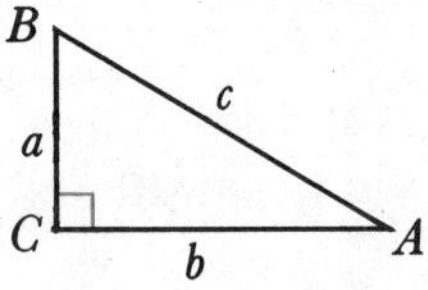

11. $a = 5, b = 12$ **12.** $a = 8, b = 15$

13. $a = 4, b = 4$ **14.** $a = 5, b = 10$

15. $c = 41, a = 40$ **16.** $c = 20, a = 16$

17. $c = 16, b = 9$ **18.** $c = 12, b = 8$

19–24. Determine if a triangle with sides of the given lengths is a right triangle.

19. 9, 12, 15 **20.** 15, 20, 25 **21.** 5, 8, 9

22. 10, 24, 26 **23.** 16, 30, 34 **24.** 20, 40, 60

25. A 40-meter radio tower is braced with a cable that is tied 30 meters from the base. How long must the cable be? (Disregard the amount of cable needed for tying.)

Ex. 25

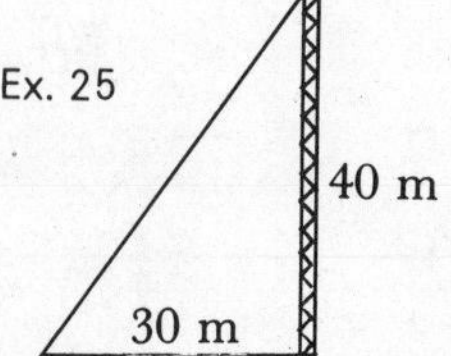

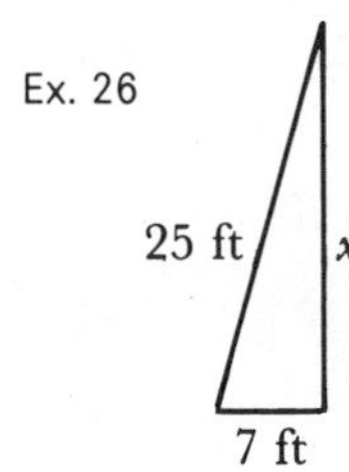

26. A 25-foot ladder leans against a building so that the foot of the ladder is 7 feet from the base of the building. How high up on the building does the ladder reach?

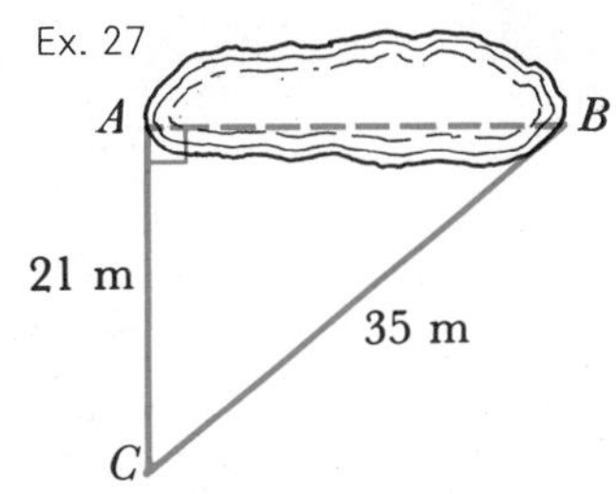

27. A surveyor wants to find the distance from point A to point B. Since the distance cannot be measured directly, a right triangle is laid off as in the figure. $AC = 21$ m and $BC = 35$ m. How long is AB?

Ex. 28

18 km

x

24 km

28. A ship is 18 kilometers south and 24 kilometers east of its starting point. How far is the ship from its starting point?

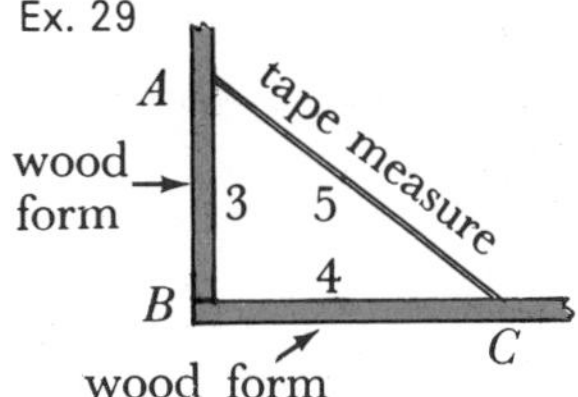

29. In laying out wood forms into which concrete will be poured, cement masons often use a 3-4-5 triangle. Is $\angle ABC$ a right angle? Why?

Ex. 30

fence

5

13

12

fence

30. A fence installer wants to square off the corner of a fence. A triangle is measured as shown. Does the corner form a right angle? Why?

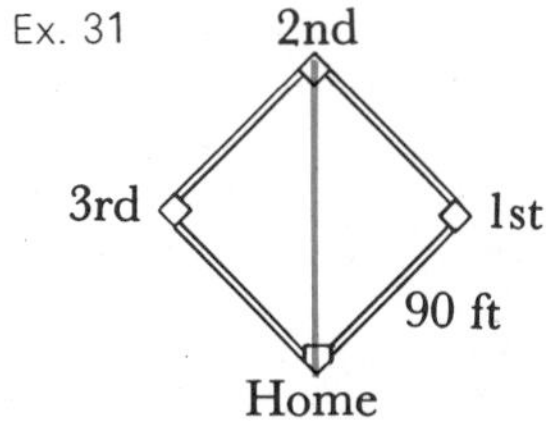

31. A baseball diamond (square) is 90 feet on each side. If the catcher throws from home plate to second base, how far is the ball thrown (to the nearest tenth of a foot)?

Ex. 32

1 m

2 m

32. A rectangular gate is braced with a board connecting opposite corners. If the gate is 2 meters by 1 meter, how long must the brace be (to the nearest hundredth of a meter)?

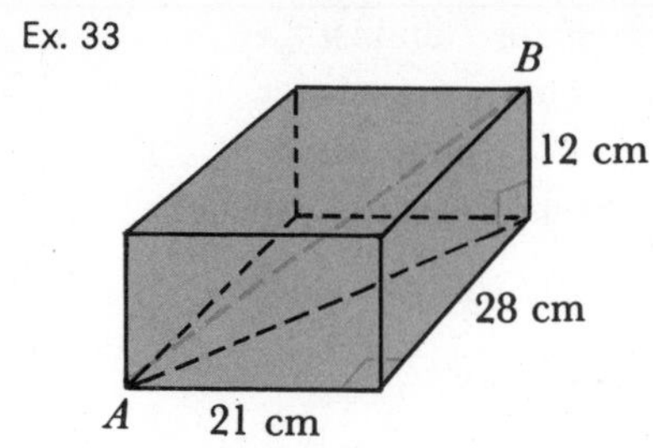

Ⓒ **33.** A box has a length, width, and height of 28 cm, 21 cm, and 12 cm. How long is a diagonal of the box? (A diagonal joins opposite corners, such as A and B in the figure.)
HINT: Apply the Pythagorean Theorem twice.

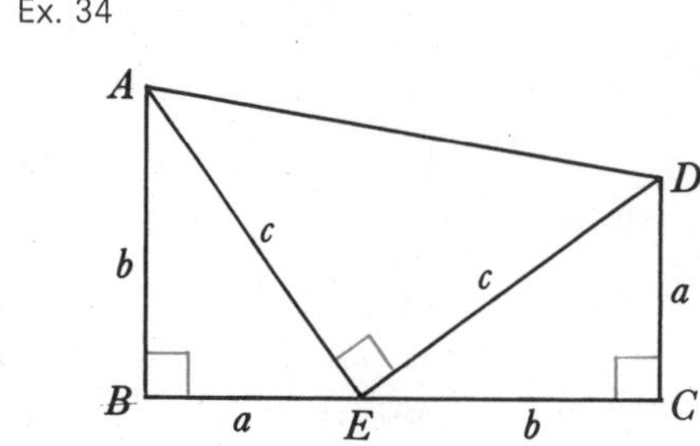

34. President James Garfield discovered a proof of the Pythagorean Theorem in 1876 while he was a member of the House of Representatives, five years before he became President. The proof involves finding the area of $ABCD$ in two different ways, first using three triangles and then as a trapezoid. Show that $c^2 = a^2 + b^2$.

THE WHEEL OF THEODORUS

Theodorus was a Greek philosopher who lived about 425 B.C. It is said that he discovered the construction below. Therefore, it is called the "wheel of Theodorus."

Notice how the "wheel of Theodorus" enables us to construct segments having measures of $\sqrt{1}$, $\sqrt{2}$, $\sqrt{3}$, $\sqrt{4}$, $\sqrt{5}$, ...

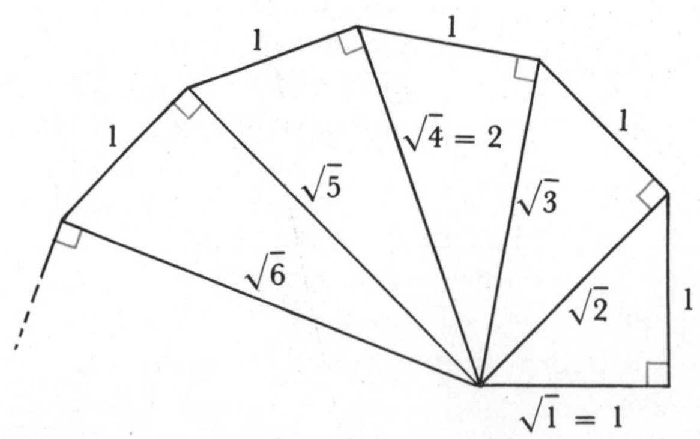

Construct a wheel of your own. What is the measure of the last segment that can be constructed before the wheel overlaps?

If you construct a wheel (or parts of it) by using unit segments that are 1 decimeter long, you can estimate $\sqrt{2}$, $\sqrt{3}$, $\sqrt{5}$, and so on, to the nearest hundredth by measuring to the nearest millimeter.

GEOMETRY AT WORK

INDUSTRIAL PRODUCTION

Millions of people in the United States work in industrial production. These workers are employed mostly in factories. Semiskilled workers, such as assemblers and certain machine operators, may need only brief on-the-job training. Skilled workers, such as patternmakers and machinists, may have to complete a 3- or 4-year apprenticeship program.

For most jobs in industrial production a high-school diploma is not required. But many employers prefer high-school graduates who have taken such courses as machine shop and blueprint reading. A knowledge of geometry can also be very helpful in getting a good job and in successfully completing the training program.

A welder might have to solve a problem like the following:

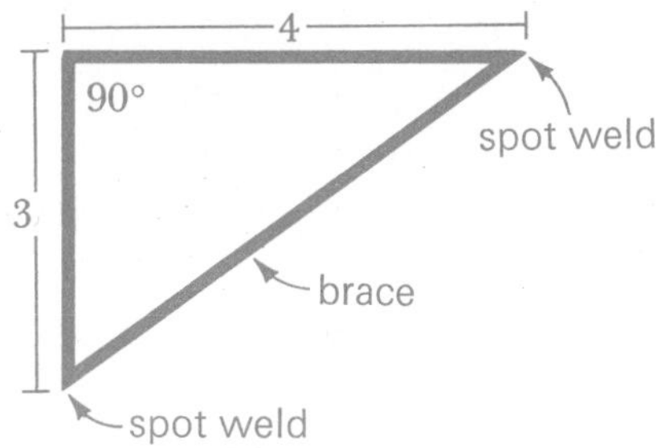

How long a metal rod is needed for the brace?

Joe Tritsch

9.6 Special Right Triangles

Isosceles Right Triangle

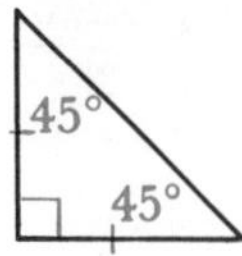

30-60-90° Triangle

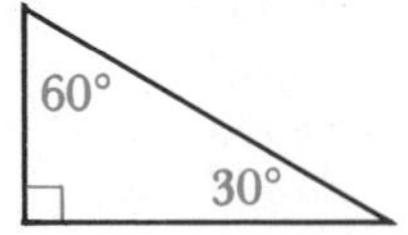

The two triangles at the left have properties that are sometimes quite useful.

Isosceles Right Triangle Theorem

In an isosceles right triangle, the length of the hypotenuse is $\sqrt{2}$ times the length of either leg.

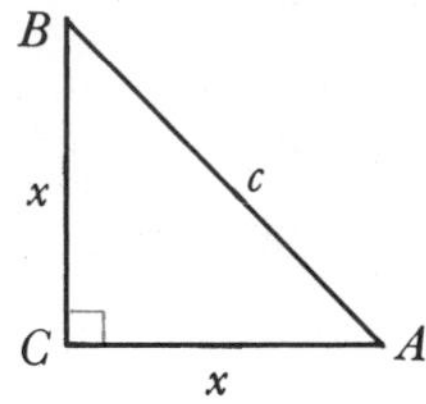

Given: Isosceles right $\triangle ABC$ with $m\angle C = 90$, $BC = AC = x$, $BA = c$

Prove: $c = x\sqrt{2}$

Proof: By the Pythagorean Theorem, $c^2 = x^2 + x^2$. So $c^2 = 2x^2$. Then $c = \sqrt{2}x$ or $c = x\sqrt{2}$. (We can ignore the negative root since the side of a triangle must have a positive length.)

30-60-90° Triangle Theorem

In a 30-60-90° triangle, the length of the side opposite the 30° angle is half the length of the hypotenuse. The length of the side opposite the 60° angle is $\sqrt{3}$ times the length of the side opposite the 30° angle.

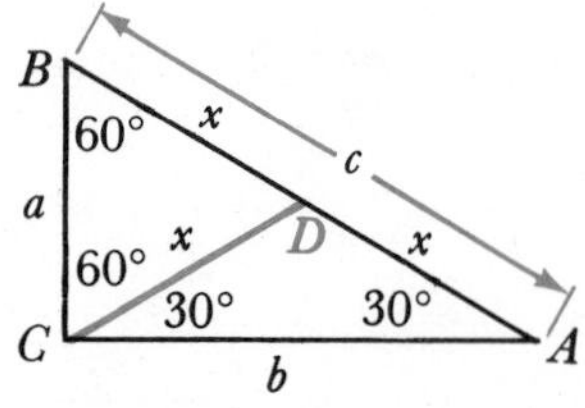

Given: Right $\triangle ABC$ with $m\angle A = 30$, $m\angle B = 60$, $m\angle C = 90$. $AB = c$, $BC = a$, $CA = b$

Prove: $a = \frac{1}{2}c$ and $b = a\sqrt{3}$

Proof: From C, draw $\overline{CD}$ so that $m\angle BCD = 60$. Let $CD = x$. By the Isosceles Triangle Theorem, $BD = x$.

Since $m\angle BCA = 90$ and $m\angle BCD = 60$, it follows that $m\angle ACD = 30$. Therefore, $\angle DCA \cong \angle CAD$, and $\triangle DCA$ is isosceles. Since $CD = x$, then $DA = x$.

$$\text{So } c = x + x = 2x \text{ or } \tfrac{1}{2}c = x.$$

Now in $\triangle BCD$, $m\angle BCD = m\angle CBD = 60$. Then $m\angle BDC = 60$. So $\triangle BCD$ is equilateral, and $a = x$. Since $\frac{1}{2}c = x$, then $\frac{1}{2}c = a$ or $a = \frac{1}{2}c$.

By the Pythagorean Theorem, ▶ $c^2 = a^2 + b^2$

Since $a = \frac{1}{2}c$, ▶

$$c^2 = (\tfrac{1}{2}c)^2 + b^2$$

$$c^2 = \tfrac{1}{4}c^2 + b^2$$

$$\tfrac{3}{4}c^2 = b^2$$

$$\frac{\sqrt{3}}{2}c = b$$

Substituting $2a$ for c, ▶ $\sqrt{3}a = b$ or $b = a\sqrt{3}$

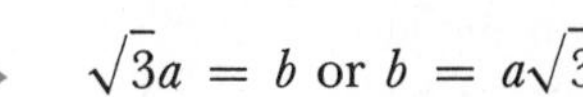

Examples: Find the missing length(s) in each triangle.

1.

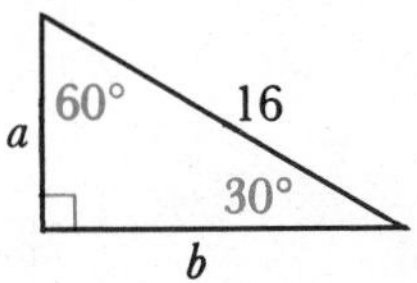

By the 30-60-90° Triangle Theorem, $a = \frac{1}{2} \cdot 16 = 8$ and $b = 8\sqrt{3}$.

2.

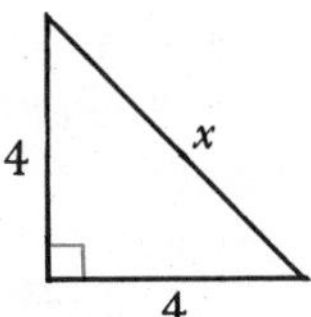

By the Isosceles Right Triangle Theorem, $x = 4\sqrt{2}$.

Exercises 9.6

Ⓐ **1.** In an isosceles right triangle, the length of the hypotenuse equals the length of either leg multiplied by ______.

2. In a 30-60-90° triangle, the length of the side opposite the 30° angle is ______ the length of the hypotenuse.

3. In a 30-60-90° triangle, the length of the side opposite the 60° angle equals the length of the side opposite the 30° angle multiplied by ______.

4. In an isosceles right triangle, each acute angle has a measure of ______.

Ⓑ **5–12.** Given the length of a leg of an isosceles right triangle, find the length of the hypotenuse.

5. 7	**6.** 10	**7.** $\frac{1}{2}$	**8.** $\frac{1}{4}$
9. $\sqrt{2}$	**10.** $\sqrt{3}$	**11.** $3\sqrt{3}$	**12.** $5\sqrt{2}$

13–20. Given the length of the hypotenuse of a 30-60-90° triangle, find the length of (**a**) the side opposite the 30° angle and (**b**) the side opposite the 60° angle.

13. 14 **14.** 20 **15.** 1 **16.** 3

17. $\frac{1}{2}$ **18.** $\frac{1}{3}$ **19.** $\sqrt{2}$ **20.** $\sqrt{3}$

21–24. Given the length of the hypotenuse of an isosceles right triangle, find the length of a leg.

21. 10 **22.** 12 **23.** $4\sqrt{2}$ **24.** $\sqrt{10}$

25–28. Given the length of the side opposite the 30° angle in a 30-60-90° triangle, find the length of (**a**) the side opposite the 60° angle and (**b**) the hypotenuse.

25. 6 **26.** 18 **27.** $\sqrt{3}$ **28.** $8\sqrt{3}$

29–32. Find the missing length(s) in each triangle.

29.

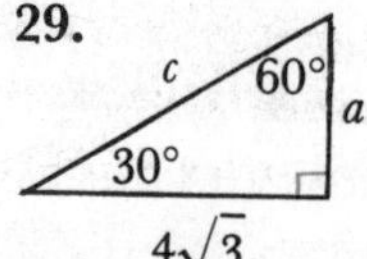

30.

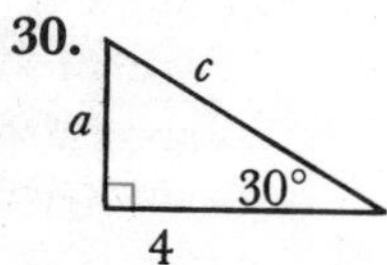

31.

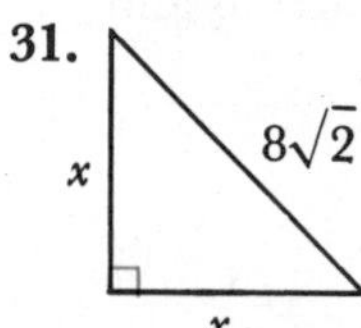

32.

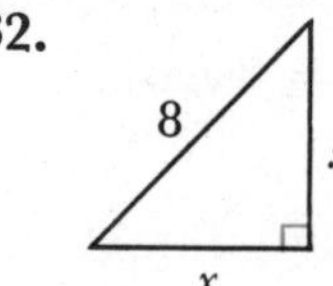

33–36. Find the length of the altitude in each triangle.

33.

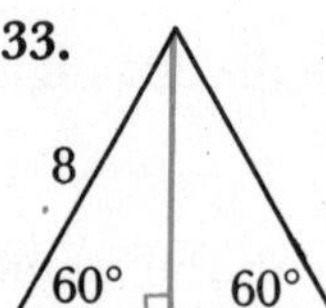

34.

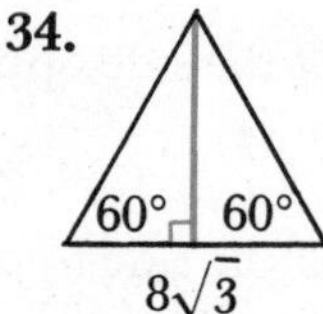

35.

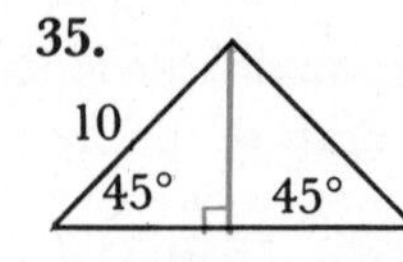

36.

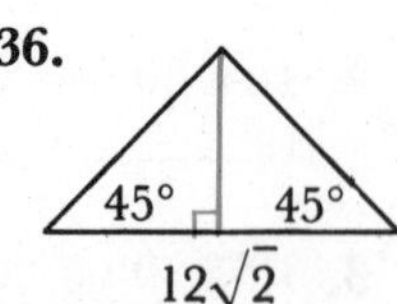

37–40. Find each answer to the nearest tenth. $\sqrt{2} \approx 1.414$, $\sqrt{3} \approx 1.732$

Ex. 37

28 cm

28 cm

Ex. 38

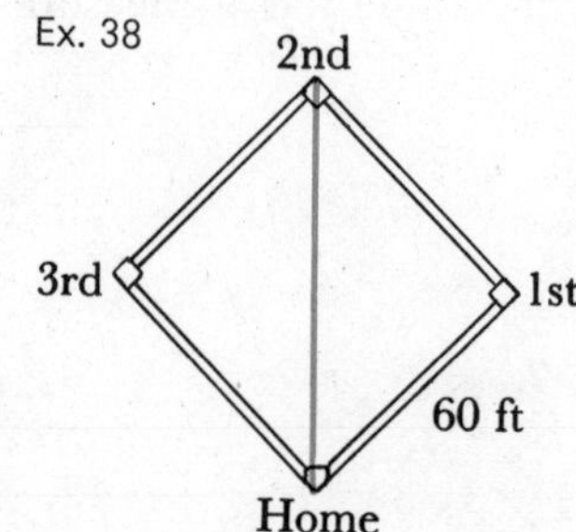

37. A brace is made for a bookshelf as shown in the figure. How long must the brace be?

38. A softball diamond (square) is 60 feet on a side. If the ball is thrown from home plate to second base, how far must it be thrown?

39. A ramp is inclined so that it makes a 60° angle with the ground. How long must the ramp be so that it reaches a point that is 42 cm above the ground?

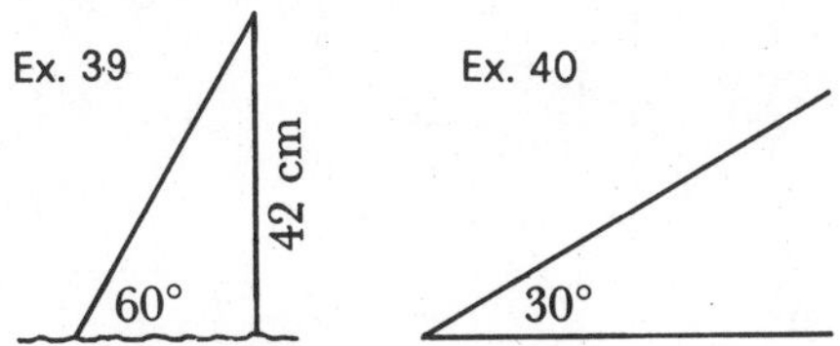

40. At the General Motors Proving Ground in Milford, Michigan, there is a hill with a 30° incline (see figure) for testing tracked vehicles like bulldozers. On this hill, for every meter that a vehicle moves horizontally, how much would it move vertically?

Courtesy Caterpillar Tractor Co.

construction: a 30-60-90° triangle

1. Pick a unit length AB and construct a perpendicular at one endpoint of $\overline{AB}$.

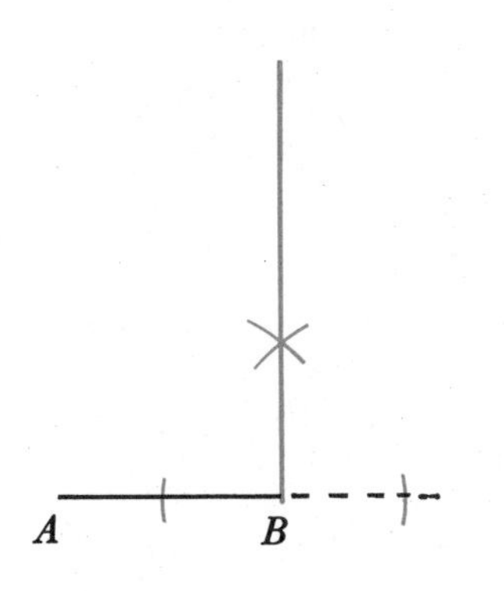

2. Extend $\overline{AB}$ and construct $\overline{BC}$ so that $\overline{AB} \cong \overline{BC}$.

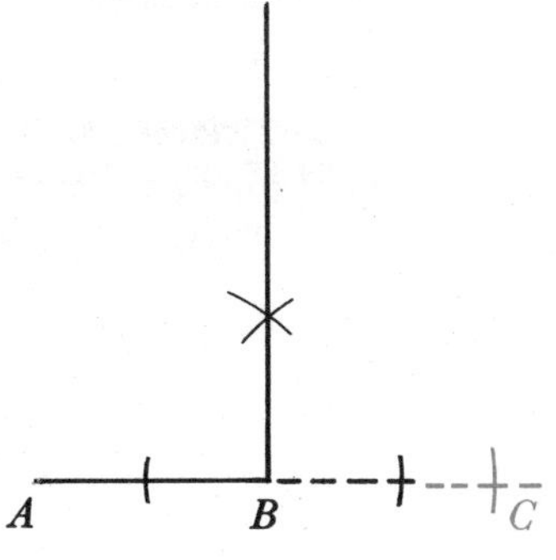

3. With A as center and radius AC, construct an arc intersecting the perpendicular at D. $\triangle DAB$ is a 30-60-90° triangle.

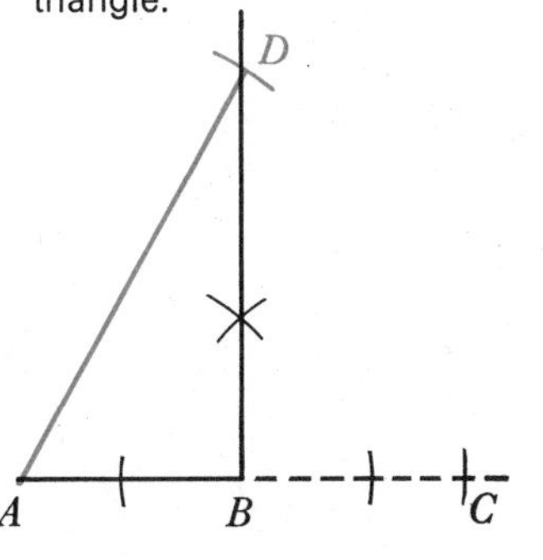

© 41. Construct a 15° angle. HINT: Construct a 30-60-90° triangle and then bisect one of the angles.

42. Construct a 75° angle. HINT: Use the construction in Exercise 41.

43. Construct a 105° angle.

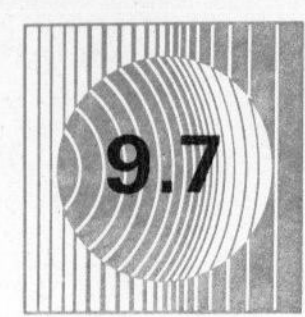

9.7 Transformations: Size Changes

In Chapter 10, we discuss figures with the same shape but different sizes. The material in this section will be useful at that time.

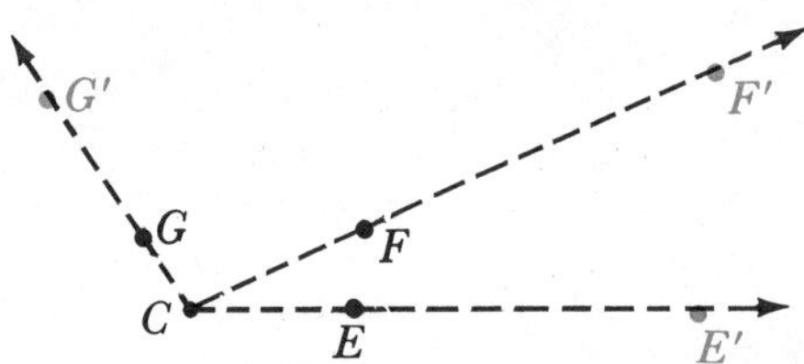

Look at the figure shown at the left. Rays are drawn from point C through E, F, and G. Then points E', F', and G' are marked off so that each one is 3 times as far from C as E, F, and G are.

We say E', F', and G' are the images of E, F, and G under a *size change* with magnitude 3 and center C. In general,

Let C be a point and let k be a *positive* real number. For any point A, let A' be the point on $\overrightarrow{CA}$ whose distance from C is k times the distance from C to A. That is, $A'C = k \cdot AC$. This transformation is called a **size change** with magnitude k and center C.

Example 1:

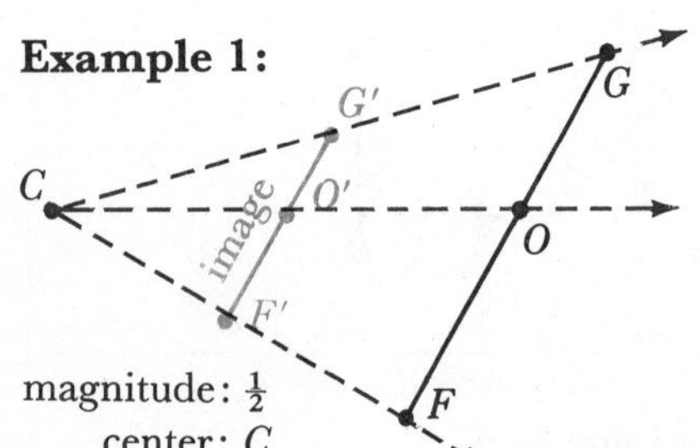

magnitude: $\frac{1}{2}$
center: C

Example 2:

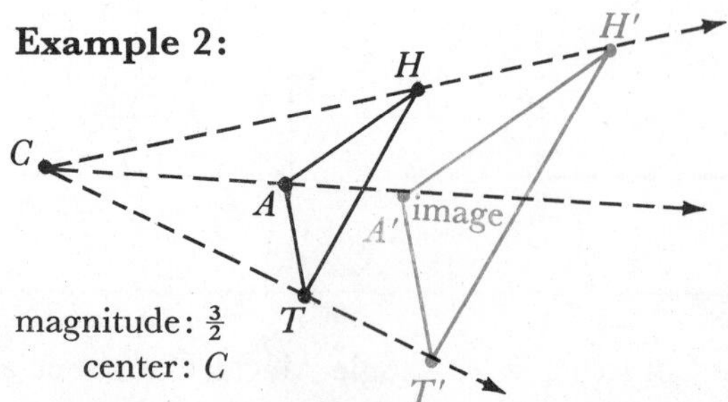

magnitude: $\frac{3}{2}$
center: C

Notice that when $k < 1$, the size change is a *contraction*. The image points are closer to the center than the original points are. When $k > 1$, the size change is an *expansion*, and the image points are farther from the center than the original points are.

The preceding examples show that some properties remain the same under a size change. For instance, in Example 1, G, O, and F are collinear, and their images under the size change are collinear. Also O is between G and F, and O' is between G' and F' under the size change.

In Example 2, $\angle H$ and $\angle H'$ have the same measure. So do $\angle A$ and $\angle A'$, as well as $\angle T$ and $\angle T'$.

Consequently, the following should seem reasonable:

Each size change preserves

a. collinearity, **b.** betweenness, and **c.** angle measure.

Exercises 9.7

Ⓐ **1.** In a size change of magnitude 2, the distance from each image point to the center is _____ the distance from each original point to the center.

2. P' is the image of P under a size change of magnitude $\frac{1}{4}$, center A. If $AP = 4$, then $AP' =$ _____.

3. E' is the image of E under a size change of magnitude 4, center A. If $AE' = 8$, then $AE =$ _____.

4. Which of the following properties are *not* preserved under a size change?

a. collinearity **b.** distance **c.** angle measure

5. In a contraction, which point is farther from the center, the image or the original point?

6. A size change with magnitude greater than 1 is called a(n) _____.

Ⓑ **7–10.** *C* is the center of a size change. A point and its image (in orange) are given. Find the magnitude.

7.

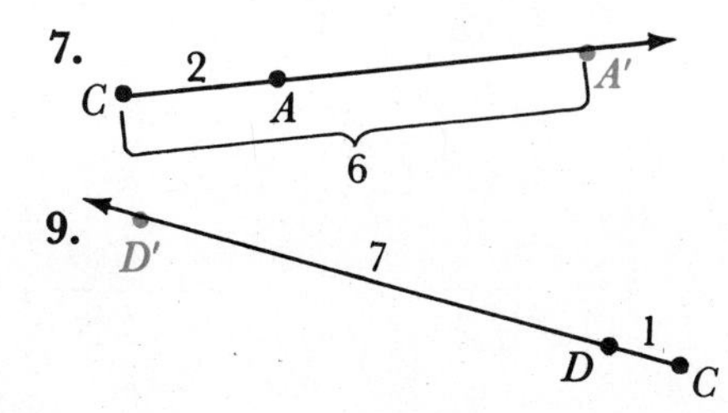

8.

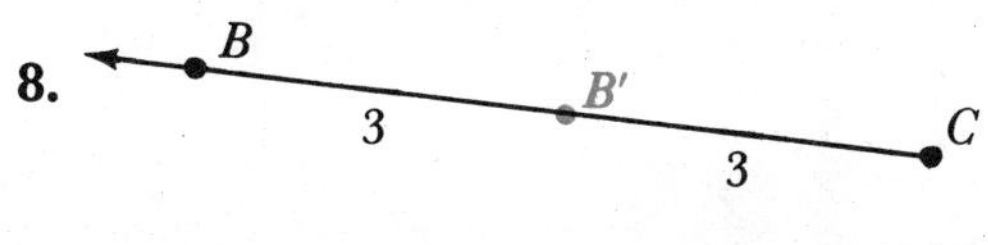

10.

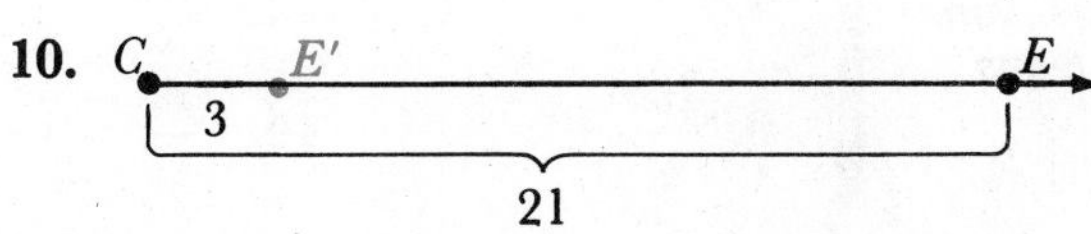

11–14. For each exercise, copy the given figure. Draw the image of each point under a size change with center C and the given magnitude.

11. 2

12. $\frac{1}{2}$

13. $\frac{1}{4}$

14. $\frac{3}{2}$

•B

•A

•C

D•

15–18. For each exercise, copy the given figure. Draw the image under a size change with center C and the given magnitude.

15. 2 **16.** $\frac{1}{2}$ **17.** $\frac{1}{2}$ **18.** 2

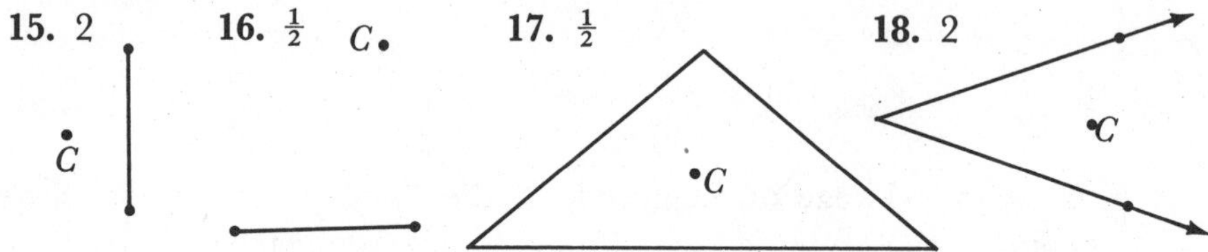

19–22. The points A through P are equally spaced on the ray shown. Consider a size change with center A. What is the image of G when the transformation has the given magnitude?

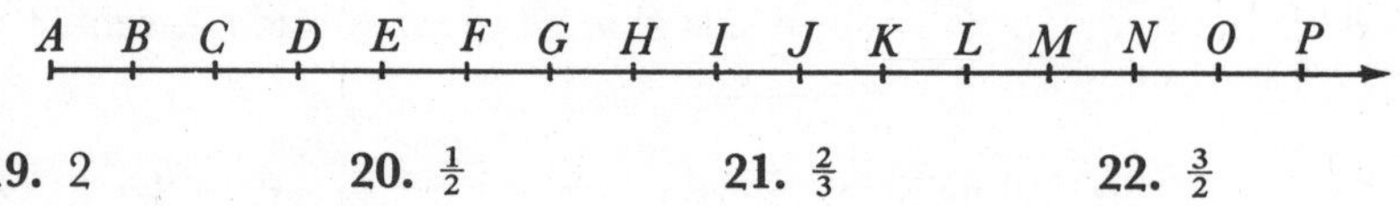

19. 2 **20.** $\frac{1}{2}$ **21.** $\frac{2}{3}$ **22.** $\frac{3}{2}$

© **23.** What happens in a size change when $k = 1$? In particular, what are the images of A, B, C, and D under a size change with center Q, magnitude 1?

B• •D

•C

A• •Q

Algebra Review

Review this skill:

- *reducing fractions to lowest terms*

Reduce each fraction to lowest terms.

1. $\frac{2}{4}$ **2.** $\frac{5}{25}$ **3.** $\frac{10}{100}$ **4.** $\frac{36}{81}$

5. $\frac{12}{48}$ **6.** $\frac{19}{76}$ **7.** $\frac{3x}{3y}$ **8.** $\frac{4a}{5a}$

9. $\frac{16x^2}{24x}$ **10.** $\frac{5y^3}{15y}$ **11.** $\frac{7xy}{49x^4y}$ **12.** $\frac{10a^2b^2}{25a^5b}$

■ Chapter 9 Review ■

1–4. Find the area of each rectangle or square. (ℓ stands for length, w for width, and s for length of a side of a square.) **9.1**

1. $\ell = 16$ cm, $w = 14$ cm **2.** $\ell = 3.5$ cm, $w = 20$ mm

3. $s = 1\frac{1}{2}$ **4.** $s = 5.6$

5. A rectangle has an area of 450 and a length of 25. Find the width.

6–8. Find the area of each triangle. **9.2**

6.

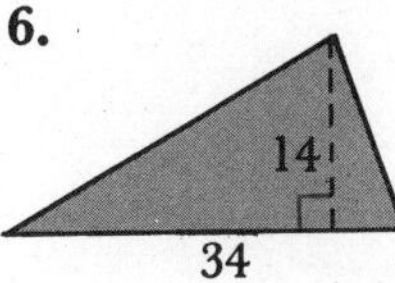

7.

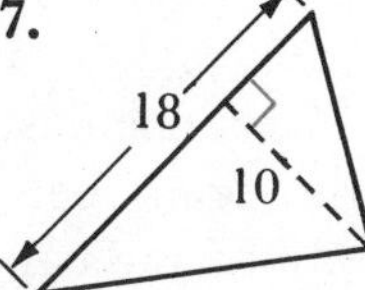

8.

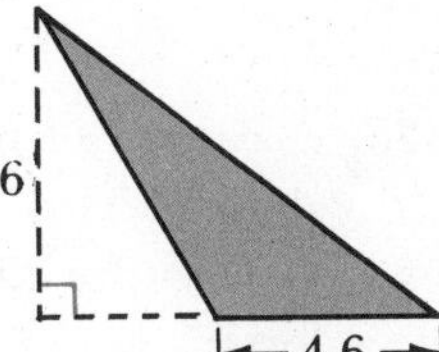

9–10. Find the area of each parallelogram.

9. $b = 6.3$, $h = 1.9$ **10.** $b = 3\frac{1}{4}$, $h = 7$

11–13. Find the area of each trapezoid. **9.3**

11.

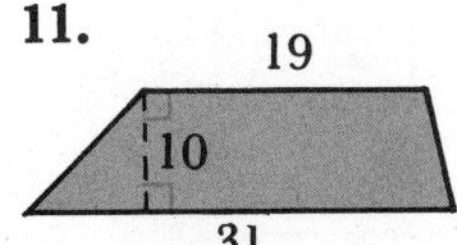

12.

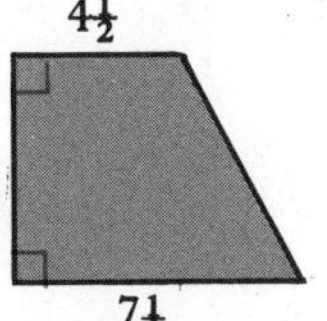

13.

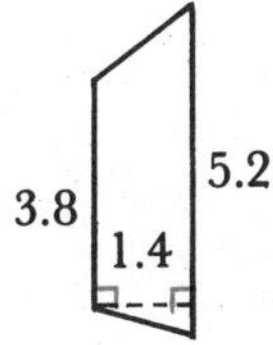

14–16. Find the area of each rhombus.

14.

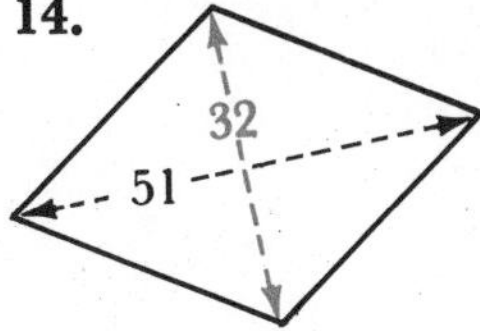

15.

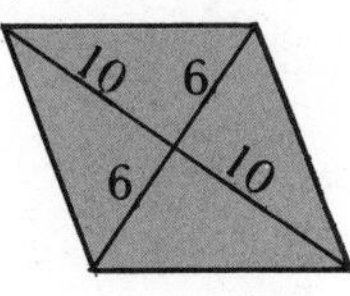

16.

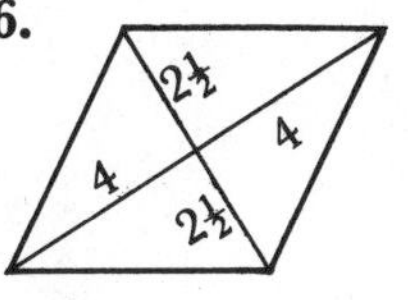

17–20. Simplify each radical. **9.4**

17. $\sqrt{27}$ **18.** $\sqrt{\frac{5}{36}}$ **19.** $\sqrt{\frac{1}{3}}$ **20.** $\frac{2}{\sqrt{3}}$

21–22. Use the table on page 562 to find each square root to the nearest tenth. You will first have to simplify each radical.

21. $\sqrt{300}$ **22.** $\sqrt{250}$

9.5 **23–25.** Find the missing length in each right triangle.

23.

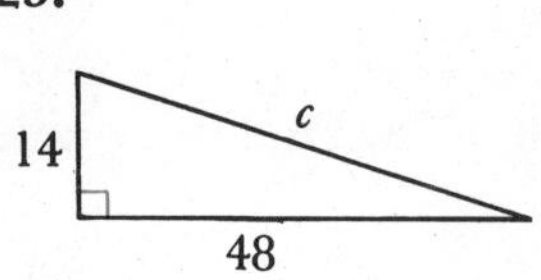

24.

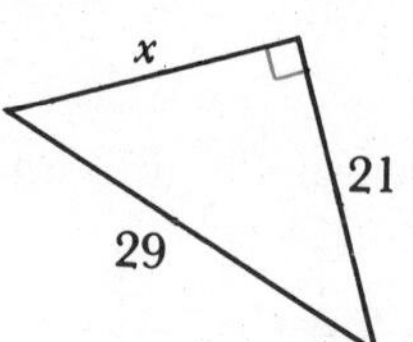

25.

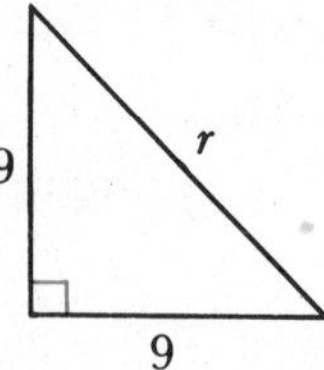

26. A carpenter makes a brace for a shelf as shown. How long must the brace be? (Leave the answer in simplified radical form.)

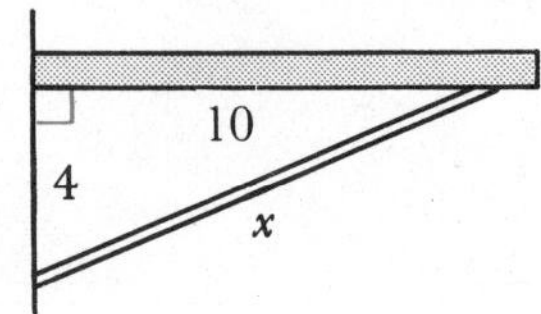

9.6 **27–29.** Find the missing lengths.

27.

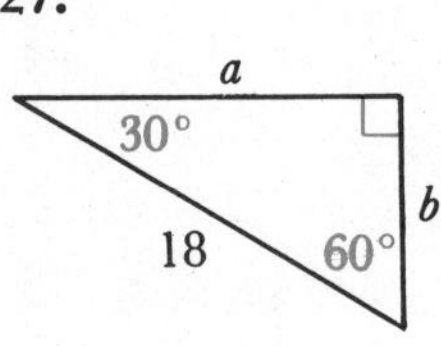

28.

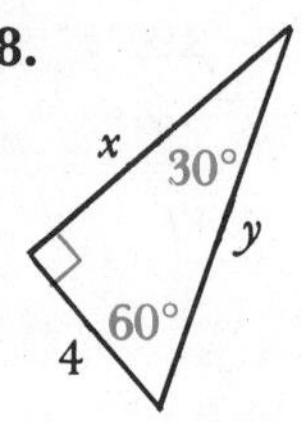

29.

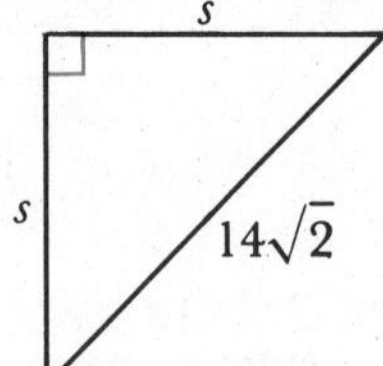

30. A square frame has a diagonal brace as shown. If the square is 30 centimeters on a side, how long is the brace?

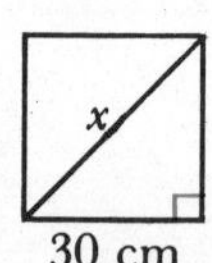

9.7 **31–32.** *C* is the center of a size change. A point and its image are given. Find the magnitude.

31.

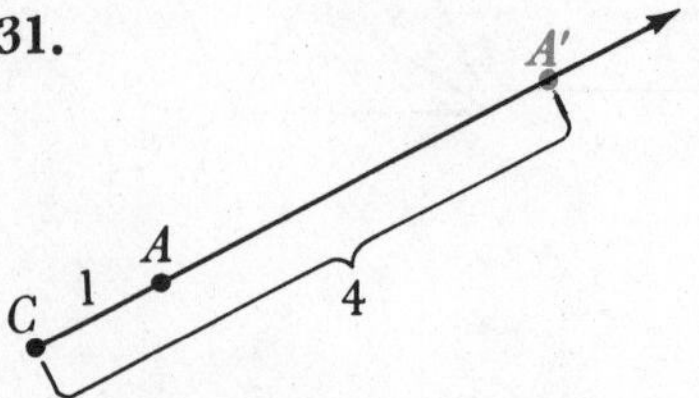

32.

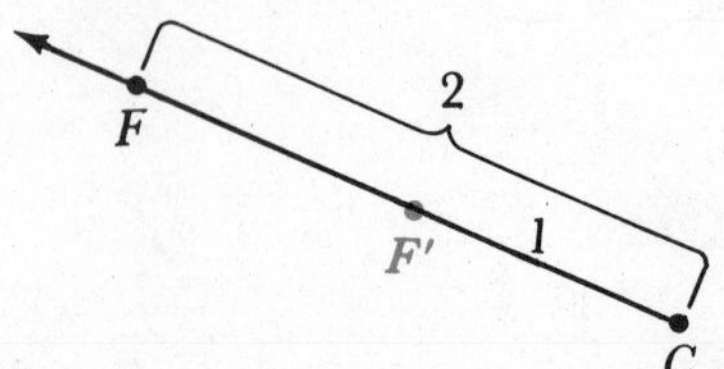

Chapter 9 Test

1. A rectangular lot has a length of 38 m and a width of 21 m. Find its area.

2. A square is 4.5 m on a side. What is its area?

3. A triangle has a base of $4\frac{1}{2}$, and its height is 10. What is its area?

4. A parallelogram has a base of 60, and its height is 73. What is its area?

5. A trapezoid has bases of 32 and 41. The height is 24. Find its area.

6. A rhombus has diagonals of $8\frac{1}{2}$ and 16. Find its area.

7–10. Simplify each radical.

7. $\sqrt{125}$ 8. $\sqrt{\frac{1}{8}}$ 9. $\sqrt{\frac{64}{81}}$ 10. $\frac{2}{\sqrt{5}}$

11–12. Use the Pythagorean Theorem to find the missing length in each right triangle.

11.

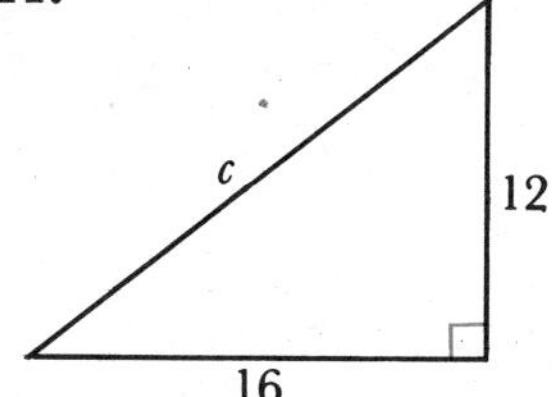

12.

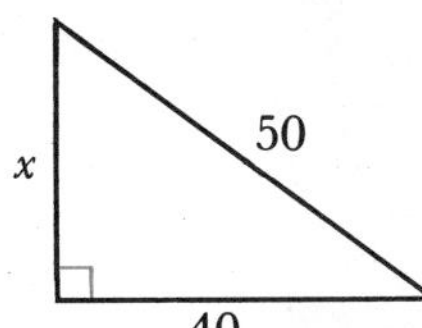

13. Can the lengths of the sides of a right triangle be 27, 36, and 45? Give a reason.

14–15. Find the missing lengths.

14.

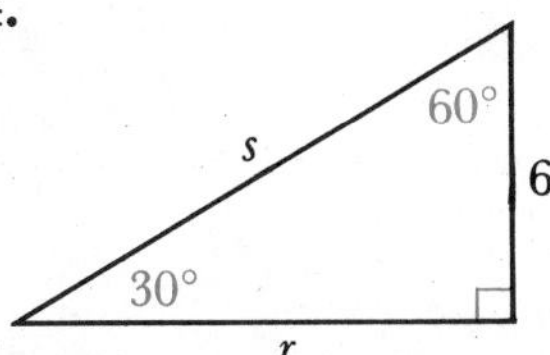

15.

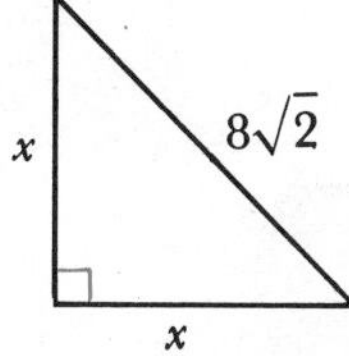

16. C is the center of a size change. A point and its image are given. Find the magnitude.

10

E' E 2 C

MINI-CHAPTER: RUBBER-SHEET GEOMETRY

If the picture of a fish at the left were drawn on a rubber sheet, some interesting results would occur if you could stretch, shrink, and distort the sheet (without tearing it).

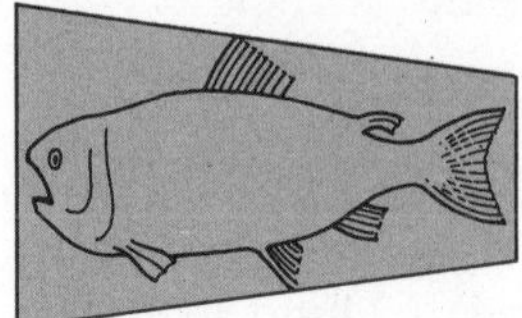

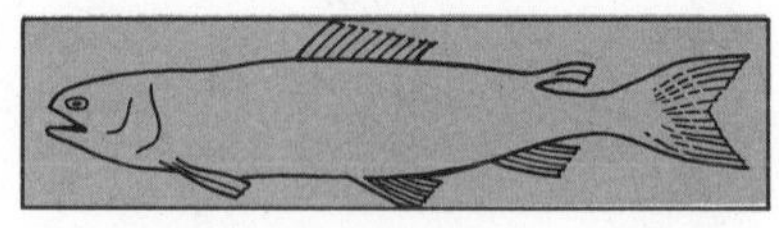

Even though the creatures above are different in many ways, they are still fish.

A whole branch of mathematics called *topology* deals with the ways that surfaces can be twisted, bent, pulled, stretched, or otherwise deformed from one shape into another. A topologist is interested in the properties that remain unchanged after all these transformations have taken place.

Photo Research International

When you look at a doughnut and a coffee cup, you probably don't see that they have anything in common. Yet to a topologist, they are equivalent. One could be transformed into the other by twisting, bending, and shaping. But in either case, there is one hole. A topologist would say that both have *genus one*. Notice how some objects that look very different can have the same genus.

GENUS 0 (no holes) GENUS 1 GENUS 2

Which objects have genus 0? Genus 1? Genus 2? Genus 3 or more?

EXPERIMENT 1

At a party you may have played a game where you were tied to another person by two cords or ropes as shown in the photograph. The object was to get loose from your partner without untying or cutting the cords. Try it! HINT: Loop your cord under the wrist loop of your partner. Then pull your cord over the hand of your partner.

Frank Kuechmann

EXPERIMENT 2

A German mathematician named Augustus Moebius discovered an interesting object that has only one surface. It is called a Moebius strip in his honor. To make one, take an ordinary strip of paper. First give the strip a half twist and then connect the ends to form a closed ring.

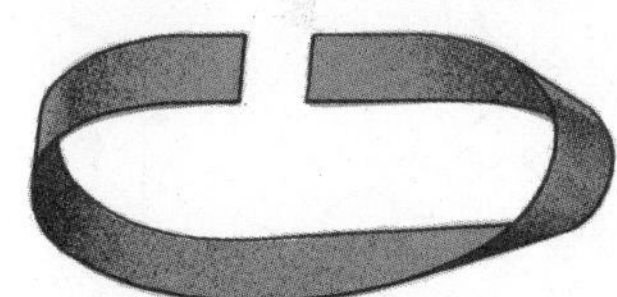

An ordinary sheet of paper has two surfaces. You could color one side red and the other side green. Use colored pencils and try to color a Moebius strip that way. What happens?

fig. 1

An interesting thing happens if you try to "halve" a Moebius strip. Try it. See figure 1.

fig. 2

Next make another Moebius strip and make the cut one third of the way in from the edge. See figure 2. What happens this time?

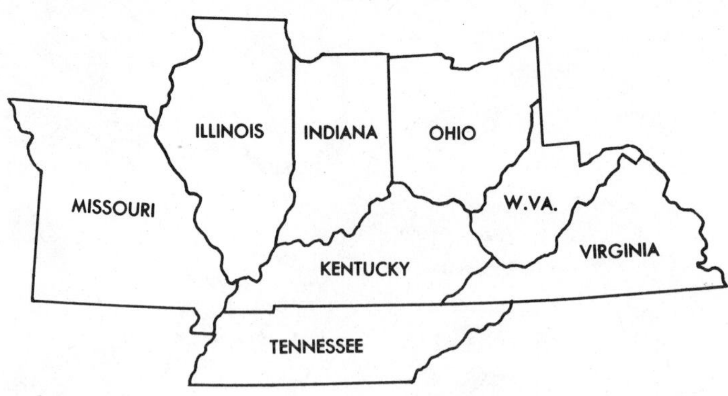

EXPERIMENT 3

Copy the map shown at the left and color it so that no two bordering states have the same color. Use a minimum of colors.

If you use more than four colors, something is wrong. Mapmakers have known for years that only four colors are needed for a flat map.

Yet mathematicians always want to prove things. So for years they looked for a proof of this fact. The four-color map theorem was one of the great unsolved problems in mathematics till just recently. Finally in 1976, a group of mathematicians at the University of Illinois proved that four colors are enough to color any flat map. However, they had to use computers in order to prove it.

Jordan Curves and Mazes

Would you guess that figures 1 and 2 below have something in common? One is a simple circle. The other is a circle that has been bent out of shape but is still a plane figure that does not intersect itself. We call such a figure a Jordan curve. Like a circle, it has an inside and and an outside. To get from the inside to the outside, the figure must be crossed at least once.

fig. 1

A is inside the circle.

B is actually outside the curve.

fig. 2

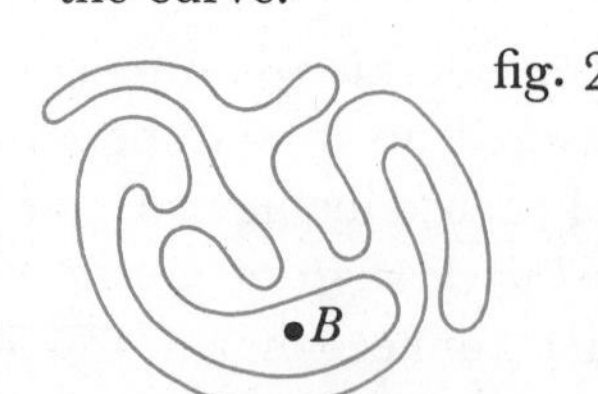

A quick way to tell if a point is inside or outside a Jordan curve is to connect it by a straight line to the outside. If the line crosses the curve an even number of times, the point is outside the curve. If the line crosses the curve an odd number of times, the point is inside the curve.

The figure at the left is a Jordan curve. Decide if points *A* and *B* are inside or outside the curve.

A maze is another kind of figure that looks like a Jordan curve. However, it is very different because it has an entrance or exit. So a maze can be said to have no inside. All the paths in a maze connect to the outside without crossing any boundaries.

Mazes made of shrubbery were once very popular in Europe. The one shown at the right is in Williamsburg, Virginia. It is a reproduction of the most famous garden maze, at Hampton Court, England.

Colonial Williamsburg Foundation

The maze shown below is a diagram of the Hampton Court maze. The goal is to get to the open area in the center. To get to the center, use this rule: Place either hand on any wall and then take no paths that require you to lift your hand from the wall.

Courtesy Kraft Systems

10 SIMILAR POLYGONS

You are familiar with objects that have the *same shape* but not the same size—enlargements or reductions of photos, scale models of airplanes or buildings, and so on.

In geometry, figures that are exactly the same shape—whether or not they are the same size—are called **similar figures.**

- Some polygons are similar.
- Some triangles are similar.
- All squares are similar.
- All equilateral triangles are similar.

Ratios are used to compare sizes of similar figures.

Ratio and Proportion

Suppose your school team won 8 out of 10 meets and lost 2. You might describe their record by using any of these *ratios:*

meets won to total meets: 8 to 10 or $\frac{8}{10}$ or 8:10

meets lost to total meets: 2 to 10 or $\frac{2}{10}$ or 2:10

meets won to meets lost: 8 to 2 or $\frac{8}{2}$ or 8:2

Photri

A **ratio** is a comparison of numbers by division. A ratio can be written in any of the ways above, but we will usually use a fraction. Equivalent fractions express **equivalent ratios.**

Example 1: a. $\frac{8}{10} = \frac{4}{5}$ **b.** $\frac{8}{2} = \frac{4}{1}$ **c.** $\frac{2}{3} = \frac{4}{6}$ **d.** $\frac{3}{4} = \frac{6}{8} = \frac{9}{12}$

When a ratio is expressed by a fraction that cannot be reduced, the fraction and the ratio are in *lowest terms.*

A true statement that ratios are equal is a **proportion.** (The equations in the example above are proportions.) Here are some expressions used in talking about proportions. Assume $b \neq 0$ and $d \neq 0$.

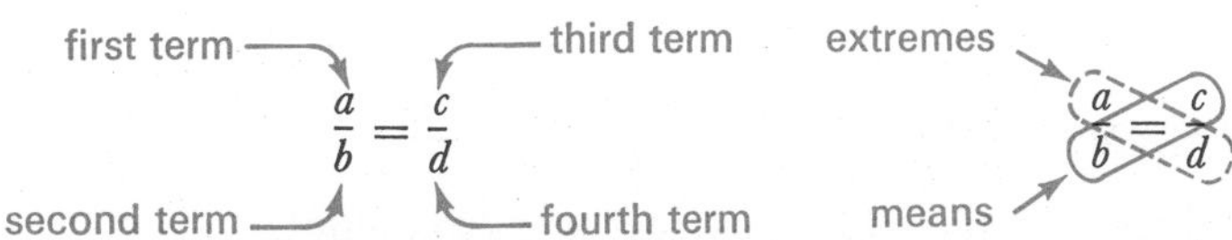

The multiplication and division properties of = can be used to show that, if no term is zero, the five equations below are equivalent.

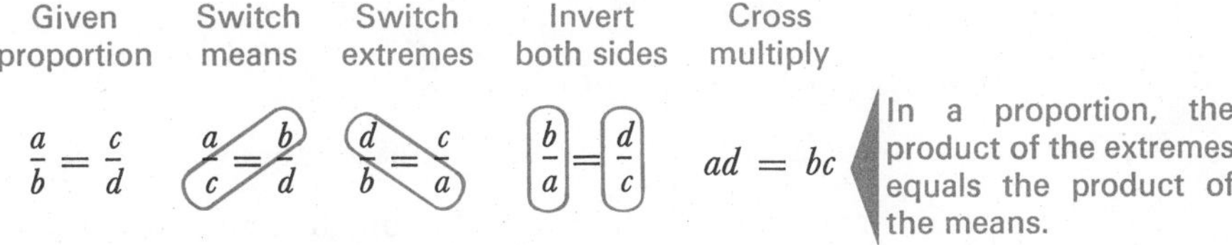

In a proportion, the product of the extremes equals the product of the means.

Example 2:

Given proportion	Switch means	Switch extremes	Invert both sides	Cross multiply
$\frac{2}{5} = \frac{4}{10}$	$\frac{2}{4} = \frac{5}{10}$	$\frac{10}{5} = \frac{4}{2}$	$\frac{5}{2} = \frac{10}{4}$	$2 \cdot 10 = 5 \cdot 4$

If one term of a proportion contains a variable, solving for the variable is called *solving the proportion.*

Example 3: Solve.

a. $\frac{x}{3} = \frac{4}{5}$	**b.** $\frac{y}{5} = \frac{12}{15}$
$x = \frac{12}{5}$ Multiply both sides by 3.	$\frac{y}{5} = \frac{4}{5}$ Reduce $\frac{12}{15}$.
	$y = 4$ Multiply both sides by 5.
c. $\frac{2}{n} = \frac{3}{8}$	**d.** $\frac{3m}{4} = \frac{5}{2}$
$16 = 3n$ Cross multiply.	$3m = 10$ Multiply both sides by 4.
$\frac{16}{3} = n$ Divide both sides by 3.	$m = \frac{10}{3}$ Divide both sides by 3.

The properties of equality also let us use any two equations to set up a proportion. Assume $c \neq 0$ and $d \neq 0$.

If $a = b$ and $c = d$, ▶ then $\frac{a}{c} = \frac{b}{d}$.

Example 4: If $x = 2$ and $y = 3$, ▶ then $\frac{x}{y} = \frac{2}{3}$.

Exercises 10.1

Ⓐ **1.** A ratio compares two numbers by ______.

2. Equivalent ratios are expressed by equivalent ______.

3. A ratio in lowest terms is expressed by a ______ in lowest terms.

4–10. Let $\frac{m}{n} = \frac{5}{3}$.

4. This equation is an example of a ______.

5. The means are ______.

6. The extremes are ______.

7. The second term is ______.

8. The fourth term is ______.

9. $\frac{3}{n} =$ ______

10. $5n =$ ______

11. If $\frac{r}{5} = \frac{4}{10}$, then $r =$ ______.

12. If $s = 3$ and $4 = t$, then $\frac{s}{4} =$ ______.

Ⓑ **13–16.** Reduce each ratio to lowest terms.

13. $\frac{3}{12}$ **14.** $\frac{4}{24}$ **15.** $\frac{28}{50}$ **16.** $\frac{12}{60}$

17–20. Write four equivalent equations, as in Example 2.

17. $\frac{s}{t} = \frac{4}{5}$ **18.** $\frac{p}{r} = \frac{3}{7}$ **19.** $4g = 3h$ **20.** $7n = 6k$

21–26. Use the given equations to find a ratio equivalent to $\frac{x}{y}$.

21. $x = 3, y = 7$ **22.** $x = 9, y = 5$ **23.** $x = 12, 5 = y$

24. $11 = x, y = 3$ **25.** $2x = 13, 2y = 15$ **26.** $3x = 4, 3y = 7$

27–38. Solve.

27. $\frac{n}{5} = \frac{3}{8}$ **28.** $\frac{r}{6} = \frac{2}{5}$ **29.** $\frac{s}{7} = \frac{3}{14}$ **30.** $\frac{t}{5} = \frac{7}{15}$

31. $\frac{4}{m} = \frac{5}{9}$ **32.** $\frac{5}{7} = \frac{3}{x}$ **33.** $\frac{c}{5} = \frac{24}{18}$ **34.** $\frac{d}{3} = \frac{15}{25}$

35. $\frac{3}{5} = \frac{18}{e}$ **36.** $\frac{24}{f} = \frac{4}{7}$ **37.** $\frac{2a}{5} = \frac{4}{7}$ **38.** $\frac{5b}{2} = \frac{6}{7}$

Ⓒ **39–46.** Let $\frac{a}{c} = \frac{b}{d}$. Show that each statement is true.

39. If $a = b$, then $c = d$. **40.** If $c = d$, then $a = b$.

41. If $a = c$, then $b = d$. **42.** If $b = c$, then $b^2 = ad$.

43. $\frac{5a}{c} = \frac{5b}{d}$ **44.** $\frac{3a}{3c} = \frac{b}{d}$

45. $\frac{a + c}{c} = \frac{b + d}{d}$ **46.** $\frac{a - c}{c} = \frac{b - d}{d}$

47–48. Show that the given proportion lets you conclude that $\frac{a}{c} = \frac{b}{d}$.

47. $\frac{a + c}{c} = \frac{b + d}{d}$ **48.** $\frac{a - c}{c} = \frac{b - d}{d}$

49–52. Write as a ratio in lowest terms. For example, $3\% = \frac{3}{100}$.

49. 23% **50.** 147% **51.** 2.5% **52.** 0.01%

RATIOS AROUND YOU

RATIOS IN ADS AND NEWS

Dogs prefer the taste of new improved Gravy Train® DOG FOOD 3 to 1.

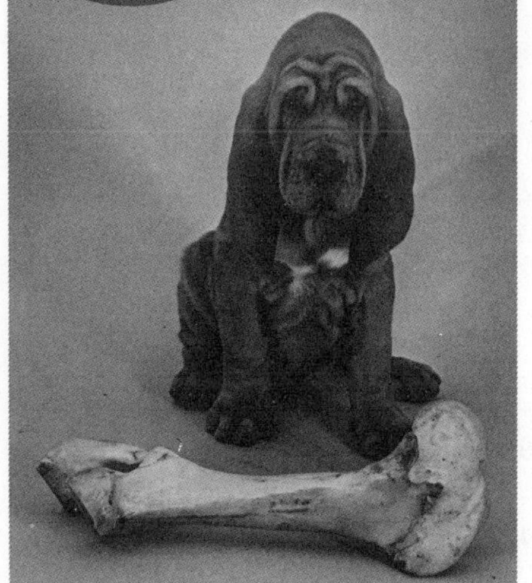
Photri

In tests, we gave dogs Gravy Train and new improved Gravy Train. And you know what happened? 3 out of 4 dogs preferred the new to the old. That's 3 to 1.

Reprinted courtesy General Foods Corp.

This advertisement compares a new product and an older product from the same company.

Which of the ratios below is $\frac{3}{4}$? Which is $\frac{3}{1}$?

a. dogs that preferred the new product to dogs that preferred the old product

b. dogs that preferred the new product to total dogs tested

c. total dogs tested to dogs that preferred the old product

If only 4 dogs were tested, how many preferred the new product? The old?

If 48 dogs were tested, how many preferred the new product? The old?

If 27 of the dogs tested preferred the new product, how many dogs were tested?

> AN INDUSTRY study shows three out of four buyers of 1977 model cars are equipping them with the larger, often optional V-8 engines. Only one out of five chooses a 6-cylinder engine and one out of 20 a 4-cylinder.

Reprinted courtesy Chicago Tribune

• • •

This newspaper item from early 1977 shows one reason why the world's supply of gasoline is rapidly being used up.

What is the ratio of **a.** V-8 buyers to all buyers?
b. 6-cylinder buyers to all buyers?
c. 4-cylinder buyers to all buyers?

Out of every 20 car buyers, how many buy each type of car?

What is the ratio of **a.** V-8 buyers to 6-cylinder buyers?
b. 4-cylinder buyers to V-8 buyers?

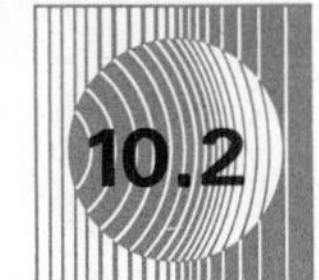

What Are Similar Polygons?

Suppose you draw a polygon, photograph it, and then have photo prints of two different sizes made. The photos should show polygons of exactly the same shape. This means that

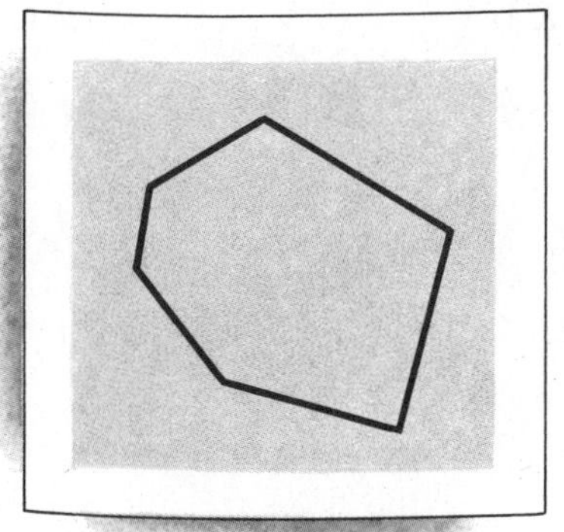

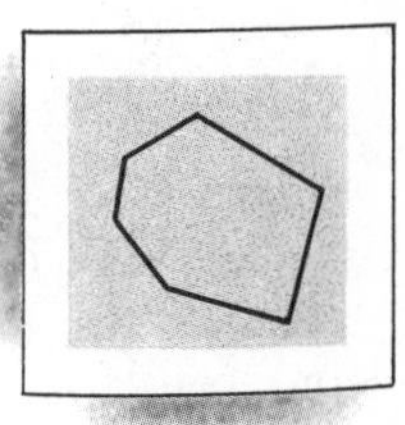

- Any angle of the polygon is the same size on both photos.
- If a side of the polygon on one photo is half as long as on the other photo, all sides compare the same way.

The polygons in the two photos are *similar*.

As in the case of *congruent* polygons, there is a one-to-one correspondence between the vertices of *similar* polygons. This leads to pairs of corresponding angles and pairs of corresponding sides.

is similar to

	$ABCDE \sim RSTUV$		
corresponding angles	$\angle A$ and $\angle R$	$\overline{AB}$ and $\overline{RS}$	corresponding sides
	$\angle B$ and $\angle S$	$\overline{BC}$ and $\overline{ST}$	
	$\angle C$ and $\angle T$	$\overline{CD}$ and $\overline{TU}$	
	$\angle D$ and $\angle U$	$\overline{DE}$ and $\overline{UV}$	
	$\angle E$ and $\angle V$	$\overline{EA}$ and $\overline{VR}$	

Similar polygons are polygons for which corresponding angles are congruent and the ratios of corresponding sides are equal. NOTE: *Ratio of sides* means "ratio of their lengths."

Example 1: $\triangle ABC \sim \triangle DEF$

Congruent angles	Equal ratios
$\angle A \cong \angle D$	$\frac{AB}{DE} = \frac{8}{6} = \frac{4}{3}$
$\angle B \cong \angle E$	$\frac{BC}{EF} = \frac{16}{12} = \frac{4}{3}$
$\angle C \cong \angle F$	$\frac{AC}{DF} = \frac{20}{15} = \frac{4}{3}$

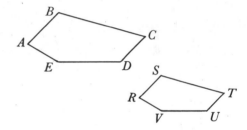

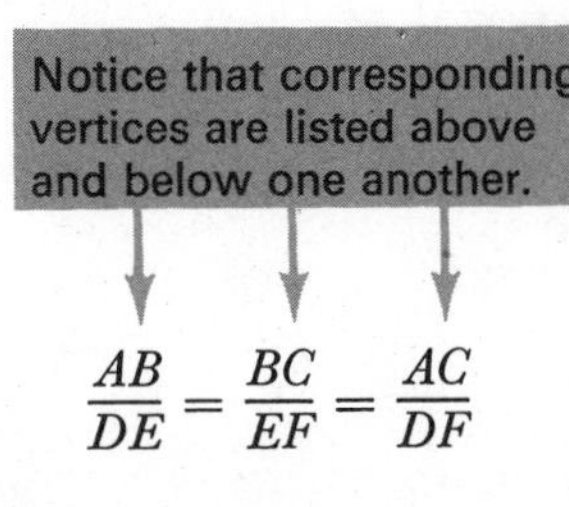

Notice that corresponding vertices are listed above and below one another.
$\frac{AB}{DE} = \frac{BC}{EF} = \frac{AC}{DF}$

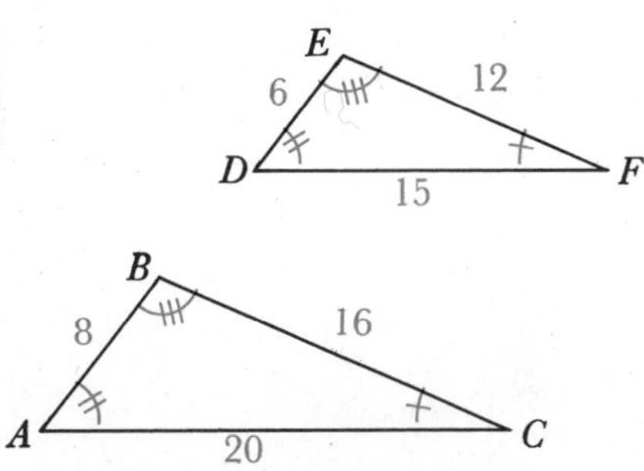

Example 2:

$PQRS \sim JKMN$

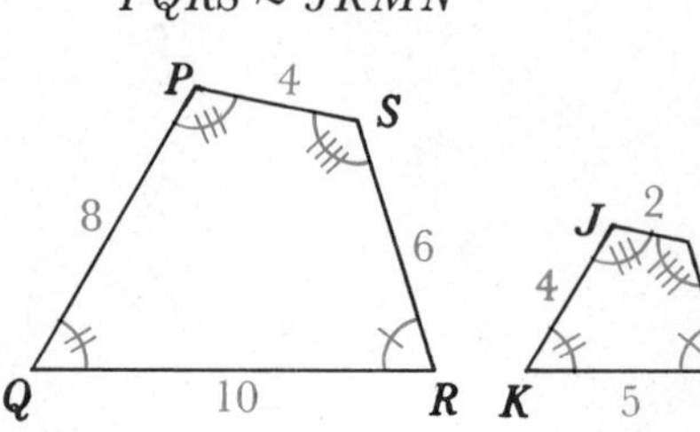

Congruent angles	Equal ratios
$\angle J \cong \angle P$	$\frac{JK}{PQ} = \frac{4}{8} = \frac{1}{2}$
$\angle K \cong \angle Q$	$\frac{KM}{QR} = \frac{5}{10} = \frac{1}{2}$
$\angle M \cong \angle R$	$\frac{MN}{RS} = \frac{3}{6} = \frac{1}{2}$
$\angle N \cong \angle S$	$\frac{NJ}{SP} = \frac{2}{4} = \frac{1}{2}$

$$\frac{JK}{PQ} = \frac{KM}{QR} = \frac{MN}{RS} = \frac{NJ}{SP}$$

When the ratios of corresponding sides are equal, as above, we say the sides are **proportional.** The common ratio is called the **ratio of similarity**. In Examples 1 and 2, the ratio of similarity is

$\frac{4}{3}$ for $\triangle ABC \sim \triangle DEF$	$\frac{1}{2}$ for $JKMN \sim PQRS$
$\frac{3}{4}$ for $\triangle DEF \sim \triangle ABC$	$\frac{2}{1}$ for $PQRS \sim JKMN$

If two polygons are congruent, their corresponding angles are congruent. And since corresponding sides have the same length, they are proportional, with ratio of similarity $\frac{1}{1}$. Therefore,

Theorem  Congruent polygons are similar polygons. 

If two figures are similar and we know the measures of some of their parts, we may be able to find the measures of the other parts.

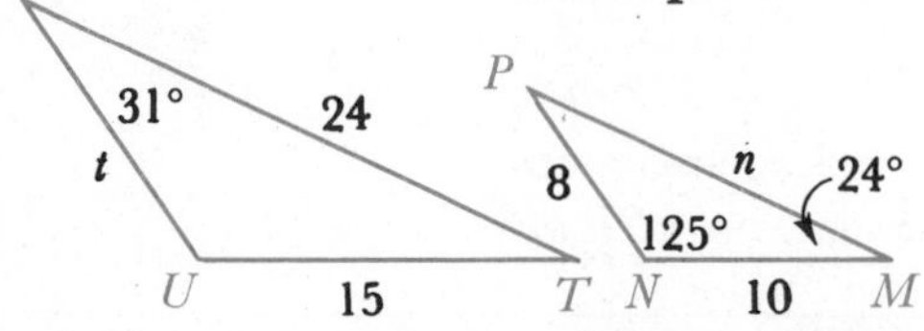

Example 3: If $\triangle MNP \sim \triangle TUV$, find the five missing measures.

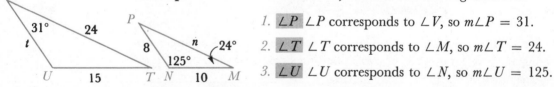

1. $\angle P$ $\angle P$ corresponds to $\angle V$, so $m\angle P = 31$.
2. $\angle T$ $\angle T$ corresponds to $\angle M$, so $m\angle T = 24$.
3. $\angle U$ $\angle U$ corresponds to $\angle N$, so $m\angle U = 125$.
4. MP Corresponding sides are proportional, so

$$\frac{MN}{TU} = \frac{MP}{TV}$$

Substitute $\frac{10}{15} = \frac{n}{24}$

Solve $240 = 15n$

$n = 16$

So $MP = 16$.

5. UV Use another proportion.

$$\frac{MN}{TU} = \frac{NP}{UV}$$

Substitute $\frac{10}{15} = \frac{8}{t}$

Solve $10t = 120$

$t = 12$

So $UV = 12$.

Exercises 10.2

Ⓐ **1–14.** Suppose $\triangle KMN \sim \triangle PDR$ and $\frac{KM}{PD} = \frac{1}{3}$.

Ex. 1–14

1. Name the corresponding sides.

2. Name the congruent angles.

3. What is the ratio of each side of $\triangle KMN$ to the corresponding side of $\triangle PDR$?

4. What is the ratio of each side of $\triangle PDR$ to the corresponding side of $\triangle KMN$?

5. Each side of $\triangle PDR$ is ______ times as long as the corresponding side of $\triangle KMN$.

6. Each side of $\triangle KMN$ is ______ times as long as the corresponding side of $\triangle PDR$.

7. If $KM = 2$, then $PD =$ ______.

8. If $MN = 5$, then $DR =$ ______.

9. If $PD = 12$, then $KM =$ ______.

10. If $PR = 6$, then $KN =$ ______.

11. If $KN = \frac{1}{3}$, $PR =$ ______.

12. If $DR = 1$, $MN =$ ______.

13. If $m\angle M = 43$, m______ $= 43$.

14. If $\overline{KN} \perp \overline{MN}$, ______ $\perp$ ______.

Ⓑ **15–26.** Refer to the figures.

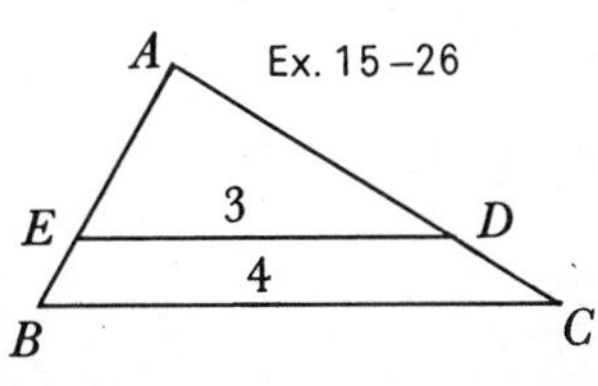

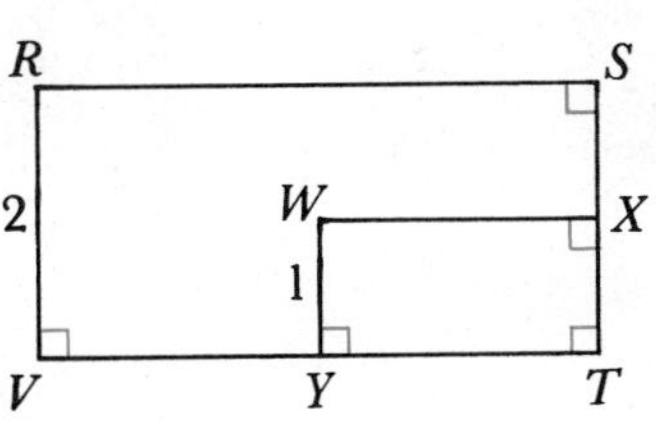

15. For $\triangle AED \sim \triangle ABC$, the ratio of similarity is ______.

16. For $\triangle ABC \sim \triangle AED$, the ratio of similarity is ______.

17. If $\triangle AED \sim \triangle ABC$, then $AD =$ ______ $\cdot AC$.

18. If $\frac{AE}{AB} = \frac{1}{2}$, then $\triangle AED$ (is, is not) similar to $\triangle ABC$.

19. For $RSTV \sim WXTY$, the ratio of similarity is ______.

20. For $WXTY \sim RSTV$, the ratio of similarity is ______.

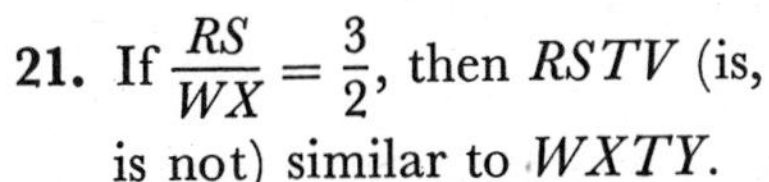

21. If $\frac{RS}{WX} = \frac{3}{2}$, then $RSTV$ (is, is not) similar to $WXTY$.

22. If $RSTV \sim WXTY$, then $WX =$ ______ $\cdot RS$.

23. If $RSTV \sim WXTY$, then $ST =$ ______ $\cdot XT$.

24. If $RSTV \sim WXTY$, then $VT =$ ______ $\cdot YT$.

25. If $WX = 3$ and $RS = 4$, then $RSTV$ (is, is not) similar to $WXTY$.

26. If $VT = 6$ and $YT = 3$, then $RSTV$ (is, is not) similar to $WXTY$.

27–30. Find all missing measures.

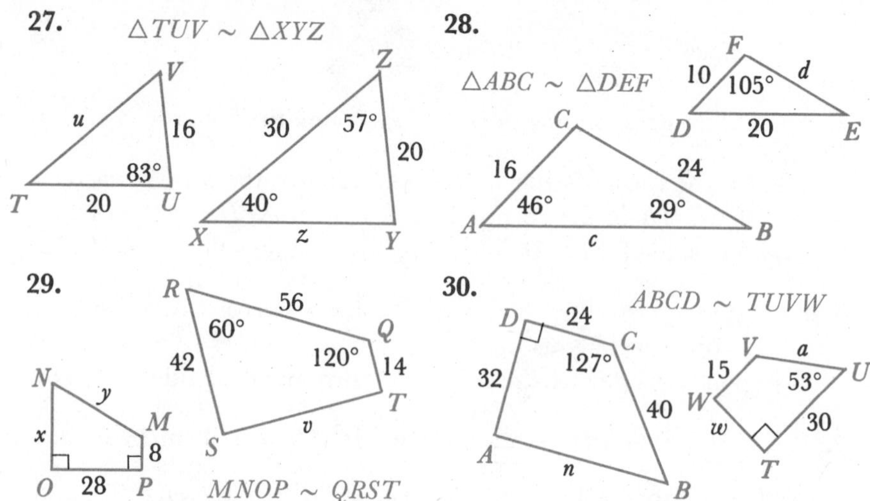

31. If a photographic negative 24 mm wide by 35 mm long is enlarged to make a picture 12 cm wide, how long will the picture be?

32. If a photographic negative 24 mm wide by 35 mm long is enlarged to make a picture 28 cm long, how wide will the picture be?

Courtesy Revell, Inc.

33–40. The ratio of a full-size car to its scale model is $\frac{25}{2}$. Complete the tables.

	Corresponding measures			Corresponding measures	
	on car	on model		on car	on model
33.	2.5 m		**34.**		20 cm
35.		18 cm	**36.**	0.45 m	
37.	90°		**38.**		90°
39.		45°	**40.**	$32\frac{1}{2}°$	

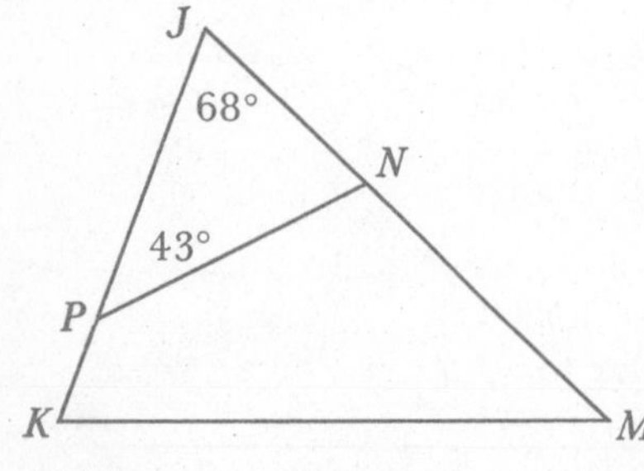

41–44. In the figure, $\triangle JPN \sim \triangle JMK$. HINT: Redraw the triangles so they don't overlap.

41. If $JP = 3$, $JM = 5$, and $JK = 4$, then $JN =$ ______.

42. If $PN = 3$, $MK = 5$, and $JN = 2$, then $JK =$ ______.

43. Find $m\angle M$.

44. Find $m\angle K$.

45. Given: $\angle A \cong \angle M$, $\overline{AB} \cong \overline{BC}$, $\overline{MN} \cong \overline{NP}$, $\dfrac{AB}{MN} = \dfrac{AC}{MP}$

Prove: $\triangle ABC \sim \triangle MNP$

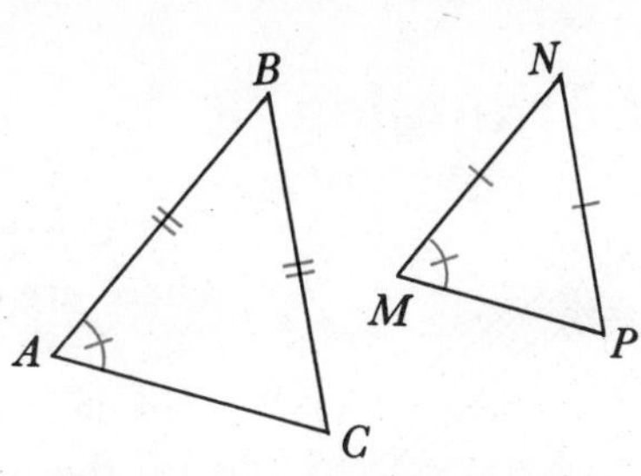

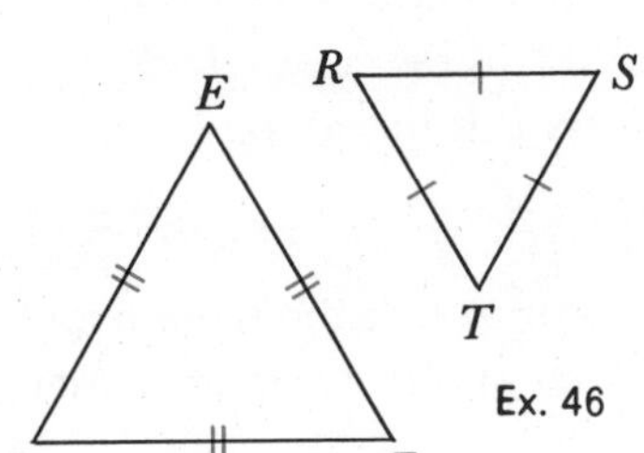

Ex. 46

46. Given: $\triangle DEF$ and $\triangle RST$ are equilateral.

Prove: $\triangle DEF \sim \triangle RST$

© **47.** Given: Rhombus $RSTV$, rhombus $YUWX$, $\angle R \cong \angle Y$

Prove: $RSTV \sim YUWX$

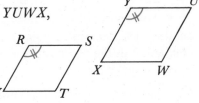

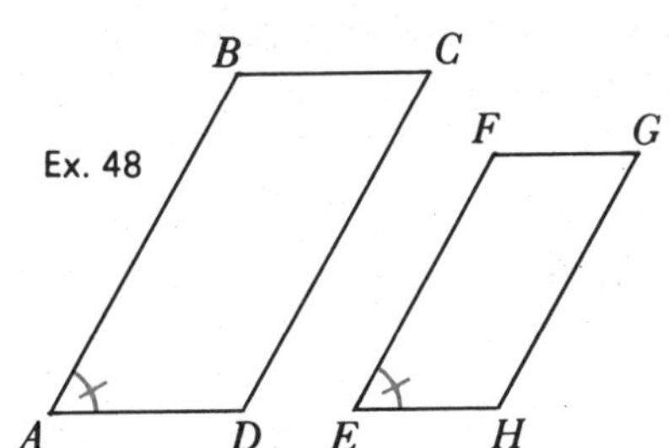

Ex. 48

48. Given: ▱$ABCD$, ▱$EFGH$, $\angle A \cong \angle E$, $\dfrac{AB}{EF} = \dfrac{BC}{FG}$

Prove: ▱$ABCD$ ~ ▱$EFGH$

49. Given: ▭$HIJK$, ▭$NOPQ$, $\dfrac{IJ}{OP} = \dfrac{KJ}{QP}$

Prove: ▭$HIJK$ ~ ▭$NOPQ$

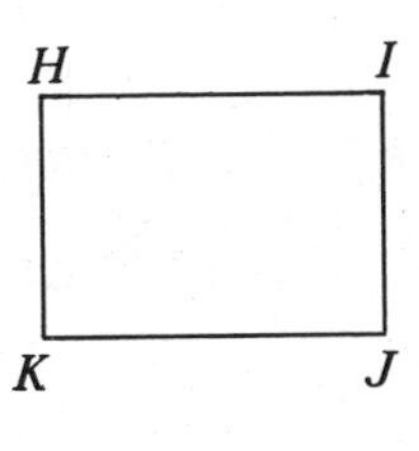

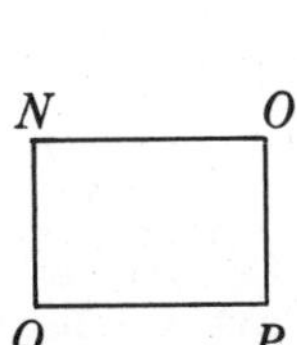

50. A tape measure that was originally 20 m long has stretched uniformly to 20.1 m. This tape is to be used to lay out a rectangular foundation 8 m wide by 12 m long. What will the dimensions of the foundation read on the tape?

51. The *pitch* of a roof is found by dividing the rise by the span. If a roof has pitch $\frac{3}{8}$ and a total rise of 9 feet, what is the rafter length?

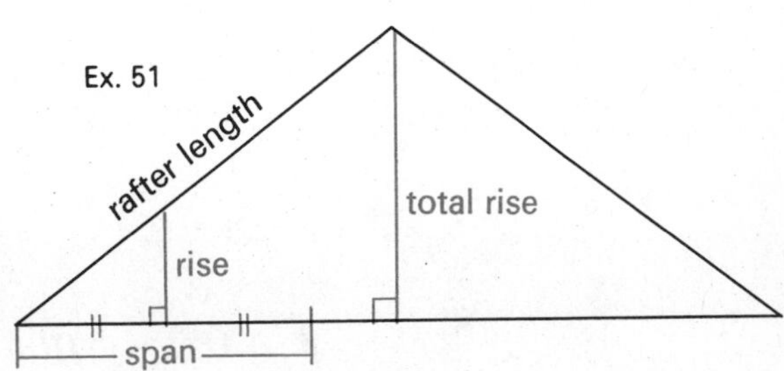

Ex. 51

10.3 Similar Triangles

Corresponding angles of the triangles shown here are congruent. Do the triangles appear to be similar? Can you draw a triangle that is not similar to these but whose angles are congruent to the angles of these triangles? The next postulate answers this question.

AAA Similarity Postulate

Angle-Angle-Angle Similarity Postulate: If the three angles of one triangle are congruent to the three angles of another triangle, the triangles are similar.

But if two angles of one triangle are congruent to two angles of another, the remaining angles are congruent. So one pair of angles mentioned in the postulate above is not needed. That is,

AA Similarity Theorem

Angle-Angle Similarity Theorem: If two angles of one triangle are congruent to two angles of another triangle, the triangles are similar.

The next two theorems are corollaries of the AA Similarity Theorem.

Theorem

In $\triangle ABC$ (see figure below), when line ℓ intersects side $\overline{AB}$ at D and side $\overline{BC}$ at E,

a. If $\ell \parallel \overline{AC}$, then $\triangle ABC \sim \triangle DBE$.

b. If $\triangle ABC \sim \triangle DBE$, then $\ell \parallel \overline{AC}$.

Part a. Given: $\ell \parallel \overline{AC}$

Prove: $\triangle ABC \sim \triangle DBE$

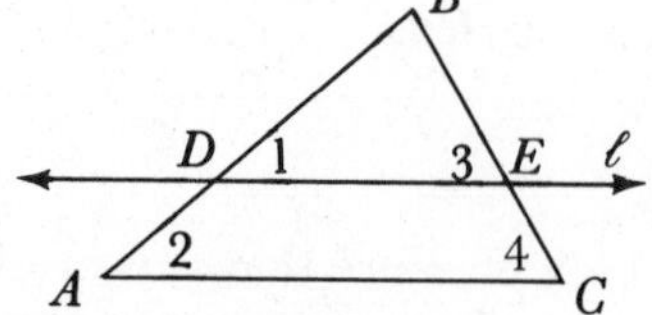

Proof:

STATEMENTS	REASONS
1. $\ell \parallel \overline{AC}$	1. Given
2. $\angle 1 \cong \angle 2$, $\angle 3 \cong \angle 4$	2. If 2 lines are $\parallel$, corres. $\angle$s are $\cong$. ($\overleftrightarrow{AB}$ is a transversal of ℓ and $\overleftrightarrow{AC}$, and so is $\overleftrightarrow{BC}$.)
3. $\triangle ABC \sim \triangle DBE$	3. AA Similarity Theorem

This proves part **a** of the theorem. The proof of part **b**, the converse, is Exercise 19.

The proof of the theorem below is outlined in Exercises 21–24.

Triangles similar to the same triangle are similar to each other.

Theorem

Exercises 10.3

Ⓐ **1.** If $\triangle XYZ \sim \triangle RTS$ and $\triangle HIJ \sim \triangle RTS$, is $\triangle XYZ \sim \triangle HIJ$? Why?

2–6. Refer to the figure.

2. If $\overleftrightarrow{DR} \parallel \overleftrightarrow{PM}$, $\triangle PTM \sim$ ______.

3. If $\triangle DRT \sim \triangle PMT$, then $\overline{PM} \parallel$ ______.

4. If $\triangle DTR \sim \triangle PTM$, then $\frac{PT}{DT} =$ ______ $=$ ______.

5. If $\angle DRT \cong$ ______, $\triangle RTD \sim \triangle MTP$.

6. If $\triangle DTR \sim \triangle PTM$, $\angle TDR \cong$ ______.

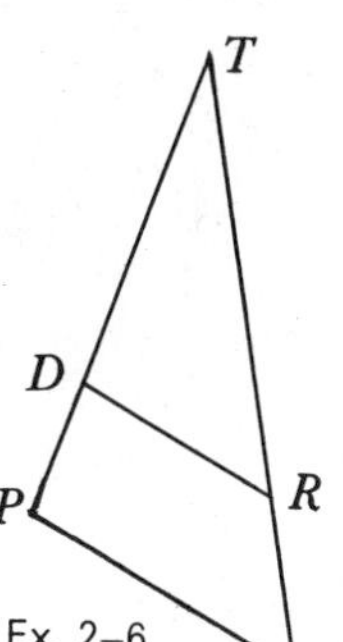

Ex. 2–6

7. Which triangles below are similar?

a.
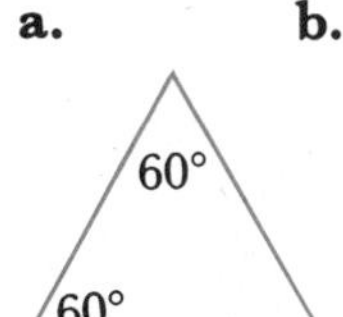

b.
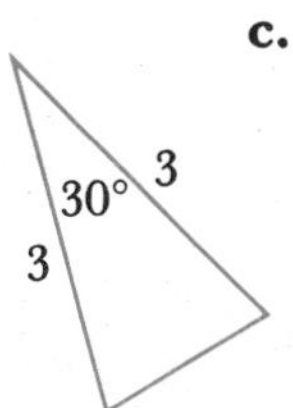

c.
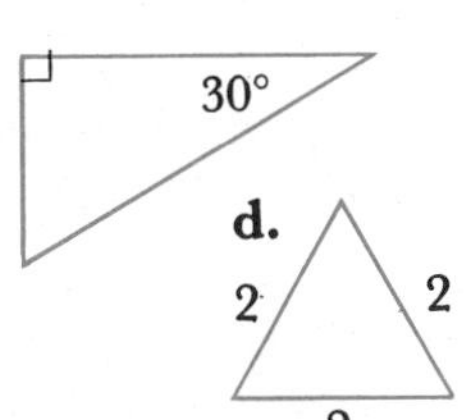

d.
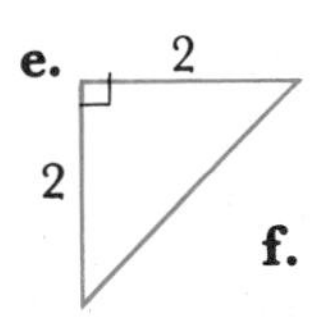

e.

f.
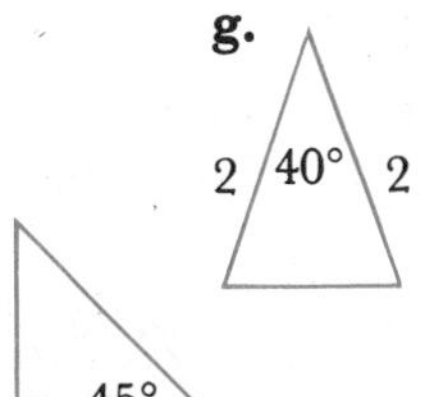

g.

h.
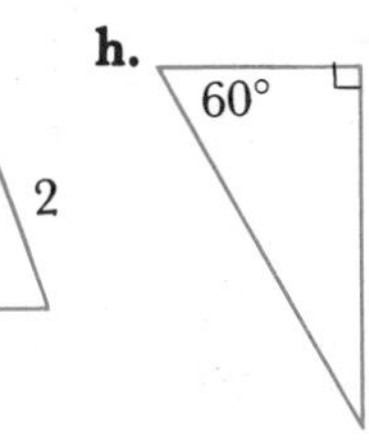

8. Which of these statements result from the AA Similarity Theorem?

a. All equilateral triangles are similar.

b. All isosceles triangles are similar.

c. All right triangles are similar.

d. All isosceles right triangles are similar.

e. All 30-60-90° triangles are similar.

Ⓑ **9–10.** Which triangles are similar?

9. **a.** **b.** **c.** **d.**

10.

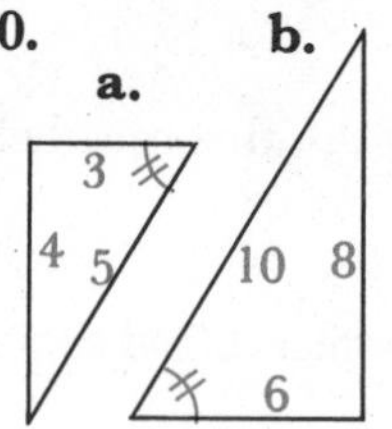

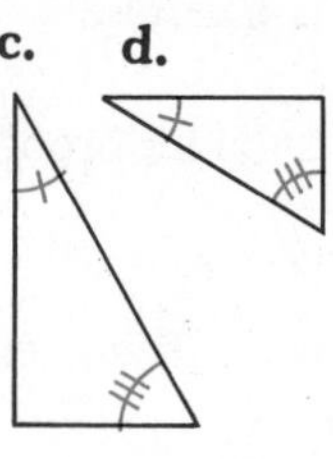

11–18. Refer to the figures below.

11. Given: $\ell \parallel n$

Prove: $\triangle ABD \sim \triangle ACE$

12. Given: $k \parallel \ell$

Prove: $\triangle BCD \sim \triangle ACF$

13. Given: $k \parallel n$

Prove: $\triangle ADF \sim \triangle EDC$

14. Given: $k \parallel n$

Prove: $\dfrac{DC}{DF} = \dfrac{ED}{AD}$

Ex. 11–14

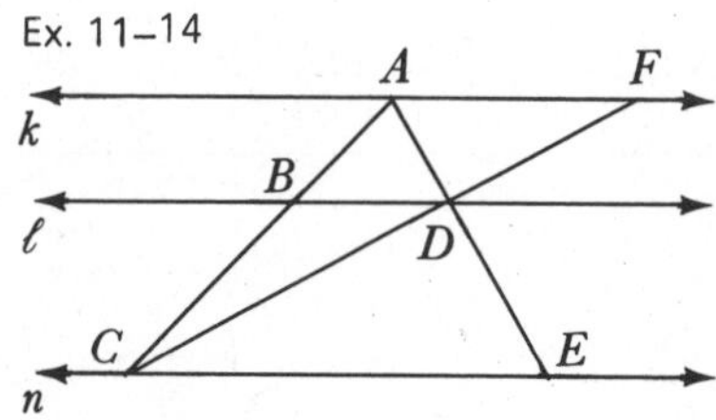

Ex. 15–18

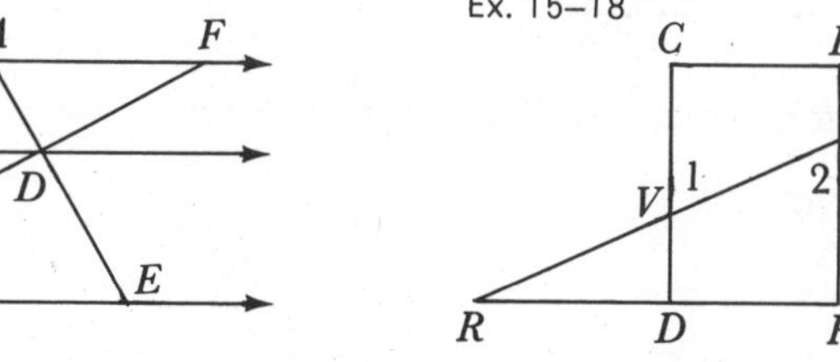

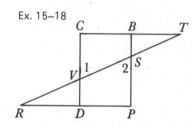

15. Given: $\overline{CD} \perp \overline{CT}$, $\overline{BP} \perp \overline{CT}$

Prove: $\triangle SPR \sim \triangle VDR$

16. Given: $\overline{RP} \perp \overline{CD}$, $\overline{RP} \perp \overline{BP}$

Prove: $\triangle TSB \sim \triangle TVC$

17. Given: $\angle 1 \cong \angle 2$

Prove: $\dfrac{RV}{RS} = \dfrac{RD}{RP}$

18. Given: $\angle 1 \cong \angle 2$

Prove: $\dfrac{CT}{BT} = \dfrac{VT}{ST}$

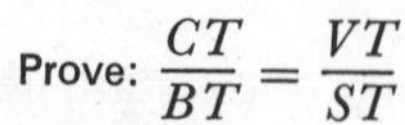

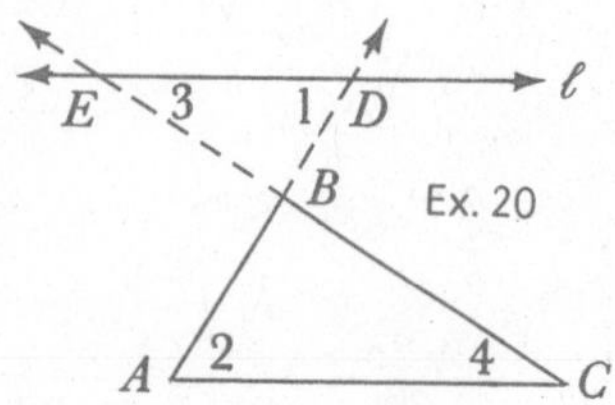

19. Prove part **b** of the second theorem on page 334. (Use the figure with part **a.**)

20. Prove that the second theorem on page 334 is true if the line intersects the lines containing the sides of the triangle. (See the figure at the left.)

21–24. Complete this proof that triangles similar to the same triangle are similar to each other.

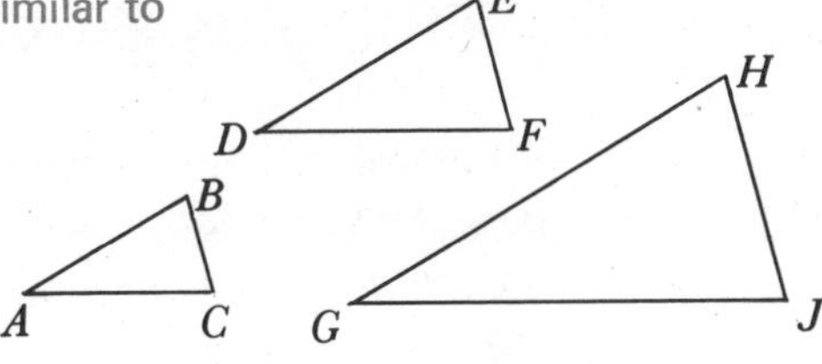

Given: $\triangle ABC \sim \triangle DEF$, $\triangle ABC \sim \triangle GHJ$

Prove: $\triangle DEF \sim \triangle GHJ$

Proof:

STATEMENTS	REASONS
1. $\angle A \cong \angle D$, $\angle B \cong \angle E$, $\angle A \cong \angle G$, $\angle B \cong \angle H$	1. **21.**
2. $\angle D \cong \angle G$, $\angle E \cong \angle H$	2. **22.**
3. **23.**	3. **24.**

© **25.** Why, in the projection system shown, are segments in the image on the screen proportional to segments in the picture? HINT: The picture, lens, and screen are parallel.

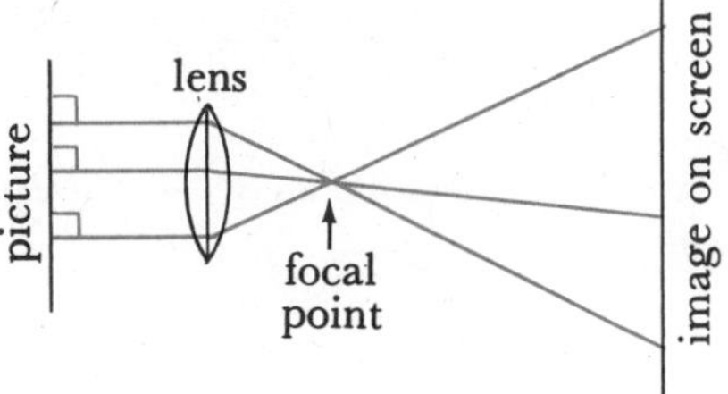

26. Prove that if the sides of one triangle are parallel to the sides of another triangle, the triangles are similar. HINT: Use a line containing a side of one triangle both as a transversal and as a line parallel to a side of the other triangle.

27. Prove that if the lines containing the sides of one triangle are perpendicular to the lines containing the sides of another triangle, the triangles are similar. HINT: Extend the sides of the triangles to form four right triangles. Use vertical and complementary angles.

Algebra Review

Review these skills:

- *adding polynomials*
- *subtracting polynomials*

Simplify.

1. $(2x + 5) + (7x + 3)$ **2.** $(3y - 2) + (8y + 4)$

3. $(9n - 3) + (2n - 4)$ **4.** $(2a^2 + 4a + 1) + (3a^2 + 7a - 2)$

5. $(x^2 - 2) + (3x^2 + 2)$ **6.** $(c^2 - 2c + 3) + (c - 5)$

7. $(5n + 2) - (2n + 5)$ **8.** $(4a - 6) - (3a - 2)$

9. $(3y^2 - 5) - (y^2 - 5)$ **10.** $(6x^2 + 7x - 3) - (2x^2 - 4x + 5)$

11. $(6v^2 + 4) - (3v + 2)$ **12.** $(5t^2 - 2t + 3) - (t - 3)$

10.4 Proving Triangles Similar

In earlier chapters, we considered different ways to prove triangles *congruent* (SAS, SSS, ASA, and AAS). In the preceding section, we stated that triangles can be proved *similar* by AAA. But this is more than is needed, since we can prove the AA Similarity Theorem. Now we consider other ways to prove triangles similar.

SAS Similarity Theorem

Side-Angle-Side Similarity Theorem: If two sides of one triangle are proportional to two sides of another triangle and the included angles are congruent, then the triangles are similar.

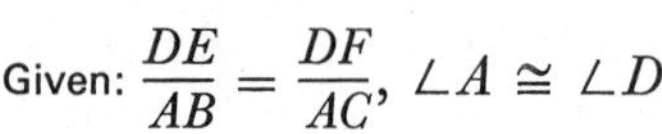

Given: $\frac{DE}{AB} = \frac{DF}{AC}$, $\angle A \cong \angle D$

Prove: $\triangle ABC \sim \triangle DEF$

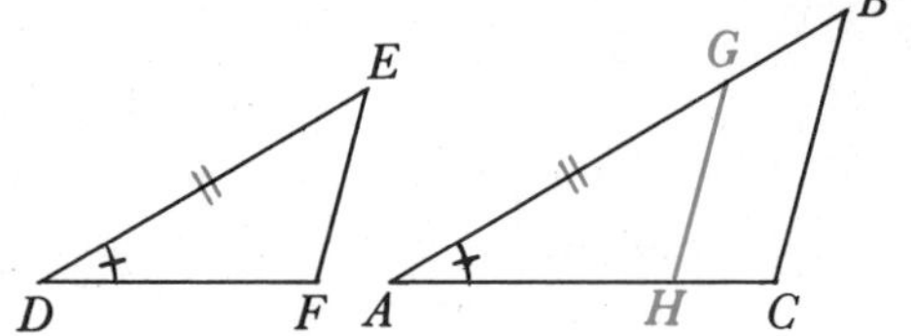

Proof:

STATEMENTS	REASONS
1. On $\overrightarrow{AB}$, let $AG = DE$, so $\overline{AG} \cong \overline{DE}$.	1. Point Plotting Theorem (p. 27)
2. Through G, draw $\overline{GH} \parallel \overline{BC}$.	2. Parallel Postulate
3. $\triangle AGH \sim \triangle ABC$	3. If a line $\parallel$ to one side of a $\triangle$ intersects the other two sides, a similar $\triangle$ is formed.
4. $\frac{AG}{AB} = \frac{AH}{AC}$	4. Definition of similar polygons
5. $\frac{DE}{AB} = \frac{DF}{AC}$	5. Given
6. $\frac{AG}{AB} = \frac{DF}{AC}$	6. Substitution (steps 1 and 5)
7. $\frac{AH}{AC} = \frac{DF}{AC}$	7. Substitution (steps 4 and 6)
8. $AH = DF$, so $\overline{AH} \cong \overline{DF}$.	8. Multiply both sides by AC.
9. $\angle A \cong \angle D$	9. Given
10. $\triangle AGH \cong \triangle DEF$	10. SAS Postulate (steps 1, 8, and 9)
11. $\triangle AGH \sim \triangle DEF$	11. $\cong$ polygons are $\sim$.
12. $\triangle ABC \sim \triangle DEF$	12. $\triangle$s $\sim$ to the same $\triangle$ are $\sim$.

Similar triangles are triangles for which

corresponding angles are congruent — The AAA Postulate says this alone gives similar triangles.

and corresponding sides are proportional. — We can now prove that this alone gives similar triangles.

Side-Side-Side Similarity Theorem: If the sides of one triangle are proportional to the corresponding sides of another triangle, the triangles are similar.

SSS Similarity Theorem

Given: $\dfrac{SR}{OM} = \dfrac{ST}{OP} = \dfrac{RT}{MP}$

Prove: $\triangle RST \sim \triangle MOP$

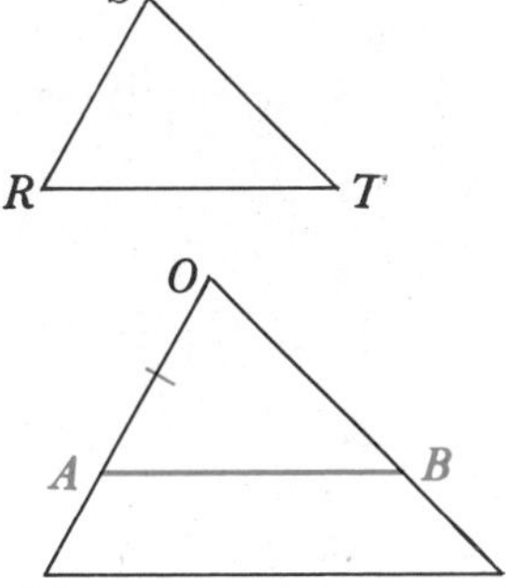

[*Plan:* Let $\overline{OA} \cong \overline{SR}$ and $\overline{AB} \parallel \overline{MP}$. Then $\triangle AOB \sim \triangle MOP$. Use proportions from this similarity and the given information to prove $\triangle RST \cong \triangle AOB$ by SSS.]

The proof of this theorem is in Exercise 39.

Do we need an ASA Similarity Theorem or an AAS Similarity Theorem for triangles? In each of these cases, two pairs of corresponding angles are congruent. This is enough to prove the triangles similar by AA. So neither theorem is needed.

The figures at the right show why triangles *cannot* be proved similar by SSA—just as triangles cannot be proved congruent by SSA.

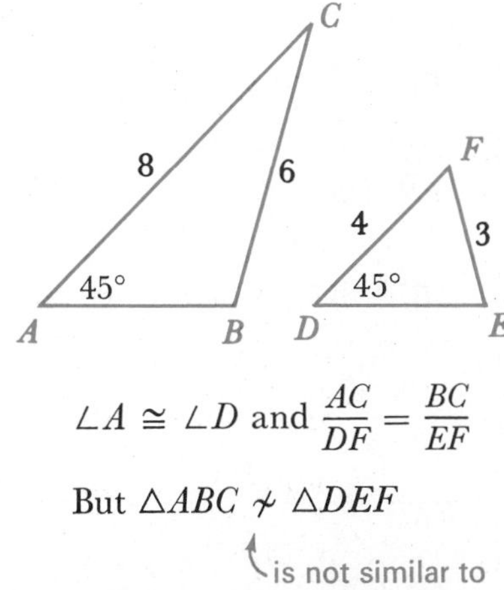

$\angle A \cong \angle D$ and $\dfrac{AC}{DF} = \dfrac{BC}{EF}$

But $\triangle ABC \nsim \triangle DEF$

↑ is not similar to

Exercises 10.4

Ⓐ **1–3.** *Multiple choice:* List *all* possible choices.

a. SAS **b.** SSS **c.** ASA **d.** AAS **e.** SSA **f.** AA

1. We stated a postulate or theorem for proving triangles congruent by ______.

2. We stated a theorem for proving triangles similar by ______.

3. Because of the AA Similarity Theorem, a(n) ______ Similarity Theorem is not needed.

4–10. State each postulate or theorem.

4. SAS Postulate

5. SAS Similarity Theorem

6. SSS Postulate

7. SSS Similarity Theorem

8. ASA Postulate

9. AA Similarity Theorem

10. AAS Theorem

11–16. Given the figures and the information below, can you conclude that $\triangle ABC \sim \triangle DEF$? If so, by which theorem?

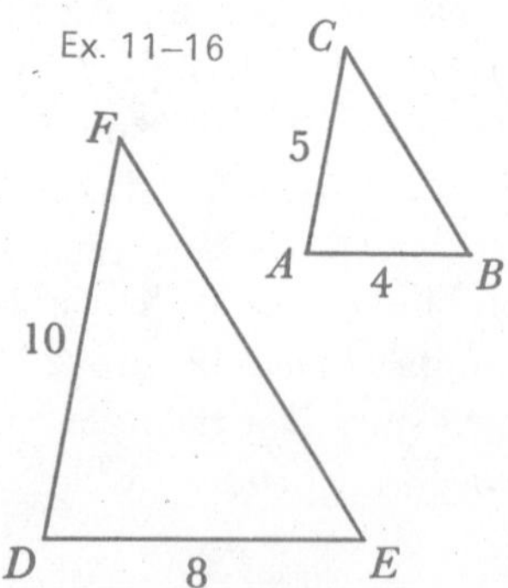

11. $\angle A \cong \angle D$

12. $\angle B \cong \angle E$

13. $\frac{BC}{EF} = \frac{1}{2}$

14. $BC = 6$, $EF = 12$

15. $\frac{BC}{EF} = \frac{3}{5}$

16. $BC = 6$, $EF = 11$

Ⓑ **17–18.** Which triangles are similar?

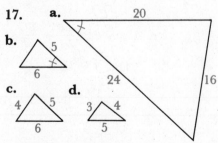

17. **a.** 20, 24, 16 **b.** 5, 6 **c.** 4, 5, 6 **d.** 3, 4, 5

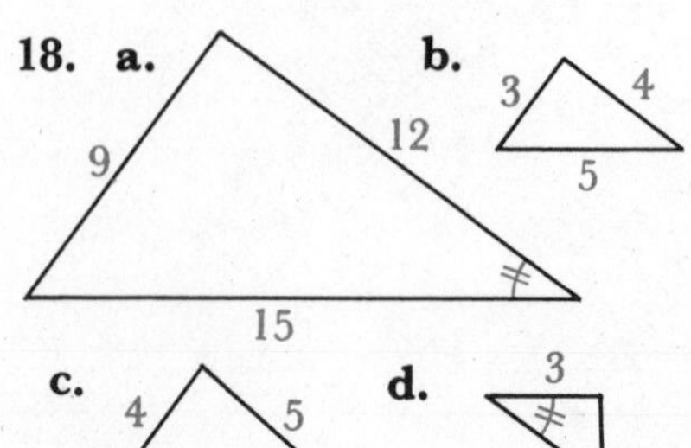

19–24. Given the figures and the information below, can you conclude that $\triangle KMN \sim \triangle RPS$? If so, by which theorem?

19. $m\angle M = 80$, $m\angle P = 80$

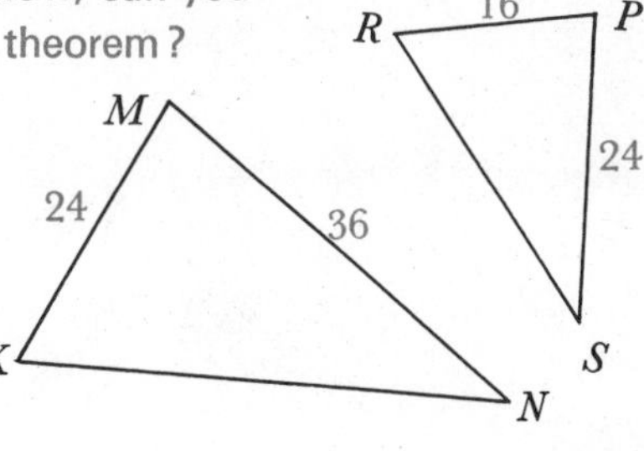

20. $m\angle M = 80$, $m\angle R = 80$

21. $m\angle M = 80$, $m\angle R + m\angle S = 100$

22. $\frac{RS}{KN} = \frac{2}{3}$

23. $RS = 26$, $KN = 40$

24. $KN = MN$, $RS = PS$

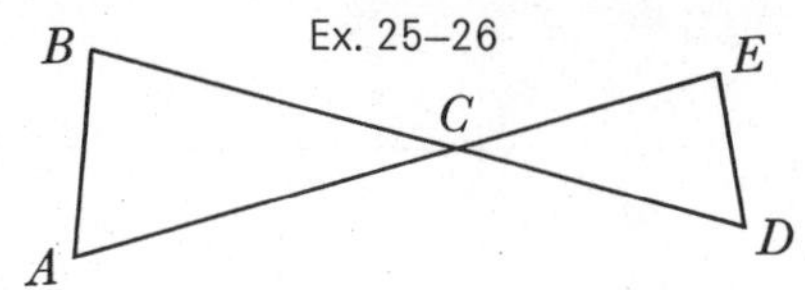

25. Given: $\frac{BC}{EC} = \frac{AC}{DC}$

Prove: $\triangle ACB \sim \triangle DCE$

26. Given: $\angle A \cong \angle D$

Prove: $\triangle ACB \sim \triangle DCE$

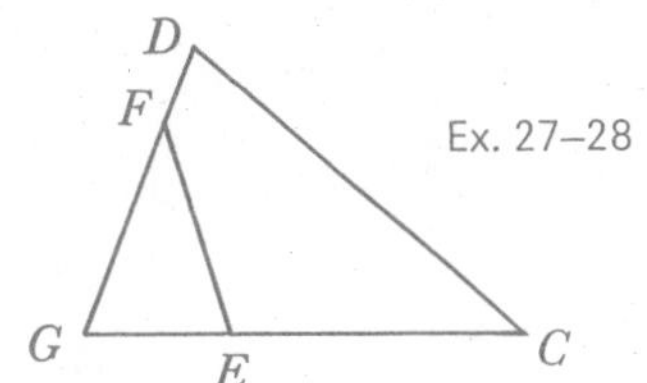

27. Given: $GF = \frac{1}{2}GC$,
$GE = \frac{1}{2}GD$,
$EF = \frac{1}{2}DC$

Prove: $\triangle GFE \sim \triangle GCD$

28. Given: $GF = \frac{1}{2}DC$,
$GE = \frac{1}{2}DG$,
$EF = \frac{1}{2}GC$

Prove: $\triangle GFE \sim \triangle DCG$

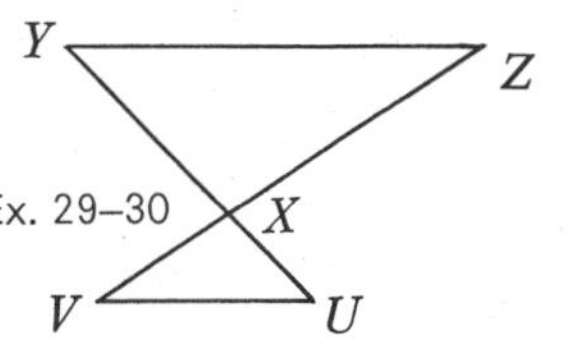

29. Given: $\overline{YZ} \parallel \overline{UV}$

Prove: $\frac{XY}{XU} = \frac{YZ}{UV}$

30. Given: $\frac{XY}{XU} = \frac{XZ}{XV}$

Prove: $\overline{YZ} \parallel \overline{UV}$

31–36. If something cannot be measured directly, it may be possible to find its approximate size by using similar triangles to make an *indirect measurement*, as shown in the figures.

31. If the shadow of the tree is 14 m long and the shadow of the person, who is 1.8 m tall, is 4 m long, how tall is the tree?

Brent Jones

32. If the shadow of the tree is 20 m long and the shadow of the person, who is 190 cm tall, is 250 cm long, how tall is the tree?

33. A pole 3 m high has a shadow 5 m long when the shadow of a nearby building is 110 m long. How tall is the building?

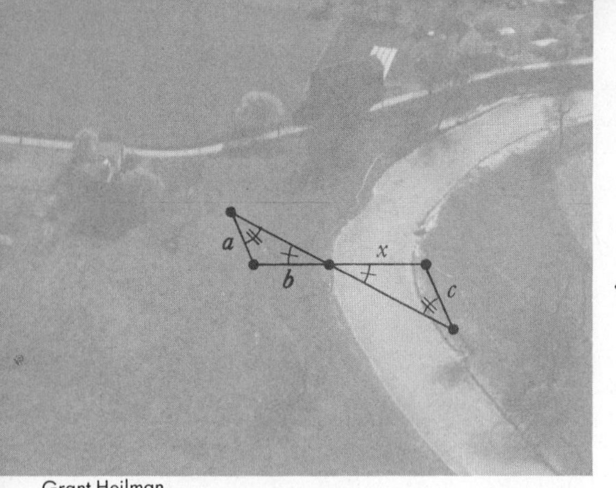

Grant Heilman

34. A flagpole 4 m high has a shadow 6 m long when the shadow of a nearby monument is 45 m long. How tall is the monument?

◀ 35. By measurement, $a = 9$ m, $b = 15$ m, and $c = 12$ m. How long is x?

◀ 36. By measurement, $a = 8$ m, $b = 12$ m, and $c = 15$ m. How long is x?

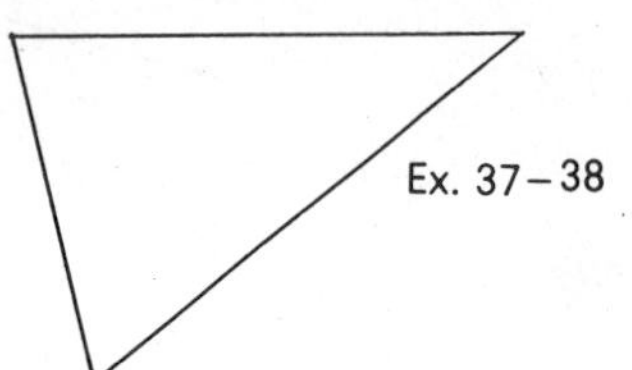
Ex. 37–38

37–38. *Constructions:* Use the SAS Similarity Theorem as a basis for the construction. Then repeat the construction using the SSS Similarity Theorem.

37. Construct $\triangle XYZ \sim \triangle RST$ so that $XY = 2RS$.

38. Construct $\triangle XYZ \sim \triangle RST$ so that $XY = 3RS$.

Ⓒ 39. Copy the figure and restatement of the SSS Similarity Theorem on page 339. Then complete the proof.

Proof:

STATEMENTS	REASONS
1. On $\overrightarrow{OM}$, let $OA = SR$, so $\overline{OA} \cong \overline{SR}$.	1. ______
2. Through A, draw $\overline{AB} \parallel \overline{MP}$.	2. ______
3. $\triangle AOB \sim \triangle MOP$	3. ______
4. $\frac{OA}{OM} = \frac{OB}{OP} = \frac{AB}{MP}$	4. ______
5. $\frac{SR}{OM} = \frac{ST}{OP} = \frac{RT}{MP}$	5. ______
6. $\frac{OA}{OM} = \frac{SR}{OM}$	6. Divide both sides of $OA = SR$ by OM (see step 1).
7. $\frac{OB}{OP} = \frac{ST}{OP}, \frac{AB}{MP} = \frac{RT}{MP}$	7. ______
8. $OB = ST$, so $\overline{OB} \cong \overline{ST}$. $AB = RT$, so $\overline{AB} \cong \overline{RT}$.	8. ______
9. $\triangle RST \cong \triangle AOB$	9. ______
10. $\triangle RST \sim \triangle AOB$	10. ______
11. $\triangle RST \sim \triangle MOP$	11. ______

1–5. Let $\frac{3}{n} = \frac{5}{x}$.

1. Name the means.

2. Name the extremes.

3. The given equation is an example of a ______.

4. $3x =$ ______

5. $\frac{3}{5} =$ ______

6. Solve: $\frac{5}{4} = \frac{t}{12}$

7. If $p = 2$ and $6 = r$, $\frac{p}{6} =$ ______

8–11. For $\triangle PDC \sim \triangle RST$, the ratio of similarity is $\frac{2}{3}$.

8. $\frac{PD}{RS} =$ ______

9. If $m\angle S = 35$, ______ $= 35$.

10. $\frac{RT}{PC} =$ ______

11. If $DC = 6$, then $ST =$ ______.

12–14. State each similarity theorem.

12. AA

13. SAS

14. SSS

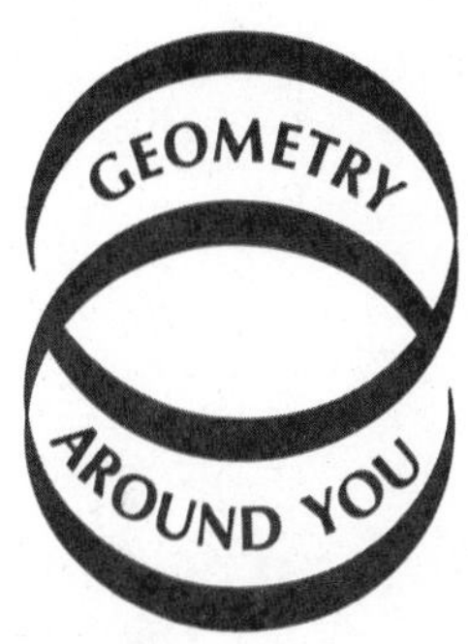

GET THE PICTURE?

Each picture on a strip of motion-picture film is called a *frame*. When the picture is projected onto a flat screen, parallel to the film plane, the outlines of the frame and of the projected picture are similar rectangles. The ratio of frame height to frame width depends on the type of camera and the film size. Some frame ratios are shown below. Notice that 16 mm film is used for both commercial and home movies.

<table>
<tr><td></td><td colspan="4">commercial movies</td><td>home movies</td></tr>
<tr><td rowspan="2">film size</td><td colspan="2">wide screen</td><td colspan="3">normal screen</td></tr>
<tr><td>70 mm</td><td>35 mm</td><td>35 mm,</td><td>16 mm,</td><td>8 mm</td></tr>
<tr><td>frame height / frame width</td><td>$\frac{2}{5}$</td><td>$\frac{4}{7}$</td><td colspan="3">$\frac{3}{4}$</td></tr>
</table>

If the picture is to fit the screen closely, how wide does a screen of the given height have to be for each frame ratio above?

1. 9 m **2.** 10 m **3.** 7 m **4.** 18.4 m

When a movie is shown on television, part of the picture may be lost because the outline of the screen on the TV set is not similar to the outline of the film frame. Two commonly used height-to-width ratios for TV screens are $\frac{3}{4}$ and $\frac{4}{5}$. Which is best for showing normal-screen movies? For 70 mm wide-screen movies? For 35 mm wide-screen movies?

10.5 Similar Right Triangles

In Chapter 5, we considered special theorems for proving *right* triangles *congruent* (LL, HL, HA, and LA). There are also special ways to prove that *right* triangles are *similar*.

LL Similarity Theorem

Leg-Leg Similarity Theorem: If the legs of one right triangle are proportional to the legs of another right triangle, then the triangles are similar.

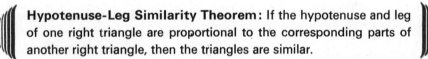

Given: $\angle C$ and $\angle F$ are right angles,
$\frac{AC}{DF} = \frac{BC}{EF}$

Prove: $\triangle ABC \sim \triangle DEF$

Proof:

STATEMENTS	REASONS
1. $\angle C$ and $\angle F$ are rt. $\angle$s.	1. Given
2. $\angle C \cong \angle F$	2. All rt. $\angle$s are $\cong$.
3. $\frac{AC}{DF} = \frac{BC}{EF}$	3. Given
4. $\triangle ABC \sim \triangle DEF$	4. SAS Similarity Theorem

The next theorem is proved in Exercise 44.

HL Similarity Theorem

Hypotenuse-Leg Similarity Theorem: If the hypotenuse and leg of one right triangle are proportional to the corresponding parts of another right triangle, then the triangles are similar.

Do we need an HA Similarity Theorem or an LA Similarity Theorem for right triangles? In each of these cases, a pair of acute angles are congruent. Since the right angles are also congruent, the two triangles are similar by AA. So neither of these theorems is needed. We can, however, prove two other theorems about right-triangle similarity.

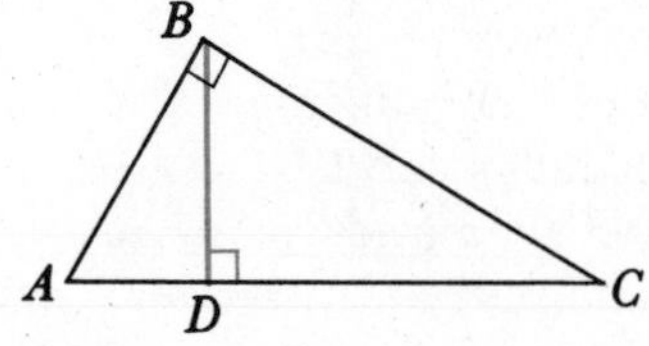

An altitude to the hypotenuse of a right triangle forms two smaller right triangles. They may not look much like the original triangle, but they are in fact the same shape. The three triangles are shown separately in the next figure.

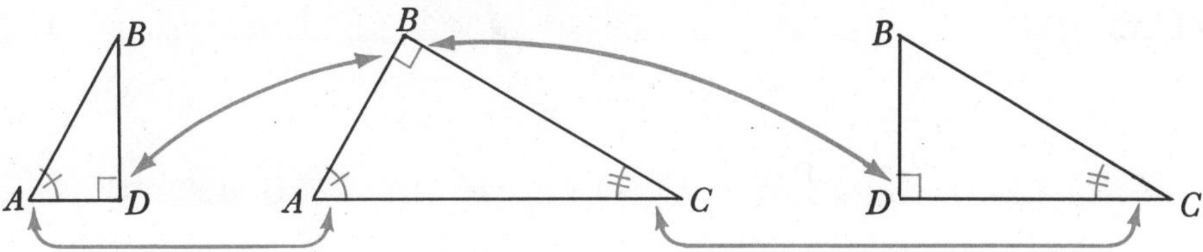

right angles

So, by the AA Similarity Theorem, $\triangle ADB \sim \triangle ABC \sim \triangle BDC$. That is,

common angles

In a right triangle, the sides and the altitude to the hypotenuse form two triangles that are similar to the given triangle and to each other. — **Theorem**

Since the triangles are similar, corresponding sides are proportional.

	$\triangle ADB \sim \triangle BDC$	$\triangle ABC \sim \triangle BDC$	$\triangle ADB \sim \triangle ABC$
corresponding sides ▶ corresponding sides ▶	$\frac{AD}{BD} = \frac{BD}{CD}$	$\frac{AC}{BC} = \frac{BC}{DC}$	$\frac{AD}{AB} = \frac{AB}{AC}$

When both *means* of a proportion are the same number, as in the proportions above, that number is called the **geometric mean** of the extremes. The three proportions can now be described in one theorem.

Theorem

For any right triangle and the altitude to its hypotenuse,

a. The altitude is the geometric mean of the segments into which it separates the hypotenuse.

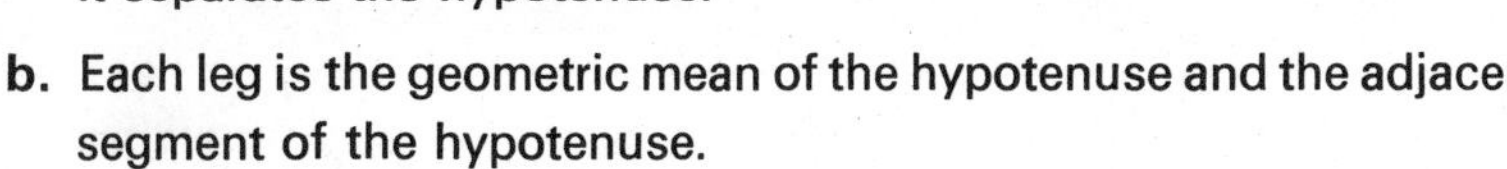

b. Each leg is the geometric mean of the hypotenuse and the adjacent segment of the hypotenuse.

Examples:

1.

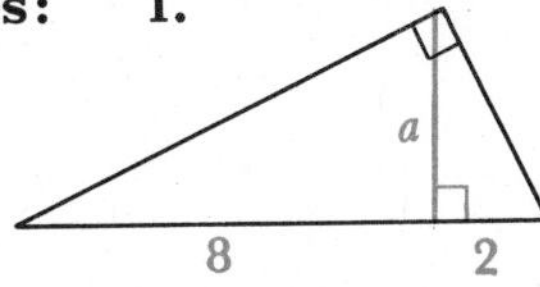

$\frac{2}{a} = \frac{a}{8}$ By part **a** above

$a^2 = 16$ Cross multiply.

$a = 4$ Take the (positive) square root of both sides.

2.

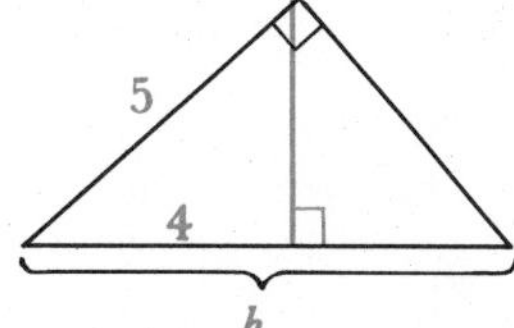

$\frac{4}{5} = \frac{5}{h}$ By part **b** above

$4h = 25$ Cross multiply.

$h = \frac{25}{4}$ Divide both sides by 4.

Exercises 10.5

Ⓐ **1–3.** *Multiple choice:* List *all* possible choices.

a. LL **b.** HL **c.** HA **d.** LA

1. We stated a theorem for proving right triangles congruent by ______.

2. We stated a theorem for proving right triangles similar by ______.

3. Because of the AA Similarity Theorem, a(n) ______ Similarity Theorem is not needed.

4–9. State each theorem.

4. LL Theorem

5. LL Similarity Theorem

6. HL Theorem

7. HL Similarity Theorem

8. HA Theorem

9. LA Theorem

10–15. Given the figures and the information below, can you conclude that $\triangle ABC \sim \triangle DEF$? If so, by which theorem?

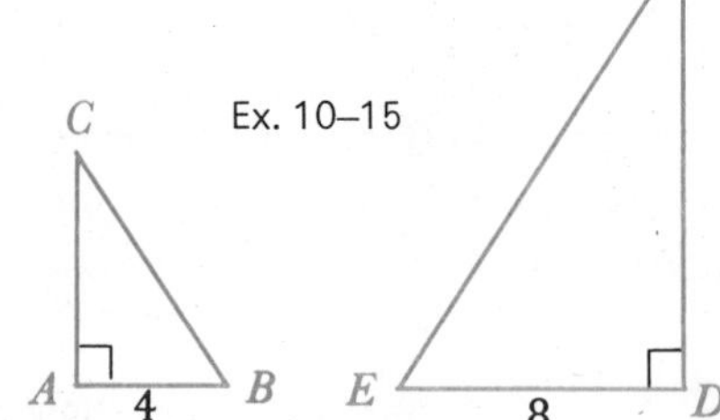

10. $\frac{AC}{DF} = \frac{1}{2}$

11. $\frac{BC}{EF} = \frac{1}{2}$

12. $\frac{AC}{DF} = \frac{3}{5}$

13. $AC = 5,\ DF = 10$

14. $\angle B \cong \angle E$

15. $BC = 6,\ EF = 12$

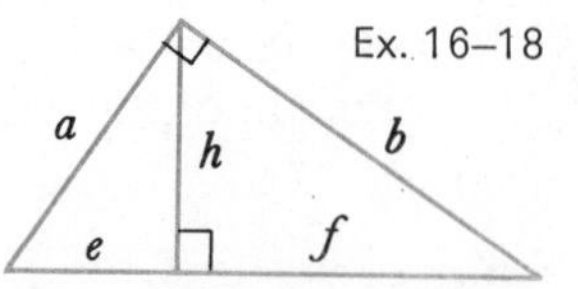

16–18. Refer to the figure.

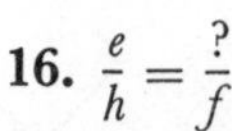

16. $\frac{e}{h} = \frac{?}{f}$

17. $\frac{e}{a} = \frac{?}{e + f}$

18. $\frac{f}{?} = \frac{?}{e + f}$

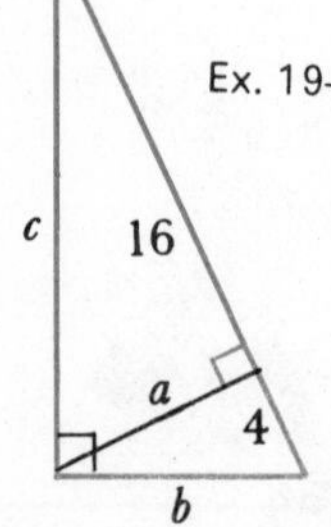

Ex. 19–26

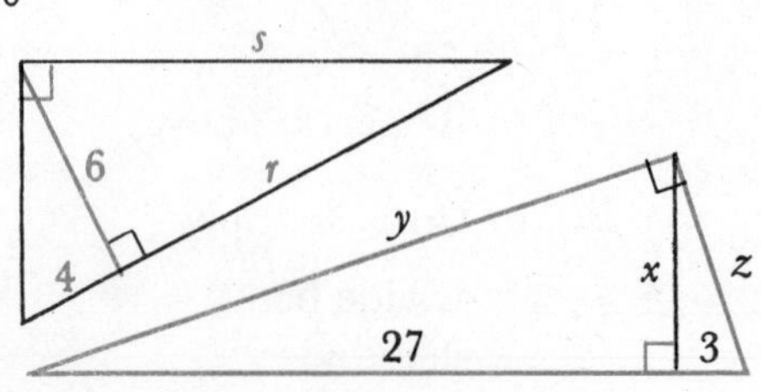

Ⓑ **19–26.** Refer to the figures. Find each length.

19. a **20.** x **21.** b **22.** y

23. c **24.** z **25.** r **26.** s

27. Given: $\angle Y$ and $\angle V$ are rt. $\angle$s.
Prove: $\triangle XYZ \sim \triangle XVW$

Ex. 27

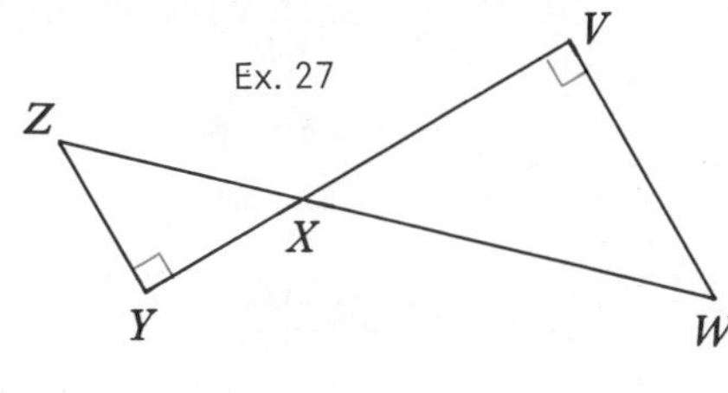

28. Given: $\overline{AC} \perp \overline{DE}$, $\frac{AC}{BC} = \frac{DC}{EC}$
Prove: $\triangle ADC \sim \triangle BEC$

Ex. 28–30

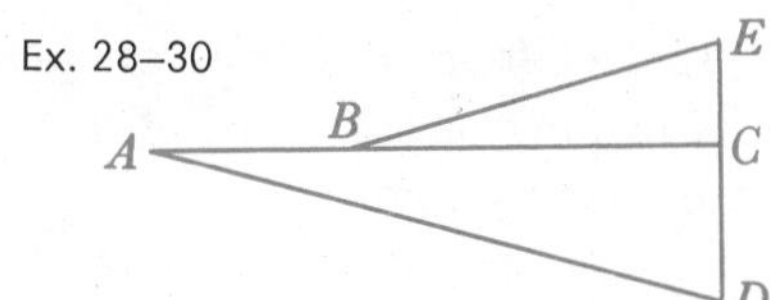

29. Given: $\overline{AC} \perp \overline{DE}$, $\frac{AD}{BE} = \frac{DC}{EC}$
Prove: $\triangle ADC \sim \triangle BEC$

30. Given: $\overline{AC} \perp \overline{DE}$, $\angle D \cong \angle E$
Prove: $\triangle ACD \sim \triangle BCE$

31. The person is 166 cm tall and stands 90 cm from the mirror. If the mirror is 495 cm from the base of the tower, how high is the tower?

32. The person is 160 cm tall and stands 120 cm from the mirror, which is 675 cm from the base of the tower. How high is the tower?

Ex. 31–32

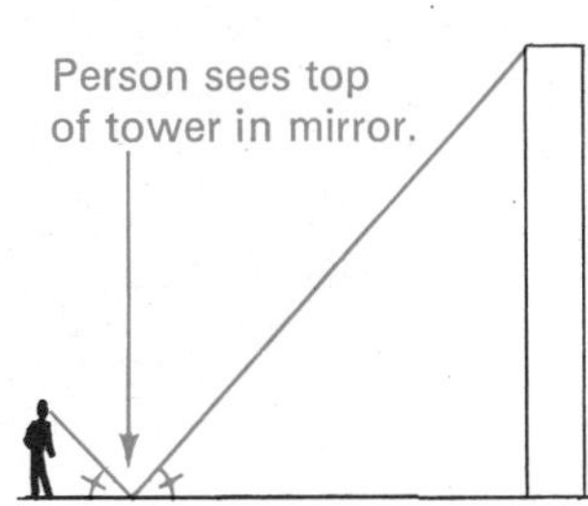

Brent Jones

construction: the geometric mean of two segments

1. Given: $\overline{AB}$, $\overline{CD}$

A B C D

2. On any line ℓ, construct $\overline{A'B'} \cong \overline{AB}$ and $\overline{B'D'} \cong \overline{CD}$. Construct $\overrightarrow{B'P} \perp \overline{A'D'}$ at B'.

P A′ B′ D′ ℓ

3. Construct M, the midpoint of $\overline{A'D'}$. From M, mark off $\overline{MT} \cong \overline{MD'}$. $\angle A'TD'$ is a right angle.

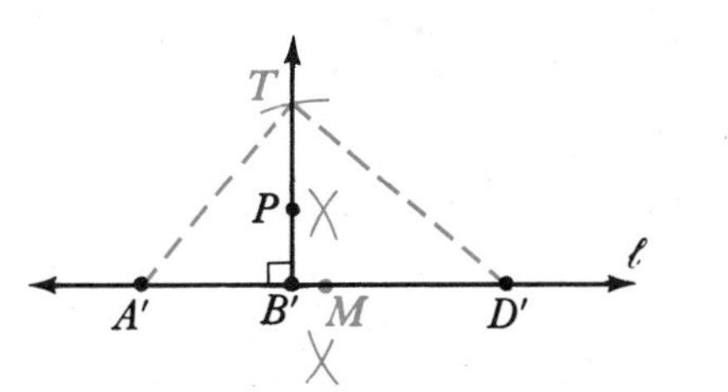

33–36. Refer to right $\triangle A'TD'$ in step 3 above.

33. The geometric mean of $A'B'$ and $B'D'$ is ______.

34. The geometric mean of $A'B'$ and $A'D'$ is ______.

35. The geometric mean of $B'D'$ and $A'D'$ is ______.

36. The geometric mean of AB and CD in step 1 is ______.

37–40. Draw $\overline{MN}$, $\overline{RS}$, and $\overline{TV}$ so that $MN = 8$ cm, $RS = 5$ cm, and $TV = 3$ cm. Then construct the geometric mean of the lengths listed.

37. MN, RS 38. MN, TV 39. $MN + TV, RS$ 40. $MN + RS, TV$

Ⓒ **41–42.** For the lengths listed, identify the geometric mean in one of the constructions for Exercises 37–40.

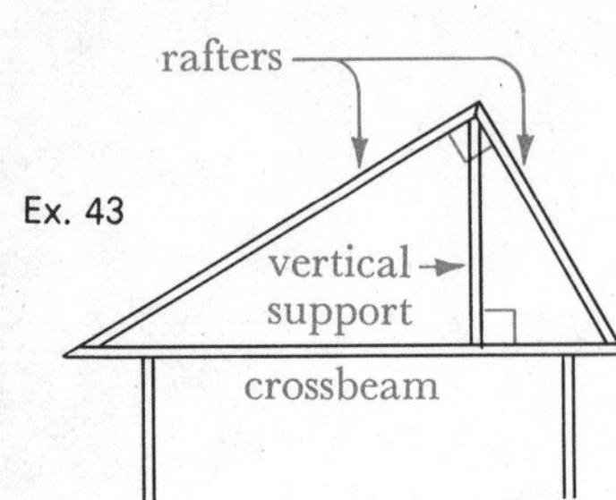

41. $MN + RS$, MN **42.** $MN + TV$, TV

43. The rafters of this roof meet at a right angle. The vertical support is 15 feet long and rests on a 34-foot crossbeam. How far from the ends of the crossbeam is the base of the support?

44. Copy and complete this proof of the HL Similarity Theorem.

Given: $\angle C$ and $\angle F$ are right angles, $\frac{DE}{AB} = \frac{DF}{AC}$

Prove: $\triangle ABC \sim \triangle DEF$

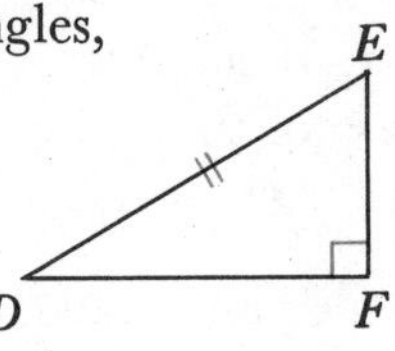

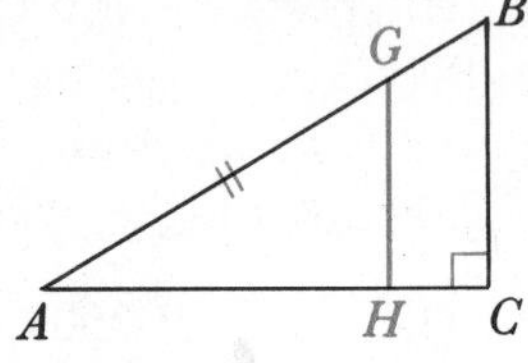

Proof:

STATEMENTS	REASONS
1. On $\overrightarrow{AB}$, let $AG = DE$, so $\overline{AG} \cong \overline{DE}$.	1. Point Plotting Theorem (p. 27)
2. Through G, draw $\overline{GH} \parallel \overline{BC}$.	2. ____
3. $\triangle AGH \sim \triangle ABC$	3. ____
4. $\angle GHA \cong \angle C$	4. ____
5. $\angle GHA$ is a rt. $\angle$.	5. Def. of $\cong$ $\angle$s and given $\angle C$ is a rt. $\angle$.
6. $\frac{AG}{AB} = \frac{AH}{AC}$	6. ____
7. $\frac{DE}{AB} = \frac{DF}{AC}$	7. ____
8. $\frac{AG}{AB} = \frac{DF}{AC}$	8. Subst. (steps 1 and 7)
9. $\frac{AH}{AC} = \frac{DF}{AC}$	9. ____
10. $AH = DF$, so $\overline{AH} \cong \overline{DF}$.	10. ____
11. $\triangle AGH \cong \triangle DEF$	11. HL Theorem (steps 1 and 10)
12. $\triangle AGH \sim \triangle DEF$	12. ____
13. $\triangle ABC \sim \triangle DEF$	13. ____

GEOMETRY AT WORK

MECHANICS AND REPAIRERS

One of the fastest growing groups of skilled workers includes mechanics and repairers—the people who keep cars, airplanes, home appliances, and other machinery working properly. These workers are trained in vocational and technical schools or on the job, often in apprenticeship programs.

Employers look for high-school graduates who have courses in mathematics, chemistry, physics, blueprint reading, and machine shop.

Mechanics and repairers must often use diagrams to recognize repair parts. A knowledge of similar figures can be helpful.

Can you match the parts in each photo with the diagram?

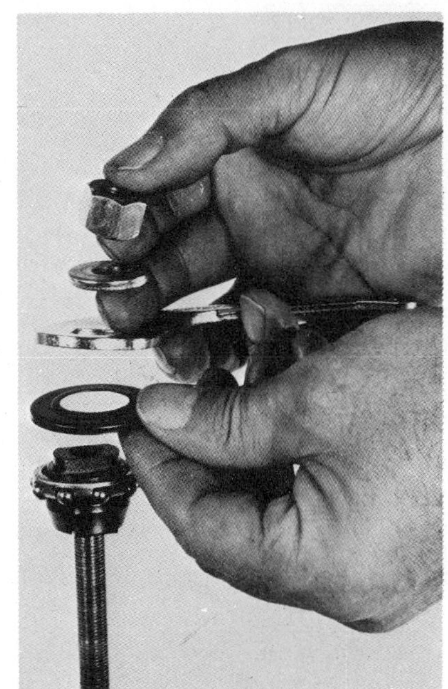

Copyright, Schwinn Bicycle Co., Chicago, Ill.

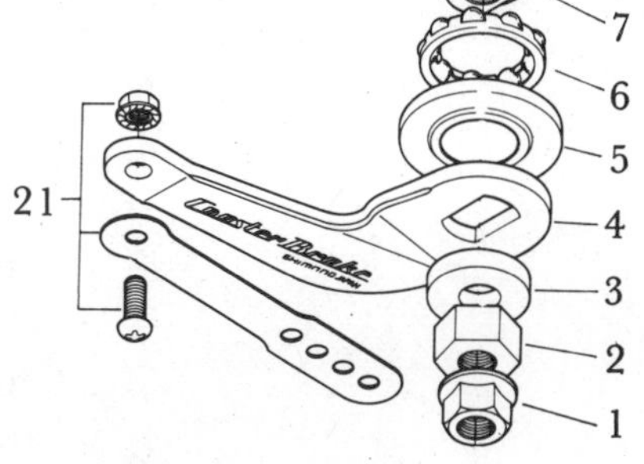

10.6 Triangle Similarity Summarized

TRIANGLES CAN BE PROVED SIMILAR BY

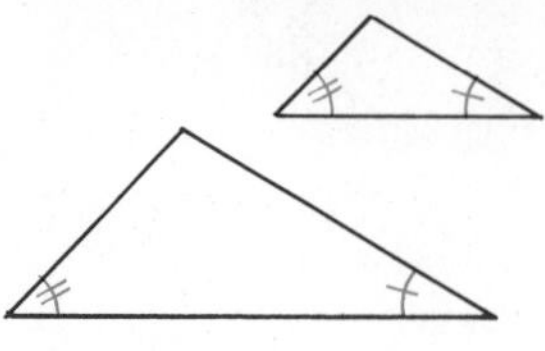

Angle-Angle Similarity Theorem

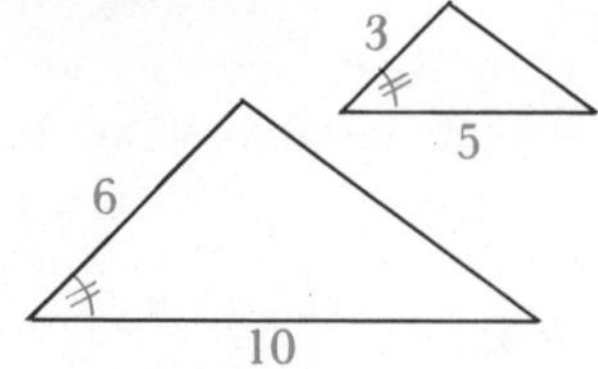

Side-Angle-Side Similarity Theorem

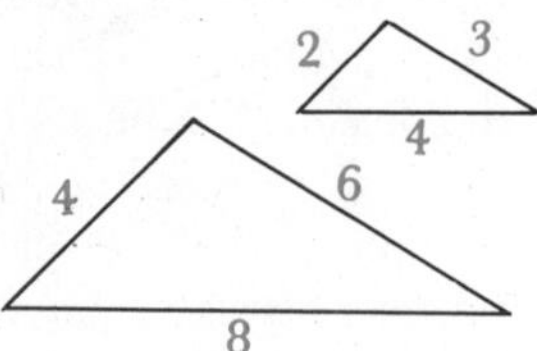

Side-Side-Side Similarity Theorem

RIGHT TRIANGLES CAN BE PROVED SIMILAR BY

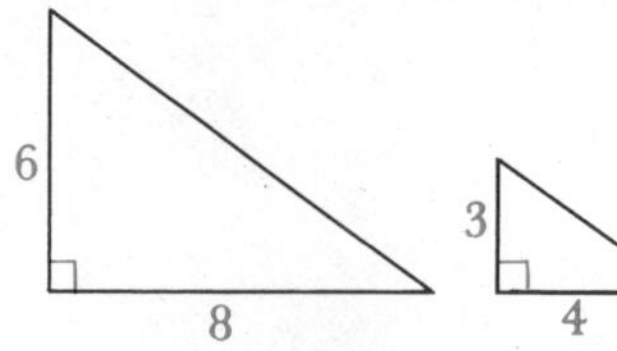

Leg-Leg Similarity Theorem

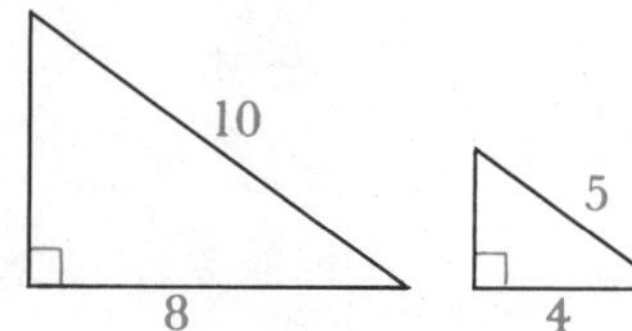

Hypotenuse-Leg Similarity Theorem

Triangles **cannot** be proved similar by Side-Side-Angle.

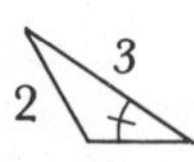

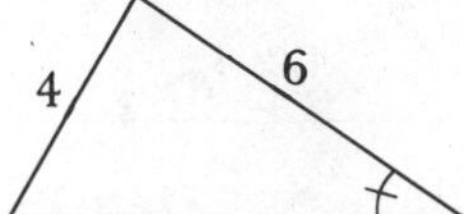

We also saw that certain cases for which we stated a congruence postulate or theorem (ASA, AAS, HA, and LA) did not have to be extended to similarity. These cases are covered by the AA Similarity Theorem.

Exercises 10.6

Ⓐ **1–6.** Using the given information, which theorem can be used to prove $\triangle ABC \sim \triangle DEF$?

1. $\angle A \cong \angle D$, $\angle C \cong \angle F$

2. $\dfrac{AB}{DE} = \dfrac{BC}{EF} = \dfrac{AC}{DF}$

3. $\dfrac{BC}{EF} = \dfrac{AC}{DF}$, $\angle C \cong \angle F$

4. $\angle C$ and $\angle F$ are rt. $\angle$s, $\dfrac{AB}{DE} = \dfrac{BC}{EF}$

5. $\angle C$ and $\angle F$ are rt. $\angle$s, $\angle B \cong \angle E$

6. $\angle C$ and $\angle F$ are rt. $\angle$s, $\dfrac{AC}{DF} = \dfrac{BC}{EF}$

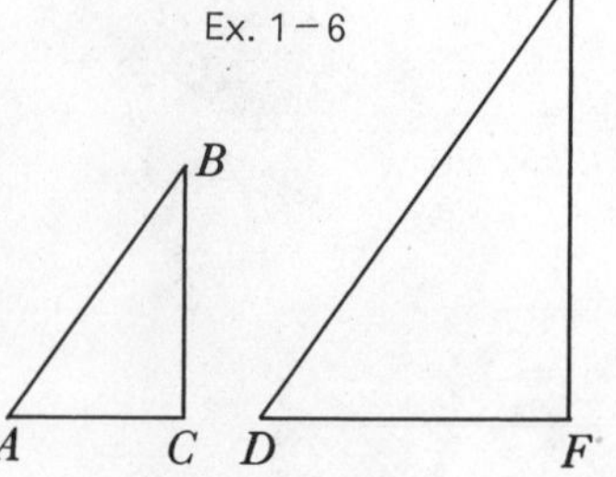

Ⓑ **7.** Given: Trapezoid $WXYZ$ with $\overline{WX} \parallel \overline{YZ}$

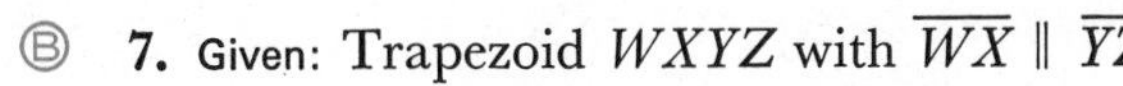

Prove: $\triangle WNX \sim \triangle YNZ$

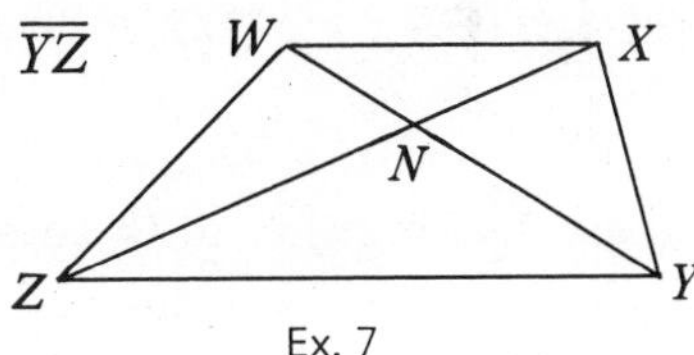

Ex. 7

8. Given: $\square HIJK$, $\dfrac{HR}{RI} = \dfrac{RK}{IJ}$

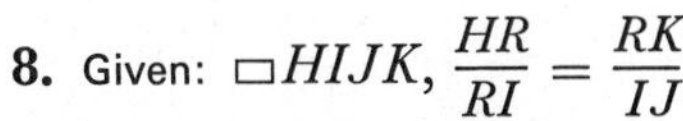

Prove: $\triangle HRK \sim \triangle RIJ$

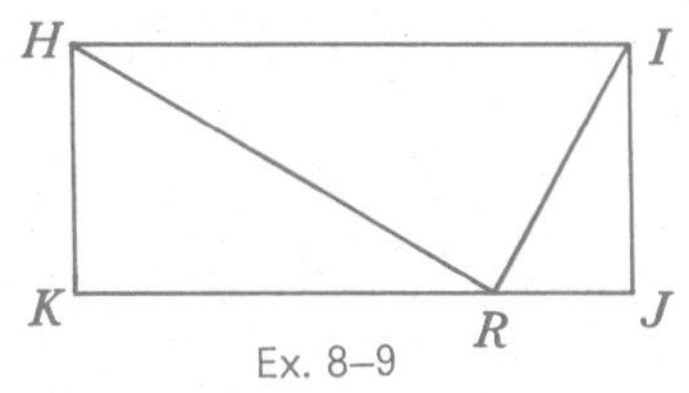

Ex. 8–9

9. Given: $\square HIJK$, $\dfrac{HI}{RH} = \dfrac{IR}{HK} = \dfrac{RH}{KR}$

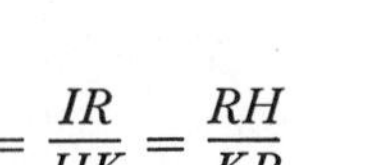

Prove: $\angle HRI$ is a rt. $\angle$.

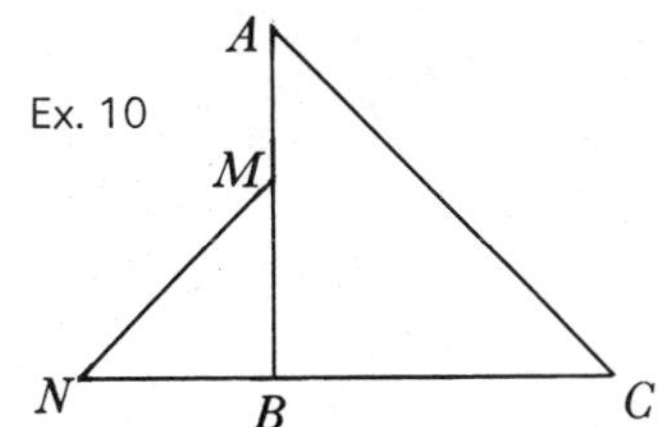

Ex. 10

10. Given: $\overline{AB} \perp \overline{NC}$ at B, $\dfrac{BN}{BC} = \dfrac{BM}{BA}$

Prove: $\angle N \cong \angle C$

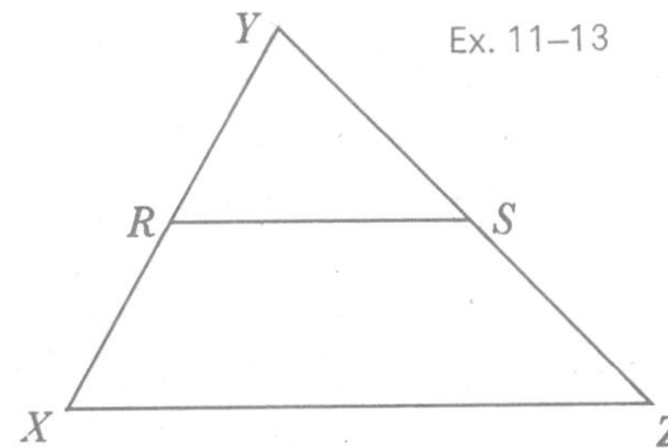

Ex. 11–13

11. Given: R is the midpoint of $\overline{XY}$,
S is the midpoint of $\overline{ZY}$.

Prove: $\triangle RYS \sim \triangle XYZ$

12. Given: $\dfrac{RY}{XY} = \dfrac{SY}{ZY}$

Prove: $\triangle RYS \sim \triangle XYZ$

13. Given: $XY = \frac{5}{2}RY$, $ZY = \frac{5}{2}SY$

Prove: $\triangle RYS \sim \triangle XYZ$

14. Given: $\square FGHI$

Prove: $\triangle HGJ \sim \triangle KIH$

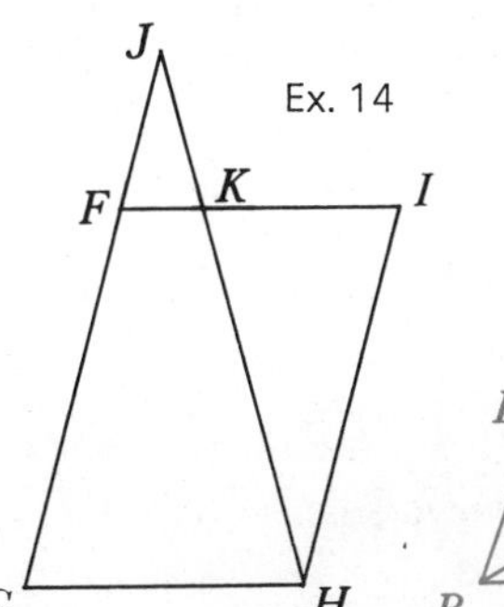

Ex. 14

Ⓒ **15.** Given: $\triangle ADB \cong \triangle AEC$

Prove: $\triangle ABC \sim \triangle AED$

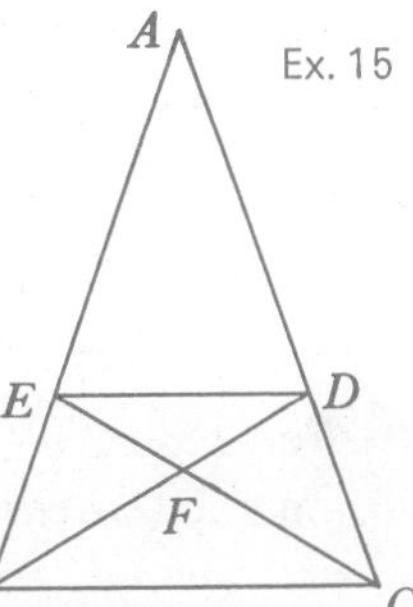

Ex. 15

10.7 Parallel Lines, Proportional Segments

On page 154, we proved that if a line parallel to one side of a triangle bisects either of the other two sides, it bisects both of them. Now we will show that no matter where this parallel line intersects the other two sides, the corresponding segments on the sides are proportional.

Gene Kuechmann

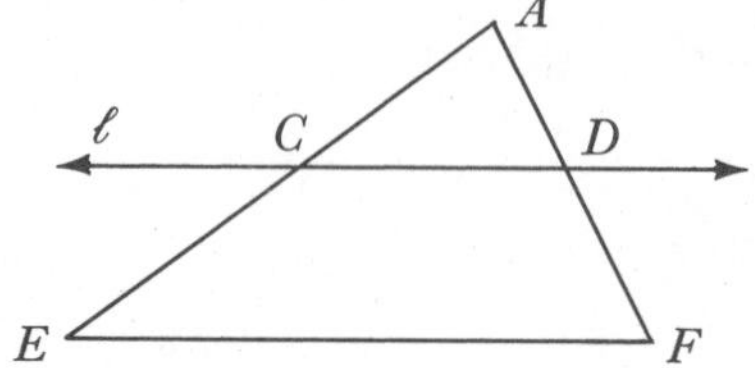

Given: $\ell \parallel \overline{EF}$

Prove: $\frac{CE}{AC} = \frac{DF}{AD}$

Proof:

STATEMENTS	REASONS
1. $\ell \parallel \overline{EF}$	1. Given
2. $\triangle AEF \sim \triangle ACD$	2. If a line $\parallel$ to 1 side of a $\triangle$ intersects the other 2 sides, a $\sim$ $\triangle$ is formed.
3. $\frac{AE}{AC} = \frac{AF}{AD}$	3. Definition of $\sim$ polygons
4. $AE = AC + CE$, $AF = AD + DF$	4. Definition of between
5. $\frac{AC + CE}{AC} = \frac{AD + DF}{AD}$	5. Substitution (steps 3 and 4)
6. $\frac{AC}{AC} + \frac{CE}{AC} = \frac{AD}{AD} + \frac{DF}{AD}$	6. Definition of addition of fractions
7. $\frac{CE}{AC} = \frac{DF}{AD}$	7. Subtract 1 from both sides. $\left(\frac{AC}{AC} = \frac{AD}{AD} = 1\right)$

The converse of the statement proved above can also be proved (see Exercise 39). The two are combined here in one theorem.

Proportional Segments Theorem for a Triangle

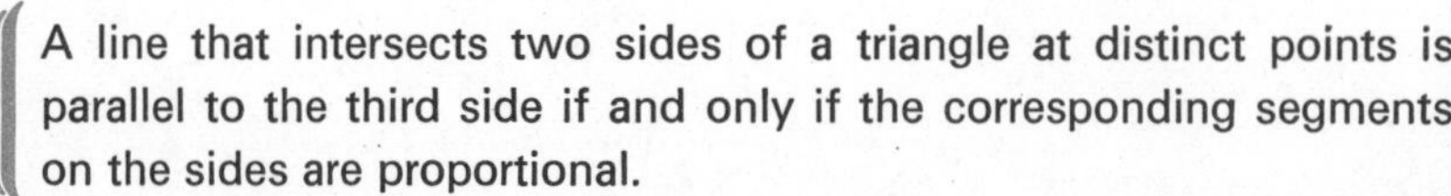

A line that intersects two sides of a triangle at distinct points is parallel to the third side if and only if the corresponding segments on the sides are proportional.

The next theorem is a corollary of the one above.

Proportional Segments Theorem for Parallels

Three parallel lines intercept proportional corresponding segments on any two transversals.

Given: $k \parallel \ell \parallel n$, transversals s and t

Prove: $\frac{AC}{CE} = \frac{BD}{DF}$

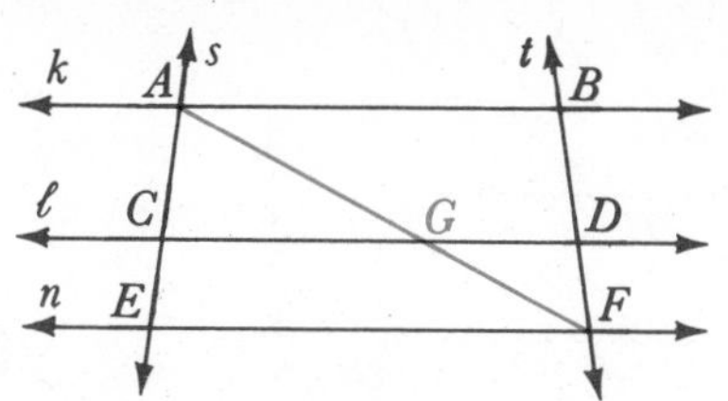

Proof:

STATEMENTS	REASONS
1. Join A and F.	1. 2 points determine a line.
2. In $\triangle AEF$, $\frac{AC}{CE} = \frac{AG}{GF}$. In $\triangle FBA$, $\frac{BD}{DF} = \frac{AG}{GF}$.	2. Proportional Segments Theorem for a $\triangle$
3. $\frac{AC}{CE} = \frac{BD}{DF}$	3. Substitution

The Proportional Segments Theorem for Parallels can be extended to any number of parallel lines and any number of transversals. But when there are more than two segments on each transversal, fractions are not the best way to express the ratios. For example,

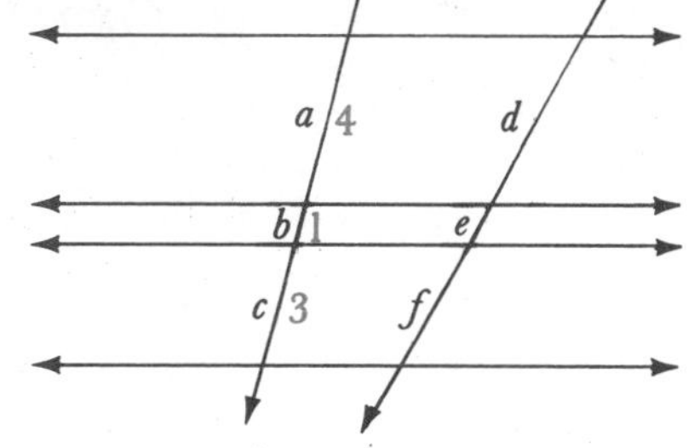

The ratios can be described by using fractions $\frac{a}{b} = \frac{4}{1}, \frac{b}{c} = \frac{1}{3}, \frac{a}{c} = \frac{4}{3}$

or by using **continued ratios.** $a:b:c = 4:1:3$

If the lines are parallel, $a:b:c = d:e:f = 4:1:3$.

Continued ratios can be used to set up proportions to be solved, but care must be taken to use *corresponding terms.*

Example: If $d:e:f = 4:1:3$ and $e = 1.5$, find d and f.

$d:e:f = 4:1:3$ $\quad \frac{d}{e} = \frac{4}{1}$ ◀ Write a proportion. ▶ $\frac{e}{f} = \frac{1}{3}$ $\quad d:e:f = 4:1:3$

$\frac{d}{1.5} = \frac{4}{1}$ ◀ Substitute 1.5 for e. ▶ $\frac{1.5}{f} = \frac{1}{3}$

$d = 6$ ◀ Solve the proportion. ▶ $f = 4.5$

Exercises 10.7

Ⓐ 1. Compare the lengths of the segments on r, in the second figure above. Are the segments in the ratio 4:1:3?

2. Compare the lengths of the segments on s, t, and $\overleftrightarrow{AF}$, at the top of the page. Do the results seem to agree with the theorem?

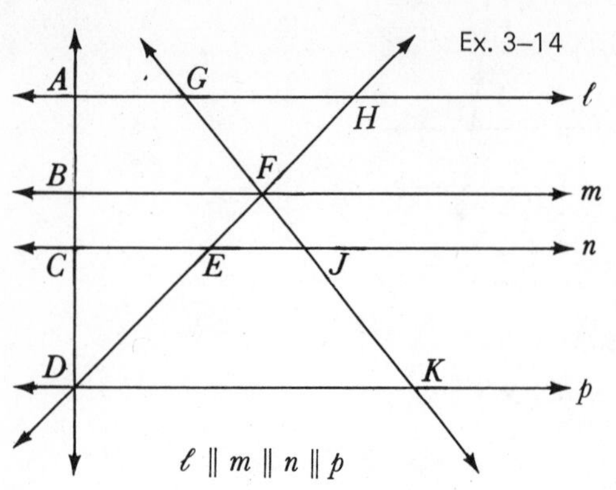

3–5. For each segment, name the corresponding segments on the other transversals in the figure.

3. $\overline{AB}$ **4.** $\overline{FJ}$ **5.** $\overline{ED}$

6–9. Refer to the figure. Name two ratios equal to the given ratio.

6. $\frac{HF}{FE}$ **7.** $\frac{GF}{FK}$ **8.** $\frac{CD}{AC}$ **9.** $\frac{DE}{EF}$

10–12. Refer to the figure. State a proportion for all sides of the given triangles.

10. $\triangle DAH$, $\triangle DBF$ **11.** $\triangle DCE$, $\triangle DAH$ **12.** $\triangle DFK$, $\triangle EFJ$

13. Use the figure to name two continued ratios equal to $AB:BC:CD$.

14. If $KJ:JF:FG = 3:1:2$, what other segments in the figure are in this same continued ratio?

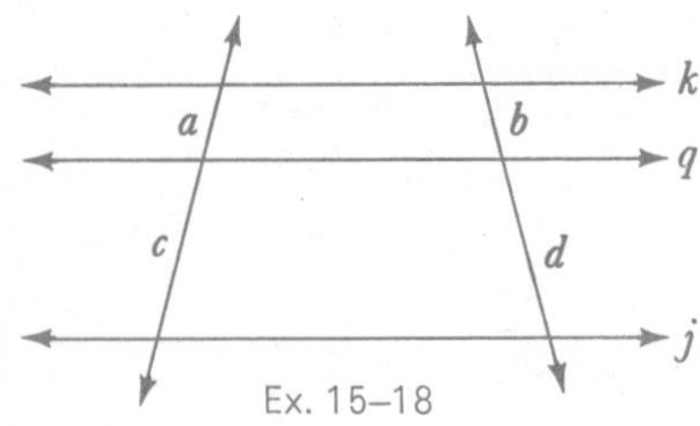

Ex. 15–18

Ⓑ **15–18.** If $k \parallel q \parallel j$ in the figure, use the given information to find the length of the fourth segment.

15. $a = 3, b = 2, c = 6$ **16.** $b = 3, c = 12, d = 9$

17. $c = 6\frac{2}{3}, d = 5, b = 3$ **18.** $b = 2, a = 3, c = 7\frac{1}{2}$

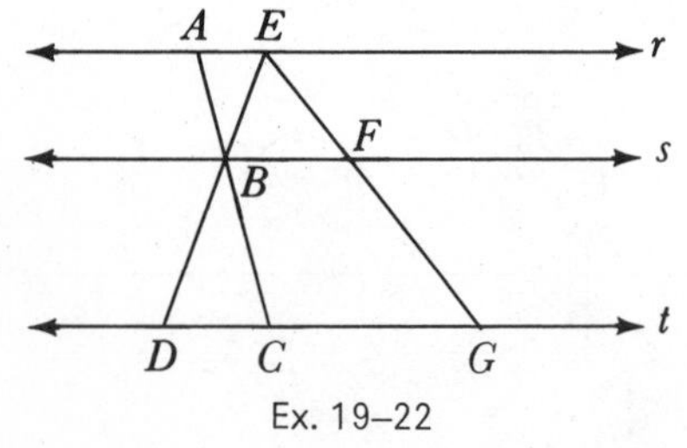

Ex. 19–22

19–22. $r \parallel s \parallel t$ in the figure.

19. If $AB = 2$, $BC = 5$, and $EB = 3$, $BD =$ ______.

20. If $BD = 6$, $BE = 3$, and $BC = 5$, $AB =$ ______.

21. If $BE = 3$, $DE = 8$, and $EG = 10$, $EF =$ ______.

22. If $EF = 3$, $BE = 2$, and $EG = 12$, $ED =$ ______.

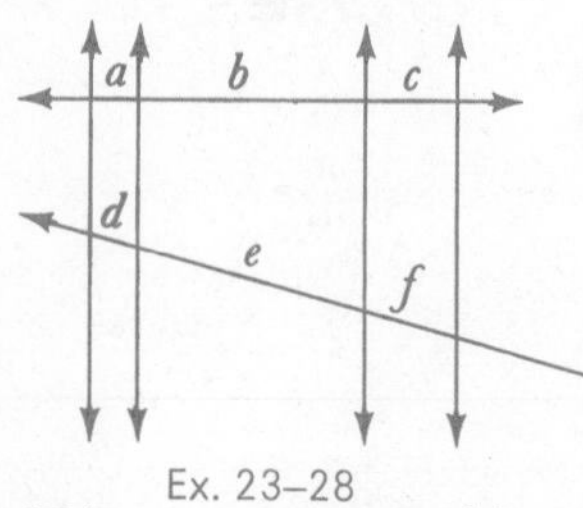

Ex. 23–28

23–28. The vertical lines in the figure are parallel; $a:b:c = 1:5:2$.

23. If $a = 3$, find b and c. **24.** If $c = 4$, find a and b.

25. $e:f:d =$ ______ **26.** $f:e:d =$ ______

27. If $e = 2.5$, find d and f. **28.** If $f = 0.5$, find d and e.

construction: separate a segment into segments in a given ratio

1. Given: Any segment $\overline{AB}$ to be separated into segments in the ratio 4:3:1

A B

2. Construct $\overrightarrow{AP}$. Mark off $4 + 3 + 1$ or 8 congruent segments on $\overrightarrow{AP}$, starting at A.

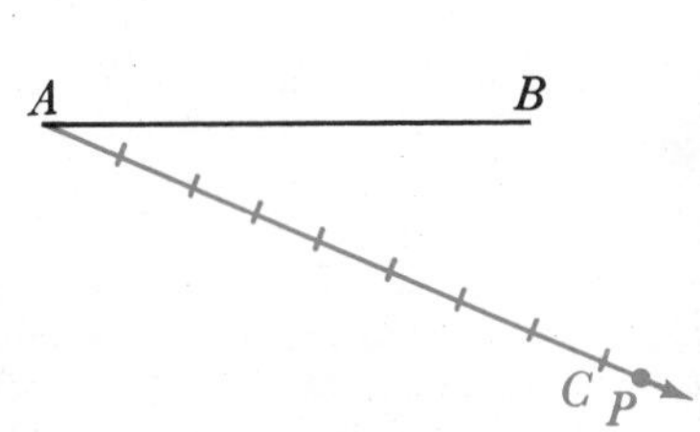

3. Join B and C. At the end of 4 segments on $\overrightarrow{AP}$ construct a parallel to $\overline{BC}$. Count off 3 more segments and construct a parallel to $\overline{BC}$.

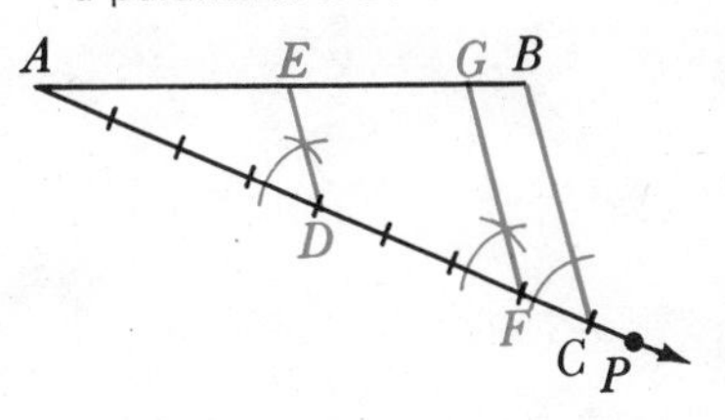

29. How is it decided how many congruent segments to mark off on $\overrightarrow{AP}$?

30. Why isn't a parallel to $\overline{BC}$ constructed at every point marked on $\overrightarrow{AP}$?

31. How are the points chosen at which to construct parallels?

32. Why is $AE:EG:GB = 4:3:1$?

33–38. Construct a segment of the given length. Then use the construction above to separate it into segments in the given ratio.

33. 6 cm, 4:2:1 **34.** 9 cm, 2:3:2 **35.** 10 cm, 2:3:4

36. 11 cm, 2:5:3 **37.** 12 cm, 2:3:5:4 **38.** 13 cm, 3:2:4:5

© **39.** Prove that if a line intersects two sides of a triangle at distinct points so that the corresponding segments on the sides are proportional, then the line is parallel to the third side. HINT: Copy the figure on page 352; interchange the *Given* and *Prove*; reverse the order of the statements (but one more statement is needed).

40. Two nonenlarging projection systems are shown. Explain why, in each case, ratios of segments in the image on the screen are equal to the ratios of segments in the picture.

41. Prove that the bisector of an angle of a triangle separates the opposite side into segments proportional to the sides they intersect.

HINT: Let $\overleftrightarrow{AE} \parallel \overline{CD}$. Write a proportion using lengths of segments on $\overline{BE}$ and $\overline{BA}$. Then prove $CE = CA$.

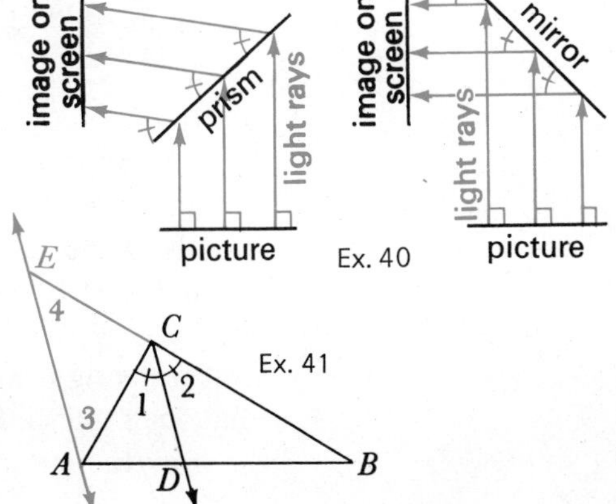

Ex. 40

Ex. 41

Areas of Similar Figures

Gene Kuechmann

Some of the oldest puzzle problems in geometry have to do with "doubling" the size of a figure. Choose a small triangle in the photograph. Then try to choose a triangle that is twice as large.

The puzzle, of course, is in the words. When is one triangle *twice as large as* another? When its sides are twice as long? Or when its area is twice as large? Do these mean the same or different things?

In the figures below, let $\triangle ABC \sim \triangle DEF$.

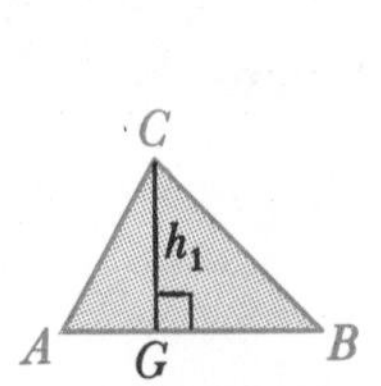

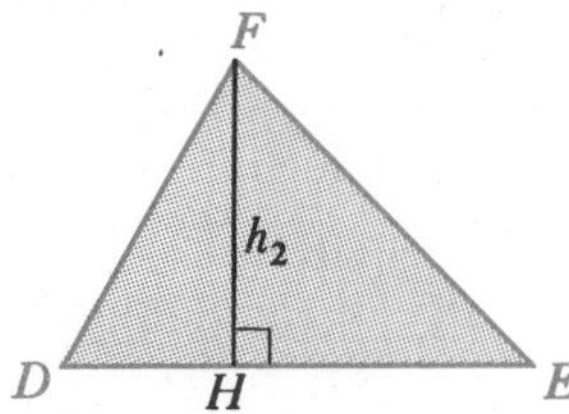

$$\text{area } \triangle ABC = \tfrac{1}{2}AB \cdot h_1$$

$$\text{area } \triangle DEF = \tfrac{1}{2}DE \cdot h_2$$

$$\frac{\text{area } \triangle ABC}{\text{area } \triangle DEF} = \frac{\frac{1}{2}AB \cdot h_1}{\frac{1}{2}DE \cdot h_2}$$

$$= \frac{AB}{DE} \cdot \frac{h_1}{h_2}$$

But $\triangle BGC \sim \triangle EHF$ by the AA Similarity Theorem, so $\dfrac{h_1}{h_2} = \dfrac{BC}{EF}$

We are given that $\triangle ABC \sim \triangle DEF$, so $\dfrac{BC}{EF} = \dfrac{AB}{DE}$

By substitution, $\dfrac{h_1}{h_2} = \dfrac{AB}{DE}$

Substituting this last result in the area proportion above, we have

$$\frac{\text{area } \triangle ABC}{\text{area } \triangle DEF} = \left(\frac{AB}{DE}\right)^2 \quad \text{and} \quad \frac{\text{area } \triangle ABC}{\text{area } \triangle DEF} = \left(\frac{h_1}{h_2}\right)^2$$

In fact, if $\overline{CG}$ and $\overline{FH}$ were corresponding medians or angle bisectors or any other corresponding segments related to the triangles, they would have the same ratio as the altitudes. So the ratio of the areas equals the square of the ratio of *any* two corresponding segments related to the triangles.

In the figures on page 357, d and e are lengths of the corresponding diagonals of similar quadrilaterals. The corresponding triangles can be proved similar using the SAS Similarity Theorem.

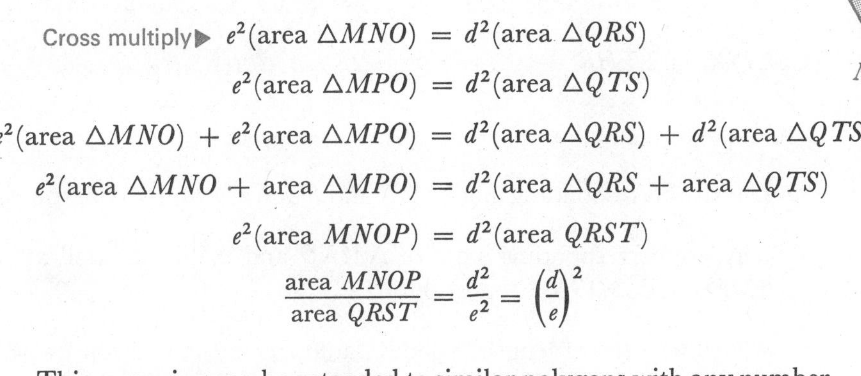

So $\dfrac{\text{area } \triangle MNO}{\text{area } \triangle QRS} = \left(\dfrac{d}{e}\right)^2 = \dfrac{d^2}{e^2}$ and $\dfrac{\text{area } \triangle MPO}{\text{area } \triangle QTS} = \left(\dfrac{d}{e}\right)^2 = \dfrac{d^2}{e^2}$

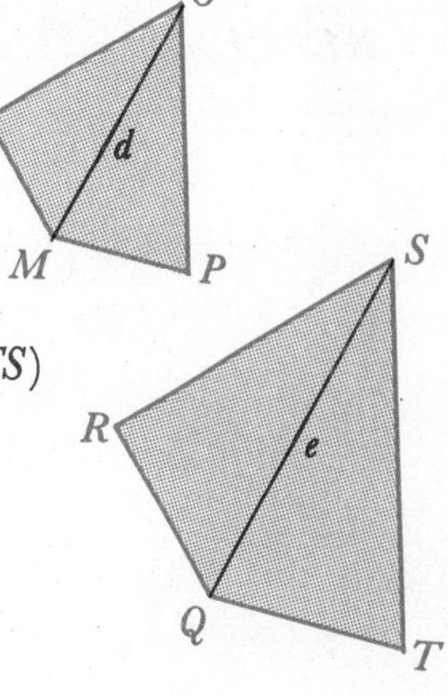

Cross multiply ▶

$$e^2(\text{area } \triangle MNO) = d^2(\text{area } \triangle QRS)$$

$$e^2(\text{area } \triangle MPO) = d^2(\text{area } \triangle QTS)$$

$$e^2(\text{area } \triangle MNO) + e^2(\text{area } \triangle MPO) = d^2(\text{area } \triangle QRS) + d^2(\text{area } \triangle QTS)$$

$$e^2(\text{area } \triangle MNO + \text{area } \triangle MPO) = d^2(\text{area } \triangle QRS + \text{area } \triangle QTS)$$

$$e^2(\text{area } MNOP) = d^2(\text{area } QRST)$$

$$\frac{\text{area } MNOP}{\text{area } QRST} = \frac{d^2}{e^2} = \left(\frac{d}{e}\right)^2$$

This reasoning can be extended to similar polygons with any number of sides, using any two corresponding segments, so we have this theorem:

The ratio of the areas of two similar polygons is the square of the ratio of any two corresponding segments.

Ratio of Areas Theorem

Examples: $\triangle ABC \sim \triangle DEF$ (See the figure on page 356.)

1. If $AB = 6$ and $DE = 9$, find $\dfrac{\text{area } \triangle ABC}{\text{area } \triangle DEF}$.

$$\frac{\text{area } \triangle ABC}{\text{area } \triangle DEF} = \left(\frac{AB}{DE}\right)^2 = \left(\tfrac{6}{9}\right)^2 = \left(\tfrac{2}{3}\right)^2 = \tfrac{4}{9}$$

2. If area $\triangle ABC = 50$ and area $\triangle DEF = 128$, find $\dfrac{BC}{EF}$.

$$\left(\frac{BC}{EF}\right)^2 = \frac{\text{area } \triangle ABC}{\text{area } \triangle DEF} = \tfrac{50}{128} = \tfrac{25}{64}$$

So, $\dfrac{BC}{EF} = \sqrt{\dfrac{25}{64}} = \dfrac{\sqrt{25}}{\sqrt{64}} = \dfrac{5}{8}$

3. If $AC = 8$, $DF = 12$, and area $\triangle ABC = 80$, find area $\triangle DEF$.

$$\frac{\text{area } \triangle ABC}{\text{area } \triangle DEF} = \left(\frac{AC}{DF}\right)^2 \blacktriangleright \frac{80}{\text{area } \triangle DEF} = \left(\frac{8}{12}\right)^2 \blacktriangleright \frac{80}{\text{area } \triangle DEF} = \left(\frac{2}{3}\right)^2$$

$$\frac{80}{\text{area } \triangle DEF} = \frac{4}{9}$$

$$4(\text{area } \triangle DEF) = 720$$

$$\text{area } \triangle DEF = 180$$

Exercises 10.8

Ⓐ **1–2.** Refer to $\triangle ABC$ and $\triangle DEF$, page 356. Why is the statement true?

1. $\angle BGC \cong \angle EHF$ **2.** $\angle B \cong \angle E$

3–7. Refer to the figures and equations at the top of page 357.

3. Why are corresponding angles at N and R and at P and T congruent?

4. Why are corresponding sides of $\triangle MNO$ and $\triangle QRS$, as well as of $\triangle MPO$ and $\triangle QTS$, proportional?

5. What five pairs of lengths besides d and e could have been used?

6. If $NP = 3$ and $RT = 5$, find the ratio of the areas.

7. If the areas are 16 and 25, find the ratio of corresponding sides.

8–12. Let $ABCDE$ and $MNOPR$ be similar polygons. Give your answers in lowest terms.

8. If $BC = 1$ and $NO = 3$, find the ratio of the areas.

9. If $BC = 2$ and $NO = 4$, find the ratio of the areas.

10. If the areas are 9 and 16, find the ratio of corresponding sides.

11. If the areas are 4 and 5, find the ratio of corresponding sides.

12. If the areas are 10 and 20, find the ratio of corresponding sides.

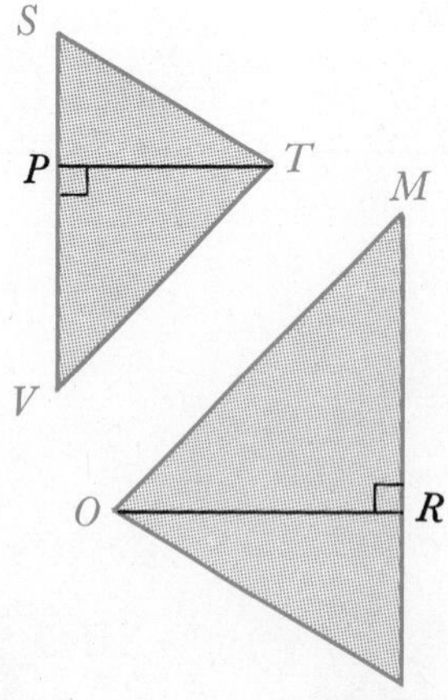

Ⓑ **13–18.** In the figure, $\triangle STV \sim \triangle LOM$. Use the given information to find the missing values.

	$\frac{ST}{LO}$	area $\triangle STV$	area $\triangle LOM$	TP	OR
13.	?	45	125	?	10
14.	?	32	98	?	14
15.	$\frac{5}{6}$	?	72	10	?
16.	$\frac{3}{4}$	?	48	9	?
17.	?	50	?	20	12
18.	?	48	?	12	15

19–20. Refer to the figure for Exercises 13–18. Let $\triangle STV \sim \triangle LOM$. Find the ratio of corresponding medians in lowest terms.

19. area $\triangle STV = 20$
area $\triangle LOM = 36$

20. area $\triangle STV = 45$
area $\triangle LOM = 48$

21–24. Let *RSTUV* and *KMNOP* be similar polygons.

21. If $RS = \sqrt{3}$ and $KM = 2\sqrt{2}$, the ratio of the areas is ______.

22. If $UV = 2\sqrt{5}$ and $OP = \sqrt{11}$, the ratio of the areas is ______.

23. If the areas are 124 and 225, the ratio of corresponding sides is ______.

24. If the areas are 125 and 169, the ratio of corresponding diagonals is ______.

Ⓒ **25.** Given: $\triangle MOP \sim \triangle QRS$, corresponding medians $\overline{OK}$ and $\overline{RL}$

Prove: $\dfrac{OK}{RL} = \dfrac{OM}{RQ}$

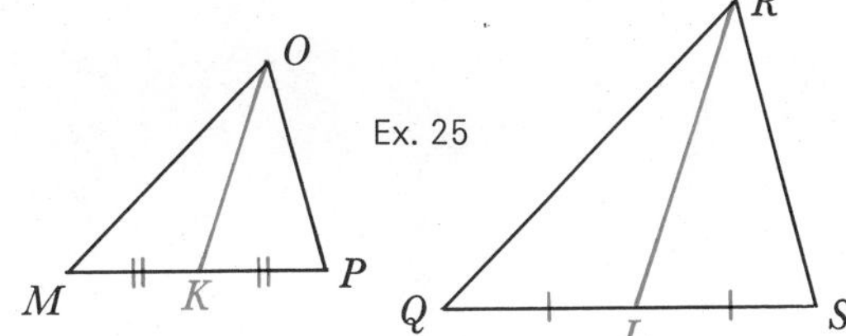

Ex. 25

26. Given: $\triangle DAB \sim \triangle CPE$, corresponding angle bisectors $\overrightarrow{AN}$ and $\overrightarrow{PT}$

Prove: $\dfrac{AN}{PT} = \dfrac{AD}{PC}$

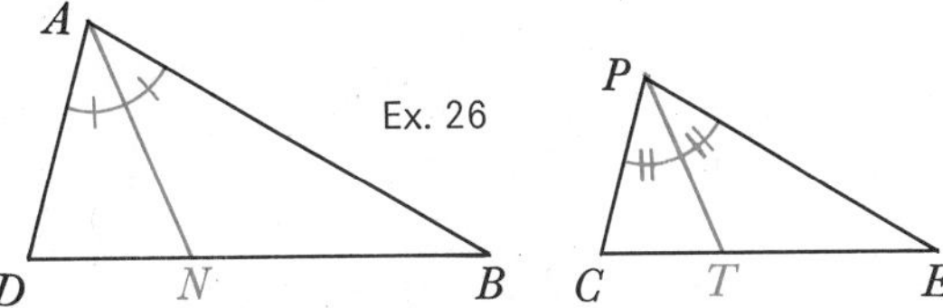

Ex. 26

Algebra Review

Review these skills:

- *dividing a polynomial by a monomial*
- *dividing a polynomial by a binomial*

Divide as indicated.

1. $\dfrac{5x^2 + 15x}{5x}$
2. $\dfrac{3n^3 - n^2}{n^2}$
3. $\dfrac{y^4 + y^2 + y}{y}$
4. $\dfrac{12a^3 - 4a^2}{-2a^2}$
5. $\dfrac{8r^3 + 3r}{4r}$
6. $\dfrac{14m^2n^2 - 21mn}{7mn}$
7. $\dfrac{18a^3b^4 + 12a^2b^3}{6ab^2}$
8. $\dfrac{x^2 + 4x + 4}{x + 2}$
9. $\dfrac{y^2 + 3y - 28}{y - 4}$
10. $\dfrac{6s^2 - 5s + 1}{2s - 1}$
11. $\dfrac{t^3 - 7t + 6}{t - 2}$
12. $\dfrac{27y^2 + 3y + 4}{3y + 1}$
13. $(x^3 + 3x^2 + 3x + 1) \div (x + 1)$
14. $(x^3 - 8) \div (x - 2)$
15. $(9c^3 - 12c^2 + c + 2) \div (3c - 2)$
16. $(y^3 + 8) \div (y + 2)$

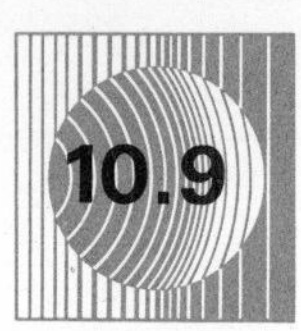

Similarity Transformations

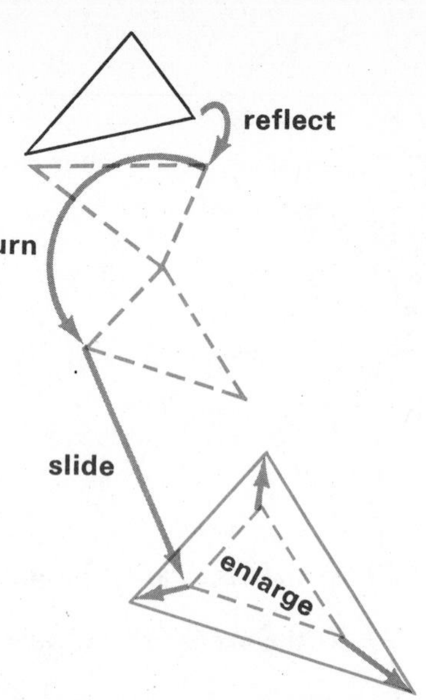

Each of these transformations preserves angle measure:

reflection	slide
turn	size change

If you applied any number of these transformations, in any order, as at the right, angle measures would be preserved. Since the angles of each image triangle are congruent to the angles of the original, all of the triangles are similar by the AA Similarity Theorem.

> Any combination of reflections, turns, slides, and size changes is a **similarity transformation.**

The magnitude of the size change (or size changes) involved in a similarity transformation determines the ratio of similarity of the figures.

Examples: **1.** $\triangle DEF$ is the image of $\triangle ABC$ under a similarity transformation that involves one size change of magnitude 4. The ratio of similarity of $\triangle DEF$ to $\triangle ABC$ is $\frac{4}{1}$.

2. $\triangle MOP$ is the image of $\triangle RST$ under a similarity transformation that involves one size change of magnitude $\frac{1}{3}$. The ratio of similarity of $\triangle MOP$ to $\triangle RST$ is $\frac{1}{3}$.

3. A similarity transformation involving size changes of magnitudes 6 and $\frac{2}{3}$ applied to $\triangle FST$ gives image $\triangle HRD$. The ratio of similarity of $\triangle HRD$ to $\triangle FST$ is $\frac{2}{3} \cdot \frac{6}{1}$, or $\frac{4}{1}$.

Exercises 10.9

Ⓐ **1.** Which of the transformations applied to the triangle above preserve congruence?

2. Which preserve similarity?

3. If a similarity transformation does not involve a size change, what is the ratio of similarity of the given figure to its image?

4. If a similarity transformation involves one size change, of magnitude k, what is the ratio of similarity of the image to the given figure? Of the given figure to its image?

Ⓑ **5–12.** Each similarity transformation involves a size transformation. Complete the chart.

	Given triangle	Image	Magnitude of size change
5.	$\triangle BDC$	$\triangle ABC$	?
6.	$\triangle ADB$	$\triangle ABC$	?
7.	$\triangle BDC$	$\triangle ADB$	?
8.	$\triangle ADB$	$\triangle BDC$	?
9.	$\triangle RVS$	?	$\frac{12}{5}$
10.	$\triangle SVR$	?	$\frac{13}{5}$
11.	$\triangle RST$	?	$\frac{5}{13}$
12.	$\triangle TSR$	?	$\frac{12}{13}$

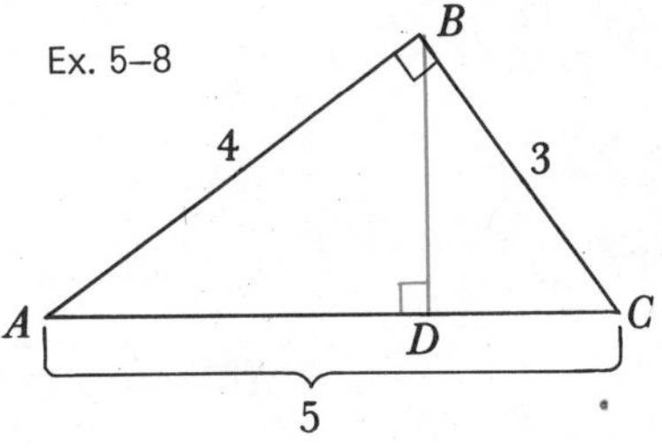

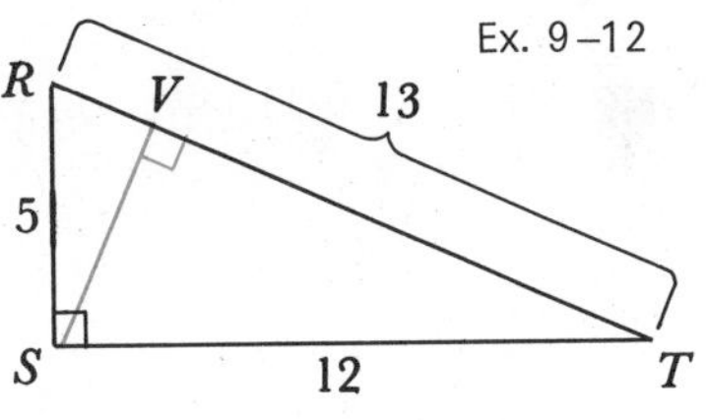

Ⓒ **13–20.** Refer to the figures above. Which transformation described below, combined with a size change and applied to the given triangle, gives the image named?

a. 90° turn around D clockwise

b. 90° turn around V counterclockwise

c. reflection over $\overleftrightarrow{BC}$ and turn around C of $m\angle C$ counterclockwise

d. reflection over $\overleftrightarrow{RS}$ and turn around R of $m\angle R$ counterclockwise

e. reflection over $\overleftrightarrow{AB}$ and turn around A of $m\angle A$ clockwise

f. reflection over $\overleftrightarrow{ST}$ and turn around T of $m\angle T$ clockwise

	Given △	Image
13.	$\triangle BDC$	$\triangle ABC$
15.	$\triangle ADB$	$\triangle ABC$
17.	$\triangle ADB$	$\triangle BDC$

	Given △	Image
14.	$\triangle SVR$	$\triangle TVS$
16.	$\triangle RST$	$\triangle SVT$
18.	$\triangle RVS$	$\triangle RST$

Chapter 10 Review

10.1

1–6. Let $\frac{a}{b} = \frac{4}{10}$.

1. $\frac{a}{b}$ and $\frac{4}{10}$ are ______ ratios.

2. Name the means and extremes.

3. $\frac{4}{10}$ (is, is not) in lowest terms.

4. $4b =$ ______

5. $\frac{a}{4} =$ ______

6. $\frac{10}{b} =$ ______

7. If $m = 3$ and $n = 5$, then $\frac{m}{n} =$ ______.

8. Solve: **a.** $\frac{x}{4} = \frac{9}{5}$ **b.** $\frac{13}{y} = \frac{2}{3}$

10.2

9. Define *similar polygons.*

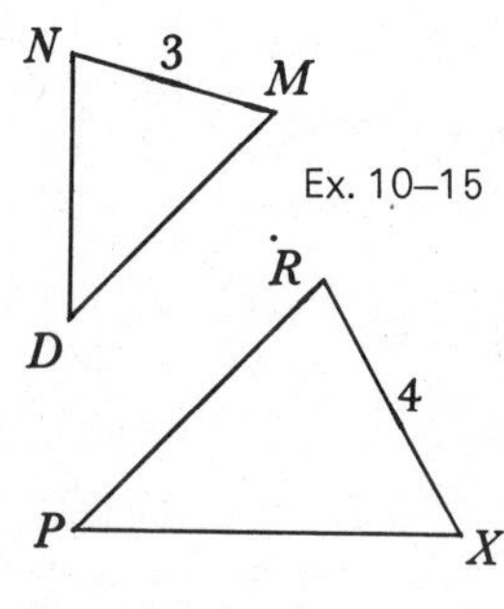

Ex. 10–15

10–15. Refer to the figures. Let $\triangle DMN \sim \triangle PXR$.

10. Name the corresponding angles and sides.

11. For $\triangle DMN \sim \triangle PXR$, the ratio of similarity is ______.

12. $MN =$ ______ $\cdot XR$

13. If $ND = 5$, $RP =$ ______.

14. $DM =$ ______ $\cdot PX$

15. If $m\angle N = 75$, ______ $= 75$.

10.3

16–25. Refer to the figures. Does the given information mean that $\triangle STV \sim \triangle ABC$?

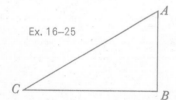

Ex. 16–25

16. $\angle A \cong \angle S$

17. $\angle B \cong \angle T$, $\angle C \cong \angle V$

18. $\angle A \cong \angle S$, $\overline{AB} \perp \overline{BC}$, $\overline{VT} \perp \overline{TS}$

19. $\triangle ABC \sim \triangle FGK$, $\triangle STV \sim \triangle FGK$

10.4

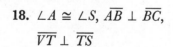

20. $\frac{AB}{ST} = \frac{BC}{TV}$

21. $\frac{AB}{ST} = \frac{AC}{SV}$, $\angle A \cong \angle S$

22. $\frac{AB}{ST} = \frac{BC}{TV} = \frac{AC}{SV}$

23. $\frac{AB}{ST} = \frac{BC}{TV}$, $\angle C \cong \angle V$

10.5

24. $m\angle B = m\angle T = 90$, $\frac{AB}{ST} = \frac{BC}{TV}$

25. $\overline{AB} \perp \overline{BC}$, $\overline{VT} \perp \overline{TS}$, $\frac{AC}{SV} = \frac{AB}{ST}$

26–31. Refer to the figure.

26. $\triangle EFH \sim$ ______ $\sim$ ______

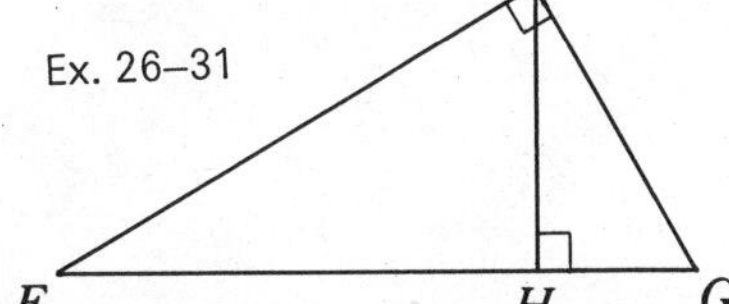

27. FH is the ______ of EH and HG.

28. The geometric mean of EH and EG is ______.

29. FG is the geometric mean of HG and ______.

30. If $FH = 6$ and $HG = 4$, then $EH =$ ______.

31. If $FG = 16$ and $EG = 64$, then $HG =$ ______.

32–41. Is the given abbreviation a part of the name of a similarity theorem in this book? If your answer is yes, state the theorem. **10.6**

32. SAS **33.** HL **34.** ASA **35.** LL **36.** SSA

37. AAS **38.** HA **39.** SSS **40.** LA **41.** AA

42–47. $k \parallel \ell \parallel n \parallel s$ in the figure. **10.7**

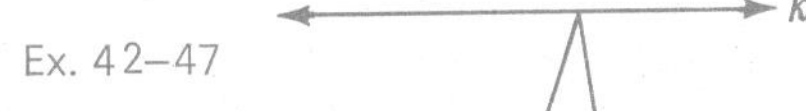

Ex. 42–47

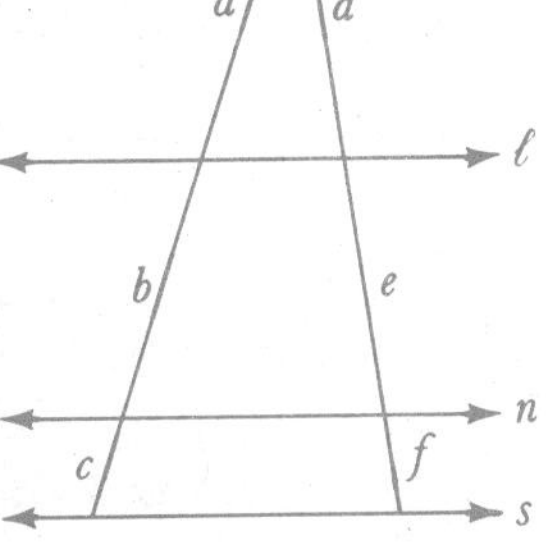

42. $\frac{a}{b} =$ ______ **43.** $\frac{c}{b} =$ ______

44. $d:e:f =$ ______ **45.** $c:b:a =$ ______

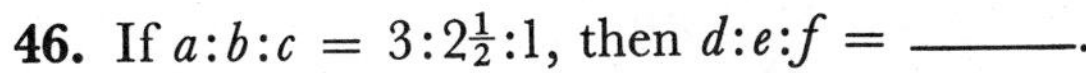

46. If $a:b:c = 3:2\frac{1}{2}:1$, then $d:e:f =$ ______.

47. If $a:b:c = 3:2\frac{1}{2}:1$ and $b = 10$, find a and c.

48–49. Refer to the figure for Exercises 16–25. **10.8**

48. If $\triangle STV \sim \triangle ABC$ and $\frac{ST}{AB} = \frac{2}{3}$, then $\frac{\text{area } \triangle STV}{\text{area } \triangle ABC} =$ ______.

49. If $\frac{\text{area } \triangle ABC}{\text{area } \triangle STV} = \frac{36}{25}$, then corresponding altitudes of $\triangle ABC$ and $\triangle STV$ have the ratio ______.

50. Define *similarity transformation.* **10.9**

51. If $\triangle VSY$ is the image of $\triangle PMT$ under a similarity transformation that involves a size change of magnitude $\frac{1}{2}$, then $\frac{VS}{PM} =$ ______.

Chapter 10 Test

1–3. Let $\frac{c}{d} = \frac{2}{3}$.

1. $\frac{c}{d} = \frac{2}{3}$ is a ______.

2. $\frac{2}{3}$ is in ______ terms.

3. If $d = 2$, then 2 is the ______ of c and 3.

4. In similar polygons, corresponding angles are ______ and the ratios of corresponding ______ are equal.

5. For $\triangle AMN \sim \triangle BDC$, if the ratio of similarity is $\frac{3}{5}$, then $\frac{AM}{BD} =$ ______.

6. Solve: $\frac{d}{7} = \frac{3}{14}$

Ex. 7–16

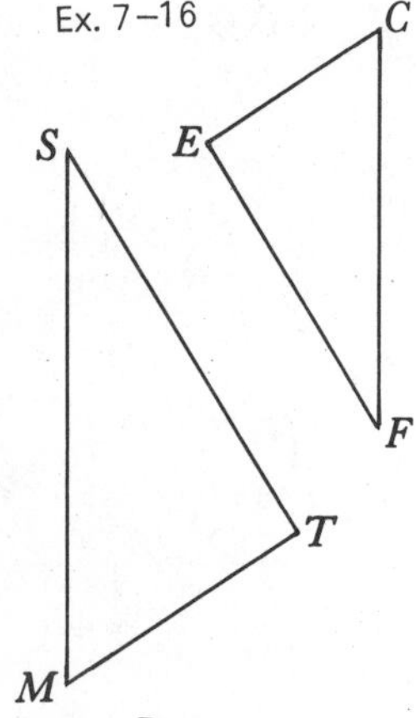

7–12. Refer to the figures. Using the given information, which theorem would be used to prove that $\triangle CFE \sim \triangle MST$?

7. $\angle F \cong \angle S$, $\angle E \cong \angle T$

8. $\overline{ST} \perp \overline{MT}$, $\overline{CE} \perp \overline{EF}$, $\angle F \cong \angle S$

9. $\frac{CF}{MS} = \frac{FE}{ST} = \frac{CE}{MT}$

10. $\triangle CFE \sim \triangle DPR$, $\triangle DPR \sim \triangle MST$

11. $\frac{CF}{MS} = \frac{FE}{ST}$, $\angle F \cong \angle S$

12. $\overline{ST} \perp \overline{TM}$, $\overline{CE} \perp \overline{EF}$, $\frac{CE}{MT} = \frac{EF}{TS}$

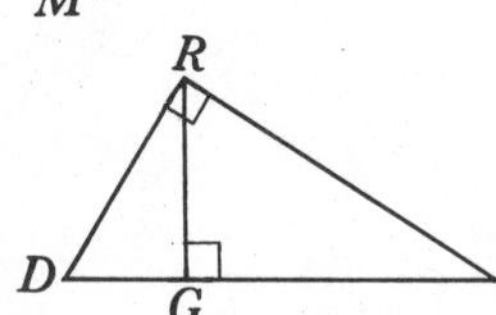

13–16. Refer to the figures. Let $\triangle CEF \sim \triangle MTS$.

13. If $\frac{CE}{MT} = \frac{5}{7}$ and $ST = 21$, then $FE =$ ______.

14. If $m\angle F = 32$, ______ $= 32$.

15. If $GR = 9$ and $PG = 27$, then $DG =$ ______.

16. If $DR = 2$ and $RP = 5$, then $\frac{\text{area } \triangle DGR}{\text{area } \triangle RGP} =$ ______.

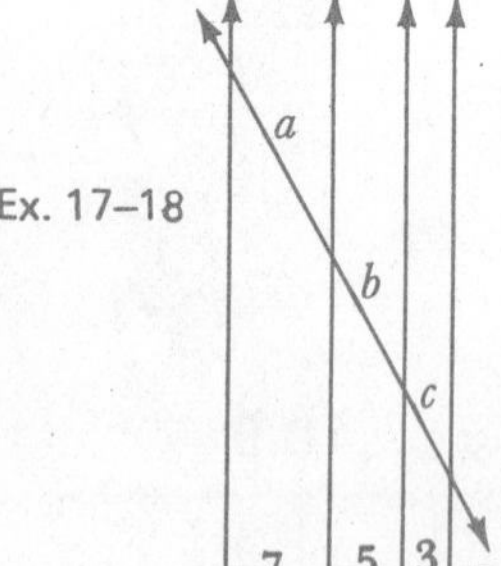

Ex. 17–18

17–18. Refer to the figure. Let $k \parallel \ell \parallel r \parallel s$.

17. $a{:}b{:}c =$ ______

18. If $c = 6$, find a and b.

19. If $\triangle A'B'C'$ is the image of $\triangle ABC$ under a similarity transformation that involves one size change, and for $\triangle A'B'C' \sim \triangle ABC$ the ratio of similarity is $\frac{2}{5}$, the size change has a magnitude of ______.

20. Given: $TU = 1$, $TW = 2$, $TV = 4$

Prove: $\triangle TUW \sim \triangle TWV$

W

V U T

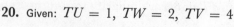

MINI-CHAPTER: TRIGONOMETRY

$\angle A$ is any acute angle. B and D are any two points on one side of $\angle A$.

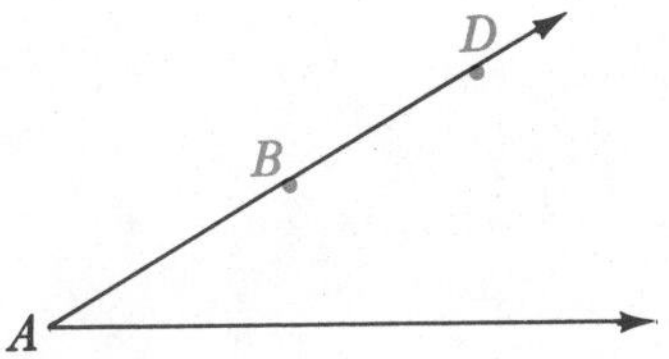

Draw $\overline{BC}$ and $\overline{DE}$ perpendicular to the other side of $\angle A$.

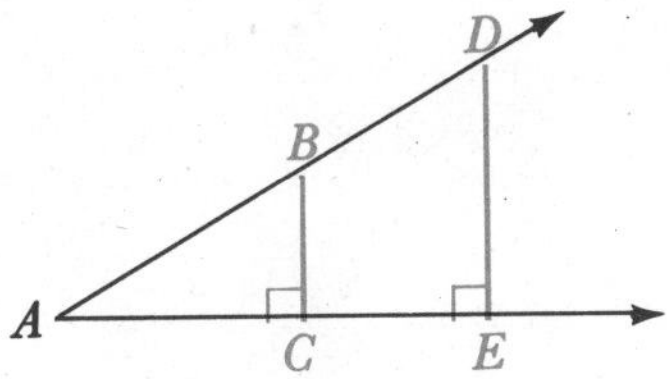

By the AA Similarity Theorem, $\triangle ACB \sim \triangle AED$

By the definition of similar polygons, $\frac{BC}{DE} = \frac{AB}{AD}$

By the properties of proportions (p. 325), $\frac{BC}{AB} = \frac{DE}{AD}$ ◀ corresponding sides ◀ corresponding sides

▲ sides of $\triangle ACB$ ▲ sides of $\triangle AED$

This shows that

> **If two triangles are similar, the ratio of any two sides of one triangle equals the ratio of the corresponding sides of the other.**

Look again at the ratio of the sides of right triangles ACB and AED. Since the triangles are different sizes, this ratio does not depend on the size of the right triangle, but only on $m\angle A$.

Side opposite $\angle A$ in each right triangle ▶ $\frac{BC}{AB} = \frac{DE}{AD}$ This ratio is called the **sine** of $m\angle A$, abbreviated sin $\angle A$.

Hypotenuse of each right triangle ▶

Example: $\sin \angle P = \frac{24}{25}$

$\sin \angle D = \frac{7}{25}$

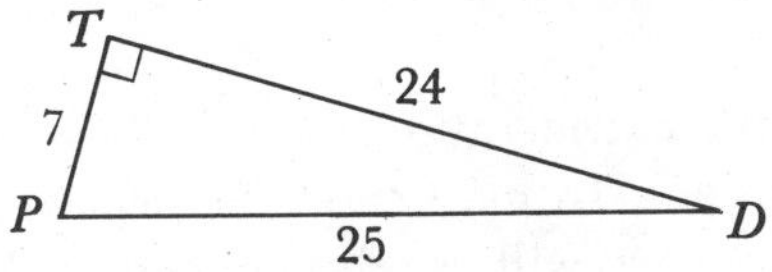

Use right triangle MNP to find sin $\angle M$. Then use each of the other two right triangles to find sin $\angle M$. Are the results equal?

Find sin $\angle MPN$. Find the sines of the angles corresponding to $\angle MPN$ in the other two triangles. (These three angles are congruent, so they have the same sine.)

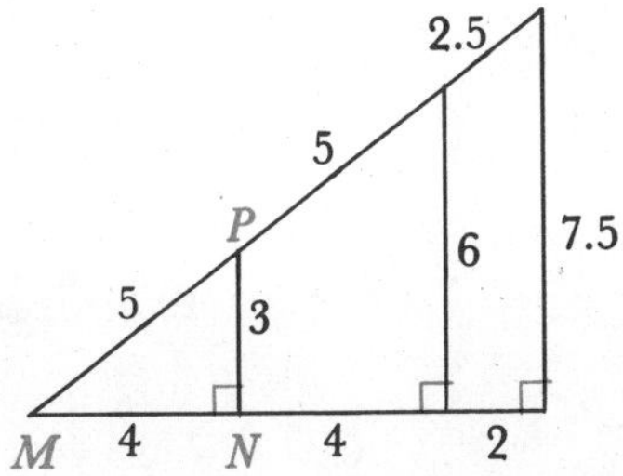

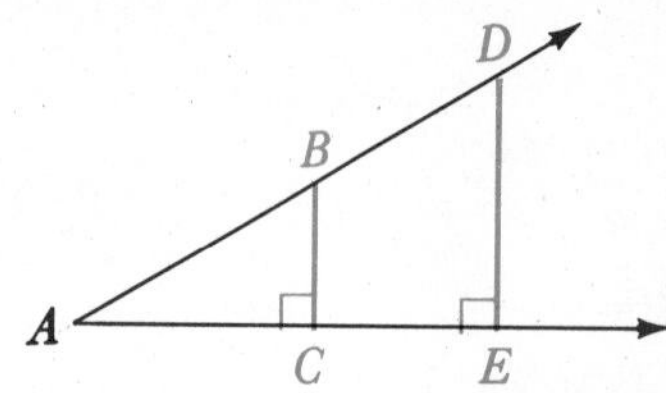

We used the ratios of the sides opposite $\angle A$ and the hypotenuses of right triangles ACB and AED to define sine of $m\angle A$. The ratios of the other pairs of corresponding sides are also equal, and these other ratios are also given special names. NOTE: The leg that is not *opposite* $\angle A$ is *adjacent* to $\angle A$.

These are called **trigonometric ratios.**

Name	Abbreviation	Ratio
sine of $m\angle A$	$\sin \angle A$	$\dfrac{\text{side opposite } \angle A}{\text{hypotenuse}}$
cosine of $m\angle A$	$\cos \angle A$	$\dfrac{\text{side adjacent to } \angle A}{\text{hypotenuse}}$
tangent of $m\angle A$	$\tan \angle A$	$\dfrac{\text{side opposite } \angle A}{\text{side adjacent to } \angle A}$

As before, the ratio of sides means the ratio of their lengths.

Exercises: Find the sine, cosine, and tangent of each acute angle.

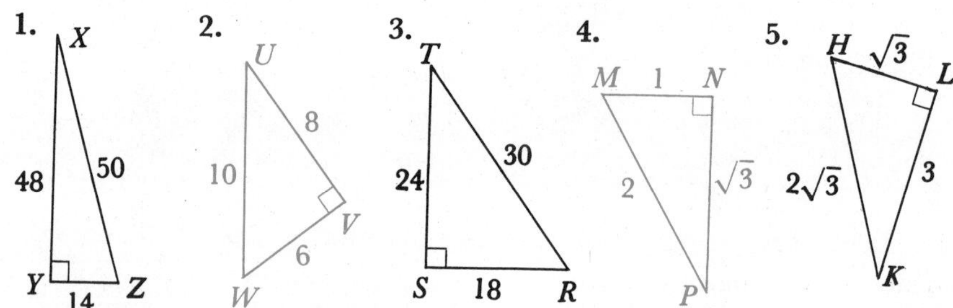

Example: $\tan \angle X = \frac{14}{48} = \frac{7}{24}$ ◀ in lowest terms

Is $\sin \angle P = \sin \angle K$ in the figures above? Is $\sin \angle M = \sin \angle H$? $m\angle P = 30$ and $m\angle M = 60$. What is $m\angle K$? $m\angle H$?

Trigonometric ratios are usually expressed using decimals rather than fractions. In most cases the decimal is an approximation, but for convenience we will use the symbol $=$ throughout.

Examples: $\sin 30^\circ = \frac{1}{2} = 0.5$

$\sin 60^\circ = \frac{1}{2}\sqrt{3} = 0.866$ (to the nearest thousandth)

Exercises: Give the sine, cosine, and tangent of each acute angle of figures 1–5 above as a decimal approximation to the nearest thousandth.

Because every angle with the same measure has the same sine, the same cosine, and the same tangent, a table can be made showing angle measures and decimal approximations for the corresponding trigonometric ratios. The table on page 368 lists approximations to the nearest thousandth for angle measures in degrees from 1° to 89°.

USING A TABLE OF APPROXIMATIONS

1. To find cos 27° ▶ Find 27 in the column headed $m\angle A$. Then look across the row to the column headed cos $\angle A$. (cos 27° = 0.891)

2. To find x, given tan x = 2.356 ▶ Find 2.356 in the column headed tan $\angle A$. Then look across the row to the column headed $m\angle A$. (x = 67°)

Exercises

Use the table to find each approximation.

1. sin 39° **2.** cos 64° **3.** tan 23° **4.** sin 45°

5. cos 45° **6.** tan 75° **7.** sin 57° **8.** cos 17°

Use the table to find each angle measure.

9. sin x = 0.485 **10.** cos y = 0.225 **11.** tan a = 6.314

12. sin r = 0.990 **13.** cos b = 0.990 **14.** tan z = 0.306

You have seen that for a given angle measure there is exactly one value for the sine, cosine, or tangent. Conversely, a given value for sin x, cos x, or tan x corresponds to exactly one x between 0° and 90°.

In the table, find sin 87° and sin 88°. In view of the statement above, how can both of the statements below be true?

sin 87° = 0.999 sin 88° = 0.999

Some hand-held calculators give approximations for trigonometric ratios. These approximations may include nine or more digits following the decimal point and may cover many more angle measures than our table does. So if you do these exercises using a calculator, you should get a more accurate result than you can get using the table. (The usefulness of this additional accuracy would depend on the accuracy of the original measurements and the use to be made of the result.)

SINES, COSINES, AND TANGENTS

$m\angle A$	sin $\angle A$	cos $\angle A$	tan $\angle A$	$m\angle A$	sin $\angle A$	cos $\angle A$	tan $\angle A$
1°	0.017	1.000	0.017	46°	0.719	0.695	1.036
2	.035	0.999	.035	47	.731	.682	1.072
3	.052	.999	.052	48	.743	.669	1.111
4	.070	.998	.070	49	.755	.656	1.150
5	.087	.996	.087	50	.766	.643	1.192
6	.105	.995	.105	51	.777	.629	1.235
7	.122	.993	.123	52	.788	.616	1.280
8	.139	.990	.141	53	.799	.602	1.327
9	.156	.988	.158	54	.809	.588	1.376
10	.174	.985	.176	55	.819	.574	1.428
11	.191	.982	.194	56	.829	.559	1.483
12	.208	.978	.213	57	.839	.545	1.540
13	.225	.974	.231	58	.848	.530	1.600
14	.242	.970	.249	59	.857	.515	1.664
15	.259	.966	.268	60	.866	.500	1.732
16	.276	.961	.287	61	.875	.485	1.804
17	.292	.956	.306	62	.883	.469	1.881
18	.309	.951	.325	63	.891	.454	1.963
19	.326	.946	.344	64	.899	.438	2.050
20	.342	.940	.364	65	.906	.423	2.145
21	.358	.934	.384	66	.914	.407	2.246
22	.375	.927	.404	67	.921	.391	2.356
23	.391	.921	.424	68	.927	.375	2.475
24	.407	.914	.445	69	.934	.358	2.605
25	.423	.906	.466	70	.940	.342	2.747
26	.438	.899	.488	71	.946	.326	2.904
27	.454	.891	.510	72	.951	.309	3.078
28	.469	.883	.532	73	.956	.292	3.271
29	.485	.875	.554	74	.961	.276	3.487
30	.500	.866	.577	75	.966	.259	3.732
31	.515	.857	.601	76	.970	.242	4.011
32	.530	.848	.625	77	.974	.225	4.331
33	.545	.839	.649	78	.978	.208	4.705
34	.559	.829	.675	79	.982	.191	5.145
35	.574	.819	.700	80	.985	.174	5.671
36	.588	.809	.727	81	.988	.156	6.314
37	.602	.799	.754	82	.990	.139	7.115
38	.616	.788	.781	83	.993	.122	8.144
39	.629	.777	.810	84	.995	.105	9.514
40	.643	.766	.839	85	.996	.087	11.430
41	.656	.755	.869	86	.998	.070	14.301
42	.669	.743	.900	87	.999	.052	19.081
43	.682	.731	.933	88	.999	.035	28.636
44	.695	.719	.966	89	1.000	.017	57.290
45	.707	.707	1.000				

Trigonometry is used in surveying, navigation, astronomy, and a number of other fields. Here are some typical applications.

How high is the kite?

$$\frac{h}{152} = \sin 40°$$
$$h = 152 \sin 40°$$
$$= 152\ (0.643)$$
$$= 97.736 \text{ m high}$$

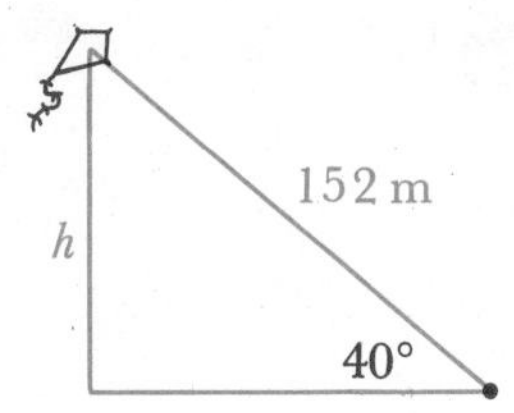

If a jet airplane takes off at an 18° angle to the runway, how high is the jet when it is over a point that is 170 m from its takeoff point?

$$\frac{a}{170} = \tan 18°$$
$$a = 170 \tan 18°$$
$$= 170\ (0.325)$$
$$= 55.25 \text{ m high}$$

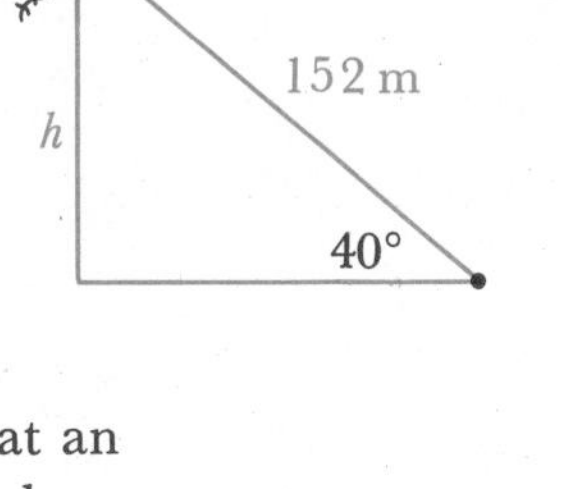

Leo de Wys, Inc.

Exercises

Use a trigonometric ratio to solve each exercise. Give your answers to the nearest hundredth or the nearest degree.

1. If a sudden wind lifted the kite shown above so the string made a 60° angle with the ground, how high would the kite be?

2. If you swam to the opposite shore on the line perpendicular to the near shore, how far would you swim?

3. If you rowed a boat back on the line that makes a 35° angle with the near shore, how far would you row?

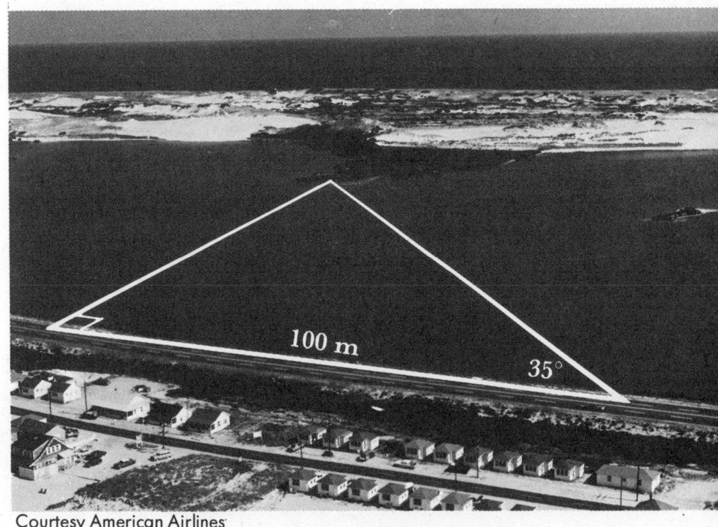

Courtesy American Airlines

4. How far above the water is the roadway of the bridge?

5. How far above the roadway does the bridge tower extend?

6. How far is the rider from the base of the rock formation?

7. How far from the rider is an eagle that is sitting on top of the rock formation?

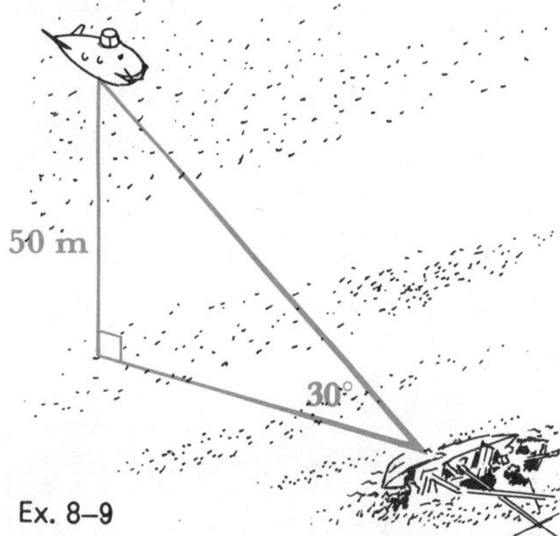

Ex. 8–9

8. How far is the submarine from the wreck on the ocean floor?

9. If the submarine drops vertically to the ocean floor from its present position, how far from the wreck will it be?

10. How far does the cable car drop vertically as it slides 21 m down the cable? How far does it drop for each foot it slides?

11. How far does the cable car travel horizontally as it slides 21 m down the cable? How far does it travel horizontally for each foot it slides?

Photos courtesy American Airlines

Ex. 12–13

Air Photographics

12. If a straight road were built from the fork at X to the intersection at Z, how long would the new road be?

13. How long would a road be from the intersection at Z to the highway at Y?

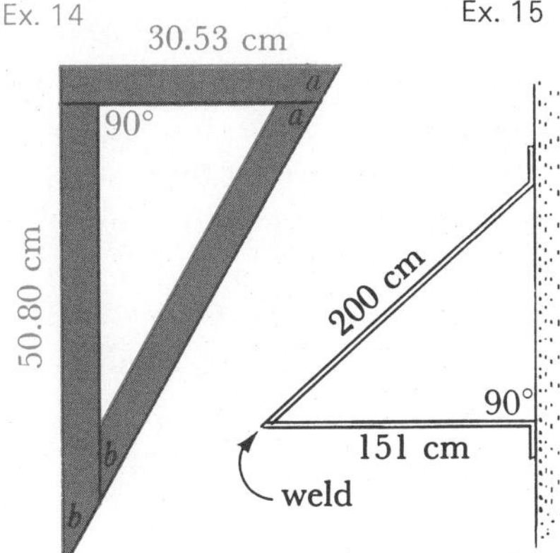

14. The wooden triangle is to be used as a shelf support. At what angles should the wood pieces be cut at a and b?

15. Two pieces of metal are to be welded into a wall bracket as shown. At what angle should the pieces be joined?

Ex. 16–17

Courtesy American Airlines

16. How far is it from the pier on the right to the ferry dock in the distance?

17. How much closer to the ferry dock is the pier on the left than the pier on the right?

18–19. When a car's brakes are the only thing keeping it from rolling downhill, the force on the brakes is $w \sin x°$, where w is the weight of the car.

18. Find the force on the brakes of a 3000-pound car parked on a 7° hill. NOTE: The force is in pounds.

19. Find the force on the brakes of a 2800-pound car parked on a 12° hill.

Ex. 18–19

Brent Jones

Chicago Rehabilitation Institute

20. A wheelchair ramp should not rise more than 1 cm for every 12 cm of horizontal distance covered. Can the ramp make an angle as large as 5° with the level ground?

21. A wheelchair ramp from the street to a curb 17.74 cm high is 2.54 m long. What angle does the ramp make with the street?

Brent Jones

22–23. To find the horizontal distance between two points on a hill, a surveyor may first measure the actual distance and then measure the angle of depression. Trigonometric ratios may then be used to find both the horizontal distance and how much lower one point is than the other.

22. If $d = 10$ m and $m\angle P = 5$, find x and y.

23. If $d = 10$ m and $m\angle P = 6$, find x and y.

24–25. To intercept 100% of the solar energy that strikes it, a flat solar-energy collector should be perpendicular to the sun's rays. If it is not, the percent (n) of solar energy it intercepts can be found by using the formula $n = 100 \cos x°$.

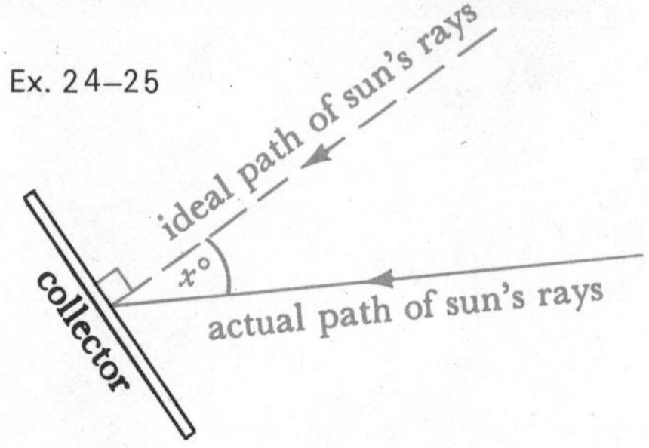

24. If the angle between the actual path of the sun's rays and the collector is 73°, what percent of the solar energy is intercepted?

25. If the sun's rays hit the ground at a 35° angle and the collector leans at a 45° angle, what percent of the solar energy is intercepted?

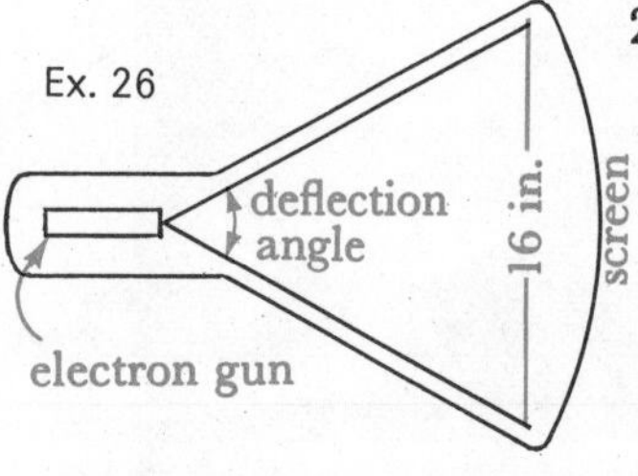

26. In a TV picture tube, the beams put out by the electron gun (at the back of the tube) form the picture on the screen. In older picture tubes, the deflection angle of the electron beams was 56°. Now that angle might be 114°. For a screen that is 16 inches from top to bottom, as shown, how much "thinner" from back to front can the TV set be made by using the larger deflection angle?

Cumulative Review: Chapters 8–10

Ch. 8

1. State the definition of a perpendicular line and plane.

2–8. Refer to the figure.

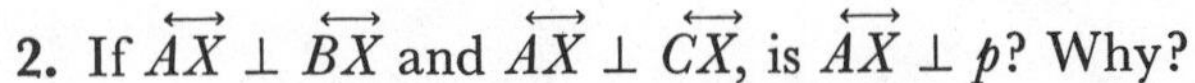

2. If $\overleftrightarrow{AX} \perp \overleftrightarrow{BX}$ and $\overleftrightarrow{AX} \perp \overleftrightarrow{CX}$, is $\overleftrightarrow{AX} \perp p$? Why?

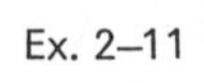

3. How many planes are perpendicular to $\overleftrightarrow{MG}$ at G?

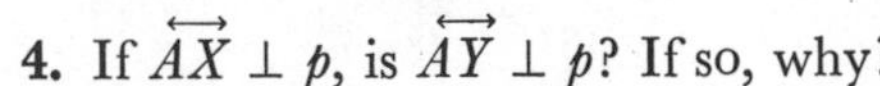

4. If $\overleftrightarrow{AX} \perp p$, is $\overleftrightarrow{AY} \perp p$? If so, why?

5. If $\overleftrightarrow{GM} \perp p$ and $\overleftrightarrow{GM} \perp \overleftrightarrow{MP}$, is $\overleftrightarrow{MP}$ in p? If so, why?

6. If $\overleftrightarrow{GM} \perp p$ and $\overleftrightarrow{AX} \perp p$, are G, M, A, and X coplanar?

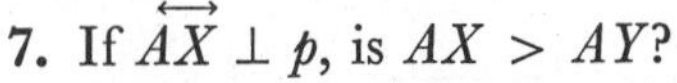

7. If $\overleftrightarrow{AX} \perp p$, is $AX > AY$?

8. When is AX the distance from A to plane p?

Ex. 2–11

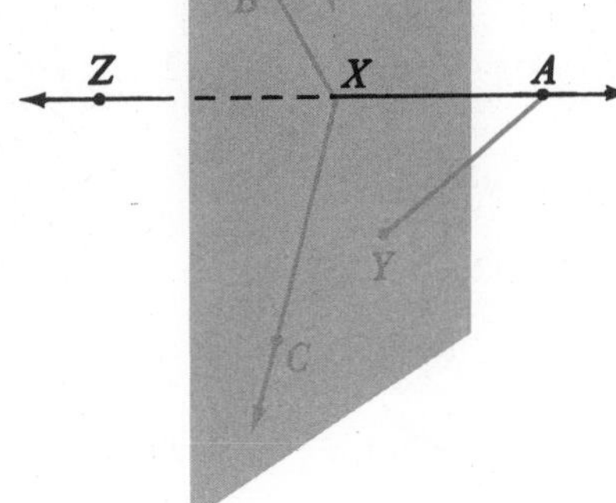

9–11. Refer to the figure. Plane p is the perpendicular bisecting plane of $\overline{AZ}$. Complete each statement.

9. $YA =$ ______ 10. $SA =$ ______

11. If $NA = NZ$, then N is ______.

Ch. 9

12–13. Find the area of each rectangle or square. (ℓ stands for length, w for width, and s for length of a side of a square.)

12. $\ell = 45$ m, $w = 42$ m 13. $s = 3\frac{1}{2}$

14. A triangle has a base with length 18.2 and a corresponding height of 14. What is the area of the triangle?

15. A parallelogram has a base with length $21\frac{1}{2}$ and a corresponding height of 6. Find its area.

16. A trapezoid has bases of lengths 14 and 22. The height is 9. Find its area.

17–20. Simplify each radical.

17. $\sqrt{45}$ 18. $\sqrt{\frac{2}{25}}$ 19. $\sqrt{\frac{1}{5}}$ 20. $\frac{3}{\sqrt{7}}$

21. A right triangle has legs of lengths 4 and 6. Find the length of the hypotenuse. (Leave your answer in simplified radical form.)

22. A triangle has sides of lengths 10, 24, and 26. Is it a right triangle?

23–24. Find the missing lengths.

23.

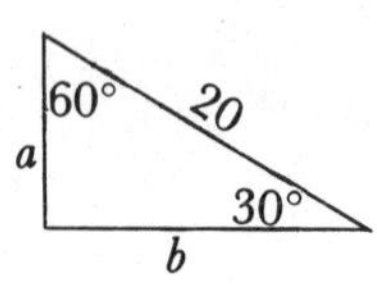

24.

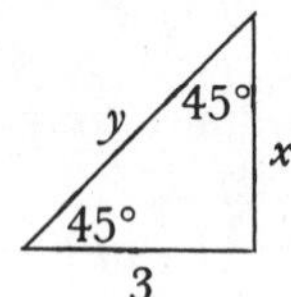

Ch. 10

25–28. Let $\frac{n}{3} = \frac{2}{t}$.

25. $nt =$ ______

26. If $n = 2$, $t =$ ______.

27. $\frac{n}{2} =$ ______

28. $\frac{t}{3} =$ ______

29. Solve: **a.** $\frac{r}{3} = \frac{4}{24}$ **b.** $\frac{2s}{5} = \frac{6}{7}$

30–39. Refer to the figures.

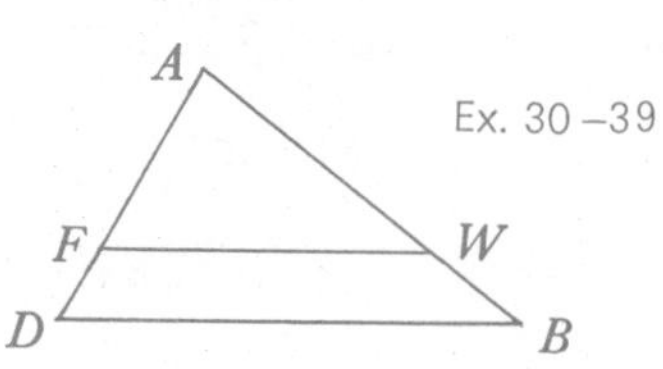

Ex. 30–39

30. Given: $\angle D \cong \angle AFW$

Prove: $\triangle DAB \sim \triangle FAW$

31. Given: $\frac{AF}{AD} = \frac{AW}{AB}$

Prove: $\triangle DAB \sim \triangle FAW$

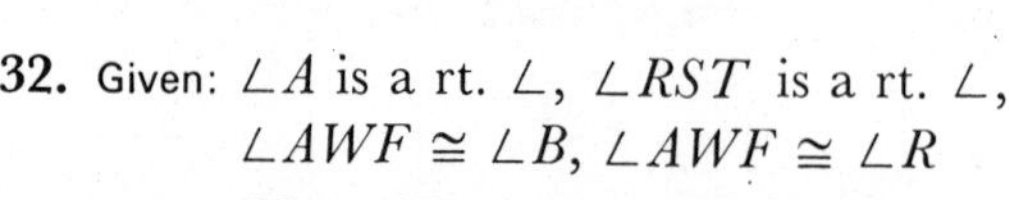

32. Given: $\angle A$ is a rt. $\angle$, $\angle RST$ is a rt. $\angle$, $\angle AWF \cong \angle B$, $\angle AWF \cong \angle R$

Prove: $\frac{RS}{BA} = \frac{ST}{AD}$

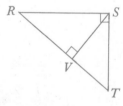

33. $\triangle TVS \sim$ ______ $\sim$ ______

34. $(RS)^2 = RT \cdot$ ______

35. $(SV)^2 = RV \cdot$ ______

36. If $ST = 2\sqrt{3}$ and $VT = 2$, then $RT =$ ______.

37. If $\overline{FW} \parallel \overline{DB}$, then $\triangle ADB \sim$ ______.

38. If $\triangle BDA \sim \triangle WFA$, then $\overline{DB} \parallel$ ______.

39. If $RS = 3$ and $RT = 4$, then $\frac{\text{area } \triangle RSV}{\text{area } \triangle RTS} =$ ______.

40. If $d{:}e{:}f = 4{:}3{:}2$ and $f = 4$, find d and e.

11 CIRCLES AND SPHERES

Zefa

11.1 Definitions

The Los Angeles Lakers

A basketball hoop is nearly a circle. In a plane, a **circle** is the set of all points at a fixed distance, the *radius*, from a given point, the *center*.

A basketball is nearly a sphere. In space, a **sphere** is the set of all points at a fixed distance, the *radius*, from a given point, the *center*.

We will define the basic terms relating to circles and spheres at the same time, since the definitions are almost identical.

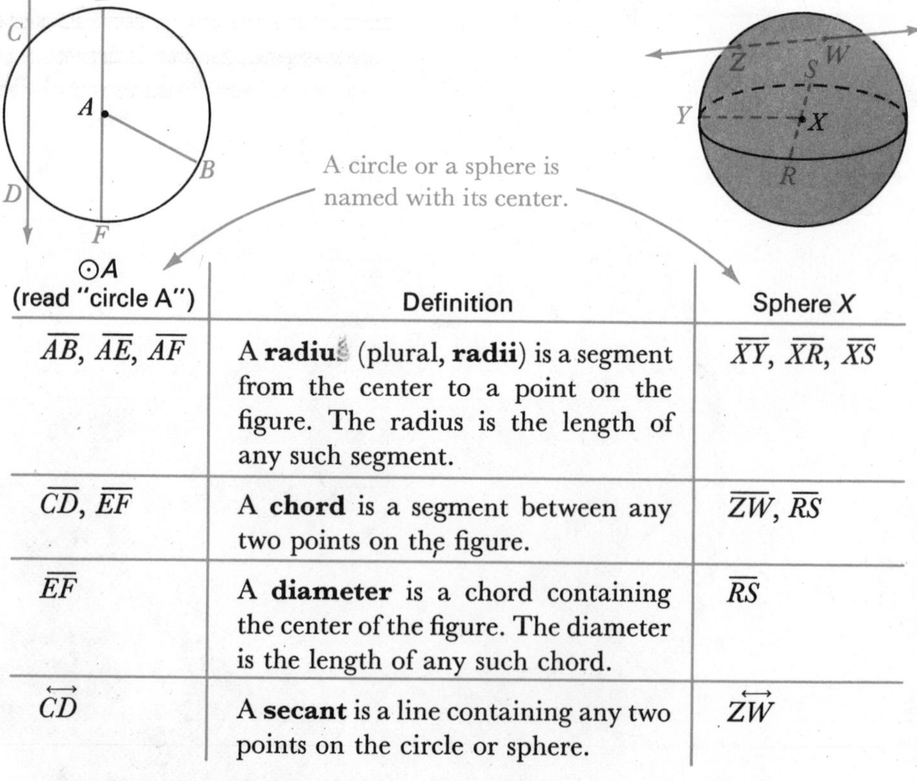

$\odot A$ (read "circle A")	Definition	Sphere X
$\overline{AB}$, $\overline{AE}$, $\overline{AF}$	A **radius** (plural, **radii**) is a segment from the center to a point on the figure. The radius is the length of any such segment.	$\overline{XY}$, $\overline{XR}$, $\overline{XS}$
$\overline{CD}$, $\overline{EF}$	A **chord** is a segment between any two points on the figure.	$\overline{ZW}$, $\overline{RS}$
$\overline{EF}$	A **diameter** is a chord containing the center of the figure. The diameter is the length of any such chord.	$\overline{RS}$
$\overleftrightarrow{CD}$	A **secant** is a line containing any two points on the circle or sphere.	$\overleftrightarrow{ZW}$

Notice that the term *radius* has been defined in two ways, as a segment and as the length of a segment. Similarly, two definitions have been given for *diameter*. It will be clear from the context which meaning is intended. For example, when we say that all radii of a circle are congruent, we mean the radii as segments. When we say that two spheres each have a radius of 3, we mean the radius as the length of a segment.

Exercises 11.1

Ⓐ **1.** Define *circle*. **2.** Define *sphere*.

3–10. What name best applies to each of the following?

3. $\overline{DT}$

4. DT

5. $\overleftrightarrow{LM}$

6. $\overline{PO}$

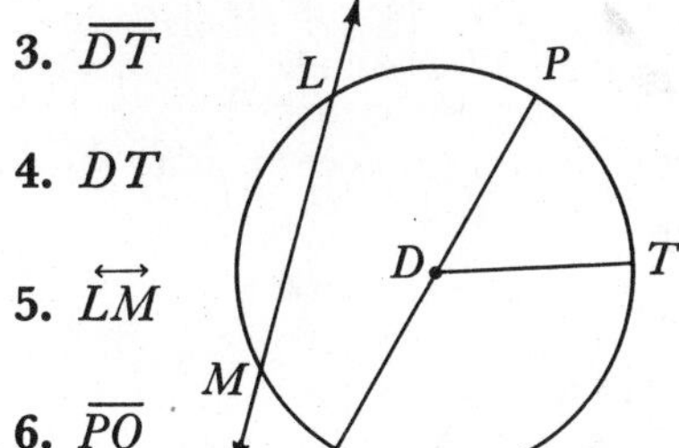

7. $\overleftrightarrow{AY}$

8. $\overline{RQ}$

9. $\overline{AY}$

10. $\overline{WR}$

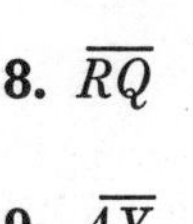

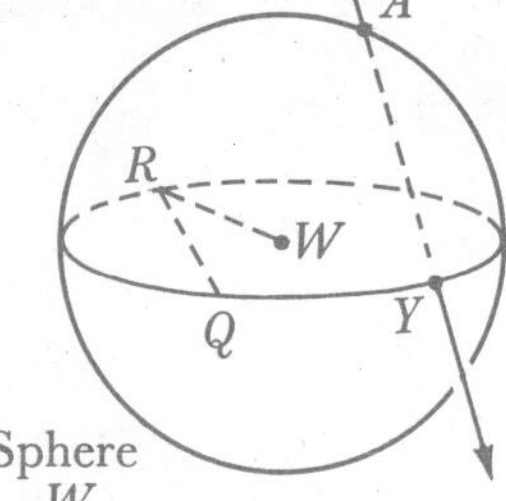

Ⓑ **11–18.** Use the appropriate figure to name the following:

11. a radius

12. three chords

13. a diameter

14. a secant

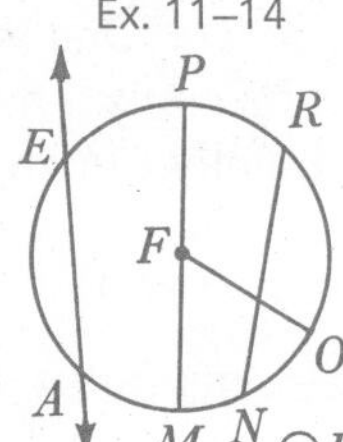

15. two radii

16. three chords

17. two secants

18. a diameter

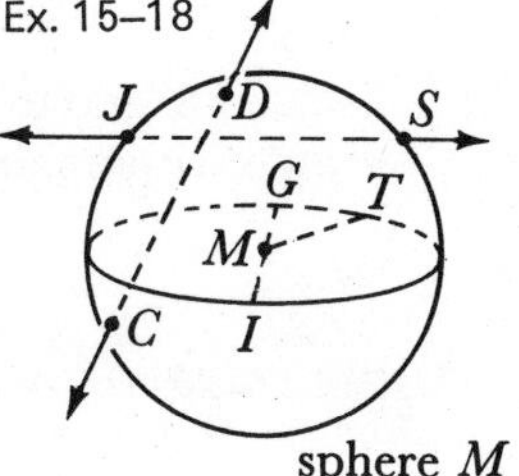

19–22. True or False?

19. All radii of a circle are congruent.

20. A diameter of a sphere is also a secant of the sphere.

21. A radius of a sphere is also a chord of the sphere.

22. A chord of a circle is always a diameter of the circle.

A

C

B

23–24. Construct a circle with

23. diameter AB

24. radius AC

construction: a circle given 3 points on the circle

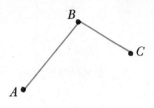

1. Given: Points A, B, and C.	2.	3.
B C A	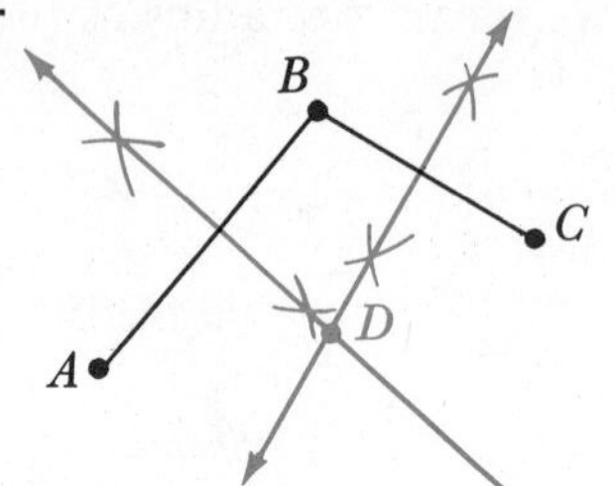	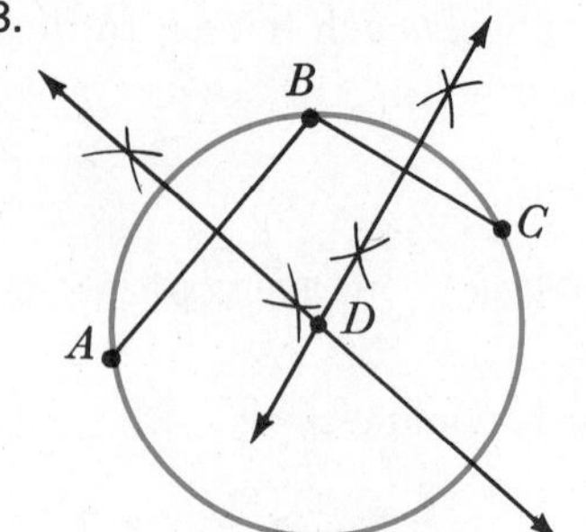
Construct any 2 segments with endpoints A, B, C.	Construct the perpendicular bisectors of the segments.	D is the center of the circle with $\overline{DA}$, $\overline{DB}$, and $\overline{DC}$ as radii.

© **25–27.** Copy points A, B, and C and construct a circle containing them.

25. B • A• C•

26. A • B• • C

27. •B A • • C

Settling the Circle

Settlers coming to south-central Ohio in 1810 found two earthwork enclosures built by prehistoric Mound Builders. One was in the shape of a square, and the other was in the shape of a circle. The people decided to settle within the circle and call their community Circleville.

Algebra Review

Review this skill:

- *multiplying and dividing rational expressions*

Multiply or divide. Express each answer in simplest form.

1. $\frac{4}{7} \cdot \frac{5}{6}$ **2.** $\frac{3}{4} \div \frac{3}{5}$ **3.** $\frac{5}{6} \cdot \frac{12}{25}$ **4.** $\frac{4}{9} \div \frac{2}{21}$

5. $\frac{a}{2} \cdot \frac{a}{6}$ **6.** $\frac{5}{d} \div \frac{6}{d}$ **7.** $\frac{2m^3}{r} \cdot \frac{r^2}{4m}$

8. $\frac{s^3}{t} \div \frac{s}{t}$ **9.** $\frac{14}{g^4} \cdot \frac{g}{24}$ **10.** $\frac{6}{z^3w} \div \frac{w^2}{15}$

11. $\frac{x^3y}{3x} \cdot \frac{2}{x^2y^2}$ **12.** $\frac{16a^2b^3}{6a} \cdot \frac{9a^2b}{4b}$ **13.** $\frac{7c^2n}{m^2n^2} \div \frac{21cm^4}{n^5}$

More About Circles

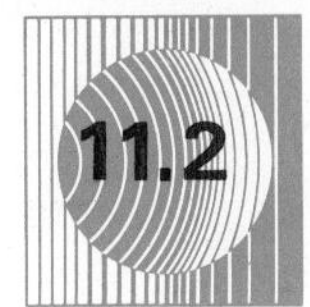

Any circle C is in some plane p. A circle separates that plane into two sets of points, the interior and exterior of the circle. The **interior** of a circle contains all the points in the plane whose distance from the center is less than the radius. The **exterior** of a circle contains all the points in the plane whose distance from the center is greater than the radius.

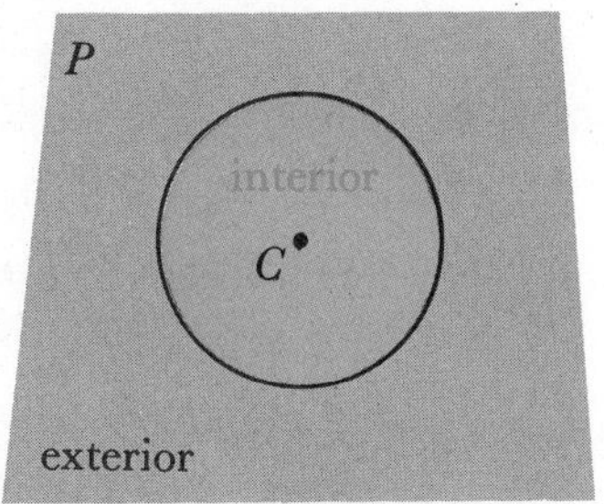

In the photo think of the pizza as a circle and its interior. If we make a cut in the pizza, not through the center, the cut could be thought of as a chord of a circle. If we now cut through the center of the pizza and bisect the first cut, the second cut will be perpendicular to the first. This is a model for part **a** of the Chord Theorem.

Chord Theorem

a. The segment containing the center of a circle and bisecting a chord that is not a diameter is perpendicular to the chord.

b. The perpendicular from the center of a circle to a chord bisects the chord.

c. In the plane of a circle, the perpendicular bisector of a chord contains the center of the circle.

Part a.

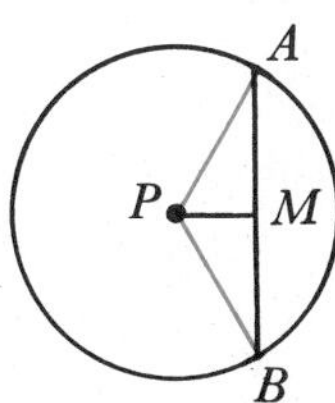

Given: $\odot P$, chord $\overline{AB}$, $\overline{PM}$ bisects $\overline{AB}$.

Prove: $\overline{PM} \perp \overline{AB}$

Proof: Since $\overline{PM}$ bisects $\overline{AB}$, $\overline{AM} \cong \overline{MB}$. We can draw radii $\overline{PA}$ and $\overline{PB}$, and $\overline{PA} \cong \overline{PB}$ because radii of a circle are congruent. $\overline{PM} \cong \overline{PM}$, so $\triangle PMA \cong \triangle PMB$ by the SSS Postulate. Then $\angle PMA \cong \angle PMB$ because they are corresponding parts. Also, $\angle PMA$ and $\angle PMB$ are supplementary because they are adjacent and their noncommon sides are opposite rays. Because they are supplementary and congruent, $\angle PMA$ and $\angle PMB$ are right angles. Therefore, $\overline{PM} \perp \overline{AB}$.

Part b.

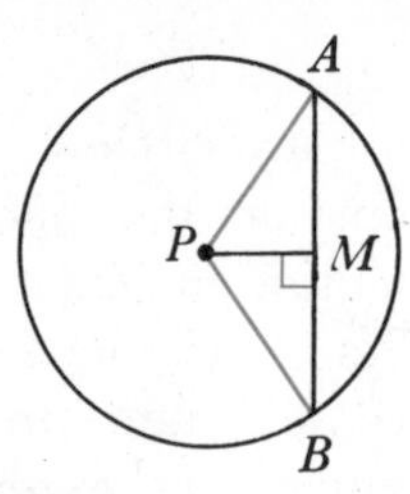

Given: $\odot P$, chord $\overline{AB}$, $\overline{PM} \perp \overline{AB}$

Prove: $AM = MB$

You'll be asked to prove part **b** in Exercise 27. Part **c** is proved in Exercises 15–18.

Dr. E.R. Degginger

Notice that the wheels in the photo are congruent, and the spokes of each wheel are the same length. Think of the wheels as a model for congruent circles. **Congruent circles** are circles whose radii are congruent.

Congruent Chords Theorem

In the same circle or in congruent circles, chords are congruent if and only if they are equidistant from the center(s) of the circle(s).

Part a.

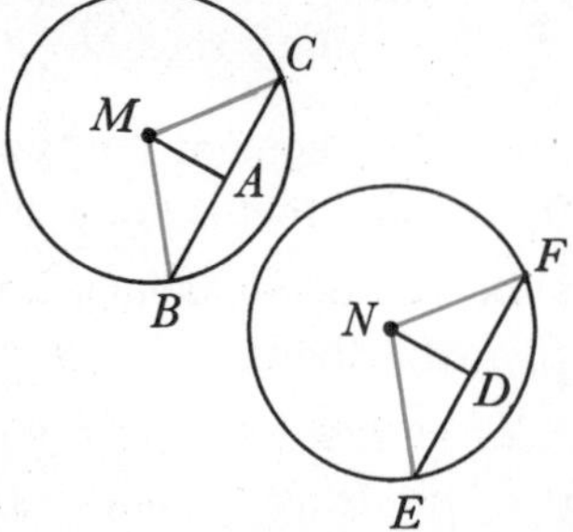

Given: $\odot M \cong \odot N$, MA the distance to $\overline{BC}$, ND the distance to $\overline{EF}$, $MA = ND$

Prove: $\overline{BC} \cong \overline{EF}$

Proof: Since MA is the distance to $\overline{BC}$ and ND is the distance to $\overline{EF}$, $\overline{MA} \perp \overline{BC}$ and $\overline{ND} \perp \overline{EF}$. So $\triangle MAC$ and $\triangle NDF$ are right $\triangle$s. Also $\overline{MC} \cong \overline{NF}$ since they are radii of congruent circles, and we are given $MA = ND$. Therefore, $\triangle MAC \cong \triangle NDF$ by the HL Theorem, so $\overline{AC} \cong \overline{DF}$. By the Chord Theorem, $\overline{MA}$ bisects $\overline{BC}$ and $\overline{ND}$ bisects $\overline{EF}$. Since $\overline{AC} \cong \overline{DF}$, $\overline{BC} \cong \overline{EF}$.

Part b.

Given: $\odot M \cong \odot N$, MA the distance to $\overline{BC}$, ND the distance to $\overline{EF}$, $\overline{BC} \cong \overline{EF}$ (See figure for part **a**.)

Prove: $MA = ND$

You'll be asked to prove part **b** in Exercise 28.

Exercises 11.2

Ⓐ **1–7.** Refer to the figure.

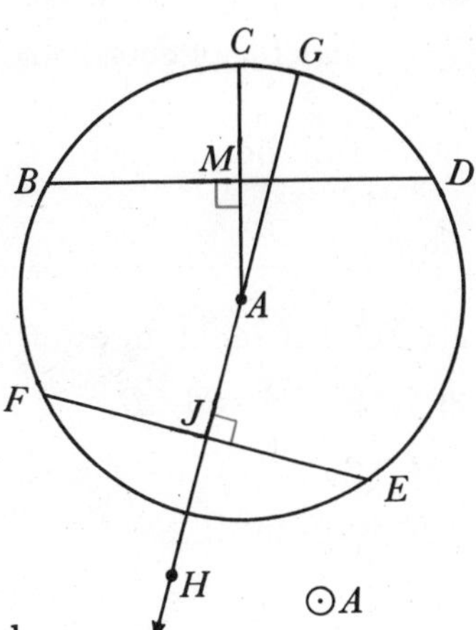

1. Name 3 points in the interior of $\odot A$.

2. Name 1 point in the exterior of $\odot A$.

3. If $\overline{AJ} \perp \overline{EF}$, $\overline{FJ} \cong$ ______.

4. If $MB = MD$, why is $\overline{AC} \perp \overline{BD}$?

5. If $\overleftrightarrow{GJ}$ is the $\perp$ bisector of $\overline{EF}$, why does $\overleftrightarrow{GJ}$ contain point A?

6. If $AM = AJ$, name 2 congruent chords.

7. If $\overline{BD} \cong \overline{EF}$, $AM =$ ______.

8. Define *congruent circles*.

Ⓑ **9–14.** State a reason for each conclusion. Refer to the figures.

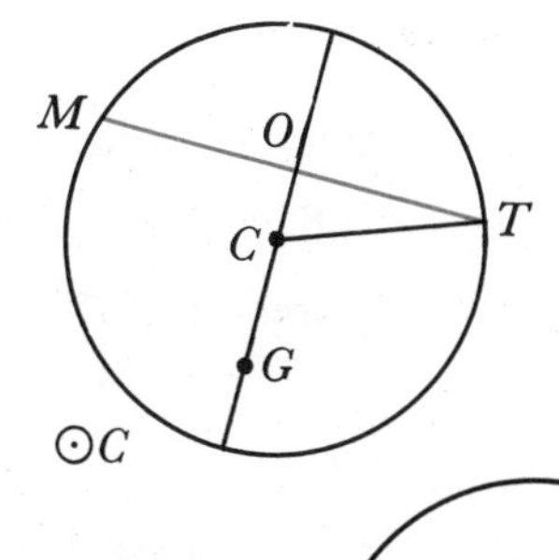

Ex. 9–14

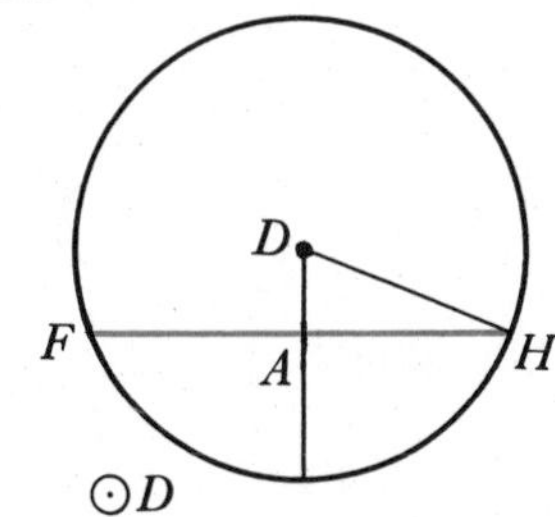

9. *Given:* $\odot C$, $\overline{CO} \perp \overline{MT}$

Conclusion: $MO = OT$

10. *Given:* $\odot C \cong \odot D$, $CO = DA$, $\overline{CO} \perp \overline{MT}$, $\overline{DA} \perp \overline{HF}$

Conclusion: $\overline{MT} \cong \overline{HF}$

11. *Given:* $\odot C \cong \odot D$

Conclusion: $\overline{CT} \cong \overline{DH}$

12. *Given:* $\odot D$, $FA = AH$

Conclusion: $\overline{DA} \perp \overline{FH}$

13. *Given:* $\odot C$, $\overleftrightarrow{GO}$ is the $\perp$ bisector of $\overline{MT}$.

Conclusion: $\overleftrightarrow{GO}$ contains C.

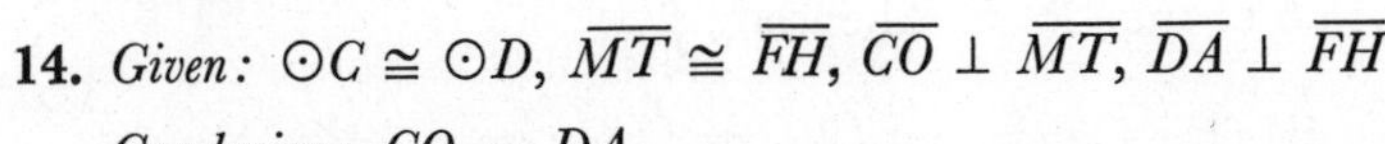

14. *Given:* $\odot C \cong \odot D$, $\overline{MT} \cong \overline{FH}$, $\overline{CO} \perp \overline{MT}$, $\overline{DA} \perp \overline{FH}$

Conclusion: $CO = DA$

15–24. Complete these proofs.

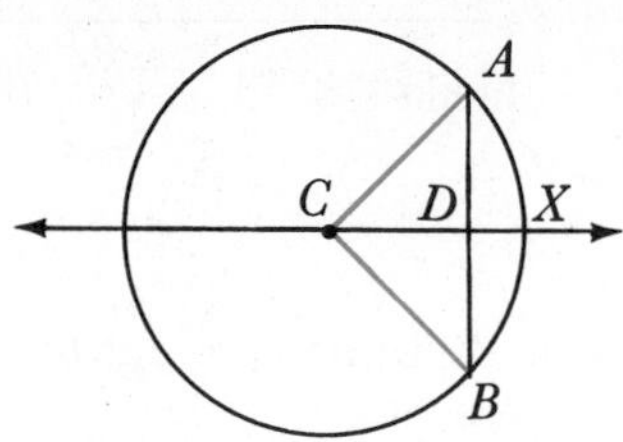

Given: $\odot C$, $\overleftrightarrow{DX}$ is the perpendicular bisector of chord $\overline{AB}$.

Prove: $\overleftrightarrow{DX}$ contains point C.

Proof:

STATEMENTS	REASONS
1. $\odot C$, $\overleftrightarrow{DX}$ the $\perp$ bisector of chord $\overline{AB}$	1. **15.**
2. Draw $\overline{CA}$ and $\overline{CB}$.	2. **16.**
3. $\overline{CA} \cong \overline{CB}$	3. **17.**
4. C is on the $\perp$ bisector of $\overline{AB}$, $\overleftrightarrow{DX}$.	4. **18.**

Given: $\odot X$ contains points Q, R, and S.

Prove: Points Q, R, and S are not collinear.

[*Plan:* Use an indirect proof.]

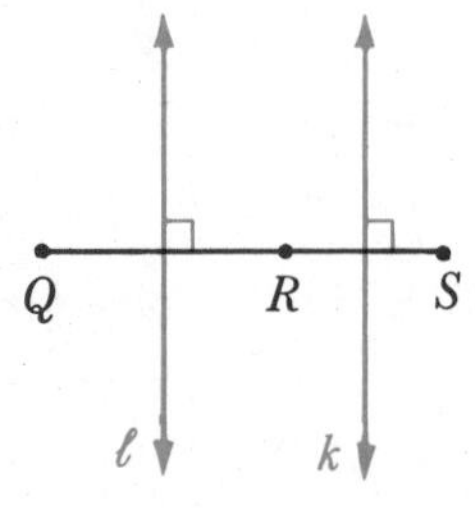

Proof:

STATEMENTS	REASONS
1. $\odot X$ contains points Q, R, and S.	1. **19.**
2. Assume Q, R, and S are collinear.	2. **20.**
3. Draw ℓ, the $\perp$ bisector of $\overline{QR}$. Draw k, the $\perp$ bisector of $\overline{RS}$.	3. **21.**
4. $\ell \parallel k$	4. **22.**
5. But, ℓ intersects k at point X.	5. **23.**
6. So, Q, R, and S are not collinear.	6. **24.**

Ex. 25–26

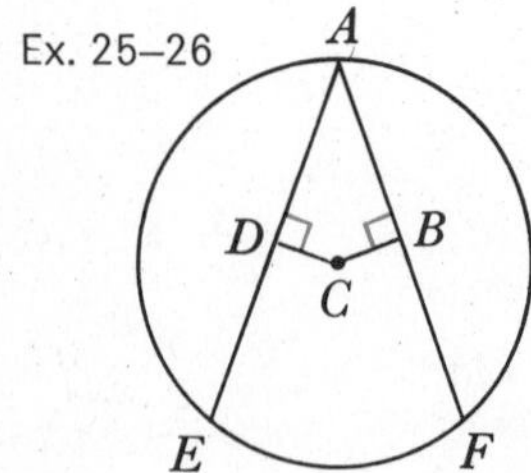

25. Given: $\odot C$, $\overline{CD} \perp \overline{AE}$, $\overline{CB} \perp \overline{AF}$, $CD = CB$

Prove: $AD = FB$

26. Given: $\odot C$, $\overline{CD} \perp \overline{AE}$, $\overline{CB} \perp \overline{AF}$, $DE = BF$

Prove: $CD = CB$

© **27.** Prove part **b** of the Chord Theorem.

28. Prove part **b** of the Congruent Chords Theorem.

} Use the figures and restatements on page 380.

Tangents

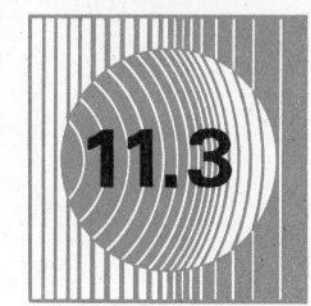

Consider a line and a circle in a plane. They may have 0, 1, or 2 points of intersection.

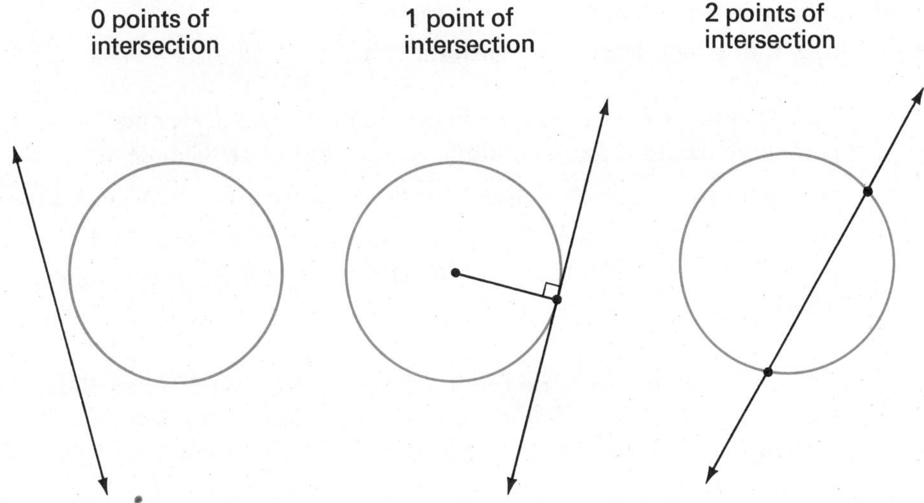

In a plane, a line that intersects a circle at exactly one point is **tangent** to the circle. The line is called a *tangent line*, and the point of intersection is called the *point of tangency*. Segments and rays may also be tangent to a circle.

In a plane, if a line contains a point in the interior of a circle, it intersects the circle in two points.

In the center figure above, notice that the radius drawn to the point of tangency is perpendicular to the tangent. We prove this as part of the next theorem.

A line is perpendicular to a radius at its outer endpoint if and only if it is tangent to the circle.

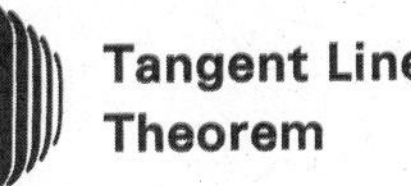

Tangent Line Theorem

Part a. If a line is perpendicular to a radius at its outer endpoint, then it is tangent to the circle.

You'll be asked to complete the proof of part **a** in Exercises 23–26.

Part b. If a line is tangent to a circle, then it is perpendicular to a radius at its outer endpoint.

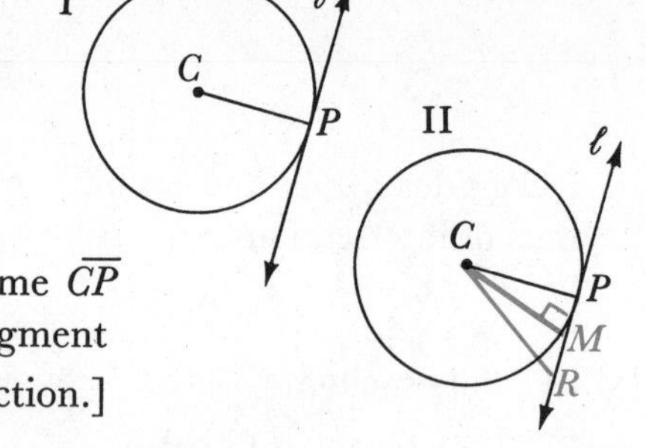

Given: Line ℓ is tangent to $\odot C$ at P.

Prove: $\overline{CP} \perp \ell$

[*Plan:* Use an indirect proof. Assume $\overline{CP}$ is not perpendicular to ℓ, so some segment $\overline{CM} \perp \ell$, which leads to a contradiction.]

Proof: Assume $\overline{CP}$ is not perpendicular to ℓ. We can draw one line, $\overleftrightarrow{CM}$, perpendicular to ℓ and containing C. See figure II. Choose R on the ray opposite $\overrightarrow{MP}$, so that $\overline{MR} \cong \overline{MP}$. To prove $\triangle CMR \cong \triangle CMP$ we know that (**1**) $\overline{CM} \cong \overline{CM}$, (**2**) $\angle CMR$ and $\angle CMP$ are right angles because $\overline{CM} \perp \ell$, and (**3**) $\overline{MR} \cong \overline{MP}$. $\triangle CMR \cong \triangle CMP$ by the LL Theorem.

Therefore, $\overline{CR} \cong \overline{CP}$ because they are corresponding parts of congruent triangles. So $\overline{CR}$, like $\overline{CP}$, must be a radius, and R must be on $\odot C$. Then both R and P would be on line ℓ and $\odot C$. This contradicts the given fact that ℓ is a tangent line. Therefore, the assumption that $\overline{CP}$ is not perpendicular to ℓ is false. A tangent is perpendicular to a radius at its outer endpoint.

Now consider the possible ways two circles can intersect.

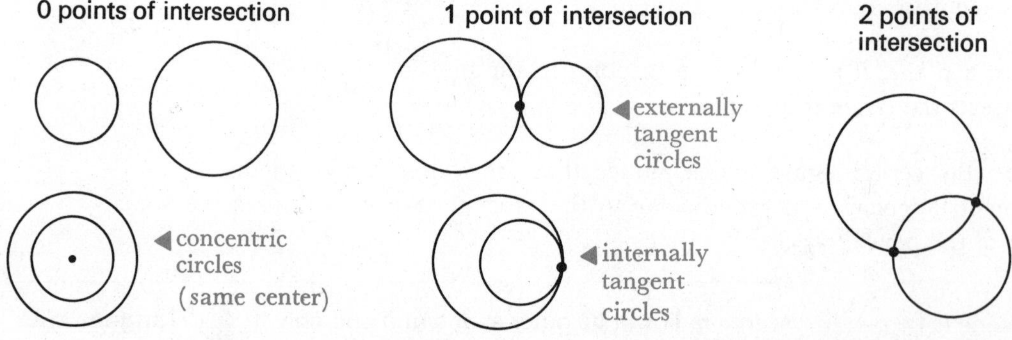

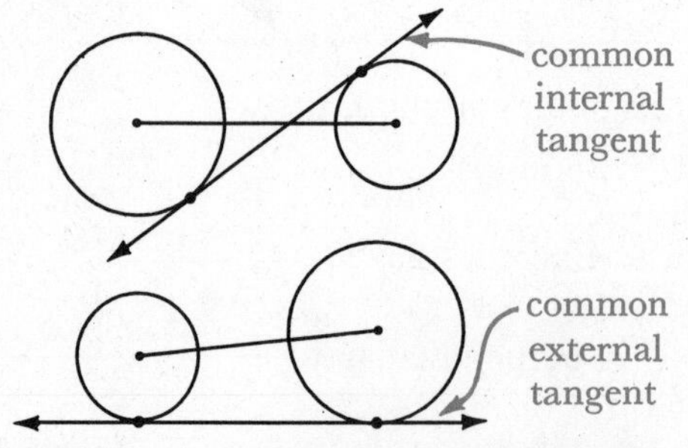

A line tangent to more than one circle is called a **common tangent.** If a common tangent intersects the segment that joins the centers of the circles, it is a *common internal tangent*.

If a common tangent does not intersect the segment that joins the centers of the circles, it is a *common external tangent.*

Exercises 11.3

Ⓐ **1–5.** Use the appropriate figure at the right to name the following:

1. a segment tangent to $\odot P$
2. a point of tangency
3. two perpendicular segments
4. a common internal tangent
5. a common external tangent

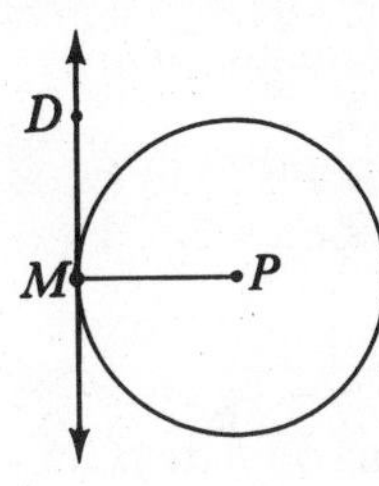

Ex. 1–3

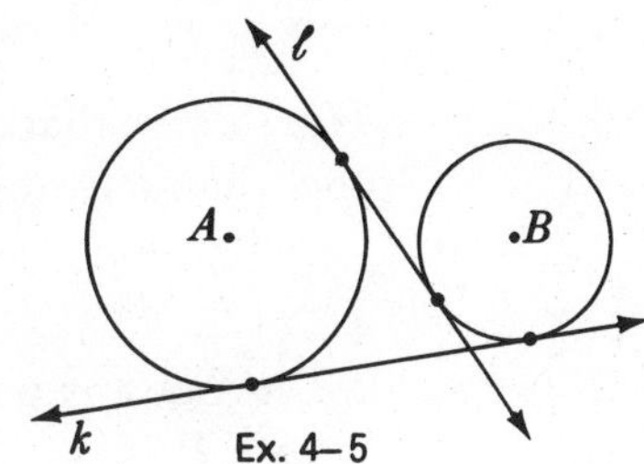

Ex. 4–5

6–8. Describe the circles with the appropriate term below.

a. externally tangent **b.** concentric **c.** internally tangent

6.

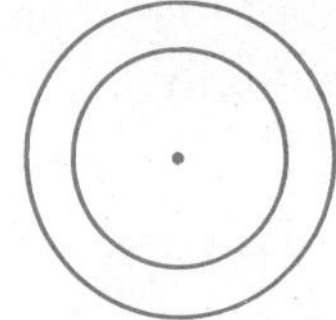

7.

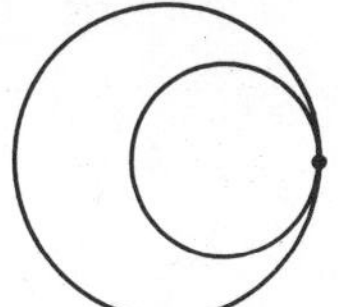

8.

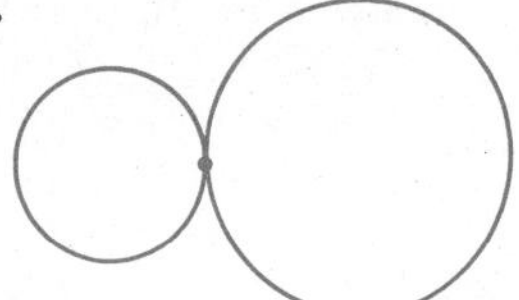

Ⓑ **9–12.** Use the figure at the right. $\overline{BA}$ and $\overline{BC}$ are tangent to $\odot X$.

9. Find AB.
10. If $m\angle ABC = 72$, find $m\angle AXC$.
11. If $m\angle AXC = 110$, find $m\angle ABC$.
12. Find BC.

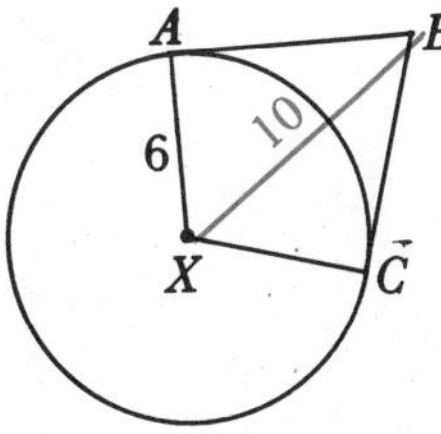

13–16. Draw two circles which can have exactly the given number of tangents—no more, no less. Draw the tangents also.

13. 1 common external tangent
14. 2 common external tangents
15. 3 common tangents
16. 4 common tangents

17–22. Find:

17. NT
18. $m\angle N$
19. $m\angle TAI$
20. $m\angle AIT$
21. NI
22. AI

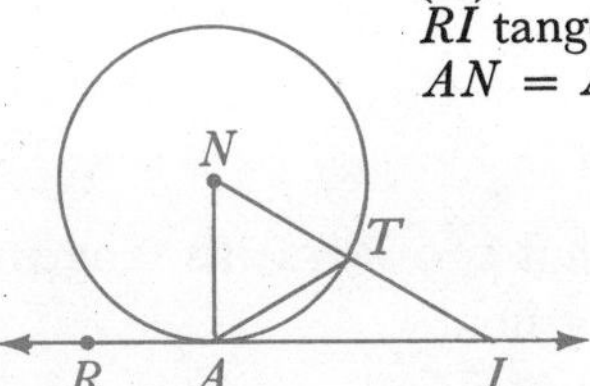

$\overleftrightarrow{RI}$ tangent to $\odot N$ at A
$AN = AT = 5$

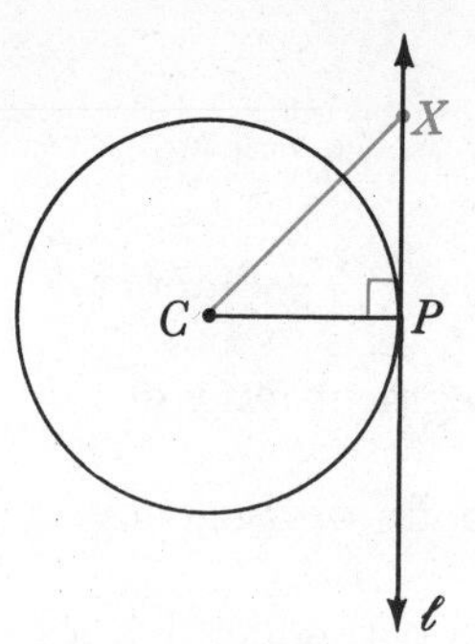

23–26. Complete the proof of part **a** of the Tangent Line Theorem.

Given: $\odot C$ with radius $\overline{CP}$, $\ell \perp \overline{CP}$ at P

Prove: Line ℓ is tangent to $\odot C$.

[*Plan:* Prove that any point of ℓ other than P cannot be on $\odot C$.]

Proof:

STATEMENTS	REASONS
1. Let X be any point on ℓ distinct from P.	1. **23.** ____
2. $\overline{CP} \perp \ell$	2. **24.** ____
3. $CP < CX$	3. **25.** ____
4. X is in the exterior of $\odot C$.	4. **26.** ____
5. Line ℓ is tangent to $\odot C$.	5. Def. of tangent line (ℓ intersects $\odot C$ at P only.)

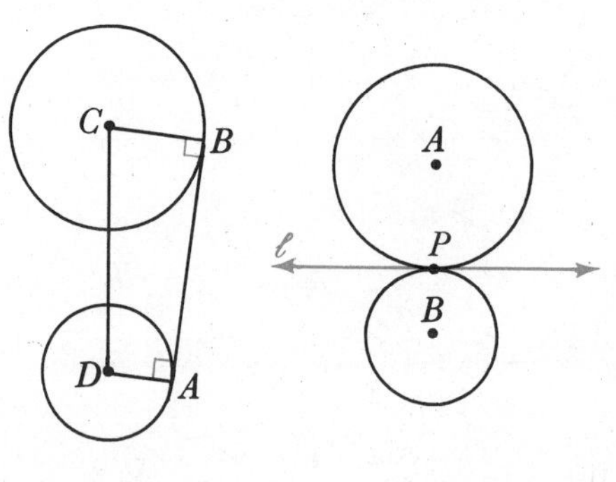

Ex. 27 Ex. 28

27. **Given:** $\overline{AB}$ is externally tangent to $\odot C$, and $\odot D$, $\overline{AB}$ is not parallel to $\overline{CD}$.

Prove: $ABCD$ is a trapezoid.

28. **Given:** $\odot A$ and $\odot B$ externally tangent at P, ℓ tangent to $\odot A$ and $\odot B$ at P.

Prove: A, P, and B are collinear.

Ⓒ **29.** Prove that the tangents to a circle at the endpoints of a diameter are parallel.

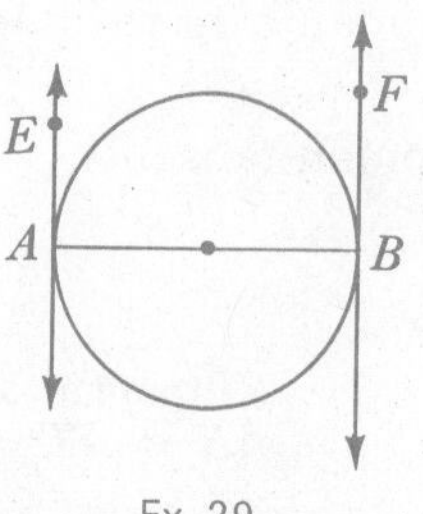

Ex. 29

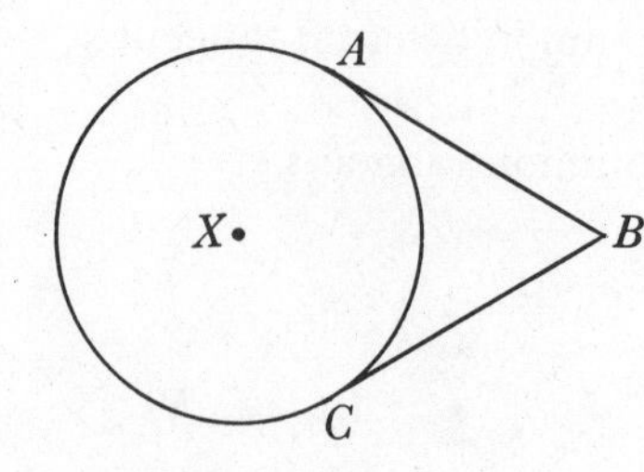

Ex. 30

30. Prove that two segments tangent to a circle from an exterior point are congruent.

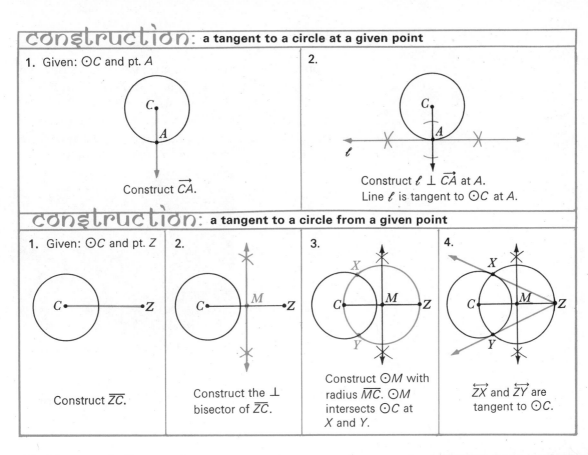

construction: a tangent to a circle at a given point

1. Given: $\odot C$ and pt. A	2.
Construct $\overrightarrow{CA}$.	Construct $\ell \perp \overrightarrow{CA}$ at A. Line ℓ is tangent to $\odot C$ at A.

construction: a tangent to a circle from a given point

1. Given: $\odot C$ and pt. Z	2.	3.	4.
Construct $\overline{ZC}$.	Construct the $\perp$ bisector of $\overline{ZC}$.	Construct $\odot M$ with radius $\overline{MC}$. $\odot M$ intersects $\odot C$ at X and Y.	$\overleftrightarrow{ZX}$ and $\overleftrightarrow{ZY}$ are tangent to $\odot C$.

31–34. Copy the figure and construct:

31. a tangent to $\odot C$ at A

32. a tangent to $\odot C$ at B

33. a tangent to $\odot C$ from D

34. a tangent to $\odot C$ from E

35. Before going to the moon, a spacecraft orbits the earth in a nearly circular path. To leave orbit and reach the moon, the spacecraft reignites the third stage of its rocket. As the spacecraft leaves orbit, its path will be tangent to the path of its orbit around the earth. Using this idea, what do you suppose it means to say "a speaker went off on a tangent"?

Harold M. Lambert

More About Spheres

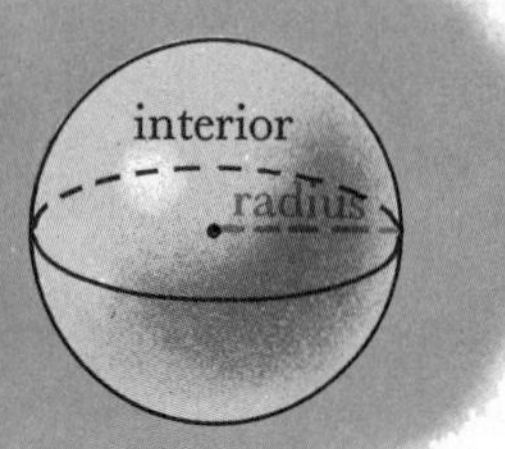

A sphere separates space into two sets, the interior and the exterior of the sphere. The **interior** of a sphere contains the points in space whose distance from the center of the sphere is less than the radius. The **exterior** of a sphere contains the points in space whose distance from the center of the sphere is greater than the radius.

Look at the photo of the Ping-Pong ball lying on the table. The ball touches the table at exactly one point. Also notice the result of slicing a Ping-Pong ball with a knife. The edge of the cut is a circle.

Consider a sphere and a plane in space. They may have 0, 1, or many points of intersection.

A plane that intersects a sphere at exactly one point is **tangent** to the sphere. The plane is called a *tangent plane* and the point of intersection is called the *point of tangency*.

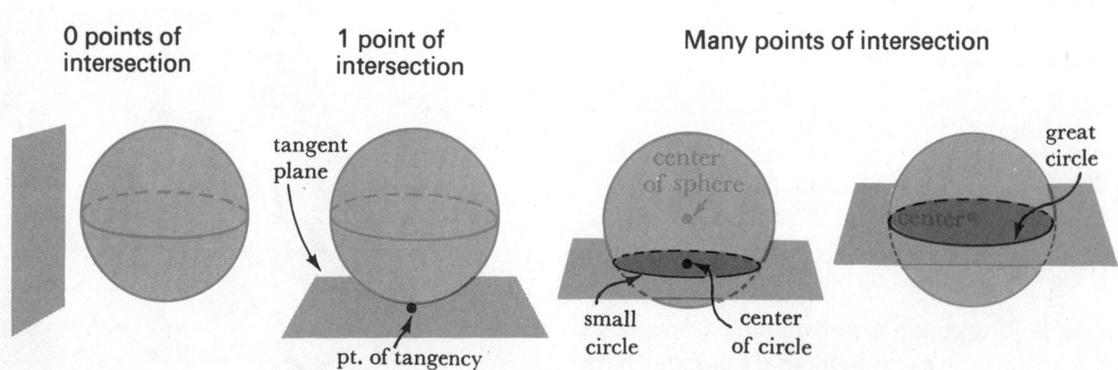

A plane that intersects a sphere at many points intersects the sphere at a circle. If the plane *does not* contain the center of the sphere, the intersection is called a *small circle*. The center of a small circle is the foot of the perpendicular from the center of the sphere to the plane. If the plane contains the center of a sphere, the intersection is called a *great circle*. A sphere and its great circles have the same radius.

The next theorem is about the intersection of a plane and a sphere and is similar to the Tangent Line Theorem.

Tangent Plane Theorem

A plane is perpendicular to a radius at its outer endpoint if and only if it is tangent to the sphere.

Part a. If a plane is perpendicular to a radius at its outer endpoint, then it is tangent to the sphere.

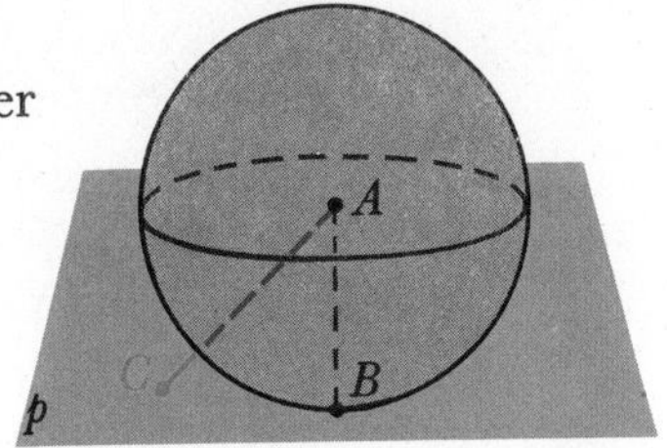

Given: Sphere A, plane $p \perp \overline{AB}$ at B

Prove: Plane p is tangent to sphere A.

Proof:

STATEMENTS	REASONS
1. $\overline{AB} \perp p$ at B	1. Given
2. Choose any point C in p so $B \neq C$.	2. A plane contains at least 3 pts.
3. $AB < AC$	3. The shortest seg. from a pt. to a plane is $\perp$ to the plane.
4. C is in the exterior of sphere A.	4. Def. of ext. of a sphere
5. Plane p is tangent to sphere A.	5. Def. of tangent plane (Plane p intersects sphere A at B only.)

Part b. If a plane is tangent to a sphere, then it is perpendicular to a radius at its outer endpoint.

Given: Plane p tangent to sphere A at B (See figure above.)

Prove: $\overline{AB} \perp p$

You'll be asked to prove part **b** in Exercise 21.

The next theorem is similar to the Chord Theorem for circles.

Chord Theorem for Spheres

a. The perpendicular from the center of a sphere to a chord bisects the chord.

b. The segment containing the center of a sphere and bisecting a chord that is not a diameter is perpendicular to the chord.

c. The perpendicular bisecting plane of a chord contains the center of the sphere.

Part a.

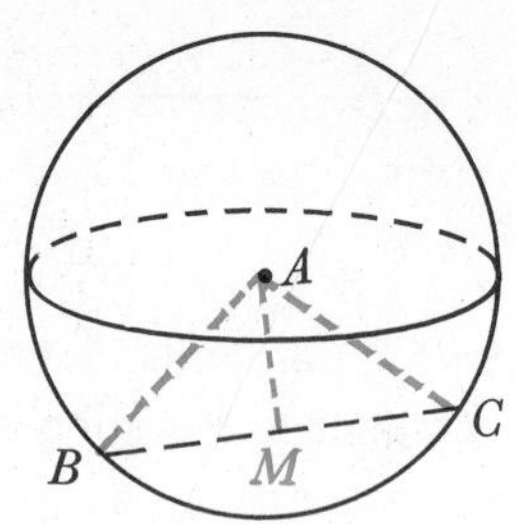

Given: Sphere A, chord $\overline{BC}$, $\overline{AM} \perp \overline{BC}$

Prove: $CM = MB$

Proof: Since $\overline{AM} \perp \overline{BC}$, $\angle AMC$ and $\angle AMB$ are right angles. We can draw congruent radii $\overline{AC}$ and $\overline{AB}$ to form right triangles AMC and AMB. $\overline{AM} \cong \overline{AM}$, so $\triangle AMC \cong \triangle AMB$ by the HL Theorem, and $MC = MB$ because they are corresponding parts.

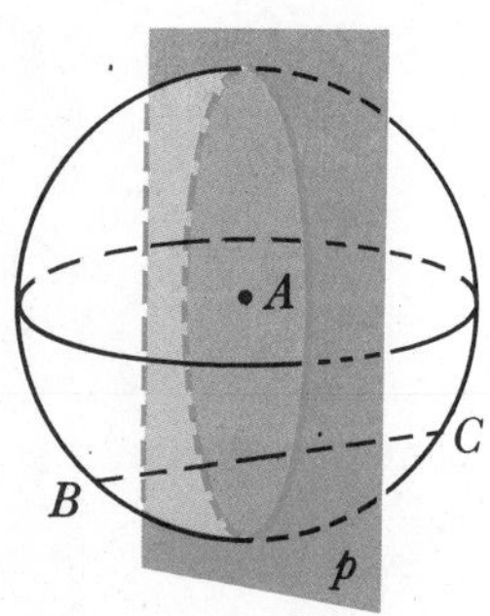

Part b. (See figure above.)

Given: Sphere A, chord $\overline{BC}$, $\overline{AM}$ bisects $\overline{BC}$.

Prove: $\overline{AM} \perp \overline{BC}$

Part c. (See figure at left.)

Given: Sphere A, plane p is the perpendicular bisecting plane of chord $\overline{BC}$.

Prove: Plane p contains point A.

You'll be asked to prove parts **b** and **c** in Exercises 22–23.

Exercises 11.4

Ⓐ **1–3.** The radius of sphere S is 9. State whether each point is on the sphere, in its interior, or in its exterior.

1. A, if $SA = 11$ **2.** B, if $SB = 7.73$ **3.** C, if $SC = \sqrt{81}$

4–9. Only point A is on sphere S and in plane p. Refer to the figure.

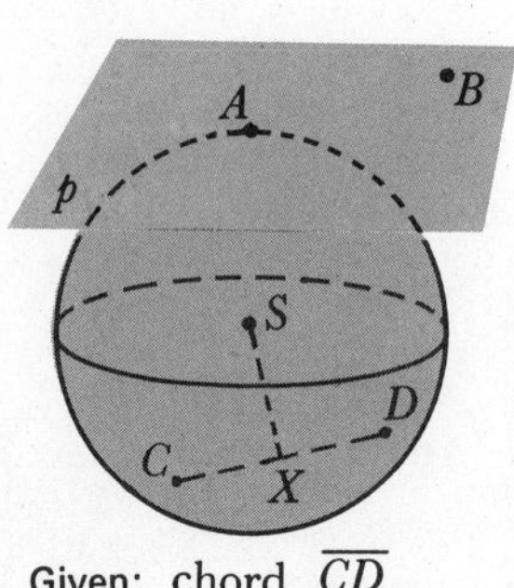

Given: chord $\overline{CD}$

4. Name all the points in the interior of sphere S.

5. Name all the points in the exterior of sphere S.

6. Why is plane p a tangent plane?

7. Name the point of tangency.

8. If $\overline{SX}$ bisects $\overline{CD}$, name 2 perpendicular segments.

9. If $\overline{SX} \perp \overline{CD}$, name two segments with the same length.

10. State the Chord Theorem for Spheres.

Ⓑ **11–14.** Points X and Y are on sphere W. M is on $\overline{XY}$.

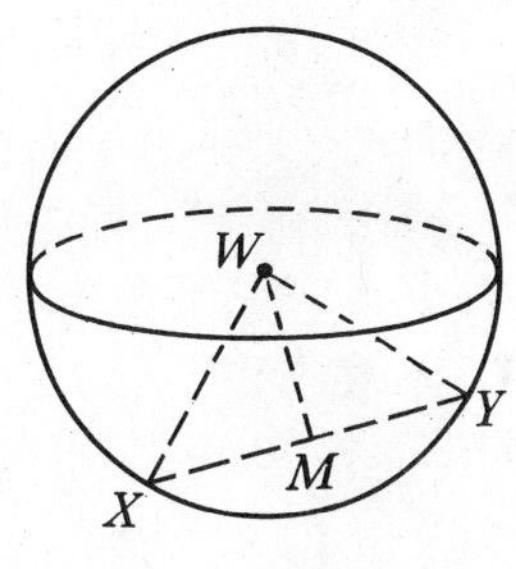

11. If $WM = 5$, and $YM = MX = 12$, find the radius of the sphere.

12. If $WX = 5$, $WM = 3$, and $\overline{WM} \perp \overline{YX}$, find YM and XM.

13. If $WY = 10$, $WM = 8$, and $\overline{WM} \perp \overline{YX}$, find YX.

14. If $XM = YM = 8$, and $WX = 10$, find WM.

15. Can two spheres be tangent to each other? Draw a figure to illustrate your answer.

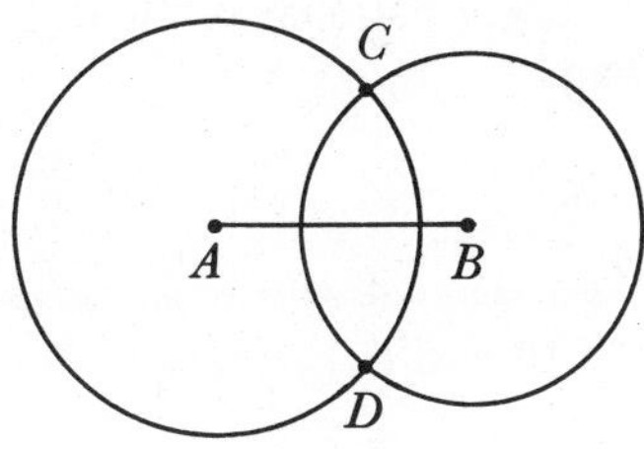

16. Circles A and B intersect at C and D. Think of rotating the figure around line AB. Two intersecting spheres, A and B, would be formed. Their intersection would be the path traced by points C and D. Describe the intersection.

17. How many great circles can a sphere have?

18. If a sphere has a radius of 10, how many small circles with radius 5 will the sphere have?

19–20. Plane p intersects sphere A at $\odot B$ and $\overline{AB} \perp p$.

19. If the radius of sphere A is 5, and $AB = 4$, find the radius of $\odot B$.

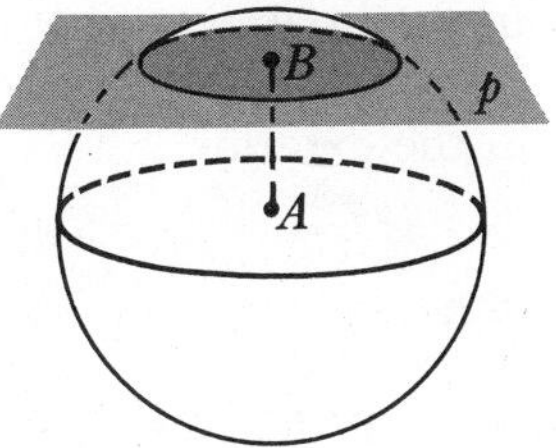

20. If $AB = 12$, and the radius of $\odot B$ is 5, find the radius of the sphere.

Ⓒ **21.** Prove part **b** of the Tangent Plane Theorem.

22. Prove part **b** of the Chord Theorem for Spheres.

23. Prove part **c** of the Chord Theorem for Spheres.

Use the figures and restatements on pages 389 and 390.

24. Make a model of two planes tangent to a sphere at the endpoints of a diameter. What can you conclude about the planes?

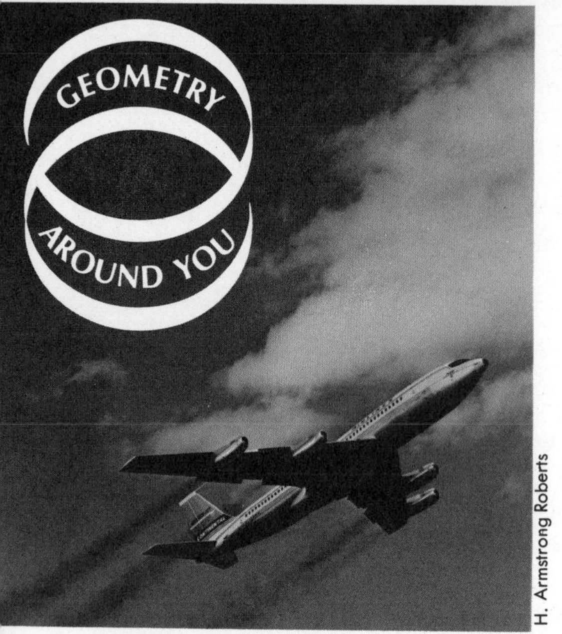

GREAT CIRCLES OF THE WORLD

Did you know that the shortest air route to Paris from New York passes over Newfoundland? Because the earth's surface is approximately a sphere, the shortest air route between any two points follows the great circle containing those two points.

1. Use a globe to trace the shortest air route
   a. between Chicago, Illinois, and Rome, Italy.
   b. between New Orleans, Louisiana, and New Delhi, India.

2. By a great-circle route which distance is shorter: Los Angeles, California, to Sydney, Australia, or Seattle, Washington, to Tokyo, Japan?

Quick Quiz
for
Sections
11.1 to 11.4

1–7. Name the following in the figure for (a) $\odot A$ and (b) sphere B.

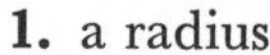

1. a radius
2. a tangent (line or plane)
3. a secant
4. a chord
5. perpendicular segments
6. a point in the interior
7. a point in the exterior

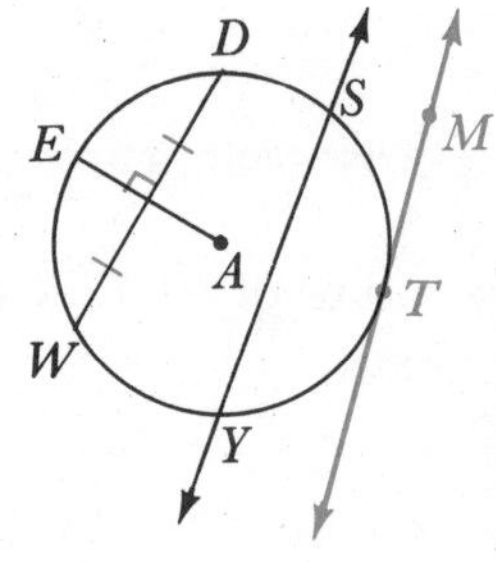

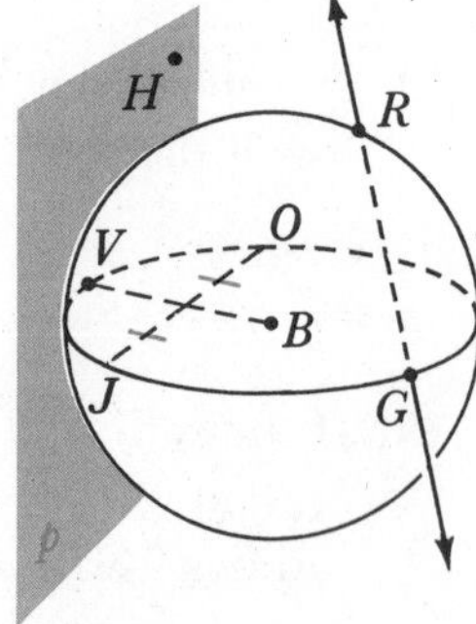

V is on sphere B and in plane p.
$BV \perp p$

8–9. Refer to the figure.

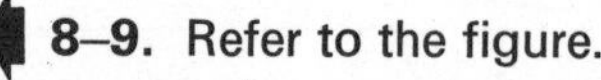

8. Find ZY. 9. Find WY.

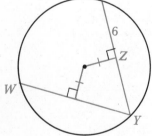

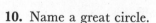

10–12. Refer to the figure.

10. Name a great circle.
11. Name a small circle.
12. Find AC.

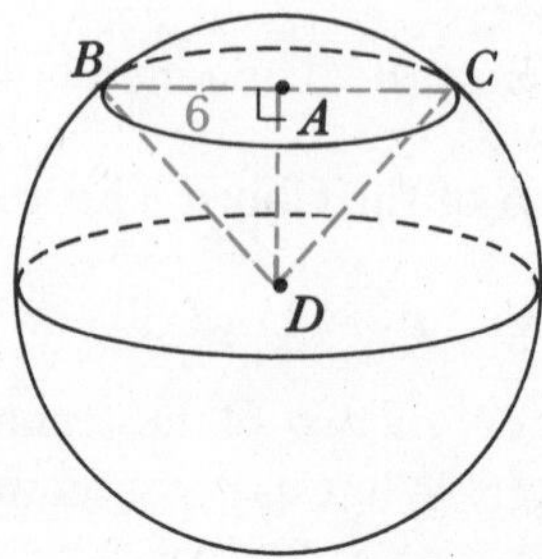

Arcs

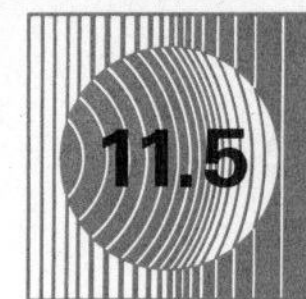

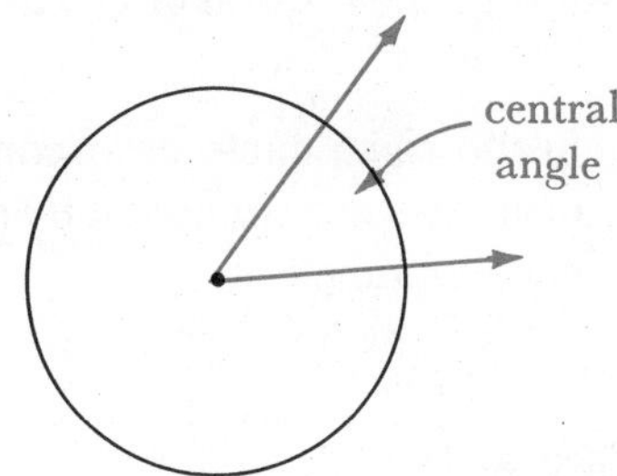

The hands of a clock form an angle whose vertex is at the center of the face of the clock. Similarly, a **central angle** is an angle whose vertex is at the center of a circle.

Name	Definition	Figure
minor arc AB or minor $\widehat{AB}$ ($\frown$ is the symbol for arc.)	the points of $\odot C$ in the interior of and on central angle ACB	minor $\widehat{AB}$; A; central angle; X; C; B; major $\widehat{AXB}$
major arc AXB or major $\widehat{AXB}$ (A major arc is always named by its endpoints and another point on the arc.)	the points of $\odot C$ in the exterior of and on central angle ACB	
semicircle $\widehat{CYD}$ (A semicircle is named by its endpoints and another point on the arc.)	an arc whose endpoints are the endpoints of a diameter	C; Semicircle $\widehat{CYD}$; Z; Y; Semicircle $\widehat{CZD}$; D

All arcs can be measured in arc degrees, and there are 360 arc degrees in a circle.

	Measure	Comments	Figure
1	$m\widehat{AN} = m\angle AGN$ (Read $m\widehat{AN}$ as "the measure of arc AN.")	The measure of a minor arc is equal to the measure of the central angle whose sides contain the endpoints of the arc.	A; N; G; D; E
2	$m\widehat{AEN} = 360 - m\widehat{AN}$	The measure of a major arc is equal to 360 (number of degrees in a circle) minus the measure of its corresponding minor arc.	
3	$m\widehat{NED} = 180$	The measure of a semicircle is 180.	

In the same circle or in congruent circles, **congruent arcs** are arcs that have the same measure.

Congruent Arcs Theorem

In the same circle or in congruent circles, two chords that are not diameters are congruent if and only if their corresponding minor arcs are congruent.

Part a.

Given: $\odot A \cong \odot D$, $\overline{BC} \cong \overline{EF}$

Prove: $\overset{\frown}{BC} \cong \overset{\frown}{EF}$

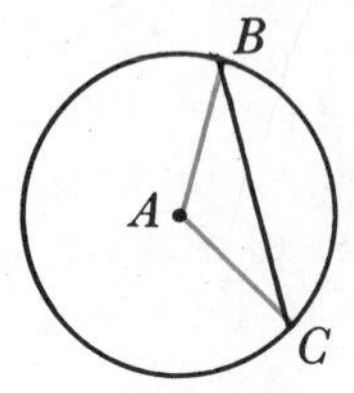

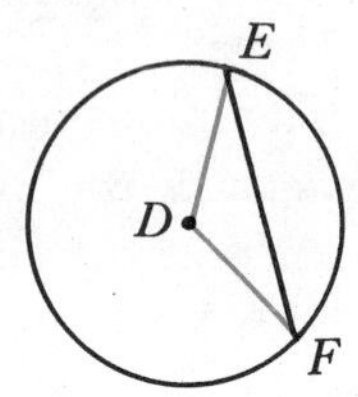

[*Plan:* Show $m\angle A = m\angle D$.]

Proof:

STATEMENTS	REASONS
1. $\overline{BC} \cong \overline{EF}$	1. Given
2. Draw radii $\overline{AB}$, $\overline{AC}$, $\overline{DE}$, and $\overline{DF}$.	2. Two pts. determine a line.
3. $\overline{AB} \cong \overline{AC} \cong \overline{DE} \cong \overline{DF}$	3. Radii of $\cong$ $\odot$s are $\cong$.
4. $\triangle ABC \cong \triangle DEF$	4. SSS Postulate
5. $m\angle A = m\angle D$	5. Corres. parts of $\cong$ $\triangle$s are $\cong$.
6. $m\overset{\frown}{BC} = m\angle A$, $m\overset{\frown}{EF} = m\angle D$	6. Def. of meas. of a minor arc
7. $m\overset{\frown}{BC} = m\overset{\frown}{EF}$	7. Substitution (steps 5 and 6)
8. $\overset{\frown}{BC} \cong \overset{\frown}{EF}$	8. Def. of $\cong$ arcs

Part b.

Given: $\odot A \cong \odot D$, $\overset{\frown}{BC} \cong \overset{\frown}{EF}$ (See figure above.)

Prove: $\overline{BC} \cong \overline{EF}$

You'll be asked to prove part **b** in Exercise 28.

Arc Addition Postulate

If Y is on $\overset{\frown}{XZ}$, then $m\overset{\frown}{XZ} = m\overset{\frown}{XY} + m\overset{\frown}{YZ}$

Example 1:

Find $m\overset{\frown}{XZ}$ if $m\overset{\frown}{XY} = 34$, and $m\overset{\frown}{YZ} = 91$.

$$\begin{aligned} m\overset{\frown}{XZ} &= m\overset{\frown}{XY} + m\overset{\frown}{YZ} \\ &= 34 + 91 \\ &= 125 \end{aligned}$$

Example 2:

Find $m\overset{\frown}{YZ}$ if $m\overset{\frown}{XY} = 34$, and $m\overset{\frown}{XZ} = 131$.

$$\begin{aligned} m\overset{\frown}{XZ} &= m\overset{\frown}{XY} + m\overset{\frown}{YZ} \\ 131 &= 34 + m\overset{\frown}{YZ} \\ 97 &= m\overset{\frown}{YZ} \end{aligned}$$

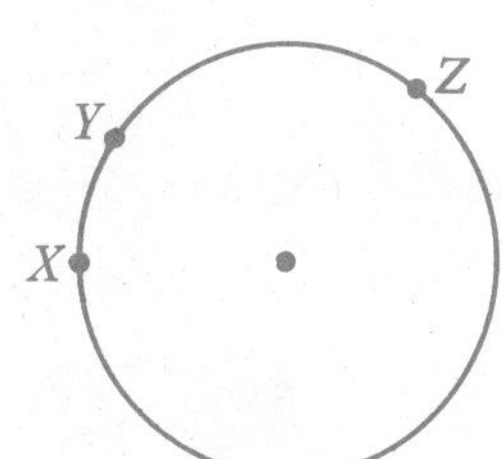

Exercises 11.5

Ⓐ **1–4.** Name the following:

1. a central angle

2. a minor arc

3. a major arc

4. a semicircle

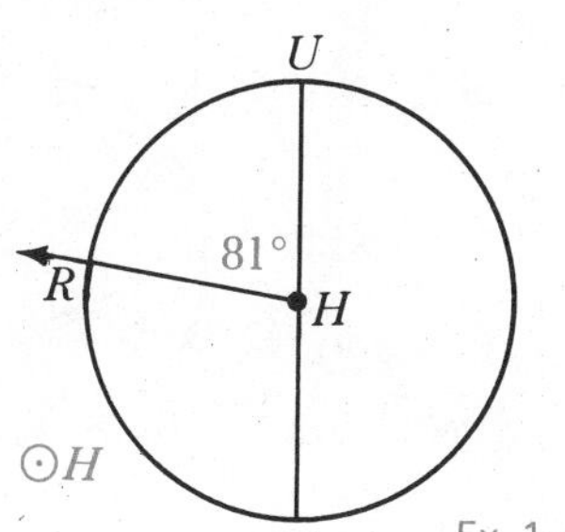

Ex. 1–8

5–8. Find the following:

5. $m\overset{\frown}{RU}$ **6.** $m\overset{\frown}{RTU}$ **7.** $m\overset{\frown}{TRU}$ **8.** $m\overset{\frown}{RT}$

9. The measure of a minor arc is between ______ and ______.

10. The measure of a major arc is between ______ and ______.

11–12. Refer to the figure.

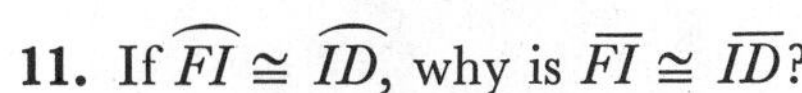

11. If $\overset{\frown}{FI} \cong \overset{\frown}{ID}$, why is $\overline{FI} \cong \overline{ID}$?

12. If $FI = 6$, and $ID = 6$, is $\overset{\frown}{FI} \cong \overset{\frown}{ID}$? Why?

Ex. 11–12

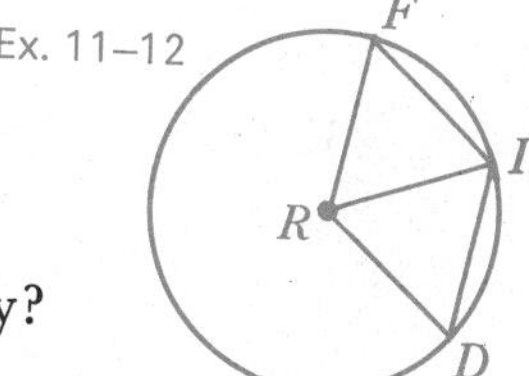

Ⓑ **13–18.** Identify each arc as a minor arc, major arc, or semicircle, and find its measure.

13. $\overset{\frown}{IR}$ **14.** $\overset{\frown}{ER}$

15. $\overset{\frown}{RIE}$ **16.** $\overset{\frown}{ERC}$

17. $\overset{\frown}{ERI}$ **18.** $\overset{\frown}{RIC}$

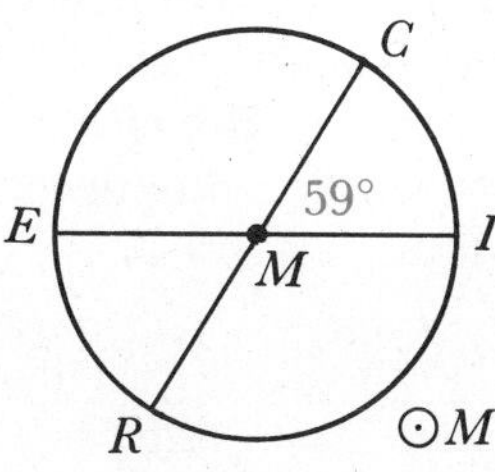

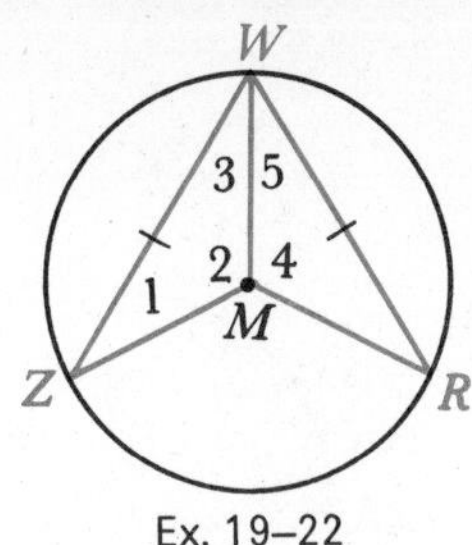

Ex. 19–22

19–22. Given $\odot M$ and $m\angle 2 = 116$, find:

19. $m\widehat{WZ}$

20. $m\angle 3$

21. $m\angle 4$

22. $m\widehat{ZR}$

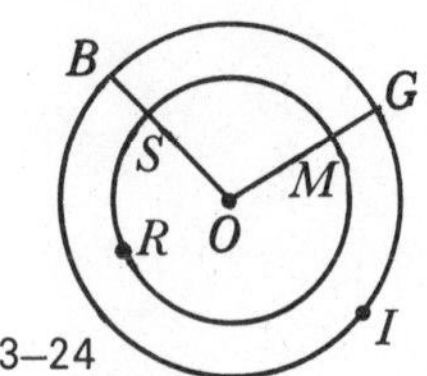

Ex. 23–24

23–24. The two circles are concentric, with center O.

23. Is $m\widehat{BG} = m\widehat{MS}$? Why?

24. If $m\angle O = 104$ find $m\widehat{BIG}$ and $m\widehat{SRM}$.

25. Given: $\odot G$, $\overline{CE} \cong \overline{DE}$

Prove: $\widehat{ECD} \cong \widehat{EDC}$

Ex. 25–26

26. Given: $\odot G$, $m\widehat{ECD} = 220$, $m\widehat{EDC} = 220$

Prove: $\triangle CED$ isosceles

Ⓒ **27.** Given: $\overline{RS}$ a diameter of $\odot C$, $\overline{RT} \parallel \overline{CV}$

Prove: $\widehat{TV} \cong \widehat{VS}$

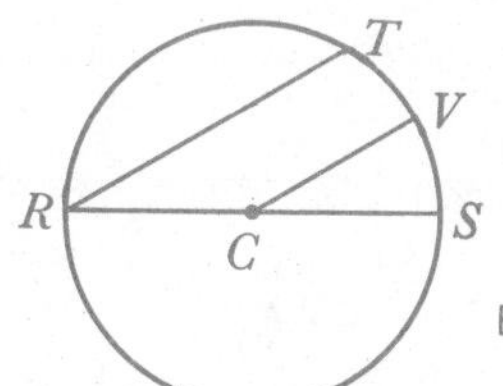

Ex. 27

28. Prove part **b** of the Congruent Arcs Theorem. Use the figure and restatement on page 394.

Arcs, Lights, Action

Some lights used in TV studios, theaters, and movie projectors are called arc lights. In an arc light, electricity leaps from one conductor or electrode to another. Air conducts the electric current and produces a flame in the shape of an arc. The electrodes become very hot which produces the strong, bright light.

Courtesy Mole-Richardson Co.

CIRCLING THE GLOBE

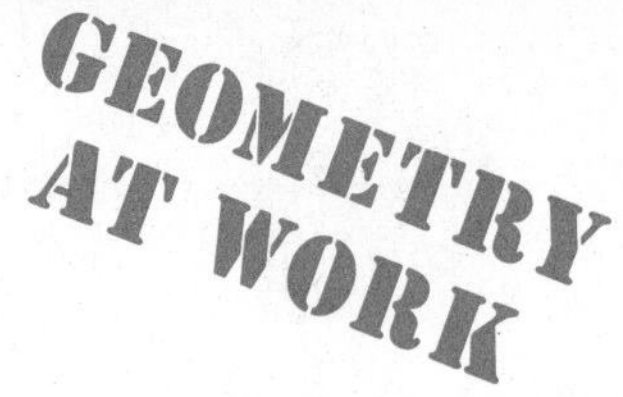

The earth, approximately a sphere, rotates about one of its diameters. The endpoints of the diameter are the North and South Poles. The diameter itself is called the polar axis. The intersection of the earth and the perpendicular bisecting plane of the polar axis is a great circle called the equator.

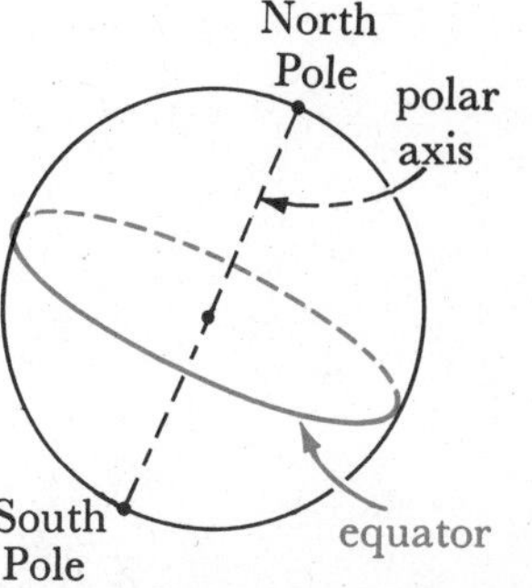

We use latitude and longitude to locate places on the earth. Latitude is the degree measure and direction, north or south of the equator, of a place or point. To find the latitude of a point A, think of a plane containing A and the polar axis and intersecting the earth in a great circle. On that great circle the measure of minor $\widehat{AE}$ between A and point E on the equator is the measure of the latitude of point A. Since A is north of the equator, the latitude of A is 50° north.

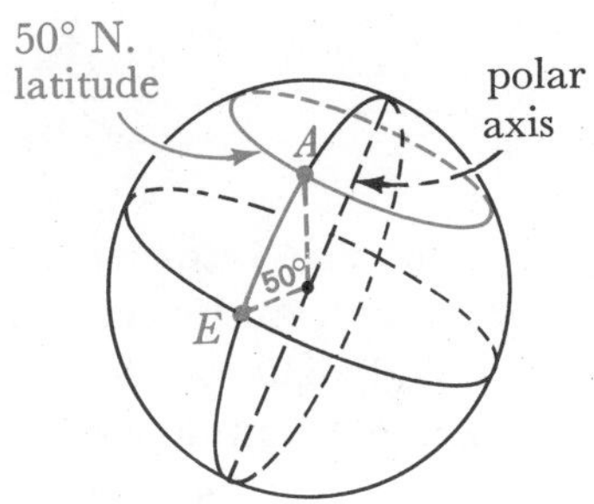

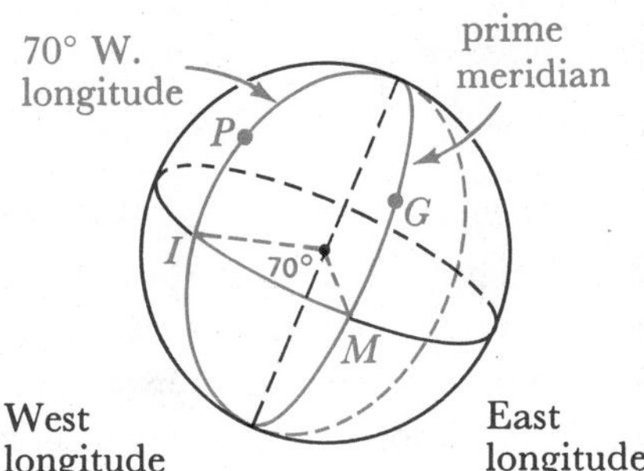

Longitude is the degree measure and direction, east or west of the prime meridian, of a point. The prime meridian is a semicircle containing G (Greenwich, England) and having the North and South Poles as endpoints. To find the longitude of point P, find the point I that is the intersection of the equator and the great circle through P and the polar axis. Also find point M, the intersection of the prime meridian and the equator. The longitude of point P is $m\widehat{IM}$. In this example, the longitude of P is 70° west.

Exercises

1–2. In a world atlas find the longitude and latitude of these places to the nearest degree.

1. Rio de Janeiro, Brazil
2. Seoul, South Korea

3–4. Identify each place having the following longitude and latitude.

3. longitude 85° east, latitude 27° north
4. longitude 0°, latitude 5° north

11.6 Inscribed Angles and Intercepted Arcs

An **inscribed angle** of a circle is an angle whose vertex is on the circle and whose sides contain two chords of the circle. Below, $\angle A$, $\angle B$, and $\angle C$ are inscribed angles while $\angle X$ and $\angle Y$ are not. Each inscribed angle is said to be *inscribed in* the arc that contains its vertex. In figures 1 and 2, each of angles A, B, and C is inscribed in the arc drawn in black.

Inscribed Angles

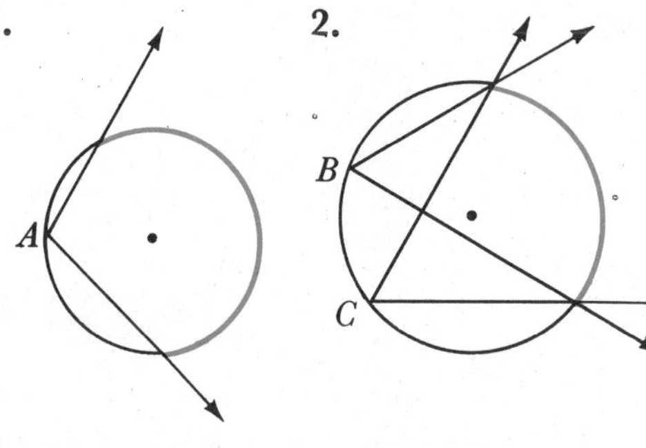

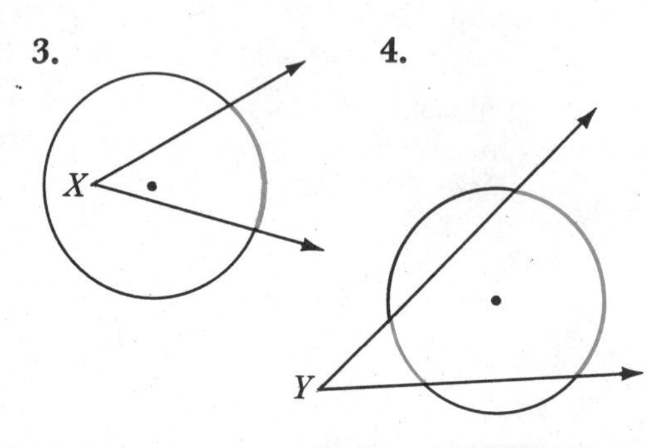

If *both* sides of an angle intersect a circle, the angle **intercepts** an arc. Each of the angles above *intercepts* the arc in red. An **intercepted arc** is in the interior of an angle, except for its endpoints which are on the angle. Notice that more than one angle may intercept an arc. (See figure 2.) Also, an angle may intercept more than one arc. (See figure 4.)

Inscribed Angle Theorem

The measure of an inscribed angle is one half the measure of its intercepted arc.

Given: $\odot C$, $\angle X$ inscribed in $\odot C$ and intercepting $\overparen{YZ}$

Prove: $m\angle X = \frac{1}{2}m\overparen{YZ}$

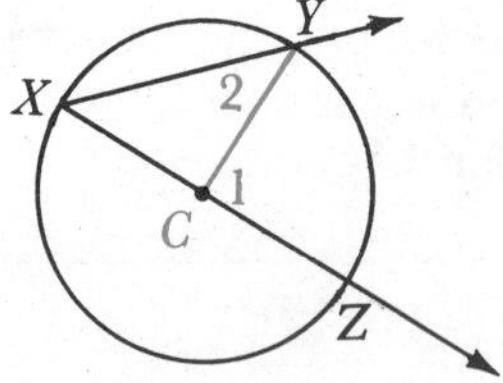

[*Plan:* To prove this theorem for any $\angle X$, we need to consider 3 cases.]

Case 1: The center of $\odot C$ is on $\angle X$. (See figure above.)

Proof:

STATEMENTS	REASONS
1. Draw $\overline{CY}$.	1. Two pts. determine a line.
2. $\overline{CX} \cong \overline{CY}$	2. Radii of a $\odot$ are $\cong$.
3. $m\angle X = m\angle 2$	3. Isosceles Triangle Thm. (p. 180)

Statements	Reasons
4. $m\angle X + m\angle 2 = m\angle 1$	**4.** Meas. of an ext. $\angle$ of a $\triangle$ = sum of measures of remote int. $\angle$s.
5. $2m\angle X = m\angle 1$	**5.** Substitution and addition
6. $m\angle X = \frac{1}{2}m\angle 1$	**6.** Multiply both sides by $\frac{1}{2}$.
7. $m\angle 1 = m\widehat{YZ}$	**7.** Def. of measure of minor arc
8. $m\angle X = \frac{1}{2}m\widehat{YZ}$	**8.** Substitution ($m\widehat{YZ}$ for $m\angle 1$ in step 6)

Case 2: C is in the interior of $\angle X$.

Case 3: C is in the exterior of $\angle X$.

You'll be asked to complete the proof of Case 2 in Exercises 25–30 and to prove Case 3 in Exercise 35.

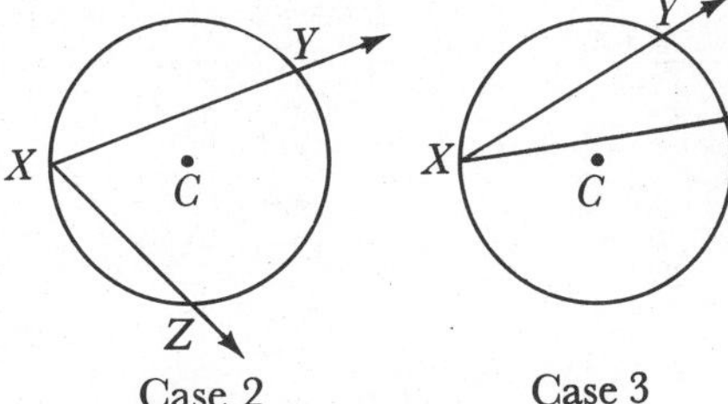

Case 2 Case 3

We can use the Inscribed Angle Theorem to prove the next two theorems. You'll be asked to prove these theorems in Exercises 33–34.

An angle inscribed in a semicircle is a right angle.

Semicircle Theorem

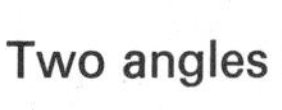

Two angles inscribed in the same arc are congruent.

Angles in Same Arc Theorem

If all the angles of a polygon are inscribed in a circle, then the polygon is *inscribed in* the circle, and the circle is *circumscribed about* the polygon.

Inscribed pentagon
Circumscribed circle

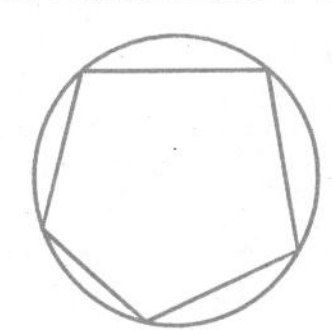

Noninscribed quadrilateral

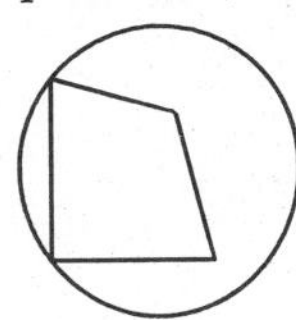

If each side of a polygon is tangent to a circle, then the polygon is *circumscribed about* the circle, and the circle is *inscribed in* the polygon.

Circumscribed triangle
Inscribed circle

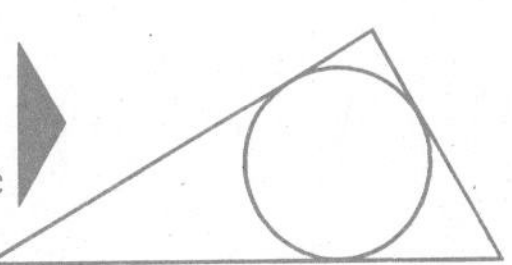

If a quadrilateral is inscribed in a circle, then its opposite angles are supplementary.

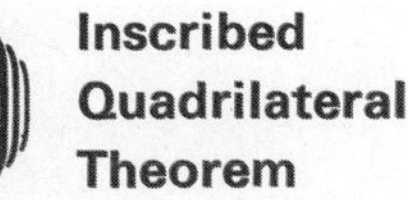

Inscribed Quadrilateral Theorem

Given: $ABCD$ inscribed in $\odot R$

Prove: $\angle A$ and $\angle C$ as well as $\angle B$ and $\angle D$ are supplementary.

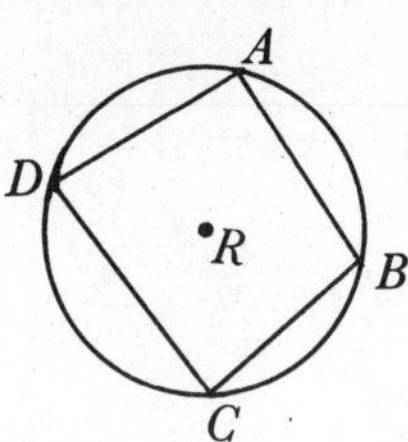

[*Plan:* Let $m\widehat{BCD} = x$. Then $m\widehat{BAD} = 360 - x$. Show $m\angle A + m\angle C = \frac{1}{2}(x + 360 - x) = 180$.]

You'll be asked to prove this theorem in Exercise 36.

Exercises 11.6

Ⓐ **1–4.** Name the intercepted arc(s) for the angle, if possible.

1.

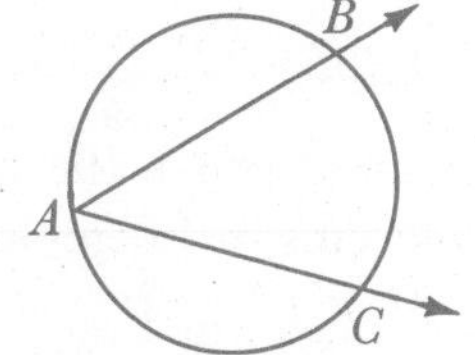

2.

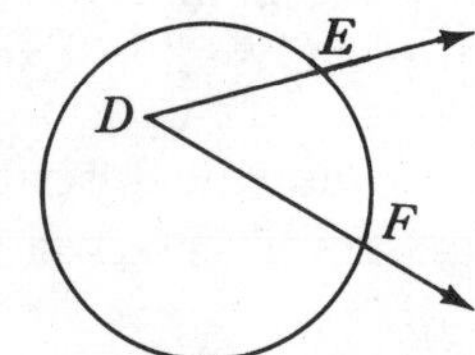

3.

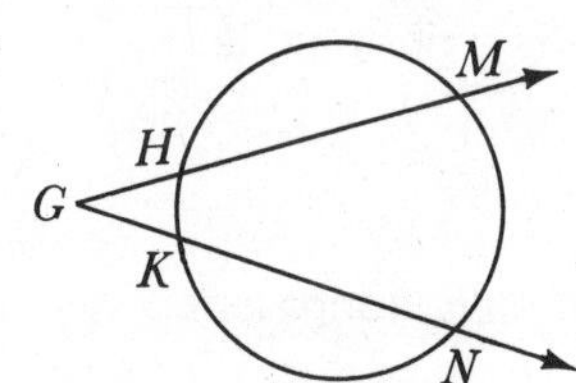

4.

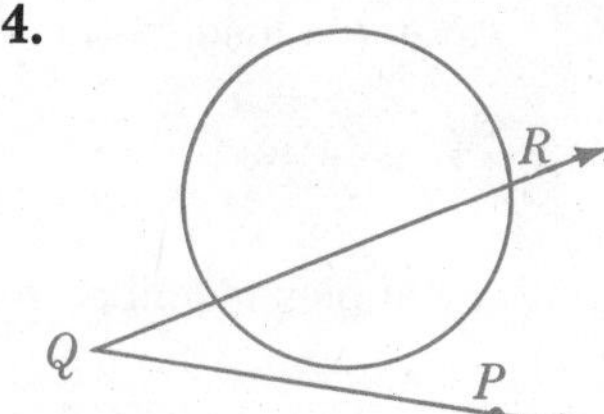

5–8. Refer to the figure.

5. Name the intercepted arc.

6. Name the arc in which the angle is inscribed.

7. If $m\widehat{XZ} = 72$, find $m\angle Y$.

8. If $m\angle Y = 41$, find $m\widehat{XZ}$.

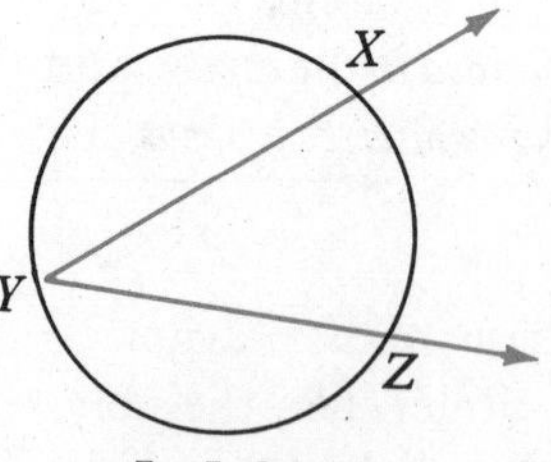

Ex. 5–8

Ⓑ **9–12.** Given $\odot T$, $m\widehat{EA} = 87$, find:

9. $m\angle ETA$

10. $m\angle H$

11. $m\angle AEH$

12. $m\angle A$

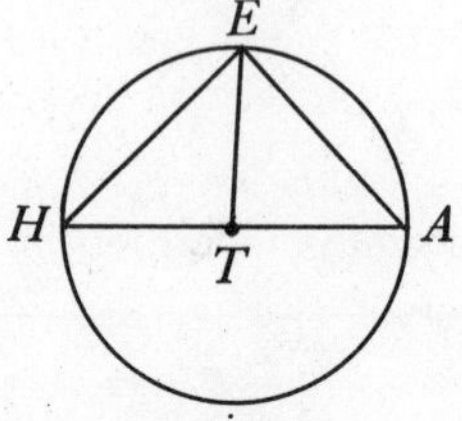

Ex. 9–12

13–18. $m\widehat{AB} = 94$, $m\angle DAC = 27$.

13. Find $m\angle ADB$. **14.** Find $m\angle ACB$.

15. Find $m\widehat{DC}$. **16.** Find $m\angle CBD$.

17. $\angle DAB$ and $\angle$______ are supplementary.

18. $\angle ABC$ and $\angle$______ are supplementary.

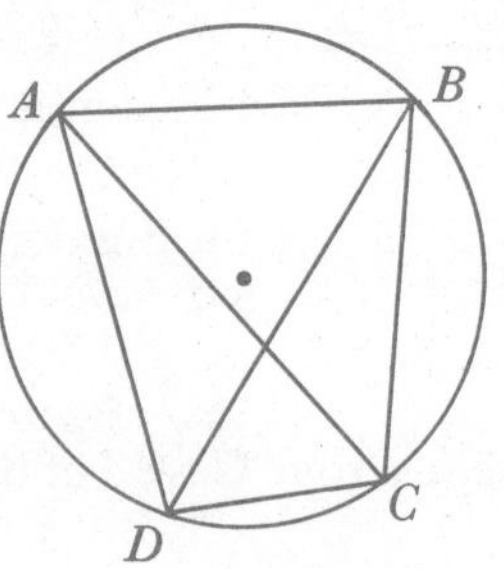

Ex. 13–18

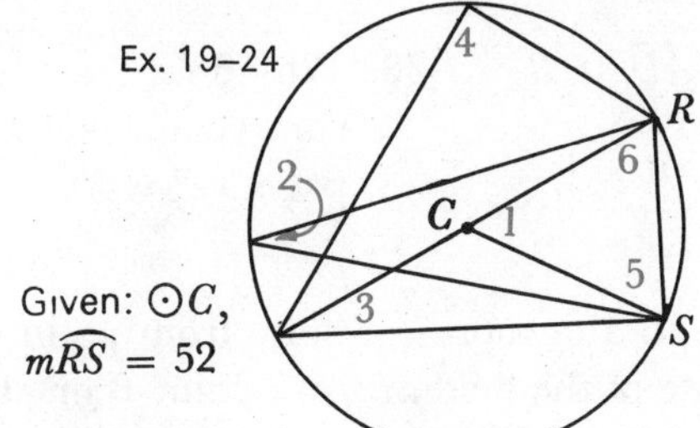

Ex. 19–24

Given: $\odot C$, $m\widehat{RS} = 52$

19–24. Refer to the figure. Find:

19. $m\angle 1$ **20.** $m\angle 2$

21. $m\angle 3$ **22.** $m\angle 4$

23. $m\angle 5$ **24.** $m\angle 6$

25–30. Give a reason for each statement.

Given: $\odot C$, $\angle YXZ$ inscribed in $\odot C$ and intercepting $\widehat{YZ}$, point C in the interior of $\angle YXZ$

Prove: $m\angle YXZ = \frac{1}{2}m\widehat{YZ}$

Proof:

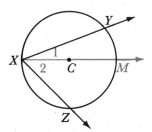

STATEMENTS	REASONS
1. $m\angle 1 = \frac{1}{2}m\widehat{YM}$	1. **25.** ____
2. $m\angle 2 = \frac{1}{2}m\widehat{MZ}$	2. **26.** ____
3. $m\angle YXZ = m\angle 1 + m\angle 2$	3. **27.** ____
4. $m\angle YXZ = \frac{1}{2}m\widehat{YM} + \frac{1}{2}m\widehat{MZ}$	4. **28.** ____
5. $m\angle YXZ = \frac{1}{2}(m\widehat{YM} + m\widehat{MZ})$	5. Distributive Prop.
6. $m\widehat{YM} + m\widehat{MZ} = m\widehat{YZ}$	6. **29.** ____
7. $m\angle YXZ = \frac{1}{2}m\widehat{YZ}$	7. **30.** ____

31. Draw a circle with an inscribed hexagon.

32. Construct a circle and inscribe a quadrilateral in it.

33. Prove the Semicircle Theorem, page 399.

34. Prove the Angles in Same Arc Theorem, page 399.

Ⓒ **35.** Prove Case 3 of the Inscribed Angle Theorem.

36. Prove the Inscribed Quadrilateral Theorem.

} Use the figures on pages 399 and 400.

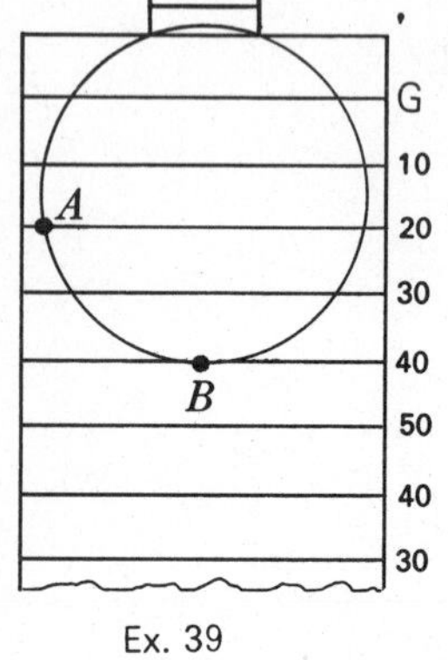

Ex. 39

37. Given: Semicircle $\widehat{ACD}$, $\overline{CB} \perp \overline{AD}$ at B

Prove: $\overline{BC}$ is the geometric mean of $\overline{AB}$ and $\overline{BD}$.

38. Why does the construction on page 347 work?

39. Does a field goal kicker have to aim more carefully from point A on the 20 yd. line near the side of the field or from point B on the 40 yd. line at the center of the field? Why?

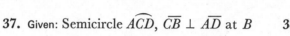

construction: triangle circumscribed about a circle

1. Given: $\odot C$

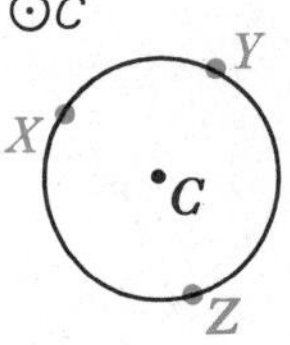

Choose points X, Y, and Z so $m\widehat{XYZ} > 180$ and no 2 points are the endpoints of a diameter.

2.

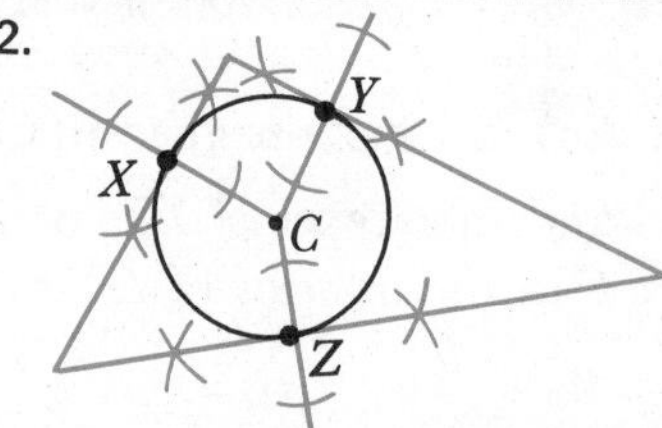

Construct tangents at X, Y, and Z. The tangents will intersect to form a triangle.

40. Circumscribe a triangle about a circle with radius 3 cm.

41. Circumscribe a triangle about a circle with radius 4 cm.

Algebra Review

Review this skill:

- *adding and subtracting rational expressions*

Add or subtract. Express each answer in simplest form.

1. $\frac{2}{9} + \frac{4}{9}$ **2.** $1 - \frac{1}{5}$ **3.** $\frac{1}{3} + \frac{3}{8}$ **4.** $\frac{7}{9} - \frac{2}{3}$

5. $\frac{2}{x} + \frac{5}{x}$ **6.** $\frac{2a}{4b} - \frac{a}{4b}$ **7.** $\frac{5}{y} + \frac{6y}{2}$

8. $\frac{2s}{3d} - \frac{5}{d}$ **9.** $\frac{9w}{10z^2} + \frac{4w^2}{6wz^2}$ **10.** $\frac{8a}{3b} - \frac{2}{ab^3}$

Angles Formed by Secants, Tangents, and Chords

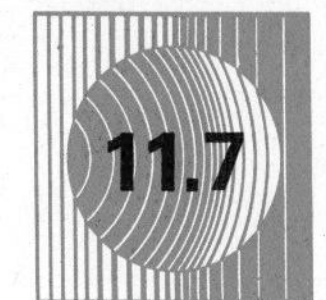

We will now use the Inscribed Angle Theorem to prove some theorems about angles formed by chords, secants, and tangents.

NOTE: In the case of chords, an angle is formed when each chord is extended. For example,

chords $\overline{AC}$ and $\overline{BD}$ intersecting at X | form $\angle AXD$ | as well as $\angle BXC$

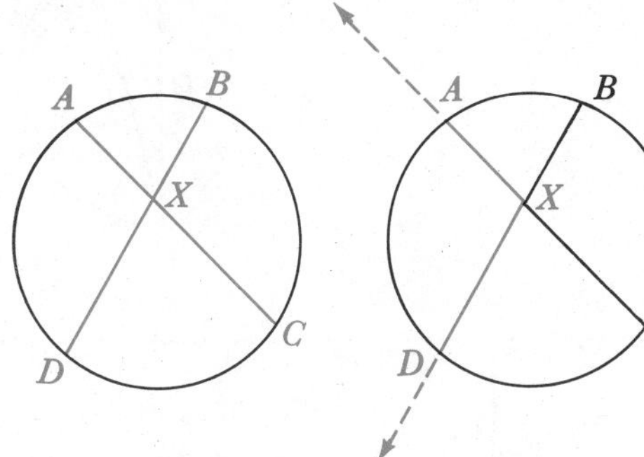

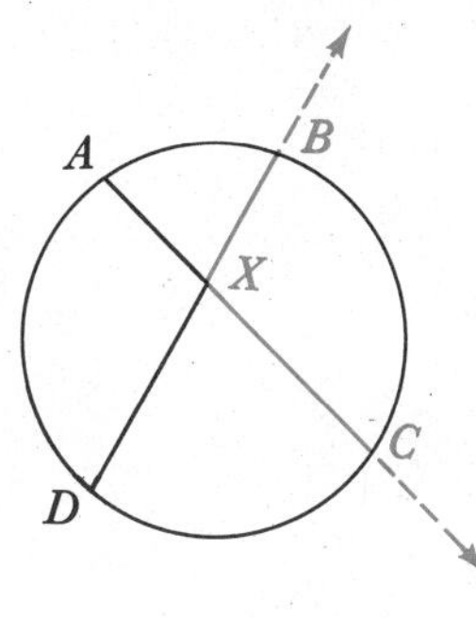

> The measure of an angle formed by two chords intersecting in the interior of a circle is equal to one half the sum of the measures of the arcs intercepted by the angle and its vertical angle.

Intersecting Chords Theorem

Given: $\odot P$, chords $\overline{BD}$ and $\overline{AC}$ intersect at X.

Prove: $m\angle AXB = \frac{1}{2}(m\widehat{AB} + m\widehat{CD})$

[*Plan:* Draw $\overline{BC}$, making $m\angle AXB = m\angle C + m\angle B$, and use the Inscribed Angle Theorem.]

The proof is asked for in Exercise 37.

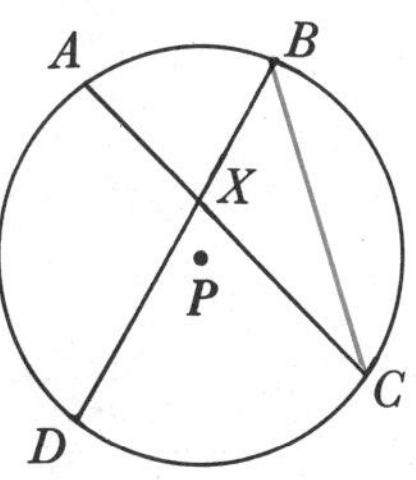

> The measure of an angle formed by a tangent and a chord is one half the measure of the intercepted arc.

Tangent and Chord Theorem

For a tangent and chord to form an angle, an endpoint of the chord must be the point of tangency. When this occurs, there are two cases possible. In each case *two* angles are actually formed.

Case 1: The chord is a diameter. In this case, $\angle ABC$ and $\angle ABD$ are right angles. (Why?) The arc that each of these angles intercepts is a semicircle (measure 180). So, $m\angle ABC = \frac{1}{2}m\widehat{AXB}$ and $m\angle ABD = \frac{1}{2}m\widehat{AYB}$.

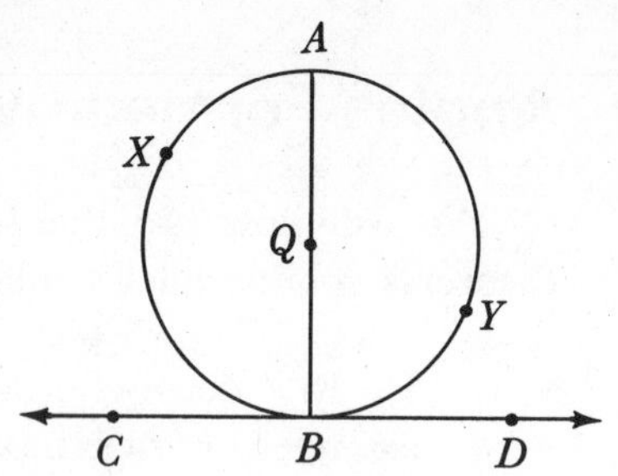

Case 2: The chord is *not* a diameter.

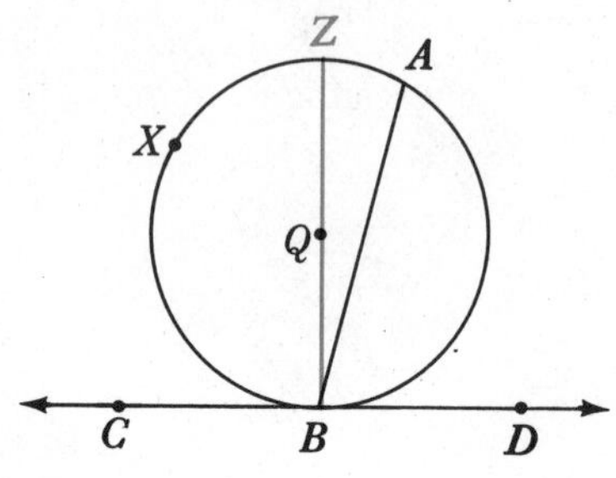

Given: $\odot Q$, chord $\overline{AB}$, $\overleftrightarrow{BC}$ is tangent to $\odot Q$ at B.

Prove: $m\angle ABC = \frac{1}{2}m\widehat{AZB}$,
$m\angle ABD = \frac{1}{2}m\widehat{AB}$

Proof:

STATEMENTS	REASONS
1. Draw $\overleftrightarrow{QB} \perp \overleftrightarrow{BC}$ intersecting $\odot Q$ at Z.	**1.** A radius is $\perp$ to a tangent at the pt. of tangency.
2. $m\angle ZBC = \frac{1}{2}m\widehat{ZXB}$, $m\angle ZBD = \frac{1}{2}m\widehat{ZAB}$	**2.** Case 1 above
3. $m\angle ABZ = \frac{1}{2}m\widehat{AZ}$	**3.** Inscribed Angle Thm.
4. $m\angle ABC = m\angle ABZ + m\angle ZBC$, $m\angle ABD = m\angle ZBD - m\angle ABZ$	**4.** Angle Addition Post. (p. 53)
5. $m\angle ABC = \frac{1}{2}m\widehat{AZ} + \frac{1}{2}m\widehat{ZXB}$, $m\angle ABD = \frac{1}{2}m\widehat{ZAB} - \frac{1}{2}m\widehat{AZ}$	**5.** Substitution (from steps 2 and 3 into step 4)
6. $m\angle ABC = \frac{1}{2}(m\widehat{AZ} + m\widehat{ZXB})$, $m\angle ABD = \frac{1}{2}(m\widehat{ZAB} - m\widehat{AZ})$	**6.** Distributive Property
7. $m\widehat{AZB} = m\widehat{AZ} + m\widehat{ZXB}$, $m\widehat{AB} = m\widehat{ZAB} - m\widehat{AZ}$	**7.** Arc Addition Post.
8. $m\angle ABC = \frac{1}{2}m\widehat{AZB}$, $m\angle ABD = \frac{1}{2}m\widehat{AB}$	**8.** Substitution

Secant and Tangent Theorem

The measure of the angle formed by two secants, a tangent and a secant, or two tangents intersecting in the exterior of a circle is one half the difference of the measures of the intercepted arcs.

Case 1: The angle is formed by two secants.

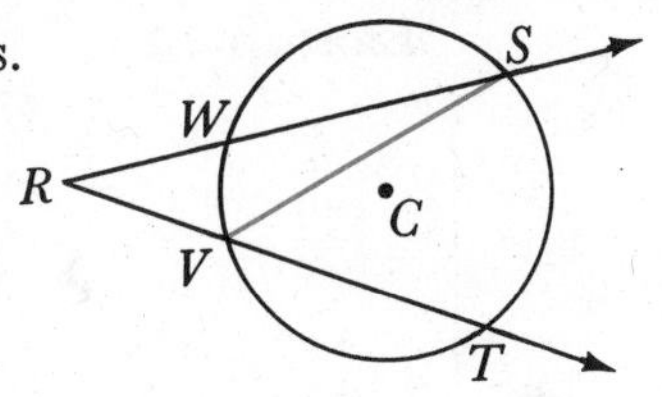

Given: $\odot C$, secants $\overleftrightarrow{RS}$ and $\overleftrightarrow{RT}$

Prove: $m\angle R = \frac{1}{2}(m\widehat{ST} - m\widehat{WV})$

Proof:

STATEMENTS	REASONS
1. $\odot C$, secants $\overleftrightarrow{RS}$ and $\overleftrightarrow{RT}$	**1.** Given
2. Draw $\overline{SV}$.	**2.** Two pts. determine a line.
3. $m\angle VSR + m\angle R = m\angle SVT$	**3.** Meas. of ext. $\angle$ of a $\triangle$ = sum of measures of remote int. $\angle$s.
4. $m\angle R = m\angle SVT - m\angle VSR$	**4.** Subtr. $m\angle VSR$ from both sides.
5. $m\angle SVT = \frac{1}{2}m\widehat{ST}$, $m\angle VSR = \frac{1}{2}m\widehat{WV}$	**5.** Inscribed Angle Theorem
6. $m\angle R = \frac{1}{2}m\widehat{ST} - \frac{1}{2}m\widehat{WV}$	**6.** Substitution
7. $m\angle R = \frac{1}{2}(m\widehat{ST} - m\widehat{WV})$	**7.** Distributive Prop.

Case 2: The angle is formed by a secant and a tangent.

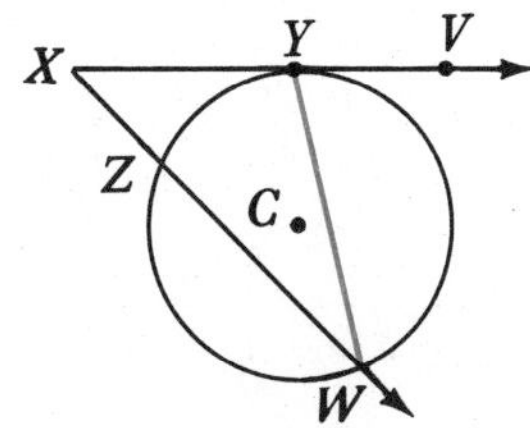

Given: $\overleftrightarrow{XY}$ tangent to $\odot C$ at Y, secant $\overleftrightarrow{XW}$

Prove: $m\angle X = \frac{1}{2}(m\widehat{YW} - m\widehat{YZ})$

[*Plan:* Draw $\overline{YW}$, and show that $m\angle X = m\angle WYV - m\angle YWX$.]

Case 3: The angle is formed by two tangents.

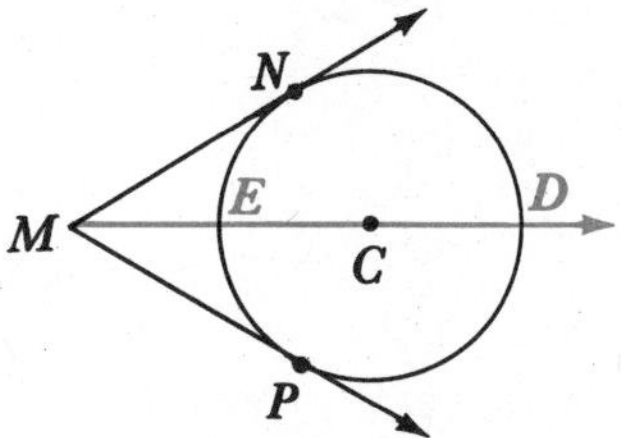

Given: $\overleftrightarrow{MN}$ tangent to $\odot C$ at N,
$\overleftrightarrow{MP}$ tangent to $\odot C$ at P

Prove: $m\angle NMP = \frac{1}{2}(m\widehat{NDP} - m\widehat{NP})$

[*Plan:* Draw $\overleftrightarrow{MC}$ and use Case 2.]

You'll be asked to prove Cases 2 and 3 in Exercises 38–39.

When deciding which theorem to use to find the measure of an angle formed by chords, secants, or tangents, it helps to look at the location of the vertex. Is it on the circle, in the interior of the circle, or in the exterior of the circle?

Example 1:

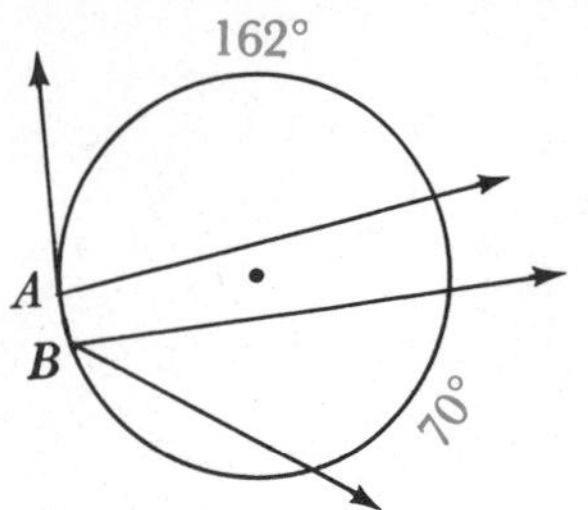

The vertex is *on the circle*, so use the Tangent and Chord or the Inscribed Angle Theorem.

$m\angle A = \frac{1}{2} \cdot 162 = 81$

$m\angle B = \frac{1}{2} \cdot 70 = 35$

Example 2:

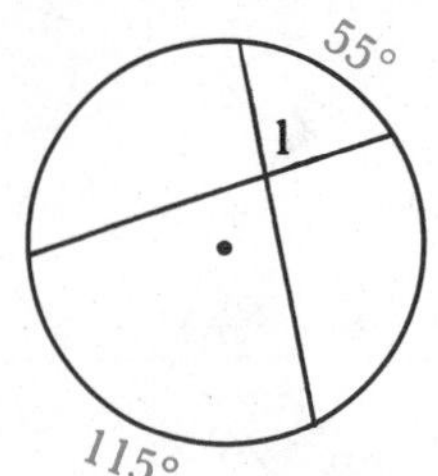

The vertex is *in the interior of the circle*, so use the Intersecting Chords Theorem.

$m\angle 1 = \frac{1}{2}(55 + 115)$

$= \frac{1}{2}(170)$

$= 85$

Example 3:

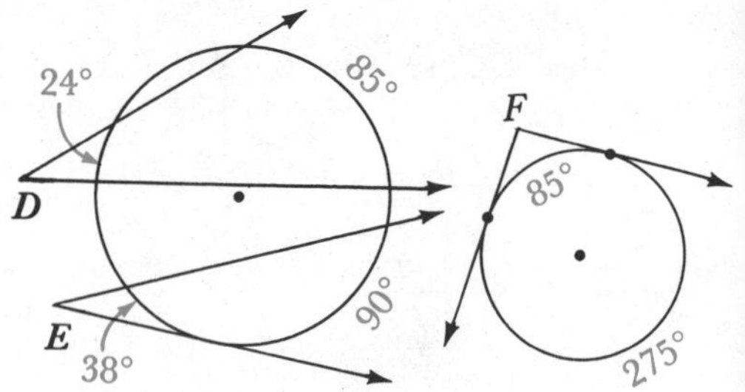

The vertex is *in the exterior of the circle*, so use the Secant and Tangent Theorem.

$m\angle D = \frac{1}{2}(85 - 24) = \frac{1}{2} \cdot 61 = 30\frac{1}{2}$

$m\angle E = \frac{1}{2}(90 - 38) = \frac{1}{2} \cdot 52 = 26$

$m\angle F = \frac{1}{2}(275 - 85) = \frac{1}{2} \cdot 190 = 95$

Exercises 11.7

Ⓐ **1–10.** Use the appropriate figure to find $m\angle 1$.

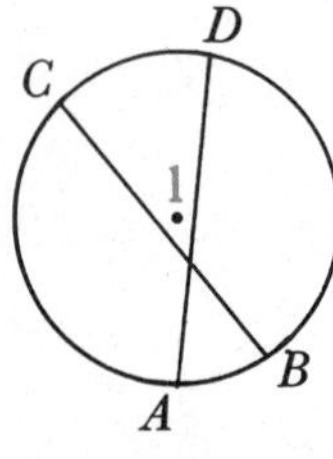

Ex. 1–2

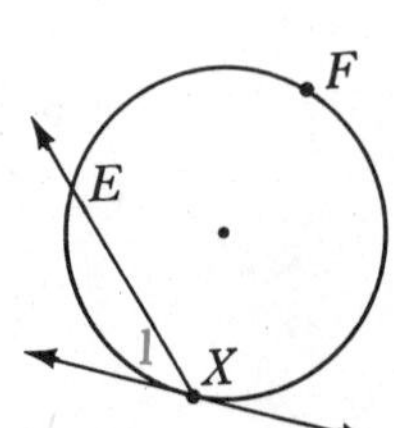

Ex. 3–4

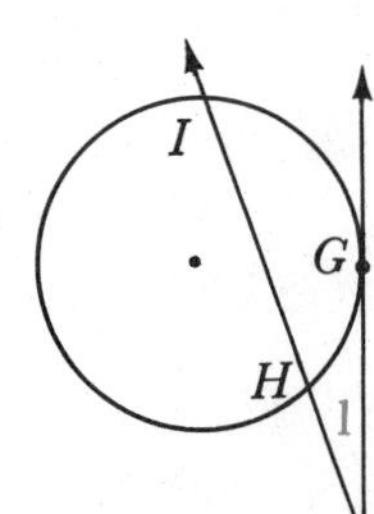

Ex. 5–6

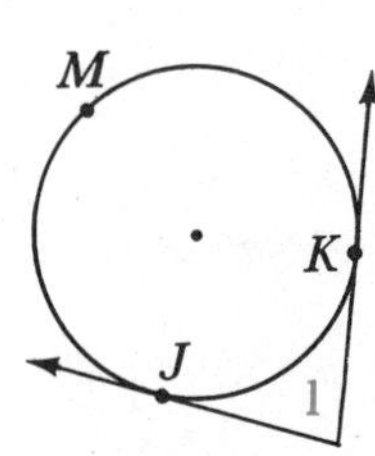

Ex. 7–8

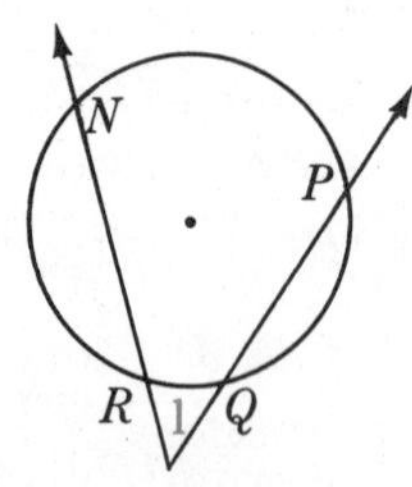

Ex. 9–10

1. $m\widehat{AB} = 36$, $m\widehat{DC} = 64$

2. $m\widehat{AB} = 40$, $m\widehat{DC} = 50$

3. $m\widehat{XE} = 102$

4. $m\widehat{EFX} = 280$

5. $m\widehat{GI} = 88$, $m\widehat{GH} = 48$

6. $m\widehat{GH} = 50$, $m\widehat{GI} = 90$

7. $m\widehat{JK} = 100$

8. $m\widehat{JMK} = 260$

9. $m\widehat{NP} = 128$, $m\widehat{RQ} = 30$

10. $m\widehat{NP} = 123$, $m\widehat{RQ} = 23$

Ⓑ **11–16.** $\overleftrightarrow{DF}$ is tangent to $\odot P$ at D. Find:

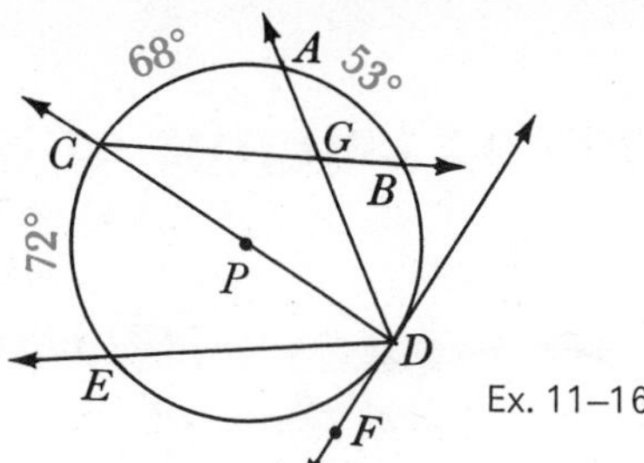

Ex. 11–16

11. $m\angle AGC$ **12.** $m\angle FDA$

13. $m\angle BCD$ **14.** $m\angle CDF$

15. $m\angle FDE$ **16.** $m\angle AGB$

17–24. $\overleftrightarrow{DN}$ and $\overleftrightarrow{DR}$ are tangent to $\odot C$. Find:

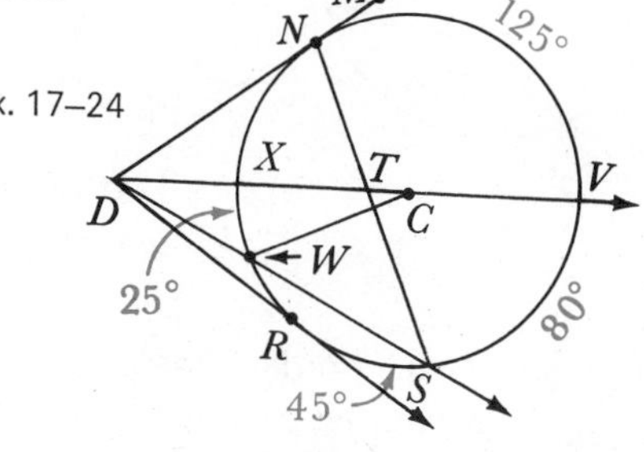

Ex. 17–24

17. $m\angle MNS$ **18.** $m\angle RDS$

19. $m\angle SDV$ **20.** $m\angle VTS$

21. $m\angle NDV$ **22.** $m\angle NDR$

23. $m\angle STX$ **24.** $m\angle SDM$

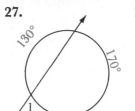

25–28. Use the appropriate figure.

25.

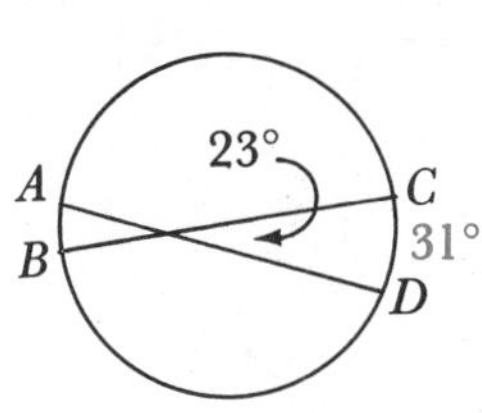

Find $m\overset{\frown}{AB}$.

26.

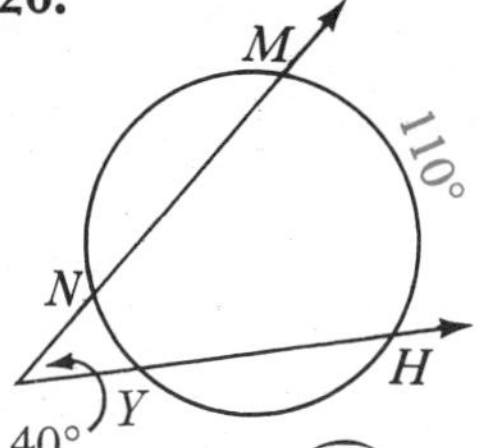

Find $m\overset{\frown}{NY}$.

27.

130°

170°

1

Find $m\angle 1$.

28.

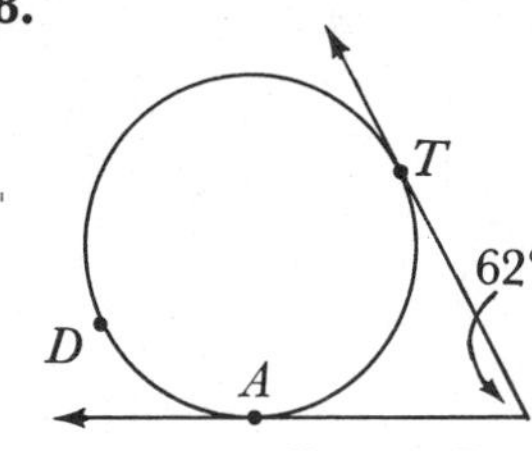

Find $m\overset{\frown}{TDA}$, $m\overset{\frown}{TA}$.

Ⓒ **29–36.** $\overleftrightarrow{TM}$ and $\overleftrightarrow{TC}$ are tangent to $\odot G$. Find:

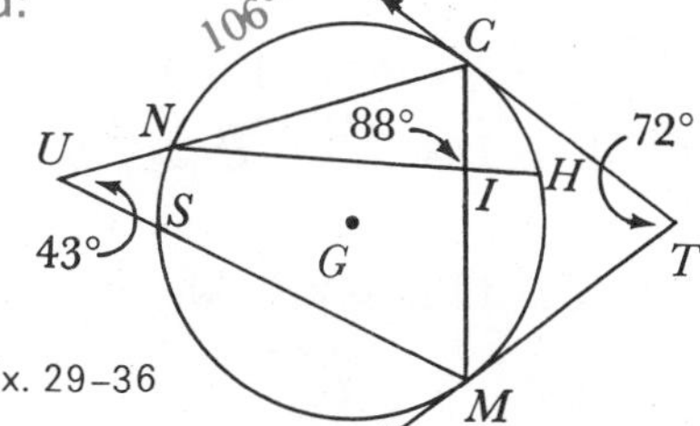

Ex. 29–36

29. $m\angle CMT$ **30.** $m\overset{\frown}{MHC}$

31. $m\overset{\frown}{MH}$ **32.** $m\overset{\frown}{SCM}$

33. $m\overset{\frown}{MNC}$ **34.** $m\overset{\frown}{SM}$

35. $m\overset{\frown}{NS}$ **36.** $m\angle HNC$

37. Prove the Intersecting Chords Theorem.

38. Prove Case 2 of the Secant and Tangent Theorem.

39. Prove Case 3 of the Secant and Tangent Theorem.

} Use the figures and restatements on pages 403 and 405.

40. Construct a circle. Mark off 36 arcs of 10°. Label the points M_1, M_2, M_3, $\cdots$, M_{36}. Draw $\overline{M_1M_9}$, $\overline{M_3M_{10}}$, $\overline{M_5M_{11}}$, $\overline{M_7M_{12}}$, $\cdots$, $\overline{M_{35}M_8}$. Notice the curve that appears. The mathematical name for the curve is *cardioid*.

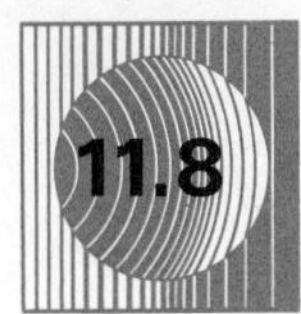

11.8 Circles and Lengths of Segments

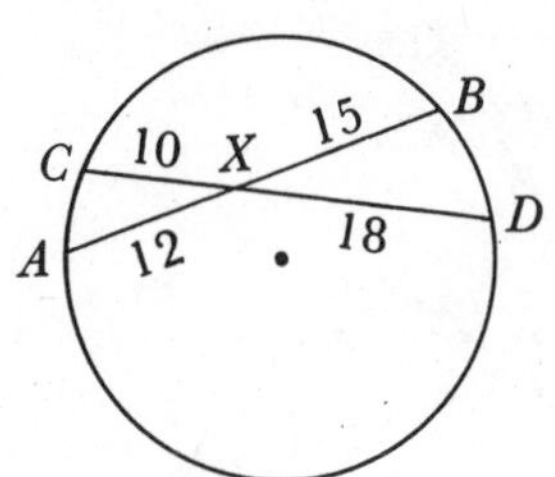

Look at the circle at the left. Chords $\overline{AB}$ and $\overline{CD}$ intersect at X. In millimeters, the measures of the segments are $AX = 12$ mm, $BX = 15$ mm, $CX = 10$ mm, and $DX = 18$ mm. Notice that

$$AX \cdot BX = CX \cdot DX$$
$$12 \cdot 15 = 10 \cdot 18$$
$$180 = 180$$

Is this relationship between the lengths of the segments always true? Consider the next theorem.

Segments of Chords Theorem If two chords intersect in the interior of a circle, the product of the lengths of the segments of one chord is equal to the product of the lengths of the segments of the other chord.

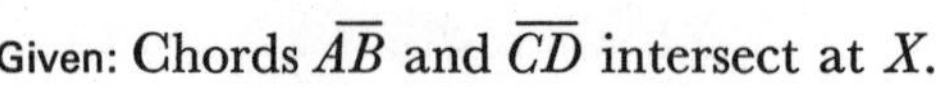

Given: Chords $\overline{AB}$ and $\overline{CD}$ intersect at X.

Prove: $AX \cdot BX = CX \cdot DX$

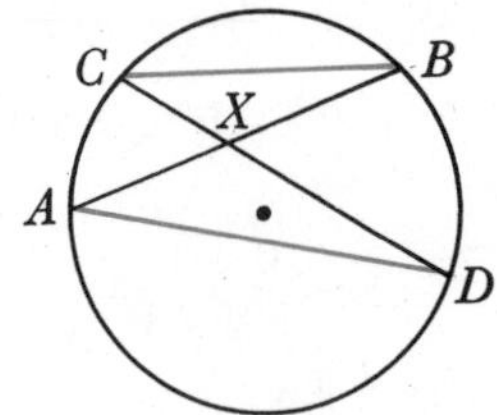

Proof:

STATEMENTS	REASONS
1. Chords $\overline{AB}$ and $\overline{CD}$ intersect at X.	1. Given
2. Draw $\overline{BC}$ and $\overline{AD}$.	2. Two pts. determine a line.
3. $\angle A \cong \angle C$, $\angle D \cong \angle B$	3. Two $\angle$s inscribed in the same arc are $\cong$.
4. $\triangle AXD \sim \triangle CXB$	4. AA Similarity Theorem
5. $\frac{AX}{CX} = \frac{DX}{BX}$	5. Corres. sides of $\sim$ $\triangle$s are proportional.
6. $AX \cdot BX = CX \cdot DX$	6. Cross multiply.

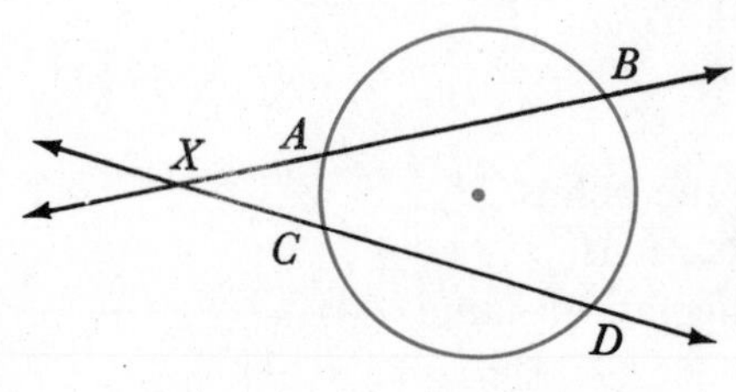

Consider two secants that intersect at a point X. $\overline{XB}$ and $\overline{XD}$ are called **secant segments** because part of each segment is in the exterior of the circle. $\overline{XA}$ is the *external part* of secant segment $\overline{XB}$, and $\overline{XC}$ is the external part of $\overline{XD}$. We now prove the Segments of Secants Theorem, which is closely related to the Segments of Chords Theorem.

If two secants intersect at a point in the exterior of a circle, the length of one secant segment times the length of its external part is equal to the length of the other secant segment times the length of its external part.

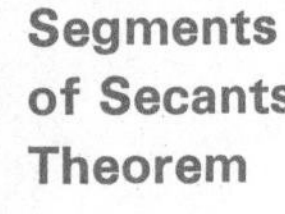

Given: Secant segments $\overline{XB}$ and $\overline{XD}$

Prove: $XB \cdot XA = XD \cdot XC$

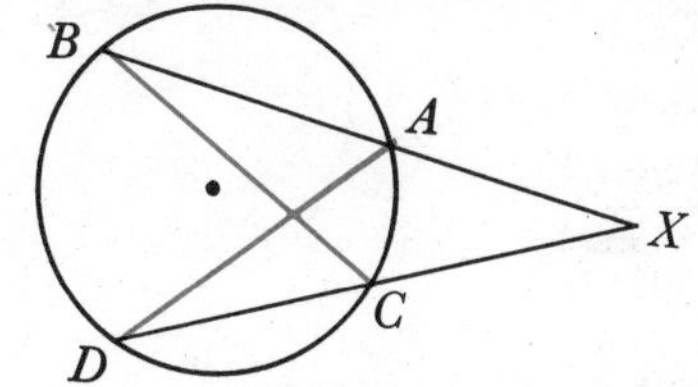

Proof:

STATEMENTS	REASONS
1. Secant segments $\overline{XB}$ and $\overline{XD}$	1. Given
2. Draw $\overline{CB}$ and $\overline{AD}$.	2. Two pts. determine a line.
3. $\angle B \cong \angle D$	3. Two $\angle$s inscribed in the same arc are $\cong$.
4. $\angle X \cong \angle X$	4. An $\angle$ is $\cong$ to itself.
5. $\triangle CXB \sim \triangle AXD$	5. AA Similarity Theorem
6. $\frac{XB}{XD} = \frac{XC}{XA}$	6. Corres. sides of $\sim$ $\triangle$s are proportional.
7. $XB \cdot XA = XD \cdot XC$	7. Cross multiply.

Notice how similar the proofs of the Segments of Chords and the Segments of Secants Theorems are.

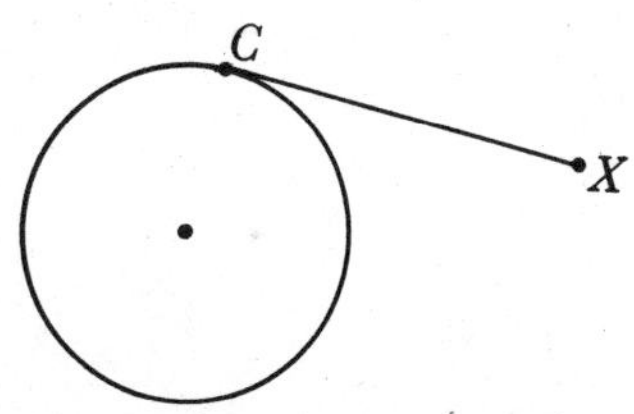

A **tangent segment** is a segment that is tangent to a circle at one of its endpoints. $\overline{XC}$ is a tangent segment.

If a tangent segment and a secant segment intersect in the exterior of a circle, the length of the tangent segment squared is equal to the product of the lengths of the secant segment and its external part.

Given: $\overline{XC}$ a tangent segment, $\overline{XB}$ a secant segment

Prove: $(XC)^2 = XB \cdot XA$

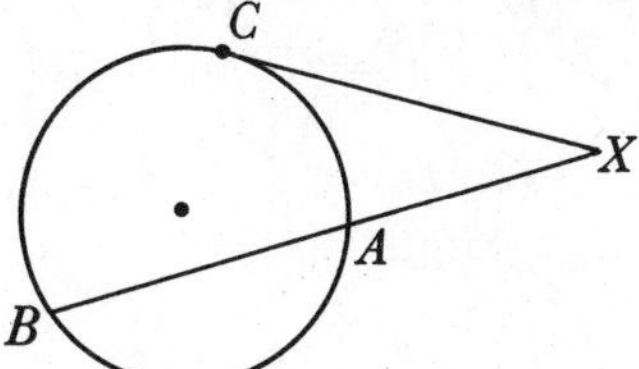

[*Plan:* Draw $\overline{CA}$ and $\overline{CB}$, and show that $\triangle ACX \sim \triangle CBX$.]

You'll be asked to prove the Tangent-Secant Segments Theorem in Exercise 23.

When finding the lengths of segments, study the figure to decide which theorem to use, as in the examples below.

Example 1:

Find x.

$8x = 6 \cdot 11$

$8x = 66$

$x = \frac{66}{8} = 8\frac{1}{4}$

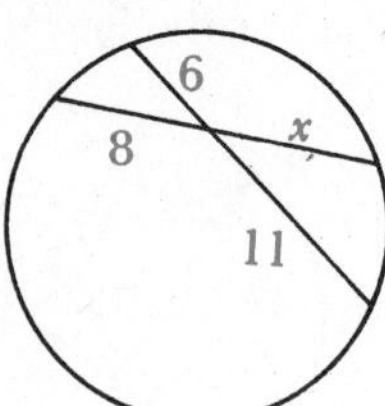

Example 2:

Find y.

$12^2 = 24 \cdot y$

$144 = 24 \cdot y$

$6 = y$

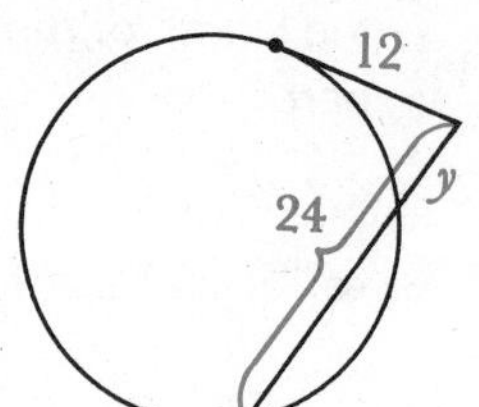

Exercises 11.8

Ⓐ **1–8.** State the equation you would use to find x.

1.

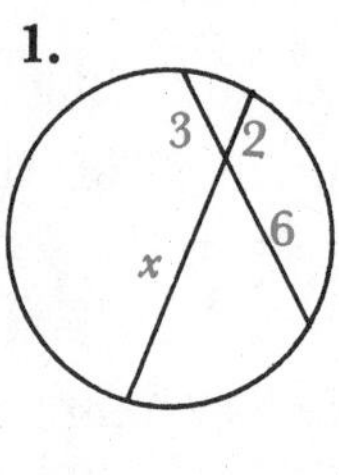

2.

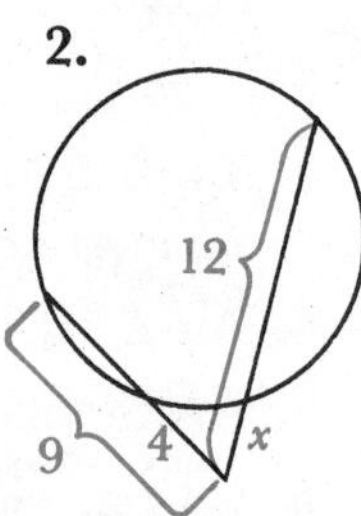

3.

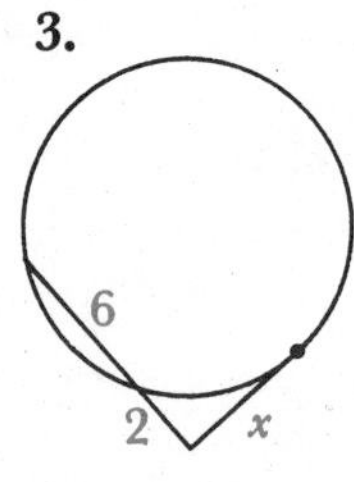

4.

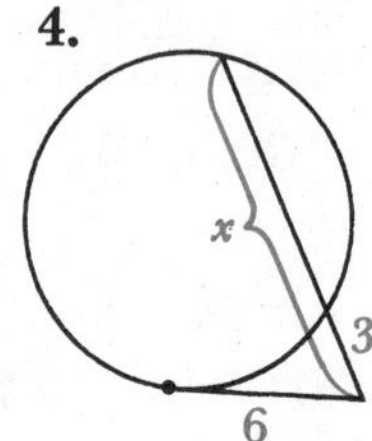

5.

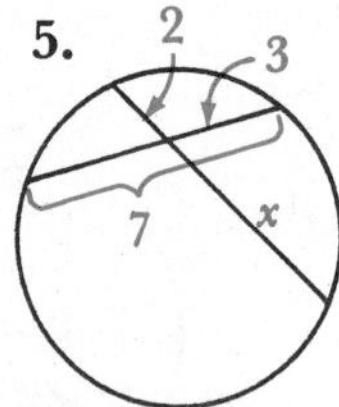

6.

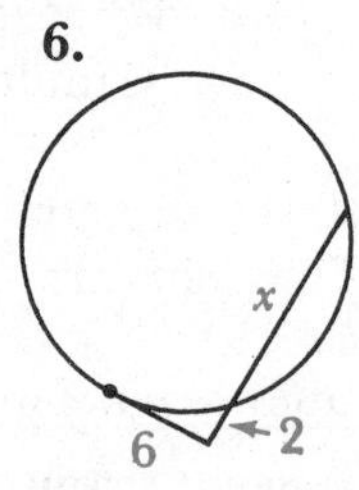

7.

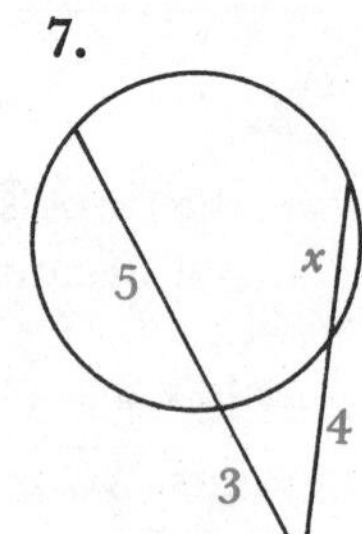

8.

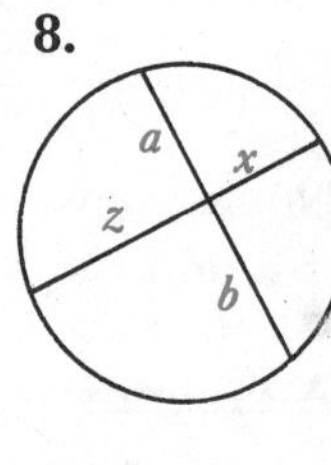

Ⓑ **9–16.** Solve for x in Exercises 1–8.

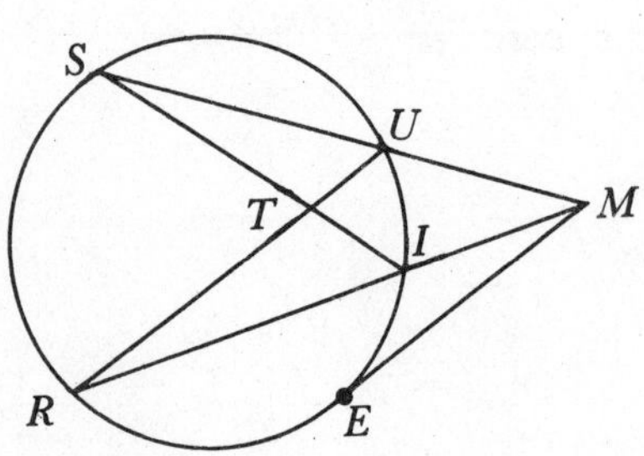

17–22. Refer to the figure.

17. $ST = 6$, $TI = 5$, $RT = 10$, find RU.

18. $SM = 21$, $RI = 14$, $RM = 22$, find UM.

19. $ME = 6$, $UM = 4$, find SM.

20. $SI = 8$, $RT = 8$, $TU = 2$, find ST.

21. $MS = 12$, $UM = 2\sqrt{3}$, $MI = 3$, find RM.

22. $IR = 6\sqrt{3}$, $MI = 3\sqrt{3}$, find ME.

Ⓒ **23.** Prove the Tangent-Secant Segments Theorem. Use the figure and restatement on page 409.

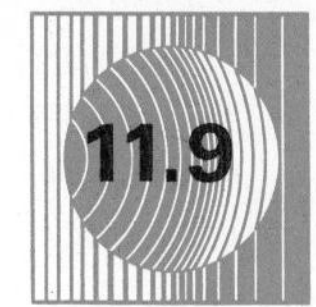

Locus

Photri

Susan is looking for a summer job. Since she wants to walk to work, she wants to find a job a mile or less from her home. Looking through the want ads of the newspaper, she circles all the jobs that satisfy that condition.

In geometry, sometimes we want to find all the points satisfying a given condition. A **locus of points** (plural, **loci**) is a geometric figure containing all the points, and only those points, that satisfy a given condition.

Example 1: In a plane, what is the locus of points 2 cm from point X?

NOTE: "In a plane" means that *all* points, those given and those in the locus, are in the same plane.

1. Make a rough drawing and find some points whose distance from X is 2 cm. (Keep finding points until you can describe the geometric figure.)

2. The locus is a circle with center X and radius 2 cm.

1.

X

2.

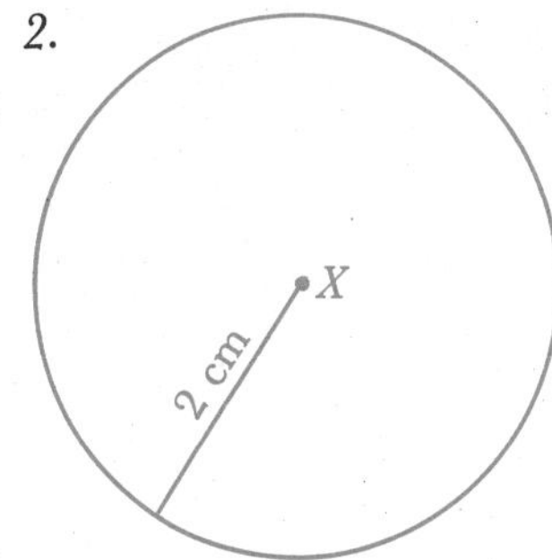

Each solution to a locus problem should have
(1) a neat drawing of the figure satisfying the given condition and
(2) a statement clearly describing the locus.

Exercises 11.9

Ⓐ **1–2.** In a plane, the locus of points 7 cm from point Z is a circle with center Z and radius 7 cm.

1. If $ZX = 7$ cm, is X in the locus?

2. If $ZW = 9$ cm, is W in the locus?

Ⓑ **3–19.** Draw and describe each locus as clearly as possible.

3. in a plane, the locus of points 2 cm from a line ℓ

4. in a plane, the locus of points equidistant from two points X and Y

5. in space, the locus of points 5 cm from a given point X

6. in space, the locus of points equidistant from points C and D

7. in a plane, the locus of points equidistant from the sides of $\angle XYZ$

8. in space, the locus of points 9 m from a given point Z

9. in a plane, the locus of points equidistant from points A and B

10. in a plane, the locus of points whose distance from the center of circle W, with radius 3 cm, is 5 cm

11. in a plane, the locus of points whose distance from point Z is less than or equal to 6 cm

12. in a plane, the locus of points 8 cm from line p

13. in a plane, the locus of points equidistant from lines ℓ and k where $\ell \parallel k$

14. in a plane, the locus of points whose distance from the center of circle C, with radius 8 cm, is 2 cm

15. in a plane, the locus of points whose distance from a point R is greater than 9 cm

16. in space, the locus of points whose distance from a point P is less than 56 mm

17. in a plane, the locus of points equidistant from $\overleftrightarrow{XZ}$ and $\overleftrightarrow{XW}$

© 18. in a plane, the locus of points equidistant from two given points X and Y and at a distance of XY from a point X

19. in space, the locus of points at a distance of 5 cm from point X and 3 cm from point Y when
   a. $XY = 8$ cm **b.** $XY = 4$ cm

Courtesy Union Pacific Railroad

20. A company that manufactures machine tools needs to build a warehouse. A cost study determined that the warehouse should be at least 30 km and no more than 50 km from the home office of the company. Describe the best location for the warehouse.

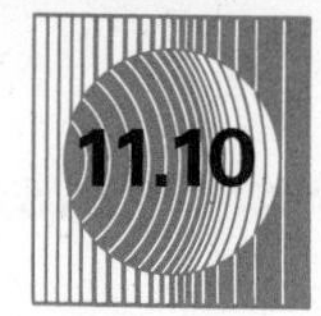

Transformations: Turns

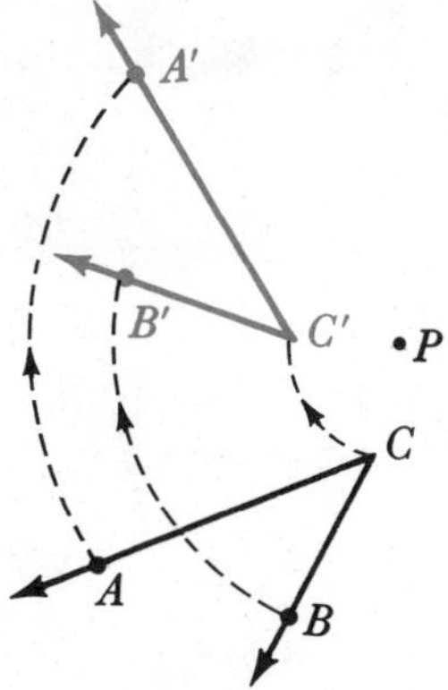

A turn in a plane is described by a center and an arc which gives the direction and magnitude of the turn. At the left the direction of the turn is clockwise and the magnitude is 80. That means that $m\widehat{AA'} = m\widehat{BB'} = m\widehat{CC'} = 80$. The center of the turn, point P, is the center of the concentric circles containing arcs $\widehat{AA'}$, $\widehat{BB'}$, $\widehat{CC'}$.

To turn $\triangle XYZ$ counterclockwise 150° with P as the center of the turn, follow these steps. Find the turn image of each vertex separately.

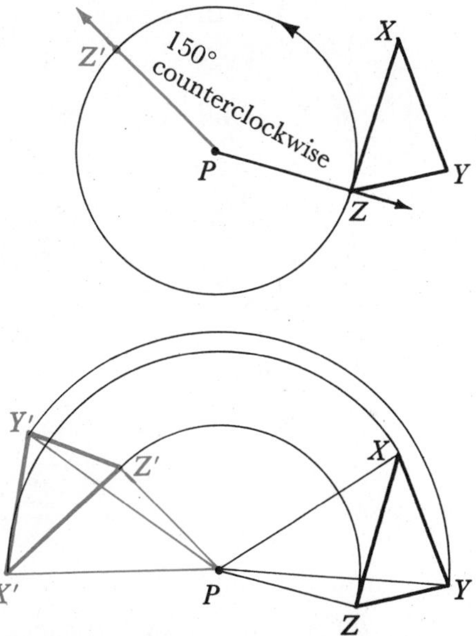

1. To find the turn image of Z, draw $\overrightarrow{PZ}$. Then draw an angle with $\overrightarrow{PZ}$ as a side and measure 150°. The direction from $\overrightarrow{PZ}$ to the other side of the angle must be counterclockwise.

2. Draw $\odot P$ with radius $\overline{PZ}$. Z' is the intersection of the new side of the angle and the circle.

3. Follow steps 1 and 2 to find the turn image of points X and Y. Notice that $\widehat{XX'}$, $\widehat{YY'}$, $\widehat{ZZ'}$ are arcs of concentric circles with center P, and have equal measure.

By measuring, we find that $XZ = X'Z'$ and $m\angle Z = m\angle Z'$. This suggests that turns preserve distance and angle measure. If a point is between points X and Z its image will be between X' and Z'. Notice that the orientation of $\triangle XYZ$ and $\triangle X'Y'Z'$ is clockwise.

Turns preserve:

1. angle measure
2. betweenness
3. collinearity
4. distance
5. orientation

Exercises 11.10

Ⓐ **1.** What is the *direction* of a turn?

2. What is the *magnitude* of a turn?

Ex. 3–4

A′ A 56° O

3–4. Refer to the figure. A' is the turn image of A around center O.

3. What is the direction of the turn?

4. What is the magnitude of the turn?

Ⓑ **5–6.** $\overline{X'Y'}$ is the turn image of $\overline{XY}$.

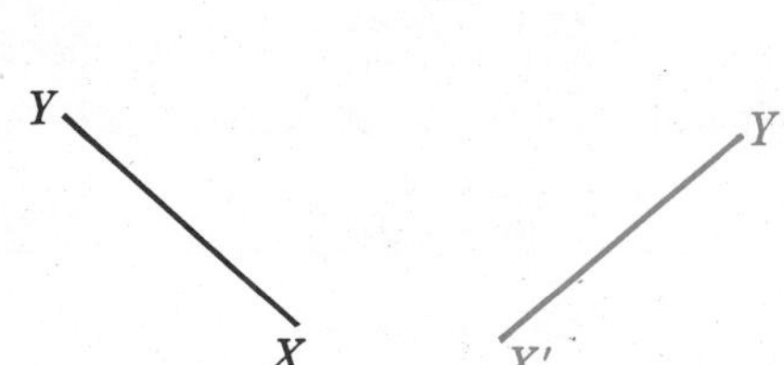

5. Name the center and direction of this turn.

6. Find the magnitude of this turn.

7–10. $A'B'C'D'$ is the turn image of $ABCD$. True or False?

7. If the orientation of $ABCD$ is clockwise, then the orientation of $A'B'C'D'$ is counterclockwise.

8. $m\angle DAB \neq m\angle D'A'B'$

9. $BC = 9$ and $B'C' = 7$ only if the turn is clockwise.

10. $m\widehat{AA'} = m\widehat{BB'}$ if $\widehat{AA'}$, $\widehat{BB'}$, and the turn have center P.

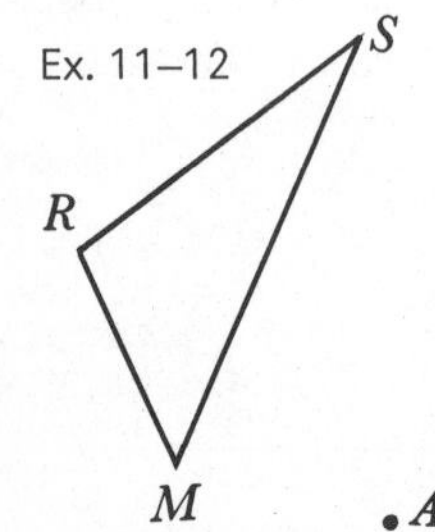

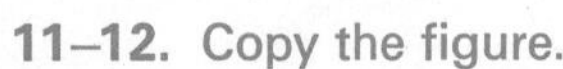

11–12. Copy the figure.

11. Turn $\triangle MSR$ 110° clockwise around center A.

12. Turn $\triangle MSR$ 70° counterclockwise around center A.

Ⓒ **13–16.** Copy $\triangle MSR$ and point A used in Exercises 11–12.

13. Draw a line ℓ through A. Draw k intersecting line ℓ at A.

14. Reflect $\triangle MSR$ over ℓ. Label the image $\triangle M'S'R'$.

15. Reflect $\triangle M'S'R'$ over k. Label the image $\triangle M''S''R''$.

16. How do $\triangle MSR$ and $\triangle M''S''R''$ appear to be related?

■ Chapter 11 Review ■

11.1

1. Define *radius* of a circle.

2. Define *diameter* of a sphere. 3. Define *secant* of a circle.

11.2

4–8. Refer to the figure.

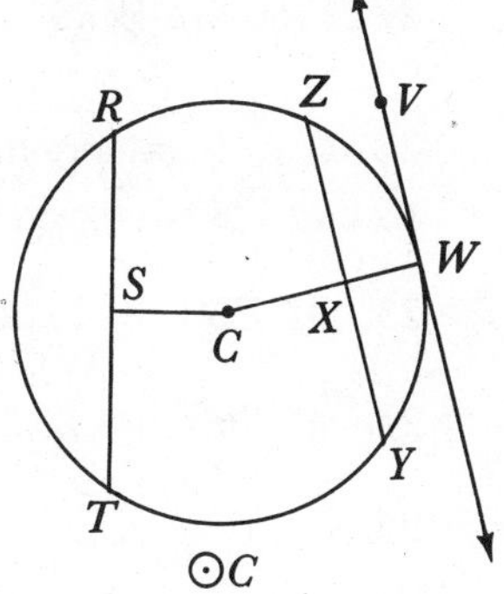

4. Name a point in the exterior of ⊙C.

5. If $\overline{CW}$ bisects chord $\overline{ZY}$, name 2 perpendicular segments.

6. If $\overline{CS} \perp \overline{RT}$, $\overline{CX} \perp \overline{ZY}$, and $CS = CX$, why is $\overline{RT} \cong \overline{ZY}$?

7. If $\overline{RT} \cong \overline{ZY}$, when is $CS = CX$?

8. If $\overline{CW} \perp \overline{WV}$, is $\overleftrightarrow{VW}$ tangent to ⊙C? Why?

11.3

9. Draw two concentric circles.

10. Draw two externally tangent circles, and then draw all their common tangents.

11.4

11–13. Sphere W is tangent to plane p at A.

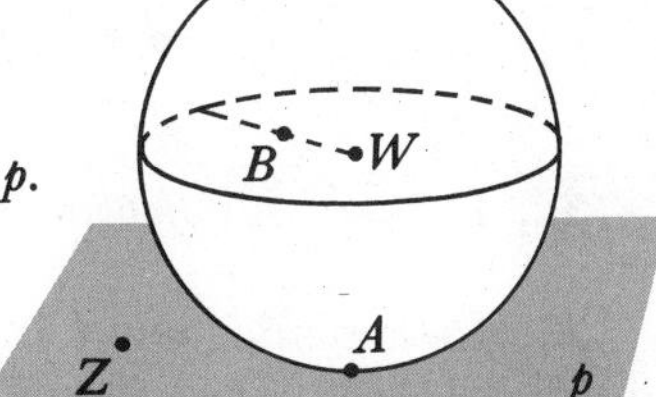

11. Name two points in the interior of the sphere.

12. Why is $\overline{WA} \perp p$?

13. If $ZA = 8$, and $WZ = 10$, find the radius of the sphere.

11.5

14–18. Given ⊙E, $m\angle BEC = 72$.

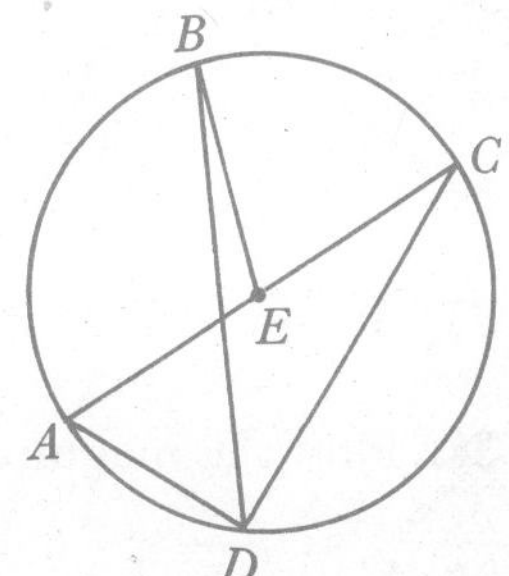

14. Name two central angles.

15. Is $\widehat{BC}$ a minor arc? Why?

16. Find $m\widehat{AB}$.

17. Name two semicircles.

18. Is $\widehat{ADB}$ a major arc? Find $m\widehat{ADB}$.

11.6 19–22. Given $\odot S$.

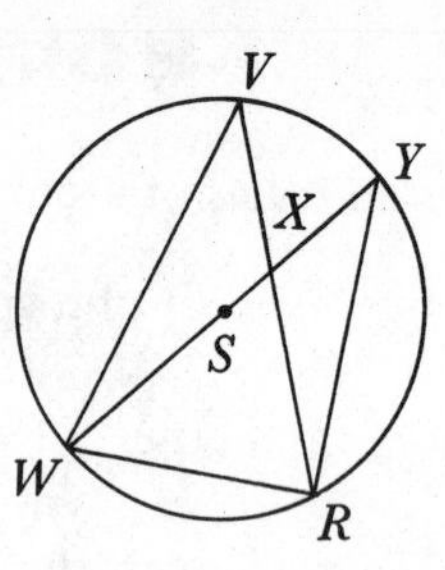

19. Name 2 inscribed angles.

20. Name the arc that $\angle RXW$ intercepts.

21. Why is $m\angle WVR = m\angle RYW$?

22. Find $m\angle WRY$.

11.7 23–31. $\overrightarrow{RS}$ is tangent to $\odot T$, $\overline{YJ}$ and $\overline{YN}$ are tangent to $\odot U$.

23. $m\angle ZXV =$ ______ $(m\overparen{ZV} +$ ______$)$

24. $m\angle SRV =$ ______

25. $m\angle Y_1 =$ ______

26. $m\angle Y_2 =$ ______

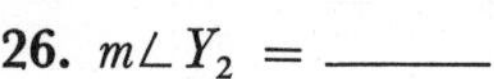

27. $m\angle Y_{123} =$ ______

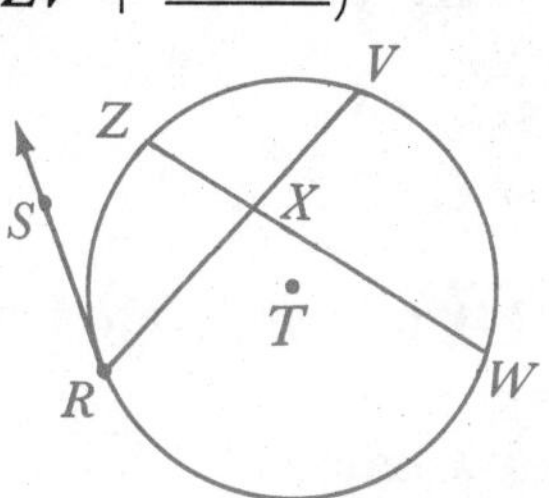

Ex. 23–24; 28–29

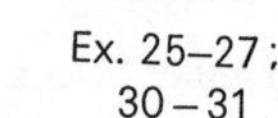

Ex. 25–27; 30–31

11.8 **28.** Is $\overline{RS}$ a tangent segment?

29. If $ZX = 3$, $XW = 8$, and $XV = 4$, then $XR =$ ______

30. If $YJ = 9$, and $YP = 3$, then $YK =$ ______

31. If $YQ = 4$, $YP = 7$, and $PK = 17$, then $QM =$ ______

11.9 **32.** Define *locus of points.*

33. In a plane, what is the locus of points whose distance from the point C is less than or equal to 4.5 cm?

34. In space, what is the locus of points equidistant from the endpoints of $\overline{AB}$?

11.10 35–38. $\triangle CDY$ is the turn image of $\triangle ABT$ around center Z.

35. State the direction of the turn.

36. Find the magnitude of the turn.

37. Find $m\overparen{BD}$. **38.** Find $m\angle AZC$.

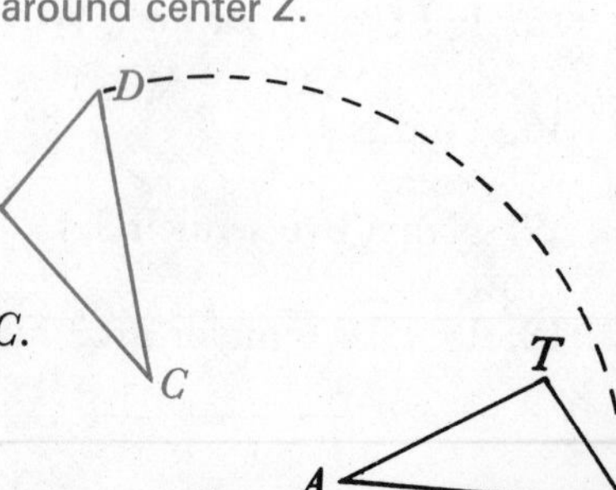

Chapter 11 Test

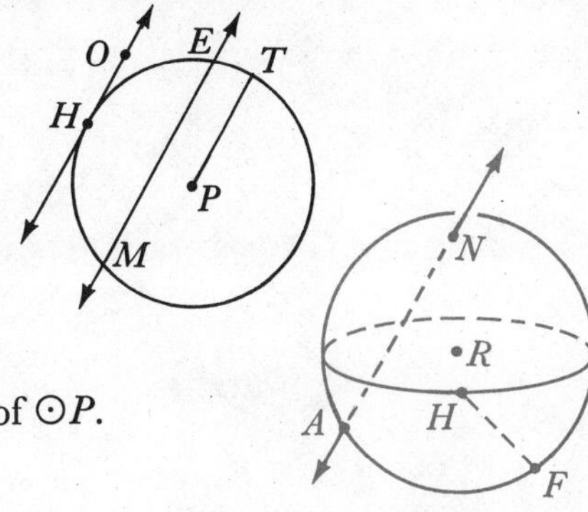

1. Name a radius of $\odot P$.
2. Name a secant of sphere R.
3. Name a chord of sphere R.
4. Name a tangent of $\odot P$.
5. Name a point in the interior of $\odot P$.

6–9. True or False?

6. If a segment bisects a chord, it is perpendicular to the chord.
7. Congruent chords of a circle are equidistant from the center of the circle.
8. All radii of a circle are congruent.
9. Any two small circles of a sphere are congruent.

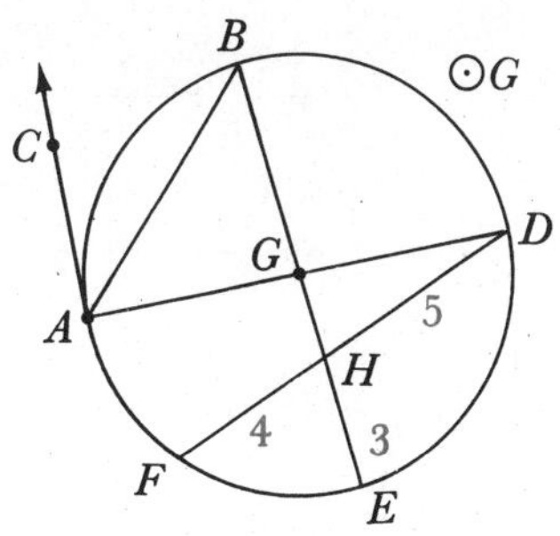

10–15. If $m\angle BAD = 46$ and $m\angle FHE = 72$, find:

10. $m\widehat{BD}$
11. $m\angle BGD$
12. $m\widehat{FE}$
13. $m\widehat{DAF}$
14. $m\angle CAD$
15. BH

16–21. $\overline{PM}$ tangent to $\odot W$ at N, $\overline{PK}$ tangent to $\odot W$ at K. Find:

16. $m\angle P$
17. $m\angle M$
18. $m\angle X$
19. VK
20. RK
21. MN

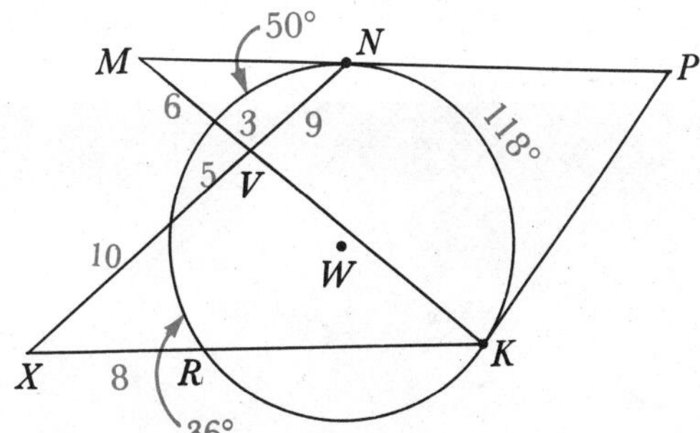

22. In a plane, what is the locus of points equidistant from two intersecting lines?

23. Copy $\triangle RTU$ and turn it 130° clockwise around center C.

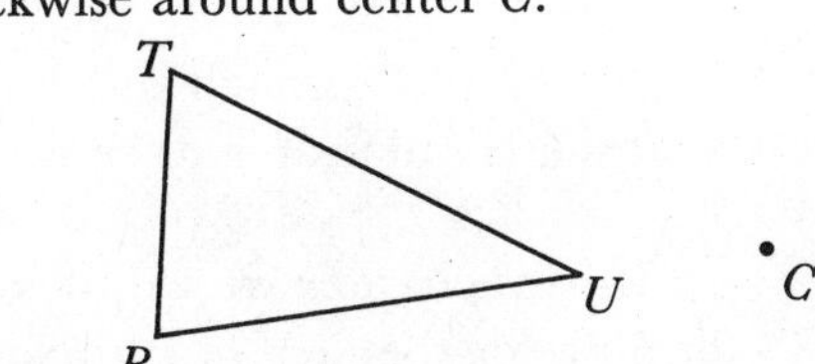

12 REGULAR POLYGONS AND CIRCLES

Photos courtesy Valmont Industries Inc.

The center-pivot irrigation system shown at the left contains a long length of pipeline attached to a water source at one end. The pipeline rotates around the water source, propelled by water pressure or electricity. As it rotates, water pumped through the pipeline irrigates a circular area as shown above.

In this chapter we will develop the formula for the area of a circle.

Inscribed Regular Polygons

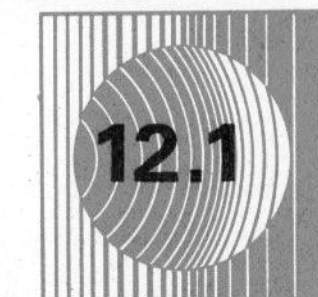

You already know that a *regular polygon* is a convex polygon that is both equilateral and equiangular. The figures below review what is meant by *inscribed* and *circumscribed* regular polygons.

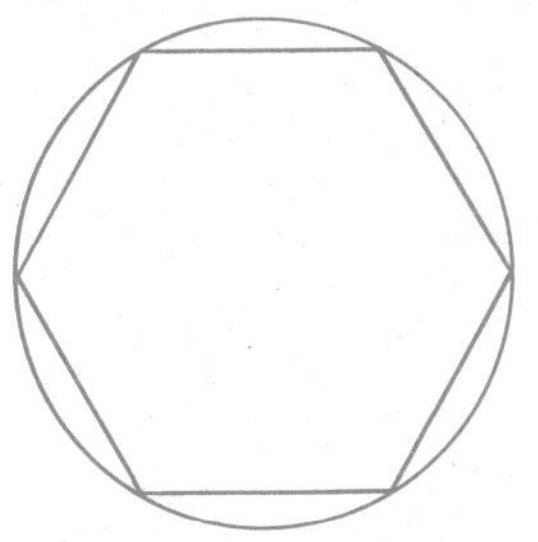

inscribed polygon
circumscribed circle

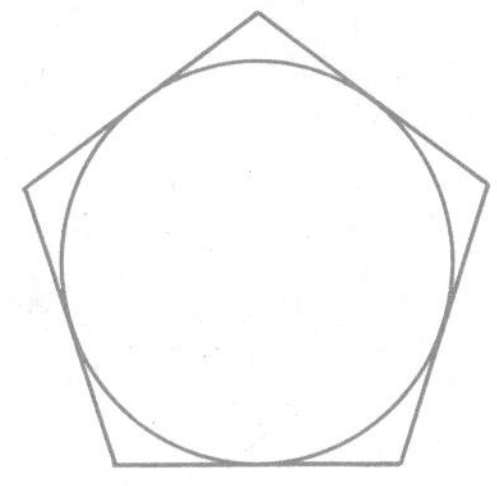

inscribed circle
circumscribed polygon

Courtesy Illinois Institute of Technology

For regular polygons inscribed in a circle, the following terms are often used:

The **center** of a regular polygon is the center of its circumscribed circle.

A **radius** of a regular polygon is a segment that joins its center to a vertex.

An **apothem** of a regular polygon is a perpendicular segment from its center to one of its sides.

A **central angle** of a regular polygon is an angle determined by two radii drawn to the endpoints of a side.

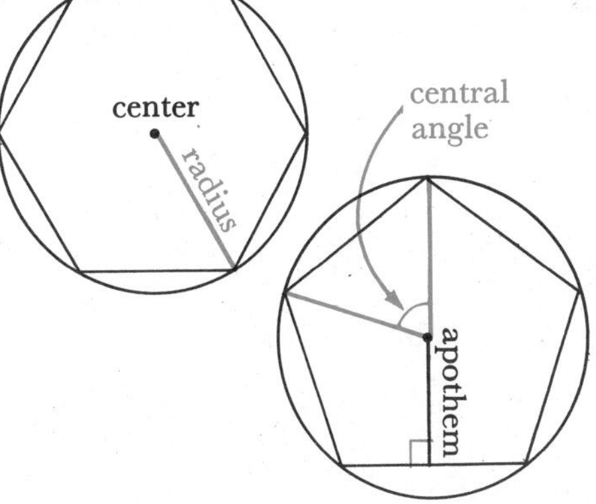

A regular polygon of n sides inscribed in a circle would cut off n congruent arcs, each having degree measure $\frac{360}{n}$. Since each of these arcs is intercepted by a central angle of the regular polygon, we could prove the following theorem:

Theorem

The degree measure of a central angle of a regular polygon of n sides is $\frac{360}{n}$.

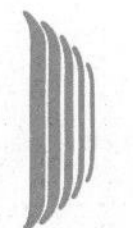

Example: Regular hexagon $ABCDEF$ with sides of length 8 is inscribed in $\odot O$. Find the lengths of the apothem $\overline{OG}$ and the radius $\overline{OA}$.

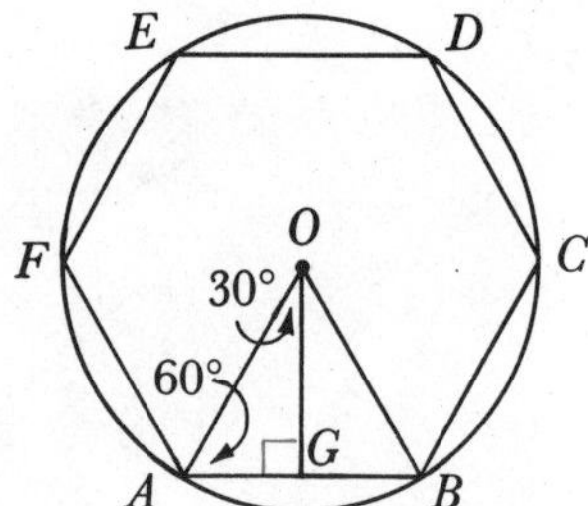

Consider $\triangle OAB$. By the theorem on page 419, $m\angle AOB = 60$. Since $\overline{OA} \cong \overline{OB}$, $\angle OAB \cong \angle OBA$. So, $m\angle OAB = m\angle OBA = 60$. Then $\triangle OAG$ is a 30-60-90° triangle. Since $\overline{OG}$ bisects $\overline{AB}$, $AG = 4$. Then, by the 30-60-90° Triangle Theorem, page 310, $OA = 2 \cdot AG = 8$ and $OG = AG \cdot \sqrt{3} = 4\sqrt{3}$.

Area Theorem for a Regular Polygon

The area (A) of a regular polygon is equal to one half of the length (a) of its apothem times its perimeter (p).

$$A = \tfrac{1}{2}ap$$

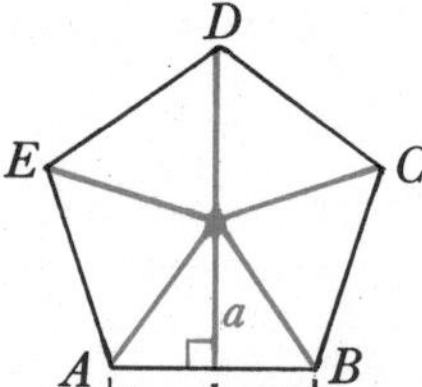

Given: Regular polygon $ABCDE$ with apothem of length a, perimeter p, and area A

Prove: $A = \frac{1}{2}ap$

Sketch of proof: Draw radii dividing the polygon into congruent triangles. Each triangle has an area equal to $\frac{1}{2}ab$ (where b is the length of one side of the polygon). If the polygon has n sides, then the total area is $n(\frac{1}{2}ab)$. So,

$$A = \tfrac{1}{2}a(nb)$$
$$= \tfrac{1}{2}ap$$

From Section 5.2, we know $p = nb$.

Exercises 12.1

Ⓐ **1–6.** Refer to the figure where O is the center of the circle and $ABCD$ is an inscribed square.

1. $\overline{OA}$ is a(n) (radius, apothem) of $ABCD$.
2. $\overline{OR}$ is a(n) (radius, apothem) of $ABCD$.
3. The center of $ABCD$ is ______.
4. $\angle AOB$ is a ______ angle.
5. $ABCD$ is (circumscribed about, inscribed in) circle O.
6. Circle O is (circumscribed about, inscribed in) $ABCD$.

Ⓑ **7–10.** Find the number of degrees in the central angle of a regular polygon having

7. 3 sides **8.** 5 sides **9.** 6 sides **10.** 36 sides

11–24. Regular hexagon *MONKEY* with sides of length 20 is inscribed in circle *P*. Square *LAMB* with sides of length 4 is inscribed in circle *R*.

Ex. 11–18

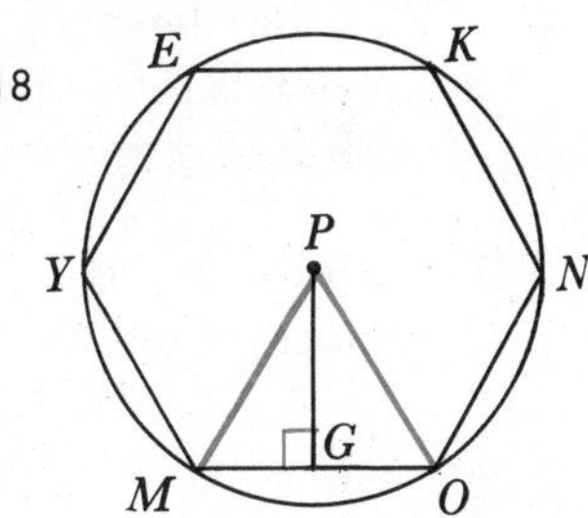

11. What is $m\angle MPO$?

12. Is $m\angle PMO = m\angle POM$?

13. What is $m\angle PMO$?

14. What is $m\angle MGP$?

15. What is $m\angle MPG$?

Ex. 19–24

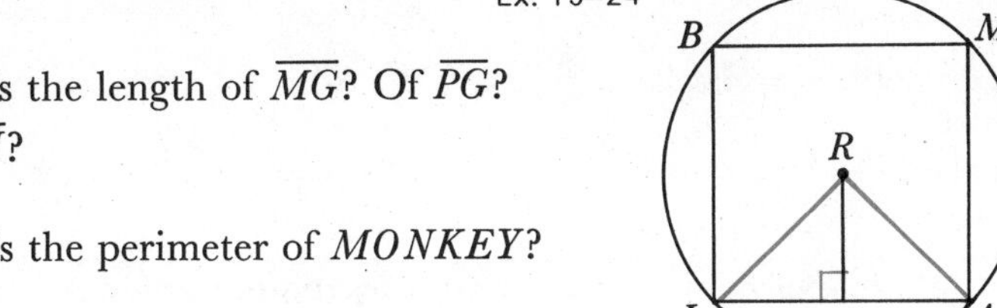

16. What is the length of $\overline{MG}$? Of $\overline{PG}$? Of $\overline{PM}$?

17. What is the perimeter of *MONKEY*?

18. What is the area of *MONKEY*?

19. What is $m\angle LRA$?

20. Is $m\angle RLA = m\angle RAL$?

21. What is $m\angle RLA$?

22. What is $m\angle LRT$?

23. What is the length of $\overline{LT}$? Of $\overline{RT}$? Of $\overline{LR}$?

24. What is the perimeter of *LAMB*? The area?

25–28. Find the length of the apothem for each inscribed regular hexagon or square. HINT: Draw radii and consider special right triangles.

25.

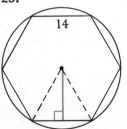

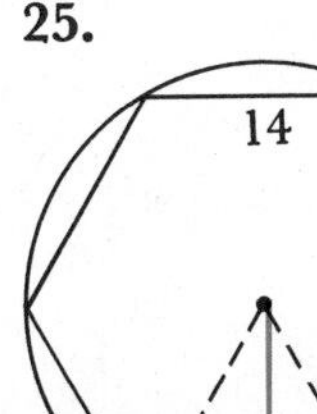

26.

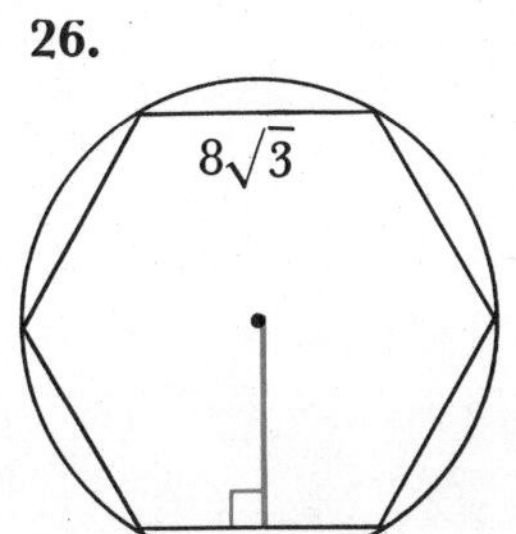

27.

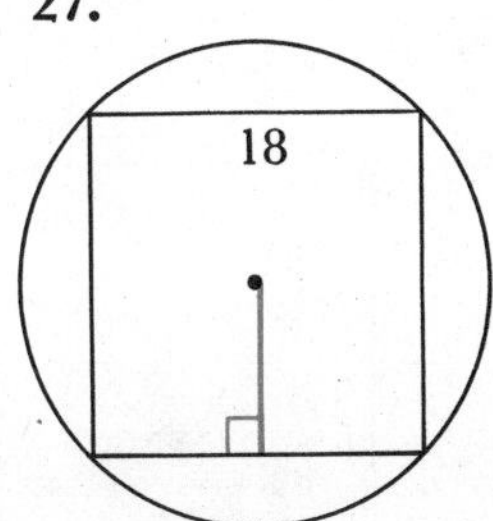

28.

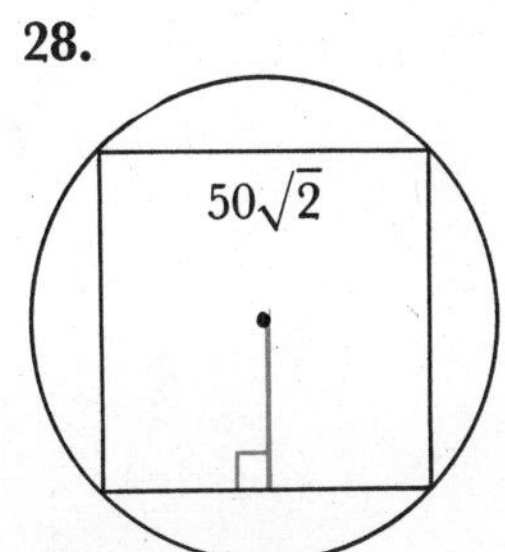

29–32. Find the length of the radius for each inscribed regular polygon.

29. inscribed regular hexagon with side of length $10\sqrt{3}$

30. inscribed regular hexagon with side of length $12\sqrt{3}$

31. inscribed square with side of length $16\sqrt{2}$

32. inscribed square with side of length 60

33. If a regular hexagon has a radius of 26 and has a circle inscribed in it, what is the radius of the inscribed circle? NOTE: The midpoint of each side of the hexagon is a point of tangency.

34. If a regular hexagon has an inscribed circle of radius $2\sqrt{3}$, what is the radius of the regular hexagon?

35–38. Find the area of each regular polygon having the given perimeter and apothem of length a.

35. $p = 48,\ a = 4\sqrt{3}$

36. $p = 28,\ a = 3\frac{1}{2}$

37. $p = 24\sqrt{3},\ a = 4$

38. $p = 60,\ a = 5\sqrt{3}$

construction: a circle circumscribed about any regular polygon

1. Construct the ⊥ bis. of one side.

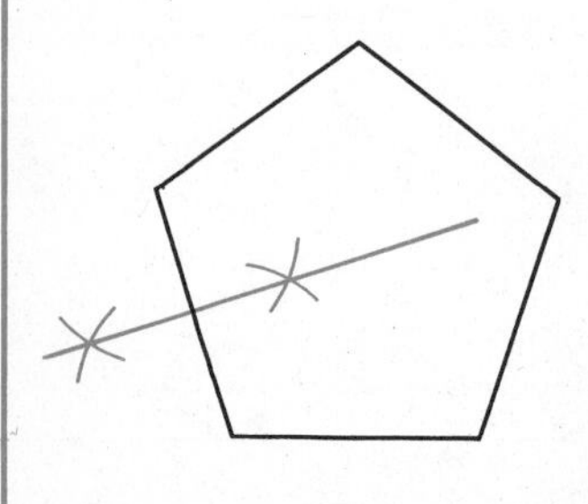

2. Construct the ⊥ bis. of another side.

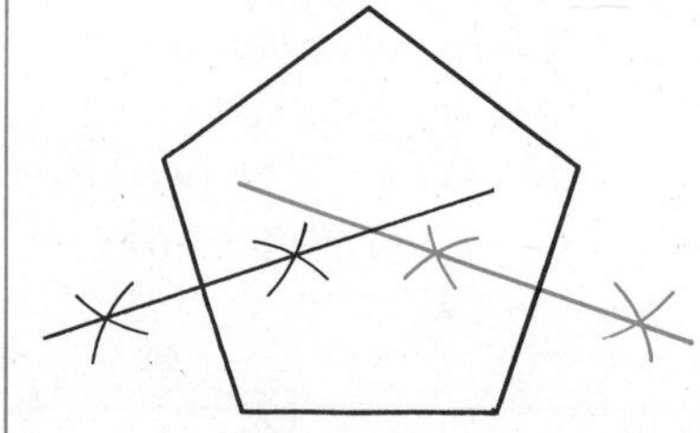

3. Use the pt. where the ⊥ bis. meet as the center O. With OR as radius, circumscribe the circle.

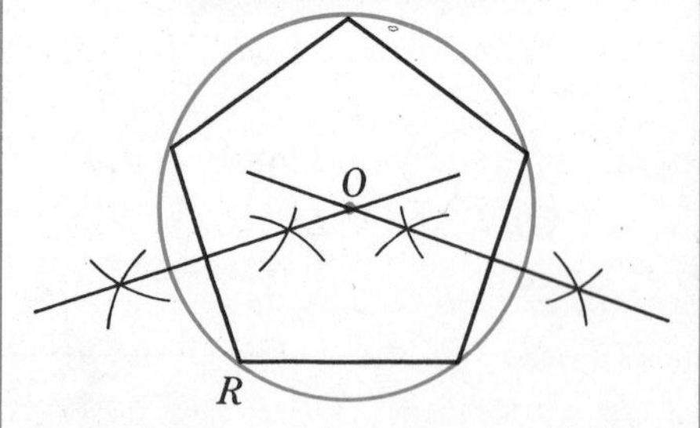

39–40. Copy each figure. Then circumscribe a circle about the polygon.

39.

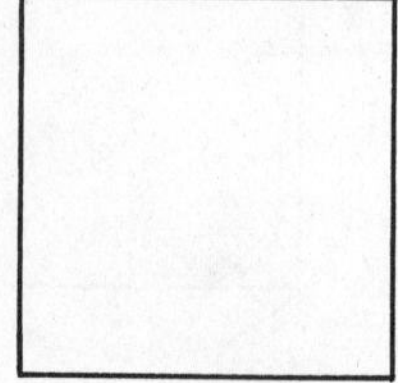

40.

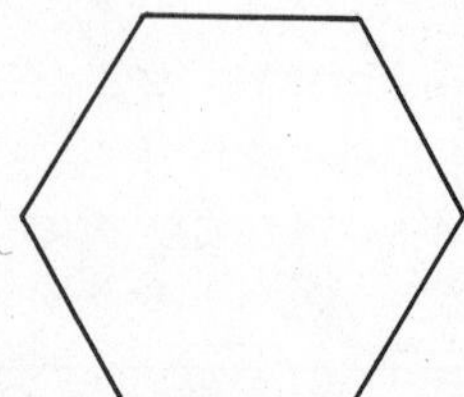

construction: a circle inscribed in any regular polygon

1. Construct an angle bisector.

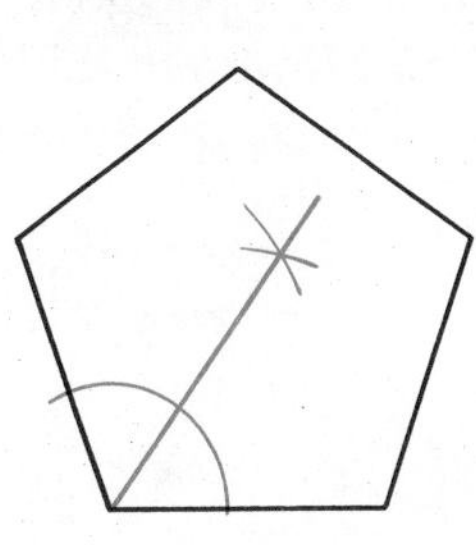

2. Construct another angle bisector.

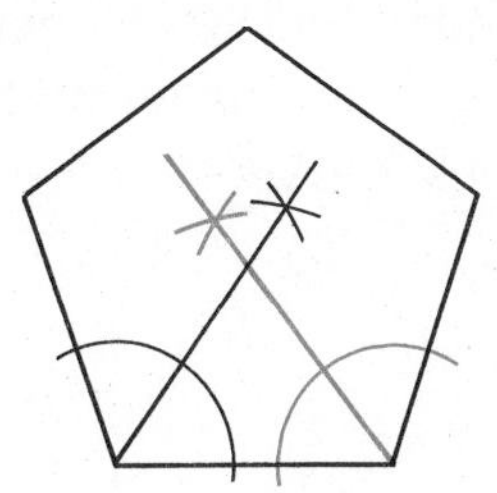

3. Construct a $\perp$ from P to one side.

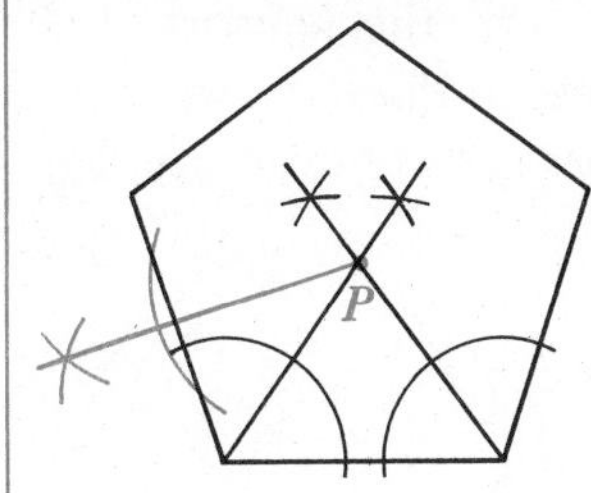

4. With P as center and radius PA, inscribe the circle.

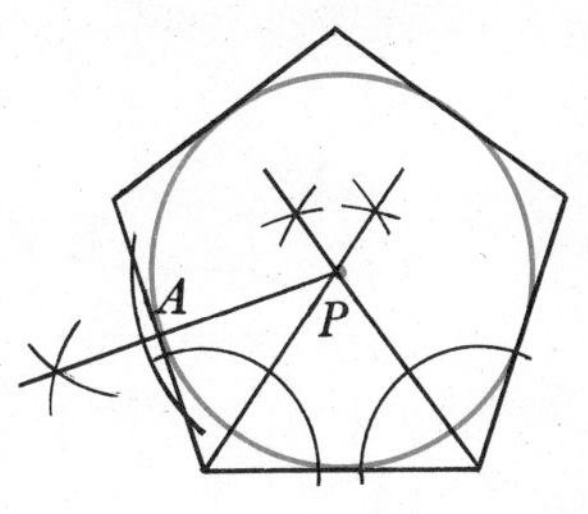

41–42. Copy each figure in Exercises 39–40. Then inscribe a circle in each polygon.

© **43.** Inscribe a square in a circle. (HINT: Draw any diameter, and then construct another diameter perpendicular to it.) Next bisect each side in order to inscribe a regular octagon in the circle.

44. Inscribe a circle in the regular octagon you constructed in Exercise 43.

45. Inscribe a regular hexagon in a circle. (See page 169.) Then bisect the sides in order to inscribe a regular 12-sided polygon (dodecagon).

Algebra Review

Review these skills:

- *factoring trinomials*
- *solving quadratics by factoring*

1–12. Factor each trinomial.

1. $x^2 - 3x - 4$	**2.** $x^2 + 5x + 6$	**3.** $x^2 - 6x + 9$
4. $x^2 + 10x + 25$	**5.** $x^2 - 2x - 15$	**6.** $x^2 + 4x - 5$
7. $2x^2 + 3x - 2$	**8.** $3x^2 + 10x + 3$	**9.** $5x^2 + 7x + 2$
10. $6x^2 + 5x + 1$	**11.** $x^2 - 49$	**12.** $25x^2 - 64$

13–20. Solve each equation by factoring.

13. $x^2 - 5x - 6 = 0$	**14.** $x^2 + 6x + 5 = 0$
15. $x^2 + 6x + 8 = 0$	**16.** $x^2 - 7x + 12 = 0$
17. $2x^2 - 3x = -1$	**18.** $3x^2 + 5x = -2$
19. $4x^2 + 7x = 2$	**20.** $5x^2 + 17x = -6$

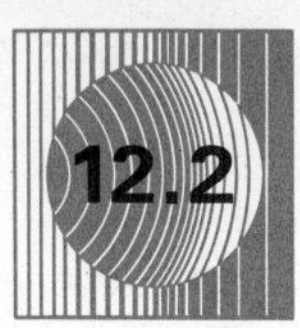

Circumference

The distance around a polygon is its *perimeter*, while the distance around a circle is its *circumference*. To find the perimeter of a polygon, we add the lengths of the sides, which are segments. However, this method does not work in finding the circumference of a circle. A circle does not contain any segments. Yet notice the polygons below.

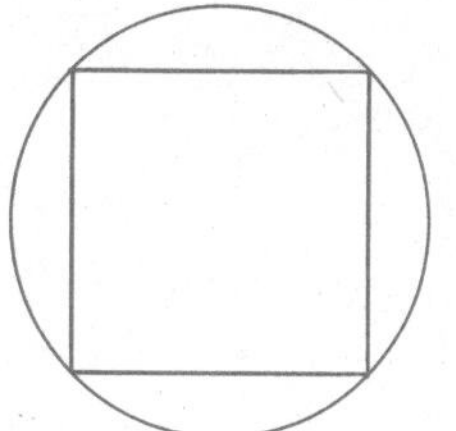
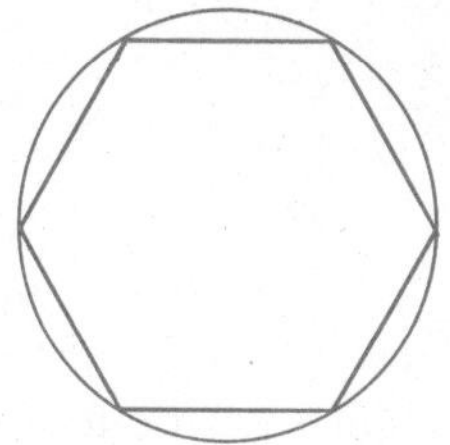
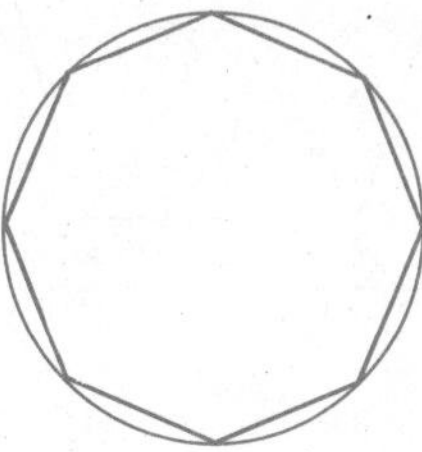
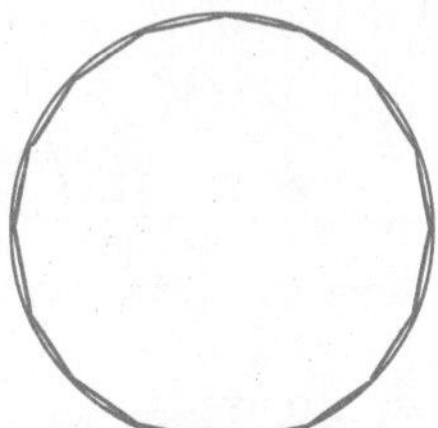

As the number of sides increases, the polygons get closer and closer to the circle. To approximate the circumference of a circle, we could find the perimeter of an inscribed polygon with a large number of sides.

We will use this idea in defining circumference. Suppose we let p be the perimeter of an inscribed regular polygon with n sides and let C be the circumference of the circle. By choosing n large enough, we can find p as close to C as we want. We say

p approaches C as a limit

or

$$p \to C$$

The **circumference** of a circle is the limit of the perimeters of the inscribed regular polygons.

The next theorem is needed to define the number π.

Theorem  **The ratio of the circumference to the diameter is the same for all circles.**

Given: $\odot O$ with radius r and circumference C, $\odot O'$ with radius r' and circumference C'

Prove: $\dfrac{C}{2r} = \dfrac{C'}{2r'}$

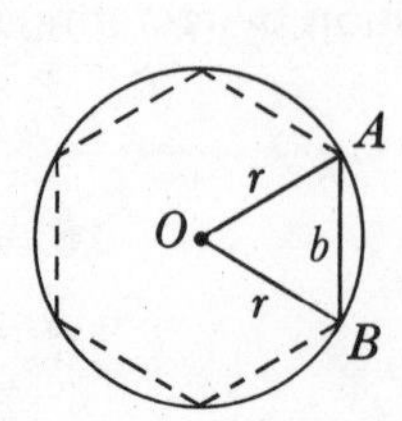

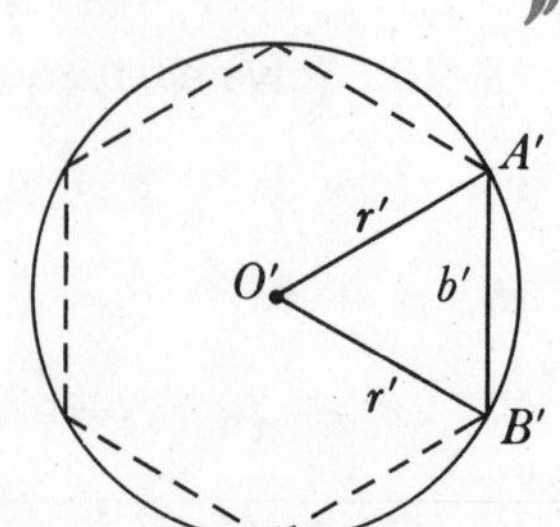

Sketch of Proof: Inscribe regular polygons with n sides having lengths of b and b'. In each circle, choose one side and draw radii to the endpoints. The two central angles are congruent because each has measure $\frac{360}{n}$. Also, the sides are proportional: $\frac{r}{r'} = \frac{r}{r'}$. Therefore, by the SAS Similarity Theorem,

$$\triangle AOB \sim \triangle A'O'B'$$

Then,

$\frac{b}{b'} = \frac{r}{r'}$	$\frac{nb}{nb'} = \frac{r}{r'}$	$\frac{p}{p'} = \frac{r}{r'}$	$\frac{p}{r} = \frac{p'}{r'}$
Corresponding sides are proportional.	Multiply left side by $\frac{n}{n}$ or 1.	Substitute. ($p = nb$ and $p' = nb'$)	Switch means.

In the above equations, p and p' are the perimeters of two polygons having n sides. We know by definition that

$$p \rightarrow C \quad \text{and} \quad p' \rightarrow C' \qquad \text{as } n \text{ increases}$$

Therefore,

$$\frac{p}{r} \rightarrow \frac{C}{r} \quad \text{and} \quad \frac{p'}{r'} \rightarrow \frac{C'}{r'}$$

Since $\frac{p}{r}$ and $\frac{p'}{r'}$ are equal, their limits are equal. Then

$\frac{C}{r} = \frac{C'}{r'}$ **Multiply both sides by $\frac{1}{2}$.** $\frac{C}{2r} = \frac{C'}{2r'}$

The ratio $\frac{C}{2r}$ is denoted by π. Since this ratio is the same for all circles, we have

$$\frac{C}{2r} = \pi \quad \text{or} \quad C = 2\pi r$$

The circumference (C) of a circle is 2π times its radius (r).

$C = 2\pi r$

Circumference Theorem

The number π is irrational. Therefore, it has a nonterminating, nonrepeating decimal expansion. But it can be approximated as closely as we want by rational numbers. Some approximations are

3   3.14 $3\frac{1}{7}$ or $\frac{22}{7}$ 3.1416 $\frac{355}{113}$ 3.14159265358979

Exercises 12.2

Ⓐ 1. The distance around a circle is called the ______.

2. The circumference of a circle is the ______ of the perimeters of the inscribed regular polygons.

3. True or False? The number π is not rational.

4. For any circle, the ratio $\frac{C}{2r}$ (where C is the circumference and r is the radius) is denoted by ______.

5. If the radius of a circle is 10, its circumference is ______ $\times\ \pi$.

6. If the radius of a circle is 7, the circumference is about ______ $\times$ $\frac{22}{7}$ or ______.

Ⓑ **7–12.** Use the given measure of a circle to find each missing number. Leave answers in terms of π.

	diameter	radius	circumference
7.	18	______	______
8.	______	12	______
9.	______	______	18π
10.	20π	______	______
11.	______	______	$14\pi^2$
12.	$50\sqrt{2}$	______	______

Courtesy Austrian National Tourist Office

13–24. Use 3.14 for π. Find each answer to the nearest tenth.

13. The diameter of a wheel is 66 centimeters. How far does the wheel roll in one complete turn?

14. One car manufacturer uses a circular test track. If the radius of the track is 1.17 kilometers, how far does a car travel in going once around the track?

15. The world's largest Ferris wheel in Vienna, Austria, has a diameter of 60 meters. What is the circumference of the wheel?

16. Many modern tires are belted. See the diagram. How long a belt is needed to encircle a tire with the dimensions shown at the right?

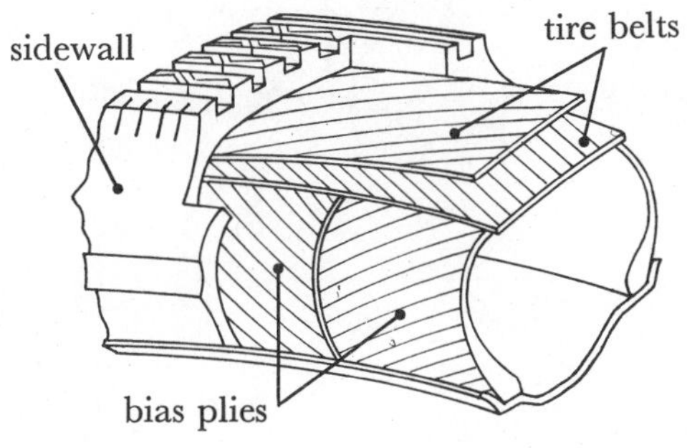

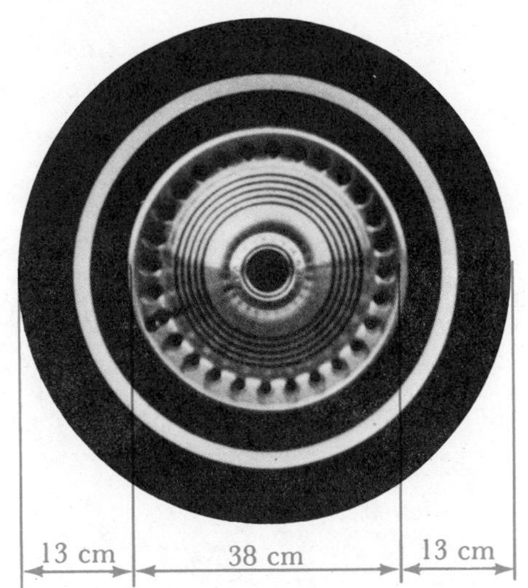

17. A strip of sheet metal 9.2 meters long is bent to form a circular outline for a flower bed. What is the diameter of the bed?

18. A log has a circumference of 123 centimeters. What is the diameter of the log?

19. The length of a side of a square is 14. Find the circumference of its inscribed circle. Of its circumscribed circle.

20. The length of a side of an equilateral triangle is $28\sqrt{3}$. Find the circumference of its inscribed circle. Of its circumscribed circle.

21. A track for track-and-field events has ends that are semicircular. (See figure.) How far does a runner travel in going once around the track?

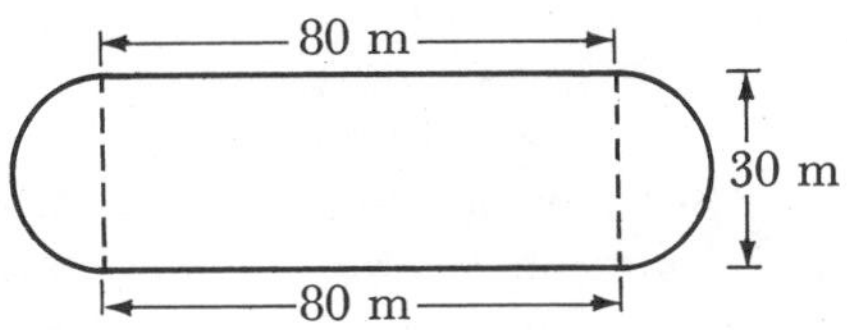

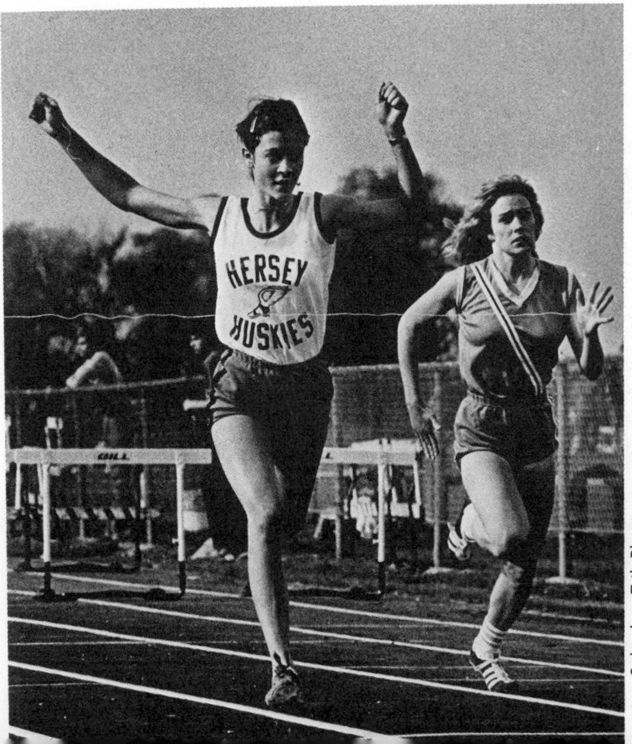

Suburban Trib Photo

22. The distance (in centimeters) that a bicycle travels with each revolution of the pedals is given by the following formula:

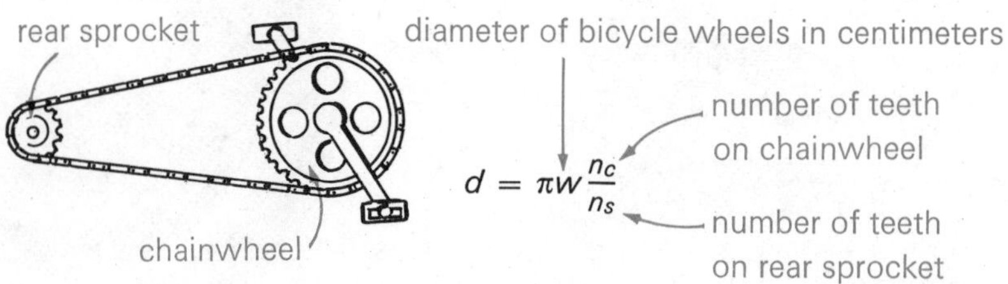

How far will a bicycle with wheels 68.6 cm in diameter travel for each revolution of the pedals if the chainwheel has 50 teeth and the rear sprocket has 28 teeth?

© 23. The earth is approximately 149 000 000 kilometers from the sun. How far does the earth travel each year in its almost circular orbit about the sun? What is a close estimate of its speed in kilometers per hour? HINT: Speed = distance ÷ time.

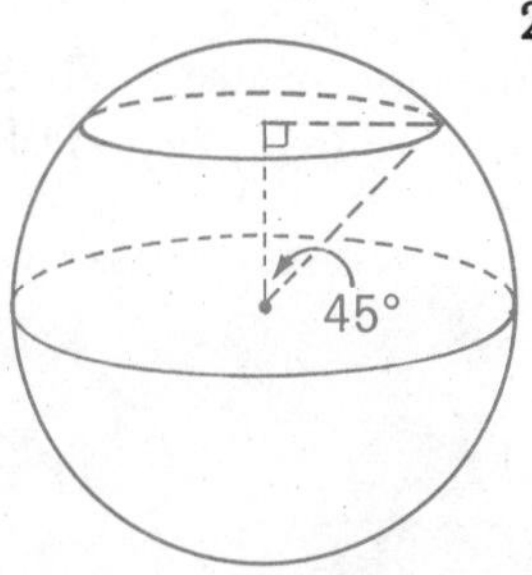

24. The radius of the earth is approximately 6336 kilometers. How far does an object at the equator travel during one complete rotation of the earth? What is the object's speed in kilometers per hour? How far does an object at latitude 45°N travel in one rotation? (Use 1.4 for $\sqrt{2}$.) What is the object's speed in kilometers per hour?

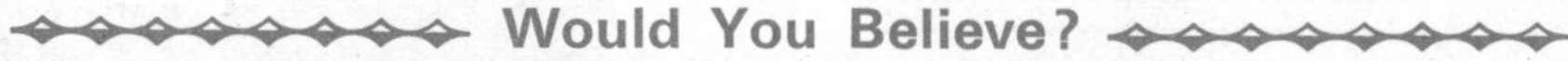

Would You Believe?

In ancient Greece it was known that regular polygons of 3, 4, 5, 6, and 15 sides could be constructed by using only a compass and a straightedge. It wasn't until 1796 that someone discovered that a regular polygon of 17 sides could be constructed with only a compass and a straightedge. Then in 1832 it was found that a regular polygon of 257 sides could be constructed. A Professor Hermes of Lingen is said to have given 10 years of his life to the problem of constructing a regular polygon of 65,537 sides!

Area of a Circle

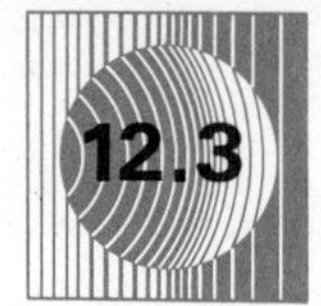

A circular region contains both the circle and its interior. For convenience, we usually refer to the area of a circle rather than to the area of a circular region.

Each regular polygon below is inscribed in a circle with radius r.

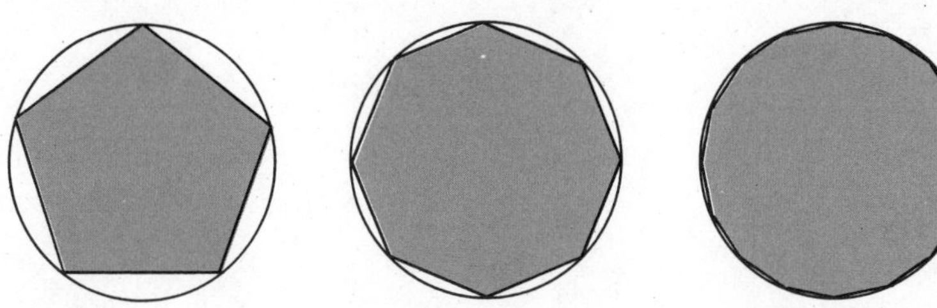

Notice how the area of each polygon gets closer and closer to the area of the circle as n, the number of sides of the polygon, increases. We already know that the formula for the area A_n of a regular polygon with n sides is

$$A_n = \tfrac{1}{2}ap \qquad (a \text{ is length of the apothem; } p \text{ is the perimeter.})$$

If A is the area of the circle, then

$$A_n \to A \qquad \text{as } n \text{ increases}$$

The area of a circle is the limit of the areas of the inscribed regular polygons.

To find the formula for the area of a circle, let's consider the following: The length a of the apothem is always less than r. But as n increases, the difference between a and r becomes smaller. So,

	$a \to r$
From Section 12.2, we have	$p \to C$
Therefore,	$\tfrac{1}{2}ap \to \tfrac{1}{2}rC$
Since, $A_n = \tfrac{1}{2}ap$,	$A_n \to \tfrac{1}{2}rC$
But, above,	$A_n \to A$
Therefore,	$A = \tfrac{1}{2}rC$
Since $C = 2\pi r$,	$A = \tfrac{1}{2}r \cdot 2\pi r$
	$A = \pi r^2$

Area Theorem for a Circle

The area (A) of a circle is π times its radius (r) squared.

$$A = \pi r^2$$

Examples:

1. Find the area of a circle with radius 28. Use $\frac{22}{7}$ for π.

$$A = \pi r^2$$

$$A = \frac{22}{7} \cdot 28 \cdot 28$$

$$A = 2464$$

2. Find the radius of a circle with area 144π.

$$A = \pi r^2$$

$$144\pi = \pi r^2$$

$$r^2 = 144$$

$$r = \pm 12$$

But the radius must be positive. So $r = 12$.

Exercises 12.3

Ⓐ 1. The area of a circle is the limit of the areas of the ______ regular polygons.

2. The formula for the area A of a circle with radius r is ______.

3. A circle has a regular pentagon and a regular hexagon inscribed in it. Which polygon has an area closer to the area of the circle?

4. If the radius of a circle is 1, its area is ______.

Ⓑ **5–12.** Use the given measure of a circle to find each missing number. Use $\frac{22}{7}$ for π.

	radius	diameter	circumference	area
5.	7	______	______	______
6.	______	70	______	______
7.	______	28	______	______
8.	42	______	______	______
9.	______	______	56π	______
10.	______	______	84π	______
11.	______	______	______	144π
12.	______	______	______	81π

13–16. Find each shaded area. Use $\frac{22}{7}$ for π. All angles are right angles.

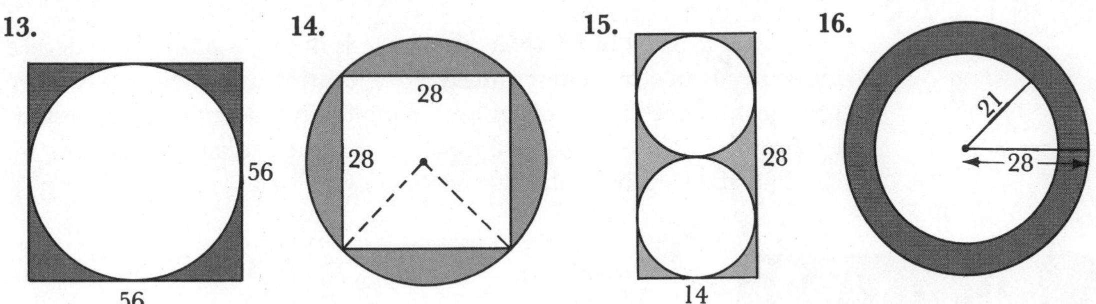

17–21. Use 3.14 for π.

17. The center-pivot method of irrigation mentioned on page 418 involves a pipeline that is rotated about a fixed point, thus forming a circular area of irrigated land. If the pipeline extends 92 meters from the center, what is the area of ground irrigated by the pipeline?

18. The largest pizza ever baked was made at Pizza Pete's in Chicago. (Source: *The Guinness Book of World Records.*) It had a diameter of 21 feet. What was its area? An ordinary small pizza has a diameter of 12 inches. How many small pizzas would you have to consume to eat as much pizza as the world's largest pizza contained?

19. A circular tabletop is cut from a square sheet of plywood that is 142 centimeters on a side. How much plywood is wasted if the largest possible circle is cut out?

20. Aluminum lids for cans are stamped out of rectangular sheets of aluminum that are 32 cm by 24 cm. The diameter of each lid is 8 cm. How much aluminum is wasted from each sheet?

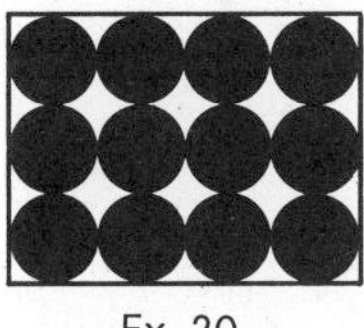
Ex. 20

© **21.** A carpenter cuts a brace from a piece of plywood as shown by the design at the right. The curved portion is made from two circular arcs, each of which is a quarter circle. Find the area of the piece wasted by the cutout.

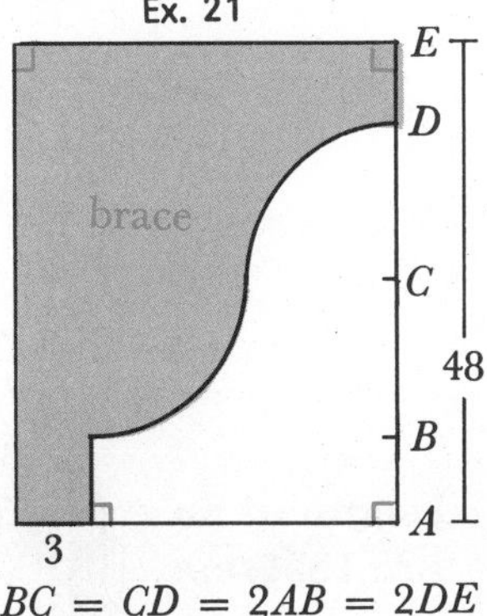

Lengths of Arcs and Areas of Sectors

As you learned in Chapter 11, an arc is part of a circle. The degree measure of an arc is determined by a central angle. Sometimes we need to find the length of an arc. We already know that the circumference of an entire circle is $2\pi r$, where r is the radius. Notice how we can find the lengths of the two arcs below.

De Wys, Inc.

Example 1:

a.

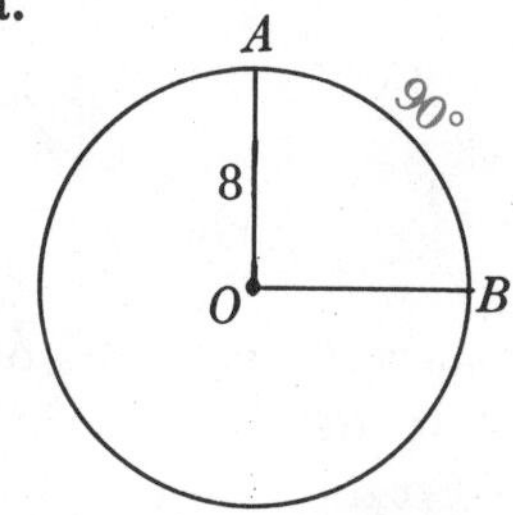

b.

C
240°
O
5
D
E

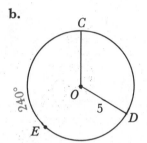

$$\text{length } \widehat{AB} = \frac{m\widehat{AB}}{360} \cdot 2\pi r = \frac{90}{360} \cdot 2\pi(8) = \frac{1}{4} \cdot 2\pi(8) = 4\pi$$

$$\text{length } \widehat{CED} = \frac{m\widehat{CED}}{360} \cdot 2\pi r = \frac{240}{360} \cdot 2\pi(5) = \frac{2}{3} \cdot 2\pi(5) = \frac{20}{3}\pi$$

In Example 1a, $m\widehat{AB} = 90$. Since the entire circle has a degree measure of 360, the length of $\widehat{AB}$ is $\frac{90}{360}$ or $\frac{1}{4}$ of the entire circumference. Likewise, in Example 1b, the length of $\widehat{CED}$ is $\frac{240}{360}$ or $\frac{2}{3}$ of the entire circumference. We can generalize these examples as follows:

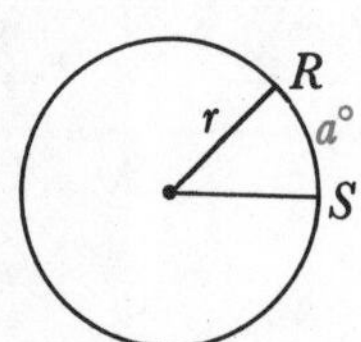

Consider $\widehat{RS}$, with degree measure a, where r is the radius of the circle. We know the circumference of the circle is $2\pi r$. Since $m\widehat{RS} = a$, the length of $\widehat{RS}$ is $\frac{a}{360}$ of $2\pi r$. Therefore, we can conclude the next theorem.

Length of an Arc Theorem

The length of an arc RS with measure $a°$ is given by the formula

$$\text{length } \widehat{RS} = \frac{a}{360} \cdot 2\pi r, \quad \text{where } r \text{ is the radius of the circle.}$$

In the figures below, the shaded portions are called sectors. A **sector** of a circle is a region bounded by an arc of the circle and the two radii to the endpoints of the arc. Two sectors are shown below.

Example 2:

a.

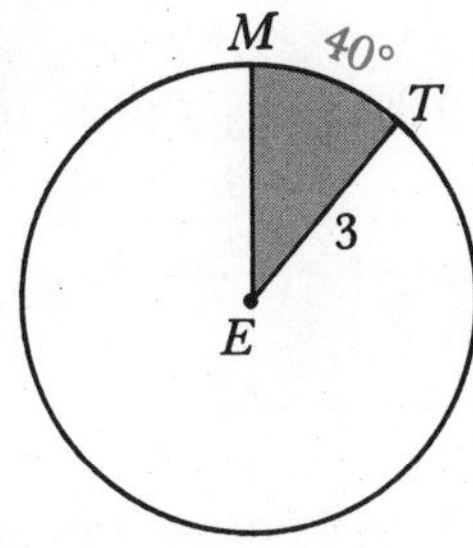

b.

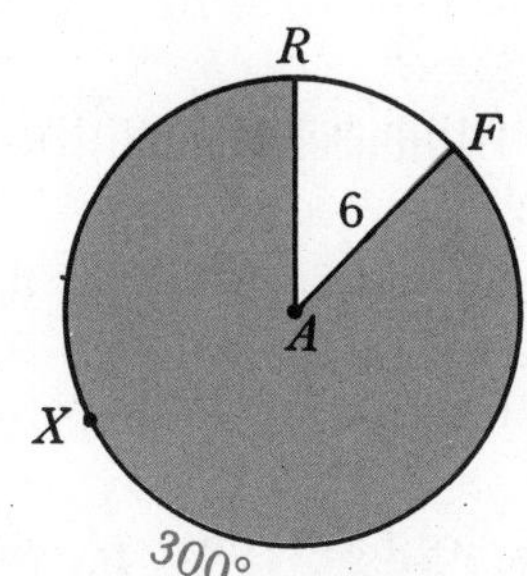

$$\text{area shaded sector} = \frac{m\widehat{MT}}{360} \cdot \pi r^2 = \tfrac{40}{360} \cdot \pi(3)^2 = \tfrac{1}{9} \cdot \pi \cdot 9 = \pi$$

$$\text{area shaded sector} = \frac{m\widehat{RXF}}{360} \cdot \pi r^2 = \tfrac{300}{360} \cdot \pi(6)^2 = \tfrac{5}{6} \cdot \pi \cdot 36 = 30\pi$$

In the preceding examples, we know the area of the entire circle is πr^2. In Example 2a, $m\widehat{MT} = 40$. So the area of the sector is $\frac{40}{360}$ or $\frac{1}{9}$ of the entire area. These examples suggest the following theorem:

The area of a sector whose arc has measure $a°$ is given by the formula

$$\text{area sector} = \frac{a}{360} \cdot \pi r^2, \quad \text{where } r \text{ is the radius of the circle.}$$

Area Theorem for a Sector

Example 3:

a. What is the radius of a circle if the length of a 40° arc ($\widehat{RS}$) is 18π?

$$\text{length } \widehat{RS} = \frac{a}{360} \cdot 2\pi r$$

$$18\pi = \tfrac{40}{360} \cdot 2\pi r$$

$$18\pi = \tfrac{1}{9} \cdot 2\pi r$$

$$18\pi = \tfrac{2}{9}\pi r$$

$$81 = r$$

b. In a circle with radius 6, a sector has area 4π. What is the degree measure of the arc of the sector?

$$\text{area sector} = \frac{a}{360} \cdot \pi r^2$$

$$4\pi = \frac{a}{360} \cdot \pi(6)^2$$

$$4\pi = \frac{a}{360} \cdot \pi(36)$$

$$40 = a$$

The two preceding theorems can be used to prove the next theorem. The proof is outlined in Exercise 37.

Corollary to Area Theorem for a Sector The area of a sector of a circle is one half the arc length times the radius.

Exercises 12.4

NOTE: Leave answers in terms of π unless told otherwise.

Ⓐ **1.** The formula for finding the length of an arc is ______.

2. The formula for finding the area of a sector is ______.

3. If an arc has a degree measure of 180, what fractional part of the entire circle is the arc?

4. If a sector has an arc with degree measure 90, what fractional part of the entire area of the circle is the area of the sector?

5–8. O is the center of the circle. $TO = 6$, and $m\widehat{TP} = 120$.

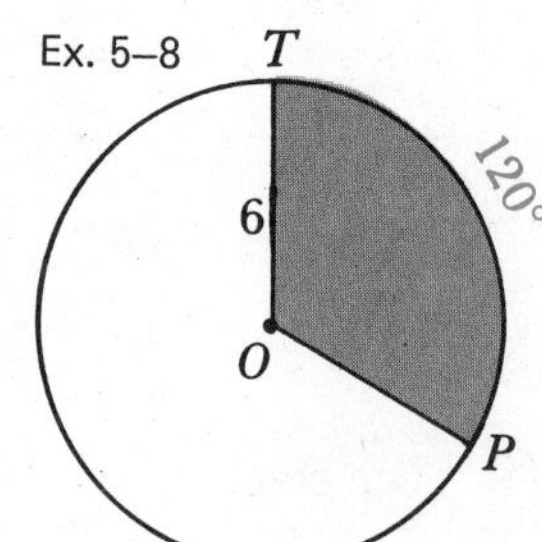

5. What is the circumference of circle O?

6. What is the length of $\widehat{TP}$?

7. What is the area of circle O?

8. What is the area of the shaded sector?

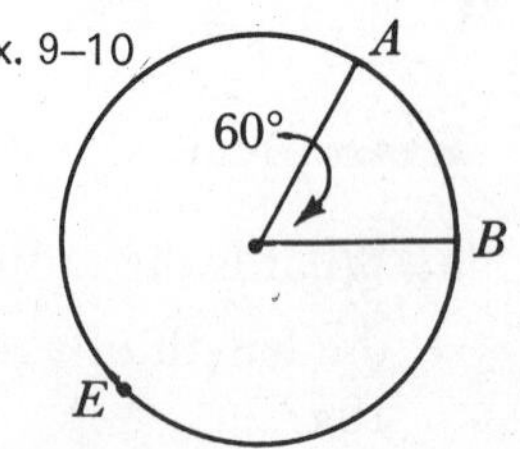

9. What is the degree measure of $\widehat{AB}$?

10. What is the degree measure of $\widehat{AEB}$?

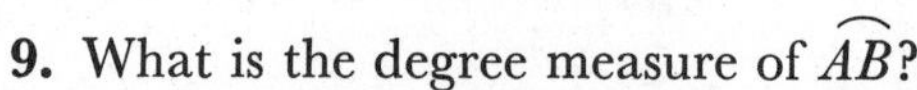

Ⓑ **11–14.** The radius of a circle is 24. Find the length of each arc having the given degree measure.

11. 60 **12.** 45 **13.** 150 **14.** 270

15. What is the radius of a circle if the length of a 90° arc is 17π?

16. What is the radius of a circle if the length of a 30° arc is 8π?

17–20. All four arcs have P as center and degree measure 60. Using the proper radius, find each arc length.

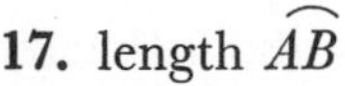

17. length $\overset{\frown}{AB}$ **18.** length $\overset{\frown}{CD}$

19. length $\overset{\frown}{EF}$ **20.** length $\overset{\frown}{GH}$

21–24. The radius of a circle is 16. Find the area of each sector whose arc has the given degree measure.

21. 180 **22.** 36 **23.** 135 **24.** 40

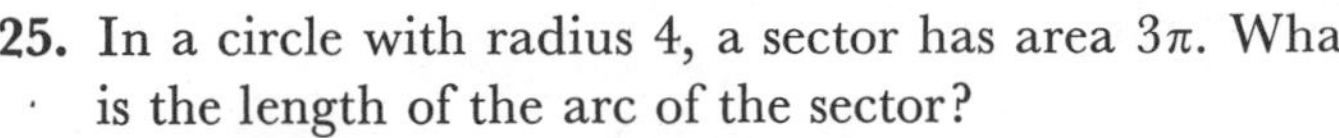

25. In a circle with radius 4, a sector has area 3π. What is the length of the arc of the sector?

26. In a circle with radius 18, a sector has area 15π. What is the length of the arc of the sector?

27. The largest four-faced clock in the world is on the Allen-Bradley Building in Milwaukee, Wisconsin. It has a 6.10-meter (20-foot) minute hand. How many meters does the tip of the minute hand travel in 1 minute? Use 3.14 for π.

Courtesy Sears, Roebuck and Co.

28. In designing skyscrapers, engineers must allow for the swaying motion of the building. The Sears Tower in Chicago has a height of 443.2 meters (1454 feet). If the top of the building moves along an arc of $\frac{1}{2}°$, how many meters is that? Use 3.14 for π.

29–30. The shaded region in the figure is called a segment of the circle. Its area can be found by subtracting the area of $\triangle AOB$ from the area of the sector with $\overset{\frown}{AB}$. Find the area of each segment if

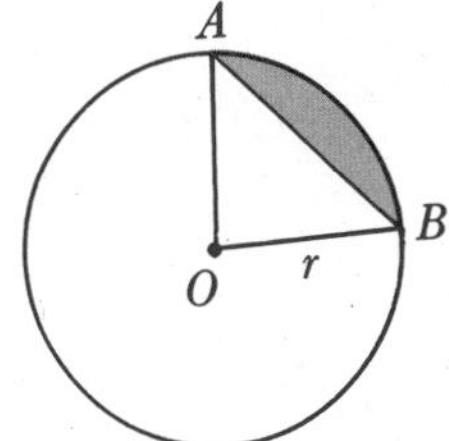

29. $r = 8$, $m\overset{\frown}{AB} = 90$ **30.** $r = 5$, $m\overset{\frown}{AB} = 60$

31–34. Use the theorem on page 434 to find the area of each sector. The arc length and radius of the circle are given in each case.

31. length $\overset{\frown}{RS} = 180$, $r = 4$ **32.** length $\overset{\frown}{RS} = 25\pi$, $r = 6$

33. length $\overset{\frown}{RS} = 42\pi$, $r = 7$ **34.** length $\overset{\frown}{RS} = 120$, $r = 10$

Ⓒ **35–36.** Use 3.14 for π.

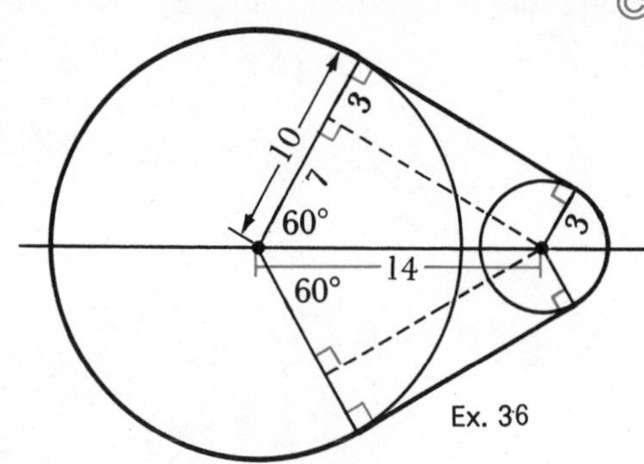

35. A cow is tied with a rope to one corner of a barn that is 12 meters long and 10 meters wide. If the rope is 15 meters long, what is the grazing area available for the cow?

36. A continuous belt fits around two wheels as shown. The wheels have radii of 10 cm and 3 cm. The distance between their centers is 14 cm. Find the length of the belt.

37. Copy and complete the proof.

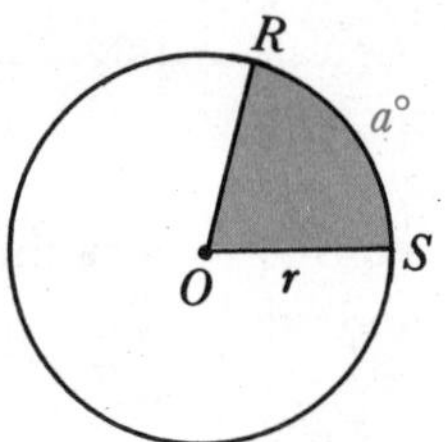

Given: $\odot O$ with radius r and $\widehat{RS}$ having degree measure a

Prove: Area shaded sector $= \frac{1}{2}(\text{length } \widehat{RS})r$

Proof: STATEMENTS	REASONS
1. Area shaded sector $= \frac{a}{360} \cdot \pi r^2$	1. _____
2. Area shaded sector $= \frac{a}{360} \cdot \pi r \cdot$ _____	2. Def. of exponent
3. Area shaded sector $= \frac{a}{360} \cdot (\_\_\_\_\_ \cdot 2)\pi r \cdot r$	3. Inv. and Ident. Props. of Mult.
4. Area shaded sector $= \frac{1}{2}\left(\frac{a}{360} \cdot 2\pi r\right) \cdot r$	4. _____ and _____ Props. of Mult.
5. Area shaded sector $= \frac{1}{2}(\text{length } \widehat{RS}) \cdot r$	5. _____

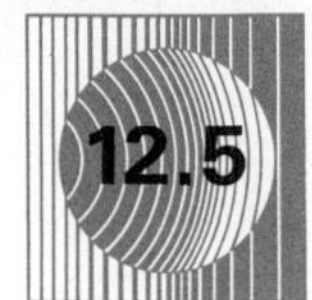

Transformations: Point Symmetry

The figures below all have something in common. If you turn this page upside down, the figures still look the same. In other words, each figure coincides with itself after it is turned 180°.

Such figures are said to have point symmetry. In order to define point symmetry, we need the following definition:

The **reflection image** of a point R over a point P is the point R' such that P is the midpoint of $\overline{RR'}$.

We say that R and R' are symmetric about P. Now we can give a better definition of point symmetry.

A set of points has **point symmetry** if and only if there is a point P such that the reflection image over P of each point in the set is also a point in the set. P is called the *center of symmetry*.

Point symmetry is a special case of a more general type of symmetry called *turn symmetry*. If a figure can be turned less than 360° so that it coincides with itself, the figure has turn symmetry.

For example, consider an equilateral triangle. It does not have point symmetry. If vertex A of the first triangle shown at the right is reflected over O, its image is not a point on the triangle. Neither is there any other point over which every point of the triangle can be reflected back onto the triangle. Nevertheless, the triangle does have turn symmetry because it can be turned 120° about O so that it coincides with itself.

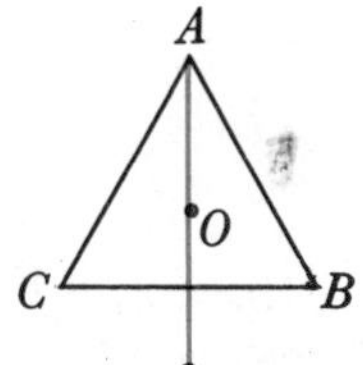

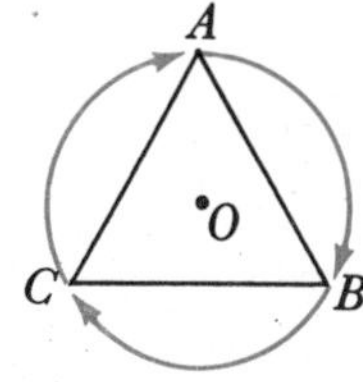

Exercises 12.5

Ⓐ **1.** The reflection image of a point Q over point P is the point Q' such that P is the ______ of $\overline{QQ'}$.

2. A set of points has ______ symmetry if and only if there is a point P such that the reflection image over P of each point in the set is also a point in the set.

3–6. Refer to the circle having center O.

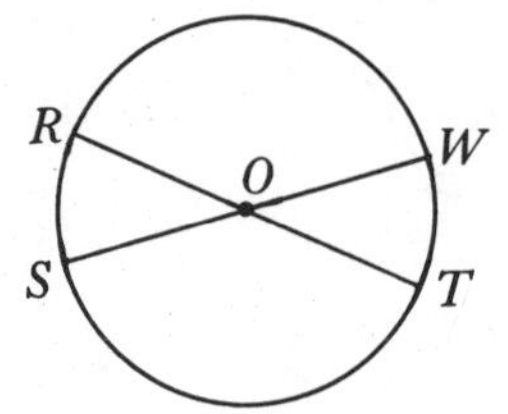

3. The reflection image of R over O is ______.

4. The reflection image of S over O is ______.

5. Does a circle have point symmetry?

6. Does a circle have turn symmetry?

Ⓑ **7–14.** Which figures have point symmetry?

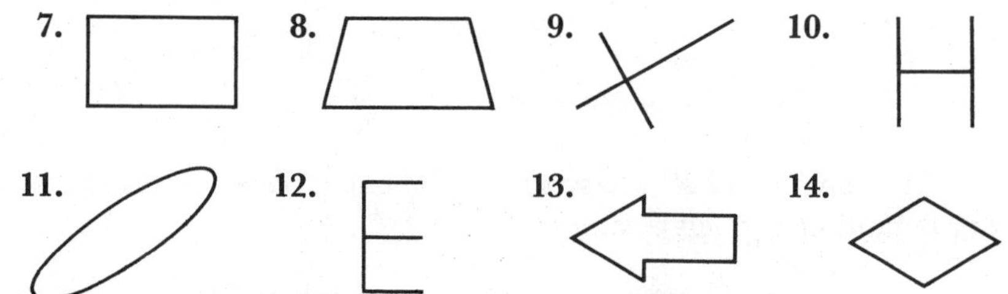

15–18. Which regular polygons below have point symmetry? Which have turn symmetry?

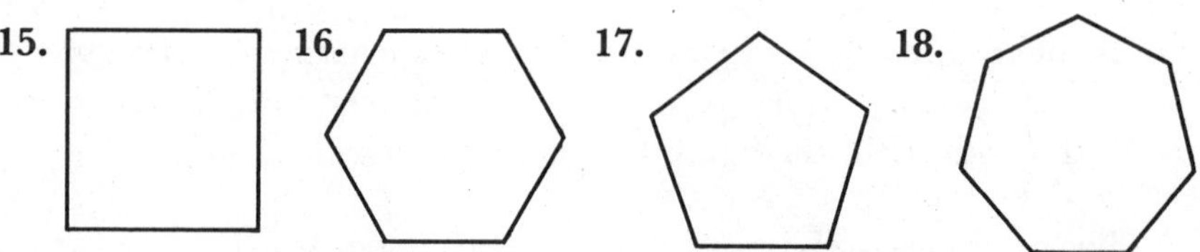

19–20. Copy each figure below. Then draw its reflection image over point P.

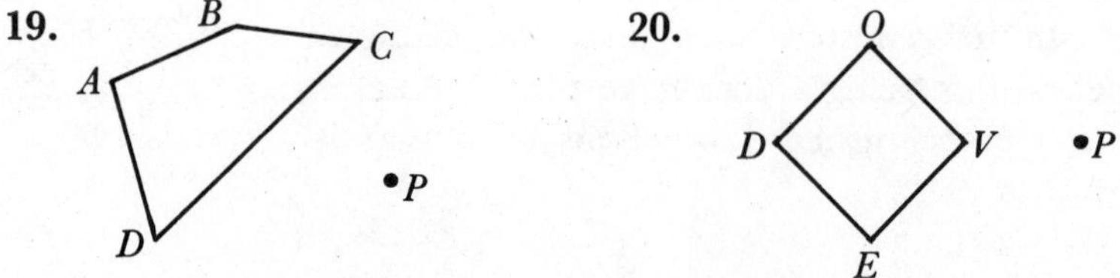

Ⓒ 21. Does each regular polygon have point symmetry? Does each regular polygon have turn symmetry? If a regular polygon has n sides, what is the smallest angle through which it can be turned in order to coincide with itself.

GEOMETRY AT WORK

CIRCLE GRAPHS

Circle graphs like the one below often appear in newspapers or magazines. In a circle graph, the area of the circle represents 100% (the whole amount). Each sector represents a certain percent of the entire amount. You can quickly compare different amounts by looking at the sizes of their sectors.

In making a circle graph, you need to remember that a circle measures 360°. Suppose you want to draw a sector that shows 25% of the entire amount. Then you must find 25% (or $\frac{1}{4}$) of 360°. Therefore, you would need to draw a sector with an arc of 90°. More generally, to represent x% of the entire amount, draw a sector with an arc that measures x% of 360°.

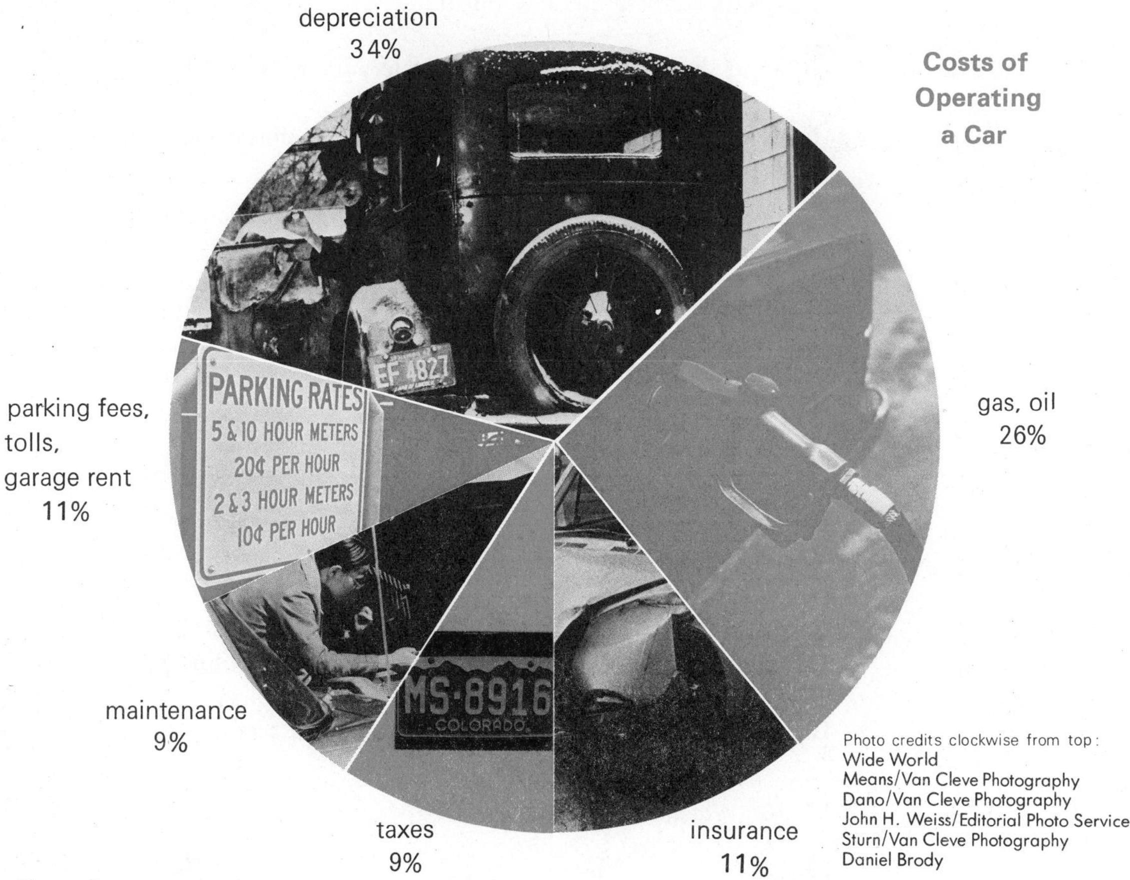

Costs of Operating a Car

Photo credits clockwise from top:
Wide World
Means/Van Cleve Photography
Dano/Van Cleve Photography
John H. Weiss/Editorial Photo Service
Sturn/Van Cleve Photography
Daniel Brody

Exercise:

Draw a circle graph to represent the sources of money for the federal government in a recent year: Individual Income Taxes, 30%; Corporation Income Taxes, 14%; Social Insurance Receipts, 26%; Excise Taxes, 9%; Borrowing, 15%; Miscellaneous, 6%.

Chapter 12 Review

12.1 1–3. Refer to the inscribed regular hexagon.

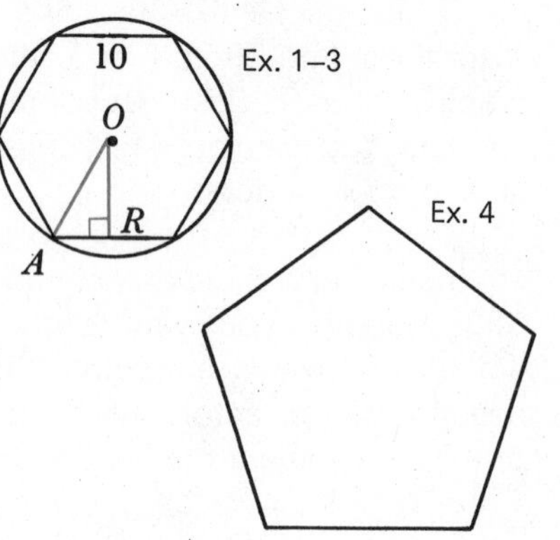

1. Find OA.
2. Find OR.
3. Find the area of the hexagon.
4. Copy the regular pentagon and circumscribe a circle about it.

12.2

5. Find the circumference of a circle with radius 140. Use $\frac{22}{7}$ for π.
6. A circle has circumference 628. Find its diameter. Use 3.14 for π.

12.3 7–10. Use the given measure of a circle to find each missing number. Leave answers in terms of π.

	radius	diameter	circumference	area
7.	8	____	____	____
8.	____	22	____	____
9.	____	____	32π	____
10.	____	____	____	64π

12.4 11–12. Leave answers in terms of π.

11. Find the length of a 30° arc in a circle with radius 7.
12. A circle has radius 10. Find the area of a sector with a 150° arc.

12.5 13–16. Which figures have point symmetry?

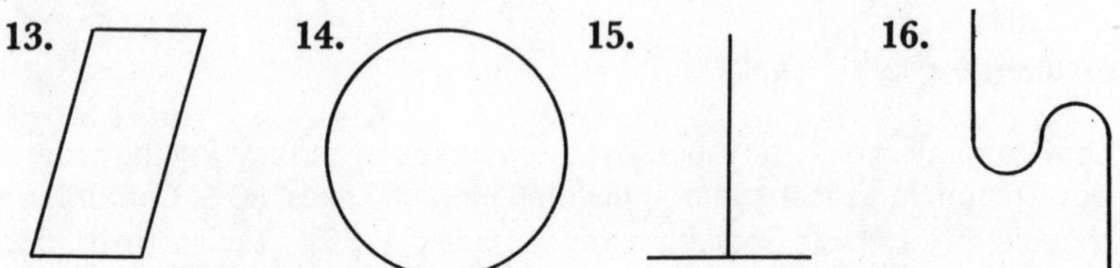

Chapter 12 Test

1–2. Equilateral $\triangle RST$ is inscribed in a circle with center O.

1. Find OA.

2. Find OR.

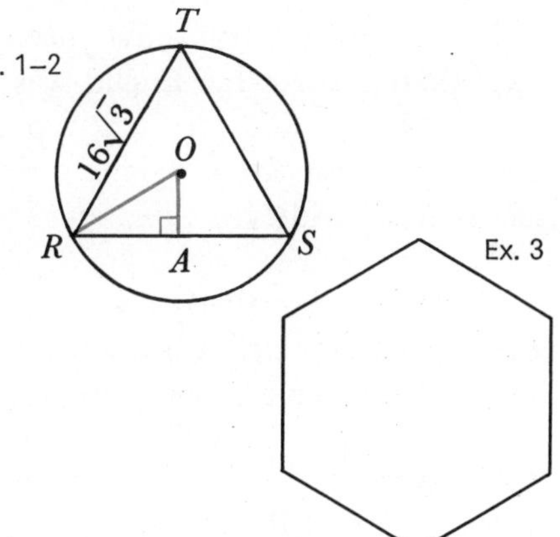

3. Copy the regular hexagon and inscribe a circle in the hexagon.

4. If a regular polygon has perimeter 84 and an apothem of length 6, what is its area?

5. Find the circumference of a circle with radius 77. Use $\frac{22}{7}$ for π.

6. Find the diameter of a circle having circumference 1256. Use 3.14 for π.

7. Find the area of a circle with radius $3\frac{1}{2}$. Use $\frac{22}{7}$ for π.

8. Find the radius of a circle with area 36π.

9–10. Leave answers in terms of π.

9. Find the length of a $100°$ arc in a circle with radius 7.

10. A circle has radius 8. Find the area of a sector with a $10°$ arc.

11–14. Which figures have point symmetry?

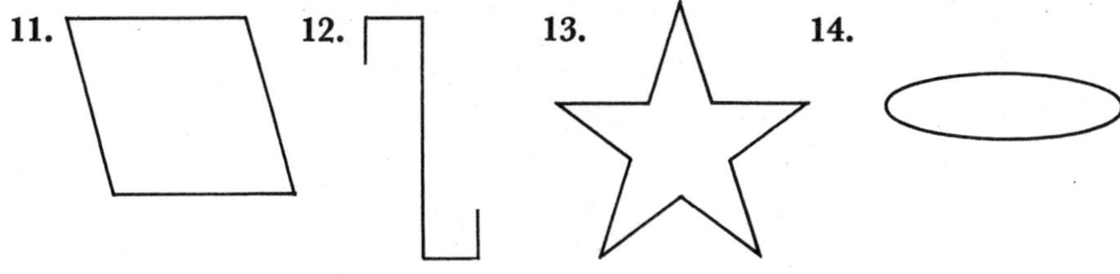

MINI-CHAPTER: OTHER GEOMETRIES

The geometry you have been studying in this book is called **Euclidean geometry.** Euclid was a Greek mathematician who lived around 300 B.C. His writings appeared in a written work called *The Elements*. Except for religious scriptures, no written work has been studied more widely.

Euclid was the first person to organize geometry into a deductive system. That is, certain basic assumptions (postulates) were stated and the rest of the development was proved from these postulates.

Probably the most famous postulate in Euclidean geometry is Euclid's Parallel Postulate.

> If a straight line falling on two straight lines makes the interior angles on the same side together less than two right angles, the two straight lines, if produced indefinitely, meet on that side on which the angles are together less than two right angles.

As you can see, the Parallel Postulate is very cumbersome and wordy. For years, mathematicians were bothered by its complex form. All the other postulates assumed by Euclid were fairly simple. So mathematicians felt it should be possible to do one of two things.

1. Prove Euclid's Parallel Postulate as a theorem. (That is, deduce it from the other postulates.)

2. Replace it with an equivalent statement which is simpler and more basic. (An equivalent statement is one that can be deduced from Euclid's Postulate, and vice versa.)

It seems that most mathematicians tried to prove the postulate as a theorem. In the process of trying to prove it, they often found other statements that are equivalent. The statement we use in this book is one such statement.

> Through a point P not on line ℓ, there is **exactly one** line parallel to ℓ.

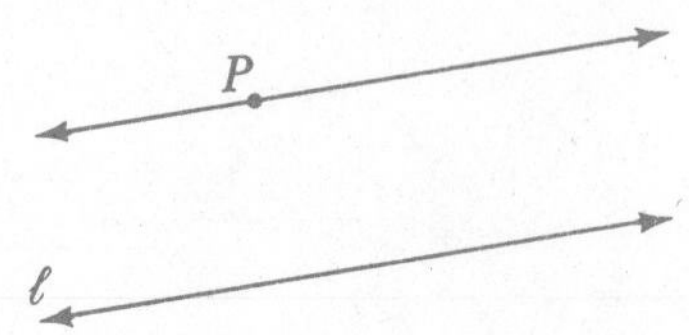

As it turns out, Euclid's Parallel Postulate cannot be proved from his other postulates. It is independent of the other postulates. It took mathematicians hundreds of years to realize this. Three persons are usually credited with making this discovery. Each of them worked independently. A Russian mathematician named Nikolai Lobachevski was the first to publish his own theories. However, János Bolyai, a Hungarian mathematician, reached this conclusion at about the same time. And later Karl Gauss, the great German mathematician, claimed to have made the discovery many years before. But he had never bothered to publish his findings. At any rate, the work of these people was to have far-reaching results.

Until that time, the geometry of Euclid was thought to be the only one possible. With the discovery that Euclid's Parallel Postulate was independent of the other postulates, the way was paved for other kinds of geometry called non-Euclidean. By replacing Euclid's Parallel Postulate with another postulate, entirely different deductions could be made.

Two other possibilities for the Parallel Postulate are

A. For any line ℓ and any point P not on ℓ, there is **more than one** line that contains P and is parallel to ℓ.

B. For any line ℓ and any point P not on ℓ, there is **no** line that contains P and is parallel to ℓ.

As you know, *point*, *line*, and *plane* are undefined terms in geometry. Yet, we often use models for these terms. With our usual models for line and plane, Postulates A and B do not make sense. But since line and plane are undefined, we can use any model that works. As it turns out, models do exist for which Postulates A and B are meaningful.

For Postulate A, let circle O and its interior be the model for "plane" and let the chords be models for "lines." Remember that *parallel* means nonintersecting.

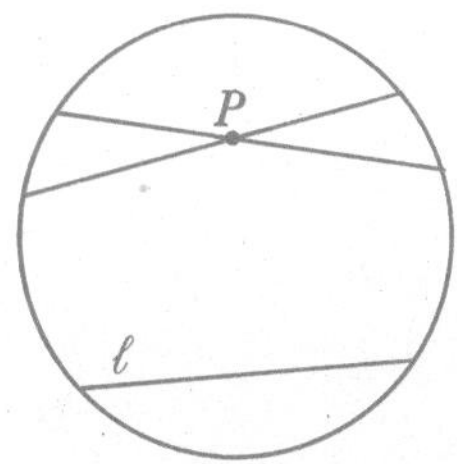

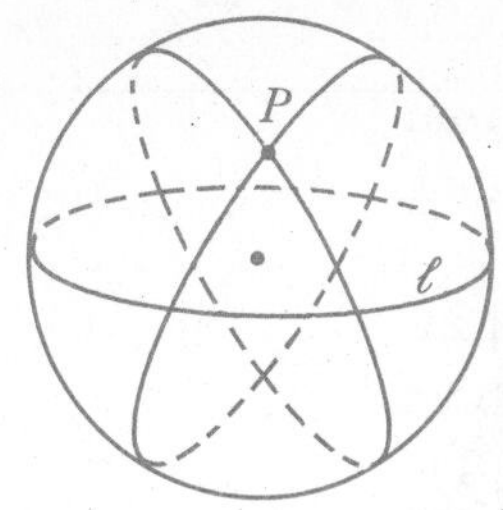

For Postulate B, another model is necessary. Suppose "plane" means sphere and "line" means a great circle on the sphere. (The plane of a great circle passes through the center of a sphere. For example, on the earth, the equator and all circles through the poles are great circles.)

The type of geometry that assumes Postulate A is usually called Lobachevskian (or hyperbolic) geometry. The type of geometry that assumes Postulate B is called Riemannian (or elliptic) geometry. (Georg Riemann, a German mathematician, discovered the non-Euclidean geometry named after him.) The two models just given are not the only possible ones for these geometries.

When non-Euclidean geometry was first developed, no one thought it had any useful applications. But Albert Einstein used concepts from Riemannian geometry in developing his famous theory of relativity.

The following chart shows how different results occur, according to which Parallel Postulate is accepted.

Euclidean	Lobachevskian	Riemannian
There is one and only one line through a given point parallel to a given line.	There is more than one line through a given point parallel to a given line.	There is no line through a given point parallel to a given line.
The sum of the measures of the angles of a triangle is 180.	The sum of the measures of the angles of a triangle is less than 180.	The sum of the measures of the angles of a triangle is more than 180.
Two parallel lines are everywhere equidistant.	Two parallel lines are not equidistant. They approach each other in one direction and diverge in the opposite direction.	There are no parallel lines. Each line intersects every other line.

The chart above shows only a few of the differences among the three kinds of geometry. It might be pointed out, however, that many theorems are the same, no matter what kind of geometry is being used. This is to be expected since most other postulates are the same. But those theorems that depend on the Parallel Postulate are different.

PARALLEL LINES AND PLANES 13

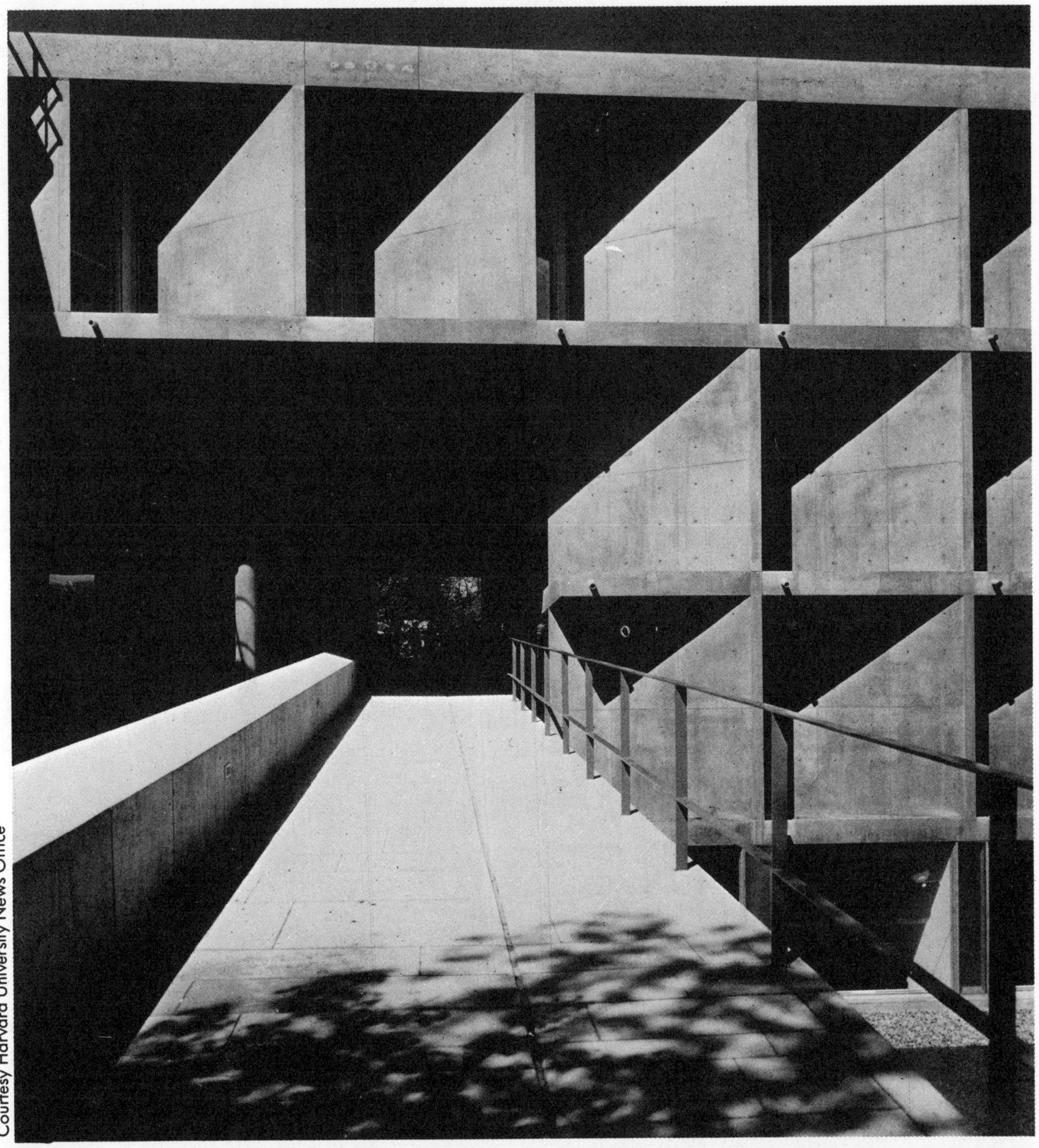

Courtesy Harvard University News Office

Two *planes* are **parallel** if and only if they do not intersect. Also a *line* and a *plane* are **parallel** if and only if they do not intersect. Notice the models of parallel planes and of a line parallel to a plane above.

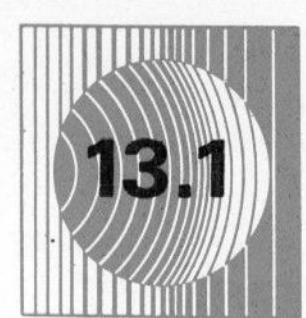

13.1 Some Theorems on Parallel Lines and Planes

Earlier, we used the symbol ∥ for parallel lines. Now, we also use it for parallel planes. If planes A and B are parallel, we write $A \parallel B$ or $B \parallel A$. If line ℓ and plane C are parallel, we write $\ell \parallel C$ or $C \parallel \ell$.

It's reasonable to expect parallel planes to have properties like those of parallel lines. But when we talk about parallel lines and planes together in space, we have to be careful. For example,

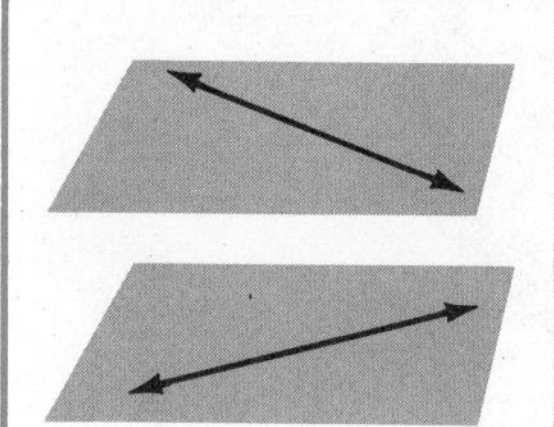	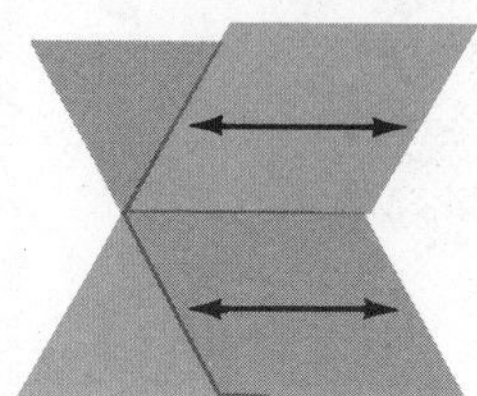	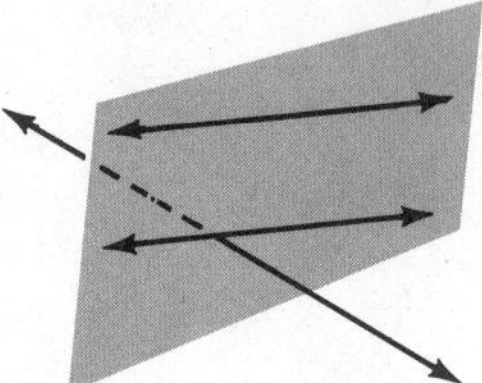	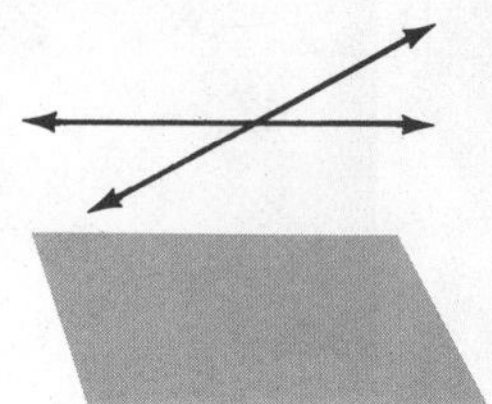
Lines in parallel planes are not always parallel. They might be skew lines.	Parallel lines may be in intersecting planes.	A line in space may intersect only one of two parallel lines.	Intersecting lines may both be parallel to the same plane.

In space, lines can intersect, be parallel, or be skew. But planes either intersect, or they are parallel.

Since the intersection of two planes is a line, the intersection of two parallel planes by a third plane will be two lines. In fact,

Theorem **If two parallel planes are intersected by a third plane, the lines of intersection are parallel.**

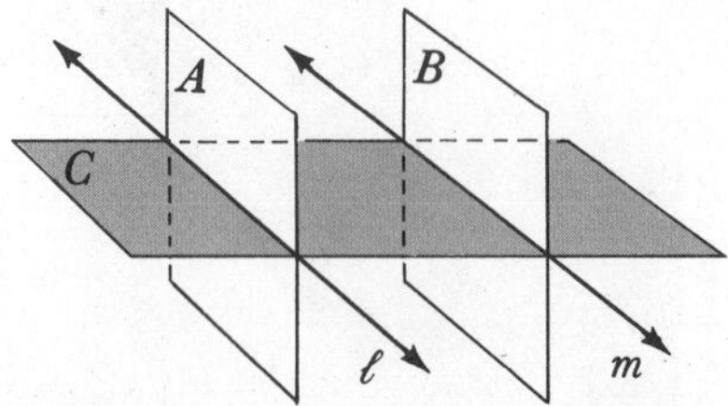

Given: Planes A and B are parallel, plane C intersects A and B at lines ℓ and m.

Prove: $\ell \parallel m$

Proof:

STATEMENTS	REASONS
1. ℓ and m are coplanar.	**1.** Given ℓ and m both in plane C
2. ℓ and m do not intersect.	**2.** Given ℓ in plane A, m in plane B, and $A \parallel B$
3. $\ell \parallel m$	**3.** Definition of parallel lines

You can illustrate the next theorem by holding a pencil perpendicular to your desk. Then place a book on the other end of the pencil, and hold the book parallel to the desk.

If a line is perpendicular to one of two parallel planes, it is perpendicular to the other.

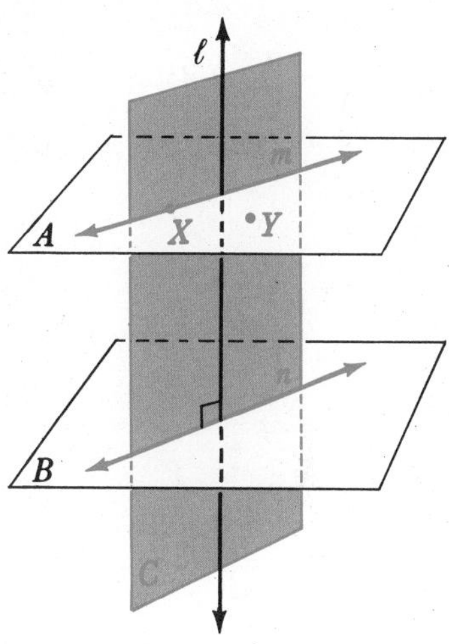

In the figure, planes A and B are parallel, and line ℓ is perpendicular to plane B. We could prove $\ell \perp A$ by showing that there are two intersecting lines in A perpendicular to ℓ (Basic Theorem for Perpendiculars, page 270).

Pick a point X in A but not on ℓ. Point X and line ℓ determine plane C, which intersects A and B at lines m and n. If a plane intersects two parallel planes, the lines of intersection are parallel; therefore, $m \parallel n$. Since $m \parallel n$ and $\ell \perp n$ (why?), $\ell \perp m$ (why?).

By choosing another point Y in A and repeating the process, we can show there exists a second line in A perpendicular to ℓ. And $\ell \perp A$ by the Basic Theorem for Perpendiculars.

The next two theorems give conditions to look for when determining if two planes are parallel.

Two planes perpendicular to the same line are parallel.

Given: Line $\ell \perp$ plane P at point X, line $\ell \perp$ plane Q at point Y.

Prove: $P \parallel Q$

I

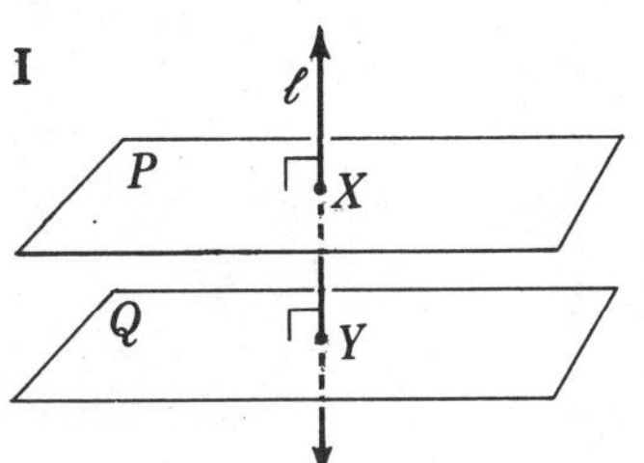

II

Proof:

STATEMENTS	REASONS
1. Assume P is not parallel to Q.	1. Assume opposite for indirect proof.
2. There is a point Z in both P and Q. (See figure II.)	2. Two planes intersect at a line. (Let Z be any point on that line.)
3. But, there is only one plane through Z perpendicular to ℓ.	3. Perpendicular Line and Plane Postulates, part **a** (p. 273)
4. So, $P \parallel Q$.	4. Principle of Indirect Reasoning

Theorem  Two planes parallel to a third plane are parallel. 

Given: Plane $A \parallel$ plane C,
plane $B \parallel$ plane C.

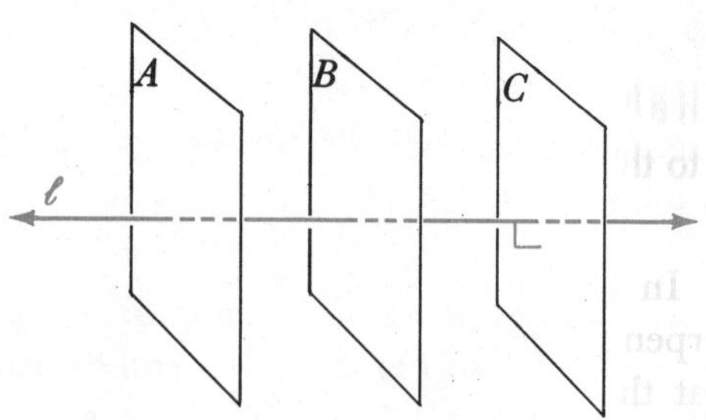

Prove: $A \parallel B$

Proof:

STATEMENTS	REASONS
1. $A \parallel C$ and $B \parallel C$	1. Given
2. Let line ℓ be perpendicular to plane C.	2. There is a line $\perp$ to C at any point of C.
3. $\ell \perp A$ and $\ell \perp B$	3. A line $\perp$ to one of two $\parallel$ planes is $\perp$ to the other.
4. $A \parallel B$	4. Two planes $\perp$ to the same line are $\parallel$.

NOTE: If planes A, B, and C are parallel, we can write $A \parallel B \parallel C$.

Exercises 13.1

Ⓐ **1–10.** True or False? (Use the figure.)

1. $A \parallel B$ **2.** $A \parallel C$

3. $m \perp \ell$ **4.** $m \perp B$

5. $n \perp \ell$ **6.** $m \parallel n$

7. $m \parallel B$ **8.** $n \parallel C$

9. $\ell \parallel C$ **10.** $\ell \perp C$

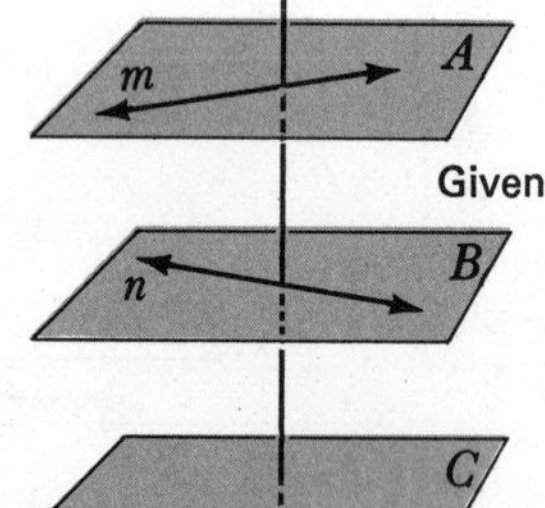

Given: $\ell \perp A$, $\ell \perp B$, m is in A and intersects ℓ, n is in B and intersects ℓ, $B \parallel C$

Ⓑ **11–18.** True or False? Draw a sketch to illustrate each true statement. Sketch a counterexample for each false statement.

11. If a line is perpendicular to one of two parallel planes, it is perpendicular to the other.

12. If two lines are parallel to the same plane, they may be perpendicular to each other.

13. If two planes are parallel to the same line, they are parallel to each other.

14. If two lines are parallel, every plane containing only one of them is parallel to the other.

15. If two planes are parallel, any line in one plane is parallel to any line in the other plane.

16. If two planes are perpendicular to the same line and are intersected by a third plane, the lines of intersection are parallel.

17. If two intersecting lines are each parallel to a plane, the plane determined by the lines is parallel to the given plane.

18. If two planes are intersected by a third plane, the lines of intersection are always parallel.

19–22. Use a theorem of this section to answer each exercise.

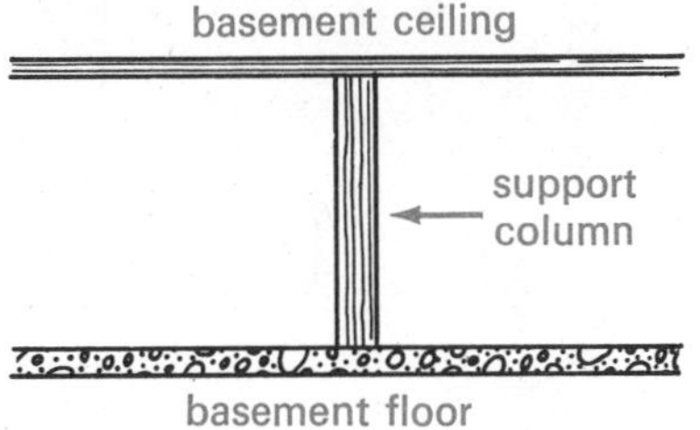

19. The basement ceiling and floor are level. (They are parallel planes.) The support column has been placed perpendicular to the floor. Is it also perpendicular to the ceiling? Why?

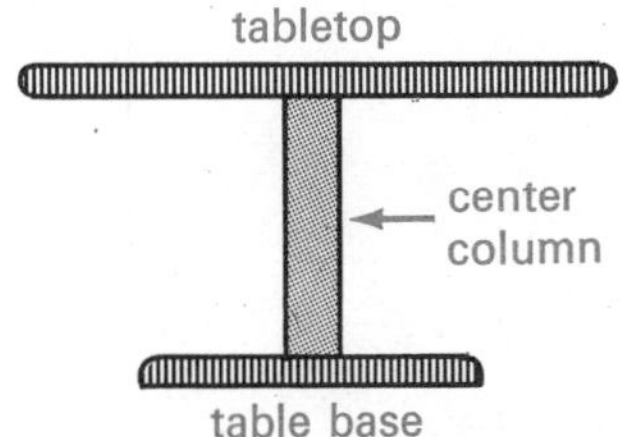

20. The tabletop has been made perpendicular to the center column, and so has the table base. Are the top and base parallel? Why?

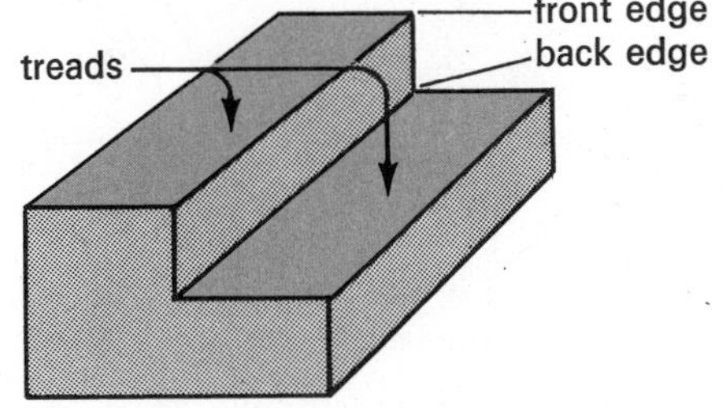

21. The treads of two steps are parallel. Is the front edge of the top step parallel to the back edge of the bottom step? Why?

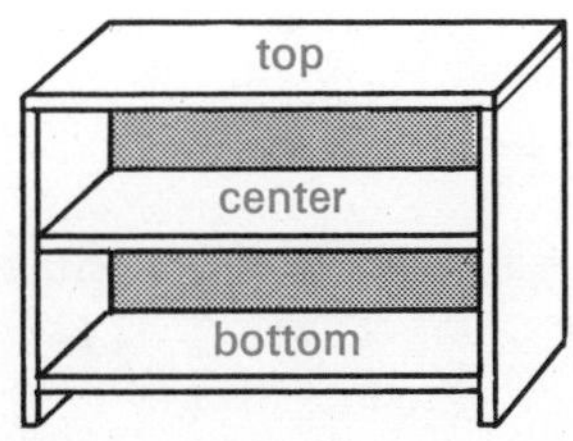

22. The top and center shelves of the bookcase have been made parallel to the bottom shelf. Are the top and center shelves parallel? Why?

23. Given: $\ell \perp A$, $\ell \perp B$, C intersects A and B at m and n.

Prove: $m \parallel n$

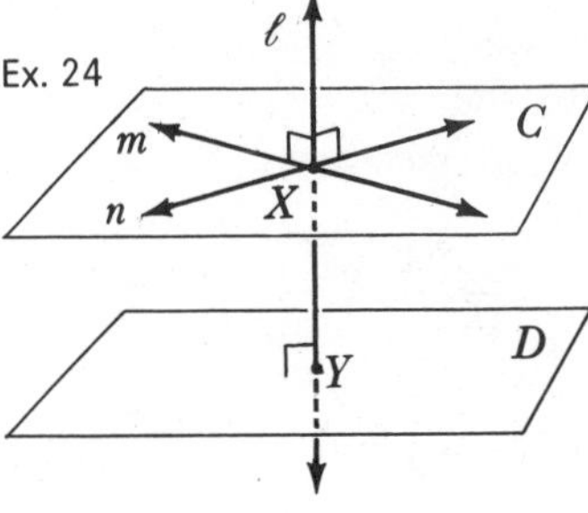

Ex. 24

24. Given: ℓ intersects planes C and D at points X and Y, m and n are in C, $\ell \perp m$, $\ell \perp n$, and $\ell \perp D$

Prove: $C \parallel D$

Ⓒ **25.** Given: $E \parallel F$, $F \parallel G$, $\ell \perp E$

Prove: $\ell \perp G$

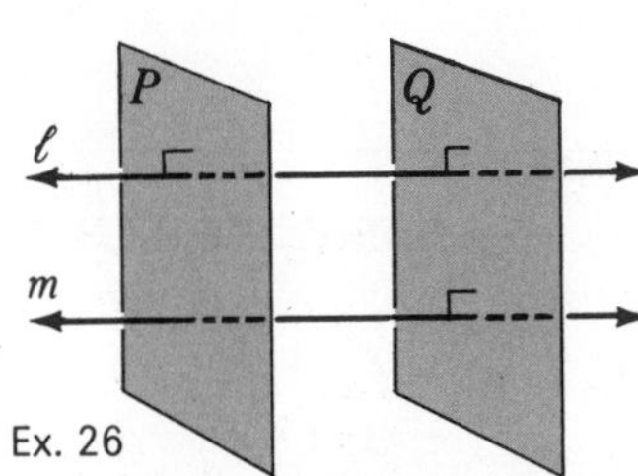

Ex. 26

26. Given: $\ell \perp P$, $\ell \perp Q$, $m \perp Q$

Prove: $m \perp P$

27. Given: Plane $a \parallel$ plane b, $\overline{YR}$ and $\overline{YS}$ are in b, $\overleftrightarrow{XY} \perp a$ at point X, $\overline{YR} \cong \overline{YS}$

Prove: $\overline{XR} \cong \overline{XS}$

HINT: What two triangles are congruent?

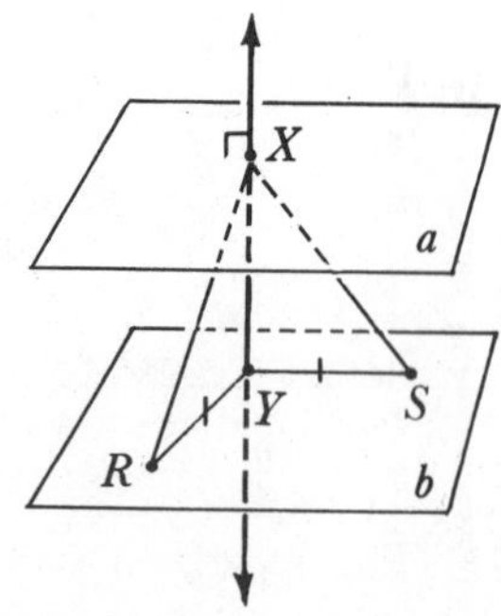

28–29. These statements about parallel planes are very much like some theorems about parallel lines in a plane. Complete each statement.

28. If three parallel planes intercept congruent segments on a line that intersects them, then they ________________.

29. If point P is not in plane r, there is exactly one plane that contains P and is ______ to r.

More Theorems on Parallel Lines and Planes

Sometimes the way in which lines are related to a plane is a clue to how they are related to each other. If two lampposts are perpendicular to the roadway, does it look as if the posts are parallel?

Two lines perpendicular to the same plane are parallel.

Theorem

Given: Line $\ell \perp$ plane P at point X, line $m \perp$ plane P at point Y.

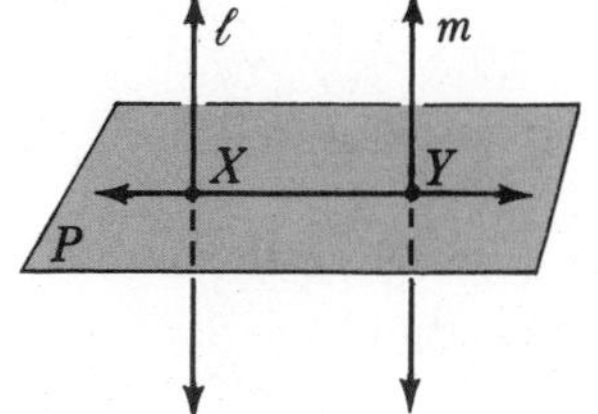

Prove: $\ell \parallel m$

Proof:

STATEMENTS	REASONS
1. $\ell \perp P$ at X, $m \perp P$ at Y.	**1.** Given
2. ℓ and m are coplanar.	**2.** Two lines $\perp$ to the same plane are coplanar.
3. $\overleftrightarrow{XY}$ is in the same plane as ℓ and m.	**3.** If two points are in a plane, so is the line through them.
4. $\ell \perp \overleftrightarrow{XY}$ and $m \perp \overleftrightarrow{XY}$	**4.** Def. of line $\perp$ to plane
5. $\ell \parallel m$	**5.** In a plane, two lines $\perp$ to the same line are $\parallel$.

The end zone of a football field illustrates the next two theorems.

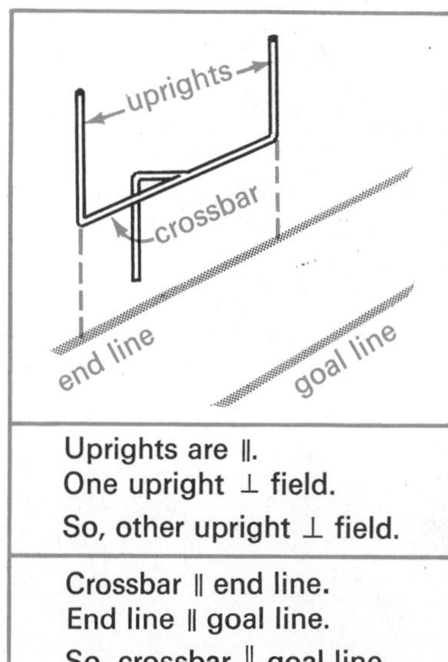

Uprights are $\parallel$.
One upright $\perp$ field.
So, other upright $\perp$ field.

Crossbar $\parallel$ end line.
End line $\parallel$ goal line.
So, crossbar $\parallel$ goal line.

Photo Trends

Theorem **If a plane is perpendicular to one of two parallel lines, it is perpendicular to the other.**

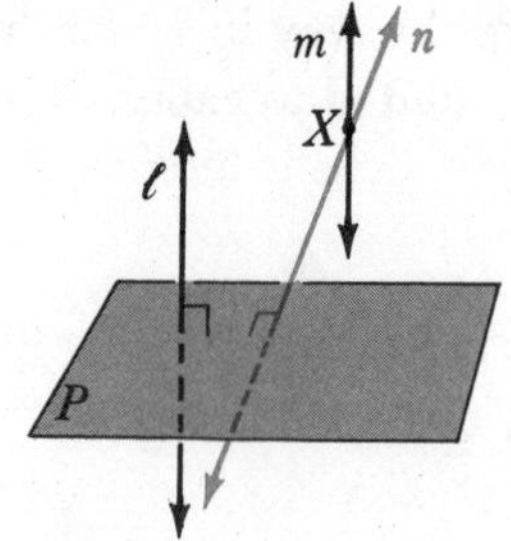

Given: Line $\ell \parallel$ line m, $\ell \perp$ plane P, point X is on m.

Prove: $P \perp m$

Proof:

STATEMENTS	REASONS
1. Let n be a line through X such that $P \perp n$.	**1.** Through a given pt., there is exactly one line $\perp$ to a given plane.
2. $\ell \perp P$	**2.** Given
3. $\ell \parallel n$	**3.** Two lines $\perp$ to the same plane are $\parallel$.
4. $\ell \parallel m$	**4.** Given
5. $m = n$	**5.** Parallel Postulate (p. 125)
6. $P \perp m$	**6.** Substitute m for n (steps 1 and 5).

Theorem **Two lines parallel to a third line are parallel.**

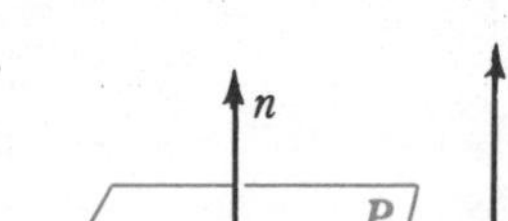

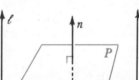

Given: $\ell \parallel n$, $m \parallel n$

Prove: $\ell \parallel m$

NOTE: Three lines do not necessarily have to be coplanar to be parallel.

Proof:

STATEMENTS	REASONS
1. Let P be a plane $\perp$ to n at any point of n.	**1.** Through a given pt., there is exactly one plane $\perp$ to a given line.
2. $\ell \parallel n$	**2.** Given
3. $\ell \perp P$	**3.** A plane $\perp$ to one of two $\parallel$ lines is $\perp$ to the other.
4. $m \parallel n$	**4.** Why?
5. $m \perp P$	**5.** Why?
6. $\ell \parallel m$	**6.** Why?

In Chapter 8 we defined the *distance from a point to a plane* as the length of the perpendicular segment from the point to the plane. We now consider *distance between parallel planes.*

Parallel planes are everywhere equidistant.

Theorem

In terms of the figure, the theorem says that if planes a and b are parallel, then all points in a are equidistant from b, and vice versa.

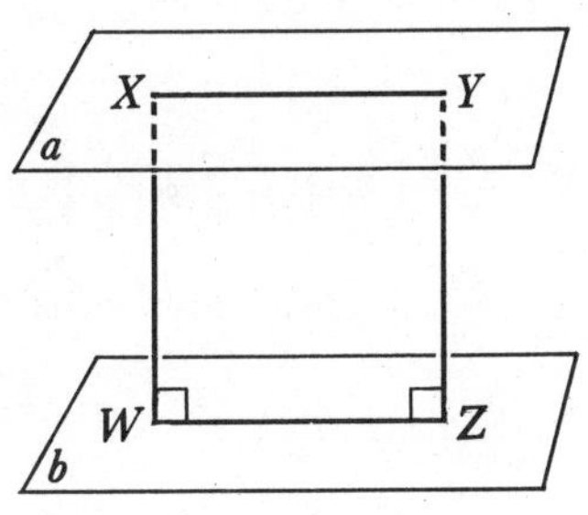

Given: $a \parallel b$, points X and Y are in a, $\overline{XW}$ and $\overline{YZ}$ are perpendicular segments from X and Y to b.

Prove: $XW = YZ$

Proof:

STATEMENTS	REASONS
1. $a \parallel b$, $\overline{XW} \perp b$, $\overline{YZ} \perp b$	**1.** Given
2. $\overleftrightarrow{XW} \parallel \overleftrightarrow{YZ}$	**2.** Two lines $\perp$ to the same plane are $\parallel$.
3. $\overleftrightarrow{XW}$ and $\overleftrightarrow{YZ}$ are in a plane.	**3.** Two $\parallel$ lines are coplanar.
4. $\overleftrightarrow{XY} \parallel \overleftrightarrow{WZ}$	**4.** Intersection of two $\parallel$ planes by third plane is two $\parallel$ lines.
5. $XYZW$ is a parallelogram.	**5.** Def. of parallelogram
6. $XW = YZ$	**6.** Opp. sides of a ▱ are $\cong$.

NOTE: What special kind of parallelogram is $XYZW$ above? Why?

Exercises 13.2

Ⓐ **1–3.** Using the words *line*(*s*) and *plane*(*s*), complete each statement in two different ways.

1. Two ______ perpendicular to the same ______ are parallel.

2. If a ______ is perpendicular to one of two parallel ______, it is perpendicular to the other.

3. Two ______ parallel to a third ______ are parallel.

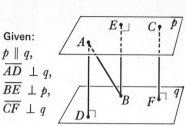

Given:
$p \parallel q$,
$\overline{AD} \perp q$,
$\overline{BE} \perp p$,
$\overline{CF} \perp q$

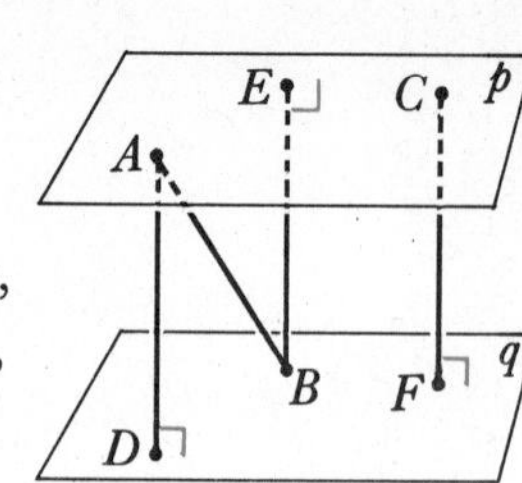

4–8. Complete each statement as a conclusion from the given.

4. $\overline{AD} \perp$ ______ 5. $\overline{BE} \perp$ ______

6. $\overline{CF} \perp$ ______ 7. $\overline{AD} \parallel$ ______ $\parallel$ ______

8. $AD =$ ______ $=$ ______

Ⓑ 9–12. Refer to the figure. Use a theorem to answer each question, and state the theorem.

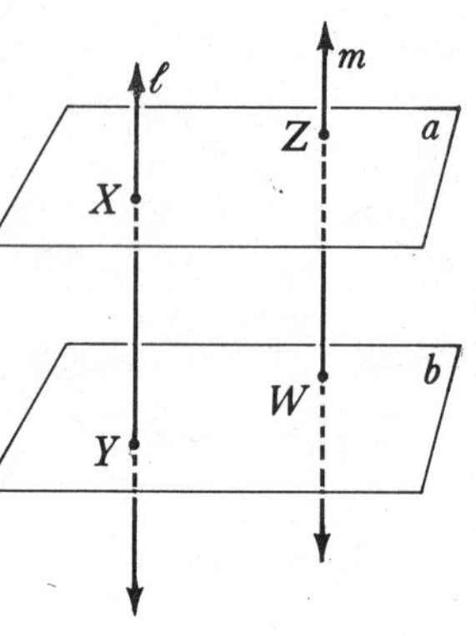

9. If $\ell \parallel m$ and $a \perp \ell$, is $a \perp m$?

10. If $\ell \perp a$ and $m \perp a$, is $\ell \parallel m$?

11. If $a \parallel b$, $\ell \perp b$, and $m \perp b$, is $XY = ZW$?

12. If $\ell \parallel m$, $\ell \perp a$, and $m \perp b$, is $a \parallel b$? (Two theorems needed.)

13–16. True or False? Draw a sketch to illustrate each true statement. Sketch a counterexample for each false statement.

13. If a plane is perpendicular to one of two parallel lines, it is perpendicular to the other.

14. If points X and Y are both in one of two parallel planes, the distances from X and Y to the other plane are equal.

15. If three lines are parallel, they are in the same plane.

16. If a line is in a plane, a perpendicular to the line is perpendicular to the plane.

Given: $\overleftrightarrow{AB} \perp e$, $\overleftrightarrow{AB} \perp f$, $\overleftrightarrow{BH}$ and $\overleftrightarrow{AB}$ determine a plane intersecting e at $\overleftrightarrow{CA}$, $\overleftrightarrow{BK}$ and $\overleftrightarrow{AB}$ determine a plane intersecting e at $\overleftrightarrow{AD}$, $AC = BH$, $AD = BK$

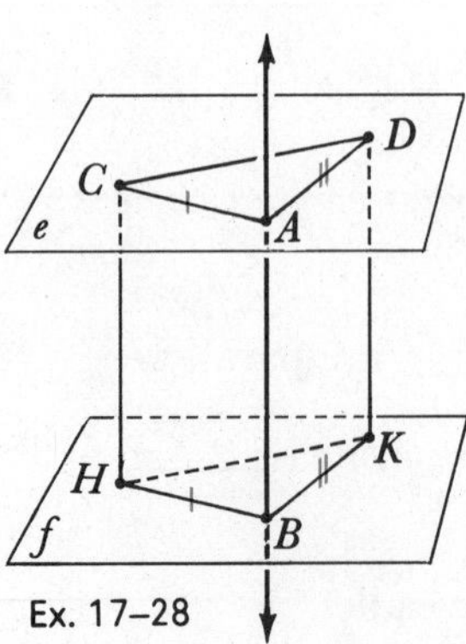

Ex. 17–28

17–28. This is a sequence of statements as in a proof. Give a reason for each statement.

17. $e \parallel f$

18. $\overline{AC} \parallel \overline{BH}$ and $\overline{AD} \parallel \overline{BK}$

19. $\overline{AC} \cong \overline{BH}$ and $\overline{AD} \cong \overline{BK}$

20. $BACH$ and $BADK$ are parallelograms.

21. $\overline{CH} \parallel \overline{AB}$ and $\overline{AB} \parallel \overline{DK}$

22. $\overline{CH} \parallel \overline{DK}$

23. $\overline{CH} \cong \overline{AB}$ and $\overline{AB} \cong \overline{DK}$

24. $\overline{CH} \cong \overline{DK}$

25. *CHKD* is a parallelogram.

26. $\overline{CD} \cong \overline{HK}$

27. $\triangle CAD \cong \triangle HBK$

28. $\angle CAD \cong \angle HBK$

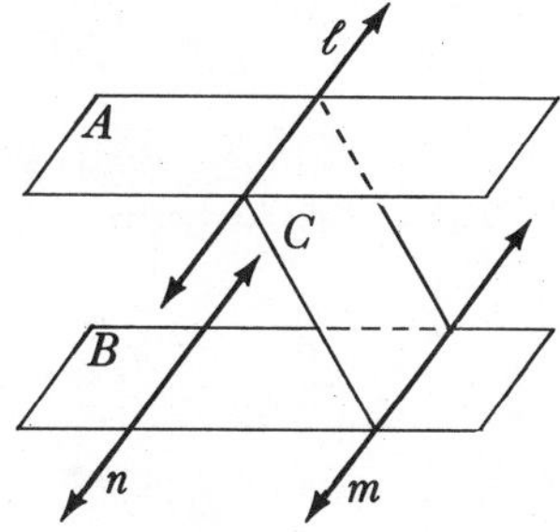

29. Given: $A \parallel B$,
C intersects A and B at ℓ and m,
$m \parallel n$

Prove: $\ell \parallel n$

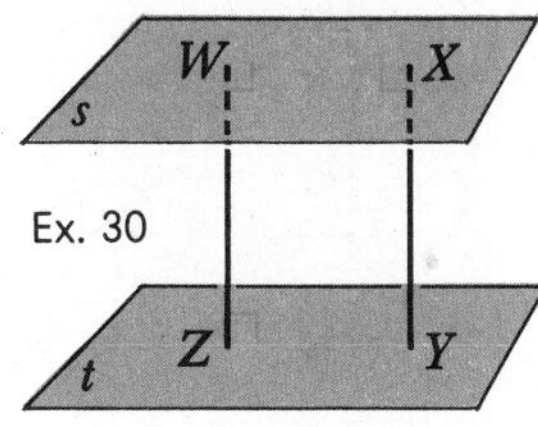

Ex. 30

30. Given: W and X are in s, Z and Y are in t,
$\overleftrightarrow{WZ} \perp s$, $\overleftrightarrow{XY} \perp s$, $\overleftrightarrow{WZ} \perp t$

Prove: $\overleftrightarrow{XY} \perp t$

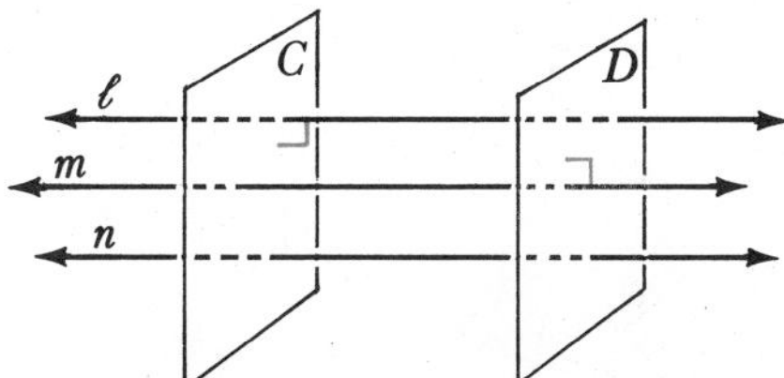

31. Given: $C \parallel D$, $\ell \perp C$,
$m \perp D$, $\ell \parallel n$

Prove: $m \parallel n$

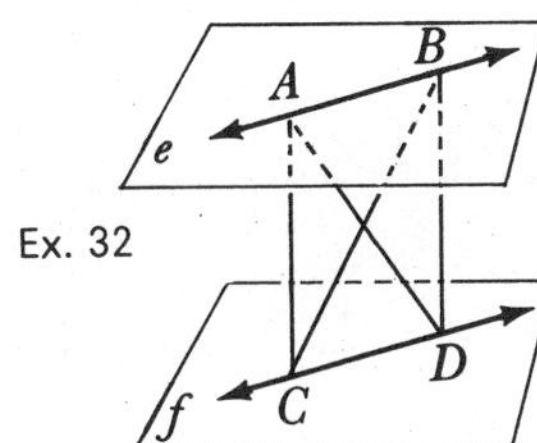

Ex. 32

32. Given: $e \parallel f$, $\overleftrightarrow{AB}$ is in e, $\overleftrightarrow{CD}$ is in f,
$\overline{AC} \perp e$, $\overline{BD} \perp e$

Prove: $\overline{AD}$ and $\overline{BC}$ bisect each other.

HINT: Diagonals of a ▱ bisect.

© 33. Given: Planes m and n intersect at $\overleftrightarrow{XY}$; m and n
intersect planes a and b at $\overleftrightarrow{XU}$, $\overleftrightarrow{YV}$, $\overleftrightarrow{XW}$,
and $\overleftrightarrow{YZ}$; $a \parallel b$; $XW = YZ$; $XU = YV$

Prove: $\angle WXU \cong \angle ZYV$

HINT: Show $\overleftrightarrow{XY} \parallel \overleftrightarrow{UV} \parallel \overleftrightarrow{WZ}$ and $UVZW$ is a ▱.

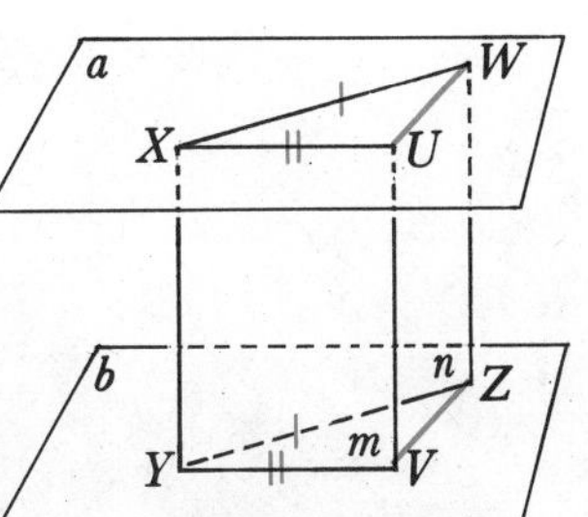

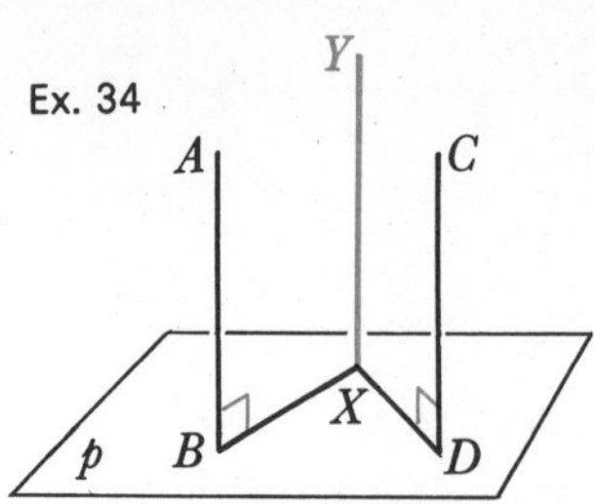

34. Given: $\overline{XB}$ and $\overline{XD}$ in plane p, $\overline{AB} \perp \overline{XB}$, $\overline{CD} \perp \overline{XD}$, $\overline{AB} \parallel \overline{CD}$

Prove: $\overline{AB} \perp p$, $\overline{CD} \perp p$

HINT: Introduce $\overleftrightarrow{YX} \parallel \overline{AB}$, and show $\overleftrightarrow{YX} \perp p$.

35. Given: Planes a and b intersect at line ℓ, point P is in a, $\overline{PQ}$ is the perpendicular segment from P to b.

Describe the locus of points in a that are a distance of PQ from b.

HINT: The points are on both sides of ℓ.

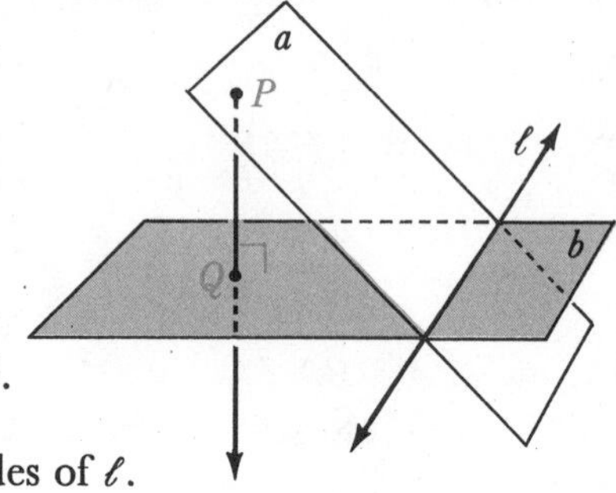

36–39. Use a theorem of this section to answer each exercise.

36. Two legs on one end of a table are made perpendicular to the tabletop. Are the legs parallel? Why?

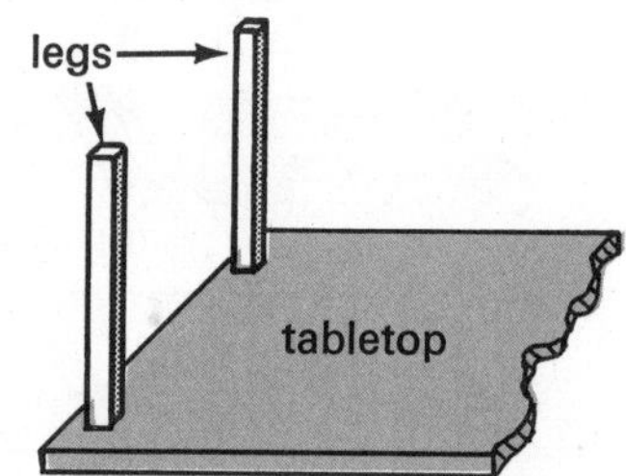

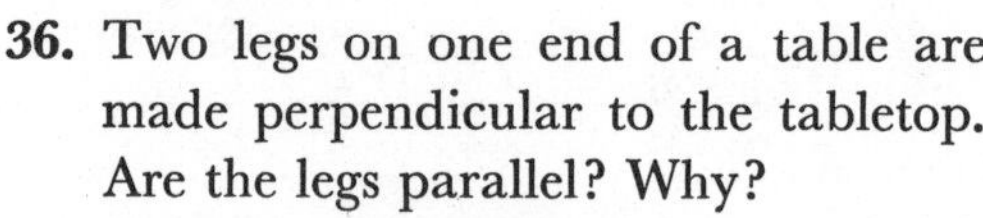

37. An end table is made by fastening the top and base with three rods. The top and base are parallel. Are the rods equal in length?

38. The net on a tennis court is held by two parallel posts. One post is perpendicular to the court. Is the other post perpendicular to the court? Why?

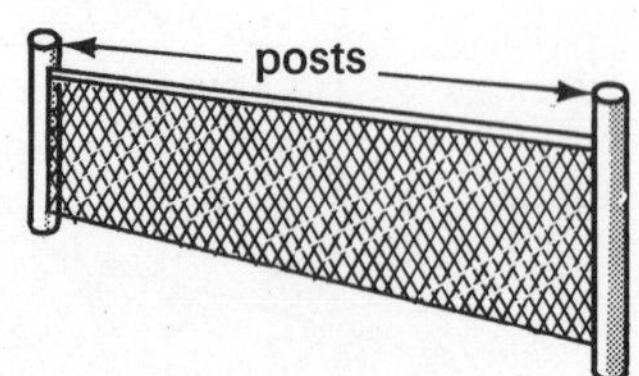

Official Photograph U. S. Navy

39. Three airplanes are flying in V-formation. Each outside airplane keeps its path parallel to the straight path of the middle airplane. Are the paths of the two outside airplanes parallel? Why?

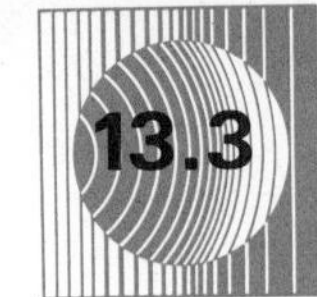

Dihedral Angles

When two lines in a plane intersect at a point, four angles are formed. Two planes in space intersecting at a line also form four figures. Each figure is called a dihedral angle.

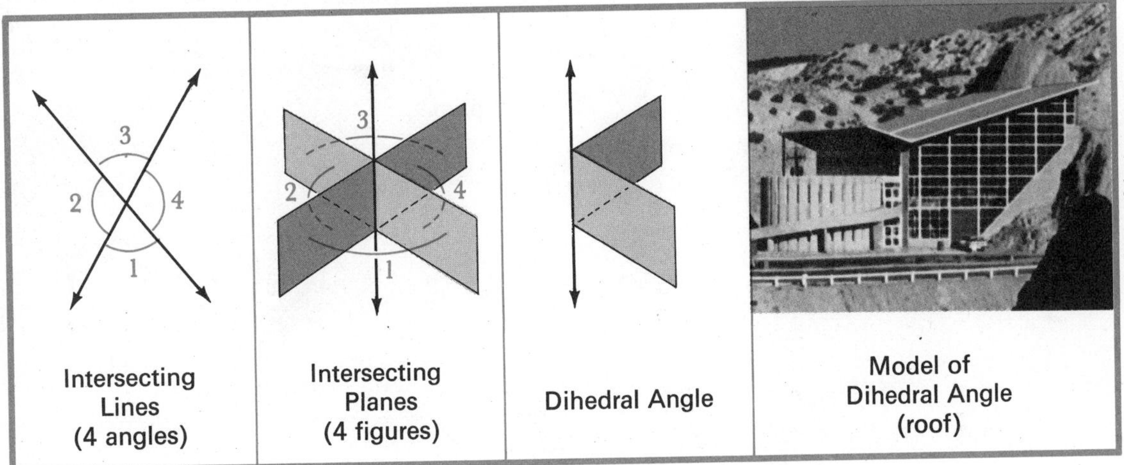

Intersecting Lines (4 angles) | Intersecting Planes (4 figures) | Dihedral Angle | Model of Dihedral Angle (roof)

U. S. Dept. of the Interior National Park Service

A **dihedral angle** is formed by a line and two noncoplanar half planes that have the line as their common edge. The line and either half plane is a *face* (or *side*) of the dihedral angle. The line is the *edge* of the dihedral angle. How is the definition of *angle* (in a plane) similar to the definition of *dihedral angle*?

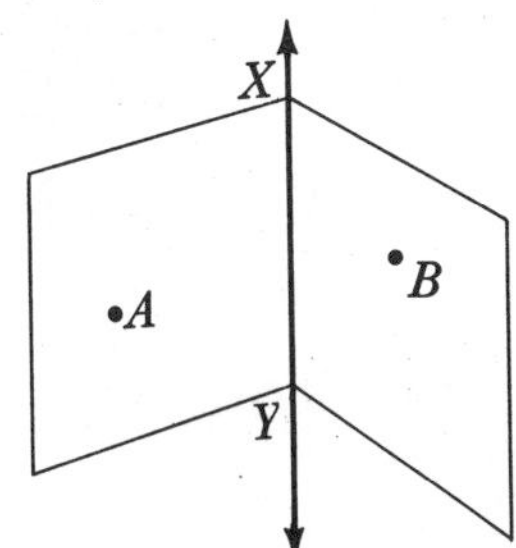

A dihedral angle with edge $\overleftrightarrow{XY}$, point A in one face, and point B in the other face is named

$$\angle A\text{-}\overleftrightarrow{XY}\text{-}B, \text{ or}$$

$$\angle \overleftrightarrow{XY} \text{ if}$$

there is no question as to which dihedral angle has $\overleftrightarrow{XY}$ as its edge.

A **plane angle** of a dihedral angle is the intersection of the dihedral angle and a plane perpendicular to the edge of the dihedral angle. If $p \perp \overleftrightarrow{XY}$ at Q, then $\angle RQS$ is a plane angle of $\angle A\text{-}\overleftrightarrow{XY}\text{-}B$. Also, $\overrightarrow{QR} \perp \overleftrightarrow{XY}$, and $\overrightarrow{QS} \perp \overleftrightarrow{XY}$. Why? We will take the definition of *plane angle* to mean that the sides of the plane angle are perpendicular to the edge of the dihedral angle.

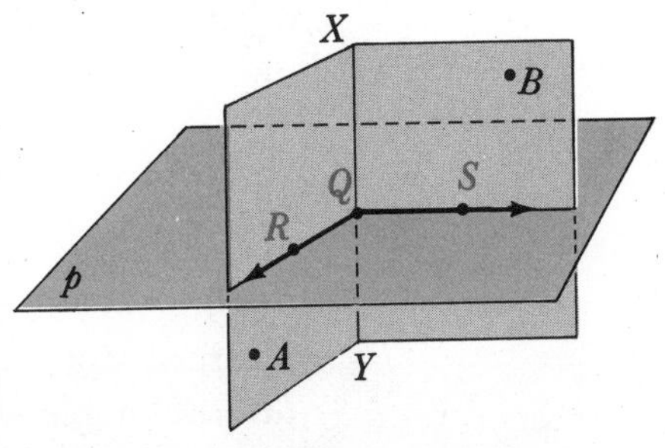

At each point of a line there is exactly one plane perpendicular to the line. Therefore, each dihedral angle has infinitely many plane angles. But we can show that all the plane angles are congruent.

Theorem  **The plane angles of a dihedral angle are congruent.** 

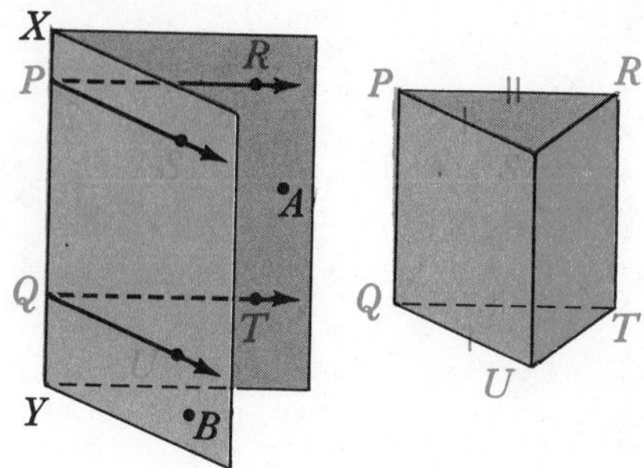

Given: $\angle RPS$ and $\angle TQU$ are plane angles of $\angle A\text{-}\overleftrightarrow{XY}\text{-}B$, $\overline{RP} \cong \overline{TQ}$, $\overline{SP} \cong \overline{UQ}$

Prove: $\angle RPS \cong \angle TQU$

Proof:

STATEMENTS	REASONS
1. $\overline{RP} \perp \overleftrightarrow{XY}$, $\overline{TQ} \perp \overleftrightarrow{XY}$, $\overline{SP} \perp \overleftrightarrow{XY}$, $\overline{UQ} \perp \overleftrightarrow{XY}$	**1.** Given $\angle$s *RPS* and *TQU* are plane angles, def. of plane angles
2. $\overline{RP} \parallel \overline{TQ}$, $\overline{SP} \parallel \overline{UQ}$	**2.** In a plane, two lines $\perp$ to the same line are $\parallel$.
3. $\overline{RP} \cong \overline{TQ}$, $\overline{SP} \cong \overline{UQ}$	**3.** Given
4. *RPQT* and *SPQU* are ▱s.	**4.** Pair of opp. sides are $\parallel$ and $\cong$.
5. $\overline{RT} \parallel \overline{PQ} \parallel \overline{SU}$	**5.** Opp. sides of a ▱ are $\parallel$, and 2 lines $\parallel$ to the same line are $\parallel$.
6. $\overline{RT} \cong \overline{PQ}$, $\overline{PQ} \cong \overline{SU}$	**6.** Opp. sides of a ▱ are $\cong$.
7. $\overline{RT} \cong \overline{SU}$	**7.** Segs. $\cong$ to the same seg. are $\cong$.
8. *RSUT* is a ▱.	**8.** Same as reason 4
9. $\overline{RS} \cong \overline{TU}$	**9.** Same as reason 6
10. $\triangle RPS \cong \triangle TQU$	**10.** SSS Postulate
11. $\angle RPS \cong \angle TQU$	**11.** Corres. parts of $\cong$ $\triangle$s are $\cong$.

Now we can say that the **measure** of a dihedral angle is the measure of any of its plane angles. And a **right dihedral angle** is a dihedral angle whose plane angles are right angles. The definitions of *acute* and *obtuse dihedral angles* are left for you to furnish in the exercises.

Exercises 13.3

Ⓐ **1–2.** Name the following:

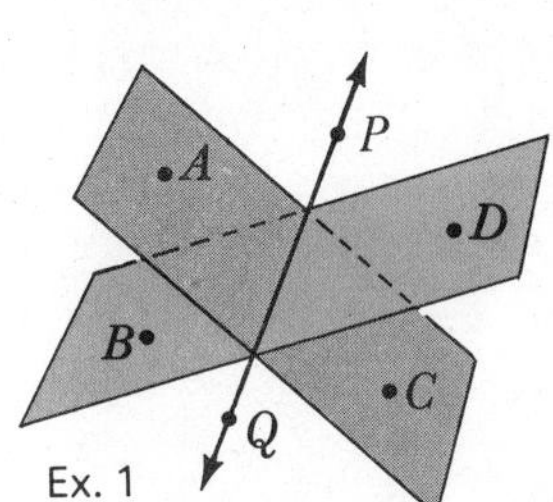

1. four dihedral angles

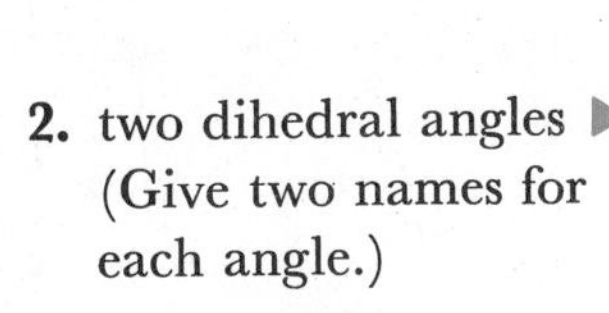

2. two dihedral angles (Give two names for each angle.)

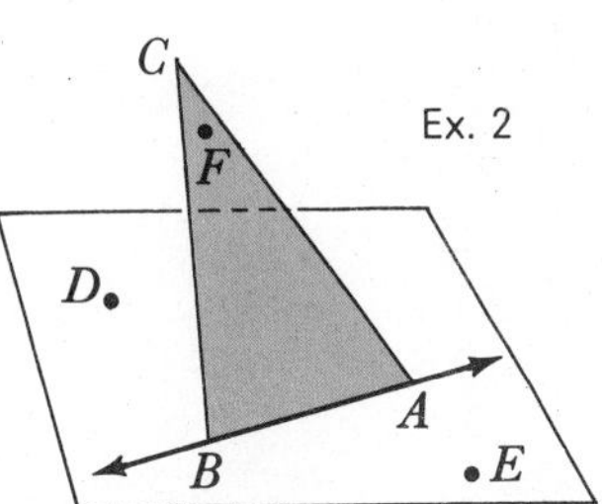

3. Find models of three dihedral angles in your classroom.

4–10. $\angle ARB$ is a plane angle of $\angle \overleftrightarrow{XY}$.

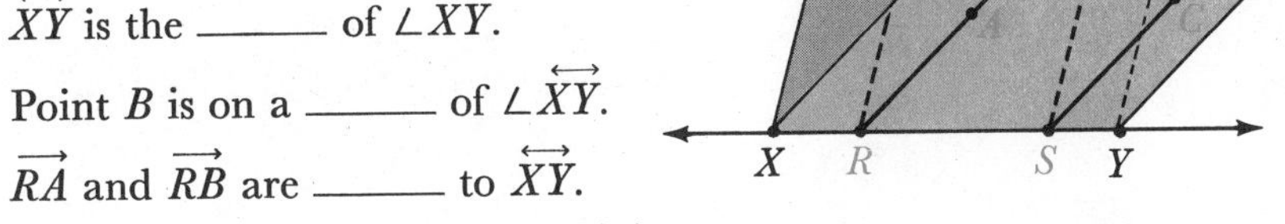

4. $\overleftrightarrow{XY}$ is the ______ of $\angle \overleftrightarrow{XY}$.

5. Point B is on a ______ of $\angle \overleftrightarrow{XY}$.

6. $\overrightarrow{RA}$ and $\overrightarrow{RB}$ are ______ to $\overleftrightarrow{XY}$.

7. If $\angle CSD$ is a plane angle of $\angle \overleftrightarrow{XY}$, then $\angle CSD$ ______ $\angle ARB$.

8. If $m\angle ARB = 45$, then $m\angle \overleftrightarrow{XY} =$ ______. **9.** $m\angle ARS =$ ______

10. If $\angle ARB$ is a right angle, then $\angle \overleftrightarrow{XY}$ is a ______ dihedral angle.

Ⓑ **11–12.** Name the following:

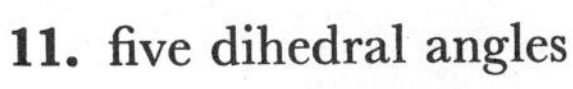

11. five dihedral angles

12. six dihedral angles

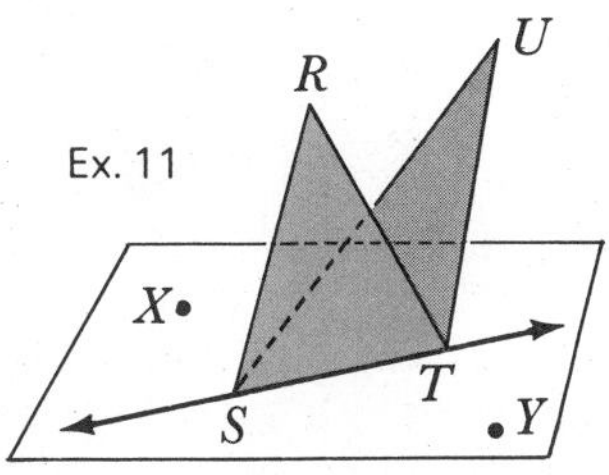

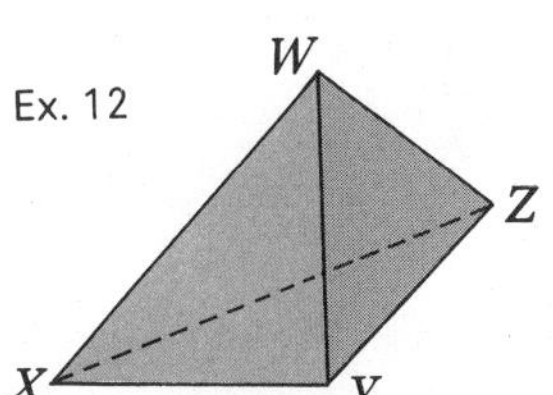

13–16. Give a reason for each statement.

13. $m\angle AQB = m\angle X\text{-}\overleftrightarrow{RS}\text{-}Y$

14. $\overrightarrow{QA} \perp \overleftrightarrow{RS}$ and $\overrightarrow{QB} \perp \overleftrightarrow{RS}$

15. If $\overrightarrow{QC} \perp \overleftrightarrow{RS}$ and $\overrightarrow{QA} \perp \overleftrightarrow{RS}$, then

(**a**) $\overrightarrow{QC}$ and $\overrightarrow{QA}$ are in a plane $\perp$ to $\overleftrightarrow{RS}$ at Q.

(**b**) $\angle CQA$ is a plane angle of $\angle Z\text{-}\overleftrightarrow{RS}\text{-}X$.

16. $\angle X\text{-}\overleftrightarrow{RS}\text{-}Y$ is a right dihedral angle if $m\angle AQB = 90$.

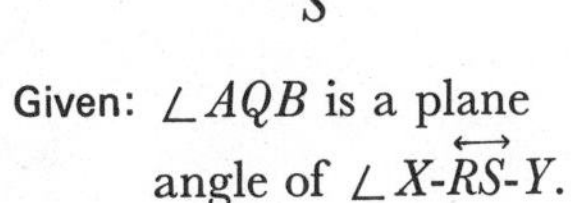

Given: $\angle AQB$ is a plane angle of $\angle X\text{-}\overleftrightarrow{RS}\text{-}Y$.

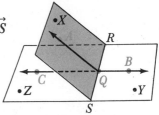

Given: $\overline{WX} \perp \overline{XY}$,
$\overline{XY} \perp \overline{XZ}$,
$\overline{XZ} \perp \overline{WX}$

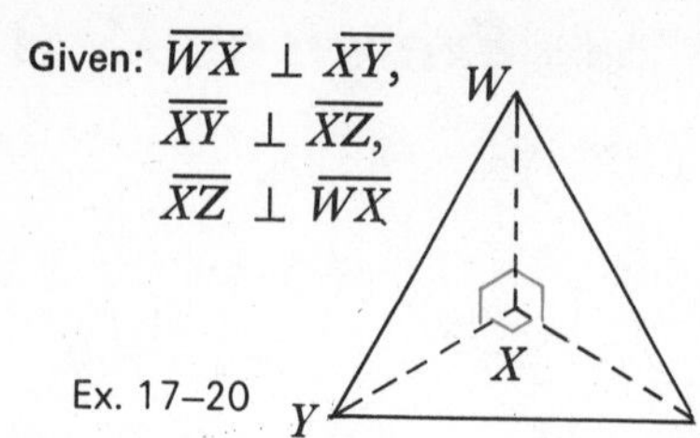

Ex. 17–20

17–20. Name the following:

17. a plane angle of $\angle W\text{-}\overleftrightarrow{XY}\text{-}Z$

18. the dihedral angle for which $\angle YXZ$ is a plane angle

19. the dihedral angle for which $\angle WXY$ is a plane angle

20. a dihedral angle whose measure is 90

21–24. Find the measure of each dihedral angle.

Given: $\overrightarrow{QA}$, $\overrightarrow{QD}$, and $\overleftrightarrow{XY}$ are $\perp$ to $\overleftrightarrow{BC}$ at Q,
$m\angle AQX = 125$, $m\angle DQX = 55$

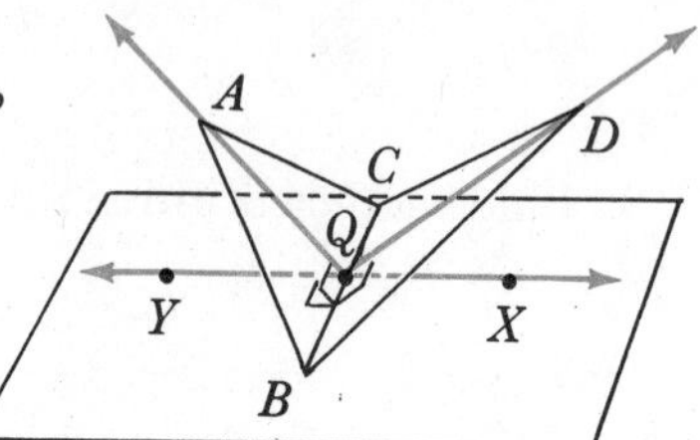

21. $\angle D\text{-}\overleftrightarrow{BC}\text{-}X$

22. $\angle A\text{-}\overleftrightarrow{BC}\text{-}D$

23. $\angle A\text{-}\overleftrightarrow{BC}\text{-}Y$

24. $\angle Y\text{-}\overleftrightarrow{BC}\text{-}D$

Ex. 25

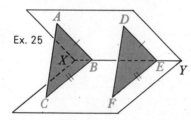

25. Given: $\angle ABC$ and $\angle DEF$ are plane angles of $\angle A\text{-}\overleftrightarrow{XY}\text{-}F$,
$\overline{AB} \cong \overline{DE}$, $\overline{BC} \cong \overline{EF}$

Prove: $\overline{AC} \cong \overline{DF}$

26. Given: $\angle FDE$ is a plane angle of $\angle \overleftrightarrow{DA}$,
$\angle DEF$ is a plane angle of $\angle \overleftrightarrow{EB}$,
$\angle EFD$ is a plane angle of $\angle \overleftrightarrow{FC}$,
$m\angle \overleftrightarrow{DA} = 50$, $m\angle \overleftrightarrow{EB} = 70$

Prove: $m\angle \overleftrightarrow{FC} = 60$

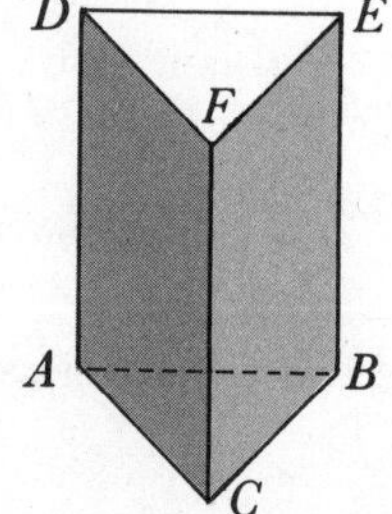

27–34. Using the definitions in Chapter 2 as a guide, define these terms. (*Example:* **Congruent dihedral angles** are dihedral angles that have the same measure.) Also draw a sketch for each definition.

27. acute dihedral angle

28. obtuse dihedral angle

29. complementary dihedral angles

30. supplementary dihedral angles

31. interior of a dihedral angle

32. exterior of a dihedral angle

© **33.** adjacent dihedral angles

34. vertical dihedral angles

35. Prove this theorem: Vertical dihedral angles are congruent.

GEOMETRY AROUND YOU

DIHEDRAL ANGLES IN OBJECTS

Pictured below are objects whose sides form congruent dihedral angles. In each case shown, if a cross section of the object is taken so that the edges of the dihedral angles are perpendicular to the "plane" of the slice, the plane angles of the dihedral angles form regular polygons. For example, the cross section of the prism shows that the plane angles ($\angle A$, $\angle B$, and $\angle C$) form an equilateral triangle. Each angle measures 60°. Why? Therefore, we know that the sides of the prism form dihedral angles with a measure of 60°. Why?

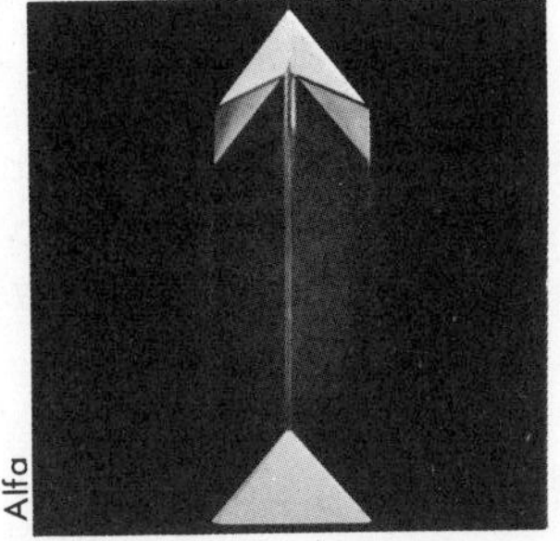

Alfa

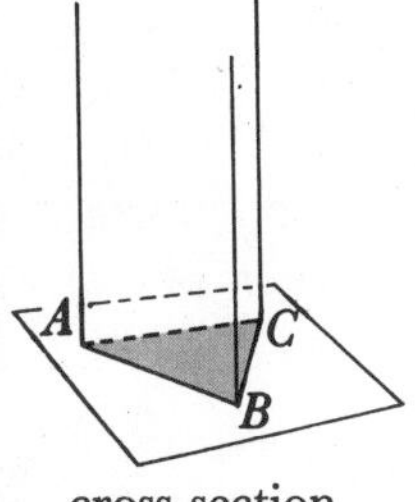

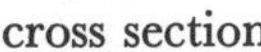

cross section

Determine the kind of regular polygon formed by plane angles of each remaining object. Then find the measure of the congruent dihedral angles. (Finding the measures of interior angles of convex polygons is covered in Section 5.3.)

Dr. E. R. Degginger

Crystal

Wide World Photos

The Pentagon

Dr. E. R. Degginger

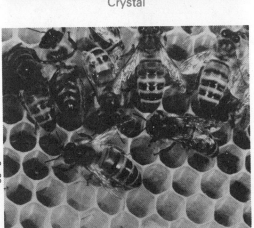

Beehive Cells

Bill Miller

Fountain

Perpendicular Planes

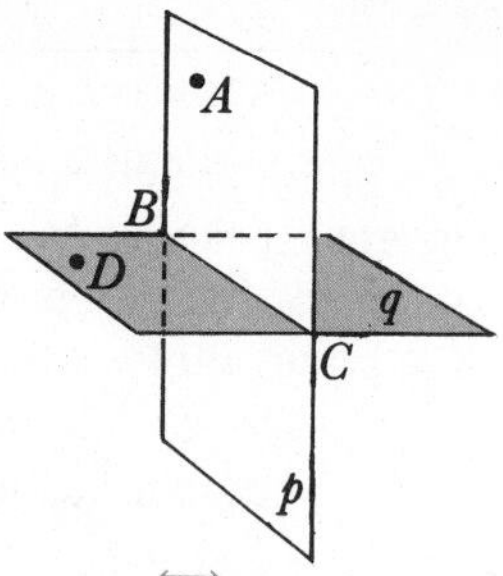

$\angle A\text{-}\overleftrightarrow{BC}\text{-}D$ is a rt. dihedral angle and $p \perp q$.

Perpendicular planes are planes that contain a right dihedral angle. In the figure, $\angle A\text{-}\overleftrightarrow{BC}\text{-}D$ is a right dihedral angle, so planes p and q are perpendicular. One model of perpendicular planes is the door and the floor of a room.

We saw that lines sometimes indicate when two planes are parallel. Lines can also tell us when planes are perpendicular. For example,

(1) Tape pencil (model line) to index card (model plane). (2) Hold pencil perpendicular to paper (another model plane). (3) Rotate pencil slowly so index card takes different positions.	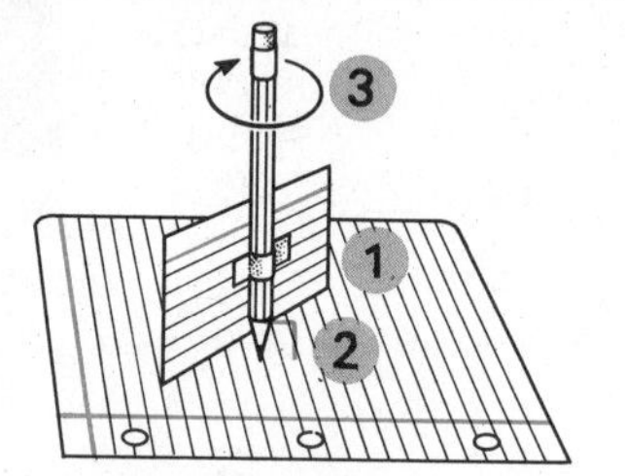

How many different planes that contain the pencil seem to be perpendicular to the paper? The theorem below gives the answer.

Theorem  **If a line is perpendicular to a given plane, then every plane containing the line is perpendicular to the given plane.** 

Given: $\overleftrightarrow{RS} \perp$ plane p at point R, plane q contains $\overleftrightarrow{RS}$ and intersects p at $\overleftrightarrow{XY}$.

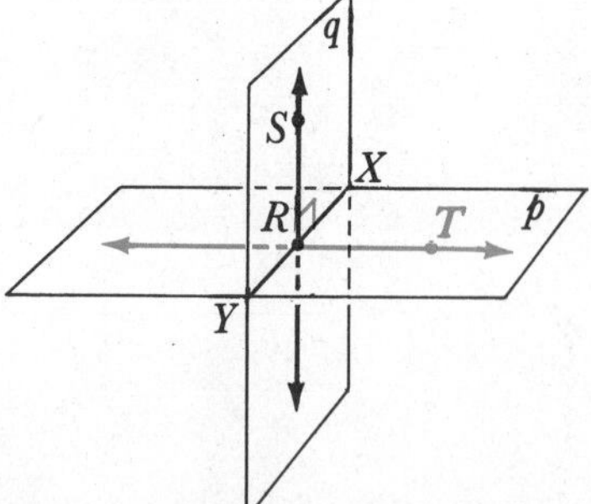

Prove: $q \perp p$

Proof:

STATEMENTS	REASONS
1. $\overleftrightarrow{RS} \perp \overleftrightarrow{XY}$	1. Given $\overleftrightarrow{RS} \perp p$ and def. of line $\perp$ to plane
2. There is a line $\overleftrightarrow{RT}$ in p such that $\overleftrightarrow{RT} \perp \overleftrightarrow{XY}$ at R.	2. In a plane, there is exactly one line $\perp$ to a line at a given pt.

3. The plane containing $\overleftrightarrow{RS}$ and $\overleftrightarrow{RT}$ is perpendicular to $\overleftrightarrow{XY}$.	3. Basic Theorem for Perpendiculars (p. 270)
4. $\angle SRT$ is a plane angle of $\angle S\text{-}\overleftrightarrow{XY}\text{-}T$.	4. Def. of plane angle
5. $\overleftrightarrow{RS} \perp \overleftrightarrow{RT}$	5. Def. of line $\perp$ to plane
6. $\angle SRT$ is a rt. $\angle$.	6. Def. of $\perp$ lines
7. $\angle S\text{-}\overleftrightarrow{XY}\text{-}T$ is a rt. dihedral $\angle$.	7. Def. of rt. dihedral $\angle$
8. $p \perp q$	8. Def. of $\perp$ planes

The next theorem gives us a way to determine if a line is perpendicular to a plane. After reading the theorem, make a model using an index card and a piece of paper as planes and a pencil as the line.

If two planes are perpendicular, a line in one of them perpendicular to their line of intersection is perpendicular to the other.

Theorem

Given: Planes p and q are perpendicular and intersect at $\overleftrightarrow{XY}$, $\overleftrightarrow{JK}$ is in q, $\overleftrightarrow{JK} \perp \overleftrightarrow{XY}$ at point J.

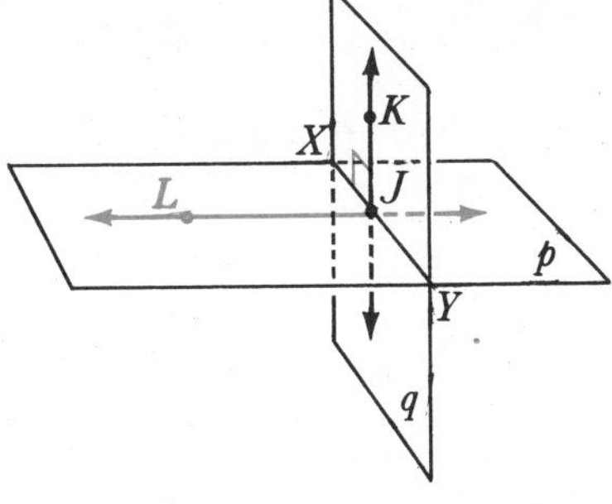

Prove: $\overleftrightarrow{JK} \perp p$

Proof:

STATEMENTS	REASONS
1. There is a line $\overleftrightarrow{JL}$ in plane p such that $\overleftrightarrow{JL} \perp \overleftrightarrow{XY}$ at J.	1. In a plane, there is exactly one line $\perp$ to a line at a given pt.
2. The plane containing $\overleftrightarrow{JK}$ and $\overleftrightarrow{JL}$ is perpendicular to $\overleftrightarrow{XY}$.	2. Given $\overleftrightarrow{JK} \perp \overleftrightarrow{XY}$ and Basic Theorem for Perpendiculars
3. $\angle KJL$ is a plane angle of $\angle K\text{-}\overleftrightarrow{XY}\text{-}L$.	3. Given p and q intersect at $\overleftrightarrow{XY}$ and def. of a plane angle
4. $\angle K\text{-}\overleftrightarrow{XY}\text{-}L$ is a right dihedral $\angle$.	4. Given $p \perp q$ and def. of $\perp$ planes
5. $\angle KJL$ is a right $\angle$.	5. Def. of rt. dihedral $\angle$
6. $\overleftrightarrow{JK} \perp \overleftrightarrow{JL}$	6. Def. of $\perp$ lines
7. $\overleftrightarrow{JK} \perp p$	7. Basic Theorem for Perpendiculars ($\overleftrightarrow{JK} \perp \overleftrightarrow{JL}$ and given $\overleftrightarrow{JK} \perp \overleftrightarrow{XY}$)

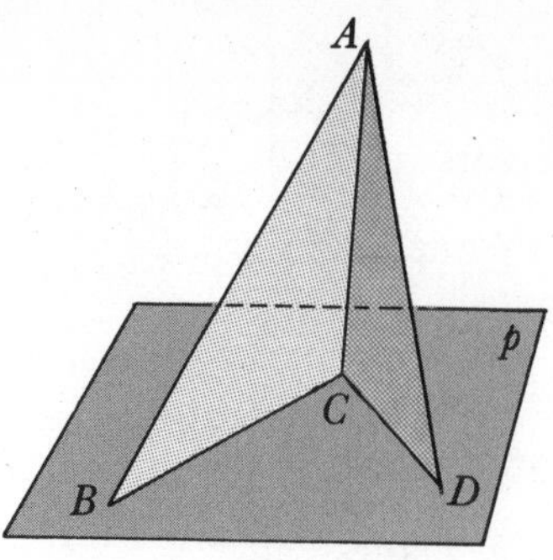

Like lines, planes can also be named by points contained in them. In the figure, B, C, and D are three noncollinear points in plane p. Another name for plane p is **plane *BCD*.** Plane ABC and plane ACD are also represented. We can also talk about plane ABD, even though it is not drawn in the figure. Remember, the three points you use in naming a plane cannot all be on the same line.

Exercises 13.4

Ⓐ **1–6.** Give a reason for each statement. (Use the figure.)

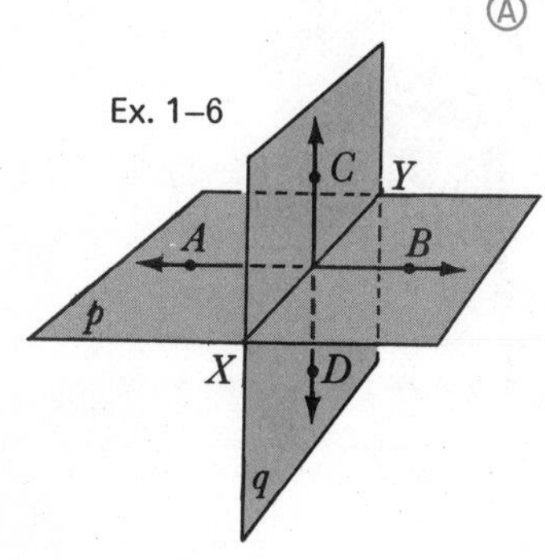

1. If $p \perp q$, then $\angle A\text{-}\overleftrightarrow{XY}\text{-}D$ is a right dihedral angle.

2. If $\angle C\text{-}\overleftrightarrow{XY}\text{-}B$ is a right dihedral angle, then $p \perp q$.

3. If $\overleftrightarrow{AB} \perp q$, then $p \perp q$.

4. If $\overleftrightarrow{CD} \perp p$, then $q \perp p$.

5. If $p \perp q$ and $\overleftrightarrow{CD} \perp \overleftrightarrow{XY}$, then $\overleftrightarrow{CD} \perp p$.

6. If $p \perp q$ and $\overleftrightarrow{AB} \perp \overleftrightarrow{XY}$, then $\overleftrightarrow{AB} \perp q$.

7–10. Name the following. (Use the figure.)

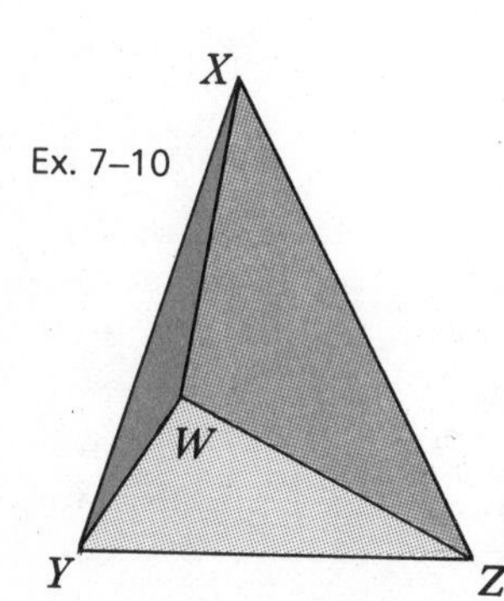

7. a right dihedral angle, if plane $XYW \perp$ plane XWZ

8. two perpendicular planes, if $\angle Y\text{-}\overleftrightarrow{ZW}\text{-}X$ is a right dihedral angle

9. two planes perpendicular to plane YZW, if $\overline{XW} \perp$ plane YZW

10. a plane perpendicular to $\overline{XW}$, if plane $XYW \perp$ plane YZW and $\overline{XW} \perp \overline{YW}$

Ⓑ **11–14.** Give a reason for each statement. (Use the figure for Exercises 7–10.)

11. If $\angle Y\text{-}\overleftrightarrow{WX}\text{-}Z$ is a rt. dihedral angle, then plane $WXY \perp$ plane WXZ.

12. If plane $WXZ \perp$ plane WYZ, then $\angle Y\text{-}\overleftrightarrow{WZ}\text{-}X$ is a rt. dihedral angle.

13. If plane $WXY \perp$ plane WYZ and $\overline{WX} \perp \overline{WY}$, then $\overline{WX} \perp$ plane WYZ.

14. If $\overline{WX} \perp$ plane WYZ, then plane $WXZ \perp$ plane WYZ.

15–22. True or False? Draw a sketch to illustrate each true statement. Sketch a counterexample for each false statement.

15. If a line is perpendicular to a plane, then there is exactly one plane that contains the line and is perpendicular to the given plane.

16. If a line is in a plane, there is exactly one plane that contains the line and is perpendicular to the given plane.

17. If two planes are perpendicular, then every line in one plane perpendicular to their line of intersection is perpendicular to the other plane.

18. If two planes are perpendicular, then every line in one plane intersecting the other plane is perpendicular to the other plane.

19. If two planes are both perpendicular to a third plane, then they are parallel.

20. If two planes are both perpendicular to the same plane and their lines of intersection with that plane are parallel, then the two planes are parallel.

21. If a line is parallel to a plane, no plane containing the line can be perpendicular to the given plane.

22. If two planes intersect and each is perpendicular to a third plane, their line of intersection is perpendicular to the third plane.

23–36. Find the measure of each angle. (Use the figures.)

23. $\angle Q\text{-}\overleftrightarrow{PS}\text{-}R$ **24.** $\angle Q\text{-}\overleftrightarrow{RS}\text{-}P$

25. $\angle QSR$ **26.** $\angle QSP$

27. $\angle QPS$ **28.** $\angle RPS$

29. $\angle PQR$ **30.** $\angle PRQ$

Ex. 23–30

P Q R S

Given: $\overline{PS} \cong \overline{QS} \cong \overline{RS}$, plane $PQS \perp$ plane PSR, plane $PSR \perp$ plane QRS, plane $QRS \perp$ plane PQS.

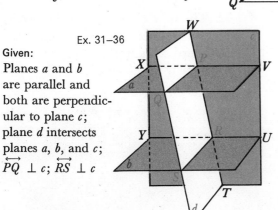

Ex. 31–36

Given: Planes a and b are parallel and both are perpendicular to plane c; plane d intersects planes a, b, and c; $\overleftrightarrow{PQ} \perp c$; $\overleftrightarrow{RS} \perp c$

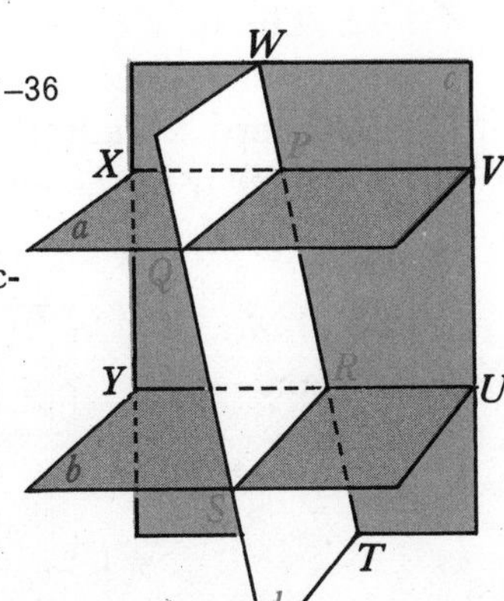

31. $\angle WPV$, if $m\angle PRU = 120$

32. $\angle WPX$, if $m\angle PRY = 60$

33. $\angle R\text{-}\overleftrightarrow{PQ}\text{-}V$, if $m\angle T\text{-}\overleftrightarrow{RS}\text{-}U = 75$

34. $\angle R\text{-}\overleftrightarrow{PQ}\text{-}X$, if $m\angle T\text{-}\overleftrightarrow{RS}\text{-}Y = 130$

35. $\angle P\text{-}\overleftrightarrow{RS}\text{-}Y$, if $m\angle V\text{-}\overleftrightarrow{PQ}\text{-}R = 50$

36. $\angle U\text{-}\overleftrightarrow{RS}\text{-}T$, if $m\angle W\text{-}\overleftrightarrow{PQ}\text{-}X = 80$

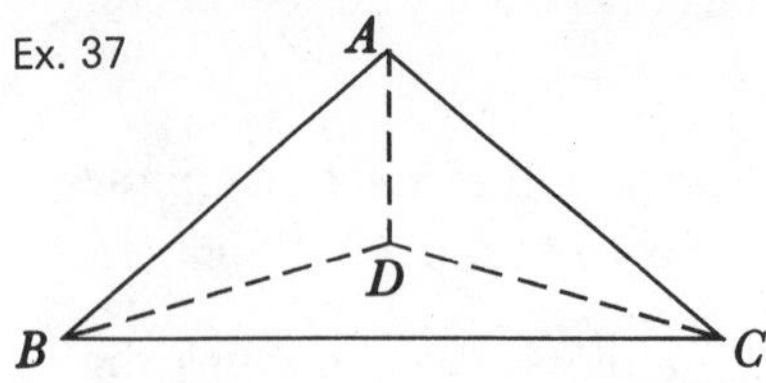

37. Given: $\overline{AD} \perp$ plane BDC.

Prove: $\angle A\text{-}\overleftrightarrow{DC}\text{-}B$ is a right dihedral angle.

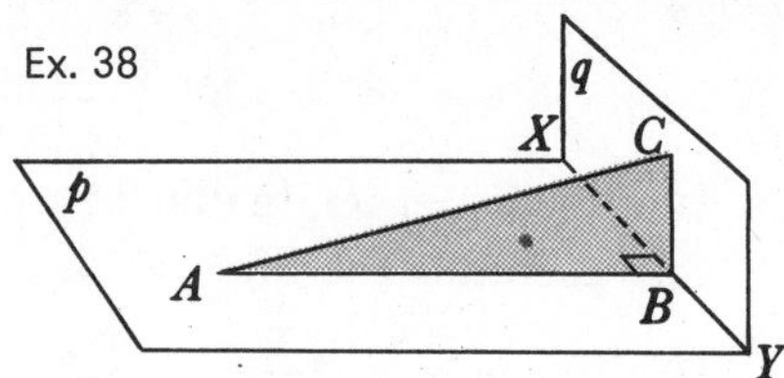

38. Given: Plane $p \perp$ plane q, $\overline{AB} \perp \overleftrightarrow{XY}$

Prove: $\triangle ABC$ is a right triangle.

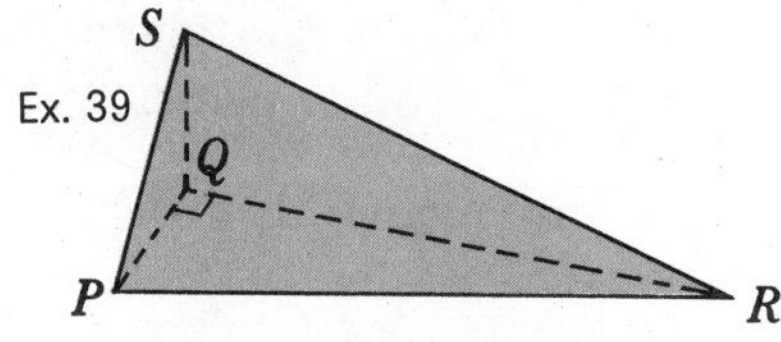

© **39.** Given: Plane $PQS \perp$ plane PQR, plane $RQS \perp$ plane PQR, $\overline{PQ} \perp \overline{RQ}$

Prove: $\overline{SQ} \perp$ plane PQR.

HINT: $\overline{PQ}$ is the intersection of two $\perp$ planes, and so is $\overline{RQ}$.

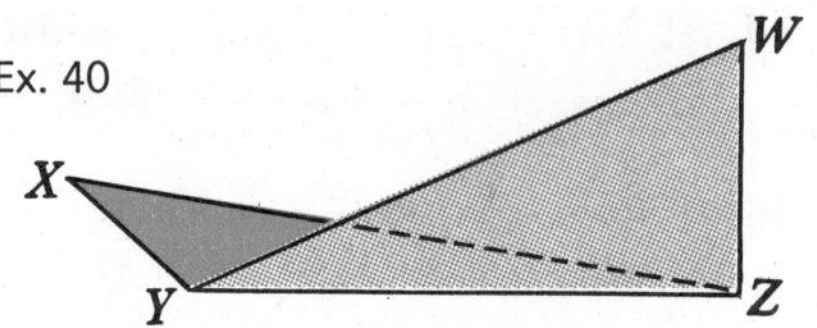

40. Given: $\overline{XY} \perp$ plane YWZ at point Y, $\angle WZY$ is a right angle.

Prove: $\overline{WZ} \perp \overline{XZ}$

HINT: Start by showing plane $XYZ \perp$ plane YWZ.

41–43. Use a theorem or definition of this section to answer each exercise.

41. The side and base of a bookend form a right dihedral angle. Are the side and base perpendicular? Why?

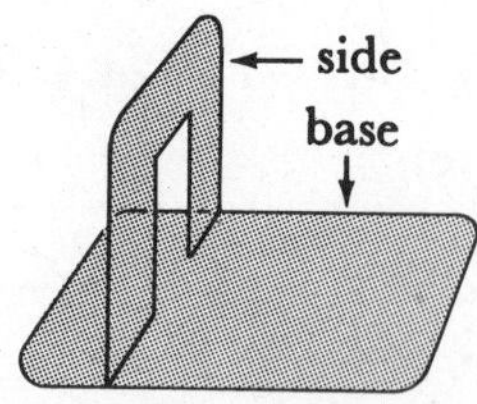

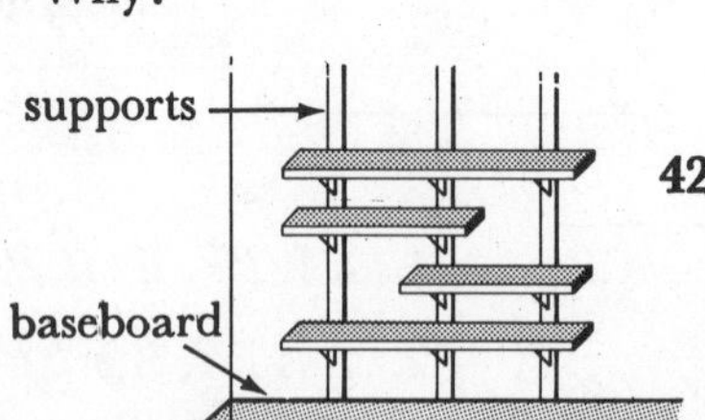

42. The shelf supports attached to the wall are perpendicular to the baseboard. Are the supports perpendicular to the floor? Why?

43. A revolving door turns on a post that is perpendicular to the floor. Are the three panels each perpendicular to the floor? Why?

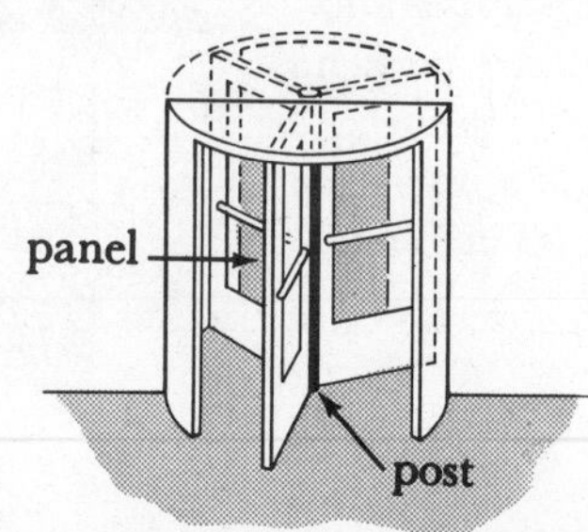

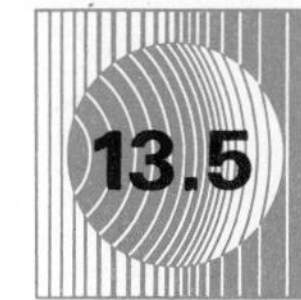

Transformations: Slides and Turns in Space

Recall that a slide in a plane can be described by its *magnitude* and *direction.* The same information is needed to describe a **slide in space.** In the diagram at the right, the heavy arrow gives both the magnitude and direction.

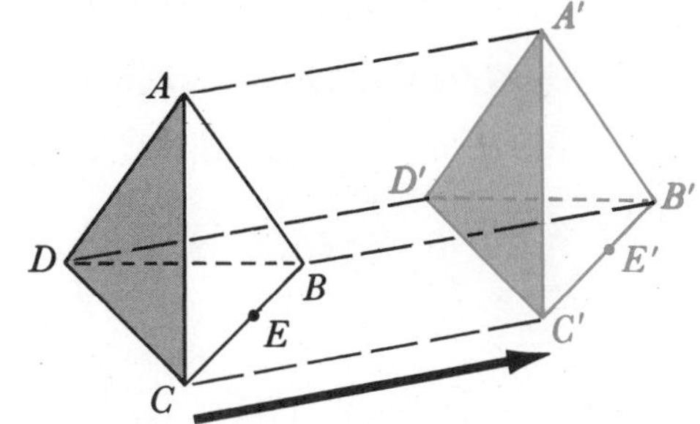

Like slides in a plane, slides in space preserve distance, collinearity, betweenness, and angle measure. Also, slides in space preserve coplanarity. Since A, B, E, and C are coplanar, their images A', B', E', and C' are coplanar.

In a plane, we turn a figure about a point. But in space, we turn a figure about a line, called the *axis of turn.* To describe a **turn in space,** we need an axis of turn and a magnitude. The magnitude is the measure of a dihedral angle such that one face contains points of the original figure, and the other face contains the images of those points.

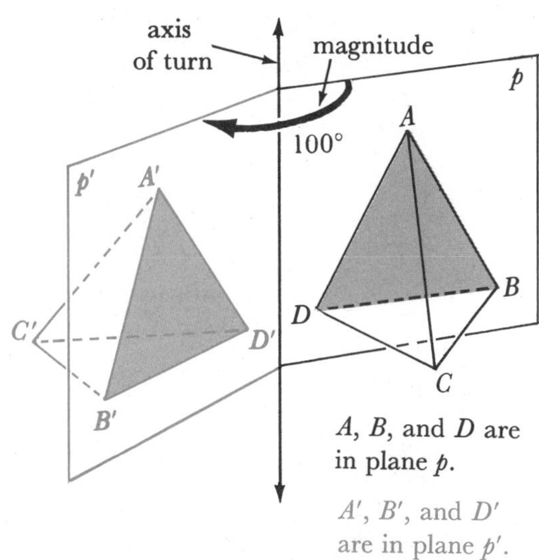

A, B, and D are in plane p.

A', B', and D' are in plane p'.

Turns in space preserve distance, collinearity, betweenness, angle measure, and coplanarity.

Exercises 13.5

Ⓐ **1–4.** Complete each statement.

1. An arrow can show the ______ and ______ of a slide in space.

2. The length of the arrow gives the ______ of the slide.

3. A turn in space is described by an ______ and a ______.

4. The ______ of a turn in space is the measure of a dihedral angle.

5–10. True or False? In space,

5. Slides preserve length.

6. Turns preserve length.

7. Turns change angle measure.

8. Slides change coplanarity.

9. Segments joining two points to their slide images are parallel.

10. If A' and B' are the turn images of A and B around axis $\overleftrightarrow{XY}$, then $\angle A\text{-}\overleftrightarrow{XY}\text{-}A' \cong \angle B\text{-}\overleftrightarrow{XY}\text{-}B'$.

Ⓑ 11–14. Tell if the model described is for a slide or a turn in space.

11. an elevator going up

12. the turning wheel of a windmill

13. a car turning a corner

14. a car riding on a level straight road

15. What is the direction of the slide in Exercise 11?

16. If an elevator goes up six floors, what is the magnitude of the slide (1 unit = 1 floor)?

17. What is the axis of turn for the turn in Exercise 12?

18. If a windmill wheel turns clockwise (as you look at it), what is the magnitude of a quarter turn?

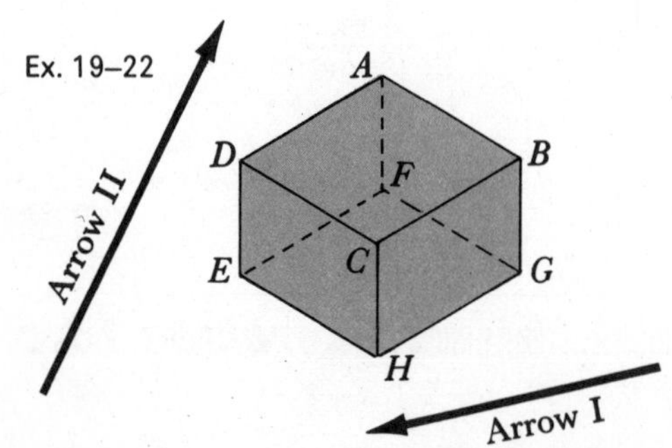

19–20. Copy and draw the image of a slide in space having the magnitude and direction given by

19. arrow I.

20. arrow II.

21–22. What is the axis of turn if the turn image of $BGHC$ is

21. $DEHC$?

22. $BGFA$?

Ⓒ 23. A slide in a plane is equivalent to successive reflections over parallel lines. (See Ex. 19–22, p. 159.) What would a slide in space be equivalent to?

24. A turn in a plane is equivalent to successive reflections over intersecting lines. (See Ex. 13–16, p. 414.) What would a turn in space be equivalent to? What would be its axis of turn?

■ Chapter 13 Review ■

1–7. Give a reason for each statement. (Use the figures.) 13.1

Ex. 1–3

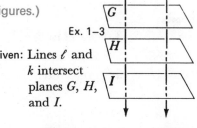

Given: Lines ℓ and k intersect planes G, H, and I.

1. If $G \parallel H$ and $\ell \perp G$, then $\ell \perp H$.

2. If $H \perp k$ and $I \perp k$, then $H \parallel I$.

3. If $G \parallel H$ and $H \parallel I$, then $G \parallel I$.

4. If $\overleftrightarrow{AB} \parallel \overleftrightarrow{CD}$ and $\overleftrightarrow{CD} \parallel \overleftrightarrow{EF}$, then $\overleftrightarrow{AB} \parallel \overleftrightarrow{EF}$. 13.2

5. If $\overleftrightarrow{CD} \parallel \overleftrightarrow{EF}$ and $p \perp \overleftrightarrow{CD}$, then $p \perp \overleftrightarrow{EF}$.

6. If $\overleftrightarrow{AB} \perp p$ and $\overleftrightarrow{CD} \perp p$, then $\overleftrightarrow{AB} \parallel \overleftrightarrow{CD}$.

7. If $p \parallel q$, $\overleftrightarrow{AB} \perp q$, and $\overleftrightarrow{CD} \perp q$, then $AB = CD$.

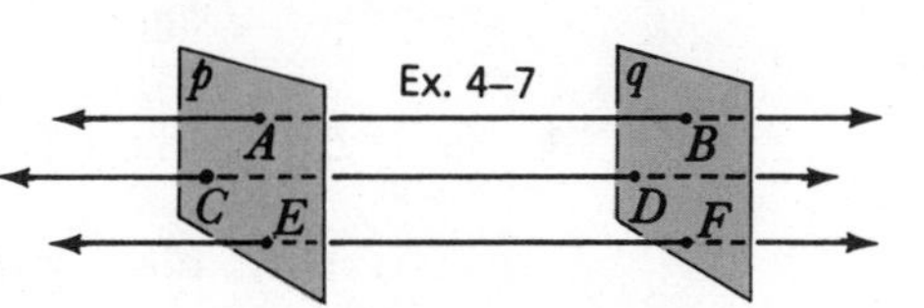

Given: $\overleftrightarrow{AB}$, $\overleftrightarrow{CD}$, and $\overleftrightarrow{EF}$ intersect planes p and q at pts. A, B, C, D, E, and F.

8–11. Complete each statement. (Use the figure.) 13.3

Given: Planes p and q intersect at $\overleftrightarrow{AB}$, $\overleftrightarrow{TU}$ is in p, $\overleftrightarrow{RS}$ is in q.

Ex. 8–11

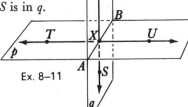

8. $\angle R\text{-}\overleftrightarrow{AB}\text{-}U$ is a _____ angle.

9. $\overleftrightarrow{AB}$ is the _____ of $\angle R\text{-}\overleftrightarrow{AB}\text{-}U$.

10. Point U is on a _____ of $\angle R\text{-}\overleftrightarrow{AB}\text{-}U$.

11. If $\angle RXU$ is a _____ angle of $\angle R\text{-}\overleftrightarrow{AB}\text{-}U$, then $m\angle R\text{-}\overleftrightarrow{AB}\text{-}U = m\angle RXU$.

12–15. Give a reason for each statement. (Use the figure.) 13.4

Given: Planes a and b intersect at $\overleftrightarrow{XY}$, $\overleftrightarrow{PQ}$ is in a, $\overleftrightarrow{RS}$ is in b.

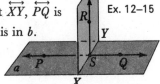

Ex. 12–15

12. If $a \perp b$, then $\angle R\text{-}\overleftrightarrow{XY}\text{-}P$ is a right dihedral angle.

13. If $\overleftrightarrow{RS} \perp a$, then $b \perp a$.

14. If $a \perp b$ and $\overleftrightarrow{PQ} \perp \overleftrightarrow{XY}$, then $\overleftrightarrow{PQ} \perp b$.

15. If $\angle Q\text{-}\overleftrightarrow{XY}\text{-}R$ is a right dihedral angle, then $a \perp b$.

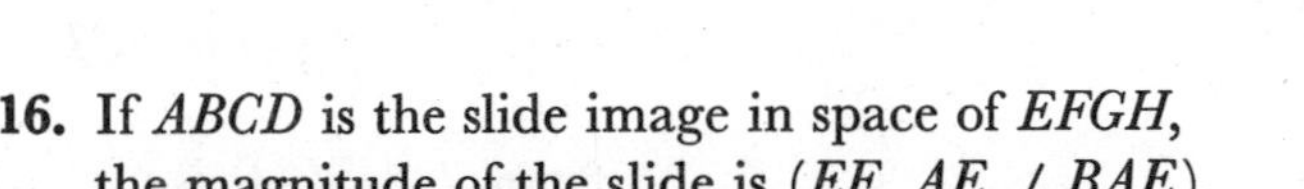

16. If $ABCD$ is the slide image in space of $EFGH$, the magnitude of the slide is (EF, AE, $\angle BAE$). 13.5

17. If $ABFE$ is the turn image in space of $CBFG$, the axis of turn is ($\angle ABC$, point B, $\overleftrightarrow{BF}$).

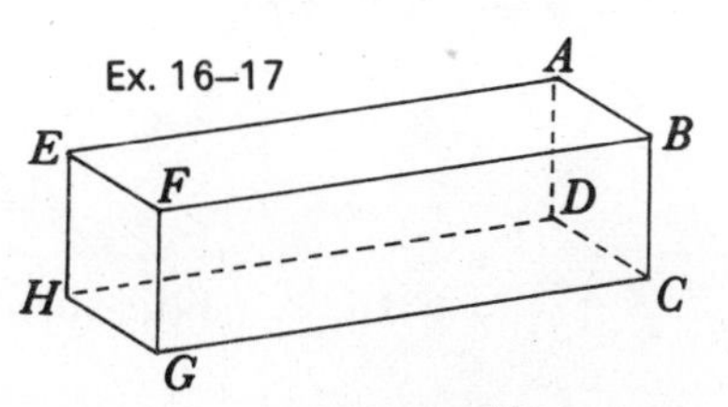

Chapter 13 Test

1–4. Write a definition for each term.

1. *parallel planes* **2.** *perpendicular planes*

3. *dihedral angle* **4.** *plane angle*

5. Name three dihedral angles.

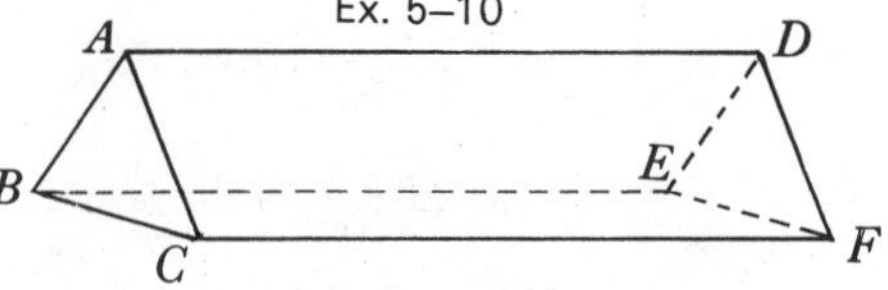

6–10 Give a reason for each statement. (Use figure at right.)

6. If $\overline{BE} \perp$ plane DEF, then $\angle DEF$ is a plane angle of $\angle A\text{-}\overleftrightarrow{BE}\text{-}F$.

7. If $\overline{AD} \perp$ plane ABC and $\overline{AD} \perp$ plane DEF, then plane $ABC \parallel$ plane DEF.

8. If $BA \perp$ plane ACF, then plane $ABC \perp$ plane ACF.

9. If $\overline{BE} \perp$ plane DEF and $\overline{CF} \perp$ plane DEF, then $\overline{BE} \parallel \overline{CF}$.

10. If $\overline{AD} \parallel \overline{CF}$ and $\overline{CF} \parallel \overline{BE}$, then $\overline{AD} \parallel \overline{BE}$.

11–13. True or False? Draw a sketch to illustrate each true statement. Sketch a counterexample for each false statement.

11. If two lines are parallel to the same plane, then they are parallel to each other.

12. If a plane is perpendicular to the edge of a dihedral angle, then it is perpendicular to each face of the dihedral angle.

13. If two planes are perpendicular to the same plane, then they are parallel.

14. Given: $\overline{AD} \perp \overline{AB}$, $\overline{AD} \perp \overline{AC}$, $\overline{AD} \perp$ plane DEF.

Prove: Plane $ABC \parallel$ plane DEF.

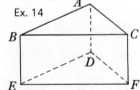

Ex. 14

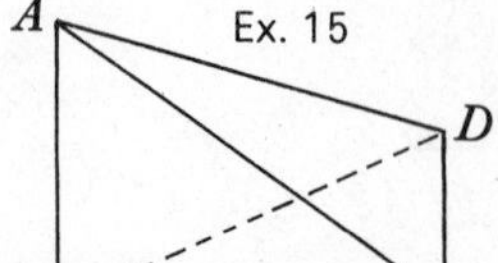

15. Given: $\overline{AB} \perp$ plane BCD.

Prove: $\angle A\text{-}\overleftrightarrow{BC}\text{-}D$ is a right dihedral angle.

16. A (slide, turn) in space is done about an axis of (slide, turn).

14 SOLIDS

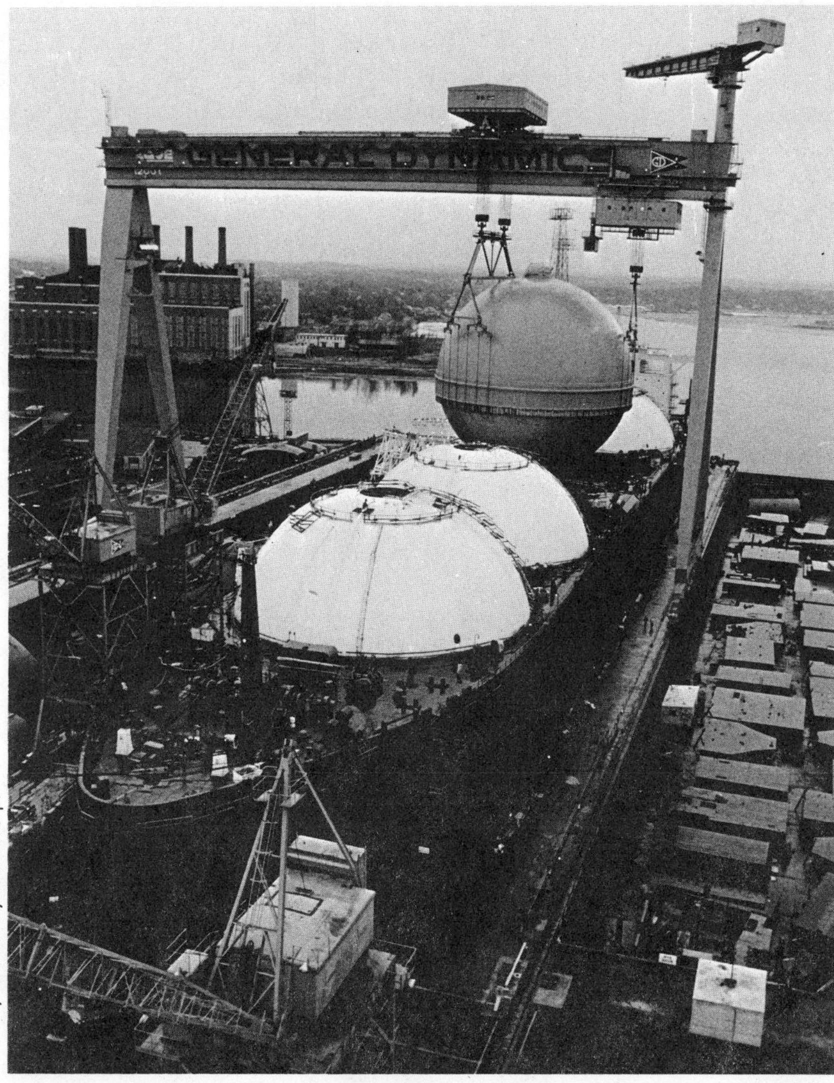

Courtesy General Dynamics Corp.

A **solid figure,** or **solid,** cannot be contained in a plane since it has three dimensions. There are two common ways to think of a solid:

1. as a surface, or shell, that encloses a part of space (*models:* an empty box and a Ping-Pong ball)

2. as the figure formed by a surface **and** the part of space that it encloses (*models:* a brick and a pool ball)

We think of a solid in the first way when we consider the area of the surface. And we use the second way when we consider its volume—the measure of the amount of space it encloses.

14.1 Polyhedrons

In a plane, a polygon is formed by joining segments at their endpoints. A polygon and its interior form a polygonal region. The 3-dimensional counterpart of a polygon is a *polyhedron.*

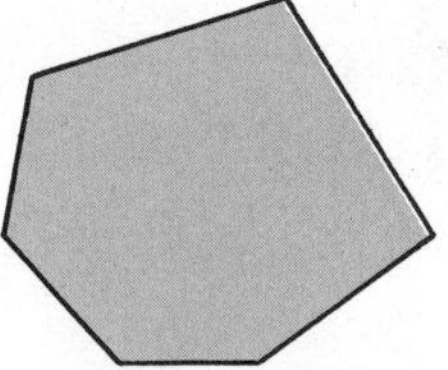

POLYGONAL REGION

POLYHEDRONS

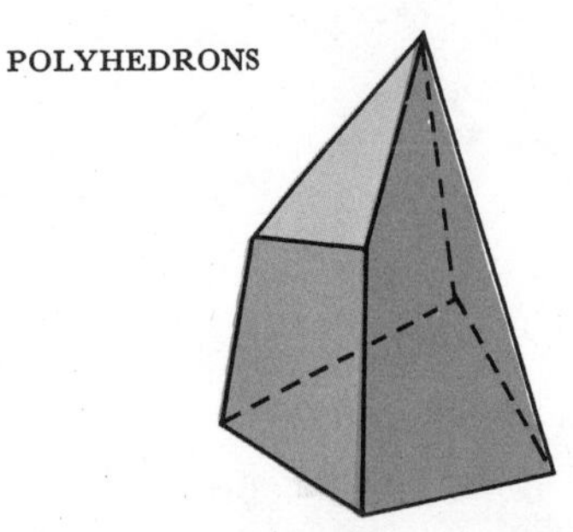

A **polyhedron** is formed by joining polygonal regions (called *faces*) at their sides (called *edges*). The faces intersect at the edges only, with each face intersecting exactly one other face at each edge. The vertices of the polygons bounding the faces are the *vertices* of the polyhedron.

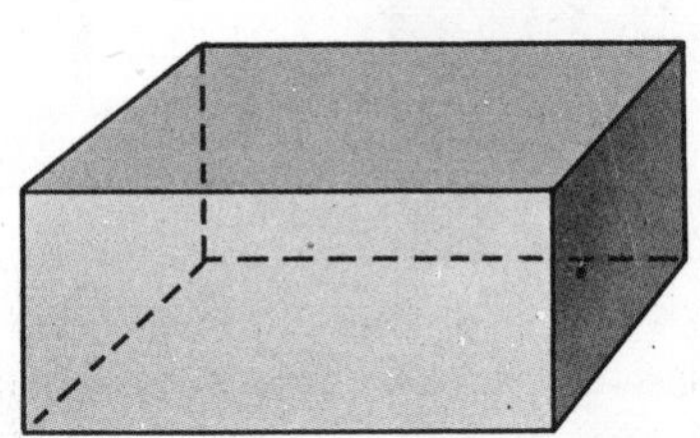

Just as a polygon separates a plane into two parts, a polyhedron separates space into two parts—the *exterior* and the *interior* of the polyhedron. If its interior is a convex set, then the polyhedron is *convex.* We will discuss only convex polyhedrons.

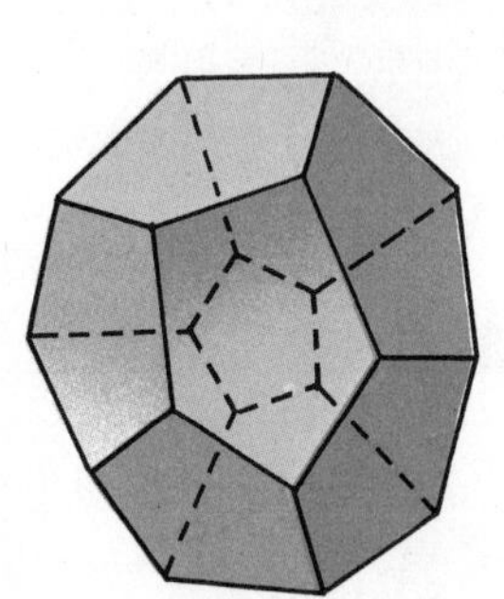

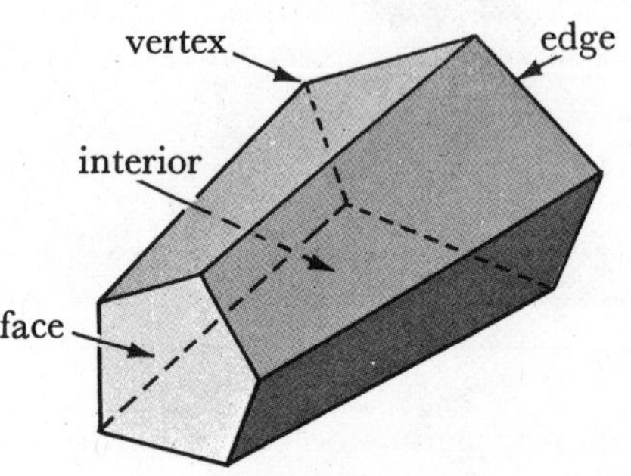

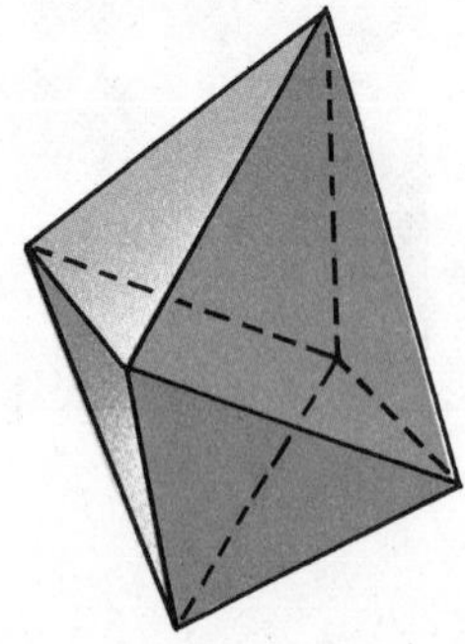

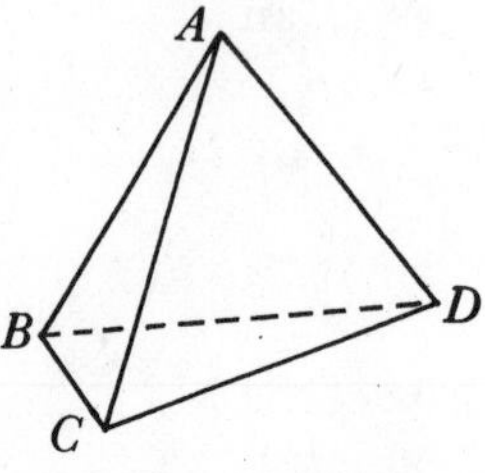

Since each face of a polyhedron is in a plane, a polyhedron is often described as a solid figure bounded by planes. Each of its edges is in the intersection of two planes, which means that each edge of the solid is in the edge of a *dihedral angle.* Two faces with a common edge determine a dihedral angle of the polyhedron. In the figure, one dihedral angle is $\angle B\text{-}\overleftrightarrow{AC}\text{-}D$.

Exercises 14.1

Ⓐ **1.** The 3-dimensional counterpart of a polygon is a ______.

2. Each ______ of a polyhedron is a polygonal region.

3. A polyhedron separates space into ______ parts.

4. A polyhedron is convex if its ______ is a convex set.

5. A polyhedron is a solid figure bounded by ______.

6. Two faces with a common edge determine a ______ of a polyhedron.

Ⓑ **7–12.** Name the following for the given solid:

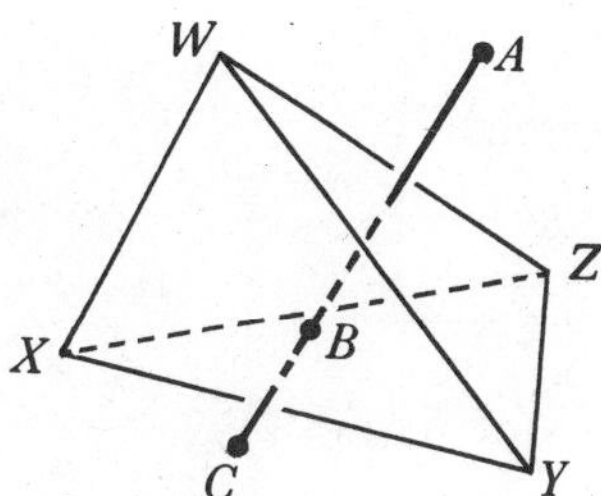

7. vertices

8. edges

9. an interior point

10. an exterior point

11. dihedral angles

12. number of faces

13–16. Is each polyhedron convex or not?

13.

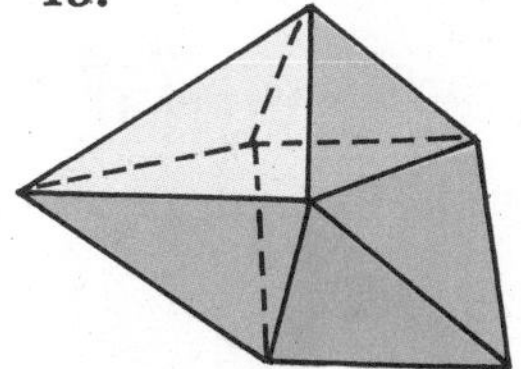

14.

15.

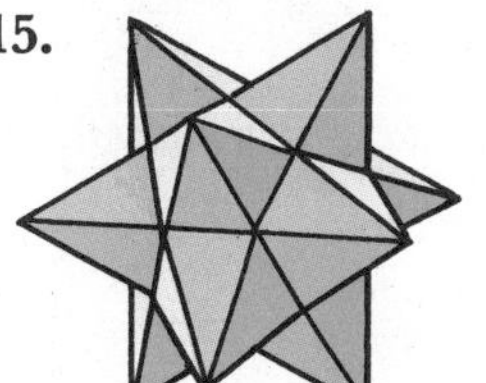

16.

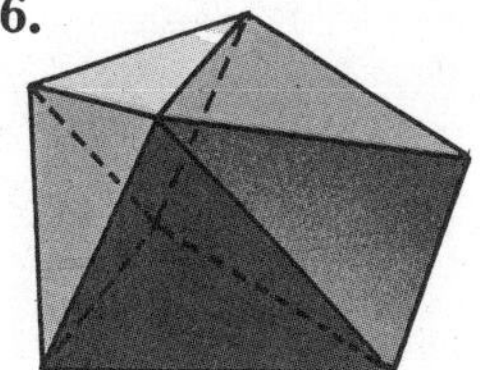

17–20. Find the number of (**a**) vertices, (**b**) faces, (**c**) edges, and (**d**) dihedral angles of each polyhedron.

17.

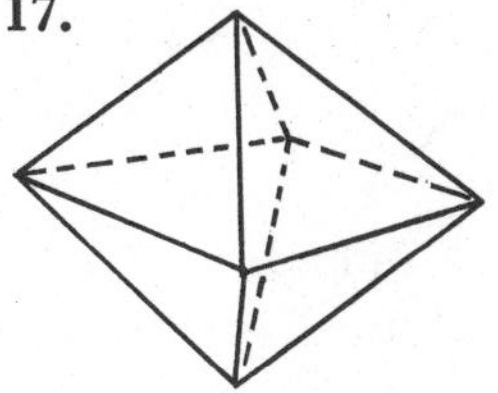

18.

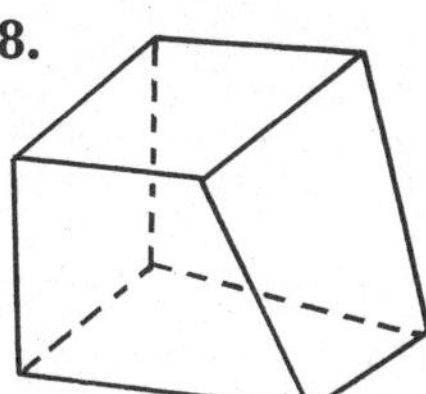

19.

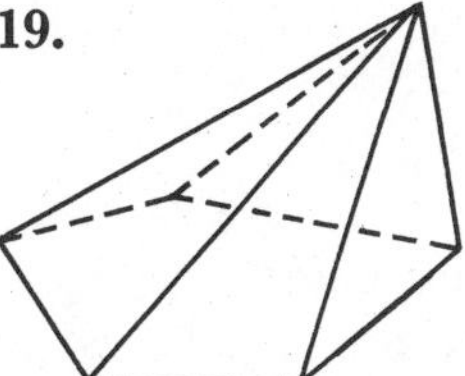

20.

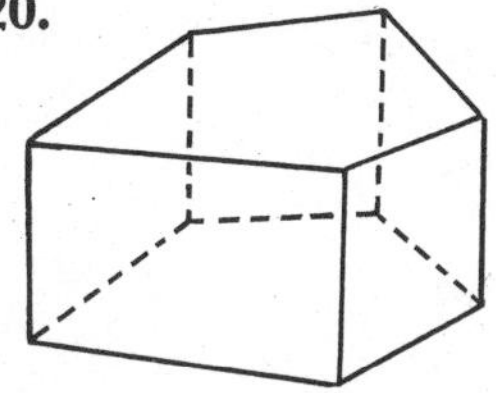

Ⓒ **21.** The least number of sides a polygon can have is three. What is the least number of faces a polyhedron can have? Sketch the solid.

22. Sketch a solid that has six faces, all triangular regions.

23. Sketch a solid that has six faces, all square regions.

14.2 Right Prisms

A **right prism** (see figure below) has two faces bounded by congruent convex polygons in parallel planes and all other faces bounded by rectangles. The faces in the parallel planes are called *bases*, and the rectangular faces are called *lateral faces*. The edges of the lateral faces that are not also edges of a base are called *lateral edges*.

An *altitude* of a right prism is any perpendicular segment from the plane of one base to the plane of the other. Therefore, all altitudes are congruent. The *height* of a right prism is the length of an altitude.

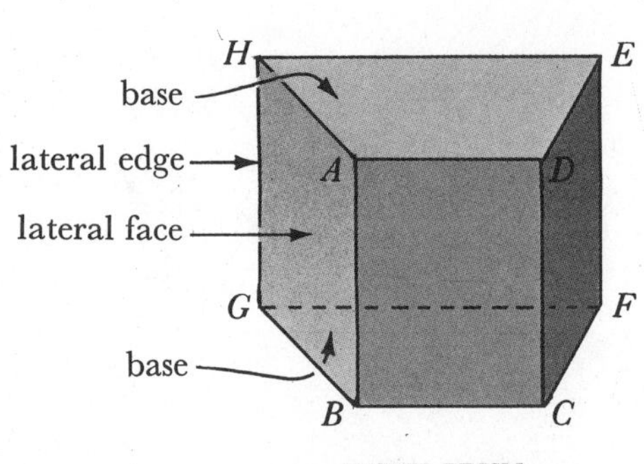

RIGHT PRISM

In the figure, $\overline{AB}$ is a side of rectangles $ABCD$ and $ABGH$. So $\overline{AB}$ is perpendicular to $\overline{BC}$ and $\overline{BG}$ and to the plane containing base $BCFG$. Similarly, $\overline{AB}$ is perpendicular to the plane containing the other base. Therefore, $\overline{AB}$ is an altitude of the prism. In fact, all lateral edges of a right prism are altitudes, and the length of any one of them is the height.

A prism is classified by the number of sides each base has. For example,

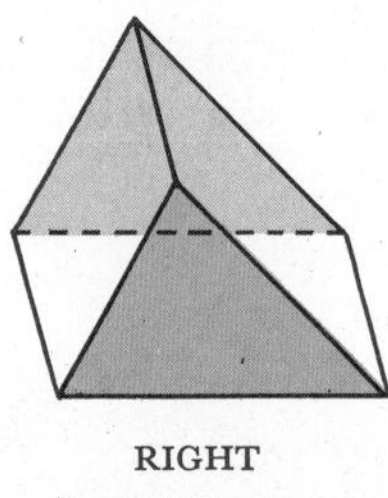
RIGHT TRIANGULAR PRISM

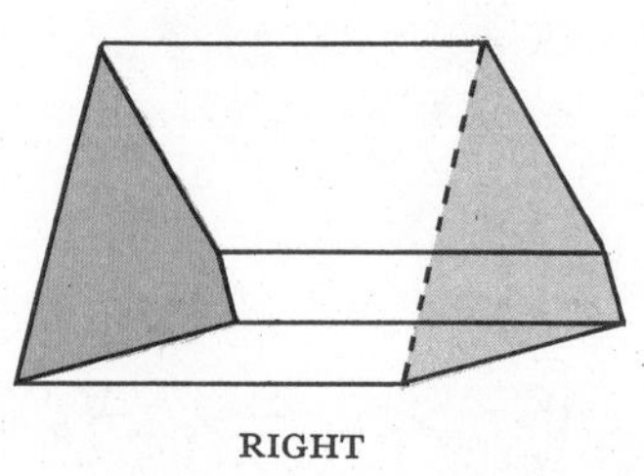
RIGHT QUADRANGULAR PRISM

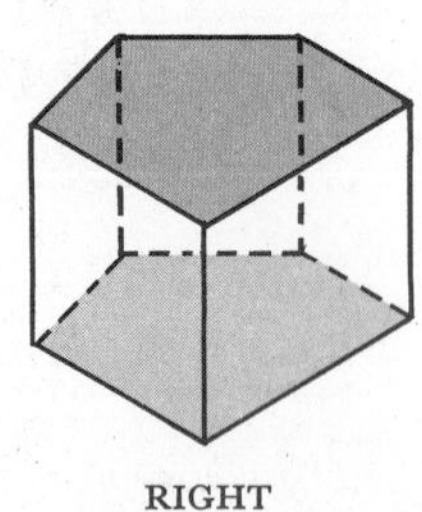
RIGHT PENTAGONAL PRISM

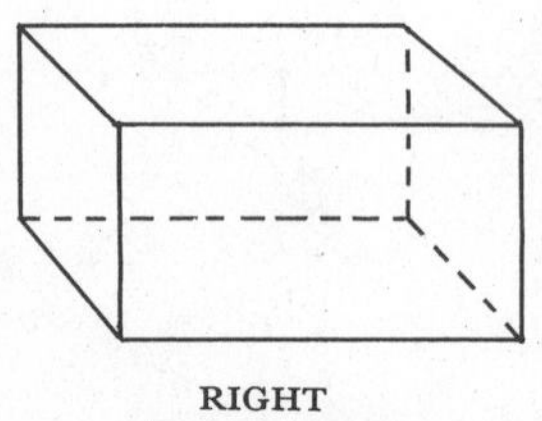
RIGHT RECTANGULAR PRISM

The bases of a **right rectangular prism** are bounded by rectangles, and any of its faces could be called a base. Cardboard boxes, bricks, and many buildings have shapes the same as right rectangular prisms. A **cube** is a right rectangular prism whose edges are all congruent (all faces are bounded by squares).

Volume is the measure of the amount of space taken up by a solid, just as area is the measure of the amount of surface covered by a polygonal region.

Volume Postulate

> For every solid, there is a unique positive number, called the volume of the solid.

To measure the volume of a solid, we must have a unit of volume. The most convenient unit is the *cubic unit.* For example, if we measure distance in centimeters and area in square centimeters, then we measure volume in cubic centimeters. NOTE: cm^3 means cubic centimeters, m^3 means cubic meters, and so on.

1 unit of length

1 square unit of area

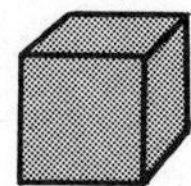
1 cubic unit of volume

Suppose a right rectangular prism has dimensions (length and width of its base and its height) that are 5 cm, 3 cm, and 4 cm.

Notice that the number of cubic centimeters needed to "cover" the base is $5 \cdot 3$, and it would take 4 such layers to "fill" the prism. So, its volume is

$$(5 \cdot 3) \cdot 4 = 60 \text{ cm}^3$$

We state this as a postulate.

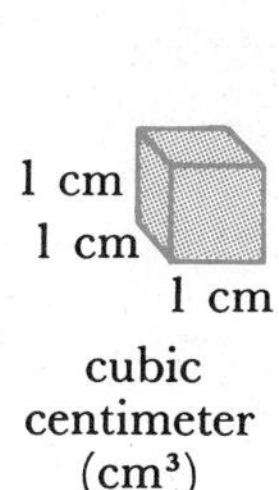

cubic centimeter (cm^3)

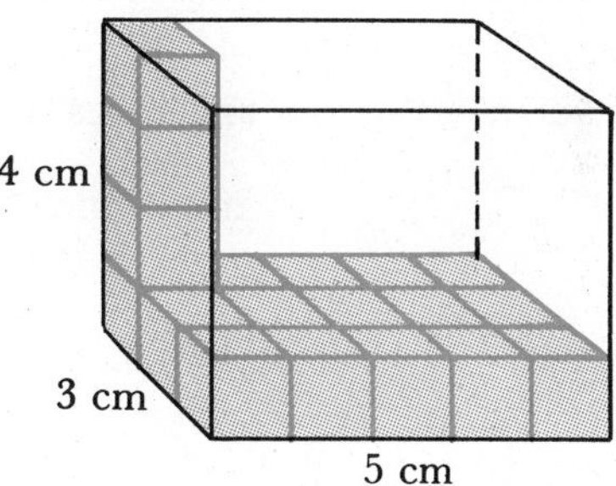

Volume Postulate for a Rectangular Prism

> The volume (V) of a right rectangular prism is equal to the area (B) of its base times its height (h).
>
> $$V = Bh$$

Example 1: Find the volume of the right rectangular prism with the given dimensions.

a. length = 3.7 m, width = 2.1 m, height = 4 m

$V = Bh$

$= (3.7 \cdot 2.1) \cdot 4$

$= 7.77 \cdot 4 = 31.08 \text{ m}^3$

b. $\ell = 4$ cm, $w = 2$ cm, $h = 52$ mm

$V = Bh$

$= (4 \cdot 2) \cdot 5.2$ ◀ 52 mm = 5.2 cm

$= 41.6 \text{ cm}^3$

Example 2: A right rectangular prism has a volume of 600 cm^3 and a height of 3 cm. Find its base area.

$V = Bh \qquad 600 = B \cdot 3 \qquad B = 200 \text{ cm}^2$

Exercises 14.2

Ⓐ 1–6. Refer to the given figure.

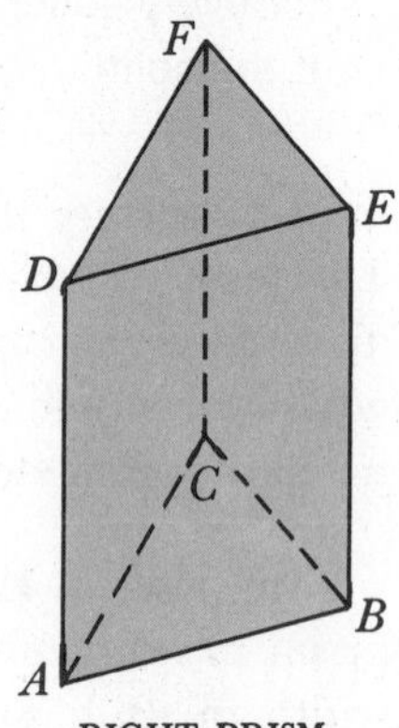

RIGHT PRISM

1. The solid is a right ______ prism.

2. Regions ______ and ______ are bases.

3. Region $BCFE$ is a ______ of the prism.

4. ______, ______, and ______ are lateral edges.

5. Lateral edges are also ______ of the prism.

6. BE is the ______ of the prism.

7–10. True or False?

7. The bases of a right prism are always bounded by rectangles.

8. Any perpendicular segment from the plane of one base of a right prism to the plane of the other is a lateral edge.

9. Any face of a right rectangular prism can be a base.

10. All faces of a cube are triangular regions.

Ⓑ 11–14. Find the volume of a cube whose edges have the given length.

11. 5.1 cm **12.** 2.5 cm **13.** e m **14.** e units

15–20. Find the volume of a right rectangular prism with the given dimensions.

15. 1.3 cm, 1.3 cm, 4 cm **16.** 10 m, 3 m, 1 m

17. 5 cm, 15 mm, 12 mm **18.** 8 cm, 25 mm, 4.5 cm

19. ℓ mm, w mm, h mm **20.** ℓ units, w units, h units

21–26. Find the following if V = volume, B = base area, and h = height of a right rectangular prism:

21. V, if $B = 16\text{ cm}^2$, $h = 8$ cm **22.** V, if $B = 3.6\text{ cm}^2$, $h = 7$ cm

23. B, if $V = 24\text{ m}^3$, $h = 6$ m **24.** B, if $V = 85\text{ mm}^3$, $h = 5$ mm

25. h, if $V = 144\text{ cm}^3$, $B = 9\text{ cm}^2$ **26.** h, if $V = 96\text{ m}^3$, $B = 2\text{ m}^2$

27–28. Find the volume of each right rectangular prism.

27.

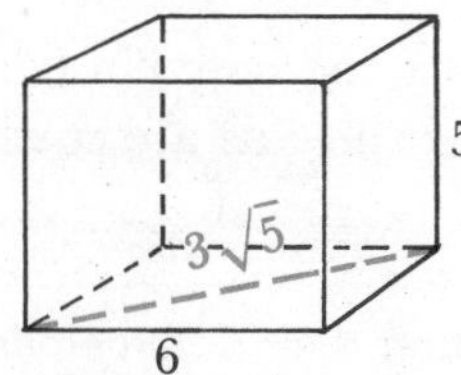

28.

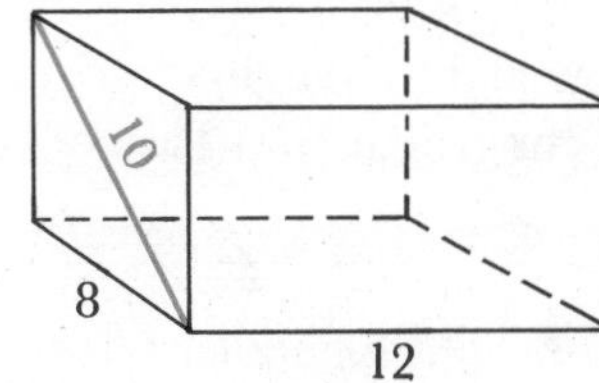

29. How many cubic centimeters are there in one cubic meter?

30. How many cubic millimeters are there in one cubic centimeter?

31–32. Determine what happens to the volume of a cube when

31. The edge is doubled.

32. The edge is halved.

© **33.** Find the volume of the cube.

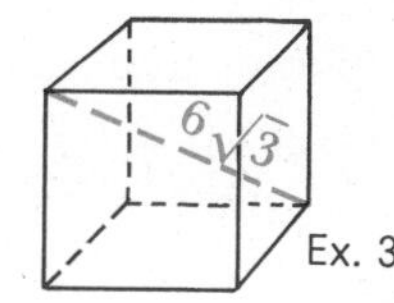

Ex. 33

Ex. 34

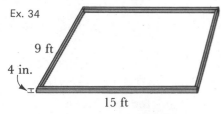

9 ft

4 in.

15 ft

34. How many cubic feet of concrete are needed to fill the rectangular form for a patio?

35. When the rock was put into the rectangular fish tank, the level of the water rose 1.25 cm. What is the volume of the rock?

Ex. 35

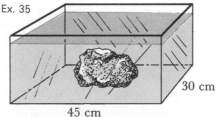

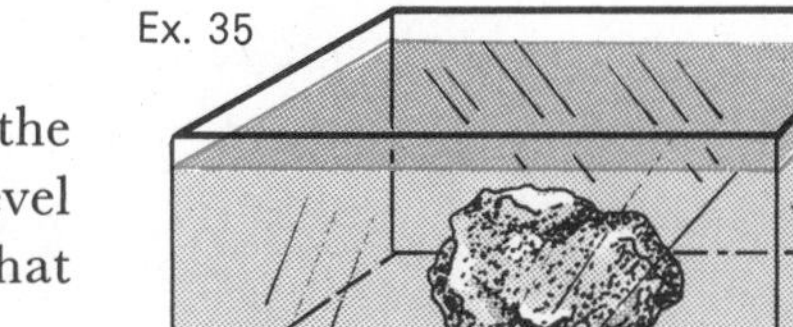

36. During a 1.5-cm rainfall, how many liters of water fell on a lawn that is 22 m long and 16 m wide? (1 liter = 1000 cm^3)

37. At the right is a pattern for a model of a right prism whose base is bounded by a trapezoid. Make a larger pattern like this one. Then make the model.

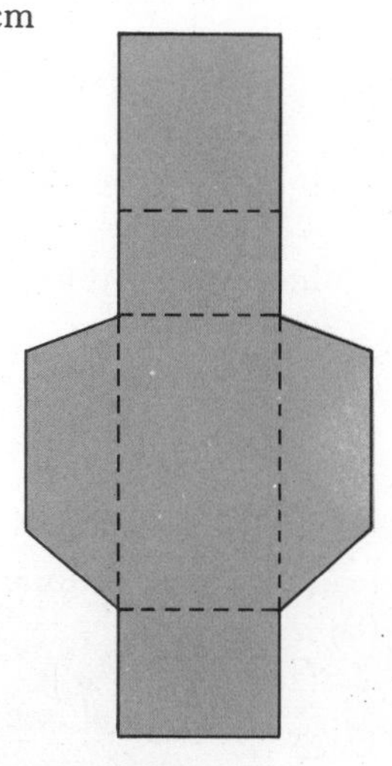

38. Make a pattern for a model of a cube whose edges are 5 cm long. Then make the model.

39. Make a pattern for a model of a right triangular prism whose base edges are all 5 cm long and whose height is 10 cm. Make the model.

More About Right Prisms

Two right triangular prisms are **congruent** if and only if a base of one is congruent to a base of the other, and their heights are equal.

Volume Postulate for Congruent Right Triangular Prisms

If two right triangular prisms are congruent, then their volumes are equal.

Volume Addition Postulate

If two solids with no common interior points form a third solid, then its volume is the sum of the volumes of the two solids.

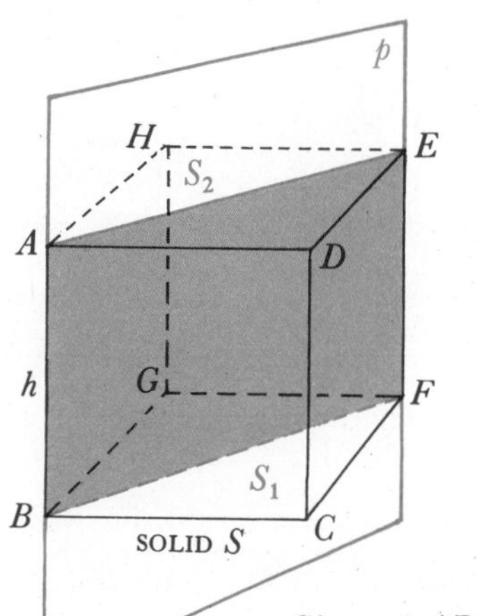

In the figure, solid S is a right rectangular prism. Therefore, its lateral edges are perpendicular to the same plane, and they are parallel. So $\overline{AB} \parallel \overline{EF}$, and both are in plane p. Plane p separates S into solids S_1 and S_2, which we can show are congruent right triangular prisms.

Since $\overline{AB} \parallel \overline{EF}$ and $\overline{AB} \cong \overline{EF}$, $ABFE$ is a parallelogram. $\overline{AB} \perp \overline{BF}$ (why?), so $ABFE$ is a rectangle. By the definition of a right prism, $ABCD$ and $DCFE$ are also rectangles. Therefore, $\overline{AE} \cong \overline{BF}$, $\overline{AD} \cong \overline{BC}$, and $\overline{DE} \cong \overline{CF}$, giving us $\triangle ADE \cong \triangle BCF$ by the SSS Postulate.

Since $\triangle ADE$ and $\triangle BCF$ are in parallel planes (why?), S_1 is a right triangular prism. S_2 is a right triangular prism by the same reasoning. S_1 and S_2 are congruent because AB, or h, is the height of both, and their bases, $\triangle BCF$ and $\triangle FGB$, are congruent ($\overline{BF}$ is a diagonal of rectangle $BCFG$). Now we can find the volume of S_1.

$\text{volume } S_1 + \text{volume } S_2 = \text{volume } S$	Volume Addition Post.
$\text{volume } S_1 + \text{volume } S_1 = \text{volume } S$	Vol. Post. for ≅ Rt. Triangular Prisms (Substitute vol. S_1 for vol. S_2.)
$2(\text{volume } S_1) = \text{volume } S$	Addition
$\text{volume } S_1 = \frac{1}{2}(\text{volume } S)$	Multiply both sides by $\frac{1}{2}$.
$\text{volume } S_1 = \frac{1}{2}(\text{area } \square BCFG)h$	Vol. Post. for Rectangular Prism
$\text{volume } S_1 = \frac{1}{2}(\text{area } \triangle BCF + \text{area } \triangle FGB)h$	Area Addition Post.
$\text{volume } S_1 = \frac{1}{2}(\text{area } \triangle BCF + \text{area } \triangle BCF)h$	Area of ≅ △s Post.
$\text{volume } S_1 = (\text{area } \triangle BCF)h$	Addition and multiplication

The volume of S_1 is equal to the area of its base times its height. In fact,

The volume (V) of any right triangular prism is equal to the area (B) of its base times its height (h).

$$V = Bh$$

Volume Theorem for a Right Triangular Prism

A convex polygon can be separated into triangles by drawing segments from one vertex to each nonconsecutive vertex. All planes that contain the same lateral edge and one other nonconsecutive lateral edge of a right prism separate the prism into right triangular prisms.

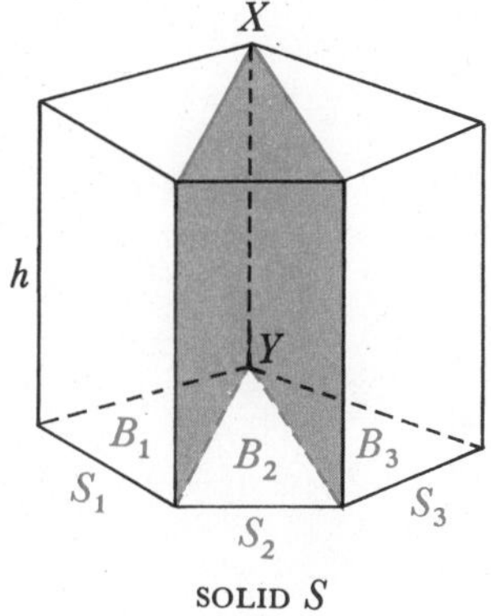

SOLID S

In the figure, right prism S with height h and base area B has been separated into right triangular prisms S_1, S_2, and S_3 whose base areas are B_1, B_2, and B_3. So,

volume S = volume S_1 + volume S_2 + volume S_3	Volume Addition Post.
$= B_1h + B_2h + B_3h$	Vol. Thm. for Rt. Triangular Prism
$= (B_1 + B_2 + B_3)h$	Distributive Property
$= Bh$	Area Addition Post.

Since a right prism with any number of base edges can be separated into right triangular prisms, we can state the next theorem.

The volume (V) of any right prism is equal to the area (B) of its base times its height (h).

$$V = Bh$$

Volume Theorem for a Right Prism

Exercises 14.3

Ⓐ **1–6.** True or False?

1. All lateral edges of a right prism are parallel.

2. All lateral edges of a right prism do not necessarily have equal lengths.

3. Right triangular prisms are congruent if their heights are equal and their bases are congruent.

4. Right triangular prisms are congruent if they have equal volumes.

5. Any right rectangular prism can be separated into two triangular prisms.

6. The volume of a right hexagonal prism is equal to the area of its base times its height.

Ⓑ **7–16.** Find the volume of each right prism.

7.

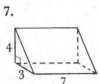

8.

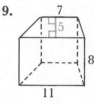

9.

10.

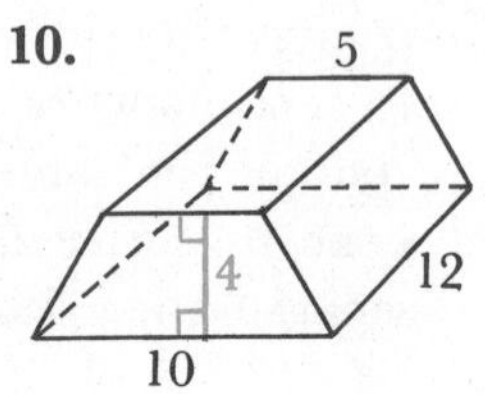

11. BASE: right triangle with legs of 5 cm and 7 cm; HEIGHT: 3.2 cm

12. BASE: isosceles right triangle with hypotenuse of $16\sqrt{2}$ mm; HEIGHT: 8.4 mm

13. BASE: parallelogram with base of 5 m and corresponding height of 5.6 m; HEIGHT: 3 m

14. BASE: rhombus with diagonals of 11.5 cm and 9.6 cm; HEIGHT: 15 cm

15. BASE: trapezoid with bases of 6 cm and 10 cm and height of 11 cm; HEIGHT: 75 mm

16. BASE: trapezoid with bases of 13.7 mm and 18.3 mm and height of 10 mm; HEIGHT: 2.5 cm

Ⓒ 17. The base of a right hexagonal prism is bounded by a regular hexagon with sides of length 6. If the prism has height 7, what is its volume?

18. Find the volume of the building.

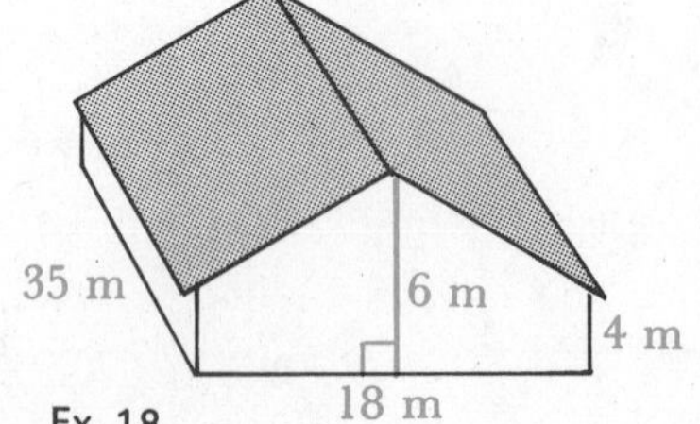

Ex. 18

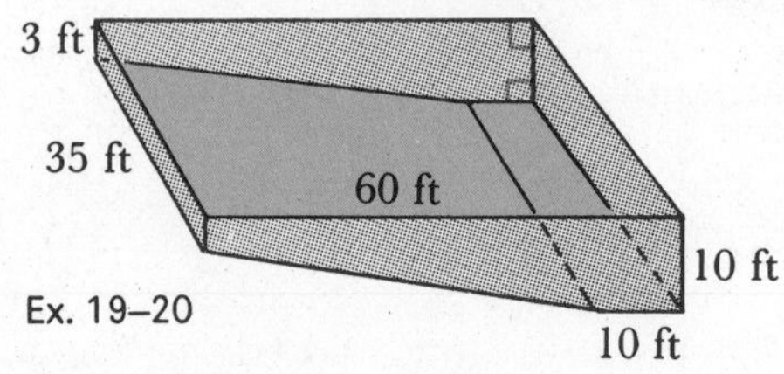

Ex. 19–20

19. How many cubic yards of dirt were removed when the swimming pool was built?

20. How many gallons of water will it take to fill the pool in Ex. 19? ($1 \text{ ft}^3 = 7\frac{1}{2}$ gallons)

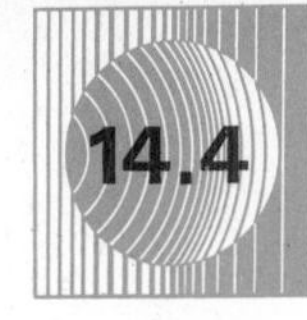

Right Circular Cylinders

A **right circular cylinder** (see figure below) has two bases that are congruent circular regions in parallel planes. The segment joining the centers of the bases, called the *axis*, is perpendicular to the planes of the bases. The *lateral surface* of the cylinder is formed by all segments that are parallel to the axis and have one endpoint on each circle bounding the bases.

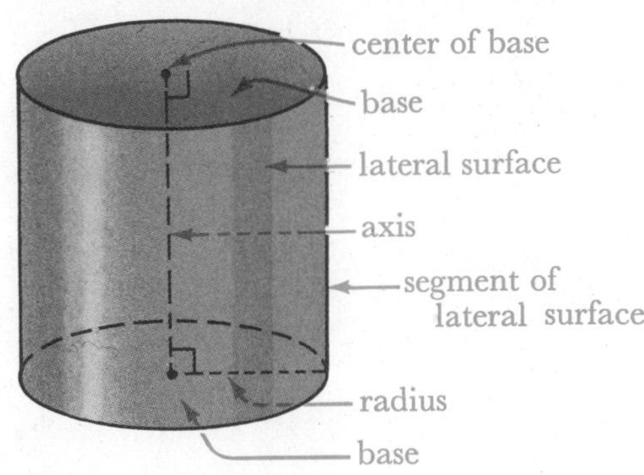

An *altitude* is any perpendicular segment from the plane of one base to the plane of the other. (The axis and all segments of the lateral surface are altitudes. Why?) The *height* is the length of an altitude. The radius of a base is the *radius* of the cylinder. Tin cans and many other containers are models of cylinders.

A right prism is *inscribed* in a right circular cylinder if the bases of the prism are inscribed in the bases of the cylinder. We can use inscribed **regular prisms** (right prisms whose bases are regular polygonal regions) to estimate the volume of a cylinder.

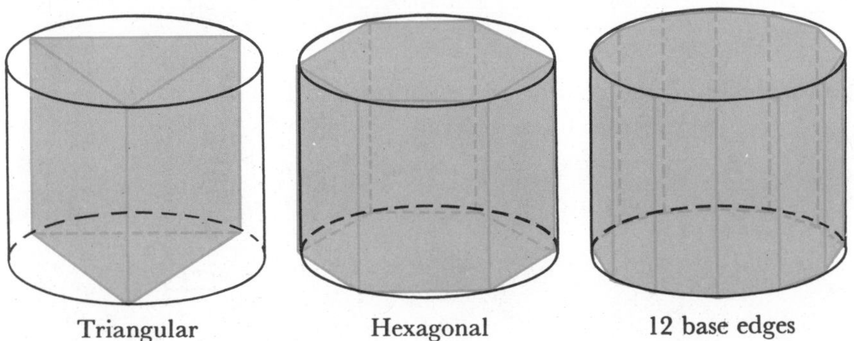

We can see that the volume of the regular triangular prism is less than the volume of the cylinder. If the number of base edges of the prism is doubled to obtain a regular hexagonal prism, its volume will be greater than the volume of the triangular prism but still less than the volume of the cylinder.

If we continue the process of doubling the base edges to obtain regular prisms, the volume of each new prism will be closer to the actual volume of the cylinder. Even the shape of the prism with many base edges is very close to the shape of the cylinder.

The process of increasing the number of base edges of the inscribed regular prisms is the 3-dimensional counterpart of the method used for finding the area of a circular region. (See Section 12.3.) And, just as the area of a circular region is the limit of the areas of its inscribed regular polygonal regions, the volume of the cylinder is the limit of the volumes of its inscribed regular prisms.

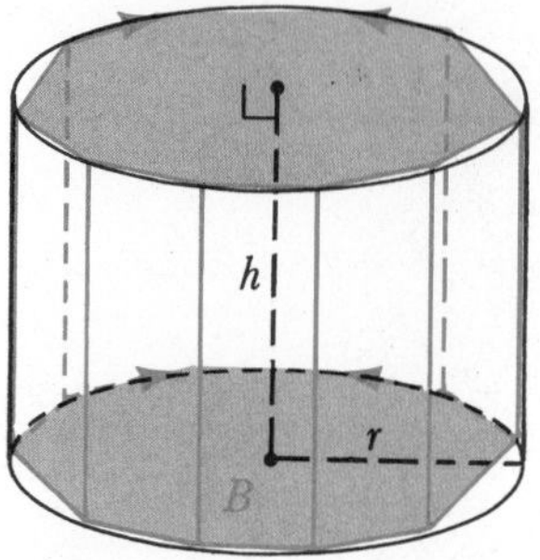

Cylinder and Inscribed Regular Prism (with many base edges)

For a right circular cylinder with height h and radius r,

$$\text{volume cylinder} = \text{limit } Bh$$

where h is the height and B is the base area of its inscribed prisms. Since the limit of B is the area of the base of the cylinder, limit $Bh = \pi r^2 h$. So,

$$\text{volume cylinder} = \pi r^2 h$$

Volume Theorem for a Right Circular Cylinder

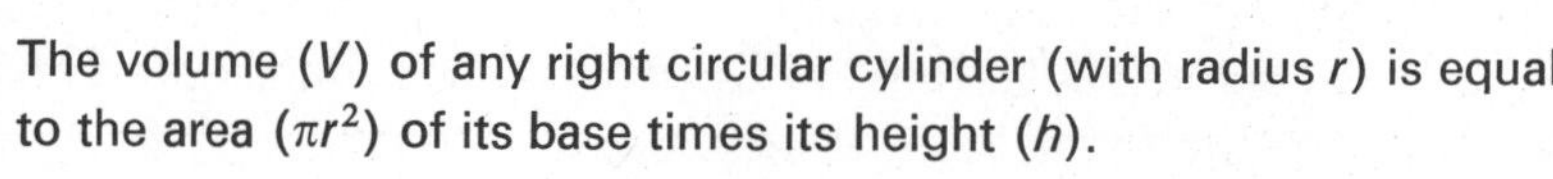
The volume (V) of any right circular cylinder (with radius r) is equal to the area (πr^2) of its base times its height (h).

$$V = \pi r^2 h$$

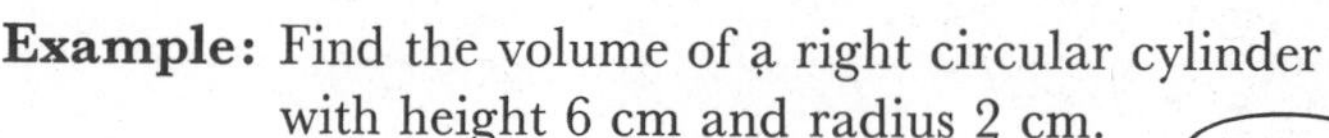
Example: Find the volume of a right circular cylinder with height 6 cm and radius 2 cm.

$$\begin{aligned} V &= \pi r^2 h \\ &= \pi(2^2)(6) \\ &= 24\pi \text{ cm}^3 \end{aligned}$$

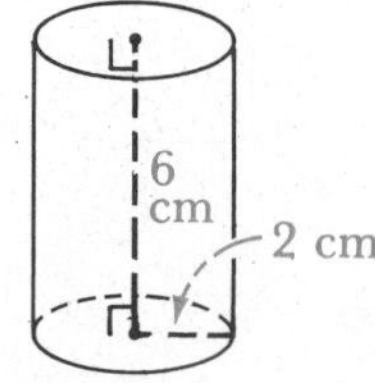

Exercises 14.4

NOTE: Leave answers in terms of π unless told otherwise.

Ⓐ **1.** If point A is the center of one base of a right circular cylinder and point B is the center of the other base, then $\overline{AB}$ is the ______.

2. The bases of a right circular cylinder are in ______ planes.

3. A segment of the lateral surface of a right circular cylinder is ______ to the axis.

4. The formula for the volume of a cylinder is ______.

5–10. True or False? Use the given figure.

5. $\overline{CD}$ is an altitude.

6. $\overline{AD}$ is a radius.

7. $AB = CE$

8. height $= BC$

9. $\overline{BC} \parallel \overline{AD}$

10. $\overline{AB} \perp \overline{BC}$

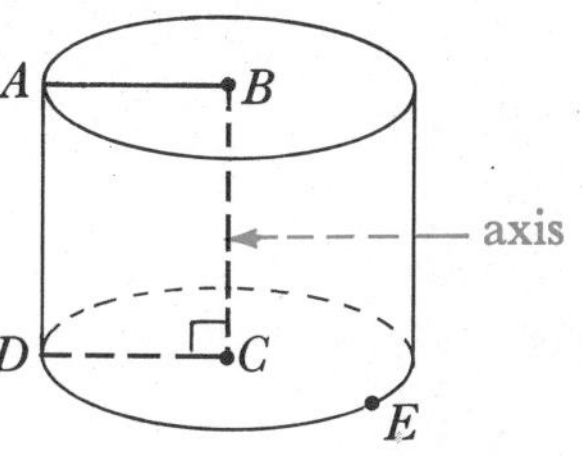

RIGHT CIRCULAR CYLINDER

Ⓑ **11–16.** Copy and complete the table for a right circular cylinder.

	Radius	Height	Volume
11.	5 cm	12 cm	?
12.	10 mm	45 mm	?
13.	2.5 m	?	50π m^3
14.	1.2 mm	?	36π mm^3
15.	?	4 cm	196π cm^3
16.	?	8 mm	968π mm^3

Courtesy Renaissance Center Partnership

17–20. Find the volume of each right circular cylinder.

17. a cylinder of height 8 whose base has a circumference of 6π

18. a cylinder of height 3 whose base has a circumference of 8π

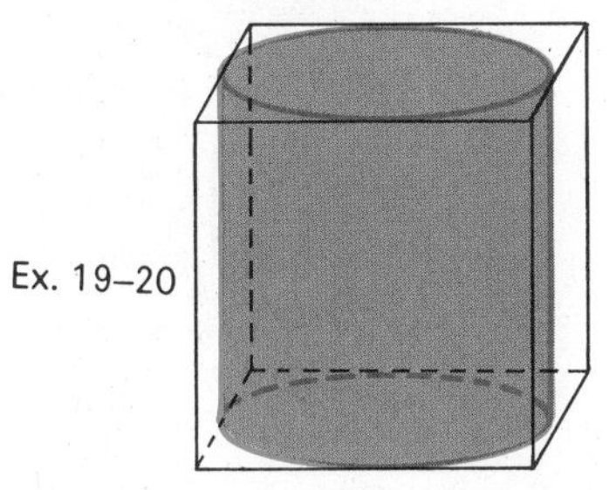
Ex. 19–20

19. a cylinder inscribed in a cube whose edge has a length of 7

20. a cylinder inscribed in a cube whose edge has a length of 9

21. The "wheels" of cheese are right circular cylinders. Which wheel has more cheese?

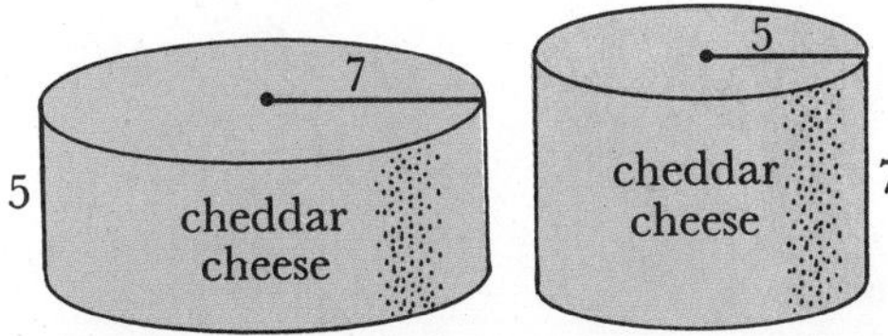

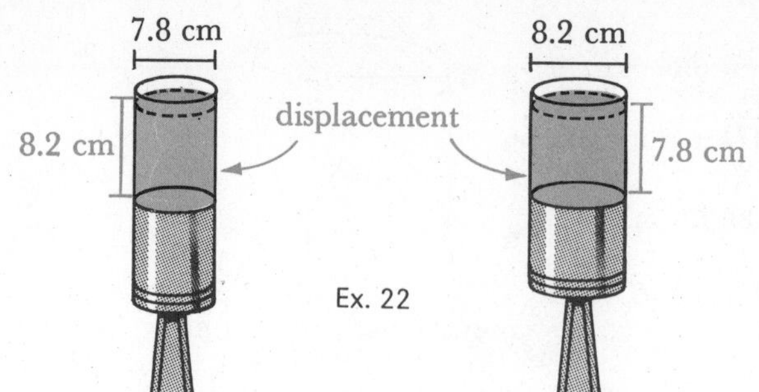

22. The cylindrical pistons in an automobile engine move up and down, displacing a certain volume. Which piston has the greater displacement?

23. How many cm³ of copper are there in 20 m of copper wire that is 1.5 mm in diameter? Use $\pi = 3.14$.

24. How many cm³ of water are used if a center-pivot irrigation system with radius 92 m covers the ground with 1.2 cm of water? Use $\pi = 3.14$. (See p. 418 and Ex. 17, p. 431.)

Ⓒ 25. Containers A and B are cylindrical. If container A holds 1 gallon, how many gallons would container B hold?

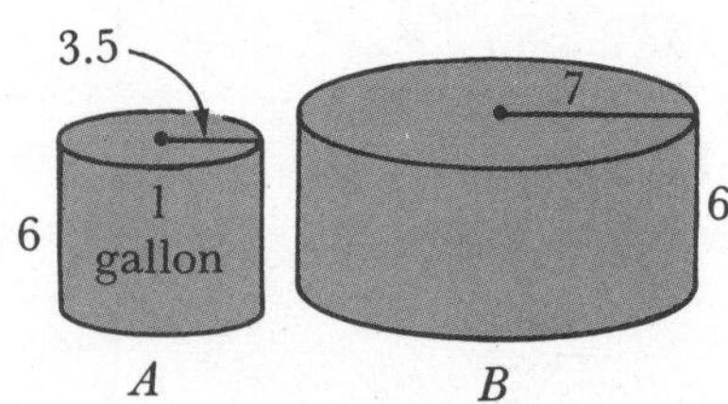

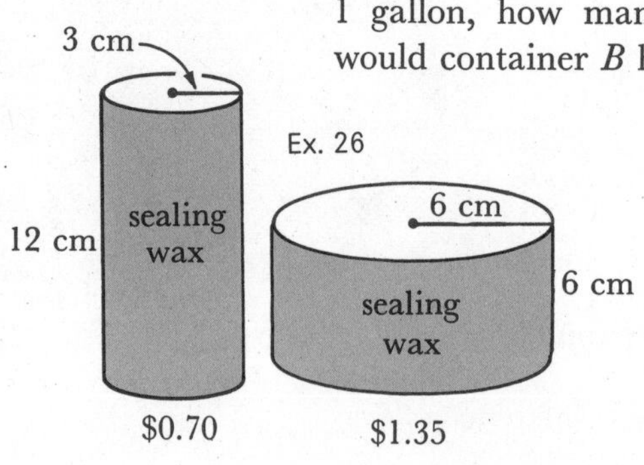

26. The cakes of sealing wax are cylindrical. Which is the better buy? Why?

27. A cube whose edge has a length of 8 is inscribed in a cylinder. Find the volume of the cylinder.

28. The outside diameter of a pipe is 6 in. If its inside diameter is $5\frac{1}{2}$ in., how many gallons of water would 30 ft of pipe hold? Use 1 gallon = 231 cubic inches, and $\pi = 3.14$.

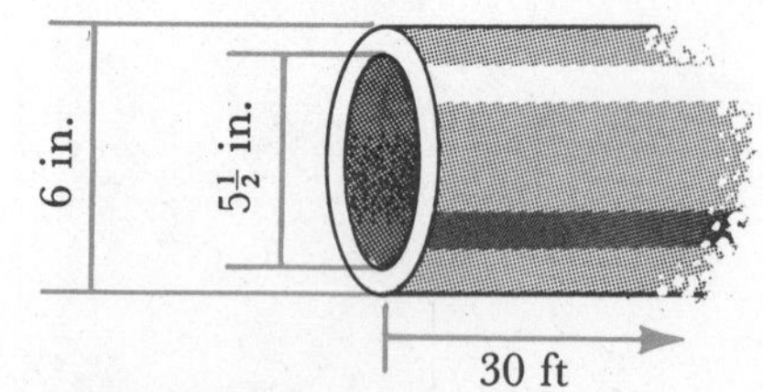

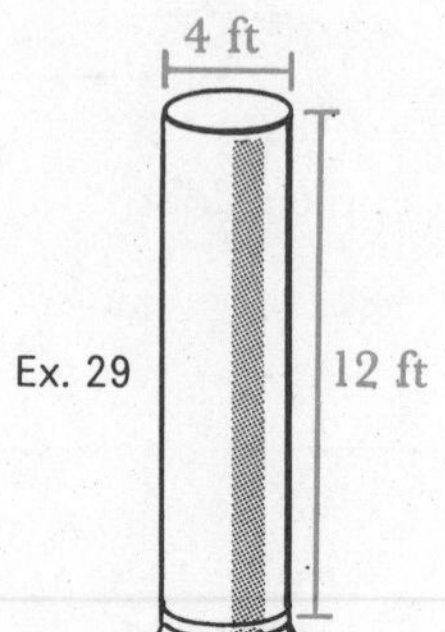

29. How many cubic feet of steel does it take to make a cylindrical tank 4 ft wide and 12 ft high if the shell of the tank is 0.24 in. thick? Use $\pi = 3.14$. HINT: The top and bottom are part of the shell.

GEOMETRIC PATTERNS

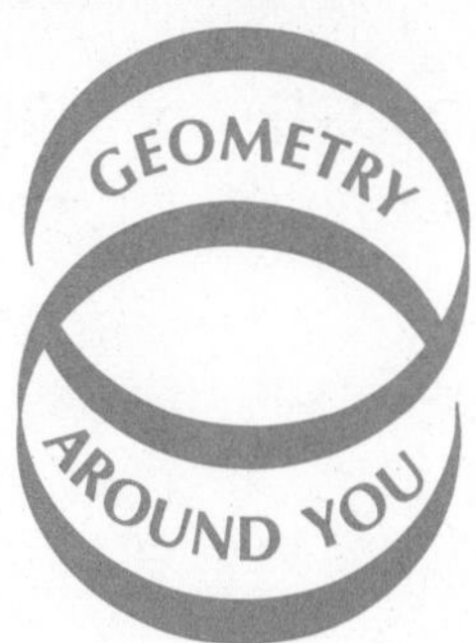

Make a kaleidoscope. Use three small rectangular mirrors of equal size and bits of colorful material (paper, plastic, or beads).

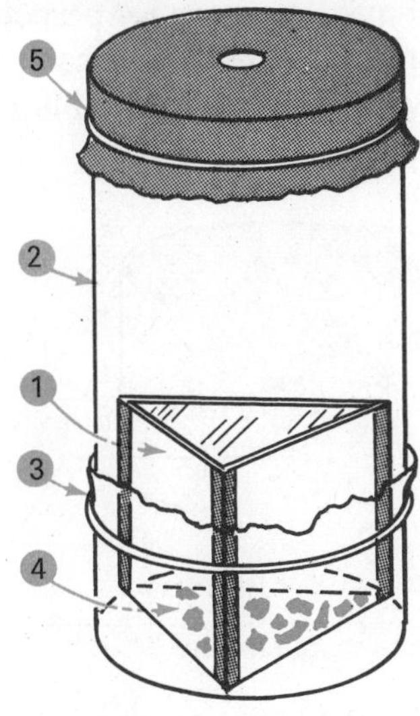

1. Tape mirrors together (front of mirrors to the inside) to form a regular triangular prism.
2. Use heavy paper to make a cylinder around the mirrors (so the prism is enclosed in the cylinder).
3. Fasten cellophane over end of cylinder with a rubber band.
4. Put colorful material into prism.
5. Fasten paper over other end of cylinder with a rubber band, and make a small hole in the center of the paper.

1. A polyhedron separates ______ into two parts.
2. The lateral faces of a right prism are always bounded by ______.
3. The volume of a right prism with base area B and height h is ______.
4. The volume of a right circular cylinder with radius r and height h is ______.

5–6. Find the volume of each right rectangular prism with the given dimensions.

5. 2.4 cm, 3.7 cm, 5 cm
6. 200 mm, 35 cm, 2 m

7–8. Find the volume of each right prism with the given base and height.

7. BASE: right triangle with legs of 4.5 cm and 8 cm; HEIGHT: 3.6 cm
8. BASE: rhombus with diagonals of 3 m and 1.2 m; HEIGHT: 4 m

9–10. Find the volume of each circular cylinder (in terms of π).

9. radius 6 cm, height 0.5 cm
10. radius 1.4 cm, height 9.6 cm

14.5 Oblique Prisms and Circular Cylinders

Oblique prisms and **oblique circular cylinders** are very much like right prisms and right circular cylinders. The same definitions apply. However, the lateral edges of an oblique prism are *not* perpendicular to the planes of the bases. Therefore, the lateral faces can be bounded by any parallelogram. Similarly, the axis of an oblique cylinder is *not* perpendicular to the planes of its bases.

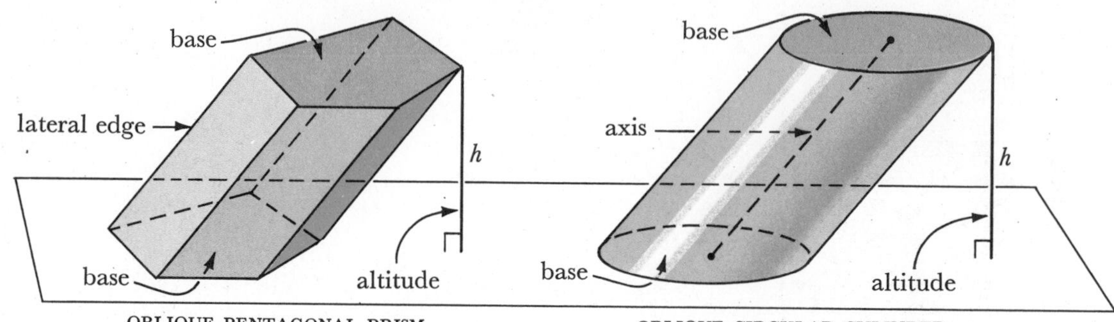

OBLIQUE PENTAGONAL PRISM

OBLIQUE CIRCULAR CYLINDER

A *cross section* of a prism or a circular cylinder (right or oblique) is the intersection of the solid with a plane parallel to the planes of bases.

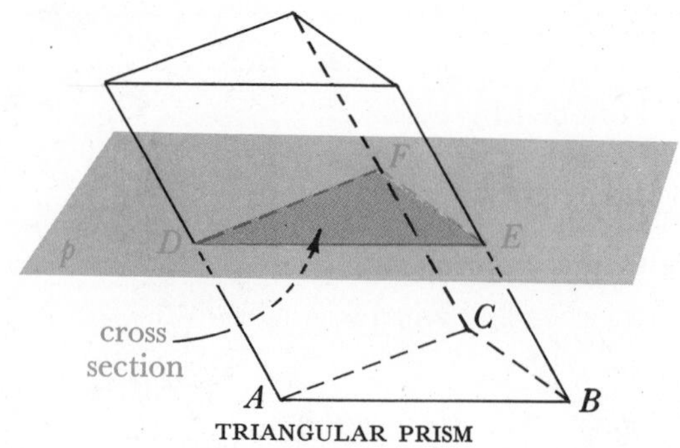

TRIANGULAR PRISM

Plane p is parallel to the planes of the bases of the triangular prism in the figure. Therefore, $\triangle DEF$ and its interior form a cross section of the prism. $\overline{AB} \parallel \overline{DE}$ and, by the definition of a prism, $\overline{AD} \parallel \overline{BE}$. So $ABED$ is a parallelogram, and $\overline{AB} \cong \overline{DE}$. We can show $\overline{BC} \cong \overline{EF}$ and $\overline{AC} \cong \overline{DF}$ by the same reasoning, and $\triangle ABC \cong \triangle DEF$ by the SSS Postulate. In fact,

Theorem All cross sections of a triangular prism are congruent to its bases.

If we separate the prism at the right into triangular prisms, its cross section and base are separated into triangular regions. The cross section of each triangular prism is congruent to its base. Since congruent triangles have equal areas, $C_1 = B_1$, $C_2 = B_2$, and $C_3 = B_3$.

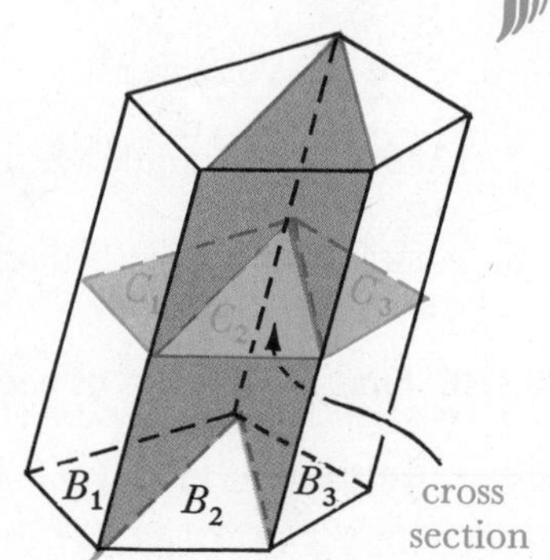

Therefore, $C_1 + C_2 + C_3 = B_1 + B_2 + B_3$

area cross section = area base

All cross sections of a prism have the same area as the base.

Prism Cross Section Theorem

There is a similar theorem for cross sections of a circular cylinder.

All cross sections of a circular cylinder have the same area as the base.

Cylinder Cross Section Theorem

The cross section of a circular cylinder is a circular region with its center on the axis of the cylinder. $\overline{BC} \parallel \overline{AD}$ by the definition of a cylinder. So $\overline{BC}$ and $\overline{AD}$ are in a plane that intersects the cross section and base. $\overline{AB} \parallel \overline{CD}$ (why?), and $ABCD$ is a parallelogram. Since $\overline{AB} \cong \overline{CD}$, the cross section and base are congruent, and they have equal areas.

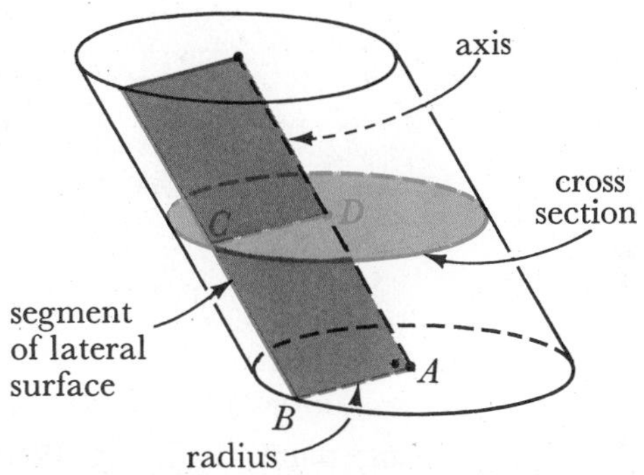

Alfa

Figure 1 is a right rectangular prism represented by a deck of very thin cards. If we "slant" an identical deck of cards, we have an oblique prism, figure 2, whose base and height are exactly like the base and height of figure 1. The volume of figure 1 is equal to the sum of the volumes of its cards. Since figure 2 is made up of exact copies of the cards, it has the same volume. Figure 3 is another deck that has been "twisted." It also represents a solid with the same volume.

Think of the cards as cross sections (no longer having volume, just area). Then any plane parallel to the bottom cards of the decks will intersect each figure at identical cards with equal areas.

An Italian mathematician, Bonaventura Cavalieri (1598–1647), was the first to make these observations about solids and their volumes.

Cavalieri's Postulate

If two solids with bases in the same plane have equal heights, and if the cross sections of both solids made by any plane parallel to the plane of the bases have equal areas, then the solids have equal volumes.

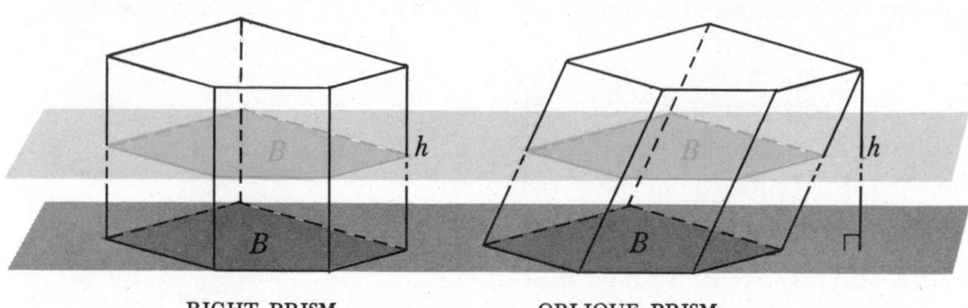

RIGHT PRISM OBLIQUE PRISM

The bases of the prisms above are in the same plane. Both prisms have base area B and height h. By the Prism Cross Section Theorem, all cross sections of each prism have area B. So the cross sections formed by any plane parallel to the plane of the bases will have area B. Therefore, by Cavalieri's Postulate,

$$\text{volume oblique prism} = \text{volume right prism}$$

In general,

Volume Theorem for a Prism

The volume (V) of any prism is equal to the area (B) of its base times its height (h)

$$V = Bh$$

The same is true for circular cylinders with equal base areas and heights.

The cylinders in the figure have equal radii and heights. Why are their volumes equal?

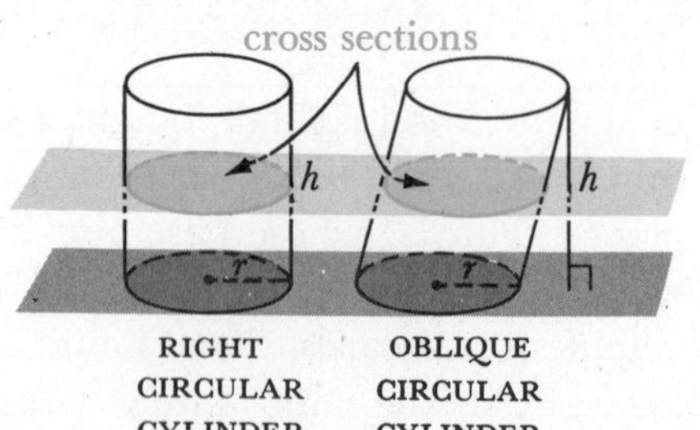

RIGHT CIRCULAR CYLINDER OBLIQUE CIRCULAR CYLINDER

Volume Theorem for a Circular Cylinder

The volume (V) of any circular cylinder (with radius r) is equal to the area (πr^2) of its base times its height (h).

$$V = \pi r^2 h$$

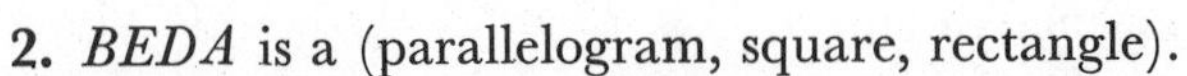

Exercises 14.5

NOTE: For cylinders, leave answers in terms of π unless told otherwise.

Ⓐ **1–12.** Use the given figures.

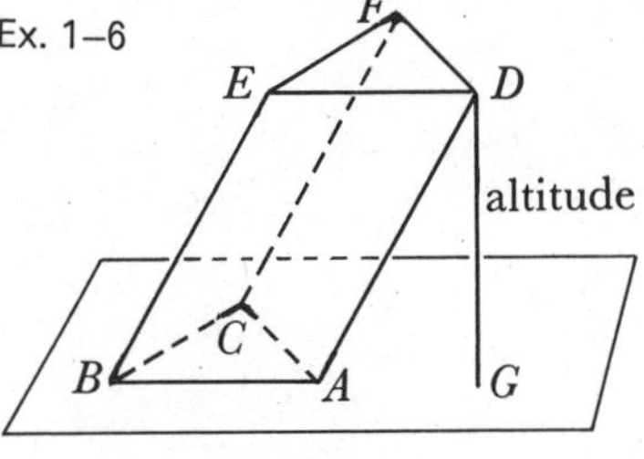

OBLIQUE PRISM

1. The prism is called an oblique ______ prism.
2. *BEDA* is a (parallelogram, square, rectangle).
3. $\overline{BE}$ is a(n) ______ of the prism.
4. $\overline{AD} \parallel$ ______ $\parallel$ ______
5. $\overline{DG}$ ______ plane *ABC*
6. *DG* is the ______ of the prism.
7. ______ is a segment of the lateral surface of the cylinder.
8. $\overline{ST}$ is the ______ of the cylinder.
9. $\overline{UT}$ is a(n) ______ of the cylinder.
10. *VY* is the ______ of the cylinder.
11. $\overline{VU} \parallel$ ______
12. Plane *VSW* ______ plane *UTY*

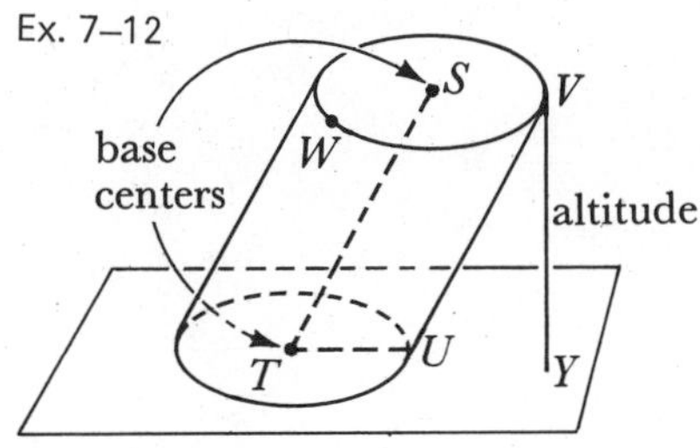

OBLIQUE CIRCULAR CYLINDER

Ⓑ **13–20.** True or False?

13. The bases of an oblique prism are not bounded by congruent polygons.
14. All lateral faces of an oblique prism are bounded by rectangles.
15. A lateral edge of an oblique prism is an altitude.
16. The bases of a circular cylinder are bounded by congruent circles.
17. The axis of an oblique cylinder is perpendicular to the planes of the bases.
18. The height of an oblique cylinder is the length of any segment of the lateral surface.
19. Any cross section of a circular cylinder has the same area as either base.
20. Some cross sections of a prism do not have the same area as either base.

21–26. Sketch each solid. Then find its volume.

21. oblique prism of height 10 cm whose base is bounded by a rectangle with length 6 cm and width 2 cm

22. oblique prism of height 7 m whose base is bounded by an equilateral triangle with a perimeter of 18 m

23. oblique cylinder of height 9 and radius 3

24. oblique cylinder of height 8.5 whose base has a diameter of 5

25. oblique cylinder of height 16 whose base has a circumference of π

26. oblique cylinder of height 3.6 whose base has a circumference of 4π

© 27–29. Determine what happens to the volume of a cylinder when

27. The radius is doubled.

28. The height is doubled.

29. Both the radius and the height are doubled.

30–32. To apply Cavalieri's Postulate, the bases of two solids do not have to be congruent, nor do they have to be bounded by the same kind of figure. Use Cavalieri's Postulate to answer each exercise.

30. Why do both prisms have the same volume?

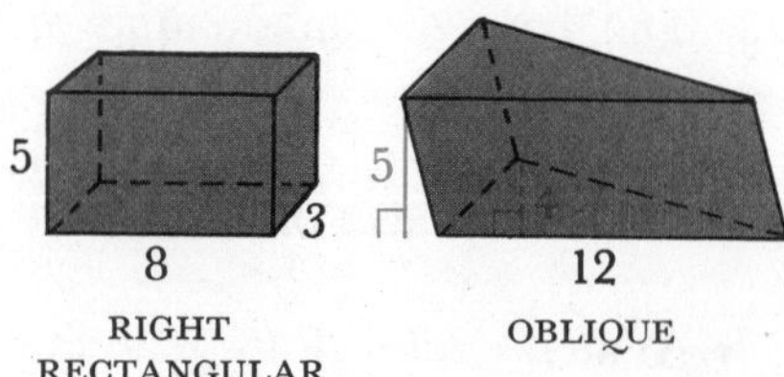

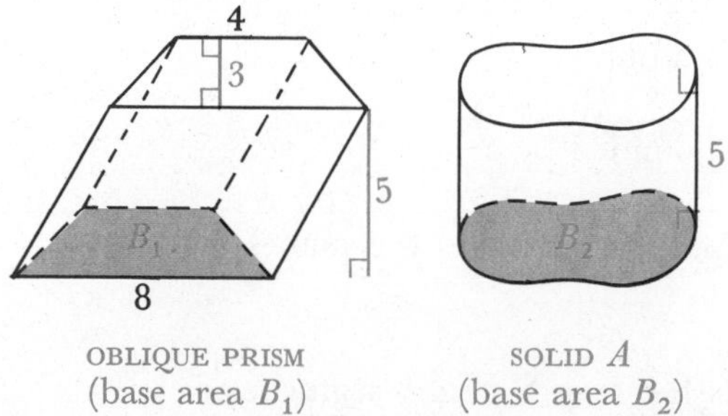

31. The areas of all cross sections of solid A are equal to B_2. If $B_1 = B_2$, why is it possible to find the volume of solid A? Find its volume.

32. $ABCD$, $RSTU$, and $VWXY$ are squares. Does Cavalieri's Postulate apply to the prism and solid Q? Why, or why not?

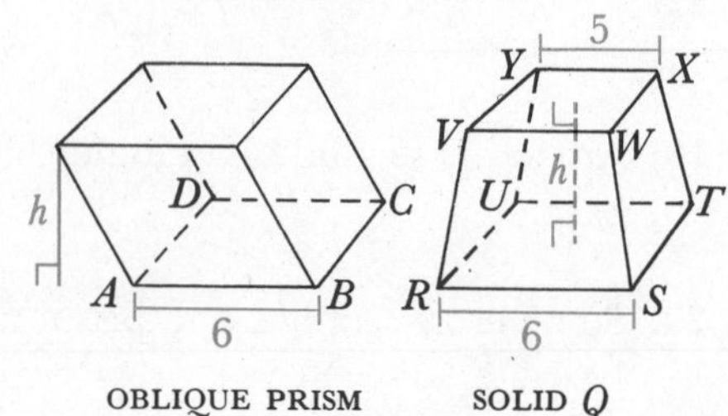

Pyramids and Cones

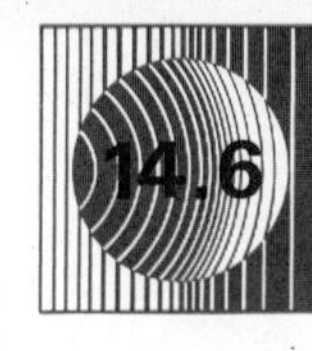

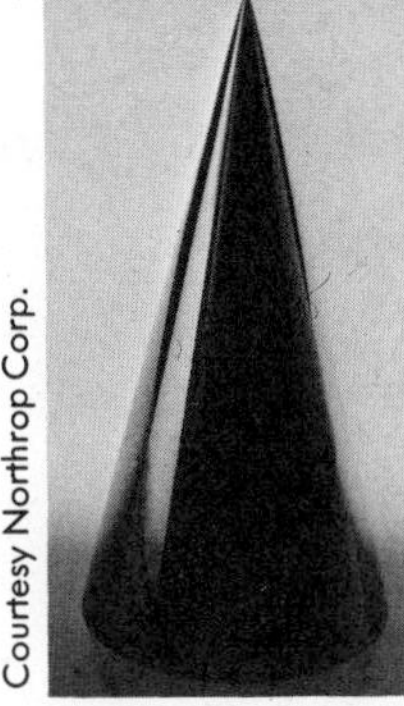

A **pyramid** has one face, called the *base*, bounded by any convex polygon. All other faces, called *lateral faces*, are bounded by triangles with a common vertex and bases that are the edges of the base of the pyramid. The common vertex of the lateral faces is the *vertex* of the pyramid. The *altitude* of the pyramid is the perpendicular segment from its vertex to the plane of its base, and the *height* is the length of the altitude.

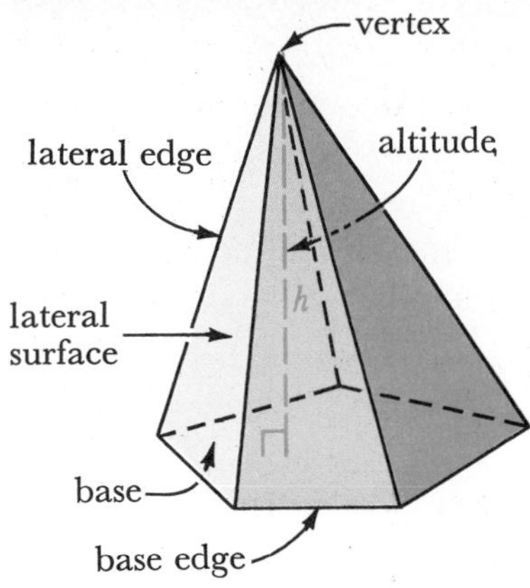

A pyramid is a **regular pyramid** if and only if its base is bounded by a regular polygon and its lateral faces are bounded by congruent isosceles triangles. A pyramid is named by the number of base edges it has. For example,

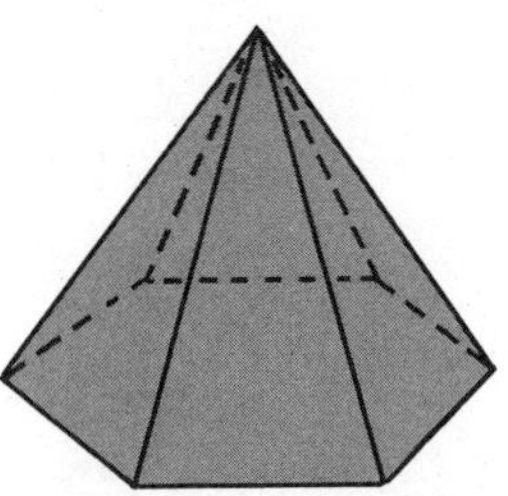

REGULAR HEXAGONAL PYRAMID

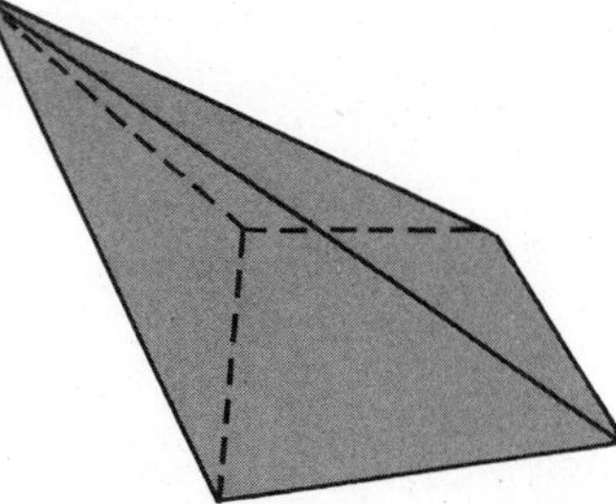

QUADRANGULAR PYRAMID

Volume Postulate for Triangular Pyramids

If two triangular pyramids have congruent bases and equal heights, then they have equal volumes.

Any triangular prism can be separated into three pyramids. In the figure below, planes XEZ and DEZ separate the prism into pyramids S_1, S_2, and S_3.

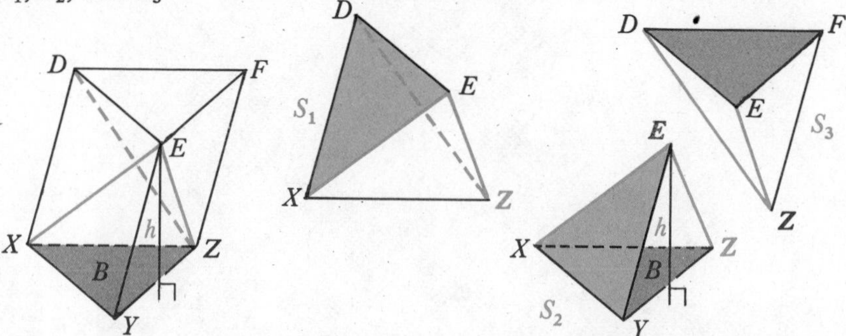

For S_1 and S_2, $\triangle XDE \cong \triangle EYX$ because $XYED$ is a parallelogram by the definition of a prism, and $\overline{XE}$ is its diagonal (a diagonal separates a parallelogram into two congruent triangles). Since $\triangle XDE$ and $\triangle EYX$ are in the same plane, the perpendicular from point Z to the plane of each base is the same segment. Therefore, S_1 and S_2 have congruent bases and equal heights. And, by the Volume Postulate for Triangular Pyramids,

$$\text{volume } S_1 = \text{volume } S_2$$

For S_3 and S_2, $\triangle DEF \cong \triangle XYZ$ because they are the bases of a prism. The perpendicular from point Z to plane DEF has the same length as the perpendicular from point E to plane XYZ. Why? And, by the Volume Postulate for Triangular Pyramids,

$$\text{volume } S_3 = \text{volume } S_2$$

By the Volume Addition Postulate and substitution,

$$\begin{aligned}
\text{volume } S_1 + \text{volume } S_2 + \text{volume } S_3 &= \text{volume prism} \\
\text{volume } S_2 + \text{volume } S_2 + \text{volume } S_2 &= \text{volume prism} \\
3(\text{volume } S_2) &= \text{volume prism} \\
\text{volume } S_2 &= \tfrac{1}{3}(\text{volume prism}) \\
\text{volume } S_2 &= \tfrac{1}{3}Bh
\end{aligned}$$

Notice that the base and altitude of the prism are the base and altitude of pyramid S_2.

Volume Theorem for a Triangular Pyramid

The volume (V) of any triangular pyramid is equal to one third the area (B) of its base times it height (h).

$$V = \tfrac{1}{3}Bh$$

Any pyramid can be separated into triangular pyramids. In the figure at right, pyramid S with base area B is separated into three pyramids. Pyramids S_1, S_2, and S_3 all have the same height h. Why?

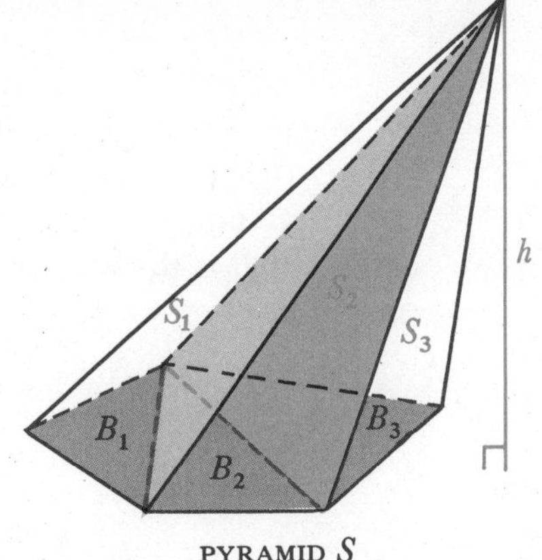

PYRAMID S

$$\begin{aligned} \text{volume } S &= \text{volume } S_1 + \text{volume } S_2 + \text{volume } S_3 \\ &= \tfrac{1}{3}B_1h + \tfrac{1}{3}B_2h + \tfrac{1}{3}B_3h \\ &= \tfrac{1}{3}(B_1 + B_2 + B_3)h \\ &= \tfrac{1}{3}Bh \end{aligned}$$

Volume Theorem for a Pyramid

The volume (V) of any pyramid is equal to one third the area (B) of its base times its height (h).

$$V = \tfrac{1}{3}Bh$$

A **circular cone** has one face, called the *base*, that is bounded by a circle and a *vertex* that is a point not in the plane of the base. All segments joining the vertex and a point on the circle bounding the base form the *lateral surface*. The segment joining the vertex to the center of the base is the *axis*.

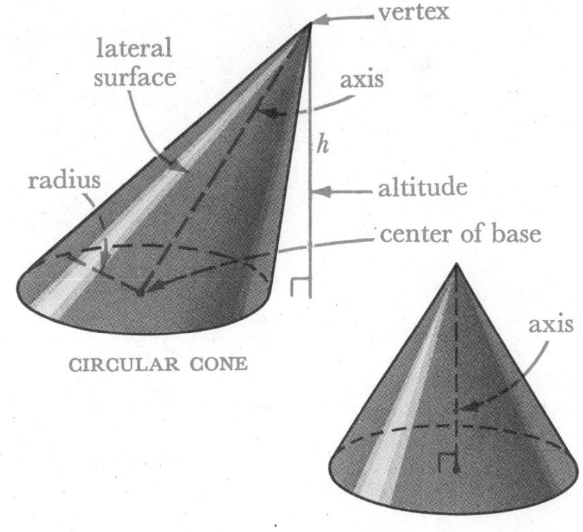

CIRCULAR CONE

RIGHT CIRCULAR CONE

The *altitude* of the cone is the perpendicular segment from the vertex to the plane of the base, and the *height* is the length of the altitude. Any radius of the base is a *radius* of the cone. A **right circular cone** is a cone whose axis is perpendicular to the plane of the base.

To find the volume of a circular cone, we will use a method similar to the one used for a right circular cylinder. A pyramid is inscribed in a cone if its base is inscribed in the base of the cone and its vertex is the same as the vertex of the cone.

INSCRIBED PYRAMIDS

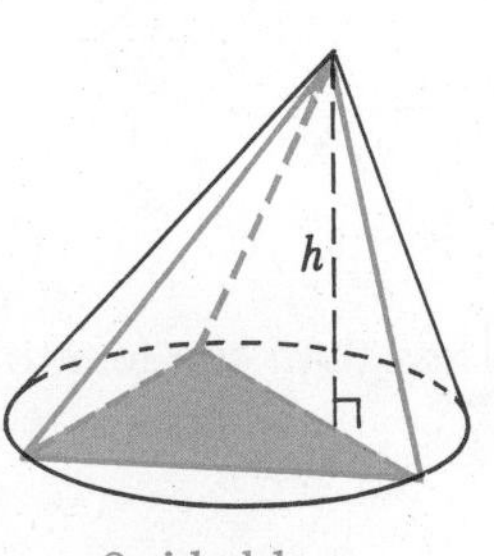

3-sided base

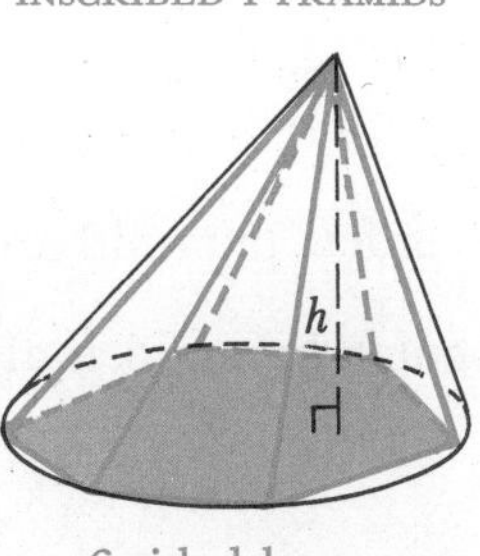

6-sided base

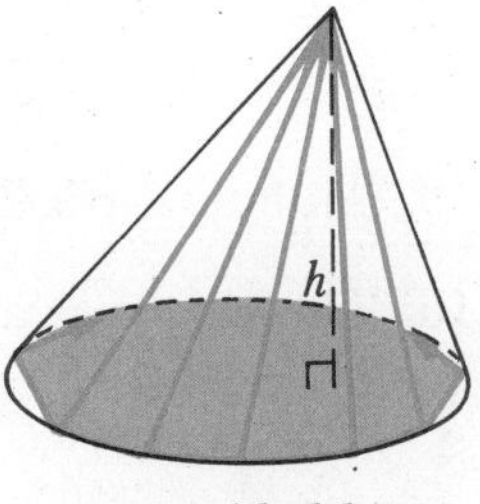

many-sided base

As the number of base edges of the inscribed pyramid increases, the shape of the pyramid begins to resemble the shape of the cone, and the volume of the pyramid is close to the volume of the cone. In fact, the volume of the cone is the limit of the volumes of its inscribed pyramids. If B is the area of the pyramid base, and h is the height, then

$$\begin{aligned}\text{volume cone} &= \text{limit volumes of pyramids}\\ &= \text{limit } \tfrac{1}{3}Bh\end{aligned}$$

The limit of B is the area of the circular base of the cone, which is πr^2, so

$$\text{volume cone} = \tfrac{1}{3}\pi r^2 h$$

In general,

Volume Theorem for a Circular Cone

The volume (V) of any circular cone (with radius r) is equal to one third the area (πr^2) of its base times its height (h).

$$V = \tfrac{1}{3}\pi r^2 h$$

Exercises 14.6

NOTE: For cones, leave answers in terms of π unless told otherwise.

Ⓐ **1–8.** Use the given figures.

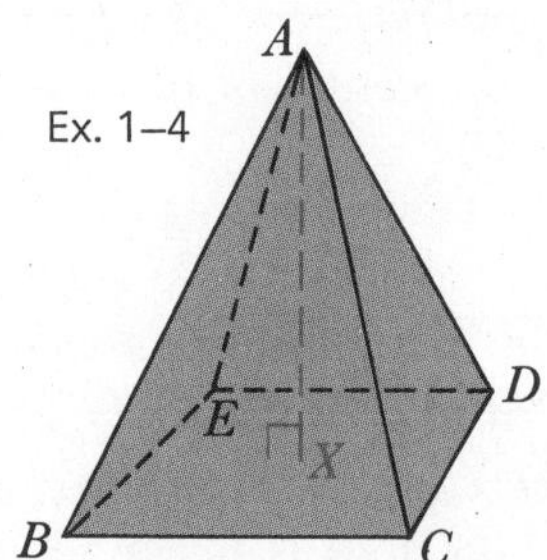

1. Point A is the ______ of the pyramid.
2. AX is the ______ of the pyramid.
3. ______ is the base of the pyramid.
4. If the pyramid is a regular pyramid, then $\triangle ABC$ is ______.

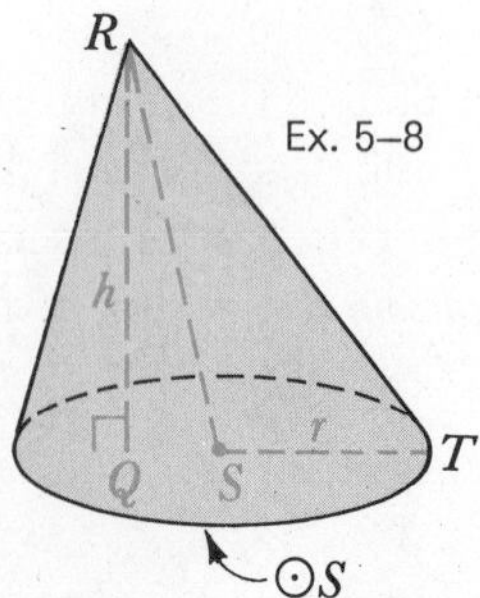

5. $\overline{RS}$ is the ______ of the circular cone.
6. $\overline{ST}$ is a(n) ______ of the cone.
7. $\overline{RQ}$ is the ______ of the cone.
8. The volume of the cone is ______.

Ⓑ **9–14.** True or False?

9. All lateral edges of a regular pyramid are congruent.
10. The height of a triangular pyramid is always less than the length of any lateral edge.

11. The axis of a right circular cone is also the altitude.

12. Any rhombus can be the base of a regular pyramid.

13. If $\overline{PQ}$, $\overline{PR}$, $\overline{PS}$, and $\overline{PT}$ are the lateral edges of a pyramid, then points Q, R, S, and T are coplanar.

14. If $\overline{AB}$ is the axis of a right circular cone with radius $\overline{BC}$, then $\triangle ABC$ is a right triangle.

15–20. Find the volume of each solid.

15.

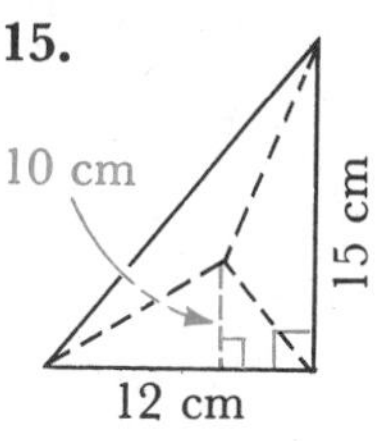

16.

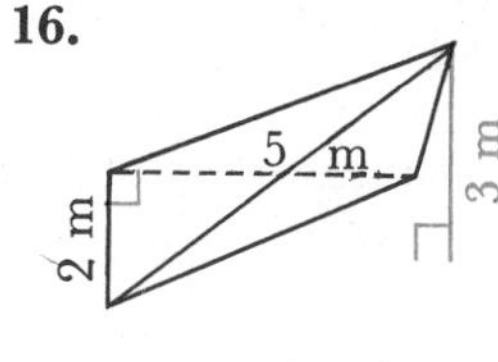

17.

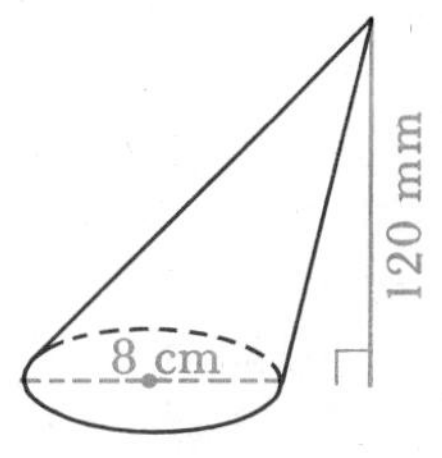

18.

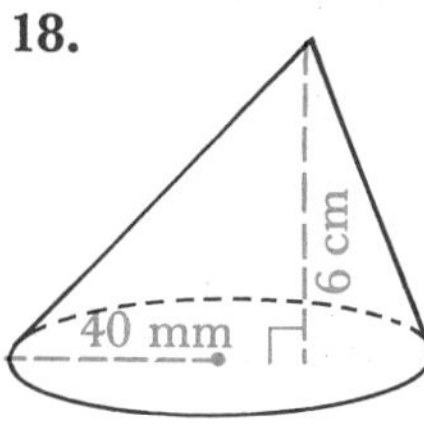

19.

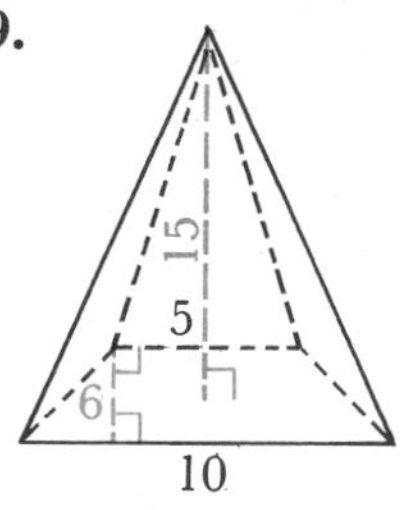

20.

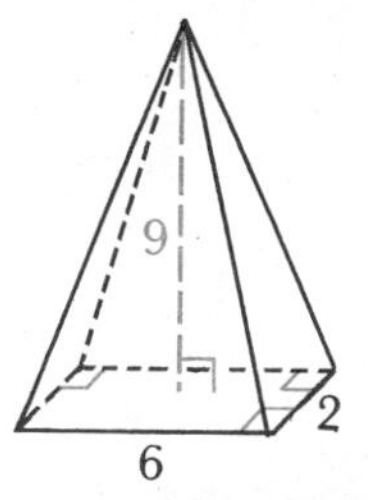

21–24. Find the following:

21. the volume of a pyramid whose height is 25 and whose base is a rhombus with diagonals of 5 and 6

22. the height of a right circular cone whose volume is 12.5π and whose base circumference is 10π

23. the base area of a regular hexagonal pyramid whose volume is 4.5 and whose height is 0.5

24. the circumference of the base of a right circular cone whose volume is 96π and whose height is 8

25. The Transamerica Pyramid Building is in San Francisco. Without its first four levels and "wings," the rest of the building is a pyramid with a square base measuring $149'$ on a side and a height of $800'$. Find the volume of the pyramid.

Courtesy Transamerica Pyramid Building

26. Road salt or grain is often unloaded in such a way that a cone is formed. Find the volume of road salt pictured at the right. (Use $\pi = 3.14$.)

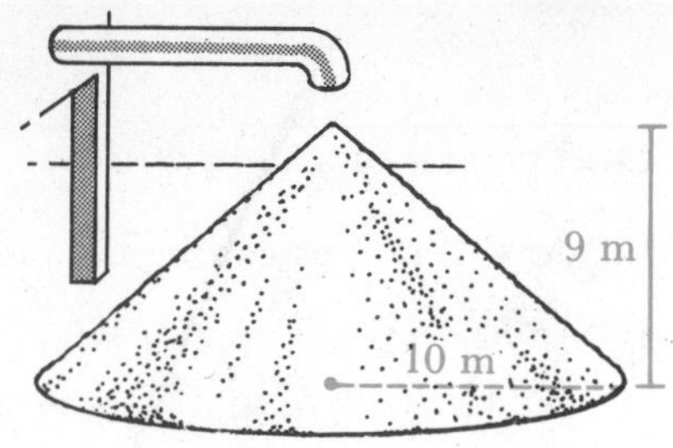

Ex. 27

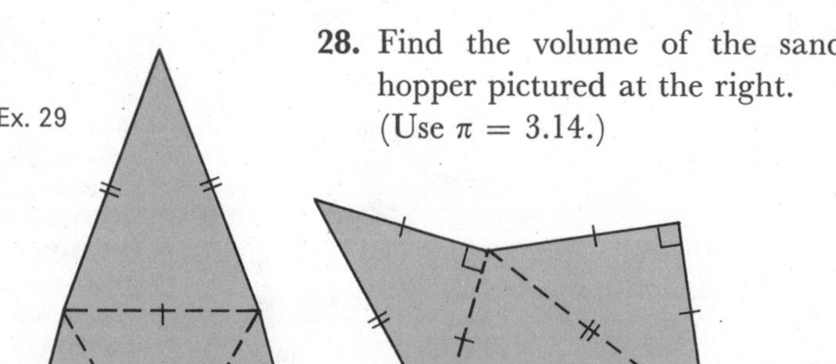

27. To install an attic fan, the volume of the attic in the building shown must be found. Find it. HINT: Together, the two ends would form a pyramid with a rectangular base of 25×10 feet.

28. Find the volume of the sand hopper pictured at the right. (Use $\pi = 3.14$.)

Ex. 29

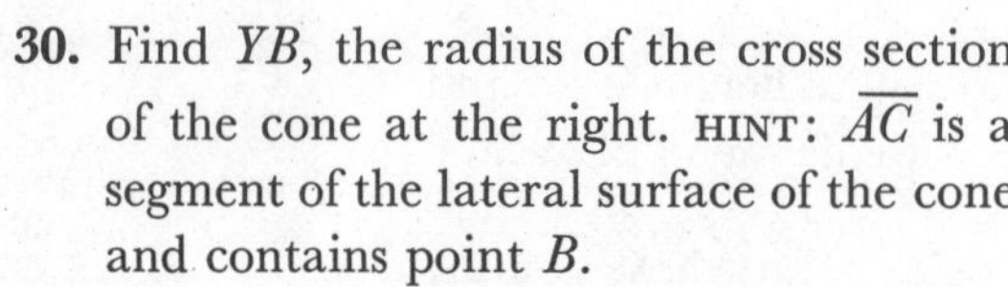

figure 1

figure 2

© 29. Trace two copies of figure 1 and one of figure 2. Make a model of a pyramid with each copy and fit them together to form a right triangular prism.

30. Find YB, the radius of the cross section of the cone at the right. HINT: $\overline{AC}$ is a segment of the lateral surface of the cone and contains point B.

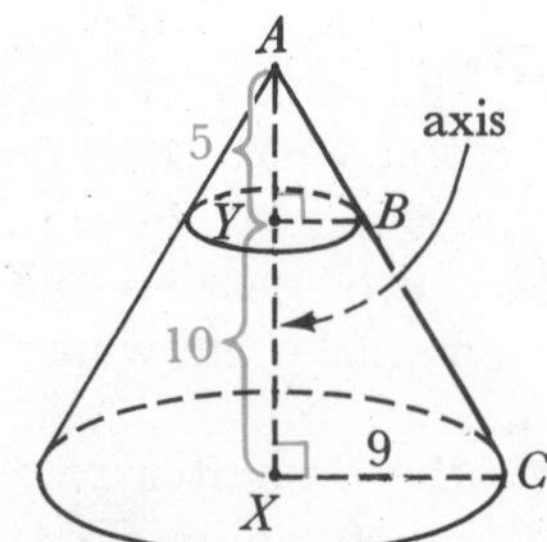

31. Find the volume of the solid that is bounded by the base and cross section of the cone in Exercise 30.

Ex. 32–33

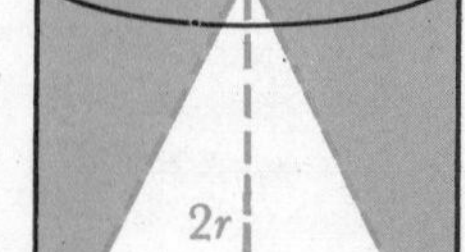

32–33. The figure at the left is a right circular cone and a right circular cylinder with the same base and axis.

32. What is the volume of the solid bounded by the lateral surface of the cone and the lateral surface and upper base of the cylinder?

33. Sketch a cross section of the solid described in Exercise 32.

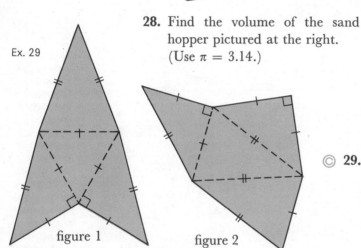

H. Armstrong Roberts

Surface Area

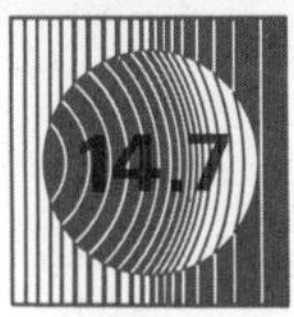

The **lateral area** (**L.A.**) of a prism or pyramid is the measure of the lateral faces; of a cylinder or cone, it is the measure of the lateral surface. The **surface area** (**S.A.**) of a solid is the measure of its total surface—including the lateral area and the base area.

For the right triangular prism below, the lateral area is the sum of the areas of its lateral faces. So,

L.A. = area $PQTS$ + area $QRUT$ + area $RPSU$.

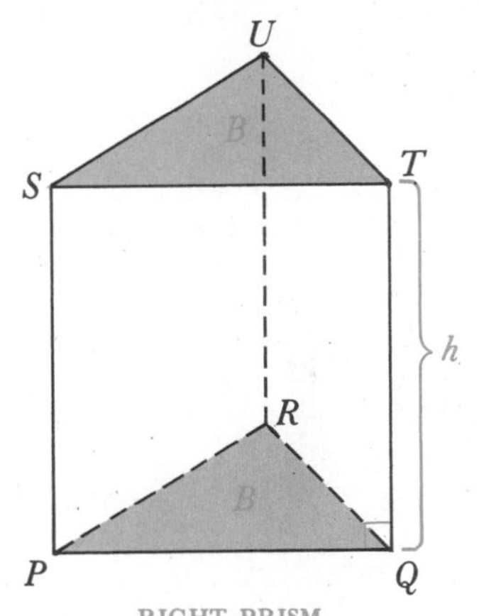

RIGHT PRISM

The prism has height h, and its lateral edges are altitudes. Therefore, $PS = QT = RU = h$. Since the lateral faces are rectangular regions,

$$\begin{aligned} \text{L.A.} &= (PQ)h + (QR)h + (RP)h \\ &= (PQ + QR + RP)h \end{aligned}$$

Notice that $PQ + QR + RP = p$, where p is the perimeter of $\triangle PQR$, the base of the prism. So,

$$\text{L.A.} = ph$$

The surface area of the prism is the sum of the areas of all its faces. The bases are congruent, and each has area B.

$$\text{S.A.} = \text{L.A.} + 2B$$

In general,

L.A. and S.A. Theorem for a Right Prism

For any right prism, lateral area (L.A.) is equal to the perimeter (p) of its base times its height (h), and surface area (S.A.) is equal to its lateral area plus twice the area (B) of its base.

$\text{L.A.} = ph$ and $\text{S.A.} = \text{L.A.} + 2B$

The lateral area of the regular pyramid below is the sum of the areas of its lateral faces.

$$\text{L.A.} = \text{area } \triangle AXY + \text{area } \triangle AYZ + \text{area } \triangle AZX$$

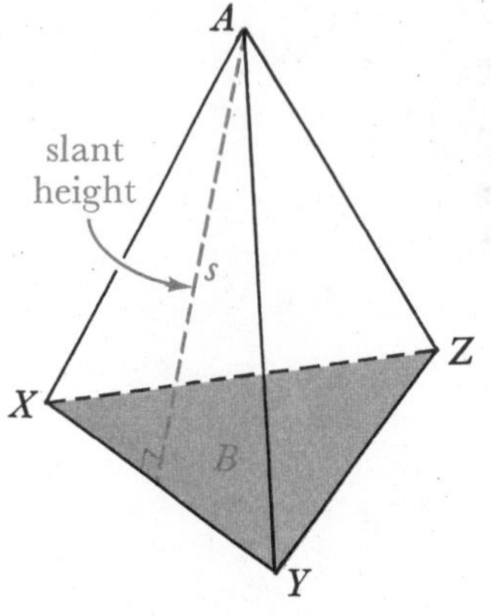

REGULAR PYRAMID

The *slant height* of a regular pyramid is the height of the triangle bounding any lateral face. The slant height (s) of the pyramid in the figure is the height of isosceles $\triangle AXY$. $\triangle AYZ$ and $\triangle AZX$ also have heights of s. Why? Therefore,

$$\begin{aligned}\text{L.A.} &= \tfrac{1}{2}(XY)s + \tfrac{1}{2}(YZ)s + \tfrac{1}{2}(ZX)s \\ &= \tfrac{1}{2}(XY + YZ + ZX)s\end{aligned}$$

But $XY + YZ + ZX = p$, the perimeter of the pyramid's base. So,

$$\text{L.A.} = \tfrac{1}{2}ps$$

The area of $\triangle XYZ$ is B, so the surface area of the pyramid is

$$\text{S.A.} = \text{L.A.} + B$$

In general,

L.A. and S.A. Theorem for a Regular Pyramid

For any regular pyramid, lateral area (L.A.) is equal to one half the perimeter (p) of its base times its slant height (s), and surface area (S.A.) is equal to its lateral area plus the area (B) of its base.

$\text{L.A.} = \tfrac{1}{2}ps$ and $\text{S.A.} = \text{L.A.} + B$

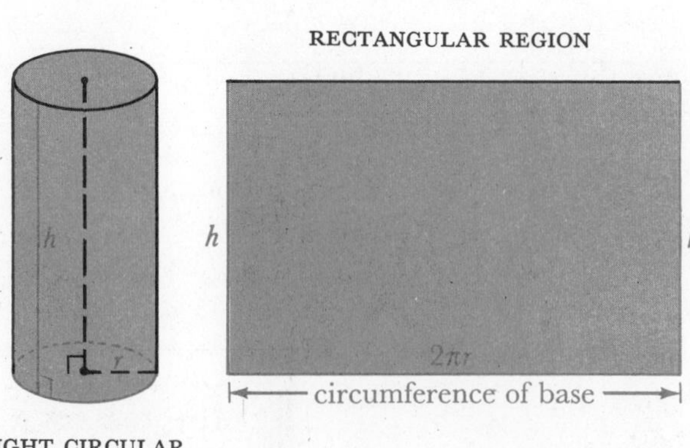

RIGHT CIRCULAR CYLINDER

To find the lateral area of a right circular cylinder, imagine "peeling" the lateral surface off the cylinder at left. The "unrolled" surface is a rectangular region. Its length is the same as the circumference of the cylinder base, and its width is the same as the height of the cylinder. The area of the rectangular region is the same as the lateral area of the cylinder. So for the cylinder,

$$\text{L.A.} = (\text{circumference of base})h$$

If the base has radius r, then its circumference is $2\pi r$, and

$$\text{L.A.} = 2\pi rh$$

The surface area of the cylinder is its lateral area plus the area of both bases. Each base has an area of πr^2, so

$$\text{S.A.} = \text{L.A.} + 2\pi r^2 = 2\pi rh + 2\pi r^2 = 2\pi r(h + r)$$

L.A. and S.A. Theorem for a Right Circular Cylinder

For any right circular cylinder, lateral area (L.A.) is equal to the circumference ($2\pi r$) of its base times its height (h), and surface area (S.A.) is equal to its lateral area plus twice the area (πr^2) of its base.

$\text{L.A.} = 2\pi rh$ and $\text{S.A.} = \text{L.A.} + 2\pi r^2 = 2\pi r(h + r)$

The *slant height* of a right circular cone is the length of any segment from the vertex to any point of the circle bounding the base. If the lateral surface of the right circular cone in the figure is "peeled off," it is a sector of a circle with radius s (the slant height of the cone). The arc length of the sector is $2\pi r$ (the circumference of the base of the cone). The area of a sector is half the arc length times the radius (see Section 12.4). So, for the cone,

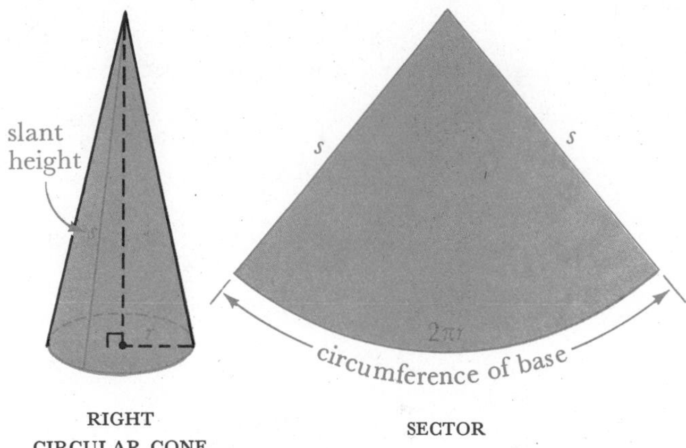

RIGHT CIRCULAR CONE

SECTOR

$$\begin{aligned}\text{L.A.} &= \text{area of sector}\\ &= \tfrac{1}{2}(\text{circumference of cone base})s\\ &= \tfrac{1}{2}(2\pi r)s\\ &= \pi rs\end{aligned}$$

The surface area of the cone is the sum of its lateral area and the area of its base, which is πr^2. So,

$$\text{S.A.} = \text{L.A.} + \pi r^2 = \pi rs + \pi r^2 = \pi r(s + r)$$

L.A. and S.A. Theorem for a Right Circular Cone

For any right circular cone, lateral area (L.A.) is equal to one half the circumference ($2\pi r$) of its base times its slant height (s), and surface area (S.A.) is equal to its lateral area plus the area (πr^2) of its base.

$\text{L.A.} = \pi rs$ and $\text{S.A.} = \text{L.A.} + \pi r^2 = \pi r(s + r)$

Exercises 14.7

NOTE: For cylinders and cones, leave answers in terms of π unless told otherwise.

Ⓐ **1.** The sum of the areas of the lateral faces of a regular pyramid is called the _____ of the pyramid.

2. The surface area of a solid is its _____ area plus its _____ area.

3. The length of a segment from the vertex of a right circular cone to a point of the circle bounding the base is called the _____.

4. The slant height of a regular pyramid is the _____ of one of its lateral faces.

5. The lateral area of a right prism of height h and base perimeter p is _____.

6. The lateral area of a regular pyramid with slant height s and base perimeter p is _____.

7. The surface area of a right circular cone of radius r and slant height s is L.A. + _____ = _____.

8. The surface area of a right circular cylinder with radius r and height h is L.A. + _____ = _____.

Ⓑ **9–12.** Find **(a)** the lateral area and **(b)** the surface area of each solid.

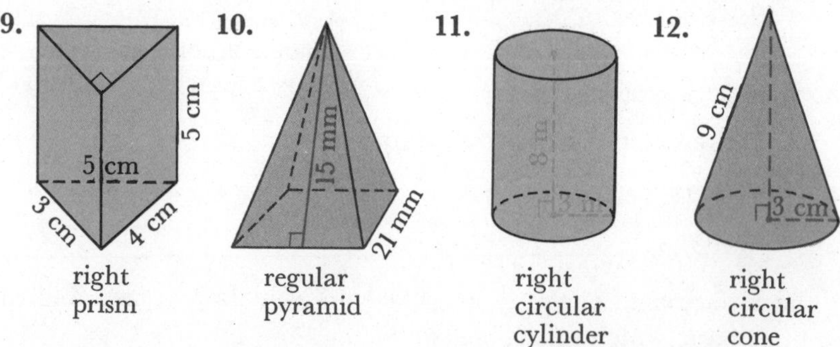

13–22. Sketch each solid. Then find **(a)** its lateral area and **(b)** its surface area.

13. right square prism with lateral edge of length 8 and base edge of length 10

14. right rectangular prism whose height is $5\frac{2}{3}$ and whose base has length 6 and width $2\frac{1}{2}$

15. cube with edge of length 3

16. cube whose volume is e^3

17. regular square pyramid with slant height of 2.5 and base edge of length 1.5

18. regular triangular pyramid with slant height of 12 and base edge of length 8

19. right circular cylinder of height 11 and radius 2

20. right circular cylinder of height 8.5 and base circumference of 5π

21. right circular cone with slant height of 9 and radius of $2\frac{1}{3}$

22. right circular cone with slant height of 20 and base diameter of 10

23–26. Solve each problem. Assume there is no waste or overlap.

23. How many square centimeters of cardboard are needed to make a box 30 cm long, 20 cm wide, and 15 cm high?

Ex. 25

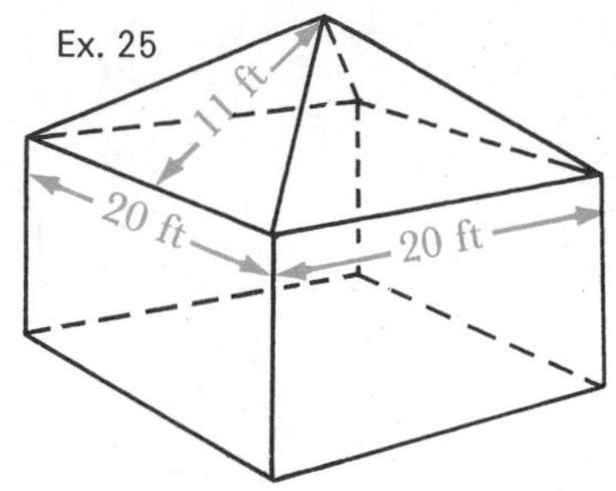

24. How many square centimeters of tin are needed to make a cylindrical tin can with a radius of 7 cm and a height of 10 cm? (Use $\frac{22}{7}$ for π.)

25. How much roofing paper is needed to cover the garage roof shown?

26. How much tin is needed to make the funnel? (Use $\frac{22}{7}$ for π.)

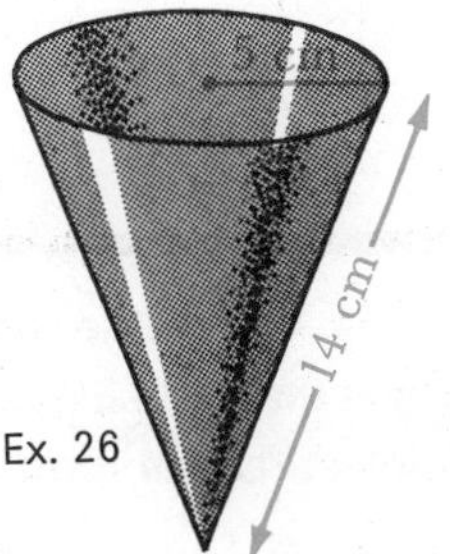

Ex. 26

Ex. 27

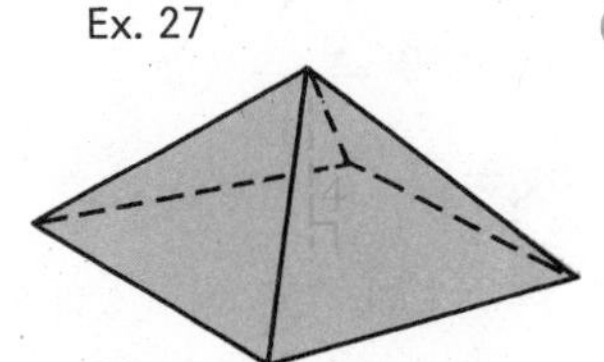

Ⓒ 27. The altitude of any regular pyramid contains the center of the polygon bounding the base. (See Section 12.1.) Find the surface area of the regular square pyramid in the figure if its base area is 64 square units.

28. The formulas for the lateral areas of right prisms and regular pyramids cannot be used for finding the lateral areas of oblique prisms and nonregular pyramids. Why?

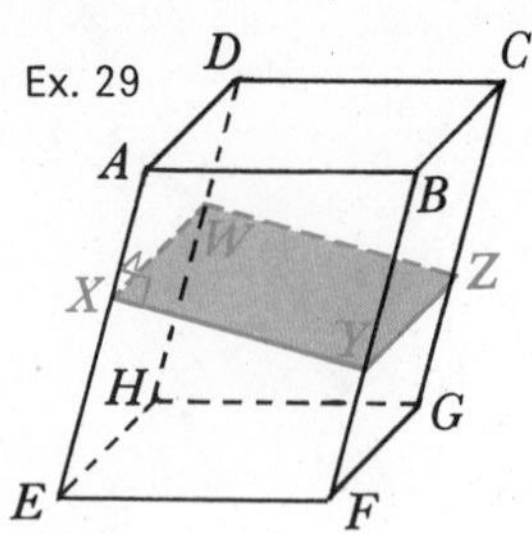

29. The intersection of the oblique prism in the figure and a plane perpendicular to $\overline{AE}$ is region $WXYZ$. Why is the lateral area of the prism equal to the perimeter of $WXYZ$ times AE?

30. Construct two 15 cm × 10 cm rectangular regions and make a model of a right circular cylinder (without bases) of height 15 cm and one of height 10 cm. Which cylinder has the greater lateral area? The greater surface area (if each had bases)?

31. Construct a semicircular region of radius 8 cm and make a model of a right circular cone (without a base). What would be the radius of the circle needed to fit this cone with a base?

32. Find both the surface area and volume for each right rectangular prism. (Does it seem that the cube is the right rectangular prism that encloses the greatest volume for a given surface area?)

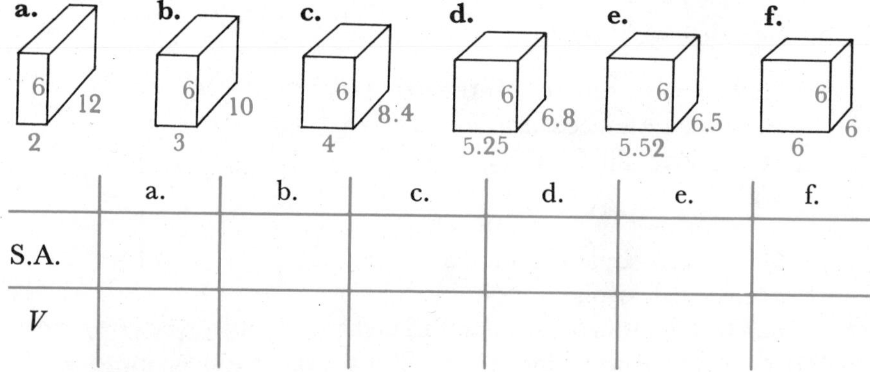

	a.	b.	c.	d.	e.	f.
S.A.						
V						

Algebra Review

Review this skill:

- *solving quadratic equations using the quadratic formula*

Solve by using the quadratic formula, shown at the right. Express irrational roots in simplest radical form.

If $ax^2 + bx + c = 0$,

$$x = \frac{-b \pm \sqrt{b^2 - 4ac}}{2a}.$$

1. $x^2 + 3x + 2 = 0$

2. $x^2 - 4x + 3 = 0$

3. $5t^2 + 2t - 3 = 0$

4. $y^2 + 6y = 2$

5. $x^2 + 1 = 4x$

6. $3s^2 + 6s + 1 = 0$

7. $2p^2 = 4p - 1$

8. $2n^2 = 3 - 6n$

9. $x^2 = 5x + 4$

10. $2w^2 + 4w - 8 = 0$

11. $y^2 + 2\sqrt{3}y + 3 = 0$

12. $t^2 - 2t + \frac{2}{3} = 0$

GEOMETRY AT WORK

GEOMETRIC BIOLOGY

Biologists have found that for warm-blooded animals the metabolic rate (and, therefore, the amount of food that must be eaten in a given time) is related to the ratio of surface area to volume. The higher the ratio, the higher the metabolic rate.

Estimate the size of a rabbit by a right rectangular prism of length 0.4 m, width 0.12 m, and height 0.14 m. Estimate the size of a person by a right rectangular prism of length 0.34 m, width 0.25 m, and height 1.7 m. Find the ratio of surface area to volume for each. Which has the higher metabolic rate?

Harold M. Lambert

Leonard Lee Rue III
Van Cleve Photography

Estimate the size of a lion by a right circular cylinder with radius 0.4 m and height 2.3 m. Estimate the size of a hippopotamus by a right circular cylinder with radius 0.75 m and height 2.7 m. Find the ratio of surface area to volume for each. Which has the higher metabolic rate?

ard Lee Rue III/Van Cleve Photography

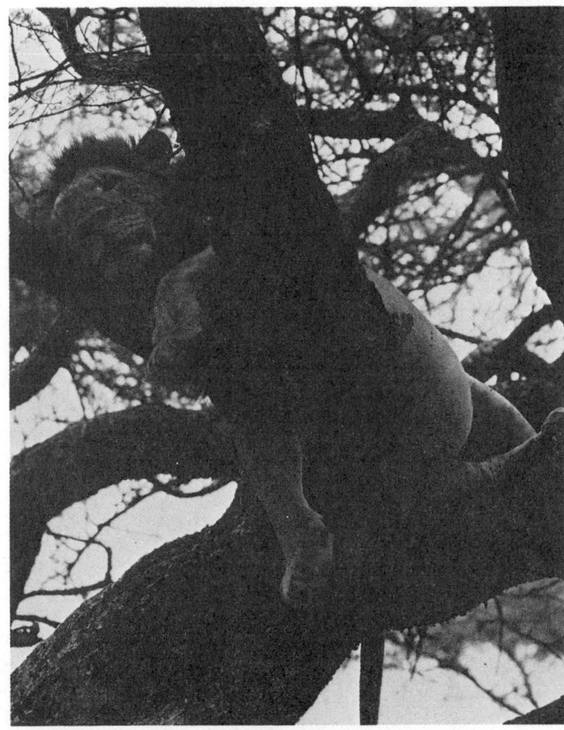

Leonard Lee Rue III/Van Cleve Photography

Spheres

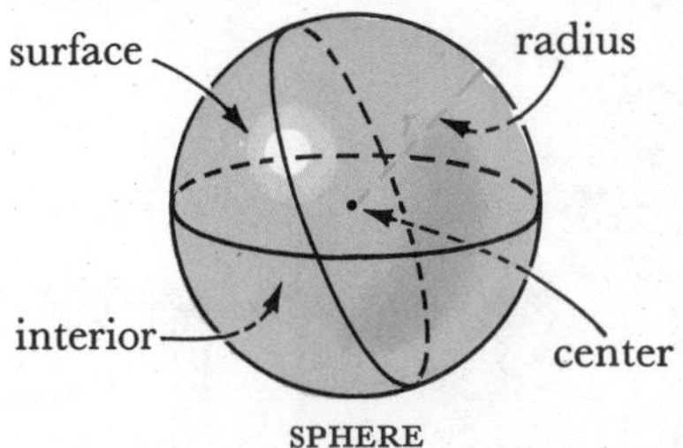

SPHERE

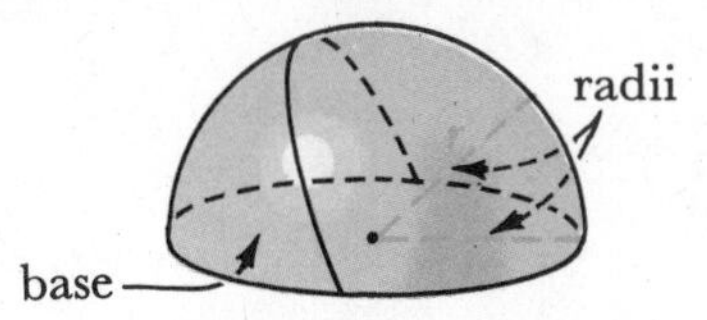

HEMISPHERE

In Chapter 11, a sphere was defined as all points in space that are a given distance (the radius) from a given point (the center). When we refer to the volume of a sphere, we mean, of course, the volume of a solid formed by the sphere and its interior.

Any plane containing the center separates a sphere into two solids of equal volume called **hemispheres.** The *base* of each hemisphere is bounded by a great circle.

In the figure below, a right circular cone is inscribed in a hemisphere that is inscribed in a right circular cylinder. All three solids have the same base. The heights of the cone and cylinder are equal to the radius of the hemisphere.

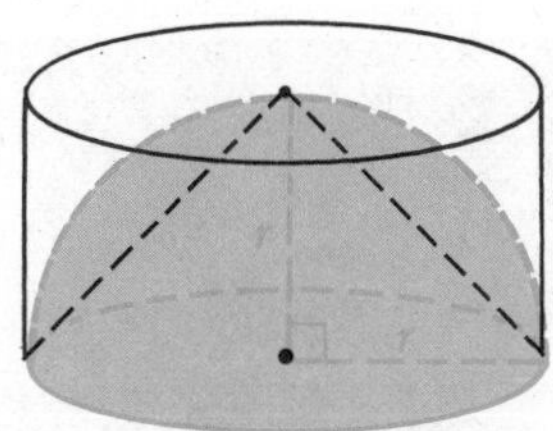

The volume of the hemisphere appears to be somewhere between the volumes of the cone and cylinder. Although we will not prove it, the average of the volumes of the cone and cylinder is equal to the volume of the hemisphere.

$$\text{volume cone} = \tfrac{1}{3}\pi r^2 r = \tfrac{1}{3}\pi r^3$$

$$\text{volume cylinder} = \pi r^2 r = \pi r^3$$

$$\text{volume hemisphere} = \tfrac{1}{2}(\tfrac{1}{3}\pi r^3 + \pi r^3) = \tfrac{2}{3}\pi r^3$$

Since the volume of the hemisphere is half the volume of a sphere with the same radius,

$$\begin{aligned}\text{volume sphere} &= 2(\tfrac{2}{3}\pi r^3)\\ &= \tfrac{4}{3}\pi r^3\end{aligned}$$

Volume Theorem for a Sphere

The volume (V) of any sphere is $\frac{4}{3}\pi$ times its radius (r) cubed.

$$V = \tfrac{4}{3}\pi r^3$$

Imagine the surface of a sphere to be made up of many small regions as in the figure at right. Let n be the number of regions.

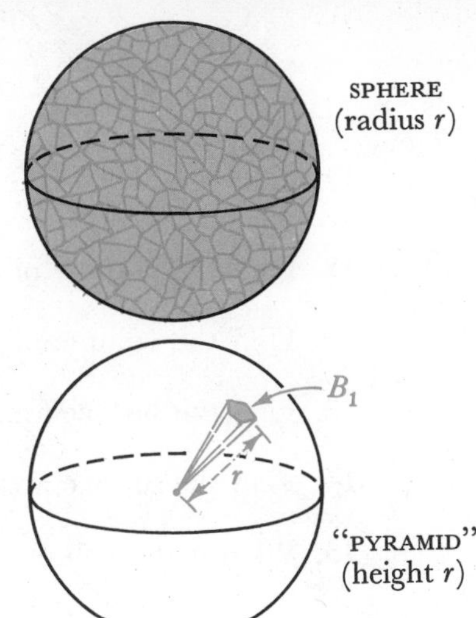

The segments from the center of the sphere to the boundary of each region separate the sphere into n small "pyramids" with slightly curved bases. Each pyramid has height r, the radius of the sphere. If B_1 is the area of the base of one pyramid, the volume of that pyramid is $\frac{1}{3}B_1r$. The sum of the volumes of all n pyramids is the volume of the sphere. So,

$$\tfrac{1}{3}B_1r + \tfrac{1}{3}B_2r + \cdots + \tfrac{1}{3}B_nr = \text{volume sphere} = \tfrac{4}{3}\pi r^3$$

$$\tfrac{1}{3}r(B_1 + B_2 + \cdots + B_n) = \tfrac{4}{3}\pi r^3$$

Since the sum of the areas of the pyramid bases is the surface area of the sphere, $B_1 + B_2 + \cdots + B_n =$ surface area sphere. And

$$\tfrac{1}{3}r(\text{surface area sphere}) = \tfrac{4}{3}\pi r^3$$

$$\text{surface area sphere} = 4\pi r^2$$

This is not a proof of the formula for surface area. However, the formula can be proved using more advanced mathematics.

The surface area (S.A.) of any sphere is 4π times its radius (r) squared.

S.A. $= 4\pi r^2$

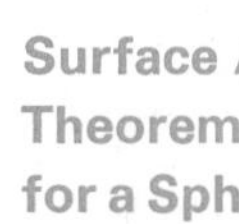

Surface Area Theorem for a Sphere

Exercises 14.8

NOTE: Leave answers in terms of π unless told otherwise.

Ⓐ **1–6.** Refer to the given figure.

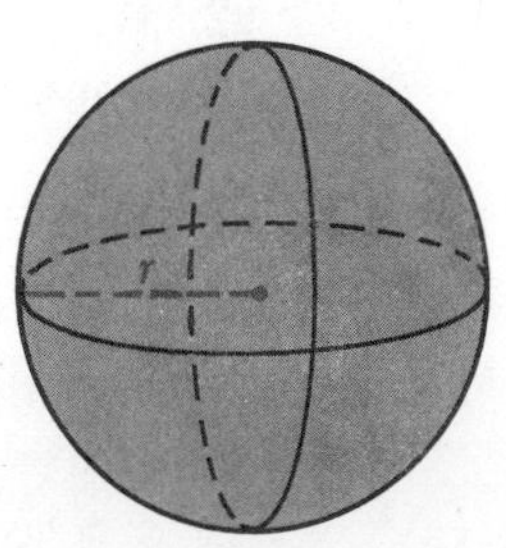

1. The radius of the sphere is ______.

2. The surface area of the sphere is ______.

3. The volume of the sphere is ______.

4. If $r = 2$, the surface area of the sphere is ______.

5. If $r = 3$, the volume of the sphere is ______.

6. The volume of a hemisphere of radius r is ______.

Ⓑ **7–10.** Find the volume and surface area of a sphere of the given radius.

7. 6 cm **8.** 1.5 m **9.** 4.5 mm **10.** $\frac{1}{2}d$ units

11. Find the volume of a sphere with surface area 100π square units.

12. Find the volume of a sphere with surface area 144π square units.

13. Find the surface area of a sphere with volume 288π cubic units.

14. Find the surface area of a sphere with volume 36π cubic units.

15. What is the volume of a sphere formed by spinning a semicircular region around its diameter, which is 18 cm in length?

16. What is the surface area of a solid formed by spinning the sector in the figure around one radius?

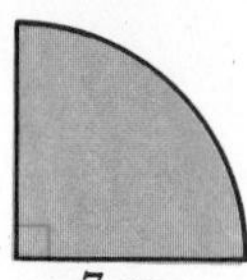

17. If the radius of a sphere is doubled, what happens to the surface area and volume of the sphere?

18. What is the ratio of the volume of a sphere of radius 6 to the volume of a sphere of radius 9?

19. What is the ratio of the area of a great circle of a sphere to the surface area of the sphere?

20. A water tank is the shape of a hemisphere. If it took 5 gallons of paint to cover its base, how much paint will it take to cover its curved surface?

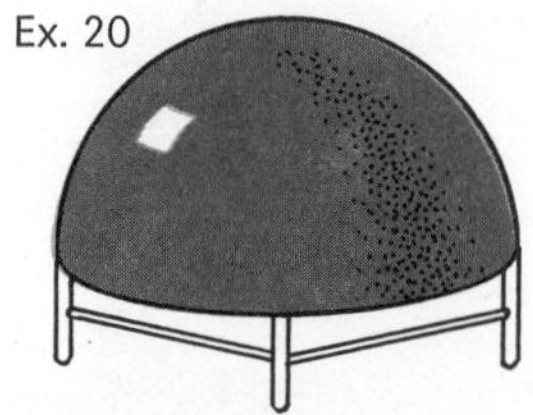
Ex. 20

21. What is the volume of the smallest right circular cylinder that can hold a sphere of diameter 14 cm?

22. What is the volume of the smallest box that will hold a soccer ball whose diameter is 22 cm?

23. Find the radius, surface area, and volume of a sphere whose surface area is x square units and whose volume is x cubic units.

24. Find the radius, surface area, and volume of a sphere whose surface area is x square units and whose volume is y cubic units such that $x > y$.

© **25.** The diameter of the earth is about 12 800 km. About 70% of the earth's surface is covered by water. How many square kilometers of land are there? (Use $\pi = 3.14$.)

26. A steel ball bearing has a radius of 1 cm. How much steel is needed to make 1000 such ball bearings? (Use $\pi = 3.14$.)

27. The ship pictured on page 471 is being equipped with spherical tanks that will carry liquefied natural gas. The inside diameter of each tank is 120 ft. How many ft^3 will each tank hold? (Use $\pi = 3.14$.)

28–30. In the figure below, solid S contains all points of the right circular cylinder (height $2r$, radius r) that are not points of the right circular cones (each with height r, radius r, vertex X). The sphere has radius r. A plane parallel to the base of the cylinder intersects solid S at a distance of h from the vertex of the cones and the sphere at a distance of h from its center.

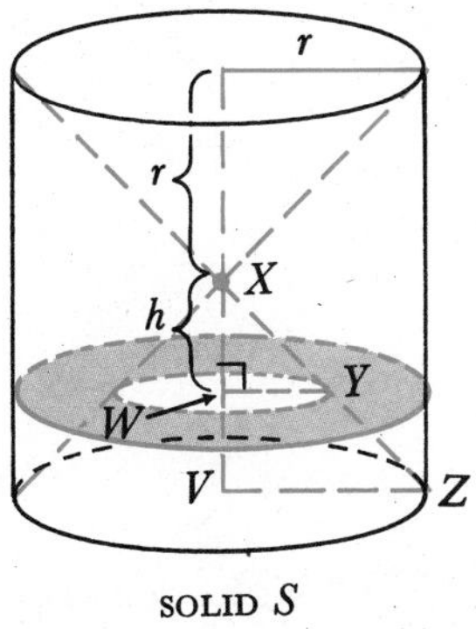

SOLID S

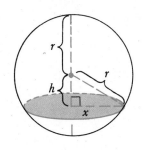

SPHERE

28. Why does the cross section of solid S have an inside radius of h? (See Ex. 30, p. 496.) Find the area of this cross section.

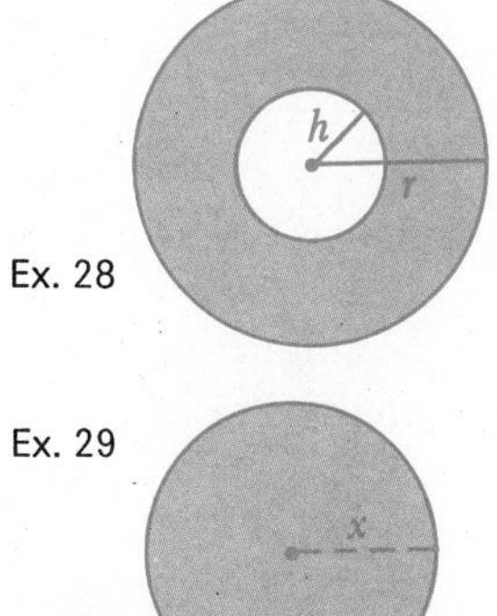

Ex. 28

29. Why is the cross section of the sphere a circular region? Find the area of the cross section in terms of h and r.

Ex. 29

30. What do the results of Ex. 28 and 29 and Cavalieri's Postulate imply about the volumes of solid S and the sphere? Using solid S, find this volume.

14.9 Transformations: Plane Symmetry

The 3-dimensional counterpart of line symmetry (see section 5.10) is **plane symmetry.** If a figure can be separated into two "congruent halves" by a plane, the figure has plane symmetry (also called *reflection symmetry with respect to a plane*). A figure that has plane symmetry can be reflected over a plane so that the figure is its own reflection image. The reflecting plane is called a **symmetry plane** of the figure.

A regular triangular prism has four symmetry planes.

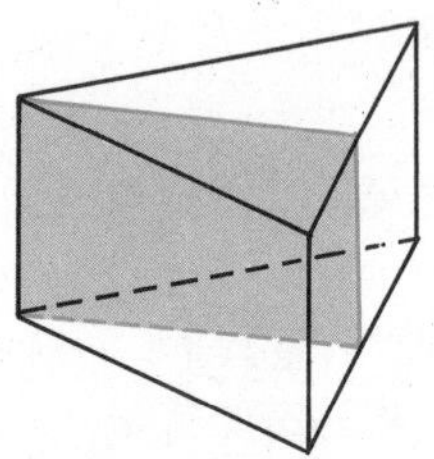

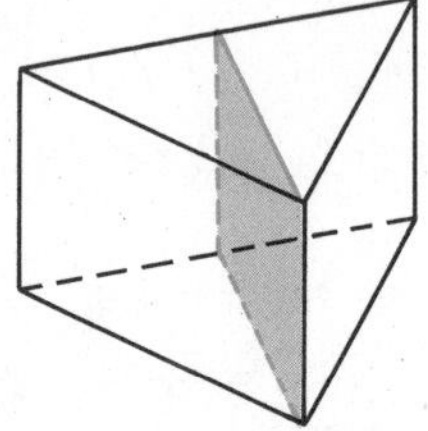

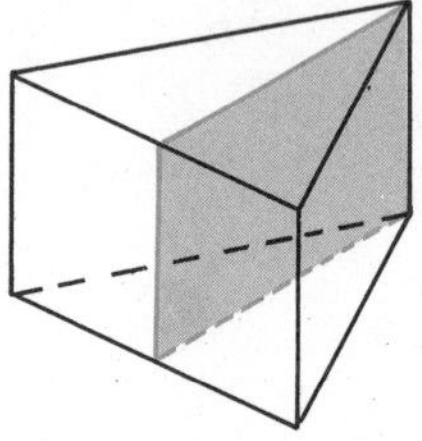

Three symmetry planes contain a symmetry line of each base.

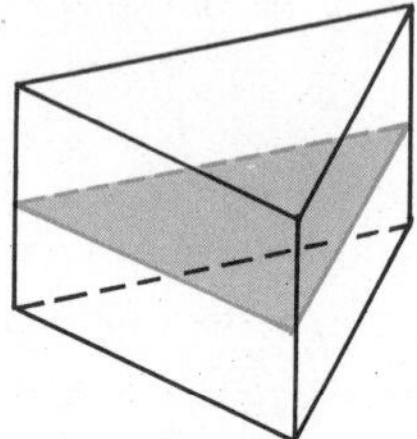

The fourth symmetry plane bisects each lateral edge.

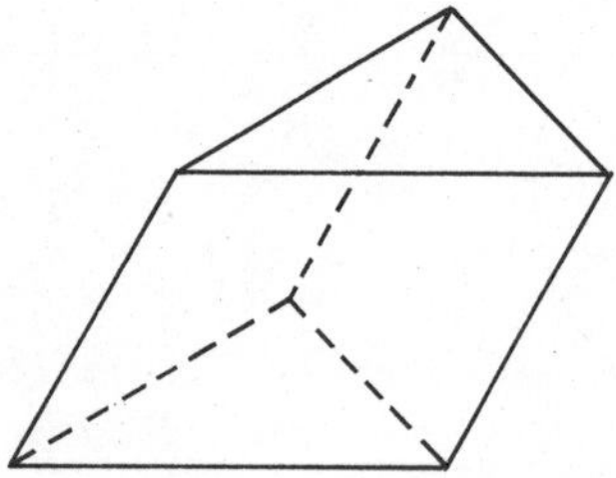

This oblique triangular prism has no symmetry planes.

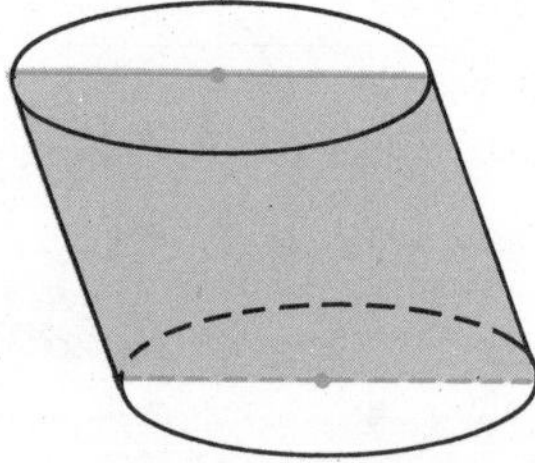

An oblique circular cylinder has exactly one symmetry plane.

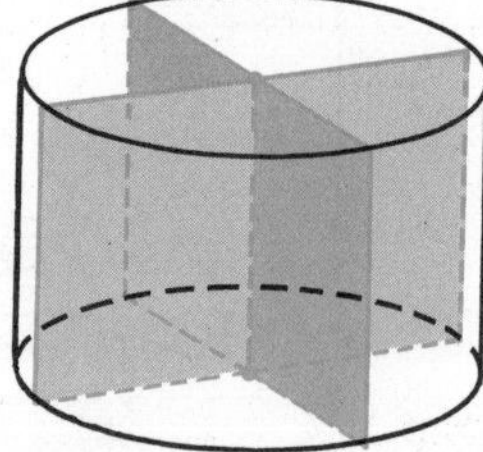

A right circular cylinder has infinitely many symmetry planes (each plane that contains its axis and the perpendicular bisecting plane of its axis).

Exercises 14.9

Ⓐ **1.** If a figure can be separated into two "congruent halves" by a plane, the figure has ______.

2. A figure that has plane symmetry can be reflected over a plane so that the figure is its own ______.

3. A regular triangular prism has ______ symmetry plane(s).

4. A figure (must have at least one, may have no) symmetry plane(s).

Ⓑ **5–18.** Determine how many symmetry planes each type of solid has. (Draw sketches or use models if necessary.)

5. a right rectangular prism, no faces square

6. a regular square pyramid

7. a rectangular pyramid, base not a square, lateral faces isosceles

8. a right square prism, not a cube

9. a regular pentagonal prism, lateral faces not square

10. a regular hexagonal prism, lateral faces not square

11. a right circular cone

12. a nonright circular cone

13. a triangular pyramid, all faces scalene

14. a sphere

Ⓒ **15.** a cube

16. a triangular pyramid, all faces equilateral

SYMMETRY IN NATURE

Many plants and animals have plane symmetry (called bilateral symmetry in biology). The leaf has bilateral symmetry because it can be separated into two identical parts by a plane. The reflection of one half of the leaf over the plane is the other half. Which of the plants and animals below have bilateral symmetry?

Dr. E. R. Degginger

Camerique

Cactus

Leonard Lee Rue III
Van Cleve Photography

Butterfly

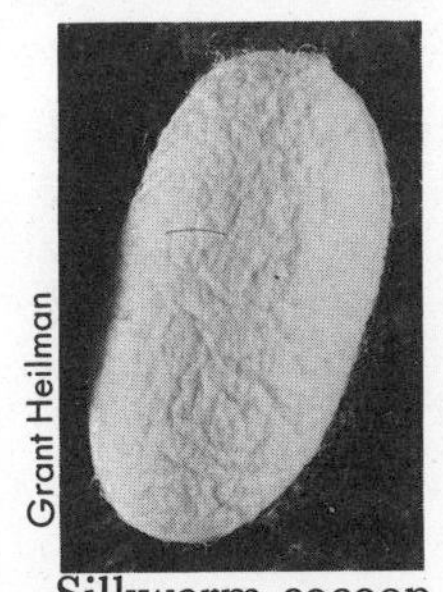
Grant Heilman

Silkworm cocoon

Field Museum of Natural History

Lobster

Dr. E. R. Degginger

Cat

■ Chapter 14 Review ■

14.1 **1–4.** Give the number of each for the given polyhedron.

1. vertices **2.** edges

3. faces **4.** dihedral angles

5. Is the polyhedron for Ex. 1–4 convex?

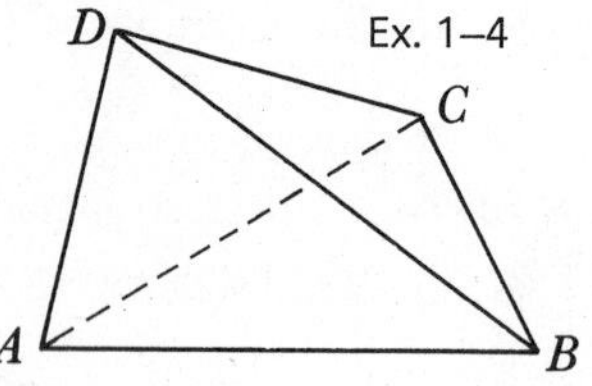

14.2 **6–10.** True or False? Use the given figure.

6. Plane $ABC \parallel$ plane DEF.

7. $\overline{AD} \parallel \overline{BE} \parallel \overline{CF}$ **8.** $\triangle ABC \cong \triangle DEF$

9. The prism is right rectangular.

10. $\overline{AC}$ and $\overline{DF}$ are altitudes of the prism.

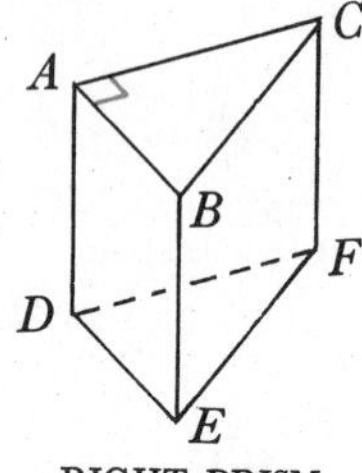

RIGHT PRISM

11. If a box is $10 \times 12 \times 8$ cm, what is its volume?

14.3 **12.** If $AB = 5$, $AC = 6$, and $AD = 10$, find the volume of the prism shown above.

13. Find the volume of a right hexagonal prism with a base area of 1.85 m^2 and a height of 0.23 m.

14.4 **14–18.** Refer to the given cylinder.

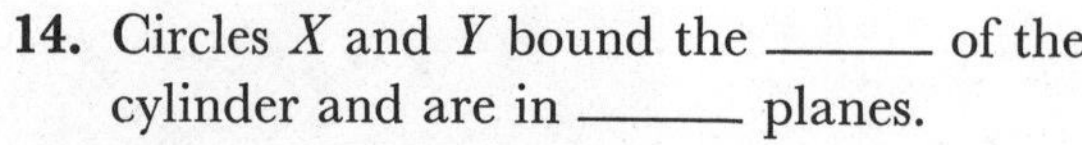

14. Circles X and Y bound the ______ of the cylinder and are in ______ planes.

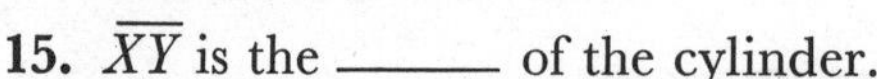

15. $\overline{XY}$ is the ______ of the cylinder.

16. YZ is the ______ of the cylinder.

17. XY is the ______ of the cylinder.

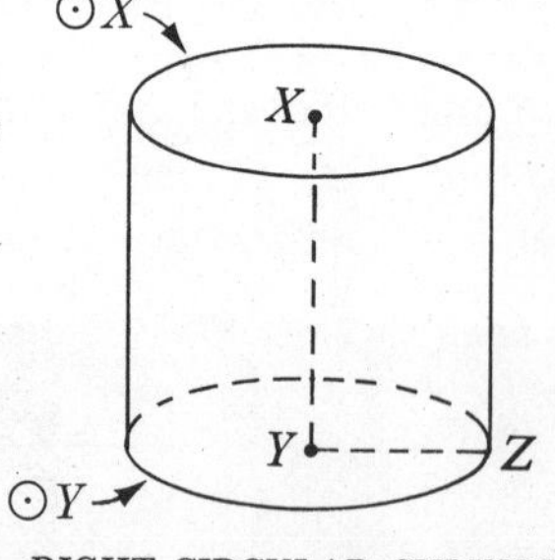

RIGHT CIRCULAR CYLINDER

18. If $XY = 10$ m and $YZ = 4$ m, find the volume in terms of π.

14.5 **19–23.** True or False?

19. The bases of an oblique prism are bounded by congruent polygons.

20. A lateral edge of an oblique prism can also be an altitude.

21. The height of an oblique circular cylinder is the length of the axis.

22. All segments of the lateral surface of an oblique circular cylinder are parallel to the axis.

23. The area of a cross section of a cylinder (made by a plane parallel to a base) is equal to the area of the base.

24–25. Find the volume of each solid. (Use $\pi = 3.14$.)

24. an oblique prism with a square base 6 cm on a side and a height of 5 cm

25. an oblique circular cylinder with height 25 mm and radius 10 mm

14.6

26–29. Name each part for the given pyramid.

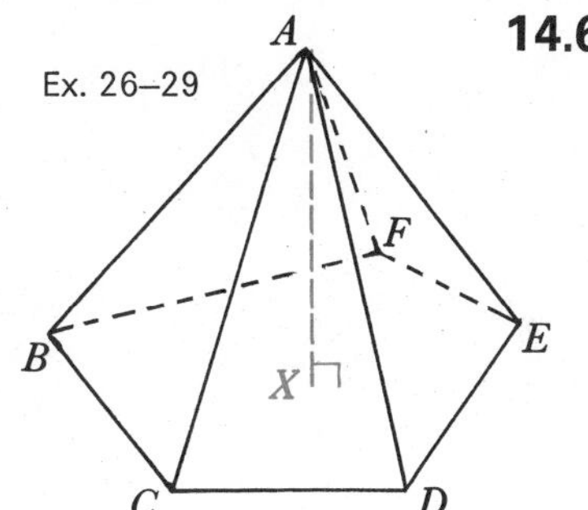

26. vertex 27. lateral edges

28. base 29. altitude

30. What kinds of polygons bound (**a**) the base and (**b**) the lateral faces of a regular pyramid?

31. Find the volume of a pyramid whose height is 12 cm and whose base area is 200 cm^2.

32–37. Refer to the given circular cone.

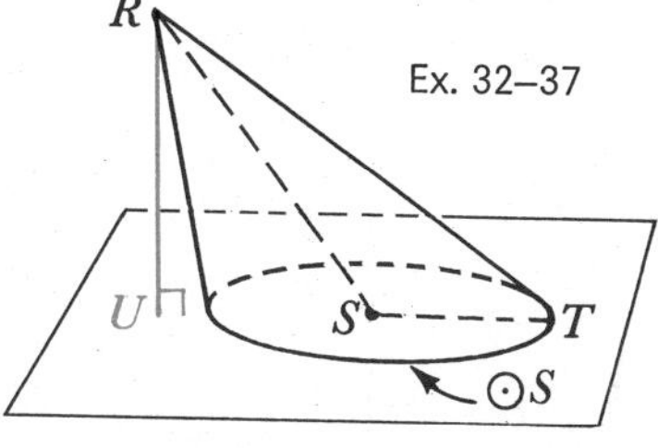

32. $\overline{RS}$ is the ______. 33. R is the ______.

34. ST is the ______. 35. RU is the ______.

36. If $\overline{RS}$ and the plane of the base are ______, then the cone is a right circular cone.

37. Find the volume in terms of π if $RU = 12$ cm and $ST = 8$ cm.

38–40. Find the lateral area and surface area of each solid. **14.7**

38. regular square pyramid with base edges of length 2 and slant height of 19

39. right circular cylinder of height 16 and radius 4

NOTE: Leave answers 39–41 in terms of π.

40. right circular cone of slant height 10 and radius 6

41. Find the volume and surface area of a sphere with radius 3 cm. **14.8**

42. The symmetry planes of a right circular cone contain its (axis, base, lateral surface). **14.9**

Chapter 14 Test

1. Each face of a polyhedron is bounded by a ______.

2. A solid whose lateral faces are bounded by rectangles is a ______.

3. A circular cylinder whose axis is perpendicular to the planes of both bases is a ______.

4. A solid with one base whose lateral faces are bounded by congruent isosceles triangles is a ______.

5. A solid that has one vertex and a circular base is a ______.

6. The measure of the amount of space enclosed by a solid is its ______.

7. The measure of the total surface of a solid is its ______.

8–13. Find the surface area and volume of each solid.

NOTE: Leave answers 10–13 in terms of π.

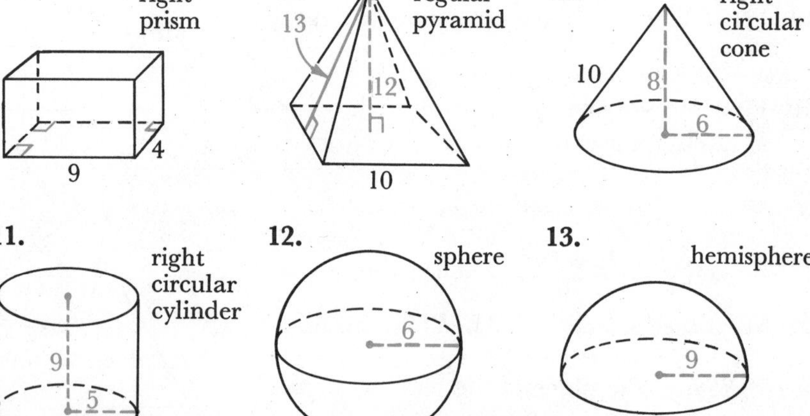

14. Find the lateral area, surface area, and volume of a cube whose edge is 5 cm long.

15. Find the surface area of a right circular cylinder whose volume is 128π cubic units and whose radius is 4 units. (Leave in terms of π.)

16. What is the radius of a sphere whose surface area is 324π cm^2?

17. What is the slant height of a regular square pyramid whose surface area is 182 cm^2 and whose base edge is 7 cm long?

18. Find the height of a circular cone with volume 256π and radius 8.

19. A right circular cylinder has (no, exactly one, many) symmetry planes.

MINI-CHAPTER: PLATONIC SOLIDS

A **regular polyhedron** is a convex polyhedron whose faces are bounded by congruent convex polygons and whose dihedral angles are congruent. Regular polyhedrons are sometimes referred to as "Platonic solids" after the Greek philosopher Plato. There are only five such solids, and Plato felt they represented fire, earth, air, water, and the universe.

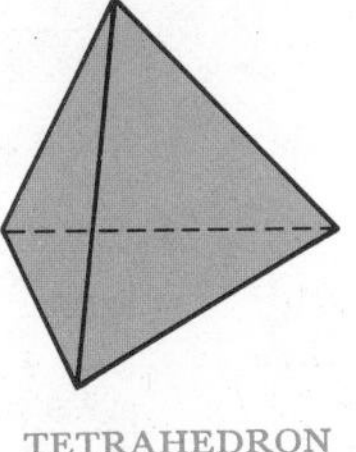

TETRAHEDRON (fire)

HEXAHEDRON (earth)

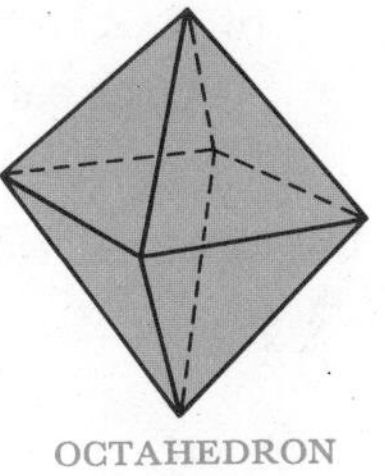

OCTAHEDRON (air)

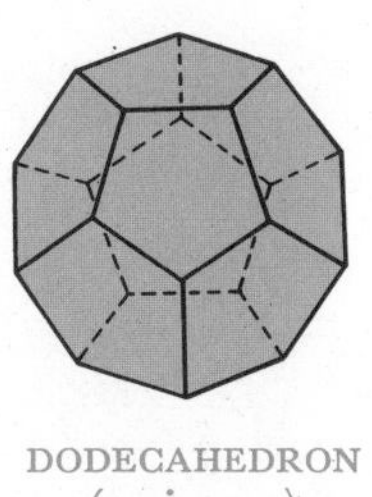

DODECAHEDRON (universe)

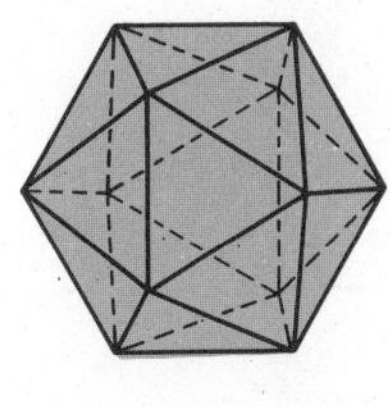

ICOSAHEDRON (water)

Each solid is named by the number of its faces. The prefix *tetra-* means four, so a tetrahedron has four faces. Which solids have 6, 8, 12, and 20 faces?

Notice that the same number of faces intersect at each vertex of any one solid. Three is the least number of faces at one vertex that will form a convex 3-dimensional corner, as in a tetrahedron. Six equilateral triangles with the same vertex are in the same plane and cannot be "folded" to form a convex 3-dimensional corner. So, *the sum of the measures of the angles of the faces at one vertex of a regular solid must be less than 360.*

60 60 60

Can be folded to form 3 faces of a tetrahedron. Sum of angle measures is less than 360.

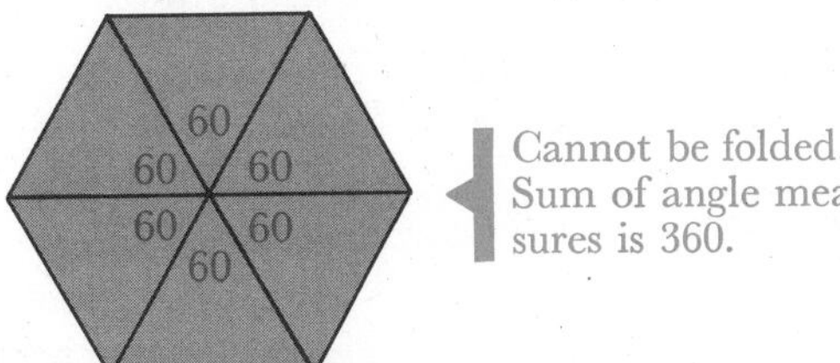

Cannot be folded. Sum of angle measures is 360.

Use the method above to show why

1. The tetrahedron, octahedron, and icosahedron are the only regular polyhedrons with faces bounded by triangles. (How many faces are at each vertex of each solid?)

2. The hexahedron is the only regular polyhedron with faces bounded by squares, and the dodecahedron is the only regular polyhedron with faces bounded by pentagons. (How many faces are at each vertex of each solid?)

3. No regular polyhedron could have faces bounded by regular polygons with more than five sides.

Copy and complete the chart below. Use the formulas below and your answers from Exercises 1–3 on page 513.

$$\text{no. of vertices of a solid} = \frac{(\text{no. of vertices of each face}) \cdot (\text{no. of faces})}{(\text{no. of faces at each vertex})}$$

$$\text{no. of edges of a solid} = \frac{(\text{no. of sides of each face}) \cdot (\text{no. of faces})}{2}$$

NOTE: 2 is the number of faces that meet at each edge of the solid.

Regular solid	No. of faces	Type of faces	No. faces at each vertex	Total no. vertices	Total no. edges
Tetrahedron	4	triangular regions	3	$\frac{3 \cdot 4}{3} = 4$	$\frac{3 \cdot 4}{2} = 6$
Hexahedron					
Octahedron					
Dodecahedron					
Icosahedron					

Enlarge the patterns below and make models of the Platonic solids. (Cut along the solid lines and fold along the dashed lines.)

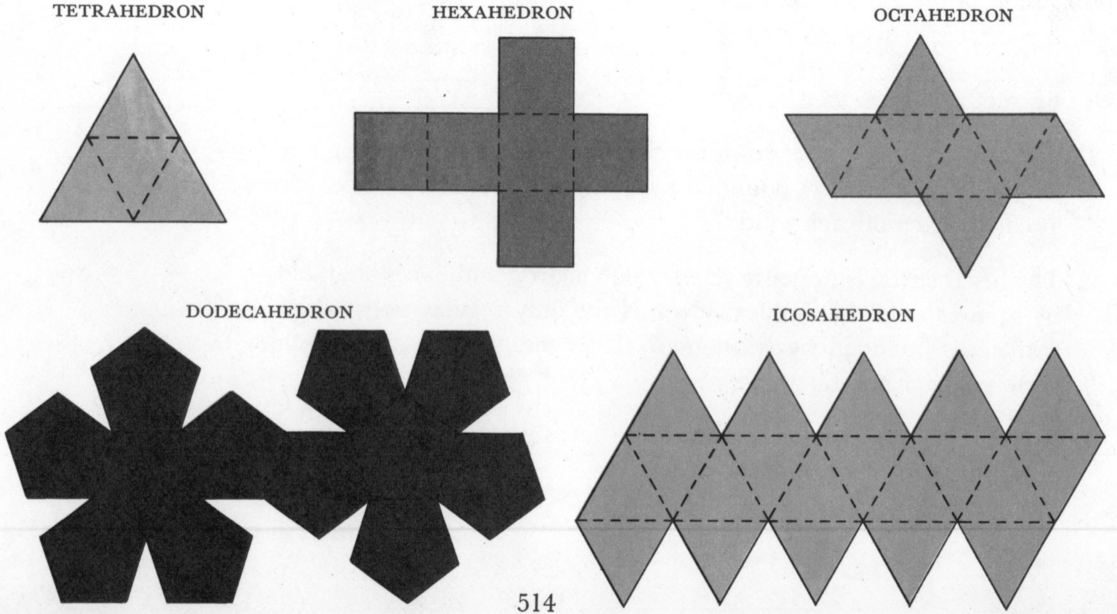

COORDINATE GEOMETRY

As the photos here suggest, graphs have many uses. In this chapter, graphs will be used to study geometry.

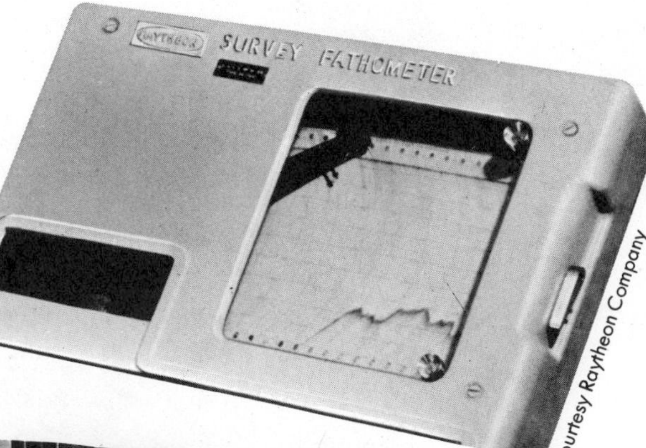

Oceanology

Courtesy Raytheon Company

Pollution control

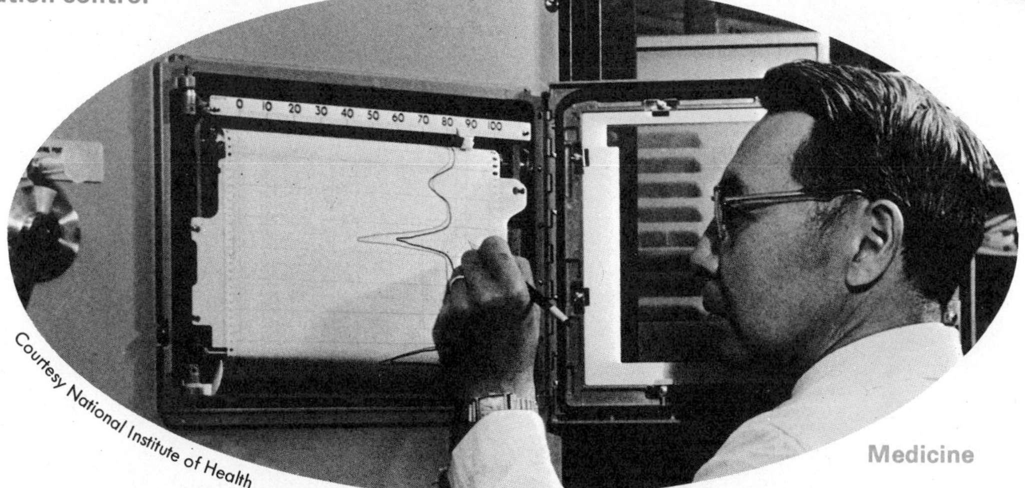

Courtesy National Institute of Health

Medicine

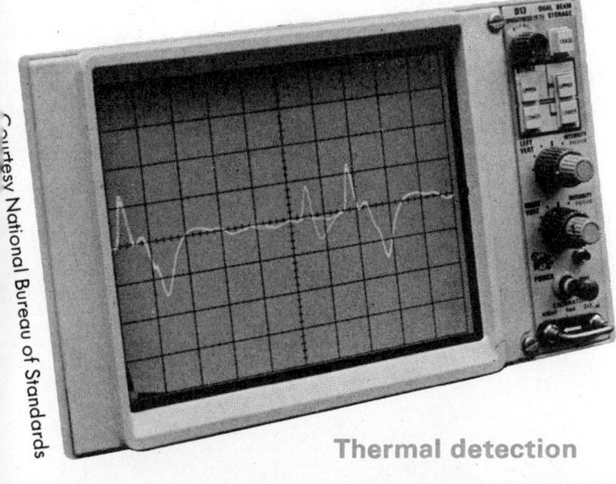

Courtesy National Bureau of Standards

Thermal detection

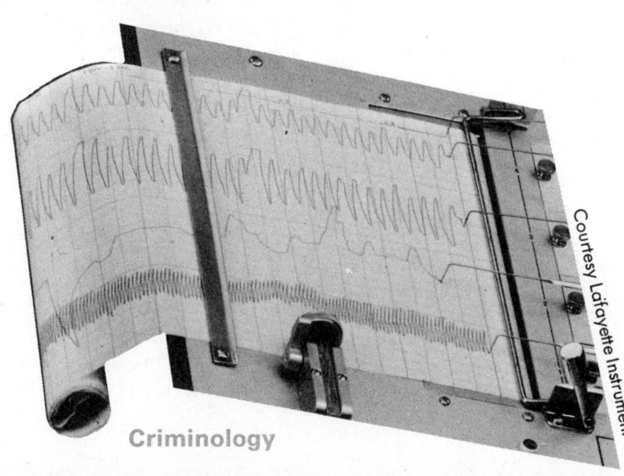

Criminology

Courtesy Lafayette Instrument Co.

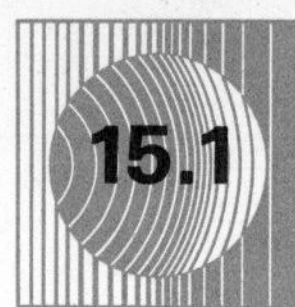

The Coordinate Plane

On a real number line, every point is matched with exactly one real number, and every real number is matched with exactly one point.

REAL NUMBER LINE

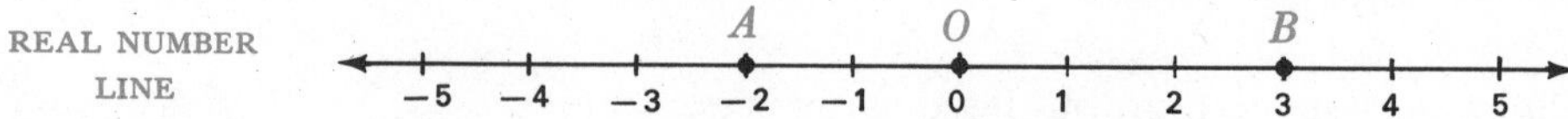

Point A has coordinate -2.
3 is the coordinate of point B.
Point O is the zero point of the line.

There is a similar system for points in a plane. Let line x be a real number line. There is a line y perpendicular to line x at its zero point. By the Ruler Postulate, the points of line y can be matched with the real numbers so that its point of intersection with line x has coordinate 0.

COORDINATE PLANE

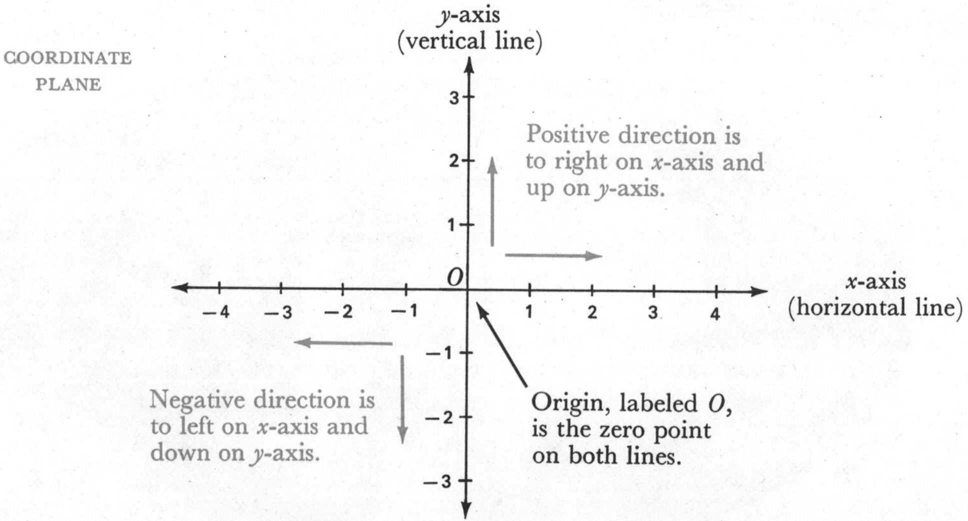

The **axes** (plural of *axis*) determine a plane called the **coordinate plane.** A point on a number line has one coordinate, and a point in the coordinate plane has a pair of coordinates.

FIRST COORDINATE: the coordinate of the foot of the perpendicular from R to the x-axis (also called the *x-coordinate* or *abscissa*)

SECOND COORDINATE: the coordinate of the foot of the perpendicular from R to the y-axis (also called the *y-coordinate* or *ordinate*)

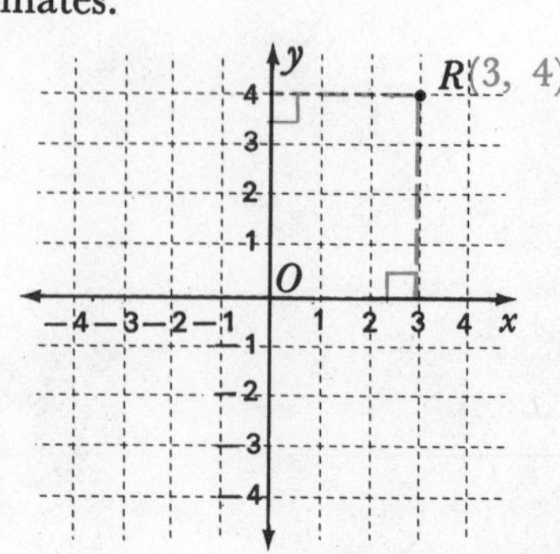

The coordinates of R are the **ordered pair** (3, 4). The coordinates of a point are an *ordered* pair because the *x-coordinate* is always named *first.* We can write $R(3, 4)$ to show that point R is at (3, 4). And we say that R is the *graph* of the ordered pair (3, 4).

Example: Name the coordinates of each point shown on the graph.

Point	Coordinates
A	(3, 1)
B	(1, 3)
C	(0, 2)
D	(−3, 4)
E	(−2, 0)
F	(−1, −2)
G	(0, −2)
H	$(1\frac{1}{2}, -2\frac{1}{2})$
I	(2, 0)
O	(0, 0)
P	(x, y)

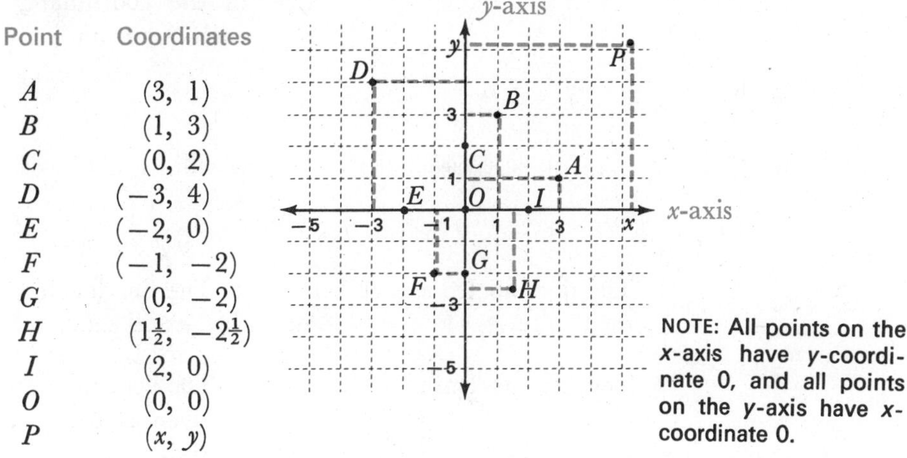

NOTE: All points on the x-axis have y-coordinate 0, and all points on the y-axis have x-coordinate 0.

In general, for every point P in the coordinate plane, there is exactly one ordered pair (x, y) of real numbers where x is the x-coordinate and y is the y-coordinate of P. Conversely, for every ordered pair (x, y) of real numbers, there is exactly one point P in the coordinate plane whose x-coordinate is x and whose y-coordinate is y.

Any line perpendicular to the y-axis is parallel to the x-axis (why?) and is a horizontal line. Lines perpendicular to the x-axis are vertical lines. An easy way to locate points on a graph is to imagine "traveling" on horizontal and vertical lines. For (−3, 2) and (2, −3), start at the origin (0, 0). Then

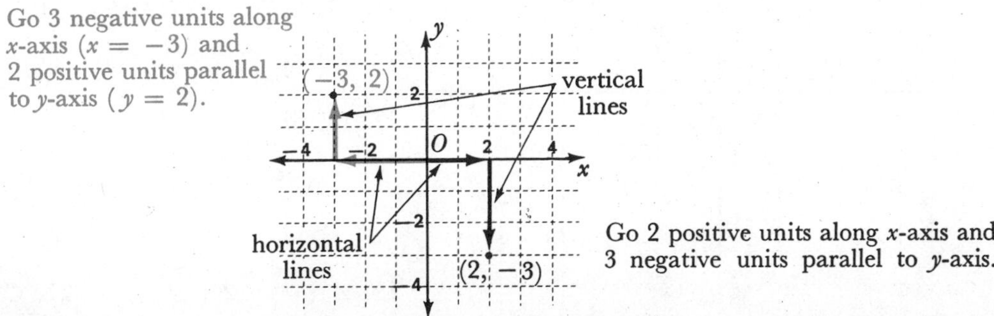

NOTE: (−3, 2) and (2, −3) are **not** the same point.

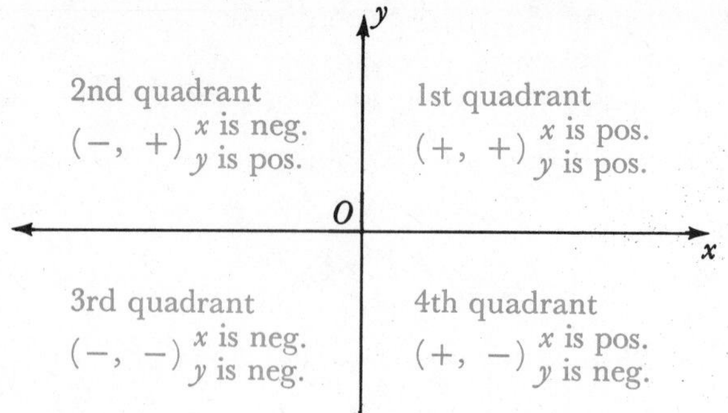

The axes separate the plane into four parts called *quadrants*, which are numbered as shown. Points on the axes are not in any of the quadrants. Notice the signs of the coordinates of points in each quadrant.

Exercises 15.1

Ⓐ **1–8.** Use the figure below to complete each statement.

1. The line labeled x is called the ______.

2. The line labeled y is called the ______.

3. The axes determine the ______ plane.

4. The coordinates of a point are given as a(n) ______ pair.

5. The first coordinate of a point is called the ______.

6. The second coordinate of a point is called the ______.

7. The point (0, 0) is called the ______.

8. The axes separate the coordinate plane into four ______.

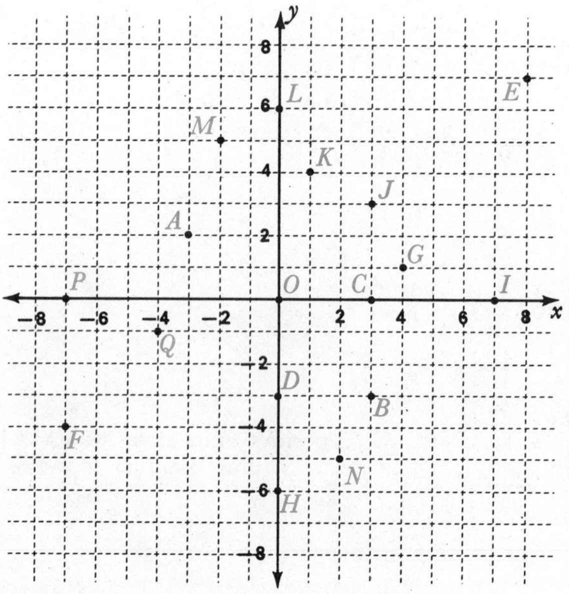

9–18. Name the point on the graph whose ordered pair is given.

9. (4, 1)	**10.** (1, 4)
11. (−2, 5)	**12.** (2, −5)
13. (7, 0)	**14.** (−7, 0)
15. (0, 6)	**16.** (0, −6)
17. (3, 3)	**18.** (−4, −1)

19–24. Name the coordinates of each point.

19. *A*	**20.** *B*	**21.** *C*
22. *D*	**23.** *E*	**24.** *O*

Ⓑ **25–34.** Graph. Use a separate pair of axes for each exercise.

25. (1, 0), (3, 0), (5, 0), (0, 0), (−2, 0), (−4, 0)

26. (0, −3), (0, −1), (0, 0), (0, 2), (0, 4), (0, 6)

27. (2, 1), (2, 3), (2, 4), (2, 0), (2, −1), (2, −2)

28. (−3, −5), (−2, −5), (−1, −5), (0, −5), (1, −5), (2, −5)

29. (−3, 2), (−1, 2), (1, 2), (1, 6), (−1, 6), (−3, 6)

30. (−2, 2), (−5, 2), (−5, −2), (−5, −4), (−2, −4), (−2, −1)

31. $(-2\frac{1}{2}, 6)$, $(-2\frac{1}{2}, 4)$, $(-2\frac{1}{2}, 2)$, $(-2\frac{1}{2}, 0)$, $(-2\frac{1}{2}, -2\frac{1}{2})$, $(2\frac{1}{2}, 0)$

32. (−8, 6), (−5, 6), (−2, 6) (0, 3), (−3, 3), (−6, 3)

33. (−2, 2), (0, 0), (2, −2), (2, −5), (0, −3), (−5, 2)

34. (0, −4), (4, 0), (8, 0), (12, −4), (8, −8), (4, −8)

35–38. Use your graphs for Exercises 25–34 to answer each exercise.

35. If the *y*-coordinate of a point is ______, then it is on the *x*-axis.

36. If the *x*-coordinate of a point is ______, then it is on the *y*-axis.

37. Points with the same __-coordinate are on the same vertical line.

38. Points with the same __-coordinate are on the same horizontal line.

39–44. Join, in the order given, the points on your graphs for Exercises 29–34. Join the last point to the first. What kind of figure is each?

45. If (1, 7) and (1, 3) are two vertices of a square that is in the 1st quadrant, name its other two vertices.

46. If (−4, −6), (−7, −1), and (−2, −4) are the vertices of a triangle, which quadrant is the triangle in?

Ⓒ **47–49.** Graph *A*(−3, 3), *B*(−3, −3), *C*(3, −3), and *D*(3, 3).

47. What is the perimeter of *ABCD*?

48. What is the length of $\overline{AC}$?

49. Name (**a**) four points that appear to be on $\overline{AC}$, (**b**) four points that appear to be on $\overline{BD}$, and (**c**) one point that appears to be on both $\overline{AC}$ and $\overline{BD}$.

15.2 Distance Formula

On a number line, the distance between two points is the absolute value of the difference of their coordinates.

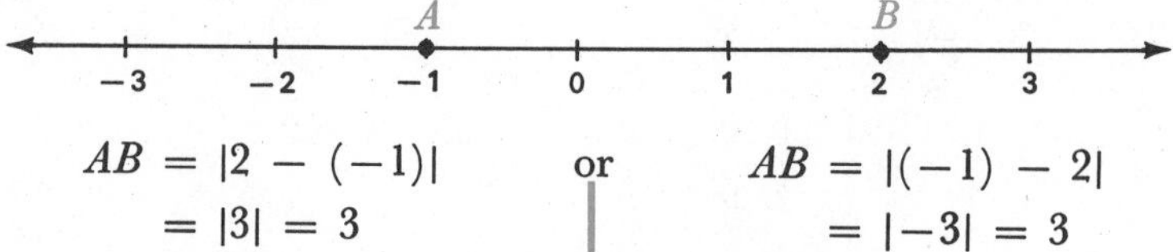

$$AB = |2 - (-1)| = |3| = 3 \quad \text{or} \quad AB = |(-1) - 2| = |-3| = 3$$

In the coordinate plane, all points on a horizontal line have the same y-coordinate. So we can use the method for distance on a number line to find AB for $A(-3, 2)$ and $B(4, 2)$ below.

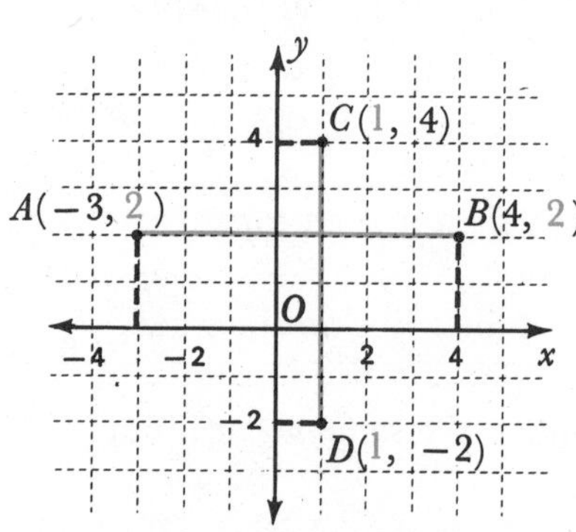

$$AB = |\text{difference of } x\text{-coordinates}| = |4 - (-3)| = |7| = 7$$

Similarly, all points on a vertical line have the same x-coordinate. For $C(1, 4)$ and $D(1, -2)$,

$$CD = |\text{difference of } y\text{-coordinates}| = |-2 - 4| = |-6| = 6$$

We can use the method above and the Pythagorean Theorem to find the distance between points not on horizontal or vertical lines.

Below, point P is at $(-2, 1)$ and point Q is at $(2, 4)$. The horizontal line through P and the vertical line through Q intersect at point R. Since R is on the same vertical line as Q, its x-coordinate is 2. R is on the same horizontal line as P, so its y-coordinate is 1. $\triangle PQR$ is a right triangle. Why?

By the method above, $PR = |2 - (-2)| = 4$

$QR = |4 - 1| = 3$

By the Pythagorean Theorem and substitution,

$$(PQ)^2 = (PR)^2 + (QR)^2$$
$$(PQ)^2 = 4^2 + 3^2$$
$$(PQ)^2 = 25$$

And, $\sqrt{(PQ)^2} = \sqrt{25}$

$$PQ = 5$$

A formula for the distance between points in the coordinate plane can be found by letting P and Q be any points at (x_1, y_1) and (x_2, y_2). The *subscripts* $_1$ and $_2$ indicate that x_1 and x_2 (or y_1 and y_2) can have different values.

The horizontal and vertical lines through P and Q intersect at point $R(x_2, y_1)$. Why? So,

$$(PQ)^2 = (PR)^2 + (QR)^2$$
$$= |x_2 - x_1|^2 + |y_2 - y_1|^2$$

Since for any number n, $|n|^2 = n^2$, even when $n < 0$ (why?), we can write

$$(PQ)^2 = (x_2 - x_1)^2 + (y_2 - y_1)^2$$

By taking the square root of both sides of the equation, we get

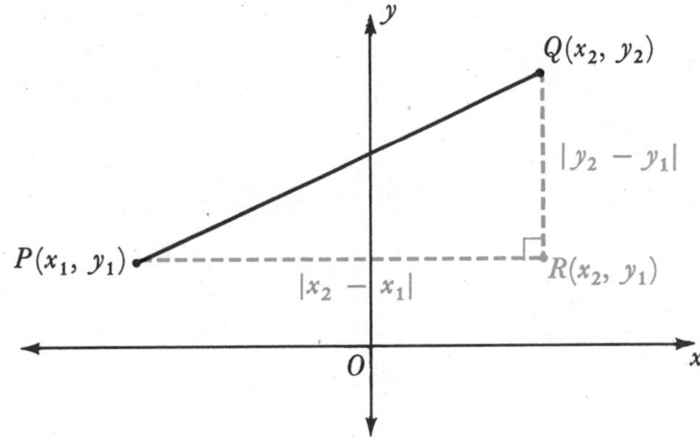

If P is a point at (x_1, y_1) and Q is another point at (x_2, y_2), then the distance from P to Q is

$$PQ = \sqrt{(x_2 - x_1)^2 + (y_2 - y_1)^2}$$

Distance Formula Theorem

NOTE: Distance is always a positive number. Why?

Example: Use the distance formula to find PQ for $P(6, 3)$ and $Q(-3, 0)$.

Let $(x_1, y_1) = (6, 3)$ and $(x_2, y_2) = (-3, 0)$. Then $x_1 = 6, y_1 = 3$, $x_2 = -3$, and $y_2 = 0$.

$$PQ = \sqrt{(x_2 - x_1)^2 + (y_2 - y_1)^2}$$
$$= \sqrt{(-3 - 6)^2 + (0 - 3)^2}$$
$$= \sqrt{(-9)^2 + (-3)^2}$$
$$= \sqrt{81 + 9} = \sqrt{90} = 3\sqrt{10}$$

Simplify radical.

Exercises 15.2

Ⓐ **1.** $\sqrt{(x_2 - x_1)^2 + (y_2 - y_1)^2}$ is the ______ from $P(x_1, x_2)$ to $Q(y_1, y_2)$.

2. If P is at $(3, 0)$, Q is at $(2, 5)$, and $x_1 = 3$, then $y_1 =$ ______, $x_2 =$ ______, and $y_2 =$ ______.

3. If P is at $(1, 0)$ and Q is at $(4, 0)$, then $PQ =$ ______.

4. If P is at $(0, -6)$ and Q is at $(0, -2)$, then $PQ =$ ______.

5. If P is at $(3, 2)$ and Q is at $(-1, 2)$, then $PQ =$ ______.

6. Can the distance between points P and Q be a negative number?

Ⓑ 7. A vertical line through $A(2, 6)$ and a horizontal line through $B(7, -3)$ intersect at point C. Find the coordinates of C.

8. A horizontal line through $A(2, 6)$ and a vertical line through $B(7, -3)$ intersect at point C. Find the coordinates of C.

9–20. Find the distance between the given points. Simplify radicals.

9. $(0, 0), (5, 12)$

10. $(-2, -4), (0, 0)$

11. $(1, 5), (1, -8)$

12. $(-2, -1), (7, -1)$

13. $(3, 4), (7, 2)$

14. $(-3, -6), (-4, -1)$

15. $(-10, 5), (6, -1)$

16. $(12, -8), (-2, 2)$

17. $(11, 8), (35, 15)$

18. $(101, -106), (1, -6)$

19. $(5, 5), (-5, -5)$

20. $(-8, 8), (8, -8)$

21–28. Use the distance formula and a graph to answer each exercise.

21. Is $\triangle ABC$ isosceles if A is at $(-3, 1)$, B is at $(5, 1)$, and C is at $(1, 5)$?

22. Is $\triangle PQR$ equilateral if P is at $(3, -4)$, Q is at $(5, -2)$, and R is at $(6, -5)$?

23. Find the lengths of the diagonals of a quadrilateral with vertices $A(1, -2)$, $B(5, -2)$, $C(6, 1)$, and $D(2, 1)$.

24. Are the diagonals of quadrilateral $JKLM$ with vertices $J(3, 1)$, $K(7, -2)$, $L(1, -3)$, and $M(-1, -1)$ equal in length?

25. Using the Pythagorean Theorem, show that a triangle with vertices $A(-3, 3)$, $B(-5, 6)$, and $C(0, 5)$ is a right triangle.

26. Using the Pythagorean Theorem, show that a triangle with vertices $D(3, 0)$, $E(4, -3)$, and $F(1, -2)$ is not a right triangle.

Ⓒ 27. A segment has endpoints $P(3, 4)$ and $Q(6, y)$. Find two possible values for y if $PQ = 5$.

28. Can a triangle with vertices $A(0, -2)$, $B(-2, 2)$, and $C(2, 0)$ be inscribed in a circle of radius 2 and center at the origin?

29. Name the coordinates of four points, each on an axis, that are on a circle of radius 5 and center at the origin.

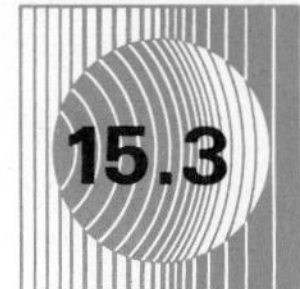

Midpoint Formula

In the graph below $P(-2, 2)$ and $Q(4, 2)$ are the endpoints of a horizontal segment. M is the midpoint of $\overline{PQ}$, and its y-coordinate is 2. Why? Let x be its x-coordinate. Since $\overline{PM}$ and $\overline{MQ}$ are horizontal,

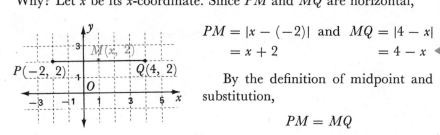

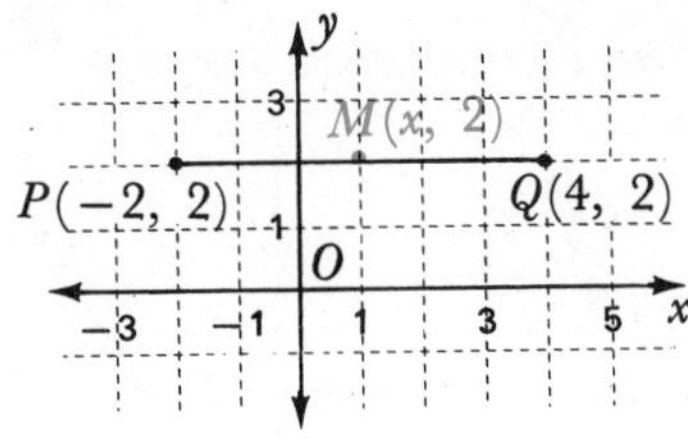

$$PM = |x - (-2)| \text{ and } MQ = |4 - x|$$
$$= x + 2 \qquad\qquad = 4 - x$$

Since $-2 < x < 4$, $x + 2 > 0$ and $4 - x > 0$. So we can eliminate the absolute value signs.

By the definition of midpoint and substitution,

$$PM = MQ$$
$$x + 2 = 4 - x$$
$$2x = 2$$
$$x = 1$$

So, M is at $(1, 2)$.

Let P be at $(x_1, 2)$ and Q at $(x_2, 2)$ with $x_1 < x_2$. Then midpoint M is at $(x, 2)$ and $x_1 < x < x_2$.

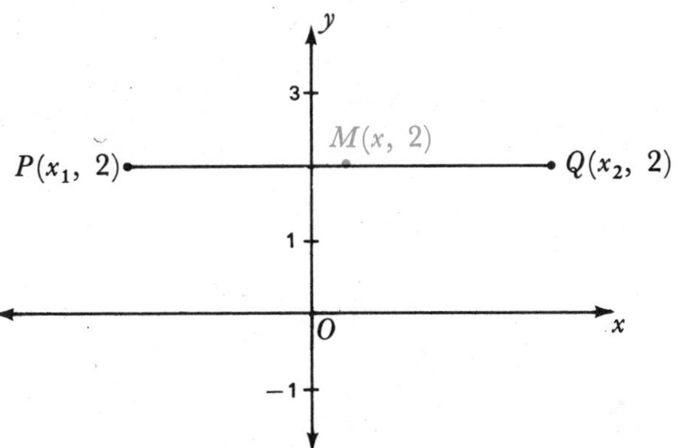

$$PM = |x - x_1| \quad \text{and} \quad MQ = |x_2 - x|$$
$$= x - x_1 \qquad\qquad = x_2 - x$$

$$PM = MQ$$
$$x - x_1 = x_2 - x$$
$$2x = x_1 + x_2$$
$$x = \frac{x_1 + x_2}{2}$$

And M is at $\left(\frac{x_1 + x_2}{2}, 2\right)$. Notice that the x-coordinate of M is the average of the x-coordinates of the endpoints. For $P(-2, 2)$ and $Q(4, 2)$ above, the x-coordinate of M is 1, which is the average of -2 and 4.

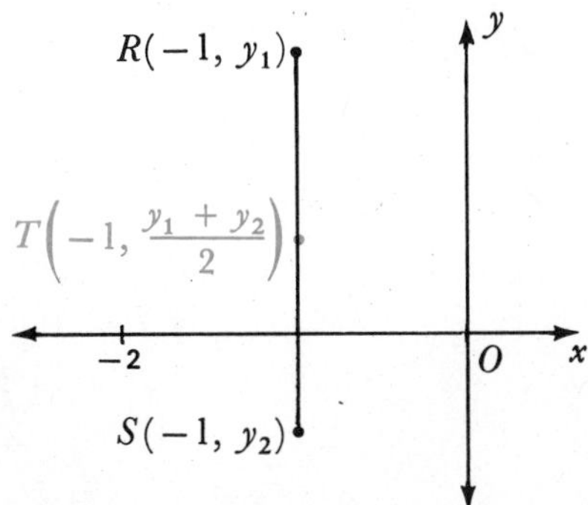

Using that same type of reasoning, we find that the y-coordinate of the midpoint of a vertical segment is the average of the y-coordinates of the endpoints. For $R(-1, y_1)$ and $S(-1, y_2)$, midpoint T of $\overline{RS}$ is

$$T\left(-1, \frac{y_1 + y_2}{2}\right)$$

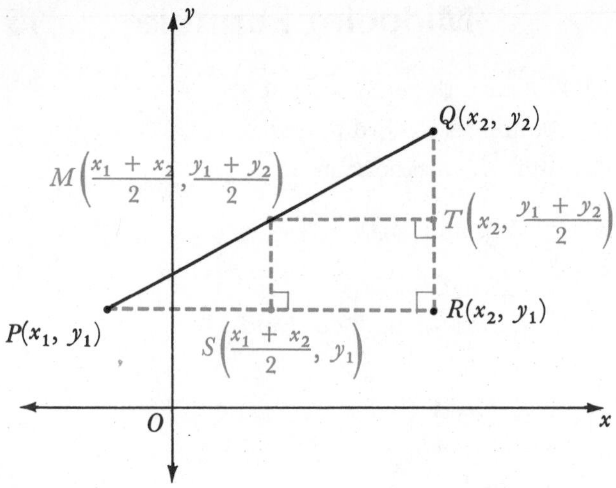

Now we can find the coordinates of the midpoint of $\overline{PQ}$ at left, which is not horizontal or vertical. The horizontal and vertical lines through $P(x_1, y_1)$ and $Q(x_2, y_2)$ give us $R(x_2, y_1)$. Why? $\overline{PR}$ is a horizontal segment, so its midpoint S is at

$$S\left(\frac{x_1 + x_2}{2}, y_1\right)$$

$\overline{QR}$ is a vertical segment, so its midpoint T is at

$$T\left(x_2, \frac{y_1 + y_2}{2}\right)$$

The horizontal segment through T and the vertical segment through S both intersect $\overline{PQ}$ at its midpoint M. (If a line parallel to one side of a triangle bisects either of the other two sides, it bisects both of them.) The x-coordinate of M is the same as the x-coordinate of S, and the y-coordinate of M is the same as the y-coordinate of T. Why?

Midpoint Formula Theorem

If point P is at (x_1, y_1) and point Q is at (x_2, y_2), then the midpoint M of $\overline{PQ}$ is

$$M\left(\frac{x_1 + x_2}{2}, \frac{y_1 + y_2}{2}\right)$$

Example 1: Find the coordinates of the midpoint of a segment whose endpoints are at $(-2, 6)$ and $(3, -2)$.

Midpoint formula: $\left(\frac{x_1 + x_2}{2}, \frac{y_1 + y_2}{2}\right)$

$$\frac{x_1 + x_2}{2} = \frac{-2 + 3}{2} = \frac{1}{2} \quad \text{and} \quad \frac{y_1 + y_2}{2} = \frac{6 + (-2)}{2} = 2$$

The midpoint is at $(\frac{1}{2}, 2)$.

Example 2: $M(-1, -3)$ is the midpoint of $\overline{PQ}$. If P is at $(-3, 2)$, find the coordinates of Q.

1. Let Q have coordinates (x, y). By the midpoint formula, the midpoint of $\overline{PQ}$ is

$$\left(\frac{x - 3}{2}, \frac{y + 2}{2}\right)$$

2. We are given that $M(-1, -3)$ is the midpoint of $\overline{PQ}$. So

$$\frac{x-3}{2} = -1 \quad \text{and} \quad \frac{y+2}{2} = -3$$

$$x - 3 = -2 \qquad y + 2 = -6$$

$$x = 1 \qquad y = -8$$

So Q is at $(1, -8)$.

Exercises 15.3

Ⓐ **1–12.** What are the coordinates of the midpoint of the segment joining each pair of points?

1. $(0, 0), (4, 0)$ **2.** $(0, 0), (-4, 0)$ **3.** $(0, 0), (0, 6)$

4. $(0, 0), (0, -6)$ **5.** $(1, 0), (7, 0)$ **6.** $(0, -1), (0, -5)$

7. $(4, 0), (-4, 0)$ **8.** $(0, -3), (0, 3)$ **9.** $(1, 0), (-3, 0)$

10. $(0, 1), (0, -9)$ **11.** $(1, 6), (1, 10)$ **12.** $(3, 1), (7, 1)$

13. For $P(x_1, y_1)$ and $Q(x_2, y_2)$, $M\left(\frac{x_1 + x_2}{2}, \frac{y_1 + y_2}{2}\right)$ is the ______ of $\overline{PQ}$.

14. If M is the midpoint of $\overline{PQ}$, then PM ______ MQ ______ $\frac{1}{2}PQ$.

Ⓑ **15–26.** Using the midpoint formula, find the coordinates of the midpoint of the segment joining each pair of points.

15. $(0, 8), (4, 2)$ **16.** $(3, 10), (1, 0)$ **17.** $(-5, 7), (-7, 5)$

18. $(13, -9), (9, -13)$ **19.** $(7, 3), (8, 4)$ **20.** $(-6, -5), (9, -5)$

21. $(\frac{2}{3}, \frac{1}{2}), (0, 1)$ **22.** $(-\frac{5}{8}, \frac{3}{4}), (-\frac{3}{8}, \frac{1}{2})$ **23.** $(\sqrt{2}, \sqrt{3}), (\sqrt{2}, 3\sqrt{3})$

24. $(\sqrt{5}, 3\sqrt{7}), (\sqrt{5}, \sqrt{7})$ **25.** $(a, 0), (b, 0)$ **26.** $(a, b), (c, d)$

27. Find the coordinates of the midpoint of each side of a triangle with vertices at (3, 5), (6, −4), and (−1, 1).

28. Find the coordinates of the midpoint of each side of a quadrilateral with vertices at (−2, −4), (7, −8), (4, −3), and (−5, 2).

29. Find the length of each median of a triangle with vertices at (−1, 6), (−3, −2), and (7, −4).

30. Find the perimeter of the figure whose vertices are the midpoints of a quadrilateral with vertices at (7, 4), (1, 8), (−3, 4), and (3, −2).

31. A rectangle has vertices $A(-6, 4)$, $B(-6, -1)$, $C(2, -1)$, and $D(2, 4)$. Show that its diagonals have the same midpoint.

32. A parallelogram has vertices $P(7, 3)$, $Q(12, 7)$, $R(10, -2)$, and $S(5, -6)$. Show that its diagonals have the same midpoint.

33–38. One endpoint and the midpoint of a segment are given. Use the midpoint formula to find the coordinates of the second endpoint.

33. endpt. (3, 5), midpt. (−2, 1)

34. endpt. (5, 7), midpt. $(6, 3\frac{1}{2})$

35. endpt. (4, 7), midpt. (6, 3)

36. endpt. (−1, 4), midpt. (1, 1)

37. endpt. $(a, 0)$, midpt. $(0, a)$

38. endpt. (a, b), midpt. (c, d)

© **39.** Use the distance formula to show that $Q(1, -1)$ is the midpoint of the segment with endpoints $A(4, 1)$ and $B(-2, -3)$.

40. Points A and B are the endpoints of a segment that contains point C. For the given coordinates of A and B, find the coordinates (x, y) of C so that $AC = r \cdot CB$.

a. $A(x_1, 0)$, $B(x_2, 0)$

b. $A(0, y_1)$, $B(0, y_2)$

c. $A(x_1, y_1)$, $B(x_2, y_2)$ HINT: Use your results from parts **a** and **b.**

41–42. Use the results from Exercise 40 to find the coordinates of point C on $\overline{AB}$ so that $AC = r \cdot CB$.

41. $A(-3, -2)$, $B(6, 4)$, $r = \frac{1}{2}$

42. $A(2, 5)$, $B(6, -3)$, $r = 3$

43. Find the coordinates of the two points that trisect (separate into three congruent parts) the segment with endpoints (−1, −4) and (5, 8).

1. Armstrong Roberts

Slope

The "steepness" or "slope" of a stairway is the ratio of "riser" to "tread." The riser is the *vertical change* (or *rise*) of each step, and the tread is the *horizontal change* (or *run*) of each step. For the stairway shown,

$$\text{slope} = \frac{\text{vertical change}}{\text{horizontal change}} = \frac{5}{9}$$

The slope of a nonvertical line is defined in a similar way. By looking at the graph of points A, B, and C on line ℓ below, we can find the slope of the line.

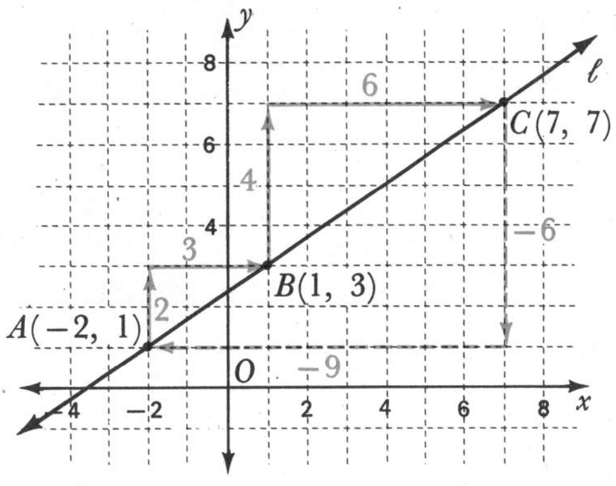

From point A to point B

$$\frac{\text{vertical change}}{\text{horizontal change}} = \frac{\text{2 units up}}{\text{3 units right}} = \frac{+2}{+3} = \frac{2}{3}$$

From point B to point C

$$\frac{\text{vertical change}}{\text{horizontal change}} = \frac{\text{4 units up}}{\text{6 units right}} = \frac{+4}{+6} = \frac{2}{3}$$

From point C to point A

$$\frac{\text{vertical change}}{\text{horizontal change}} = \frac{\text{6 units down}}{\text{9 units left}} = \frac{-6}{-9} = \frac{2}{3}$$

The slope of line ℓ is $\frac{2}{3}$. Notice that the slope of ℓ is the same no matter which two points are used. Also, segments on the same line have the same slope (slope of $\overline{AB}$ = slope of $\overline{BC}$ = slope of $\overline{CA} = \frac{2}{3}$).

Another way to find the slope is to subtract the coordinates of the points.

From A to B: $\dfrac{\text{vert. change}}{\text{horiz. change}} = \dfrac{\text{difference of } y\text{-coordinates}}{\text{difference of } x\text{-coordinates}} = \dfrac{3 - 1}{1 - (-2)} = \dfrac{2}{3}$

From C to A: $\dfrac{\text{vert. change}}{\text{horiz. change}} = \dfrac{\text{difference of } y\text{-coordinates}}{\text{difference of } x\text{-coordinates}} = \dfrac{1 - 7}{-2 - 7} = \dfrac{-6}{-9} = \dfrac{2}{3}$

In general, the **slope of a nonvertical line** is the ratio

$\dfrac{\text{difference of } y\text{-coordinates}}{\text{difference of } x\text{-coordinates}}$ for any two points on the line.

Slope Formula Theorem

The slope m of a line that contains points at (x_1, y_1) and (x_2, y_2) when $x_1 \neq x_2$ is $m = \dfrac{y_2 - y_1}{x_2 - x_1}$.

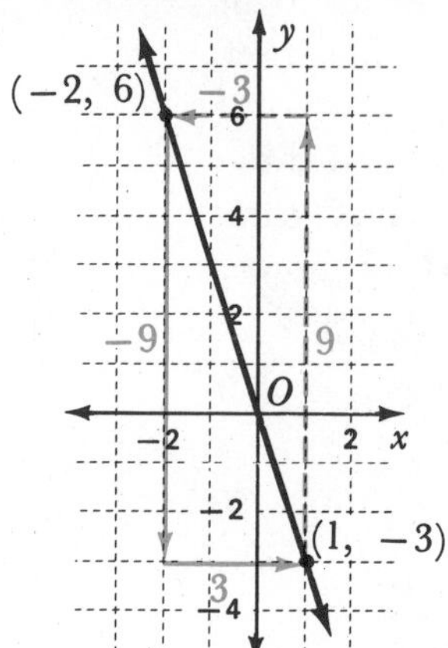

Example 1: Find the slope of the line that contains points at $(-2, 6)$ and $(1, -3)$.

Let $(x_1, y_1) = (-2, 6)$ and $(x_2, y_2) = (1, -3)$.

$$m = \frac{y_2 - y_1}{x_2 - x_1} = \frac{-3 - 6}{1 - (-2)} = \frac{-9}{3} = -3$$

or

Let $(x_1, y_1) = (1, -3)$ and $(x_2, y_2) = (-2, 6)$.

$$m = \frac{y_2 - y_1}{x_2 - x_1} = \frac{6 - (-3)}{-2 - 1} = \frac{9}{-3} = -3$$

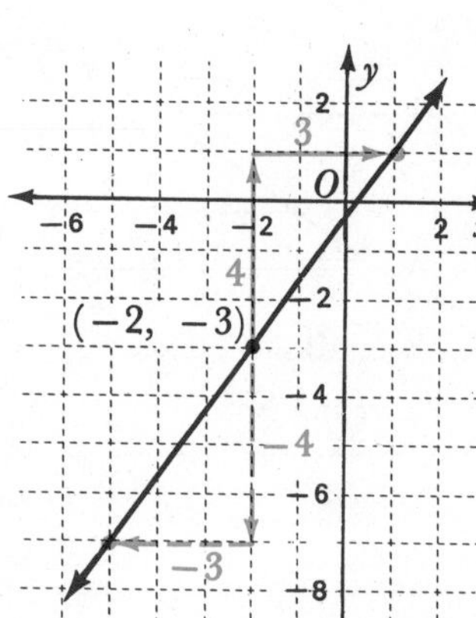

Example 2: Graph the line with slope $\frac{4}{3}$ and point $(-2, -3)$.

- Graph $(-2, -3)$.
- The slope is $\frac{4}{3}$. From $(-2, -3)$, go 4 units up and 3 units right to find a second point.
- For a third point, go 4 units down and 3 units left.
- Draw the line.

NOTE: Since two points determine a line, the third point is found as a check. If the three points are not collinear, a mistake has been made.

Not only can the slope of a line be positive or negative, it can be zero. And, some lines have no slope.

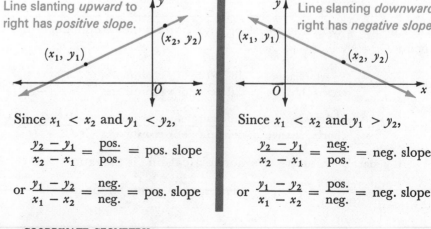

Line slanting *upward* to right has *positive slope.*

y (x_2, y_2) (x_1, y_1) O x

Since $x_1 < x_2$ and $y_1 < y_2$,

$$\frac{y_2 - y_1}{x_2 - x_1} = \frac{\text{pos.}}{\text{pos.}} = \text{pos. slope}$$

or $$\frac{y_1 - y_2}{x_1 - x_2} = \frac{\text{neg.}}{\text{neg.}} = \text{pos. slope}$$

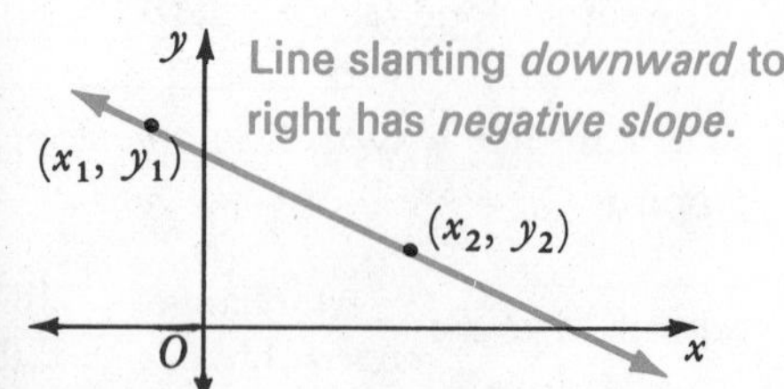

Since $x_1 < x_2$ and $y_1 > y_2$,

$$\frac{y_2 - y_1}{x_2 - x_1} = \frac{\text{neg.}}{\text{pos.}} = \text{neg. slope}$$

or $$\frac{y_1 - y_2}{x_1 - x_2} = \frac{\text{pos.}}{\text{neg.}} = \text{neg. slope}$$

Horizontal line has *zero slope.*

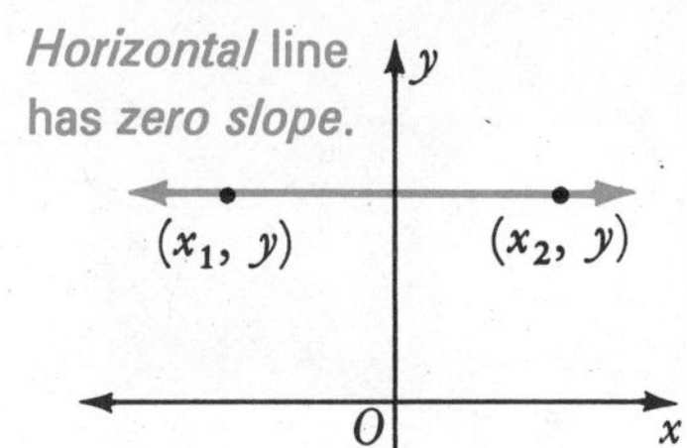

Since $y = y$,

$$\frac{y - y}{x_2 - x_1} = \frac{0}{x_2 - x_1} = 0$$

or $$\frac{y - y}{x_1 - x_2} = \frac{0}{x_1 - x_2} = 0$$

Vertical line has *no slope.*

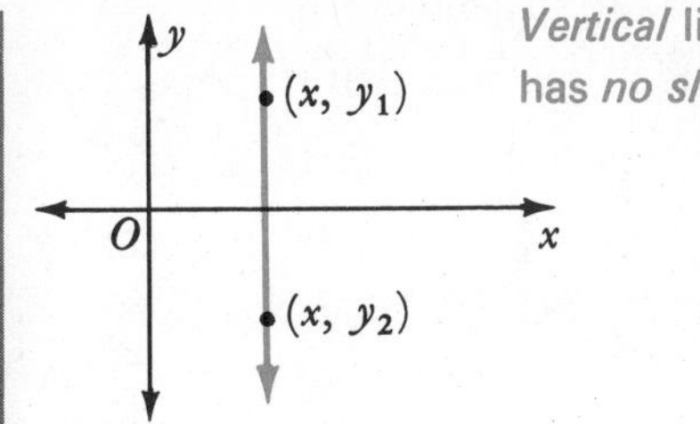

Since $x = x$,

$$\frac{y_2 - y_1}{x - x} = \frac{y_2 - y_1}{0}, \text{ which is undefined}$$

or $$\frac{y_1 - y_2}{x - x} = \frac{y_1 - y_2}{0}, \text{ which is undefined}$$

Exercises 15.4

Ⓐ **1.** Describe a line whose slope is (**a**) positive, (**b**) negative, (**c**) zero.

2. Describe a line that has no slope.

3. The slope of a line is the ratio of what two differences?

4. Which equations below show a correct way to find the slope of the line through (8, 7) and (5, 2)?

a. $\frac{8-5}{7-2} = \frac{3}{5}$ **b.** $\frac{7-2}{8-5} = \frac{5}{3}$ **c.** $\frac{5-8}{2-7} = \frac{3}{5}$ **d.** $\frac{2-7}{5-8} = \frac{5}{3}$

5. Find the slope of the line that contains (0, 0) and the given point.

a. (4, 7) **b.** (−4, 3) **c.** (−2, −5) **d.** (3, 0) **e.** (9, −2)

6. If a line with the given slope contains the origin, give the coordinates of any other point on the line.

a. $m = \frac{2}{3}$ **b.** $m = -\frac{4}{3}$ **c.** $m = -\frac{1}{5}$ **d.** $m = \frac{7}{2}$ **e.** $m = 0$

Ⓑ **7–22.** Find the slope of a line that contains the given points.

7. (6, 7), (3, 5) **8.** (8, 9), (4, 8) **9.** (3, 1), (15, 4)

10. (1, 10), (3, 16) **11.** (−5, 2), (−12, 4) **12.** (−3, 5), (2, 3)

13. (−3, −7), (0, −12) **14.** (−2, −6), (5, −8)

15. (1.2, 3.5), (2.4, 5.1) **16.** (6.2, 4.7), (8.2, 5.9)

17. (1.5, 2.6), (−0.3, 4.5) **18.** (2.7, 1.8), (5.2, −0.6)

19. (12000, 15200), (0, 0) **20.** (14000, 17300), (0, 0)

21. $(\frac{1}{2}, \frac{13}{4})$, $(\frac{9}{4}, \frac{1}{3})$ **22.** $(\frac{2}{3}, \frac{11}{4})$, $(\frac{7}{4}, \frac{3}{2})$

23–30. Graph the line that contains the given point and has the given slope *m*.

23. $(0,\ 0),\ m = \frac{8}{5}$

24. $(0,\ 0),\ m = \frac{7}{3}$

25. $(2,\ 5),\ m = -\frac{6}{7}$

26. $(3,\ 4),\ m = -\frac{5}{6}$

27. $(0,\ 0),\ m = 1$

28. $(0,\ 0),\ m = -1$

29. $(-2,\ 3),\ m = -\frac{5}{2}$

30. $(4,\ -3),\ m = -\frac{4}{3}$

31–34. Use slope to decide whether the three points are collinear.

31. $(0,\ 3),\ (4,\ 1),\ (6,\ -3)$

32. $(-9,\ 0),\ (0,\ 6),\ (-6,\ 2)$

33. $(6,\ 0),\ (3,\ -2),\ (0,\ -4)$

34. $(-6,\ 3),\ (-5,\ 0),\ (-3,\ -5)$

© **35–38.** Find the slope of a line that contains the given points.

35. $(a,\ b),\ (a + b,\ a)$

36. $(0,\ e),\ (e,\ 0)$

37. $(c,\ d),\ (c + 2,\ d + 2)$

38. $(e,\ f),\ (f,\ e)$

39–42. If both points are contained by a line with the given slope *m*, find the missing coordinate.

39. $m = \frac{3}{5},\ (2,\ 5),\ (?,\ 17)$

40. $m = \frac{4}{3},\ (-3,\ 7),\ (-6,\ ?)$

41. $m = -\frac{2}{3},\ (5,\ -1),\ (-1,\ ?)$

42. $m = -\frac{5}{2},\ (12,\ 3),\ (?,\ 13)$

43–46. The grade of a road is its slope expressed as a percent. For example, since $15\% = \frac{15}{100} = \frac{3}{20}$, a grade of 15% means a rise of 3 units for a run of 20 units. Find the grade for each of the following:

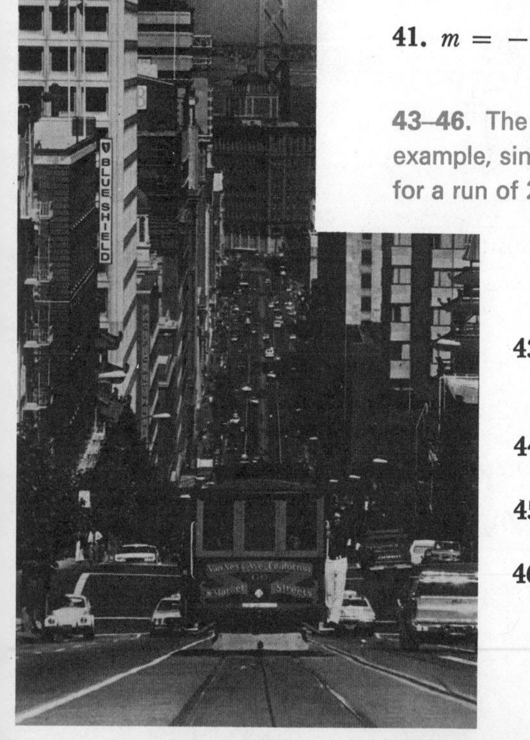

	rise (vertical change)	run (horizontal change)
43. Maximum grade on interstate highway	7 meters	100 meters
44. Road up Pike's Peak	1 meter	10 meters
45. A San Francisco street	1 meter	4 meters
46. General Motors test hill	9 meters	20 meters

Equations of Lines

Given the coordinates of two points on a line, we can graph the line. We can also describe a line algebraically with an equation.

The equations for vertical and horizontal lines are easy to find.

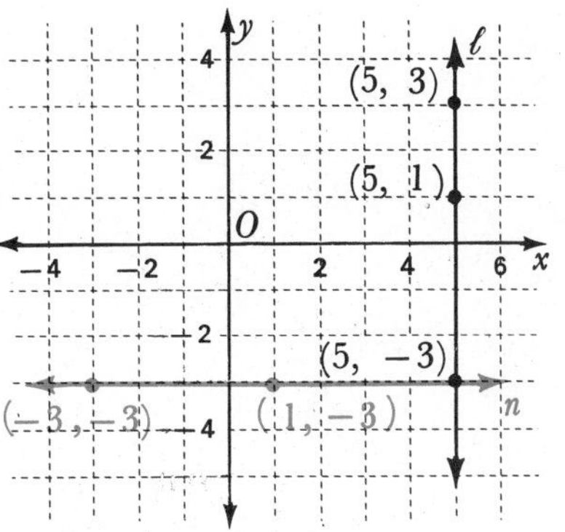

Line ℓ contains all points (x, y) whose x-coordinates are 5, and is described by the equation

$$x = 5$$

Or we can say line ℓ is the graph of equation $x = 5$.

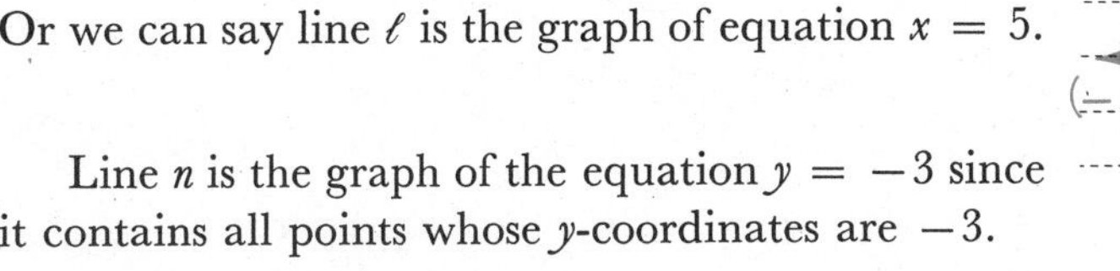

Line n is the graph of the equation $y = -3$ since it contains all points whose y-coordinates are -3.

For a line that is not horizontal or vertical, we can find an equation if we know the coordinates of one point on the line and the slope of the line. Line k contains point $(2, 3)$ and has slope $\frac{4}{5}$. Let (x, y) be any point on k different from $(2, 3)$. By the slope formula,

$$\frac{y - 3}{x - 2} = \frac{4}{5}$$

The equation has no meaning for $x = 2$ (denominator is zero) and is the equation for k without point $(2, 3)$. Multiplying both sides of the equation by $(x - 2)$, we get the equation for k:

$$y - 3 = \tfrac{4}{5}(x - 2)$$

That is, all ordered pairs (x, y) that are solutions of the equation are the coordinates of points on the line, and the coordinates of all points on the line are solutions of the equation. The equation for a line is called a *linear equation.*

The equation $y - 3 = \frac{4}{5}(x - 2)$ is in *point-slope form.* By looking at the equation, we can tell that the line has slope $\frac{4}{5}$ and contains point $(2, 3)$. In general,

If a line contains point (x_1, y_1) and has slope m, then the equation of the line is $y - y_1 = m(x - x_1)$.

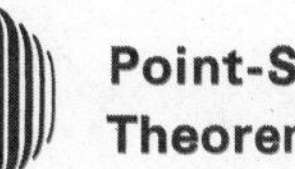

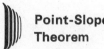

Point-Slope Theorem

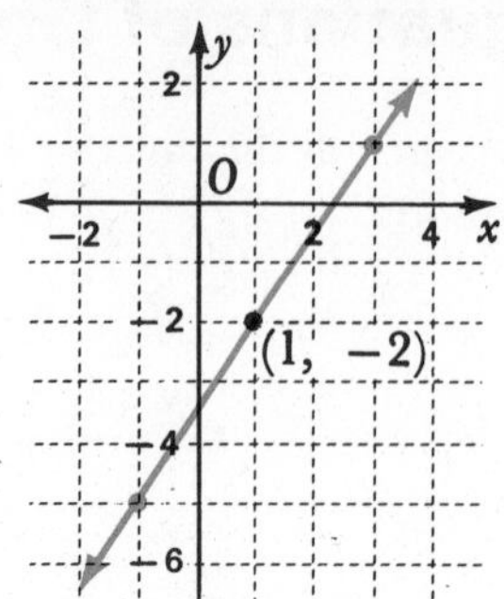

Example 1: Graph the line $y + 2 = \frac{3}{2}(x - 1)$.

- Point-slope form: $y - y_1 = m(x - x_1)$

$$y - (-2) = \tfrac{3}{2}(x - 1)$$

$m = \frac{3}{2}$ and $(x_1, y_1) = (1, -2)$

- Plot $(1, -2)$, and use the slope to find one or two other points.

- Draw line.

We can simplify the equation in Example 1.

$y + 2 = \frac{3}{2}(x - 1)$	Given
$2(y + 2) = 3(x - 1)$	Multiply both sides by 2.
$2y + 4 = 3x - 3$	Distributive property
$-3x + 2y = -7$	Add -4 and $-3x$ to both sides.
$3x - 2y = 7$	Multiply both sides by -1.

The equation is in the form $ax + by = c$, with a and b not both equal to zero. This is the *standard form* of the equation of a line. (For $3x - 2y = 7$, $a = 3$, $b = -2$, and $c = 7$.)

Given the slope and one point on a line, we can find the equation of the line.

Example 2: Point $(-3, 1)$ is on a line with slope 2. Find the equation of the line in standard form.

Use substitution and point-slope form.

$$m = 2, \ (x_1, y_1) = (-3, 1)$$

$$y - y_1 = m(x - x_1)$$
$$y - 1 = 2(x - (-3))$$
$$y - 1 = 2x + 6$$
$$-2x + y = 7 \quad \text{or} \quad 2x - y = -7$$

NOTE: If we multiply both sides of an equation by the same nonzero number, we get an equivalent equation. So, standard form is *not* unique. We usually prefer the coefficients to be integers, and the coefficient of x to be the smallest positive integer possible.

Given two points on a line, we can use the point-slope form to find the equation of the line.

Example 3: Points (7, −1) and (−8, 5) are on a line. Find the equation of the line in standard form.

- Use the given points to find the slope of the line.

$$m = \frac{5 - (-1)}{-8 - 7} = \frac{6}{-15} = -\frac{2}{5}$$

- Use the slope and one of the given points and substitute into point-slope form.

$$m = -\tfrac{2}{5}, \text{ let } (x_1, y_1) = (7, -1)$$

$$\begin{aligned} y - y_1 &= m(x - x_1) \\ y - (-1) &= -\tfrac{2}{5}(x - 7) \\ 5y + 5 &= -2x + 14 \\ 2x + 5y &= 9 \end{aligned}$$

NOTE: We could have let $(x_1, y_1) = (-8, 5)$.

Exercises 15.5

Ⓐ **1.** The equation of a line is called a ______ equation.

2. $y - 4 = \frac{2}{3}(x - 1)$ is the ______ form of an equation of a line.

3. $4x + 3y = 6$ is the ______ form of an equation of a line.

4. $y = -2$ is the equation of a line with slope ______.

5–12. Find (a) the slope of the line, if any, and (b) the coordinates of a point on the line.

5. $y = 6$

6. $x = -2$

7. $y - 1 = \frac{1}{2}(x - 3)$

8. $y - 7 = -\frac{2}{3}(x + 4)$

9. $y = 3(x + 2)$

10. $y - 4 = -x$

11. $y + 5 = \frac{4}{5}(x + 3)$

12. $y - \frac{1}{2} = -\frac{2}{7}(x + 8)$

Ⓑ **13–20.** Graph the lines in Exercises 5–12. Use a separate pair of axes for each exercise.

21–32. Find the point-slope form, and then the standard form, of the equation of a line that has the given slope and contains the given point.

	SLOPE	POINT		SLOPE	POINT
21.	$\frac{2}{3}$	(1, 4)	**22.**	$\frac{1}{2}$	(3, 7)
23.	$-\frac{1}{4}$	(4, 5)	**24.**	$-\frac{2}{7}$	(−2, 8)
25.	$\frac{3}{5}$	(−3, −8)	**26.**	−5	(−5, −1)
27.	3	(4, 0)	**28.**	−2	(−3, 0)
29.	$-\frac{2}{9}$	(0, −7)	**30.**	4	(0, 6)
31.	0	(0, −5)	**32.**	0	(−2, 1)

33–34. A line with no slope contains the given point. Find its equation.

33. (7, −4) **34.** (3, −2)

35–44. Find the standard form of the equation of a line that contains the given points.

35.	(1, 2)	(5, 3)	**36.**	(3, 7)	(1, 4)
37.	(−2, 5)	(−7, 8)	**38.**	(4, −1)	(7, −3)
39.	(−5, −8)	(−1, 0)	**40.**	(−3, −10)	(−5, −4)
41.	(3, −1)	(5, −1)	**42.**	(−7, 5)	(0, 5)
43.	(4, −6)	(4, −4)	**44.**	(−2, −3)	(−2, 7)

© **45.** If points (3, −1) and (−2, 5) are on a line, why are $y + 1 = -\frac{6}{5}(x - 3)$ and $y - 5 = -\frac{6}{5}(x + 2)$ both equations of the line?

46. Find two equations in point-slope form for the line containing (2, 4) and (−3, 1). Then show that the equations are equivalent.

47. Find two equations in point-slope form for the line containing points (x_1, y_1) and (x_2, y_2).

48. Find the equation of the line that has slope $-\frac{2}{5}$ and contains the midpoint of the segment with endpoints (−2, 6) and (3, 10).

49. Find the equations of the lines that contain the sides of a triangle with vertices at (0, −3), (5, −1), and (1, −1).

50. Find the vertices of the triangle whose sides are on the lines $y = -3$, $x = 4$, and $9x + 5y = 66$. HINT: Draw a graph.

1. Graph the ordered pairs using one pair of axes.

$$(1, 6), (6, 1), (3, -2), (-2, 3), (0, -8)$$
$$(5, 0), (-5, 0), (-7, -5), (-7, 5), (-\tfrac{1}{2}, 4)$$

2. Which ordered pairs in Exercise 1 are in the 2nd quadrant?

3. Find the distance between $(0, 0)$ and $(3, 4)$.

4. Find the distance between $(-2, -5)$ and $(-4, 1)$.

5–6. Find the coordinates of the midpoint of the segment with the given endpoints.

5. $(0, 0)$ and $(6, 4)$

6. $(-3, -8)$ and $(4, -3)$

7. A ______ line has no slope.

8. A line that has a ______ slope slants downward to the right.

9. Find the slope of the line that contains points $(2, -3)$ and $(5, 9)$.

10. The graph of $y - 1 = \frac{1}{2}(x - 3)$ has slope ______ and contains point ______.

11. Graph $y - 3 = \frac{3}{4}(x - 1)$.

12. Graph $y - 5 = -2(x + 6)$.

13–14. Find, in standard form, the equation of a line that

13. contains point $(-6, 3)$ and has slope $-\frac{1}{4}$

14. contains points $(3, 10)$ and $(-2, 3)$

GEOMETRY AT WORK

USING GRAPHS

Graphing in a coordinate plane is a useful way to record and display many different kinds of information. In applications, the units on one axis usually represent time or distance, while the units on the other axis depend on the information being graphed.

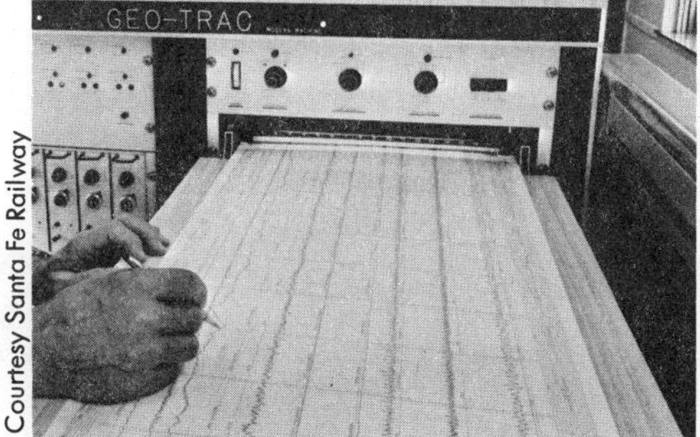

Courtesy Santa Fe Railway

The Santa Fe Railway has a special track geometry car which graphically records changes in track measurements.

Courtesy Lafayette Instrument Co.

A polygraph (lie detector) graphically records changes in breathing, blood pressure, and pulse.

15.6 More About Equations of Lines

If the equation of a line is in point-slope form, it is easy to draw the graph. But very often equations are in standard form.

The solutions of a linear equation are ordered pairs, and the graph of the solution set is a line. If we find at least two solutions, we can plot the points and draw the line.

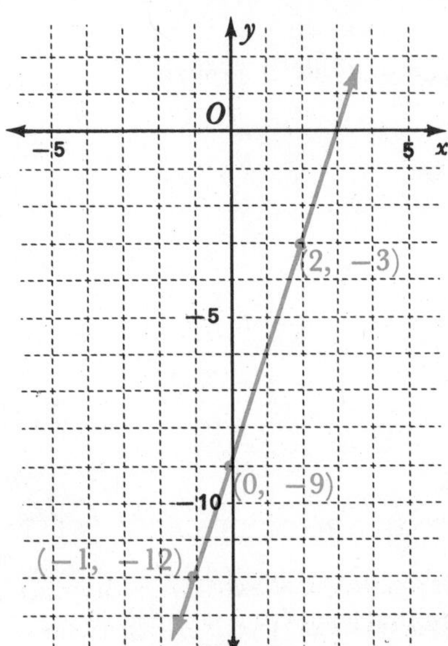

Example 1: Graph $3x - y = 9$.

- The replacement set for x, and for y, is the set of real numbers. To find a solution, let x be any real number, and then solve for y.

Let $x = 0$.
$3(0) - y = 9$
$y = -9$
→ $(0, -9)$ is a solution.

Let $x = 2$.
$3(2) - y = 9$
$y = -3$
→ $(2, -3)$ is a solution.

Let $x = -1$.
$3(-1) - y = 9$
$y = -12$
→ $(-1, -12)$ is a solution.

- Plot points and draw line.

Every nonvertical line intersects the y-axis at exactly one point. The x-coordinate of that point is 0, and the y-coordinate is called the ***y*-intercept** of the line. In Example 1, the line intersects the y-axis at $(0, -9)$, and -9 is the y-intercept.

In general, if b is the y-intercept of a line, then $(0, b)$ is on the line. Let (x, y) be any other point on the line, and let the line have slope m. Then, using the slope formula,

$$\frac{y - b}{x - 0} = m$$

$$\frac{y - b}{x} = m$$

$$y - b = mx$$

$$y = mx + b$$

(slope: m; y-intercept: b)

This form of the equation of a line is called *slope-intercept form.*

Example 2: For the graph of $y = -3x + 6$, what is the slope and the point of intersection with the y-axis?

- Use slope-intercept form: $y = mx + b$

  $y = -3x + 6$ ← y-intercept is 6.

- Slope $= -3$, and $(0, 6)$ is the point of intersection.

Example 3: Where does $y = \frac{1}{3}x$ intersect the y-axis?

- Use slope-intercept form: $y = mx + b$

  $y = \frac{1}{3}x + 0$

- Line intersects y-axis at $(0, 0)$.

Example 4: Find the slope and y-intercept of the graph of $3x - 5y = 15$.

- Solve for y: $3x - 5y = 15$

  $-5y = -3x + 15$

  $y = \frac{3}{5}x - 3$

  $y = \frac{3}{5}x + (-3)$ ← Sign must be +

- Slope $= \frac{3}{5}$, and y-intercept $= -3$.

Exercises 15.6

Ⓐ **1.** Every nonvertical line intersects the y-axis at exactly one ______.

2. If a line contains $(0, 5)$, then its y-intercept is ______.

3. The equation $y = \frac{2}{3}x + 4$ is in ______ form.

4. For $y = \frac{2}{3}x + 4$, ______ is the slope and ______ is the y-intercept.

5–14. Find the slope and y-intercept of each line.

5. $y = \frac{1}{4}x + 3$

6. $y = \frac{2}{5}x + 1$

7. $y = \frac{3}{7}x + (-4)$

8. $y = 4x + (-5)$

9. $y = -5x - 2$

10. $y = -\frac{1}{6}x - 8$

11. $y = \frac{4}{5}x$

12. $y = -\frac{9}{7}x$

13. $y = 2$

14. $y = -5$

Ⓑ **15–24.** Graph each line for Exercises 5–14. Use the y-intercept to find one point and the slope to find at least one other point.

25–34. Find three solutions for each equation and draw its graph.

25. $x + y = 4$

26. $x - y = 3$

27. $2x + 3y = 7$

28. $x + 5y = -10$

29. $6x - 4y = 30$

30. $2x - 2y = -5$

31. $-4x - 5y = 20$

32. $-3x - 8y = -24$

33. $y = \frac{1}{3}$

34. $y = -\frac{2}{5}$

35–44. For each equation in Exercises 25–34, (**a**) find the slope-intercept form and (**b**) find the slope and y-intercept of the graph.

Ⓒ **45.** Find the coordinates of the vertices of a triangle whose sides are on the graphs of $y = \frac{2}{3}x - 4$, $y = -3x - 4$, and $x = 3$.

46. Given points $A(-4, 0)$, $B(4, 0)$, and $C(0, 8)$, find the coordinates of the point on the y-axis where the medians of $\triangle ABC$ intersect.

47. Write a definition for the *x-intercept* of a line.

48. A line with slope m contains point $(a, 0)$. What might be the *x-intercept form* of the equation of the line? HINT: See Exercise 47.

Review this skill:

- *solving systems of equations*

1–3. Solve by graphing.

1. $2x - 3y = 12$
$3y = 2x + 21$

2. $y = \frac{7}{2}x - 5$
$14x - 4y = 20$

3. $5x - 2y = 3$
$3y = 2x + 1$

4–6. Solve by substitution.

4. $x = 2y$
$x + 3y = 30$

5. $y = x + 3$
$3x + 2y = 46$

6. $2y = 5x$
$3x + 4y = 39$

7–9. Solve by the multiplication-addition method.

7. $7x + 3y = 30$
$2x - 3y = 42$

8. $2x + 5y = 49$
$x - y = 7$

9. $3x + 4y = 15$
$4x - 3y = 20$

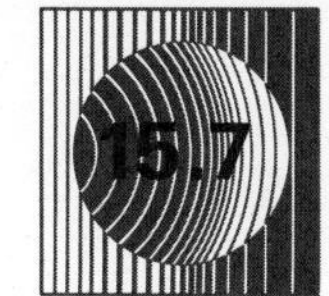

Parallel and Perpendicular Lines

If we know the slopes of two nonvertical lines, we can tell how the lines are related.

In the figure, lines ℓ and n intersect at $P(x_1, y_1)$. $Q(x_2, y_2)$ is on ℓ. Since ℓ and n are not the same line, point R on n with x_2 as its x-coordinate must have y-coordinate y_3 such that $y_3 \neq y_2$.

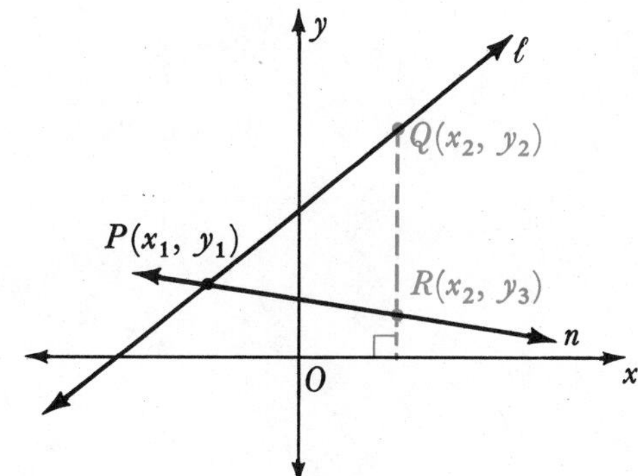

$$\text{Slope of } \ell = \frac{y_2 - y_1}{x_2 - x_1}$$

$$\text{Slope of } n = \frac{y_3 - y_1}{x_2 - x_1}$$

And $\frac{y_2 - y_1}{x_2 - x_1} \neq \frac{y_3 - y_1}{x_2 - x_1}$, since $y_3 \neq y_2$. So, intersecting lines have different slopes.

If two nonvertical lines are parallel, they have equal slopes.

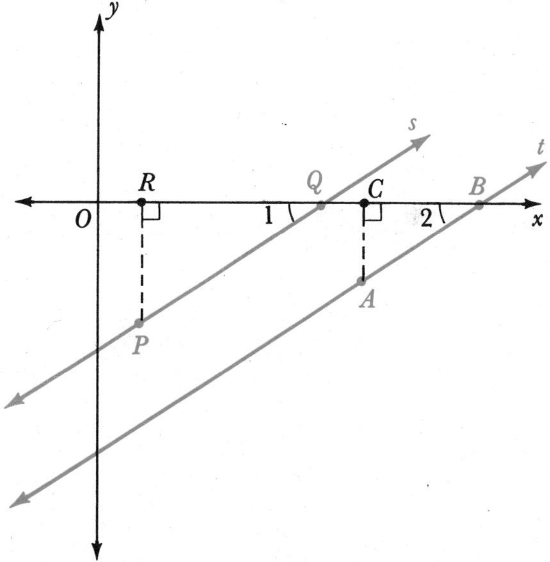

Slope of $s = \frac{PR}{RQ}$

Slope of $t = \frac{AC}{CB}$ (Def. of slope)

$\angle 1 \cong \angle 2$ (If lines are $\parallel$, corres. $\angle$s are $\cong$.)

$\angle PRQ \cong \angle ACB$ (Rt. $\angle$s are $\cong$.)

$\triangle PQR \sim \triangle ABC$ (AA Similarity Theorem)

$\frac{PR}{AC} = \frac{RQ}{CB}$ (Corres. sides of $\sim$ $\triangle$s are proportional.)

$\frac{PR}{RQ} = \frac{AC}{CB}$ (Switch means.)

Slope of s = slope of t (Substitution)

We can prove the converse. So,

Two nonvertical lines are parallel if and only if they have equal slopes.

Theorem

NOTE: Two lines with no slope are both vertical, so they are parallel.

We can also tell if two lines are perpendicular by their slopes. Below, lines ℓ'_1 and ℓ'_2 are perpendicular. By the Parallel Postulate, we can choose ℓ_1 through the origin parallel to ℓ'_1 and ℓ_2 through the origin parallel to ℓ'_2. Parallel lines have equal slopes, so whatever we prove about the slopes of ℓ_1 and ℓ_2 is also true for ℓ'_1 and ℓ'_2. Let m_1 = slope of ℓ_1 and m_2 = slope of ℓ_2. Then $m_1 = \frac{y_1}{x}$ and $m_2 = \frac{y_2}{x}$.

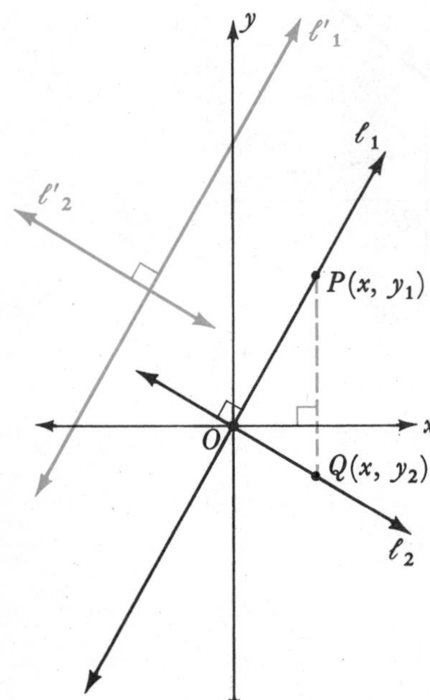

By the Pythagorean Theorem and the distance formula,

$$(PQ)^2 = (PO)^2 + (QO)^2$$

$$(\sqrt{(y_2 - y_1)^2})^2 = (\sqrt{x^2 + (y_1)^2})^2 + (\sqrt{x^2 + (y_2)^2})^2$$

$$(y_2)^2 - 2y_1y_2 + (y_1)^2 = x^2 + (y_1)^2 + x^2 + (y_2)^2$$

$$-2y_1y_2 = 2x^2$$

$$y_1y_2 = -x^2$$

Since $x \neq 0$, we can divide both sides by x^2.

$$\frac{y_1y_2}{x^2} = \frac{-x^2}{x^2}$$

$$\frac{y_1}{x} \cdot \frac{y_2}{x} = -1$$

By substituting m_1 and m_2 for $\frac{y_1}{x}$ and $\frac{y_2}{x}$,

$$m_1 \cdot m_2 = -1$$

$$m_1 = -\frac{1}{m_2}$$

The slopes of ℓ_1 and ℓ_2 (and of ℓ'_1 and ℓ'_2) are negative reciprocals of each other. By reversing the process, we could show that if their slopes are negative reciprocals, then the lines are perpendicular.

Theorem

Two nonvertical lines are perpendicular if and only if their slopes (m_1 and m_2) are negative reciprocals of each other.

$$m_1 = -\frac{1}{m_2} \qquad \text{or} \qquad m_1m_2 = -1$$

NOTE: A line with slope 0 and a line with no slope are perpendicular.

Example 1: One line contains points (5, −8) and (−6, −3). Another line contains (−9, 0) and (2, −5). Are the lines parallel?

- Find the slope of each line: $m_1 = -\frac{5}{11}$ and $m_2 = -\frac{5}{11}$
- The lines are parallel because their slopes are equal.

Example 2: Determine whether $3x - 5y = 21$ and $5x + 3y = -4$ are equations of perpendicular lines.

- Use slope-intercept form to find the slope of each line.

$y = \frac{3}{5}x - \frac{21}{5}$	$y = -\frac{5}{3}x - \frac{4}{3}$
$m_1 = \frac{3}{5}$	$m_2 = -\frac{5}{3}$

- Check to see if $m_1 \cdot m_2 = -1$.

$\frac{3}{5}(-\frac{5}{3}) = -1$, so the lines are perpendicular.

Exercises 15.7

Ⓐ 1. Nonvertical, parallel lines have ______ slopes.

2. If two lines each have no slope, then the lines are ______ and ______.

3. Two lines are perpendicular if the product of their slopes is ______.

4. A line perpendicular to a vertical line has slope ______.

5. Any line parallel to a line with slope $\frac{1}{3}$ has slope ______.

6. Any line perpendicular to a line with slope $\frac{3}{4}$ has slope ______.

7–14. Find the slope of a line **(a)** parallel to and **(b)** perpendicular to the given line.

7. $y = \frac{2}{3}x$
8. $y = -\frac{4}{5}x$
9. $y = 2x$
10. $y = -4x$
11. $y = \frac{5}{8}x + 2$
12. $y = -\frac{2}{7}x + 8$
13. $y = -\frac{3}{10}x - 7$
14. $y = -\frac{4}{9}x - \frac{2}{3}$

Ⓑ **15–22.** Each pair of points determines a line. Are the two lines in each exercise parallel, perpendicular, or neither?

15. (0, 0) and (4, 5);
(1, 6) and (−3, 1)

16. (0, 0) and (3, 7);
(2, 5) and (−5, 8)

17. (−3, 2) and (−4, −3);
(−7, 8) and (3, 6)

18. (15, −21) and (−9, −12);
(5, 3) and (−11, 9)

19. (−2, 14) and (−7, −6);
(3, 0) and (−4, 3)

20. (−8, 5) and (2, 5);
(3, 10) and (−4, 10)

21. (13, −6) and (13, 2);
(17, 9) and (−4, 9)

22. (−1, −6) and (2, 7);
(21, 7) and (8, 9)

23–28. Determine if the lines are parallel, perpendicular, or neither.

23. $2x + y = -4$
$x - 2y = 5$

24. $5x - y = -2$
$4x + 3y = 27$

25. $8x - 2y = -7$
$9x - 3y = -11$

26. $3x + 8y = 16$
$16x - 6y = -21$

27. $5y - 5x = 0$
$3y - 3x = 19$

28. $2x - 7y = 8$
$2x - 7y = -4$

29–32. Find the standard form of the equation of the line that

29. contains $(4, -1)$ and is parallel to the graph of $y = -\frac{2}{5}x + 7$.

30. contains $(0, -3)$ and is perpendicular to the graph of $y = 3x - 10$.

31. is the perpendicular bisector of the segment whose endpoints are $(3, 4)$ and $(-5, 12)$.

32. is parallel to the hypotenuse and contains the vertex of the right angle of a triangle with vertices at $(0, 10)$, $(-6, 0)$, and $(0, 0)$.

33. Show that a quadrilateral with vertices $A(-5, 4)$, $B(3, 5)$, $C(7, -2)$, and $D(-1, -3)$ is a parallelogram. HINT: Show that opposite sides are parallel.

34. Show that ▱$ABCD$ in Exercise 33 is a rhombus. HINT: Show that its diagonals are perpendicular.

35. Show that a triangle with vertices at $J(-9, 6)$, $K(12, 8)$, and $L(14, -13)$ is a right triangle.

36. $\triangle ABC$ has vertices $A(-1, -1)$, $B(9, -3)$, and $C(5, 7)$. Show that the segment joining the midpoints of $\overline{AC}$ and $\overline{BC}$ is parallel to $\overline{AB}$.

37. Find the slopes of the altitudes of $\triangle ABC$ in Exercise 36.

38. Show that a quadrilateral with vertices at $A(-7, 6)$, $B(-2, 9)$, $C(6, 4)$, and $D(9, -4)$ is a trapezoid. HINT: Show that only two sides are parallel.

Ⓒ **39.** Find the slope of the perpendicular bisector of the segment whose endpoints are $(0, a)$ and (b, c).

40. Show that the line containing points at $(0, a)$ and (c, d) is perpendicular to the line containing points at $(d, 0)$ and (a, c).

Coordinate Proofs

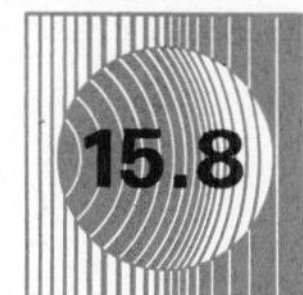

In this section, we will use the coordinate plane to do proofs. But first, we will look at the placement of geometric figures in the coordinate plane.

Below, $\triangle ABC$ is shown in different positions in the coordinate plane. Notice how much simpler the algebraic expression for AB is in figure 3 than in figures 1 and 2.

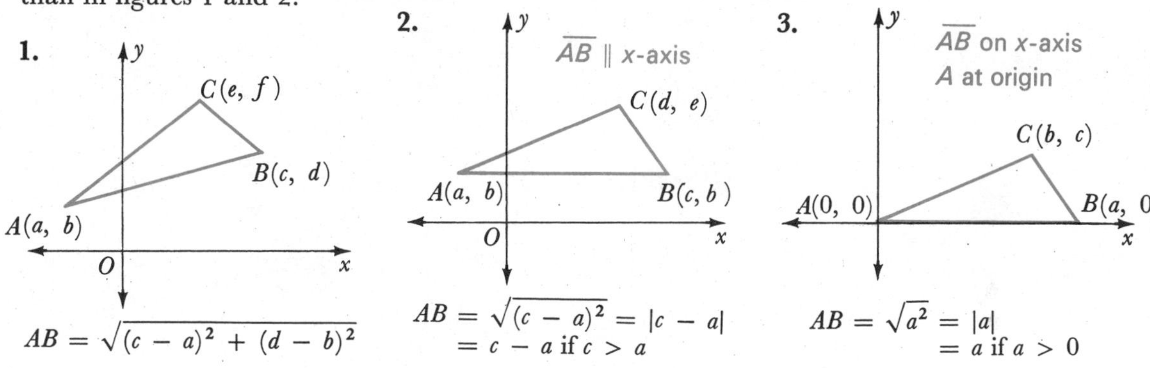

$AB = \sqrt{(c-a)^2 + (d-b)^2}$

$AB = \sqrt{(c-a)^2} = |c-a|$
$= c - a$ if $c > a$

$AB = \sqrt{a^2} = |a|$
$= a$ if $a > 0$

In general, parts of the axes are used as parts of the geometric figure so that the coordinates of the vertices can be expressed with as few variables as possible. This is done so that algebraic expressions needed in proofs will be as simple as possible. Below are just a few examples of how figures might be placed in the coordinate plane. Notice how the definition of each figure was used to assign coordinates.

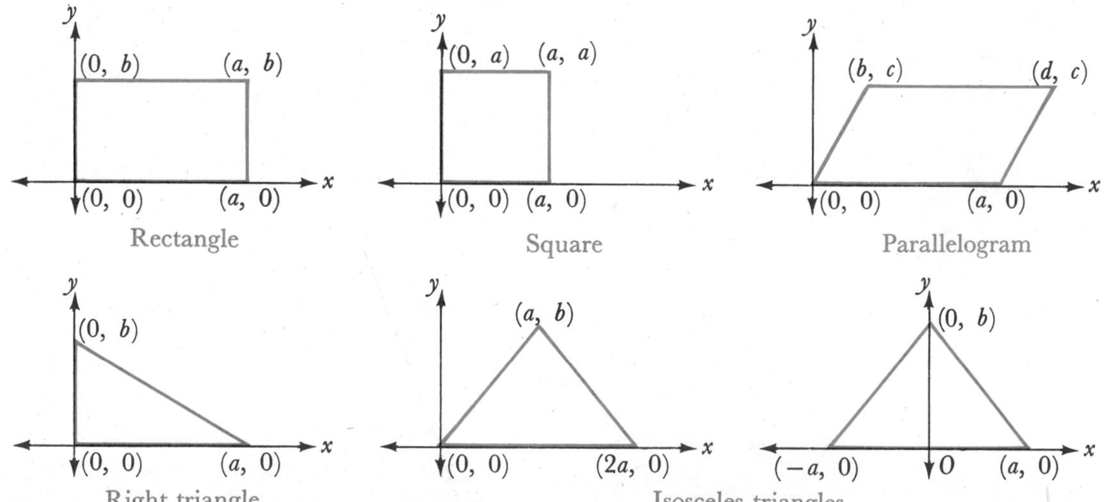

The first example of a coordinate proof shows how the distance and midpoint formulas are used in a proof.

Example 1: Prove that the length of the median to the hypotenuse of a right triangle is half the length of the hypotenuse.

Start by stating the *Given* and the *Prove* in terms of a figure in the coordinate plane.

Given: Right $\triangle ABC$ with pt. C at (0, 0), legs $\overline{CA}$ and $\overline{CB}$ on the axes, median $\overline{CM}$ to hypotenuse $\overline{AB}$

Prove: $CM = \frac{1}{2}AB$

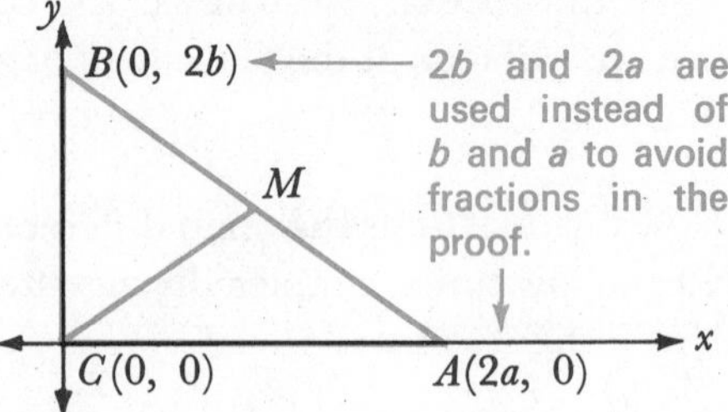

Proof: 1. By definition of median, M is the midpoint of $\overline{AB}$. And by the midpoint formula, M is at (a, b).

2. By the distance formula, $CM = \sqrt{a^2 + b^2}$

$$AB = \sqrt{(2a)^2 + (2b)^2} = 2\sqrt{a^2 + b^2}$$

$$\tfrac{1}{2}AB = \sqrt{a^2 + b^2}$$

3. By substitution, $CM = \frac{1}{2}AB$.

Before doing a proof about parallelograms, we will take a closer look at how coordinates are assigned to the vertices of a parallelogram. For $\square ABCD$ below, $\overline{AB}$ is on the x-axis with A at (0, 0). Opposite sides of a parallelogram are parallel, so $\overline{CD}$ is horizontal, and points C and D have the same y-coordinate. By the slope formula,

$$\text{slope } \overline{AD} = \frac{c}{b} \qquad \text{and} \qquad \text{slope } \overline{BC} = \frac{c}{d - a}$$

y, D(b, c), C(d, c), A(0, 0), B(a, 0), x

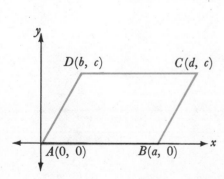

Slope of $\overline{AD}$ = slope of $\overline{BC}$ (why?). By substitution,

$$\frac{c}{b} = \frac{c}{d - a}$$

$$c(d - a) = cb$$

$$d - a = b$$

$$d = a + b$$

Notice that the x-coordinate of C is the sum of the x-coordinates of B and D.

So, the coordinates of C can be written as $(a + b, c)$. This will make proofs about parallelograms easier to do.

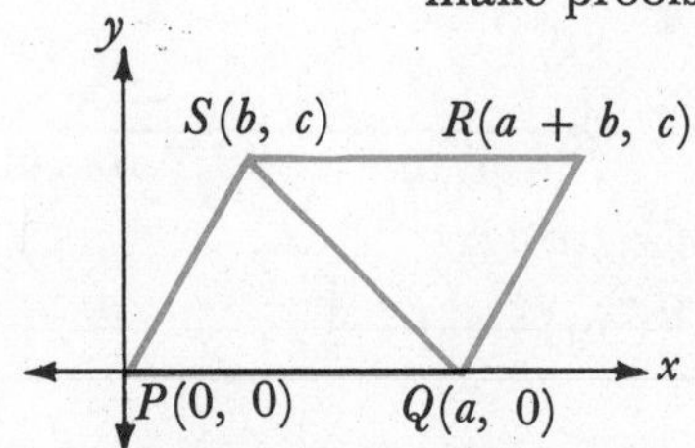

Example 2: Prove that a diagonal separates a parallelogram into two congruent triangles.

Given: $\square PQRS$ with P at (0, 0) and $\overline{PQ}$ on the x-axis

Prove: $\triangle PQS \cong \triangle RSQ$

Proof: 1. By the distance formula, $PQ = a$, $RS = a$, $PS = \sqrt{b^2 + c^2}$, and $RQ = \sqrt{b^2 + c^2}$. So, $\overline{PQ} \cong \overline{RS}$ and $\overline{PS} \cong \overline{RQ}$.

2. Since $\overline{QS} \cong \overline{QS}$, $\triangle PQS \cong \triangle RSQ$ by the SSS Postulate.

Exercises 15.8

Ⓐ **1–2.** *ABCD* below is a square. Find the coordinates of each vertex if

1. B is at $(c, 0)$. **2.** B is at $(2g, 0)$.

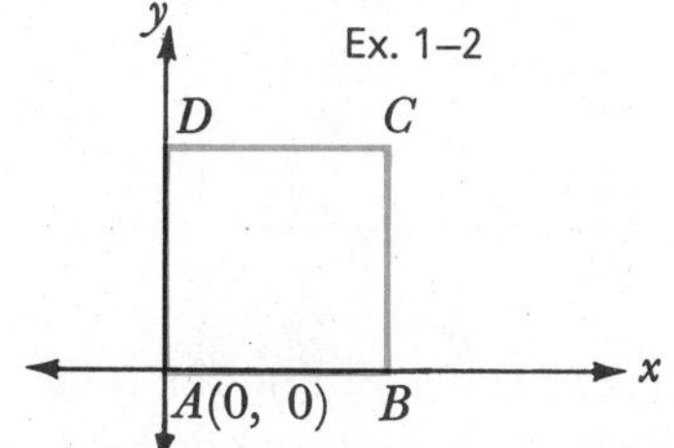

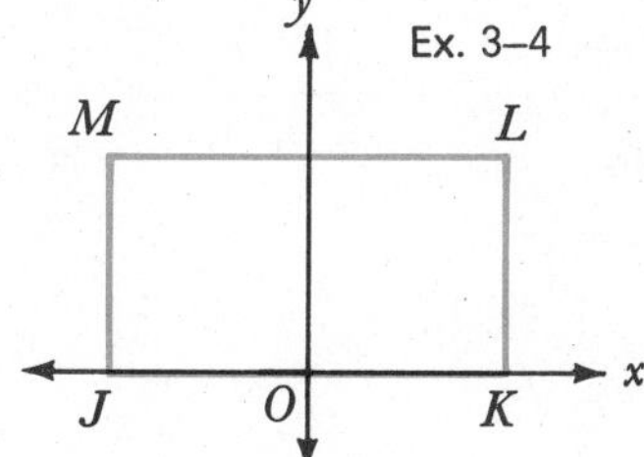

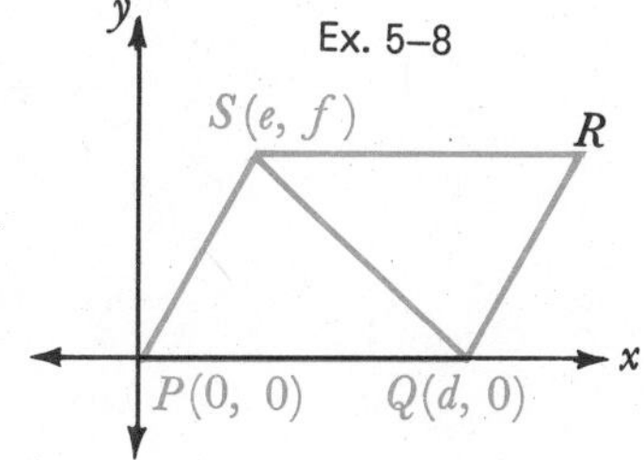

3–4. *JKLM* above is a rectangle. The y-axis is the perpendicular bisector of $\overline{JK}$. Find the coordinates of each vertex if

3. L is at (h, k). **4.** M is at $(-a, 4b)$.

5–8. *PQRS* above is a parallelogram. Find the coordinates of

5. vertex R **6.** midpt. of $\overline{PQ}$ **7.** midpt. of $\overline{PS}$ **8.** midpt. of $\overline{QS}$

Ⓑ **9–16.** Write a coordinate proof for each statement. Start by stating the *Given* and the *Prove* in terms of the given figure.

9. The opposite sides of a parallelogram are congruent.

10. The diagonals of a parallelogram bisect each other.

Ex. 9–10: y; $D(b, c)$; $C(a + b, c)$; $A(0, 0)$; $B(a, 0)$; x

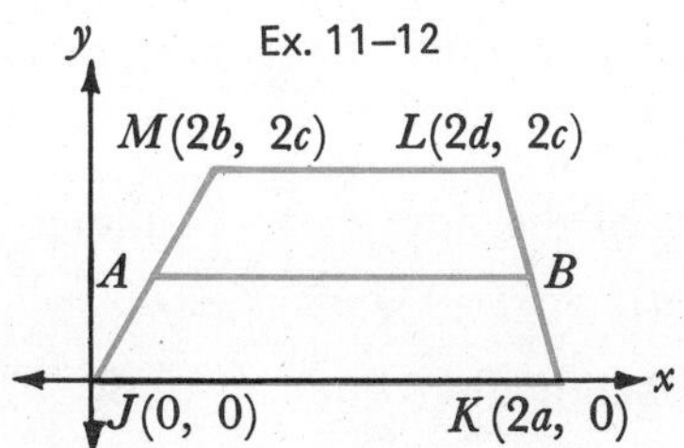

11. The midline of a trapezoid is parallel to its bases.

12. The length of the midline of a trapezoid is half the sum of the lengths of its bases.

13. The segment joining the midpoints of two sides of a triangle is parallel to the third side.

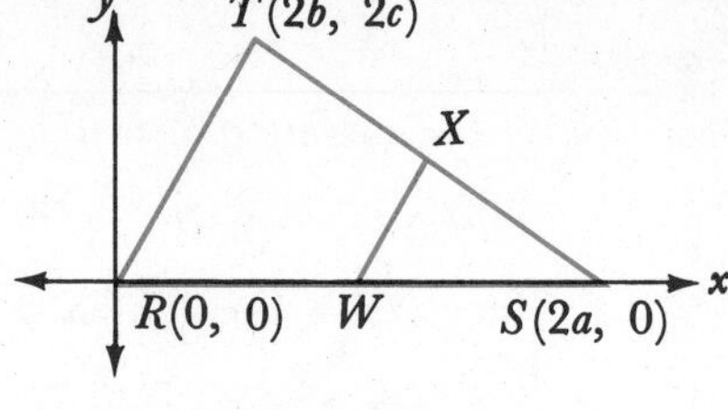

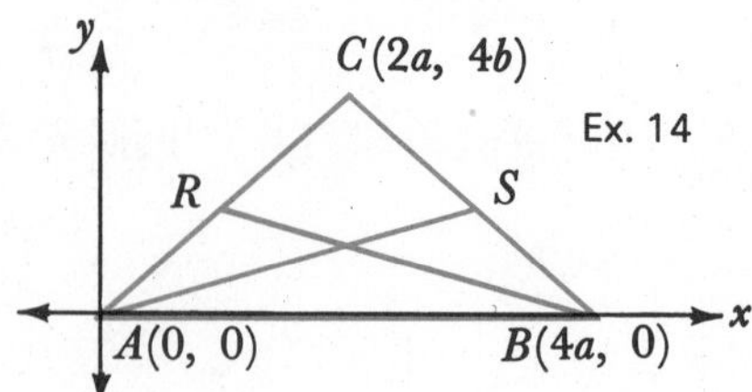

14. The medians to the legs of an isosceles triangle are congruent.

15. The diagonals of a square are perpendicular bisectors of each other.

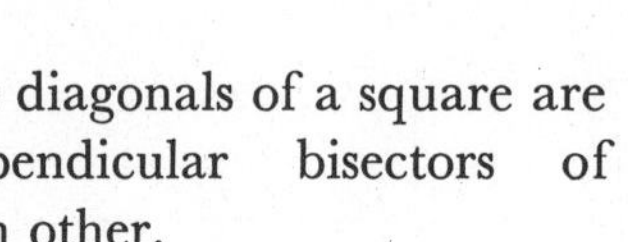

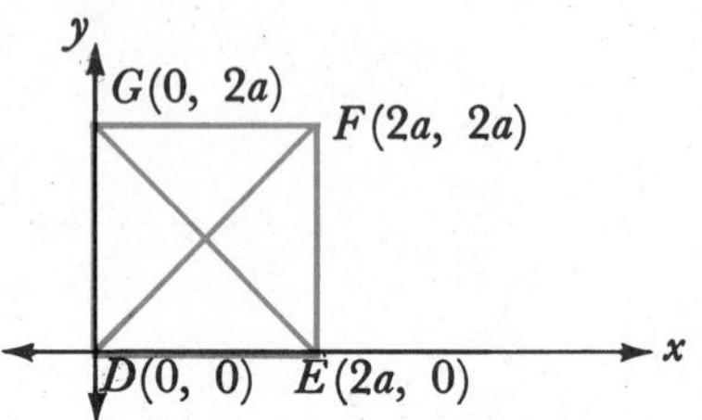

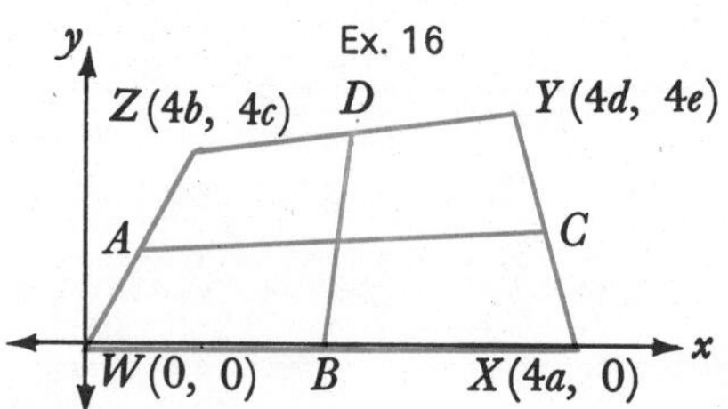

16. The segments joining the midpoints of the opposite sides of a quadrilateral bisect each other.

Ⓒ 17. *ABCD* below is an isosceles trapezoid. Find the coordinates of *C*.

18. $\triangle EFG$ below is equilateral. Find the coordinates of *G*.

19. *RSTU* below is a rhombus. Find the coordinates of *S* and *T*.

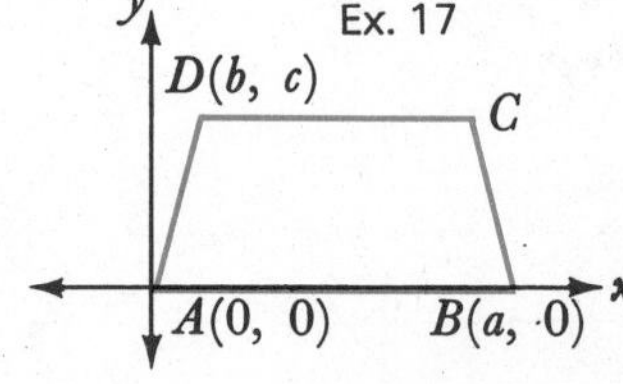

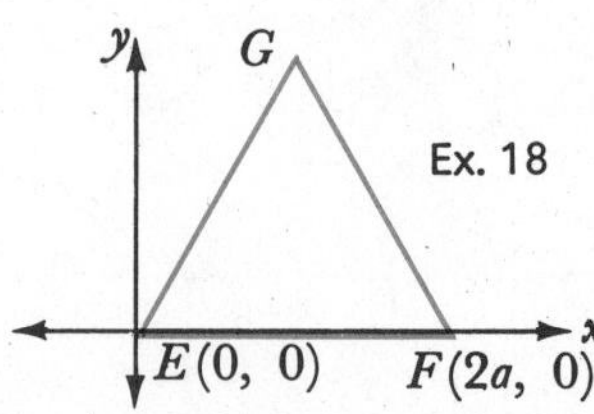

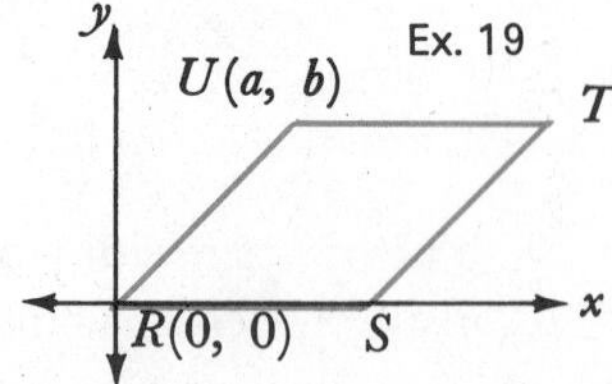

20–22. Prove each statement. Use the results from Exercises 17–19 to assign coordinates for the figure.

20. The segments joining, in order, the midpoints of the sides of an isosceles trapezoid form a rhombus.

21. The segments joining the midpoints of the sides of an equilateral triangle form an equilateral triangle.

22. The diagonals of a rhombus are perpendicular.

Locus in the Coordinate Plane

From Chapter 11, we know that a locus is a geometric figure containing all points, and only those points, that meet a given condition. The equation of a line is an algebraic condition, and its graph is the set of points whose coordinates meet that condition. A condition that uses an inequality symbol is called an **inequality.** Consider

$x \geq 1$ "is greater than or equal to"

Its graph contains all points and only those points whose x-coordinates are greater than or equal to 1. No condition is given for the y-coordinates, so y can be any real number. That is, the graph contains all points in the half plane to the right of line $x = 1$ and all points on the line. Line $x = 1$ is called the *boundary line* and is drawn as a solid line.

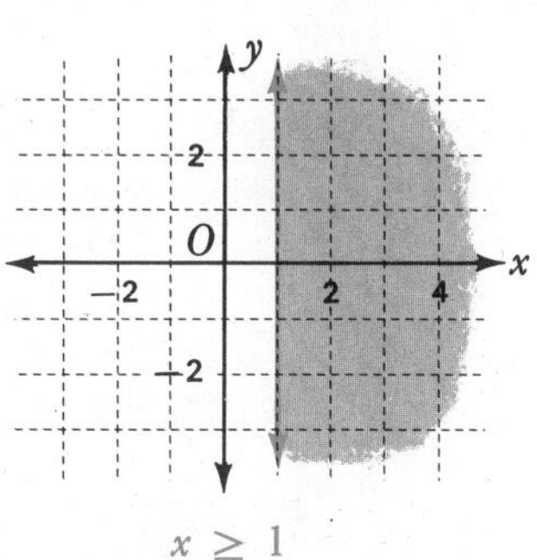

$x \geq 1$

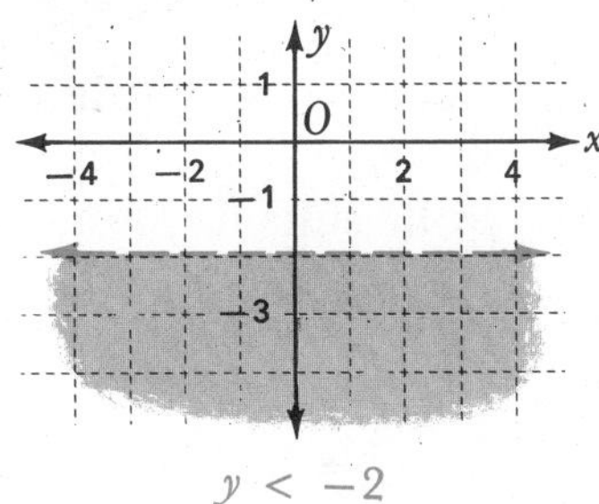

$y < -2$

The graph at the left satisfies the condition $y < -2$. Notice that points on the boundary line $y = -2$ do not satisfy the condition. The line is not part of the graph, and we show this by drawing it as a dashed line.

Example 1: Graph $y > 3x - 4$.

1. Graph boundary line $y = 3x - 4$. Draw it as a dashed line.

2. To decide which half plane to shade, pick a point on each side of the boundary line. Then check to see which one satisfies the condition.

Above: (0, 0)	Below: (3, −1)
$0 > 3(0) - 4$	$-1 > 3(3) - 4$
$0 > -4$	$-1 > 5$
True	False

Shade above the line. As a check, try another point above the line.

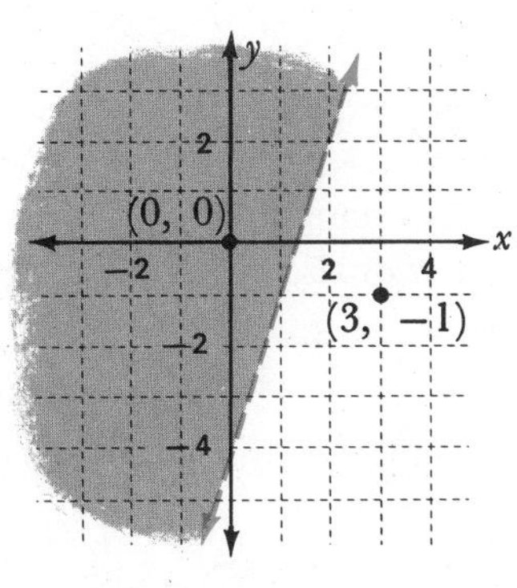

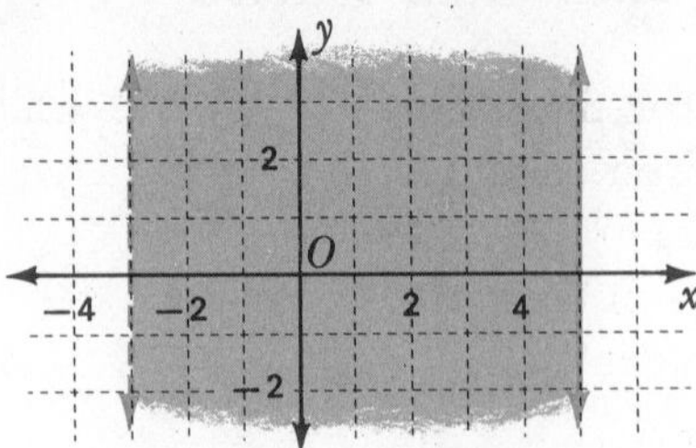

Example 2: Describe the graph of $-3 < x \leq 5$. Then draw the graph. NOTE: $-3 < x \leq 5$ means $x > -3$ **and** $x \leq 5$.

1. The graph contains all points whose x-coordinates are greater than -3 and less than or equal to 5.

2. Boundary lines are $x = -3$ (dashed) and $x = 5$ (solid). Shade between the lines.

Example 3: Draw the graph, then write an algebraic condition for the set of all points whose coordinates are both positive.

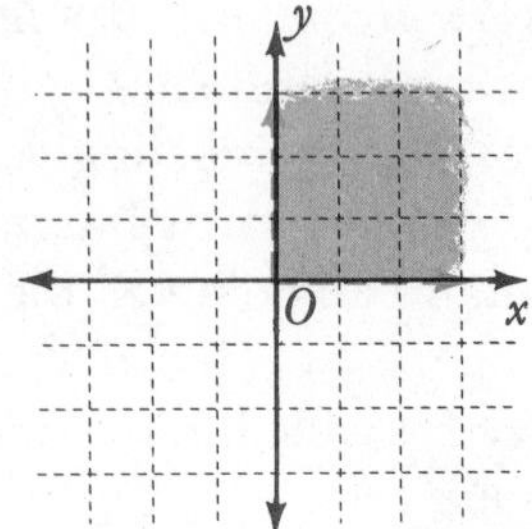

1. The graph is the 1st quadrant.

2. The algebraic condition is $x > 0$ and $y > 0$.

By using the distance formula, we can write an algebraic condition for a circle. Let the center of circle O with radius 4 be at the origin. Let $P(x, y)$ be any point on the circle. Then, by the distance formula,

$$OP = 4$$
$$\sqrt{x^2 + y^2} = 4$$
$$x^2 + y^2 = 16$$

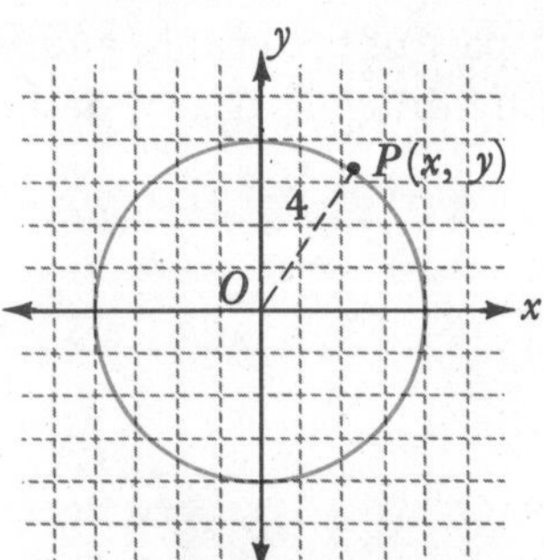

This is the equation of circle O. That is, the coordinates of all points on circle O satisfy the equation. Also, only the coordinates of points on the circle satisfy the equation.

Suppose circle A has center at $A(2, 3)$ and radius 5. If $P(x, y)$ is any point on the circle, then

$$AP = 5$$
$$\sqrt{(x - 2)^2 + (y - 3)^2} = 5$$
$$(x - 2)^2 + (y - 3)^2 = 25$$

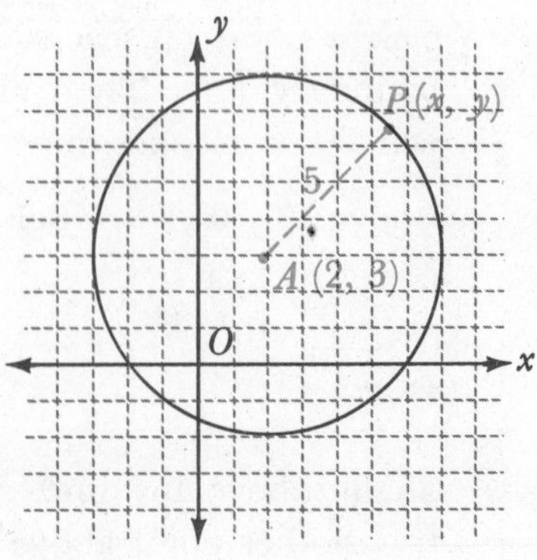

Notice how the equation tells us where the center of the circle is and what the radius of the circle is. In general,

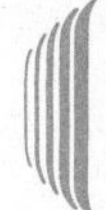

The equation of a circle with center (h, k) and radius r is

$$(x - h)^2 + (y - k)^2 = r^2$$

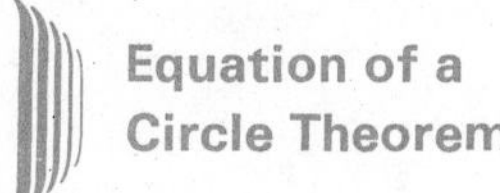

Equation of a Circle Theorem

NOTE: $x^2 + y^2 = r^2$ is the equation of a circle with center at $(0, 0)$.

Example 4: Graph $(x + 5)^2 + (y - 1)^2 = 36$.

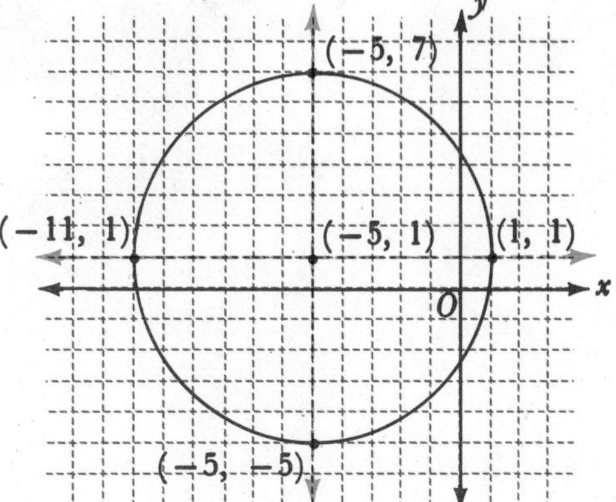

1. Find center and radius.

$$(x - (-5))^2 + (y - 1)^2 = 6^2$$

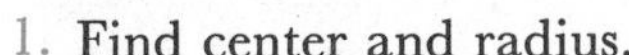

Sign must be −

Center is at $(-5, 1)$, and radius is 6.

2. Plot center. Find points on horizontal and vertical lines through the center that are 6 units from the center.

3. Draw circle.

Exercises 15.9

Ⓐ **1–12.** For each inequality, **(a)** name the boundary line(s) and **(b)** determine if its graph is a solid or a dashed line.

1. $x > 5$ **2.** $x < -2$ **3.** $y \geq 4$

4. $y \geq x$ **5.** $y < -x$ **6.** $y \geq 3x + 5$

7. $y < -\frac{2}{5}x - 4$ **8.** $y \leq \frac{1}{4}x + 1$ **9.** $-3 < y < 1$

10. $-10 < y \leq -4$ **11.** $-2 \leq x \leq 2$ **12.** $1 \leq x < 6$

13–20. Determine **(a)** the coordinates of the center and **(b)** the radius of each circle.

13. $x^2 + y^2 = 2^2$ **14.** $x^2 + y^2 = 100$

15. $x^2 + (y - 3)^2 = 9$ **16.** $(x + 1)^2 + y^2 = 36$

17. $(x - 3)^2 + (y - 8)^2 = 49$ **18.** $(x - 4)^2 + (y + 6)^2 = 81$

19. $(x + 2)^2 + (y - 5)^2 = 25$ **20.** $(x + 7)^2 + (y + 5)^2 = 64$

21–24. Determine which graph below is described by each inequality.

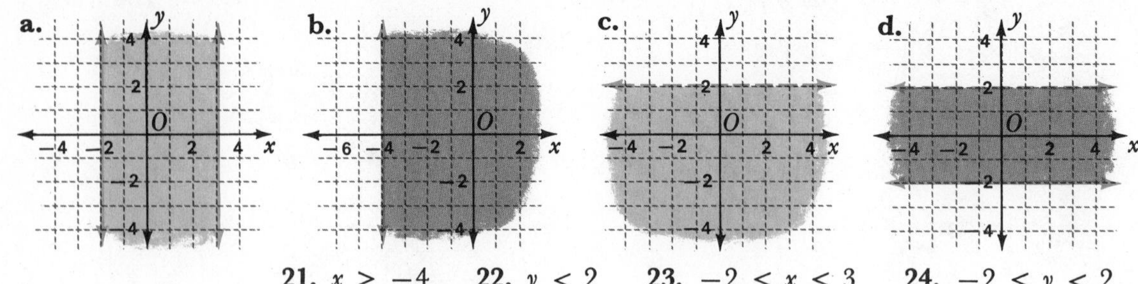

21. $x \geq -4$ 22. $y < 2$ 23. $-2 \leq x \leq 3$ 24. $-2 \leq y < 2$

Ⓑ **25–44.** Draw the graphs for Exercises 1–20. Use a separate pair of axes for each.

45–50. Solve each inequality for y. Then draw the graph.

45. $x + y < 3$ **46.** $5x + y > 7$ **47.** $y + 2 > -4$

48. $3y - 5 \leq 4$ **49.** $25x + 50y \leq -100$ **50.** $5y - 3x \geq 10$

51–63. Write an algebraic condition for each. Then draw the graph.

51. all points with x-coordinates less than 6

52. all points with y-coordinates greater than or equal to -4

53. all points whose x-coordinates have absolute values less than 5

54. all points whose y-coordinates have absolute values less than $8\frac{1}{2}$

55. all points in the 3rd quadrant

56. all points in the 4th quadrant

57. a circle with center $(0, 0)$ and radius 3

58. a circle with center $(-2, 8)$ and radius 5

59. a circle with center $(2, -3)$ that contains point $(-1, -3)$

60. a circle with center $(5, 7)$ that is tangent to the x-axis

Ⓒ **61.** a circle inscribed in a square with vertices $(-2, 5)$, $(2, 5)$, $(2, 1)$, and $(-2, 1)$

62. the interior of a circle with center $(-2, 5)$ and radius 4

63. $\triangle ABC$ and its interior, given $A(-3, -2)$, $B(0, 0)$, and $C(2, -3)$

Transformations and Coordinates

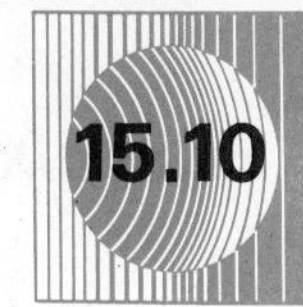

Some transformations are easy to describe with coordinates.

(x, y)	$(x + 4, y - 2)$
$A(-3, 4)$	$A'(1, 2)$
$B(0, 0)$	$B'(4, -2)$
$C(1, 3)$	$C'(5, 1)$
$D(-1, 1\frac{1}{3})$	$D'(3, -\frac{2}{3})$
$E(\frac{1}{2}, 1\frac{1}{2})$	$E'(4\frac{1}{2}, -\frac{1}{2})$

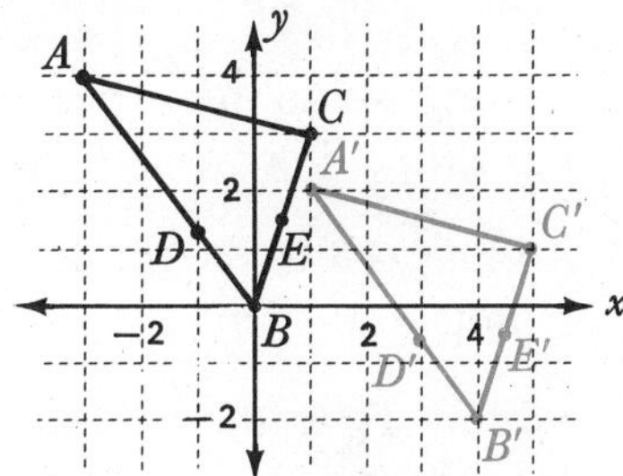

Notice that adding 4 to the x-coordinate of each point slides a figure 4 units to the right. Adding -2 to the y-coordinate of each point slides a figure 2 units down.

The magnitude of the slide is the distance between any point and its image, and can be found by the distance formula. In this case,

$$\sqrt{(-3 - 1)^2 + (4 - 2)^2} = \sqrt{16 + 4}$$
$$= \sqrt{20} = 2\sqrt{5} \approx 4.5 \quad \text{◀ magnitude}$$

A slide of magnitude $\sqrt{a^2 + b^2}$ can be described as

$$(x, y) \rightarrow (x + a, y + b)$$

where a and b are any two real numbers, (x, y) is any point in the coordinate plane, and $(x + a, y + b)$ is its image.

(x, y)	$(3x, 3y)$
$A(-1, 2)$	$A'(-3, 6)$
$B(2, 0)$	$B'(6, 0)$
$C(2, 1)$	$C'(6, 3)$
$D(1, 2)$	$D'(3, 6)$

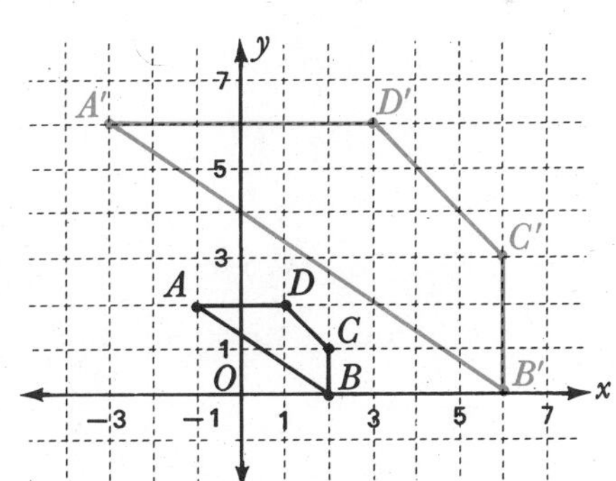

Notice that multiplying both coordinates of each point by 3 gives a size change of magnitude 3, center (0, 0).

A size change of magnitude k and center (0, 0) can be described as

$$(x, y) \rightarrow (kx, ky)$$

where k is any positive real number, (x, y) is any point in the coordinate plane, and (kx, ky) is its image.

Other transformations can be similarly described with coordinates.

Exercises 15.10

Ⓐ 1. Adding 4 to the x-coordinate of each point slides a figure ______ units to the (right, left).

2. Adding -2 to the y-coordinate of each point slides a figure ______ units (up, down).

3. Adding -3 to the ______-coordinate of each point slides a figure 3 units to the left.

4. Adding $1\frac{1}{2}$ to the ______-coordinate of each point slides a figure $1\frac{1}{2}$ units up.

5. Adding ______ to the x-coordinate and ______ to the y-coordinate of each point slides a figure 1.6 units left and 2.3 units up.

6. Multiplying both coordinates of each point of a figure by ______ gives a size change of magnitude $\frac{1}{2}$ and center (0, 0).

Ⓑ **7–18.** Draw the polygon in the coordinate plane. Then use the transformation described to draw the image of the polygon.

	VERTICES OF POLYGON	TRANSFORMATION
7.	$A(3, 5)$, $B(-2, 7)$, $C(0, 0)$	$(x, y) \to (x - 3, y + 8)$
8.	$E(4, 0)$, $F(0, -4)$, $G(3, -8)$	$(x, y) \to (x + 2, y + 10)$
9.	$H(2, 9)$, $I(7, 9)$, $J(9, 5)$, $K(2, 3)$	$(x, y) \to (x - 10, y - 2)$
10.	$L(3, 2)$, $M(8, 4)$, $N(8, 7)$, $Z(6, 7)$	$(x, y) \to (x - 9, y + 7)$
11.	$P(2, 5)$, $Q(5, 2)$, $R(5, -2)$, $S(2, -5)$	$(x, y) \to (2x, 2y)$
12.	$A(4, 4)$, $B(6, 0)$, $C(4, -4)$, $D(0, -6)$	$(x, y) \to (\frac{1}{2}x, \frac{1}{2}y)$
13.	$K(3, 6)$, $L(6, 9)$, $M(9, 0)$	$(x, y) \to (\frac{1}{3}x, \frac{1}{3}y)$
14.	$P(2, 0)$, $Q(6, 0)$, $R(6, -4)$, $S(2, -4)$	$(x, y) \to (3x, 3y)$
15.	$W(2, 5)$, $X(5, 2)$, $Y(7, 4)$, $Z(5, 8)$	$(x, y) \to (-x, y)$
16.	$A(4, 0)$, $B(6, 4)$, $C(1, 1)$	$(x, y) \to (y, x)$
17.	$G(3, -1)$, $H(7, 5)$, $I(7, 0)$	$(x, y) \to (-y, x)$
18.	$K(7, 1)$, $L(2, 0)$, $M(6, -6)$	$(x, y) \to (y, -x)$

Ⓒ **19–30.** Describe each transformation in Exercises 7–18 as a reflection, slide, turn, or size change. If a magnitude, center, or reflecting line is involved, tell what it is.

■ Chapter 15 Review ■

15.1

1. The x-axis and the y-axis determine the ______ plane.

2. The ______ of a point are given as an ordered pair.

3. The origin is the point at ______.

4. A point whose x-coordinate is ______ is on the y-axis.

5. Graph the following ordered pairs using the same pair of axes: (5, 7), (7, 5), (0, 1), (−3, 0), (−6, 2), (6, −2), (2, −6), (−6, −2)

15.2

6. What is the distance between points (x_1, y_1) and (x_2, y_2)?

7. A horizontal line through point (1, 4) and a vertical line through point (−5, −2) intersect at point ______.

8–10. Find the distance between the given points.

8. (0, 4), (5, 4)

9. (3, −2), (3, 7)

10. (−7, 5), (2, −8)

11. Is a triangle with vertices (5, −8), (−5, −1), and (3, 8) isosceles?

15.3

12–13. Find the midpoint of the segment joining each pair of points.

12. (0, 0), (6, −10)

13. $(-2\sqrt{3}, -7\sqrt{5}), (-10\sqrt{3}, -\sqrt{5})$

14. Find the midpoint of each side of a triangle with vertices (−5, −4), (−1, 3), and (3, 0).

15. If a segment has an endpoint at (−3, −7), and its midpoint is at (4, −2), find the coordinates of its other endpoint.

15.4

16–18. Find the slope of the line that contains the given points.

16. (0, 0), (3, −7)

17. (−4, −9), (7, 2)

18. $(\frac{1}{2}, \frac{5}{12}), (\frac{3}{4}, \frac{7}{8})$

19. Graph the line that contains point (5, −8) and has slope $\frac{2}{9}$.

20. Are points (0, 0), (2, 5), and (−4, −10) collinear?

15.5

21. The graph of a linear equation is a ______.

22. $y - y_1 = m(x - x_1)$ is the ______ form of an equation of a line.

23–24. Find the standard form of the equation of a line that

23. has slope 3 and contains point (4, −3)

24. contains points (2, −16) and (−34, −6)

15.6 **25.** $y = mx + b$ is the ______ form of an equation of a line.

26. The y-intercept of a line that contains point $(0, -7)$ is ______.

27. Graph $y = -2x - 3$.

28. Graph $10x - 7y = 21$.

15.7 **29.** If two nonvertical lines are parallel, then their slopes are ______.

30. If two nonvertical lines are perpendicular, then the product of their slopes is ______.

31. Are the graphs of $9x - 2y = -5$ and $4x + 6y = 9$ parallel, perpendicular, or neither?

32–33. Find the standard form of the equation of a line that

32. contains $(11, 3)$ and is perpendicular to a line with slope -5

33. contains $(0, 0)$ and is parallel to the line through $(-3, 5)$ and $(9, 1)$

15.8 **34.** If three vertices of a rectangle are at $(0, 7b)$, $(0, 0)$, and $(4a, 0)$, find the coordinates of the fourth vertex.

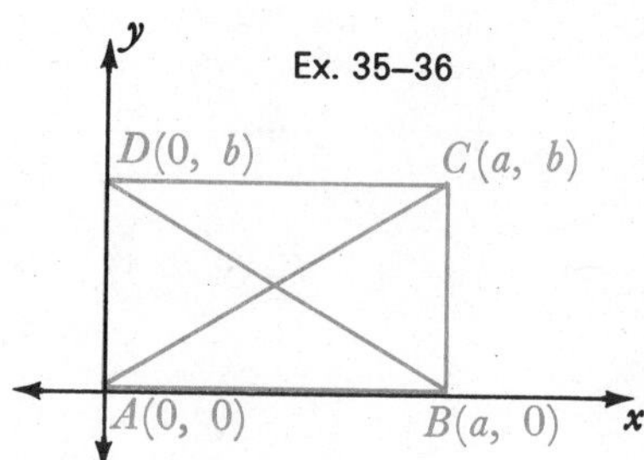

35–36. Consider this statement: The diagonals of a rectangle are congruent.

35. State the *Given* and *Prove* in terms of the given figure.

36. Write a coordinate proof of the statement.

15.9 **37–39.** Graph each inequality on a separate pair of axes.

37. $y < \frac{2}{5}x + 1$

38. $8x + 3y \geq -6$

39. $-5 \leq y < 4$

40–42. Write an algebraic condition for each. Then draw the graph.

40. all points with x-coordinates greater than -4

41. all points in the 2nd quadrant

42. a circle with center $(0, 3)$ and radius 5

15.10 **43–44.** A triangle has vertices at $A(0, 0)$, $B(4, 6)$, and $C(2, -4)$. In the coordinate plane, draw the triangle and its image using the given transformation.

43. $(x, y) \rightarrow (x + 2, y - 3)$

44. $(x, y) \rightarrow (\frac{1}{2}x, \frac{1}{2}y)$

Chapter 15 Test

1–2. Given $A(3, 7)$, $B(7, 3)$, $C(-5, 0)$, and $D(-7, 5)$,

1. Draw quadrilateral $ABCD$ in the coordinate plane.

2. Find the length of each side of quadrilateral $ABCD$.

3–4. The vertices of $\triangle RST$ are $R(6, 3)$, $S(-4, 5)$, and $T(4, 9)$.

3. Find the coordinates of the midpoint for each side of $\triangle RST$.

4. Find the slope of each side of $\triangle RST$.

5. Show that $E(-3, 5)$, $F(2, 2)$, and $G(5, 1)$ are not collinear.

6. Graph $y - 4 = \frac{2}{3}(x - 1)$.

7. Graph $3x + 4y = 12$.

8–12. Find the standard form of the equation of the line described.

8. contains points $(3, -1)$ and $(-2, 5)$

9. slope $-\frac{5}{2}$, y-intercept -2

10. slope 3, contains point $(5, -1)$

11. parallel to the graph of $y = 2x$, contains point $(0, 4)$

12. perpendicular to the graph of $y = 2x$, contains point $(-11, 2)$

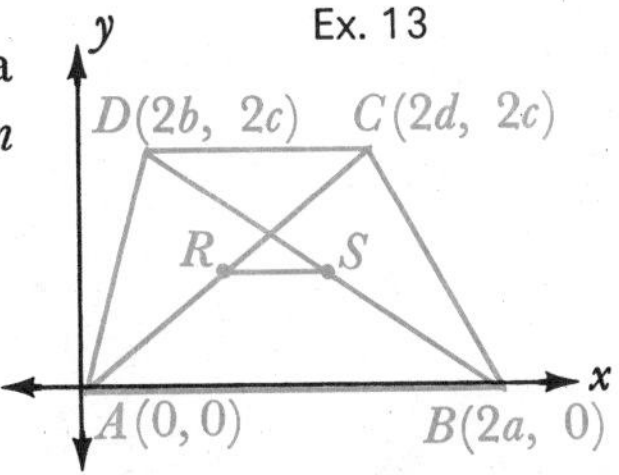

13. Prove that the segment joining the midpoints of the diagonals of a trapezoid is parallel to its bases. HINT: Start by stating the *Given* and *Prove* in terms of the given figure.

14–16. Graph each on a separate pair of axes.

14. $x < 3$

15. $-2 \leq y \leq 4$

16. $y > \frac{1}{3}x + 1$

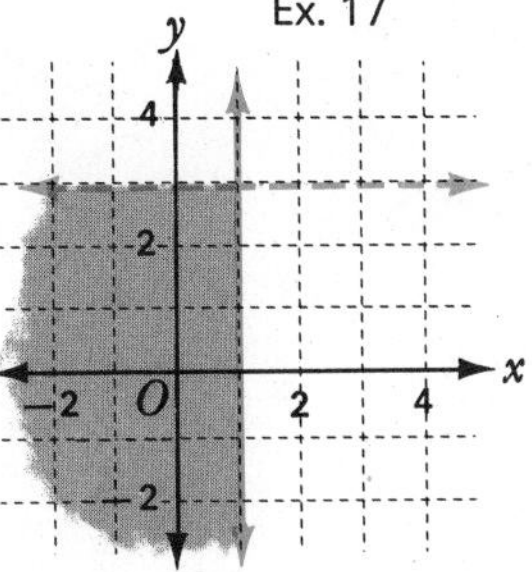

17. Write an algebraic condition to describe the graph at the right.

18. Write an algebraic condition to describe all points whose x-coordinates have absolute values less than $3\frac{1}{2}$.

19–20. Find the equation of each circle.

19. center at the origin, radius 3

20. center at $(-2, 3)$, radius 5

21–22. A triangle has vertices at $P(3, 5)$, $Q(-2, 3)$, and $R(-3, 0)$. In the coordinate plane, draw the triangle and its image using the given transformation.

21. $(x, y) \to (x - 2, y + 1)$

22. $(x, y) \to (x, -y)$

Cumulative Review: Chapters 8–15

Ch. 8

1. State the definition of a line perpendicular to a plane.

2. State the Basic Theorem for Perpendiculars.

3–7. Plane n is the perpendicular bisecting plane of $\overline{RS}$ at T. Points T, W, and U are in n. Points R, S, Z, T, and X are in plane p.

3. Is $RW = SW$? If so, why?

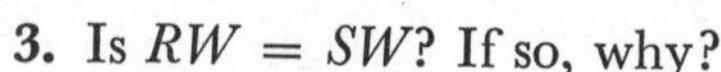

4. Is $\overleftrightarrow{TU} \perp \overleftrightarrow{RS}$? If so, why?

5. Is $RT < RW$? If so, why?

6. If $\overline{RS} \perp \overleftrightarrow{ZX}$ at T, is $\overleftrightarrow{ZX}$ in n? If so, why?

7. How many planes are perpendicular to $\overleftrightarrow{RS}$ at R?

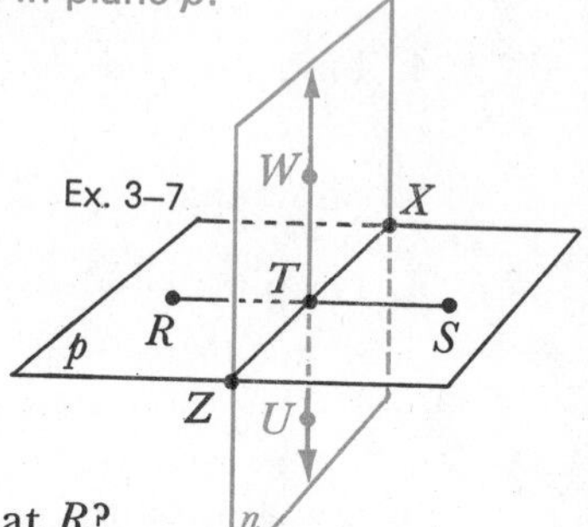

Ex. 3–7

Ch. 9

8–11. Find the area of each figure.

8. square with a side of length $2\frac{1}{2}$ cm

9. rhombus with diagonals of lengths $3\frac{1}{2}$ and 5

10. parallelogram with a base 4.2 cm long and a corresponding height of 16 mm

11. trapezoid with height 7 and bases of lengths 6 and 10

12. **Given:** $\triangle ABC$, median $\overline{AM}$, altitude $\overline{AR}$

Prove: Area $\triangle ABM$ = area $\triangle AMC$

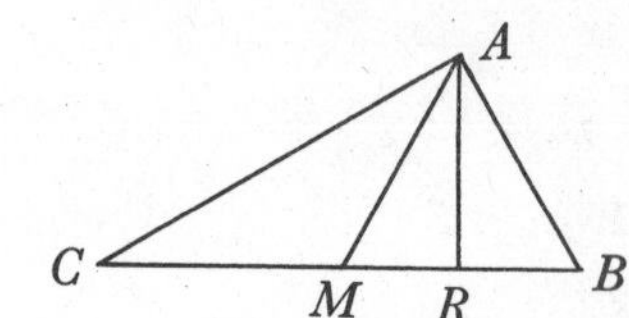

13. Simplify: **a.** $\sqrt{75}$ **b.** $\sqrt{\frac{1}{5}}$ **c.** $\dfrac{1}{\sqrt{2}}$

14. If the lengths of the legs of a right triangle are 4 and 6, find the length of the hypotenuse (in simplified radical form).

15. In a 30-60-90° triangle, the hypotenuse has length 16. Find the length of each leg.

16. Can a right triangle have sides of lengths 16, 18, and 20?

17. In $\triangle ABC$, $m\angle B = 90$. Find AB (in simplified radical form) if $AB = BC$ and $AC = 10$.

Ch. 10

18–20. Let $\frac{a}{4} = \frac{3}{b}$.

18. $ab =$ ______ **19.** $\frac{a}{3} =$ ______ **20.** If $b = 5$, $a =$ ______

21. Given: Isosceles rt. $\triangle$s XYZ and KLM
Prove: $\triangle XYZ \sim \triangle KLM$

22. Given: Trapezoid $RSTU$ with $\overline{RS} \parallel \overline{TU}$
Prove: $\triangle PRS \sim \triangle PTU$

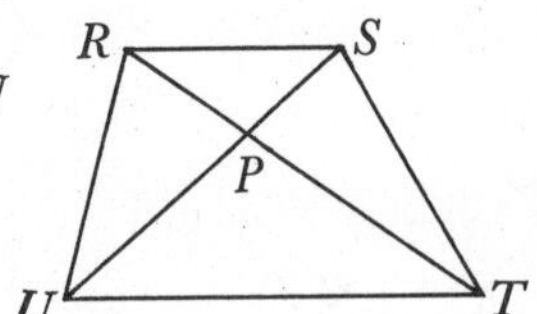

23–25. Refer to the figure.

23. $\frac{DG}{EG} = \frac{?}{GF}$ **24.** $\frac{DG}{?} = \frac{DE}{DF}$

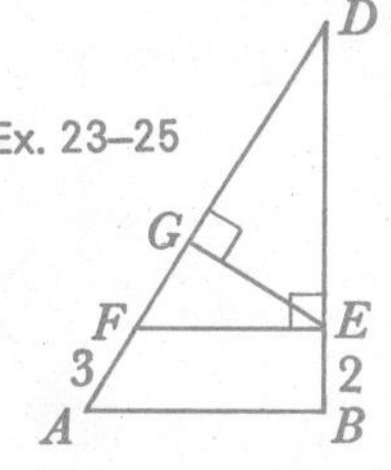

25. If $\overline{FE} \parallel \overline{AB}$ and $DE = 8$, then $DF =$ ______.

26. If $a:b:c = 2:5:3$ and $a = 6$, find b and c.

Ch. 11

27–32. $\overleftrightarrow{CA}$ is tangent to $\odot X$ at A.

27. Name 4 radii. **28.** Is $m\widehat{GAF} > 180$? Why?

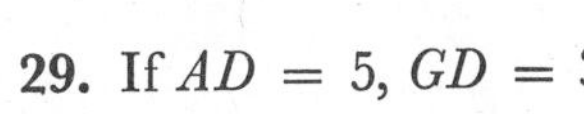

29. If $AD = 5$, $GD = 3$, $DE = 2$, find DF.

30. If $CG = 3$, $GF = 9$, find CA.

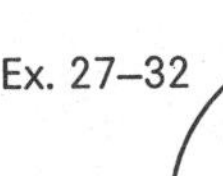

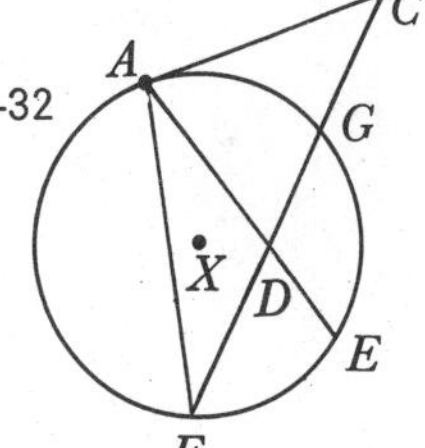

31. Find $m\angle C$ if $m\widehat{AG} = 62$ and $m\widehat{AF} = 160$.

32. Find $m\angle ADG$ if $m\widehat{AG} = 64$ and $m\widehat{FE} = 62$.

33. Given: $\odot C$, diameter $\overline{XZ}$, chords $\overline{YZ}$ and $\overline{WZ}$, $\overline{YZ} \cong \overline{WZ}$
Prove: $\triangle XYZ \cong \triangle XWZ$

34. Given: $\odot C$, chords $\overline{XY}$ and $\overline{XW}$, diameter $\overline{XZ}$, $\angle 1 \cong \angle 2$
Prove: $\overline{XY} \cong \overline{XW}$

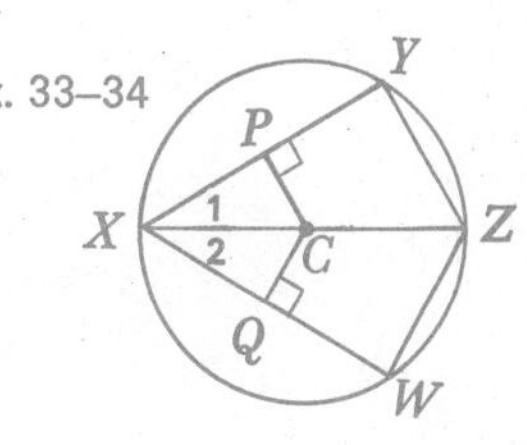

35–36. Given: Sphere M

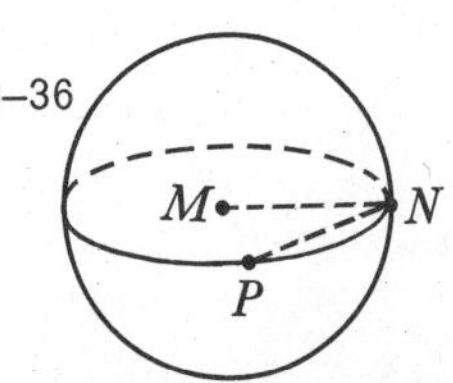

35. ______ is a chord of the sphere.

36. If T is in the interior of sphere M, then TM (=, >, <) MN.

37. If a plane and a sphere intersect at exactly one point, they are ______.

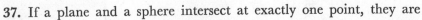

Ch. 12

38–39. Square $ABCD$ is inscribed in $\odot O$. $AB = 8$.

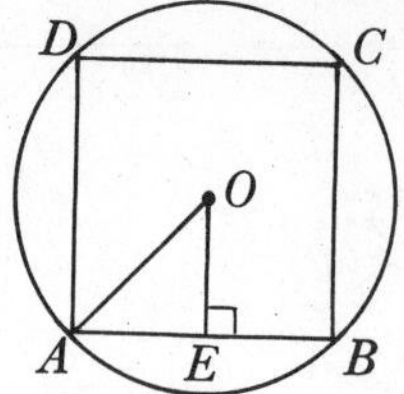

38. Find OE.

39. Find OA.

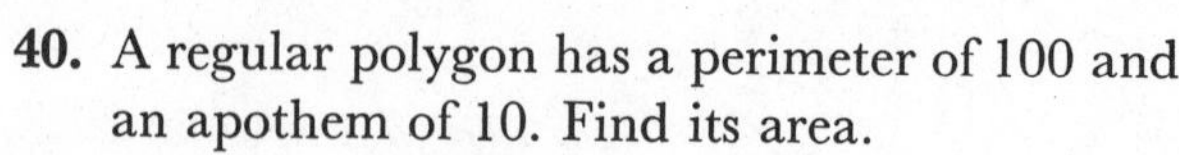

40. A regular polygon has a perimeter of 100 and an apothem of 10. Find its area.

41–44. Use the given measure of a circle to find each missing number. Leave answers in terms of π.

	radius	diameter	circumference	area
41.	5	____	____	____
42.	____	18	____	____
43.	____	____	____	16π
44.	____	____	50π	____

NOTE: **Leave answers 45–46 in terms of π.**

45. Find the length of a $135°$ arc in a circle with radius 3.

46. A circle has radius 9. Find the area of a sector with a $10°$ arc.

Ch. 13

47–51. True or False? Draw a sketch to illustrate each true statement. Sketch a counterexample for each false statement.

47. Two planes perpendicular to the same line are parallel.

48. Two planes parallel to the same line are parallel.

49. Two lines perpendicular to the same plane are parallel.

50. Two lines parallel to the same plane are parallel.

51. Three parallel lines are coplanar.

52. Given: Dihedral $\angle C\text{-}\overleftrightarrow{BY}\text{-}X$, planes ABC and XYZ are $\perp$ to $\overleftrightarrow{BY}$.

Prove: $\angle ABC \cong \angle XYZ$

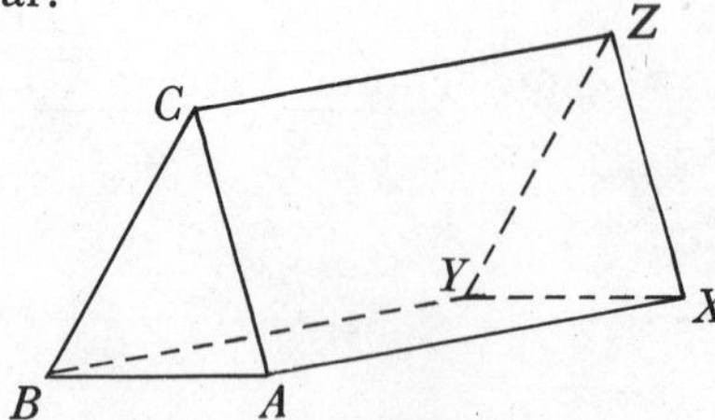

53. Given: Dihedral $\angle P\text{-}\overleftrightarrow{SQ}\text{-}R$, plane $PQR \perp \overleftrightarrow{SQ}$, $(PQ)^2 + (QR)^2 = (PR)^2$

Prove: Plane $PQS \perp$ plane RQS

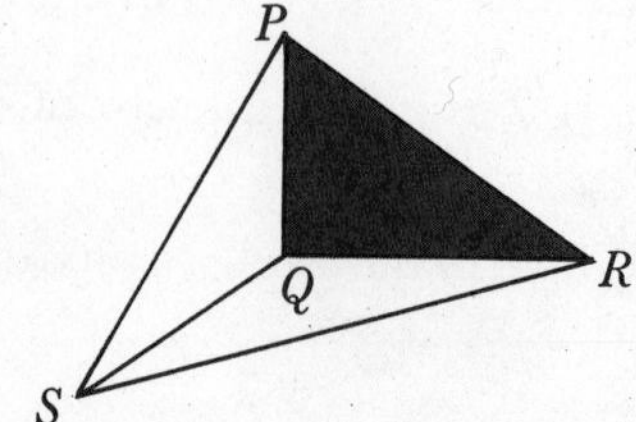

Ch. 14

NOTE: In Exercises 54–63, leave answers for cylinders, cones, and spheres in terms of π.

54–60. Find the volume of each figure.

54. right triangular prism, height 3 m, base edges of length 2 m

55. right circular cylinder, radius 42 cm, height 6.5 mm

56. oblique prism, height 13, square base with perimeter 12

57. oblique circular cylinder, radius $\frac{2}{3}$, height 12

58. circular cone, radius 6, height 2

59. triangular pyramid, height 9, base area $7\sqrt{2}$

60. sphere, radius 2.1

61–62. Find the lateral area and the surface area of each figure.

61. prism in Exercise 54

62. cylinder in Exercise 55

63. Find the surface area of a sphere with radius 11.

64. Given: A pyramid of height h whose base is a rhombus with diagonals of lengths d_1 and d_2

Prove: The volume (V) of the pyramid is equal to $\frac{1}{6}h\, d_1 d_2$.

Ch. 15

65–68. Given $A(-1, -2)$, $B(9, 5)$, $C(3, 7)$, and $D(-3, 2)$,

65. Draw quadrilateral $ABCD$ in the coordinate plane.

66. Find the coordinates of the midpoint of $\overline{BD}$.

67. Find the length of $\overline{AB}$.

68. Find the slope of $\overline{CB}$.

69–71. Refer to quadrilateral $ABCD$ in Exercises 65–68. Find the standard form of the equation of a line that

69. contains B and C

70. contains A and is parallel to $\overleftrightarrow{BC}$

71. contains the midpoint of $\overline{AD}$ and is perpendicular to $\overleftrightarrow{AD}$

72–75. Graph each on a separate pair of axes.

72. $(y - 3) = -\frac{2}{3}(x + 4)$

73. $5 \leq y < -1$

74. $5x + 6y \geq -12$

75. $x^2 + (y - 7)^2 = 64$

76. Using coordinates, prove that opposite sides of a parallelogram are congruent. HINT: Let $A(0, 0)$, $B(a, 0)$, $C(a + b, c)$, and $D(b, c)$ be the vertices of the parallelogram.

POSTULATES

NAMED THEOREMS

CONSTRUCTIONS

SYMBOLS

SQUARES AND SQUARE ROOTS

n	n^2	$\sqrt{n}$	n	n^2	$\sqrt{n}$	n	n^2	$\sqrt{n}$
1	1	1.000	**51**	2 601	7.141	**101**	10 201	10.050
2	4	1.414	**52**	2 704	7.211	**102**	10 404	10.100
3	9	1.732	**53**	2 809	7.280	**103**	10 609	10.149
4	16	2.000	**54**	2 916	7.348	**104**	10 816	10.198
5	25	2.236	**55**	3 025	7.416	**105**	11 025	10.247
6	36	2.449	**56**	3 136	7.483	**106**	11 236	10.296
7	49	2.646	**57**	3 249	7.550	**107**	11 449	10.344
8	64	2.828	**58**	3 364	7.616	**108**	11 664	10.392
9	81	3.000	**59**	3 481	7.681	**109**	11 881	10.440
10	100	3.162	**60**	3 600	7.746	**110**	12 100	10.488
11	121	3.317	**61**	3 721	7.810	**111**	12 321	10.536
12	144	3.464	**62**	3 844	7.874	**112**	12 544	10.583
13	169	3.606	**63**	3 969	7.937	**113**	12 769	10.630
14	196	3.742	**64**	4 096	8.000	**114**	12 996	10.677
15	225	3.873	**65**	4 225	8.062	**115**	13 225	10.724
16	256	4.000	**66**	4 356	8.124	**116**	13 456	10.770
17	289	4.123	**67**	4 489	8.185	**117**	13 689	10.817
18	324	4.243	**68**	4 624	8.246	**118**	13 924	10.863
19	361	4.359	**69**	4 761	8.307	**119**	14 161	10.909
20	400	4.472	**70**	4 900	8.367	**120**	14 400	10.954
21	441	4.583	**71**	5 041	8.426	**121**	14 641	11.000
22	484	4.690	**72**	5 184	8.485	**122**	14 884	11.045
23	529	4.796	**73**	5 329	8.544	**123**	15 129	11.091
24	576	4.899	**74**	5 476	8.602	**124**	15 376	11.136
25	625	5.000	**75**	5 625	8.660	**125**	15 625	11.180
26	676	5.099	**76**	5 776	8.718	**126**	15 876	11.225
27	729	5.196	**77**	5 929	8.775	**127**	16 129	11.269
28	784	5.292	**78**	6 084	8.832	**128**	16 384	11.314
29	841	5.385	**79**	6 241	8.888	**129**	16 641	11.358
30	900	5.477	**80**	6 400	8.944	**130**	16 900	11.402
31	961	5.568	**81**	6 561	9.000	**131**	17 161	11.446
32	1 024	5.657	**82**	6 724	9.055	**132**	17 424	11.489
33	1 089	5.745	**83**	6 889	9.110	**133**	17 689	11.533
34	1 156	5.831	**84**	7 056	9.165	**134**	17 956	11.576
35	1 225	5.916	**85**	7 225	9.220	**135**	18 225	11.619
36	1 296	6.000	**86**	7 396	9.274	**136**	18 496	11.662
37	1 369	6.083	**87**	7 569	9.327	**137**	18 769	11.705
38	1 444	6.164	**88**	7 744	9.381	**138**	19 044	11.747
39	1 521	6.245	**89**	7 921	9.434	**139**	19 321	11.790
40	1 600	6.325	**90**	8 100	9.487	**140**	19 600	11.832
41	1 681	6.403	**91**	8 281	9.539	**141**	19 881	11.874
42	1 764	6.481	**92**	8 464	9.592	**142**	20 164	11.916
43	1 849	6.557	**93**	8 649	9.644	**143**	20 449	11.958
44	1 936	6.633	**94**	8 836	9.695	**144**	20 736	12.000
45	2 025	6.708	**95**	9 025	9.747	**145**	21 025	12.042
46	2 116	6.782	**96**	9 216	9.798	**146**	21 316	12.083
47	2 209	6.856	**97**	9 409	9.849	**147**	21 609	12.124
48	2 304	6.928	**98**	9 604	9.899	**148**	21 904	12.166
49	2 401	7.000	**99**	9 801	9.950	**149**	22 201	12.207
50	2 500	7.071	**100**	10 000	10.000	**150**	22 500	12.247

INDEX

HOMEWORK HANDBOOK

This handbook contains model solutions and answers for selected exercises. Generally, the odd-numbered B exercises are answered, and a model solution is given for each major exercise type.

The model solutions and answers will be especially helpful when the student has had to miss some class time or when the teacher has had to shorten a class session for some unscheduled activity.

Pages 4–5 Section 1.1

19. a **21.** b **23.** e **25.** g **27.** e

29.

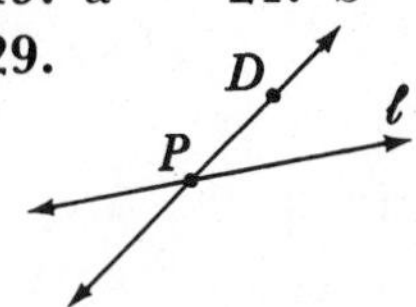

31.

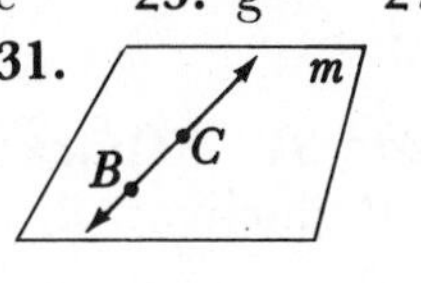

33.

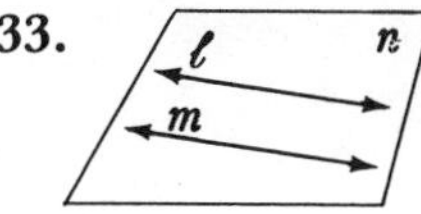

Page 8 Section 1.2

Ex. 17–27: Other answers possible

***17.** $5\frac{1}{2}$ **19.** $-3\frac{1}{2}$ **21.** $1\frac{3}{4}$

23. $3\frac{3}{8}$ **25.** 1.25 **27.** $-\frac{1}{6}$

29.

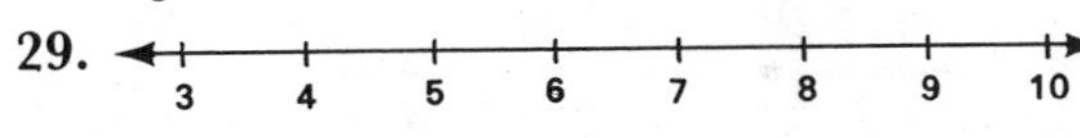

31. −8 −7 −6 −5 −4 −3 −2 −1 0

33.

35.

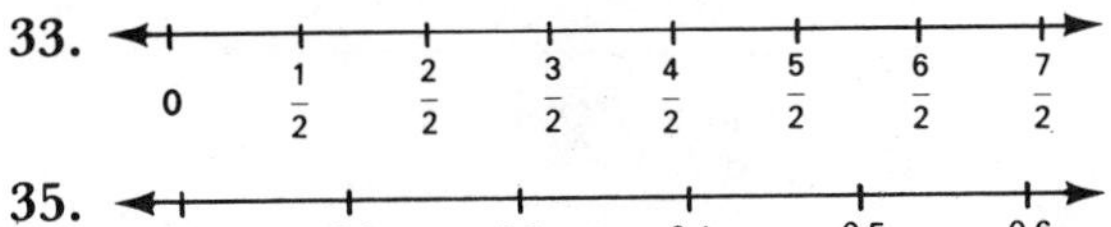

37. > **39.** = **41.** > **43.** =

**Model Solution:*

17. $\frac{1}{2}(5 + 6) = \frac{11}{2}$

$= 5\frac{1}{2}$

Page 13 Section 1.3

***17.** 7 **19.** 14 **21.** 8 **23.** 0 **25.** 16

27. 27 ***29.** 7 **31.** 15 **33.** 12 **35.** 11

37. 15 **39.** 9 **41.** 6 **43.** 94 **45.** 11

**Model Solutions:*

17. $|12 - 5|$
$= |7|$
$= 7$

29. $P: 0 \quad R: 7$
$|7 - 0|$ or $|0 - 7|$
$= |7|$ $= |-7|$
$= 7$ $= 7$

Pages 16–17 Section 1.4

21. c **23.** a **25.** g **27.** a

29. e **31.** d **33.** f

Page 17 Quick Quiz

1. Any 3 of point, line, plane, contains
2. $\overleftrightarrow{AP}$ or $\overleftrightarrow{AB}$ or $\overleftrightarrow{PB}$
3. C, A, P or C, A, B or C, P, B
4. $\overline{AB}$ or $\overline{PB}$ or $\overline{AP}$
5. $\overrightarrow{AP}$ or $\overrightarrow{AB}$
6. $\overrightarrow{PB}$
7. P
8. A rational
9. <
10. Postulate
11. Absolute value
12. Model

Pages 20–21 Section 1.5

7. A woman be President

9. A live passenger pigeon exist

11. Capital punishment is effective.

13. Capital punishment is not effective.

15. $x = 0$ **17.** $x = 1$ or $x = 0$ or any number between 0 and 1

19. b **21.** a

Page 21 Algebra Review

*1. $x = 5$ 3. $x = 9$ 5. $t = 6$ *7. $a = 3$
9. $y = 6$ 11. $y = \frac{2}{21}$ 13. $a = \frac{14}{3}$
15. $n = 1.8$ 17. $y = 5\frac{1}{2}$ 19. $a = 21$

**Model Solutions:*

1. $$\begin{array}{rcl} x + 2 &=& 7 \\ +(-2) && +(-2) \\ \hline x &=& 5 \end{array}$$

7. $$\begin{array}{rcl} 4a &=& 12 \\ \times\frac{1}{4} && \times\frac{1}{4} \\ \hline a &=& 3 \end{array}$$

Pages 24–25 Section 1.6

25. Distrib. Prop. 27. Comm. Prop. of ·
29. Ident. Prop. of + 31. Assoc. Prop. of +
33. Inv. Prop. of · 35. Ident. Prop. of ·
37. Assoc. Prop. of · 39. Inv. Prop. of +
41. If two numbers are both equal to a third number, they are equal to each other. (or Substitution)
43. Ident. Prop. of + 45. Assoc. Prop. of +
47. Distrib. Prop. 49. Mult. Prop. of 0
51. Given
Add. Prop. of =
Substitution of 12 for 3 + 9
Assoc. Prop. of +
Inv. Prop. of +
Ident. Prop. of +

Page 30 Section 1.7

13. Plane Post. 15. Midpoint Thm.
17. Number-of-Points Post.
19. Flat Plane Post. 21. Straight Line Post.

Pages 33–34 Section 1.8

7. Two intersecting lines determine a point.
9. Two planes that intersect, intersect at exactly one line.
11. A line and a point not on it are in exactly one plane.
13. Line Intersection Theorem
15. Line-Plane Intersection Theorem
17. Line-Intersection Theorem

19.

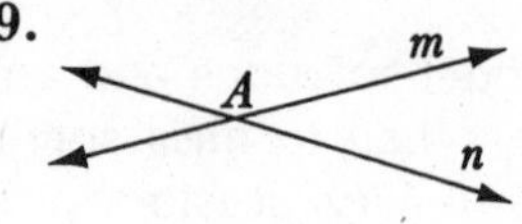

21.

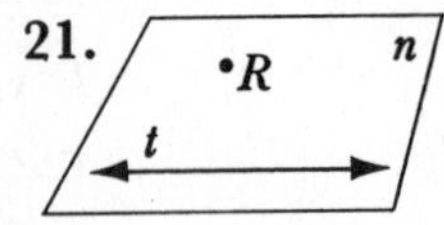

Page 34 Quick Quiz

1. Deductive 2. Theorem 3. 0 4. $\frac{1}{2}$
5. Yes 6. No 7. Yes 8. Yes

Page 37 Section 1.9

Ex. 23–35: Diagrams shown $\frac{1}{2}$ size.

23.

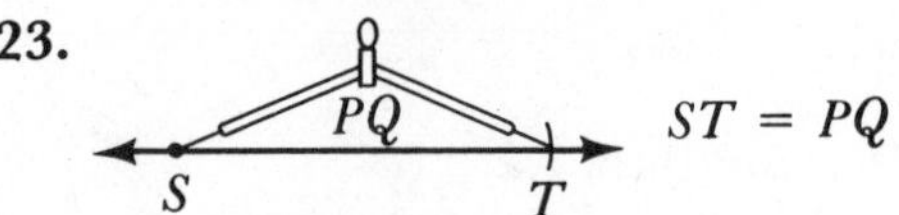

25.

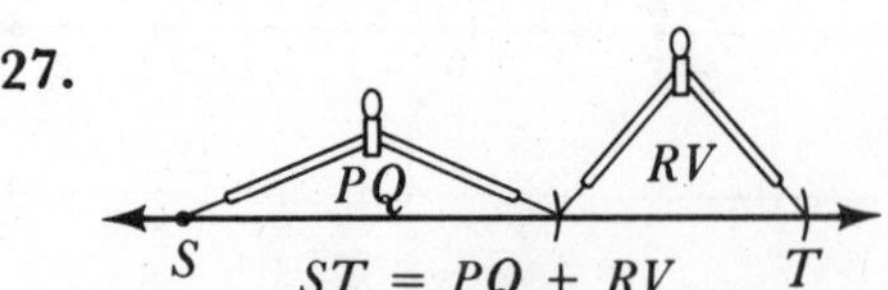

27.

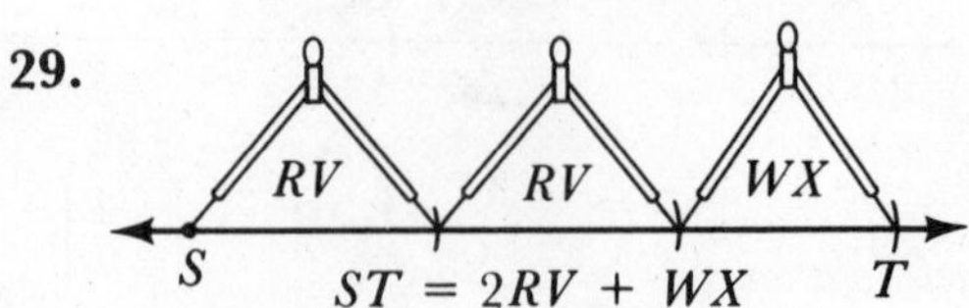

29.

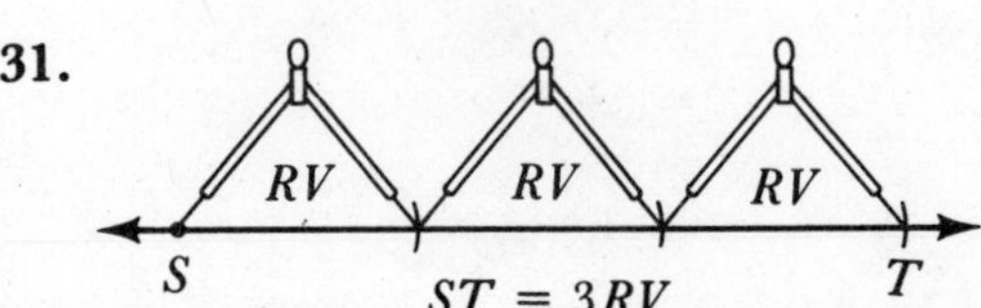

31.

S T — RV RV RV

ST = 3RV

33.

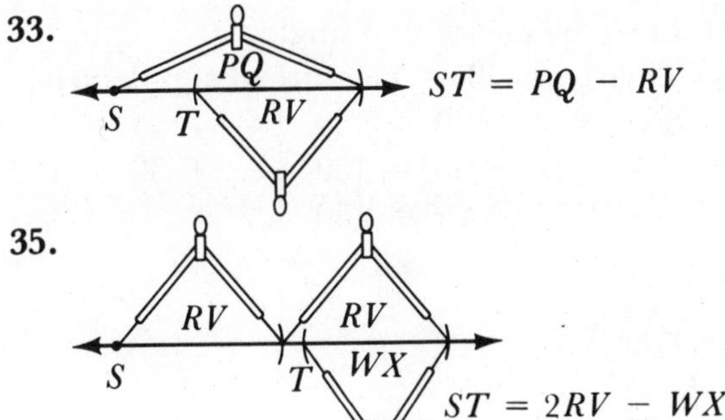

35.

Ex. 37–45: Shown in diagram below.

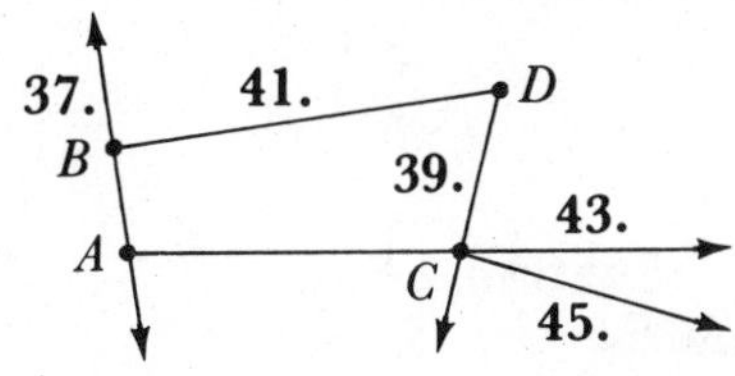

Page 39 Section 1.10
7. Slide 9. Turn 11. Reflection
13. Turn 15. Slide 17. Reflection

Pages 40–41 Chapter 1 Review
1. Point 3. Plane 5. n 7. B
9. Order 11. $>$ 13. $<$ 15. Absolute value
17. 5 19. Collinear 21. Between
23. Midpoint 25. Rays 27. Deductive
29. Hypothesis and logical conclusion
31. Assoc. Prop. of +
33. If two numbers are equal, the equation can be written with either number first.
35. Comm. Prop. of + 37. Ident. Prop. of +
39. Inv. Prop. of + 41. Mult. Prop. of 0
43. Straight Line Post.
45. Number-of-Points Post.
47. Flat Plane Post.
49. Line-Plane Intersection Thm.
51. Plane Thm., part b 53. Straightedge
57. Size change 59. Slide

Page 42 Chapter 1 Test
1. A, B, C 2. $\overleftrightarrow{PC}$ 3. D 4. P, B, C
5. A, B 6. $\overline{PC}$ 7. $\overrightarrow{CB}$ 8. A, B
9. Order 10. Coordinate
11. Absolute value 12. Distance
13. Midpoint 14. Bisects 15. Inductive
16. Deductive 17. Theorem 18. Postulate
19. Determine 20. Compass
21. Transformations
22. Straight Line Post. 23. Plane Post.
24. Plane Thm., part b
25. Line Intersection Thm.

Pages 46–47 Section 2.1
17. T 19. F 21. F 23. F
25. T 27. F 29. F 31. T

Page 47 Algebra Review
*1. $a = 7$ 3. $m = 1\frac{4}{5}$ 5. $d = 8$
*7. $x = 18$ 9. $z = 12$ 11. $g = 16\frac{2}{3}$

**Model Solutions:*

1. $4a + 7 = 35$
$+(-7) \quad +(-7)$
$4a = 28$
$\times\frac{1}{4} \quad \times\frac{1}{4}$
$a = 7$

7. $3x + 2x = 90$
$5x = 90$
$x = 18$

Pages 50–51 Section 2.2
17. Any two of $\angle CBA$, $\angle ABC$, $\angle 1$
19. $\angle HEJ$, $\angle JEK$, $\angle KEG$, $\angle HEK$, $\angle JEG$, $\angle HEG$
21. $\triangle RAS$, $\triangle RAT$, $\triangle RST$ 23. P, N
25. W, V, U, B 27. F 29. T 31. 7
33. T 35. T 37. F 39. F

2

Pages 54–55 Section 2.3

7. 144

9. 30, 135, 15

11.

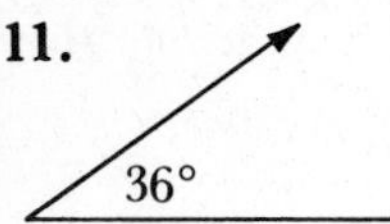

13.

76°

15. $\angle EON$, $\angle DOT$

17. 55

19. AXC

21. CXD

*23. 93

25. 72

**Model Solution:*

23. $m\angle AXC = m\angle AXB + m\angle BXC$
$= 59 + 34$
$= 93$

Page 55 Algebra Review

1. $x + 20$

3. $2x$

*5. $x + x + 6 = 180$

*7. 87, 93

**Model Solutions:*

5. Let x = one number.
Then $x + 6$ = other number.
$x + x + 6 = 180$

7. $2x + 6 = 180$
$2x = 174$
$x = 87$
$x + 6 = 93$
So the numbers are 87 and 93.

Pages 57–58 Section 2.4

7. No

*9. 80.5

*11. 149

13. 52

15. 27.7

17. $180 - n$

*19. 45, 135

*21. 75, 105

23. 135, 45

**Model Solutions:*

9. $m\angle CAX = m\angle XAY = r$
$r + r = 161$
$2r = 161$
$r = 80.5$

11. $31 + x = 180$
$x = 149$

19. $x + 3x = 180$
$4x = 180$

$x = 45$
$3x = 135$

21. Let x = measure of angle.
Then $x + 30$ = measure of supplement.
So $x + x + 30 = 180$
$2x + 30 = 180$
$2x = 150$

$x = 75$
$x + 30 = 105$

Page 59 Quick Quiz

1. T
2. F
3. F
4. T
5. F
6. F
7. T
8. F
9. T

Pages 61–63 Section 2.5

11. $\angle LCH$, $\angle SCE$

13. $\angle LCE$ and $\angle ECS$ or $\angle LCH$ and $\angle HCS$

15. $\overleftrightarrow{CE}$, $\overleftrightarrow{CH}$

17. Acute

19. Right

*21. 10

23. $61\frac{2}{3}$

25. $90 - n$

27. Perpendicular

29. T

35. Acute

37. Right

*39. 40, 50

41. 30, 60

**Model Solutions:*

21. $80 + x = 90$
$x = 10$

39. $x + x + 10 = 90$
$2x + 10 = 90$
$2x = 80$
$x = 40$
$x + 10 = 50$

Page 66 Section 2.6

11. If $\angle A \cong \angle B$, then $\angle B \cong \angle A$.

13. 93

15. $\overline{CY}$

17. $\cong$

Pages 70–71 Section 2.7

*13. T
15. F
17. T
*19. T
21. T
23. F
25. T
27. T

29. Supplements of congruent angles are congruent.
31. If two angles are congruent and supplementary, then they are right angles.
33. Vertical angles are $\cong$.
35. *Same as Ex. 31* 37. *Same as Ex. 33*

* *Model Solutions:*

13. $m\angle A_{23} + 31 = 180$ | $m\angle B_2 + 31 = 180$
$m\angle A_{23} = 149$ | $m\angle B_2 = 149$
$\angle A_{23} \cong \angle B_2$; T

19. $m\angle C_1 + 67 = 90$ | $m\angle D_2 + 67 = 90$
$m\angle C_1 = 23$ | $m\angle D_2 = 23$
$\angle C_1 \cong \angle D_2$; T

Pages 74–75 Section 2.8

17. F 19. T 21. Clockwise
23. Clockwise 25. Counterclockwise
27. 29.

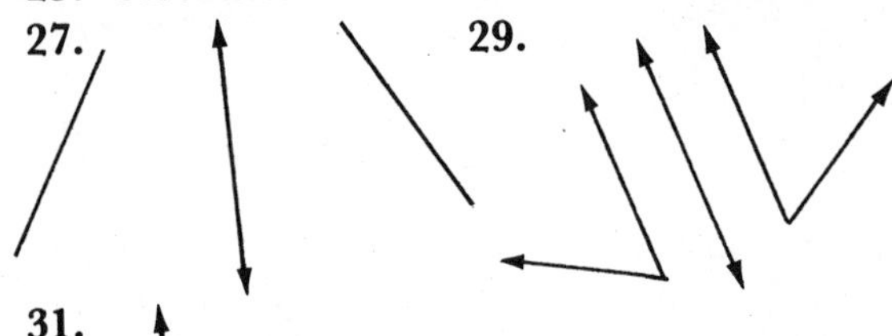

31.

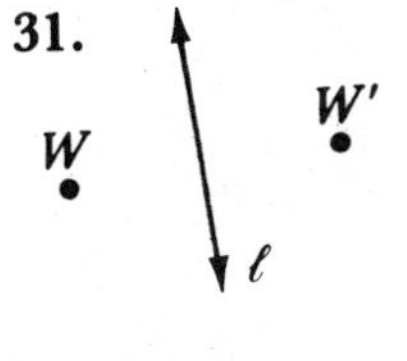

33.

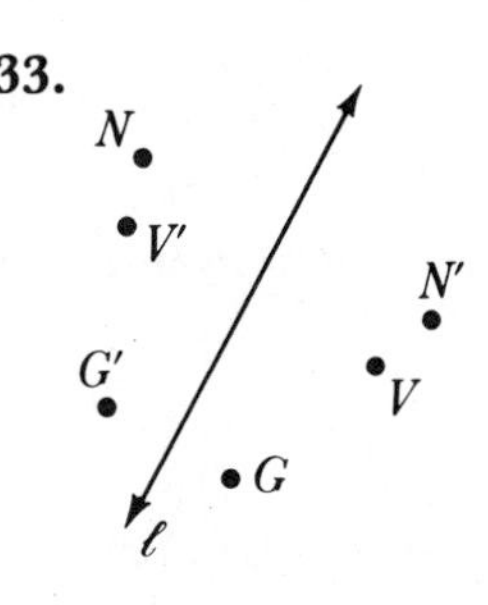

35.

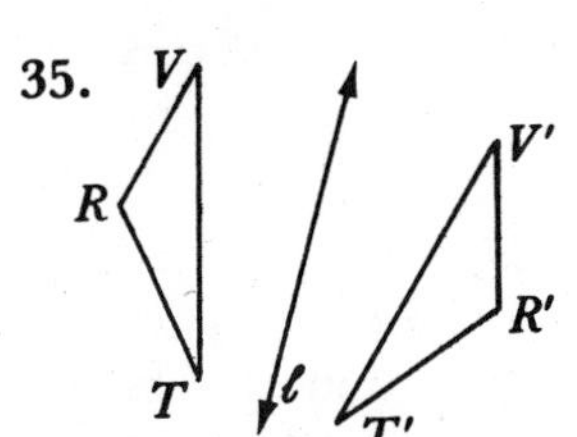

Pages 77–78 Chapter 2 Review

1. *See page 44.* 3. Yes
5. Line; half planes 7. Edge
9. *See page 48.*
11. $\triangle DFE$, $\triangle EFD$, $\triangle EDF$, $\triangle FED$, $\triangle FDE$
13. D, E, F 15. 18 17. 65
19. 36 21. 36 23. 90

25. Greater than
27. When they form right angles
29. When they have the same measure
31. $\angle B_3$ 33. A_1; A_4
35. Any 3 of betweenness, collinearity, distance, angle measure
37.

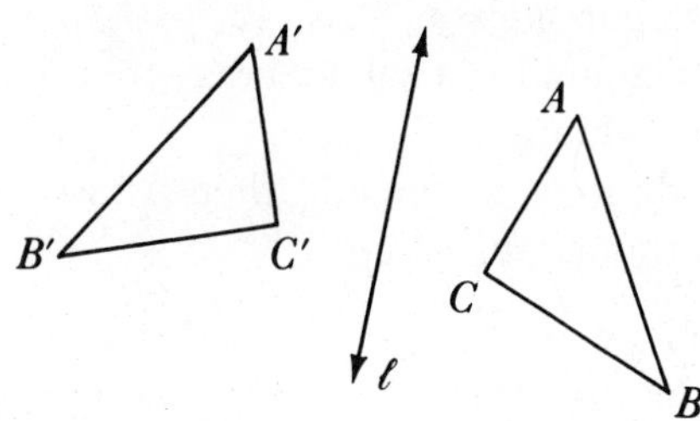

Page 79 Chapter 2 Test

1. F 2. T 3. T 4. F 5. T
6. Congruent 7. Right 8. 0; 180
9. 155 10. $\angle EAD$, $\angle EAF$ (or $\angle CAB$)
11. $\angle CAB$, $\angle EAF$ or $\angle BAF$, $\angle CAE$
12. $\angle EAC$, $\angle FAB$
13. $\overrightarrow{AD} \perp \overleftrightarrow{FC}$ or $\overleftrightarrow{FA}$ or $\overleftrightarrow{AC}$
14. 65 15. 115 16. 58 17. 52
18. 19. No

161°

20.

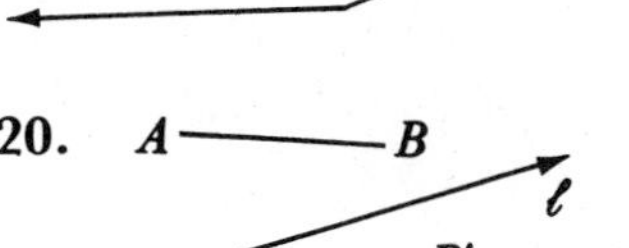

Pages 86–88 Section 3.1

7. H: there were two birds sitting on a fence
C: he would bet you which one would fly first
9. H: you brush your teeth with Superwhite
C: you will be popular
11. H: $x = 3$
C: $x^2 = 9$
13. H: $x^2 = 9$
C: $x = 3$ or $x = -3$

15. H: $\overline{AB} \cong \overline{CD}$ and $\overline{EF} \cong \overline{CD}$
C: $\overline{AB} \cong \overline{EF}$
17. H: the sum of their measures is 90
C: two angles are complementary
19. If an animal is a bird, then it can fly.
21. If a figure is a triangle, then it does not have four sides.
23. If an animal is a salamander, then it is an amphibian.
25. If a figure is a segment, then it has exactly one midpoint.
27. a 29. 31.

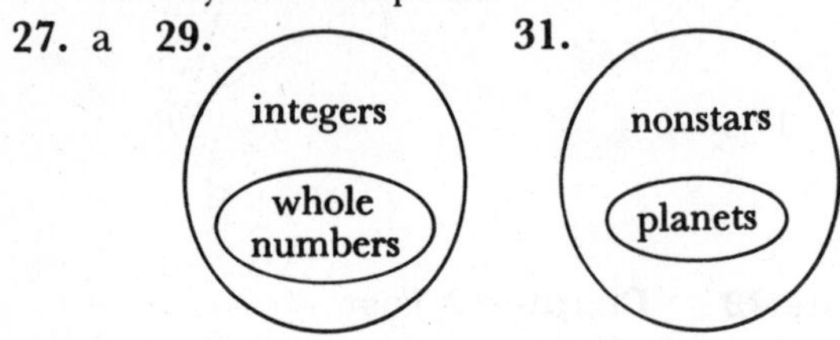

33. If a figure is a triangle, then it is contained in exactly one plane.

Pages 91–92 Section 3.2
7. Given 9. Given 11. Given
13. Given 15. Subtract BC from both sides.
17. Given 19. Given
21. Substitution (steps 2 and 4)
23. Multiply both sides by $\frac{1}{2}$.

Pages 95–96 Section 3.3
25. $\triangle RST$ 27. $\triangle SDE$ 29. $\triangle TUM$
31. $\overline{TO} \cong \overline{CA}$, $\overline{OP} \cong \overline{AR}$, $\overline{TP} \cong \overline{CR}$,
$\angle T \cong \angle C$, $\angle O \cong \angle A$, $\angle P \cong \angle R$
33. $\triangle PLA \cong \triangle KHU$, $\triangle ALP \cong \triangle UHK$,
$\triangle APL \cong \triangle UKH$, $\triangle LPA \cong \triangle HKU$

Pages 98–99 Section 3.4
7. $\triangle GFE \cong \triangle KHE$; SAS
9. Not congruent
11. $\triangle ROF \cong \triangle MOA$; ASA
13. Not congruent
15. Ex. 9 17. SAS 19. ASA
21. a. $\angle U \cong \angle L$ b. $\overline{GM} \cong \overline{TO}$

Page 101 Quick Quiz
1. H: two angles are right angles
C: they are congruent
2. If an animal is a collie, then it is a dog.
3.

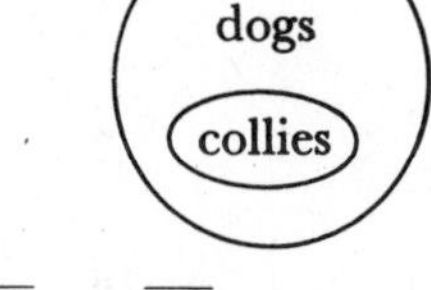

4. Given facts, postulates, definitions, previously proved theorems
5. $\overline{TE} \cong \overline{BI}$, $\overline{ED} \cong \overline{IG}$, $\overline{TD} \cong \overline{BG}$,
$\angle T \cong \angle B$, $\angle E \cong \angle I$, $\angle D \cong \angle G$
6. SSS Post. 7. ASA Post.

Pages 103–105 Section 3.5
7. SAS 9. No 11. No
13. Given 15. Given 17. Given
19. A segment is congruent to itself.
21. Given 23. Given 25. Given
27. Substitution
29. Definition of perpendicular 31. Given

Pages 107–108 Section 3.6
5. Given 7. Definition of between
9. Definition of congruent segments
11. SSS Post. 13. Given
15. Definition of perpendicular
17. Complements of congruent angles are congruent.
19. Definition of perpendicular 21. Given
23. ASA Post. (steps 5, 8, and 10)

Pages 112–113 Section 3.7

7. A segment is congruent to itself.
9. Definition of midpoint
11. Corres. parts of ≅ △s are ≅.
13. Definition of perpendicular 15. Given
17. Two points determine a line.
19. Corollary to Perpendicular Bisector Thm.

Pages 115–116 Section 3.8

(TA means *typical answer*.)

7. TA: slide, reflection
9. TA: reflection, turn
11. Opposite 13. Turn; $\overline{YC'}$ and $\overline{YZ}$
15. Yes; Corollary to Perp. Bisector Thm. (p. 111) 17. Slide, turn, reflection

Pages 118–119 Chapter 3 Review

1. H: A, B, and C are noncollinear
   C: $AB + BC > AC$
3. If an animal is a giraffe, it gargles with Listerine.
5.

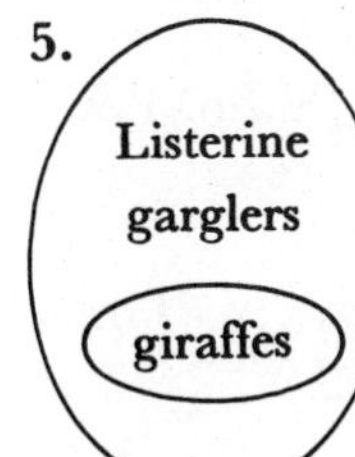

7. c 9. $\overline{TS}$ 11. $\angle A$
13. $\angle A \cong \angle Y$, $\angle R \cong \angle P$, $\angle E \cong \angle U$, $\overline{AR} \cong \overline{YP}$, $\overline{RE} \cong \overline{PU}$, $\overline{AE} \cong \overline{YU}$
15. SSS Post.
17. Given
19. ASA Post.
21. A segment is congruent to itself.
23. Corres. parts of ≅ △s are ≅.
25. Reflection

Page 120 Chapter 3 Test

1. If a number is a whole number, then it is an integer.
2. integers; whole numbers
3. **a.** $\angle T$ **b.** $\overline{PL}$ **c.** $\angle O$
4. SAS Post.
5. ASA Post.
6. Given
7. Definition of midpoint
8. Given
9. Definition of midpoint
10. Two segments congruent to the same segment are congruent.
11. Given 12. ASA Post.
13. Corres. parts of ≅ △s are ≅.
14. Slide 15. Reflection

Pages 126–127 Section 4.1

15. b 17. a 19. d 21. b
23. P is not on ℓ.
25. Perp. Line Post. (p. 60)
27. Yes; two parallel lines determine a plane.

Pages 130–131 Section 4.2

Measures of ∠s:

	1, 3	2, 4	5, 7	6, 8
*17.	62	118	62	118
19.	67	113	67	113
21.	68	112	—	—
23.	75	105	60	120

25. $\angle 4$; $\angle 6$ 27. s; t
29. $\angle 2$, $\angle 6$, $\angle 7$, $\angle 9$, $\angle 11$ 31. 35°
33. Alt. int. ∠s are ≅.

**Model Solution:*

17. $m\angle 2 + m\angle 1 = 180$ (Supp. Post.)
$118 + m\angle 1 = 180$
$m\angle 1 = 62$
$m\angle 3 = m\angle 1 = 62$ (Vert. ∠s are ≅.)
$m\angle 5 = m\angle 3 = 62$ (Alt. int. ∠s Thm.)
$m\angle 7 = m\angle 5 = 62$ (Vert. ∠s are ≅.)
$m\angle 4 = m\angle 2 = 118$ (Vert. ∠s are ≅.)
$m\angle 6 = m\angle 4 = 118$ (Alt. int. ∠s Thm.)
$m\angle 8 = m\angle 6 = 118$ (Vert. ∠s are ≅.)

Pages 134–135 Section 4.3

	$\angle$s	Meas.
*7.	1, 3, 6, 8	93
	2, 4, 5, 7	87
9.	9, 11, 14, 16	102
	10, 12, 13, 15	78
11.	1, 3, 6, 8, 9, 11, 14, 16	108
	2, 4, 5, 7, 10, 12, 13, 15	72
13.	9, 10, 11, 12, 13, 14, 15, 16	90
15.	1, 3, 6, 8, 9, 11, 14, 16	112
	2, 4, 5, 7, 10, 12, 13, 15	68
17.	1, 2, 3, 4, 5, 6, 7, 8	90

Measures of $\angle$s:

	2, 4	3	5, 7	6, 8
*19.	60	120	50	130
21.	80	100	40	140

23. Yes

25. *1.* If lines are ∥, alt. int. $\angle$s are ≅.
2. Vertical $\angle$s are ≅.
3. $\angle$s ≅ to the same $\angle$ are ≅.

******Model Solutions:*

7. $m\angle 1 + m\angle 2 = 180$ (Supp. Post.)
$m\angle 1 + 87 = 180$
$m\angle 1 = 93$

$m\angle 6 = m\angle 1 = 93$ (Vert. $\angle$s are ≅.)

$m\angle 3 = m\angle 1 = 93$ (Corres. $\angle$s Thm.)

$m\angle 8 = m\angle 3 = 93$ (Vert. $\angle$s are ≅.)

$m\angle 5 = m\angle 2 = 87$ (Vert. $\angle$s are ≅.)

$m\angle 7 = m\angle 5 = 87$ (Corres. $\angle$s Thm.)

$m\angle 4 = m\angle 7 = 87$ (Vert. $\angle$s are ≅.)

19. $m\angle 8 + m\angle 5 = 180$ (Supp. Post.)
$130 + m\angle 5 = 180$
$m\angle 5 = 50$

$m\angle 7 = m\angle 5 = 50$ (Corres. $\angle$s Thm.)

$m\angle 6 = m\angle 8 = 130$ (Vert. $\angle$s are ≅.)

$m\angle 2 = m\angle 4 = 60$ (Corres. $\angle$s Thm.)

$m\angle 3 + m\angle 4 = 180$ (If lines are ∥, int.
$m\angle 3 + 60 = 180$ $\angle$s on same side
$m\angle 3 = 120$ of trans. are supp.)

Page 135 Algebra Review

1. $x = 180$ *3. $n = 10$
5. $p = 25$ 7. $a = 61$

Model Solution:

3. $125 + 45 + n = 180$
$170 + n = 180$
$n = 10$

Page 140 Section 4.4

*13. $m\angle 1 = 72$, $m\angle 2 = 108$
15. $m\angle P = 35$, $m\angle 2 = 125$
17. $m\angle P = m\angle O = 72$, $m\angle 2 = 144$
19. $m\angle O = 82$, $m\angle 1 = 53$
*21. $m\angle 1 = 120$, $m\angle 3 = 55$, $m\angle 4 = 10$, $m\angle 5 = 65$, $m\angle 7 = 55$
23. $m\angle 2 = 72$, $m\angle 3 = 40$, $m\angle 4 = 28$, $m\angle 5 = 68$, $m\angle 6 = 112$

Model Solutions:

13. $m\angle 1 + m\angle O + m\angle P = 180$ ($\angle$ Sum
$m\angle 1 + 38 + 70 = 180$ Thm.
$m\angle 1 + 108 = 180$ for Δs)
$m\angle 1 = 72$

$m\angle 2 = m\angle O + m\angle P$ (Ext. $\angle$ Thm.)
$= 38 + 70$
$= 108$

21. $m\angle 1 + m\angle 2 = 180$ (Supp. Post.)
$m\angle 1 + 60 = 180$
$m\angle 1 = 120$
$m\angle 3 + m\angle 2 = m\angle 6$ (Ext. $\angle$ Thm.)
$m\angle 3 + 60 = 115$
$m\angle 3 = 55$
$m\angle 7 = m\angle 3 = 55$ (Def. of ≅ $\angle$s)
$m\angle 4 + m\angle 6 + m\angle 7 = 180$ ($\angle$ Sum
$m\angle 4 + 115 + 55 = 180$ Thm.
$m\angle 4 + 170 = 180$ for Δs)
$m\angle 4 = 10$
$m\angle 5 + m\angle 3 = m\angle 1$ (Ext. $\angle$ Thm.)
$m\angle 5 + 55 = 120$
$m\angle 5 = 65$

Page 140 Quick Quiz

1. $\angle 1$, $\angle 2$, $\angle 7$, $\angle 8$
2. $\angle 3$ and $\angle 5$, $\angle 4$ and $\angle 6$
3. $\angle 1$ and $\angle 5$, $\angle 2$ and $\angle 6$, $\angle 3$ and $\angle 7$, $\angle 4$ and $\angle 8$
4. $\angle 3$ and $\angle 6$, $\angle 4$ and $\angle 5$

5. 55 **6.** 112 **7.** 180 **8.** 105 **9.** T
10. F **11.** T **12.** F **13.** F **14.** T

15. If point P is not on line ℓ, there is exactly one line through P parallel to ℓ.
16. The sum of the measures of the angles of a triangle is 180.

Pages 143–144 Section 4.5

13. $\overleftrightarrow{BC} \parallel \overleftrightarrow{AD}$, transversal $\overleftrightarrow{AB}$
15. $\overleftrightarrow{BC} \parallel \overleftrightarrow{AD}$, transversal $\overleftrightarrow{CD}$

17. $\triangle RSM$	**19.** $\overline{RS}$	**21.** $\overline{PS}$
23. $\angle RSM$	**25.** 3	**27.** MS
29. $m\angle PMN$	**31.** $m\angle NRS$	**33.** 180
35. $m\angle MPN$	**37.** 105	**39.** 118

Page 147 Section 4.6

9. The diagonals bisect each other.
11. Two sides are $\parallel$ and $\cong$.
13. Opposite sides are $\cong$.
15. If two $\angle$s are supp., they are consecutive $\angle$s of a parallelogram. F
17. A segment is $\cong$ to itself.
19. Corres. parts of $\cong$ $\triangle$s are $\cong$.

Page 149 Section 4.7

9. 48	**11.** 6	**13.** 48
15. 4	**17.** 8	

Page 151 Section 4.8

11. $\overline{UT}$	**13.** 50	**15.** 12
17. 90	**19.** 7	**21.** 6

23. Since $PINK$ is a ▱ and $\overline{PI} \cong \overline{IN}$, we can prove all sides are $\cong$. So, $PINK$ is a rhombus.
25. Since $SONG$ is a rhombus and $m\angle G = 90$, we can prove $SONG$ is a rectangle. Since a rectangle has 4 rt. $\angle$s, $m\angle S = 90$.

4

Pages 155–156 Section 4.9

11. 4 **13.** 3 ***15.** 4 **17.** 12 **19.** 4

21. So sides of board are at 0 and 12. (Use marks at 2, 4, 6, 8, and 10.)
23. If corres. $\angle$s are $\cong$, lines are $\parallel$.
25. Mark off 4 $\cong$ segments on $\overrightarrow{AP}$.

* *Model Solution:*

15. $BF = \frac{1}{2}(AG + CE)$
$= \frac{1}{2}(6 + 2) = 4$

Page 159 Section 4.10

9. *See* $\triangle M'O'E'$ *below.* **11.** *See trapezoid* $N'A'M'E'$ *below.*

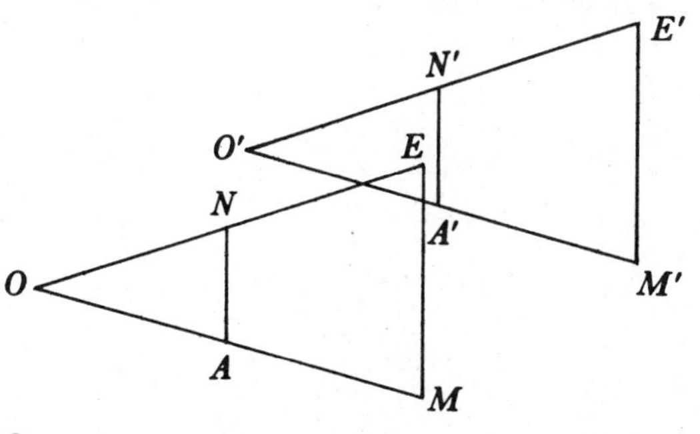

13.

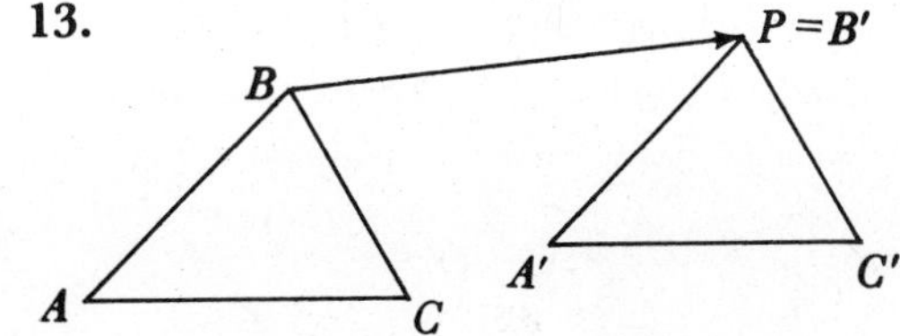

15. Yes; a line is ∥ to its slide image.

17. When a transversal intersects 2 lines, if the lines are ∥, the corres. ∠s are ≅.

Pages 160–161 Chapter 4 Review

1. a, c 3. a 5. No; Parallel Post.
7. ∠1 and ∠5 9. ∠9 11. ∠5
13. 90 15. ∠5 17. 180
19. Acute 21. T 23. F
25. F 27. T 29. No
31. Yes 33. 4 35. 180
37. Rhombus 39. Rhombus
41. If a line ∥ to 1 side of a △ bisects either of the other 2 sides, it bisects both of them.
43. Trapezoid 45. Magnitude; direction
47. $\overline{PP'}$, $\overline{TT'}$ 49. Are

Page 162 Chapter 4 Test

1. Parallel 2. Indirect
3. Alternate interior 4. Side
5. Midline 6. Trapezoid
7. ∠6 8. ∠3 9. ∠3
10. ∥ 11. 90 12. ∠2
13. *CD* 14. 90 15. 8
16. *DE* 17. a, b, c, d 18. a
19. b, d 20. c, d 21. c 22. a
23. a, b, c, d 24. b 25. Do

Page 166 Section 5.1

7. $\overline{CI}$, $\overline{IN}$, $\overline{NE}$, $\overline{EM}$, $\overline{MA}$, $\overline{AC}$
9. No; vertices are not named in order.
11. 5 13. 7 15. 9 17. 36

Ex. 19, 21. Typical answers.

19.

21.

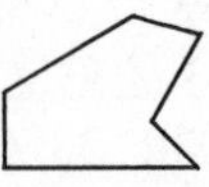

23. *There are 2.*

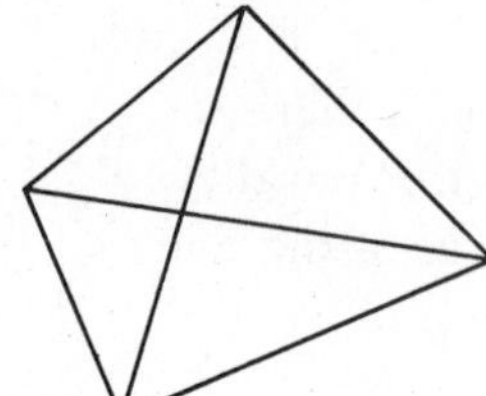

25. *There are 9.*

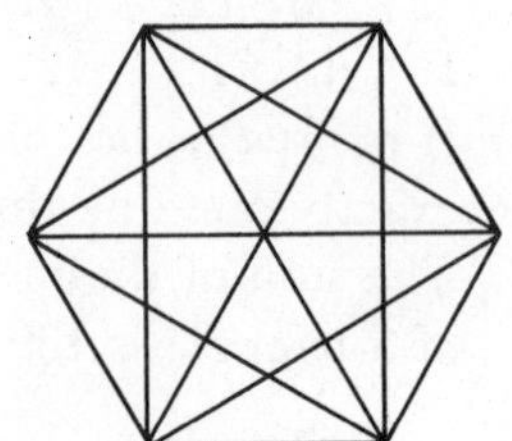

Pages 168–169 Section 5.2

7. 35 9. 118 *11. 36 cm
13. 10.2 km *15. 40 m 17. $10x$
19. No; not equiangular *21. 24 cm
23. $35 + 40x$

**Model Solutions:*

11. $P = 2(b_1 + b_2)$
$= 2(12 + 6)$
$= 2(18)$
$= 36$; 36 cm

15. $P = 2(\ell + w)$
$= 2(18 + 2)$
$= 2(20)$
$= 40$; 40 m

21. $P = ns$
$= 6 \cdot 4$
$= 24$; 24 cm

Pages 172–173 Section 5.3

	Convex polygon	No. sides	No. △s	Sum int. ∠s	Sum ext. ∠s
3.	triangle	3	1	180	360
*5.	pentagon	5	3	540	360
7.	heptagon	7	5	900	360
9.	nonagon	9	7	1260	360
11.	12-gon	12	10	1800	360
13.	20-gon	20	18	3240	360
15.	36-gon	36	34	6120	360

*17. 178 19. 128 21. **a.** 540 **b.** 360

	Regular polygon	No. sides	Meas. int. ∠	Meas. ext. ∠
23.	triangle	3	60	120
***25.**	pentagon	5	108	72
27.	heptagon	7	$128\frac{4}{7}$	$51\frac{3}{7}$
29.	nonagon	9	140	40
31.	50-gon	50	172.8	7.2
33.	12-gon	12	150	30
35.	18-gon	18	160	20

* *Model Solutions:*

5. Pentagon has 5 sides.
No. of △s = $(n - 2) = 5 - 2 = 3$
Sum of int. ∠s $= (n-2)180$
$= (5-2)180$
$= 3 \cdot 180$
$= 540$
The sum of the ext. ∠s = 360.

17. Sum of int. ∠s $= (n-2)180$
$= (5-2)180$
$= 3 \cdot 180$
$= 540$
Let x = measure of 5th ∠.
$70 + 120 + 80 + 92 + x = 540$
$362 + x = 540$
$x = 178$

25. Pentagon has 5 sides.
Measure of each int. ∠ $= \frac{180(n-2)}{n}$
$= \frac{180(5-2)}{5}$
$= \frac{\overset{36}{\cancel{180}} \cdot 3}{\underset{1}{\cancel{5}}}$
$= 108$
Measure of each ext. ∠ $= \frac{360}{n}$
$= \frac{360}{5}$
$= 72$

Pages 175–176 Section 5.4

7. 3 **9.** 4 **11.** 150 **13.** 45

15. Given:
▱$ABCD$, ▱$EFGH$,
$\angle A \cong \angle E$,
$\overline{AB} \cong \overline{EF}$, $\overline{BC} \cong \overline{FG}$
Prove:
▱$ABCD \cong$ ▱$EFGH$

Proof:

STATEMENTS	REASONS
1. ▱$ABCD$, ▱$EFGH$, $\angle A \cong \angle E$, $\overline{BC} \cong \overline{FG}$	1. Given
2. $\overline{BC} \cong \overline{AD}$, $\overline{FG} \cong \overline{EH}$	2. Opp. sides of ▱ are ≅.
3. $\overline{AD} \cong \overline{FG}$	3. Segs. ≅ to same seg. are ≅.
4. $\overline{AD} \cong \overline{EH}$	4. Same as 3.
5. $\overline{AB} \cong \overline{EF}$	5. Given
6. ▱$ABCD \cong$ ▱$EFGH$	6. SAS Thm. for ▱s

Page 176 Quick Quiz

1. *See page 164.* **2.** *See page 164.*
3. *See page 167.* **4.** 18 **5.** 24
6. 720 **7.** 360 **8.** 135 **9.** 30
10. When a side of one is ≅ to a side of the other
11. Yes; SAS Thm. for Parallelograms

Page 179 Section 5.5

5. AAS Thm. **7.** SAS Post.
9. AAS Thm. **11.** Given
13. Vertical ∠s are ≅. **15.** AAS Thm.
17. Given **19.** AAS Thm.

Pages 183–184 Section 5.6

17. 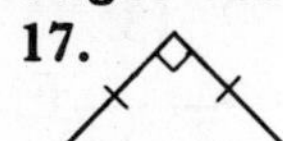

19. Impossible

21. Impossible

23.

***25.** $DE = 12$; $m\angle C = m\angle OGC = m\angle E = m\angle DOG = 65$; $m\angle OGE = m\angle D = m\angle DOC = 115$

27. $CG = OG = OC = GE = ED = DO = 8$; $CE = 16$; $m\angle C = m\angle COG = m\angle OGC = m\angle E = m\angle DOG = 60$; $m\angle OGE = m\angle D = m\angle DOC = 120$

29. $DE = 5$; $m\angle OGE = 106$; $m\angle COG = m\angle DOG = 74$; $m\angle C = m\angle E = 32$; $m\angle DOC = m\angle D = 148$

31. Every angle has a bisector.

33. Given **35.** AAS Thm.

37. If 2 $\angle$s of a $\triangle$ are $\cong$, sides opp. are $\cong$.

* *Model Solution:*

25. $DE = CO = 12$ (Def. of Isos. Trap.)

$m\angle C = m\angle OGC$ (Isos. $\triangle$ Thm.)

$m\angle C + m\angle COG + m\angle OGC = 180$ ($\angle$ Sum Thm. for $\triangle$s)

$m\angle C + 50 + m\angle C = 180$

$2m\angle C = 130$

$m\angle C = 65$

$m\angle OGC = 65$ (Subst.)

$m\angle E = m\angle C = 65$ (Isos. Trap. Thm.)

$m\angle DOG = m\angle OGC = 65$ (Alt. Int. $\angle$s Thm.)

$m\angle OGE + m\angle OGC = 180$ (Supp. Post.)

$m\angle OGE + 65 = 180$

$m\angle OGE = 115$

$m\angle DOC = m\angle COG + m\angle DOG$ ($\angle$ Add. Post)

$= 50 + 65$

$= 115$

$m\angle D = m\angle DOC = 115$ (Isos. Trap. Thm.)

Pages 187–188 Section 5.7

7. LA Thm. **9.** HL Thm. **11.** LL Thm.

13. Given **15.** Right $\angle$s are $\cong$.

17. Def. of bisector **19.** Def. of rt. $\triangle$

21. Given: $\angle 1$ and $\angle 2$ are right $\angle$s, $RS = 5$, $ST = 5$

Prove: $\triangle RSQ \cong \triangle TSQ$

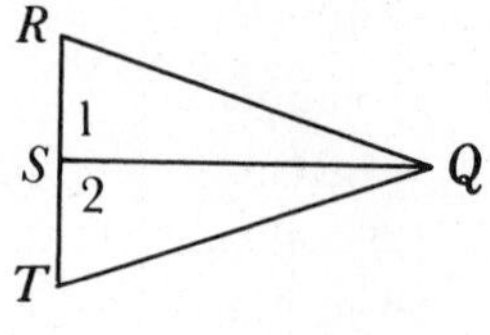

Proof:

STATEMENTS	REASONS
1. $\angle 1$ and $\angle 2$ are rt. $\angle$s.	1. Given
2. $\triangle RSQ$ and $\triangle TSQ$ are rt. $\triangle$s.	2. Def. of rt. $\triangle$
3. $RS = 5$, $ST = 5$	3. Given
4. $\overline{RS} \cong \overline{ST}$	4. Def. of $\cong$ segs.
5. $\overline{SQ} \cong \overline{SQ}$	5. Seg. is $\cong$ to itself.
6. $\triangle RSQ \cong \triangle TSQ$	6. LL Thm.

Page 190 Section 5.8

11. Given: $\overline{HP} \cong \overline{MK}$, $\angle P \cong \angle K$

Prove: $\triangle PJH \cong \triangle KJM$

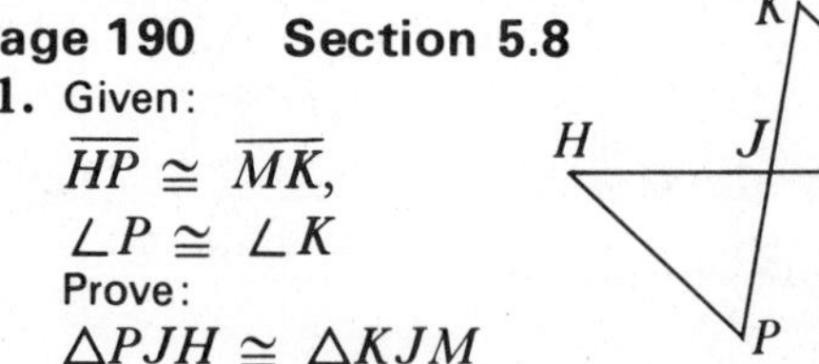

Proof:

STATEMENTS	REASONS
1. $\overline{HP} \cong \overline{MK}$, $\angle P \cong \angle K$	1. Given
2. $\angle PJH \cong \angle KJM$	2. Vert. $\angle$s are $\cong$.
3. $\triangle PJH \cong \triangle KJM$	3. AAS Thm.

13. Given: $\overleftrightarrow{PS}$ the $\perp$ bisector of $\overline{AT}$

Prove: $\triangle PRA \cong \triangle PRT$

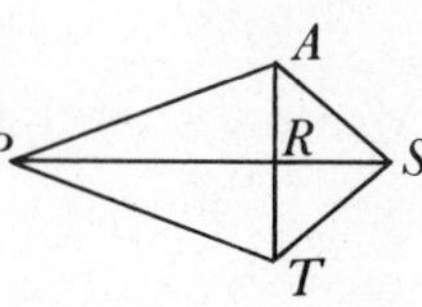

Proof:

STATEMENTS	REASONS
1. $\overline{PR} \cong \overline{PR}$	1. Seg. is $\cong$ to itself.
2. $\overleftrightarrow{PS}$ the $\perp$ bis. of $\overline{AT}$	2. Given

3. $\overline{AR} \cong \overline{TR}$	3. Def. of bis.
4. $\angle PRA$ and $\angle PRT$ are rt. $\angle$s	4. Def. of $\perp$
5. $\triangle PRA$ and $\triangle PRT$ are rt. $\triangle$s	5. Def. of rt. $\triangle$
6. $\triangle PRA \cong \triangle PRT$	6. LL Thm.

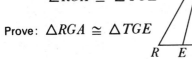

Pages 192–193 Section 5.9

7. $\overline{MN} \cong \overline{OA}$, $\overline{MP} \cong \overline{OP}$, $\overline{NP} \cong \overline{AP}$, $\angle M \cong \angle O$, $\angle P \cong \angle P$, $\angle MNP \cong \angle OAP$; $\triangle MNP \cong \triangle OAP$

9. SSS Post. **11.** SAS Post.

13. Given **15.** Seg. is $\cong$ to itself.

17. Corres. parts of $\cong$ $\triangle$s are $\cong$.

19. Opp. sides of ▱ are $\cong$.

21. Def. of rt. $\triangle$

23. Given: $\overline{GE} \cong \overline{GA}$, $\angle RGA \cong \angle TGE$

Prove: $\triangle RGA \cong \triangle TGE$

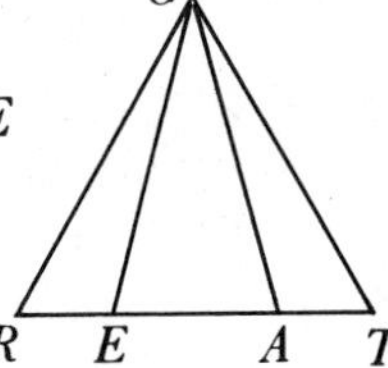

Proof: STATEMENTS	REASONS
1. $\overline{GE} \cong \overline{GA}$, $\angle RGA \cong \angle TGE$	1. Given
2. $\angle GEA \cong \angle GAE$	2. If 2 sides of $\triangle$ are $\cong$, $\angle$s opp. are $\cong$.
3. $\triangle RGA \cong \triangle TGE$	3. ASA Post.

Pages 195–196 Section 5.10

5.

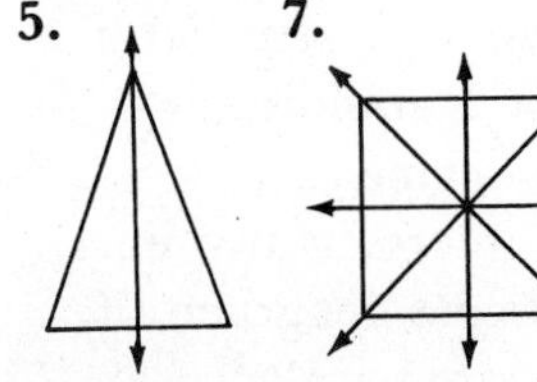

7.

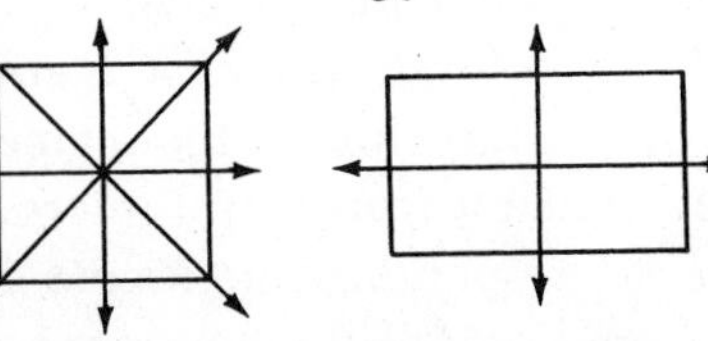

9.

11.

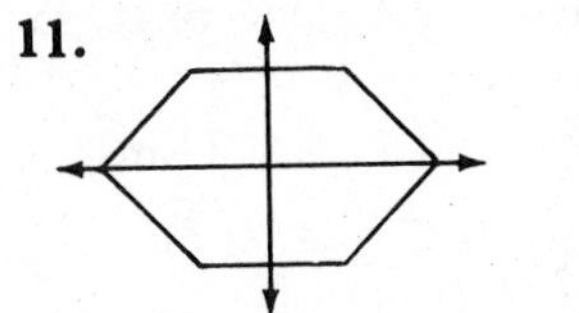

13.

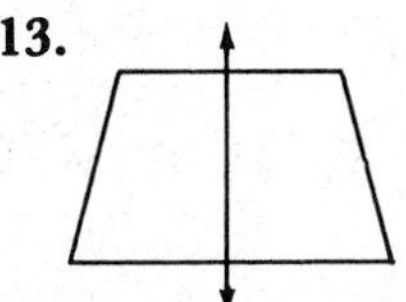

15.

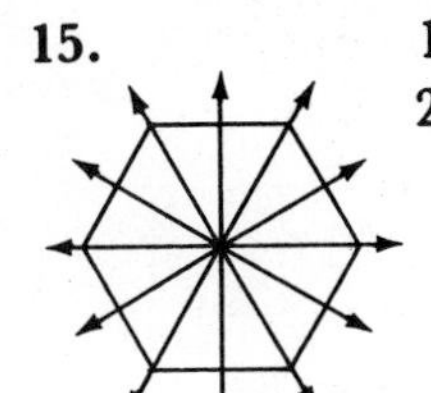

17. T **19.** T **21.** T **23.** 1 **25.** 4

Pages 197–198 Chapter 5 Review

1. *See page 164.*

3. *Typical answer:* $ABCDE$, $EDCBA$

5. 34.2 **7.** 23 **9.** 7200 **11.** 12

13. 6 **15.** 143 **17.** Right scalene

19. Equilateral

21. Given: $\angle T \cong \angle S$

Prove: $\overline{AT} \cong \overline{AS}$

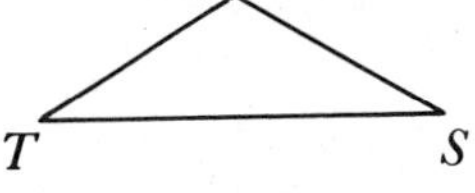

Proof: STATEMENTS	REASONS
1. $\angle T \cong \angle S$	1. Given
2. $\overline{AT} \cong \overline{AS}$	2. If 2 $\angle$s of $\triangle$ are $\cong$, sides opp. are $\cong$.

23. Given: $\angle R$ and $\angle I$ are right $\angle$s, $\overline{RV} \cong \overline{VI}$

Prove: $\triangle VER \cong \triangle VWI$

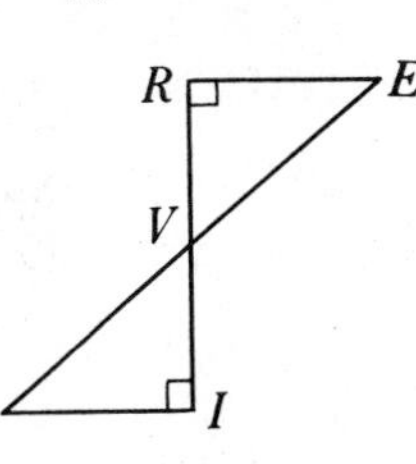

Proof: STATEMENTS	REASONS
1. $\overline{RV} \cong \overline{VI}$	1. Given
2. $\angle RVE \cong \angle IVW$	2. Vert. $\angle$s are $\cong$.
3. $\angle R$ and $\angle I$ are rt. $\angle$s.	3. Given

4. $\triangle VER$ and $\triangle \dot{V}WI$ are rt. $\triangle$s.	4. Def. of rt. $\triangle$
5. $\triangle VER \cong \triangle VWI$	5. LA Thm.

25. $\overline{RT} \cong \overline{WT}$, $\overline{RS} \cong \overline{WU}$, $\overline{ST} \cong \overline{UT}$, $\angle R \cong \angle W$, $\angle S \cong \angle U$, $\angle RTS \cong \angle WTU$

27. If 2 sides of $\triangle$ are $\cong$, $\angle$s opp. are $\cong$.

29. Given **31.** Yes **33.** Yes

Page 199 Chapter 5 Test

1. *See page 174.* **2.** *See page 167.*

3. *See page 165.*

4. Two sides do not intersect another side at both endpoints.

5. Yes **6.** Yes **7. a.** 3240 **b.** 360

8. a. 170 **b.** 10 **9.** 16.4

10. SAS Thm. for ▱s **11.** AAS Thm.

12. Given: $ABCD$ a rhombus

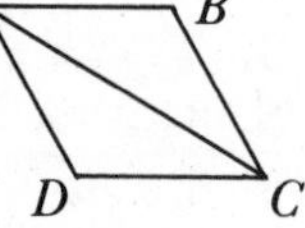

Prove: $\triangle ADC$ isosceles

Proof:

STATEMENTS	REASONS
1. $ABCD$ is a rhombus.	1. Given
2. $\overline{AD} \cong \overline{DC}$	2. Def. of rhombus
3. $\triangle ADC$ is isos.	3. Def. of isos. $\triangle$

13. Given: $\overline{MZ} \cong \overline{NZ}$, $\overline{MQ} \cong \overline{NP}$

Prove: $\triangle MQN \cong \triangle NPM$

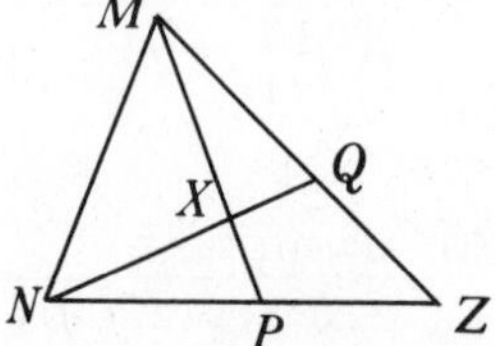

Proof:

STATEMENTS	REASONS
1. $\overline{MZ} \cong \overline{NZ}$, $\overline{MQ} \cong \overline{NP}$	1. Given
2. $\angle QMN \cong \angle PNM$	2. If 2 sides of $\triangle$ are $\cong$, $\angle$s opp. are $\cong$.
3. $\overline{MN} \cong \overrightarrow{MN}$	3. Seg. is $\cong$ to itself.
4. $\triangle MQN \cong \triangle NPM$	4. SAS Post.

14. The 4 symmetry lines contain the diagonals and the $\perp$ bisectors of the sides.

Pages 207–208 Section 6.1

(TA means *typical answer.*)

5. TA: man living in Kansas City, Mo.

7. TA: a bat **9.** $x = 5$

11. TA: $a = 5$, $b = 0$

13. $\angle A$ and $\angle B$ where $m\angle A = m\angle B = 45$

15. TA: any 2 vertical $\angle$s **17.** If 2 $\angle$s are vertical $\angle$s, the $\angle$s are $\cong$.

19. In a plane, if 2 lines are $\perp$ to the same line, the lines are $\parallel$.

21. Exercise 19 **23.** Exercise 18

Pages 211–212 Section 6.2

5. T; If a family lives on an island, it lives in Hawaii; F

7. F; If a car is a Fiat, it is a foreign car; T

9. F; If $a > 0$, then $a^2 > 0$; T

11. T; If two angles are congruent, the angles are vertical angles; F

13. T; If the alternate interior angles formed by two lines and a transversal are congruent, the lines are parallel; T

15. T; If x is a real number, x is an integer; F

17. $a = b$ if and only if $a - b = 0$.

19. An angle is a right angle if and only if its measure is 90.

21. In a plane, a point is on the perpendicular bisector of a segment if and only if the point is equidistant from the endpoints of the segment.

23. When a transversal intersects two lines, corresponding angles are congruent if and only if the lines are parallel.

25. No
27. The sum of the measures of two angles is 90 if and only if the two angles are complementary.

29. If $\frac{x^2 - y^2}{x - y} = x + y$, then $x \neq y$.

If $x \neq y$, then $\frac{x^2 - y^2}{x - y} = x + y$.

31. If an angle is an obtuse angle, its measure is greater than 90.
If its measure is greater than 90, an angle is an obtuse angle.

Page 215 Section 6.3

11. They are on the same line.
13. They are distinct collinear rays with a common endpoint.
15. Z is in the interior of $\angle BAC$, and $m\angle BAZ = m\angle CAZ$.
17. It is perpendicular to the segment at its midpoint.
19. Points are coplanar if and only if they are all in the same plane.
21. An angle is acute if and only if its measure is less than 90.
23. Lines are perpendicular if and only if the lines meet to form a 90°, or right, angle.
25. A triangle is isosceles if and only if it has at least two congruent sides.
27. A line is a transversal if and only if it intersects two or more coplanar lines at distinct points.

Pages 218–219 Section 6.4

7. Valid; affirming the hypothesis
9. Faulty; denying the hypothesis
11. $x \neq \sqrt{2}$ 13. No conclusion possible
15. $m\angle A = m\angle B$
17. No conclusion possible
19. Alt. int. $\angle$s 1 and 2 are not $\cong$.
21. Porky cannot fly.

Page 219 Quick Quiz

(TA means *typical answer.*)

1. TA: $x = -4$ 2. TA: a 50° angle
3. If x is positive, then x^2 is positive; T
4. If its measure is less than 45, an angle is acute; T
5. Yes
6. An angle is obtuse if and only if its measure is greater than 90.
7. Yes

Page 223 Section 6.5

11. Assumption for indirect proof
13. Given
15. Assumption for indirect proof
17. Given 19. Def. of rt. $\triangle$
21. LL Thm. 23. Given

Page 224 Algebra Review

1. $<$ 3. $>$ 5. $=$
*7. $x < 1$ *9. $y < 7$ 11. $x > 16$
13. $r > \frac{2}{3}$ 15. $x > 2$ *17. $x > -2$

**Model Solutions:*

7. $$\begin{array}{r} x + 2 < 3 \\ +(-2) \quad +(-2) \\ \hline x < 1 \end{array}$$

9. $$\begin{array}{r} 7y < 49 \\ \times\frac{1}{7} \quad \times\frac{1}{7} \\ \hline y < 7 \end{array}$$

17. $$\begin{array}{c} -x < 2 \\ (-1)(-x) > (-1)(2) \\ x > -2 \end{array}$$

6

Pages 227–228 Section 6.6

9. Def. of right $\triangle$
11. A segment is $\cong$ to itself.
13. Corres. parts of $\cong$ $\triangle$s are $\cong$.
15. Def. of $\perp$ 17. Given 19. HL Thm.
21. If lines are $\parallel$, interior $\angle$s on same side of a transversal are supplementary.
23. Given: $\triangle ABC$ with $\overline{AB} \cong \overline{AC}$, $\overline{CM}$ is the median to $\overline{AB}$, $\overline{BL}$ is the median to $\overline{AC}$.

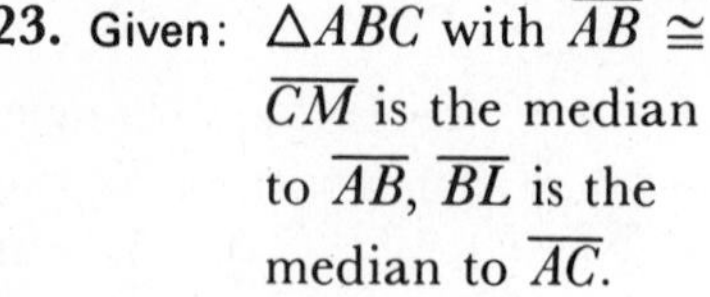

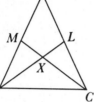

Prove: $\overline{CM} \cong \overline{BL}$

Proof:

STATEMENTS	REASONS
1. $\overline{CM}$ is the median to $\overline{AB}$, $\overline{BL}$ is the median to $\overline{AC}$.	1. Given
2. M bisects $\overline{AB}$, L bisects $\overline{AC}$.	2. Defs. of median and midpoint
3. $BM = \frac{1}{2}AB$, $CL = \frac{1}{2}AC$	3. Def. of bisect
4. $\overline{AB} \cong \overline{AC}$, so $AB = AC$.	4. Given
5. $\frac{1}{2}AB = \frac{1}{2}AC$	5. Multiply both sides by $\frac{1}{2}$.
6. $BM = CL$, so $\overline{BM} \cong \overline{CL}$	6. Substitution (steps 3 and 5)
7. $\angle ABC \cong \angle ACB$	7. If 2 sides of $\triangle$ are $\cong$, the $\angle$s opposite are $\cong$.
8. $\overline{BC} \cong \overline{BC}$	8. A seg. is $\cong$ to itself.
9. $\triangle BCL \cong \triangle CBM$	9. SAS Post.
10. $\overline{CM} \cong \overline{BL}$	10. Corres. parts of $\cong$ $\triangle$s are $\cong$.

Pages 231–232 Section 6.7

7. $\perp$ Line Post. (p. 60) 9. Substitution
11. Def. of concurrent 13. Def. of midpt.
15. Def. of median
17. Same reasoning as steps 1–6
19. Diagonals of a $\square$ bisect each other.

Page 234 Section 6.8

5. Reflections preserve distance.
7. SSS Post. 9. Def. of $\cong$ $\angle$s
11. Def. of $\cong$ segs.

Pages 235–236 Chapter 6 Review

1. F 3. Two 90° $\angle$s
5. T; If a number is a real number, it is a rational number; F
7. Yes
9. Faulty; affirming the conclusion
11. Assumption for indirect proof
13. A segment is = to itself.
15. Corres. parts of $\cong$ $\triangle$s are $\cong$.
17. Principle for Indirect Reasoning
19. Given: $\triangle TEG$ with $\overline{TG} \cong \overline{EG}$. $\overline{TL}$ is the altitude from T to $\overline{GE}$, $\overline{ER}$ is the altitude from E to $\overline{GT}$.

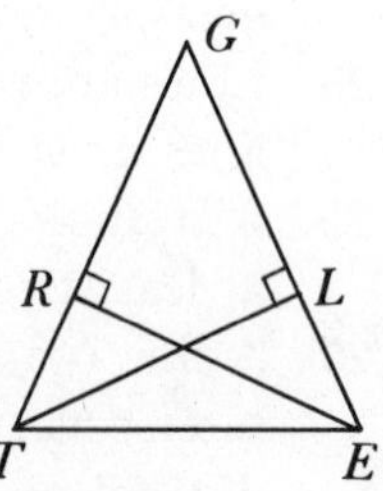

Prove: $\overline{ER} \cong \overline{TL}$

Proof:

STATEMENTS	REASONS
1. $\overline{TL}$ is the altitude from T to $\overline{GE}$, $\overline{ER}$ is the altitude from E to $\overline{GT}$.	1. Given
2. $\angle TLG$ and $\angle ERG$ are rt. $\angle$s.	2. Def. of altitude

3. $\triangle TLG$ and $\triangle ERG$ are rt. $\triangle$s.	3. Def. of rt. $\triangle$
4. $\overline{TG} \cong \overline{EG}$	4. Given
5. $\angle G \cong \angle G$	5. An $\angle$ is $\cong$ to itself.
6. $\triangle TLG \cong \triangle ERG$	6. HA Thm.
7. $\overline{ER} \cong \overline{TL}$	7. Corres. parts of $\cong$ $\triangle$s are $\cong$.

Page 237 Chapter 6 Test

1. $x = 0$
2. *Typical answer:* $\angle DEF$ and $\angle DEG$ where F is in the interior of $\angle DEG$
3. T; If the weather is usually warm, you live in Florida; F
4. T; If a triangle has three congruent sides, it has three congruent angles; T
5. If $x = 2$, then $x^3 = 8$. If $x^3 = 8$, then $x = 2$.
6. A segment is an altitude of a triangle if and only if it is a segment from a vertex perpendicular to the line containing the opposite side.
7. Faulty; affirming the conclusion
8. Valid; denying the conclusion
9. Assumption for indirect proof
10. When a transversal intersects two lines, if alternate interior angles are congruent, the lines are parallel.
11. Given
12. Principle of Indirect Reasoning
13. 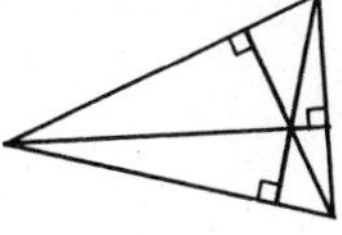
14. T

Pages 240–241 Section 7.1

9. $9 < 12$, $12 > 9$, $3 < 12$, $12 > 3$
11. $50 < 180$, $180 > 50$, $130 < 180$, $180 > 130$
13. $x < 23$, $23 > x$, $7 < 23$, $23 > 7$
15. $5 < n$, $n > 5$, $9 < n$, $n > 9$
17. $14 = 3 + 11$ **19.** $60 + 30 = 90$
21. m is not less than or equal to 12.
23. n is greater than or equal to 3.
25. t is less than or equal to 9.
27. 5 is not greater than s.
***29.** $n > 5$ ***31.** $s < 11$ ***33.** $x < 5$
35. $m > 10$ ***37.** $t < 15$ **39.** $p < 6$
41. $p < -10$ **43.** $x < 15$

* *Model Solutions:*

29.
$$n + 4 > 9$$
$$n + 4 - 4 > 9 - 4$$
$$n > 5$$

31.
$$s - 5 < 6$$
$$s - 5 + 5 < 6 + 5$$
$$s < 11$$

33.
$$4x < 20$$
$$\frac{4x}{4} < \frac{20}{4}$$
$$x < 5$$

37.
$$\frac{t}{3} < 5$$
$$3 \cdot \frac{t}{3} < 3 \cdot 5$$
$$t < 15$$

Page 243 Section 7.2

9. < **11.** > **13.** =
15. < **17.** > **19.** =
21. < **23.** $\angle$ Sum Thm. for $\triangle$s

Page 244 Algebra Review

1. $18n$ **3.** $\frac{10}{3}r$ or $\frac{10r}{3}$ **5.** $63f$

7

*7. $16p^2$ 9. $\frac{9}{25}t^2$ or $\frac{9t^2}{25}$ *11. $6s + 24$

13. $q + \frac{1}{3}$ 15. $-9d + 6$

*17. $3n^2 + 8n + 4$ 19. $d^2 - 9$

21. $m^2 - 10m + 25$ 23. $4y^2 + 4y + 1$

Model Solutions:

7. $(4p)^2 = 4^2 \cdot p^2$
$= 16p^2$

11. $6(s + 4) = 6 \cdot s + 6 \cdot 4$
$= 6s + 24$

17. $(n + \frac{2}{3})(3n + 6)$
$= n \cdot 3n + n \cdot 6 + \frac{2}{3}(3n) + \frac{2}{3}(6)$
$= 3n^2 + 6n + 2n + 4$
$= 3n^2 + 8n + 4$

Pages 248–249 Section 7.3

9. $<$ *11. $>$ 13. $>$ 15. $>$

17. $<$ 19. 4 21. 4 23. 2.4

*25. $\overline{DC}$ 27. Def. of rt. $\triangle$

29. Substitution (steps 1 and 3)

31. Def. of $\perp$

Model Solutions:

11. $m\angle G + 80 + 45 = 180$
$m\angle G = 55$
$m\angle J = 45$, so $HJ > HG$.

25. In $\triangle ABD$, $\overline{BD}$ is longest side.
In $\triangle DBC$, $m\angle DBC + 59 + 58 = 180$
$m\angle DBC + 117 = 180$
$m\angle DBC = 63$
So $DC > BD$.
$\overline{DC}$ is the longest segment in the figure.

Page 251 Section 7.4

*5. Yes 7. No 9. Yes

11. No 13. Yes 15. No

*17. 3, 23 19. 6, 16 21. $2\frac{1}{2}$, $7\frac{1}{2}$

23. 2, 17 25. No 27. Yes

Model Solutions:

5. $8 + 7 > 10$
$8 + 10 > 7$
$7 + 10 > 8$
Yes

17. $10 + x > 13$
$x > 3$
$10 + 13 > x$
$23 > x$
x is between 3 and 23.

Pages 254–255 Section 7.5

7. $>$ 9. $>$ 11. $=$ 13. $<$

15. $>$ 17. $<$ 19. $<$ 21. $>$

23. $<$ 25. Yes 27. No 29. Yes

Page 258 Section 7.6

5. Reflect D over ℓ to get D'. Let $\overline{AD'}$ intersect ℓ at P. The shortest path from A to D is along $\overline{AP}$ and $\overline{PD}$. Reflect A over ℓ to get A'. $\overline{DA'}$ also intersects ℓ at P, so the paths are the same.

7. Reflect D over m to get D'. Reflect D' over ℓ to get D''. Let $\overline{AD''}$ intersect ℓ at S. Let $\overline{SD'}$ intersect m at T. The shortest path is along $\overline{AS}$, $\overline{ST}$, and $\overline{TD}$.

Page 259 Chapter 7 Review

1. $<$ 3. $>$ 5. $p < 2$

7. $x < 11$ 9. $<$ 11. $<$

13. $>$ 15. $<$ 17. No

19. Yes 21. $<$ 23. $<$

Page 260 Chapter 7 Test

1. $<$ 2. $>$ 3. $>$ 4. $<$

5. Distance 6. $\triangle$ Inequality Thm.
7. a. $x < 15$ b. $t > 60$
8. a. No b. Yes

9. $<$	10. $>$	11. $=$	12. $>$
13. $<$	14. $>$	15. $<$	16. $>$
17. $<$	18. $>$	19. $<$	20. $<$
21. $<$	22. G		

Page 268 Section 8.1

11. T 13. Not nec. T 15. T
17. Not nec. T 19. $\angle PST$, $\angle PSR$
21. *See line ℓ and plane P in the figure for Ex. 1–4, page 267.*
23. *See proof of Plane Theorem part b, page 32.*

Page 269 Algebra Review

1. $4(a + b)$ *3. $6(2m - 3n)$
5. $ab(c - d)$ *7. $2x(x + y)$
9. $2\pi r(r + h)$ 11. $\frac{1}{3}r(B_1 + B_2 + B_3)$

**Model Solutions:*

3. $12m - 18n = 6 \cdot 2m - 6 \cdot 3n = 6(2m - 3n)$
7. $2x^2 + 2xy = 2x \cdot x + 2x \cdot y = 2x(x + y)$

Pages 271–272 Section 8.2

3. $\overline{XW} \perp \overline{WZ}$, $\overline{WZ} \perp \overline{ZY}$, $\overline{ZY} \perp \overline{YX}$, $\overline{AX} \perp \overline{XW}$, $\overline{XY} \perp \overline{XW}$
5. Not necessarily
7. $\overline{NT}$, $\overline{TO}$, and $\overline{NO}$ are $\perp$ to plane containing M, T, and S. All are $\perp$ to $\overleftrightarrow{MT}$ and $\overleftrightarrow{TS}$.

9. T 11. F 13. T 15. F

Pages 275–276 Section 8.3

9. Yes 11. Not necessarily
13. Yes; p contains every line $\perp$ to $\overleftrightarrow{AB}$ at A.
15. No; $\overleftrightarrow{BA} \perp p$, and through a given point there is exactly 1 line $\perp$ to a given plane.
17. Yes 19. No 21. Given
23. Every segment has a midpoint
25. Through a given point, there is exactly 1 plane $\perp$ to the given line.
27. If a line is in a plane, every point on the line is in the plane.

Page 280 Section 8.4

5. No; in $\triangle ADC$, $m\angle C = 90$, so other angles are acute. 7. 12
9. **Given:** Lines ℓ and k are in plane p, $\overleftrightarrow{WZ} \perp k$, $\overleftrightarrow{WZ} \perp \ell$, $\overline{XY}$ is the shortest segment from Y to plane p.

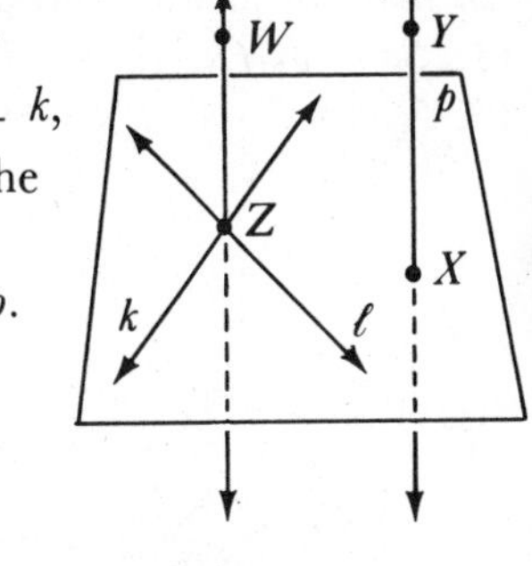

Prove:
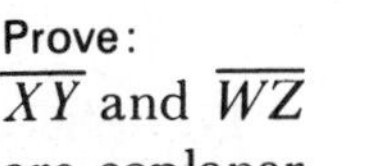
$\overline{XY}$ and $\overline{WZ}$ are coplanar.

Proof:

STATEMENTS	REASONS
1. ℓ and k in p, $\overleftrightarrow{WZ} \perp \ell$, $\overleftrightarrow{WZ} \perp k$	*1.* Given
2. $\overleftrightarrow{WZ} \perp p$	*2.* Basic Thm. for $\perp$s
3. $\overline{XY}$ is shortest segment from Y to p.	*3.* Given
4. $\overline{XY} \perp p$	*4.* The shortest seg. from a pt. to a plane is the $\perp$ seg.
5. $\overline{XY}$ and $\overline{WZ}$ are coplanar.	*5.* 2 lines $\perp$ to a plane are coplanar.

8

Pages 282–283 Section 8.5

9. *See page 281.* **11.** Yes **13.** Yes

Page 284 Chapter 8 Review

1. *See page 266.* **3.** Basic Thm. for $\perp$s **5.** Not necessarily **7.** No **9.** 90 **11.** Yes **13.** Yes; $\perp$ Bisecting Plane Thm. **15.** $\overline{ZW}$ **17.** $\perp$ bisecting plane of $\overline{AA'}$

Page 285 Chapter 8 Test

1. All; containing **2.** ℓ; P **3.** 1 **4.** T **5.** T **6.** F **7.** 1 **8.** BD **9.** Given **10.** Def. of $\perp$ line and plane **11.** *Same as Ex. 10* **12.** Basic Thm. for $\perp$s **13.** Yes **14.** Yes

Pages 289–291 Section 9.1

***13.** 247 m^2 **15.** 11.25 km^2 **17.** 1980 mm^2 **19.** 19.8 cm^2 **21.** 345 mm^2 or 3.45 cm^2 **23.** 5.29 m^2 **25.** $1\frac{7}{9}$ **27.** 2.3104 ***29.** $w = 12$ **31.** $\ell = 40$ **33.** $w = \frac{1}{4}$ **35. a.** Doubles **b.** Doubles **c.** Quadruples **37.** 10 000 **39.** 18.2 **41.** 6464 ***43.** 158 cm^2 **45.** 52 km^2 **47.** 296 cm^2

49. Given: Parallelogram $ABCD$ with diagonal $\overline{AC}$

Prove: Area $\triangle ABC = \frac{1}{2}$ area $ABCD$

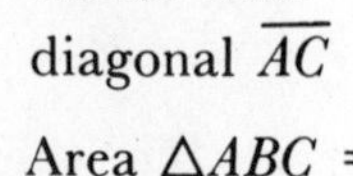

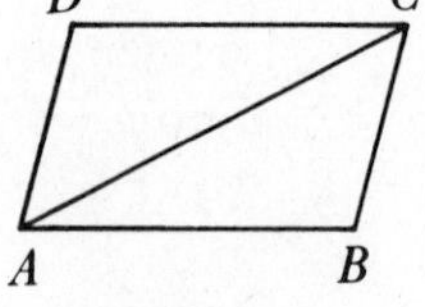

Proof: STATEMENTS	REASONS
1. $\square ABCD$ with diagonal $\overline{AC}$	*1.* Given
2. $\triangle ABC \cong \triangle CDA$	*2.* Sides and either diag. of a $\square$ form 2 $\cong$ $\triangle$s.
3. Area $\triangle ABC$ = area $\triangle CDA$	*3.* Area Post. for $\cong$ $\triangle$s
4. Area $\triangle ABC$ + area $\triangle CDA$ = area $ABCD$	*4.* Area Addition Post.
5. Area $\triangle ABC$ + area $\triangle ABC$ = area $ABCD$	*5.* Substitution (steps 3 and 4)
6. 2(area $\triangle ABC$) = area $ABCD$	*6.* Addition
7. Area $\triangle ABC$ = $\frac{1}{2}$ area $ABCD$	*7.* Multiply both sides by $\frac{1}{2}$.

******Model Solutions:*

13. $A = \ell w$
$= 19 \cdot 13$
$= 247$

29. $A = \ell w$
$228 = 19w$
$12 = w$

43.

A B 7 cm 10 cm 14 cm 6 cm

Area $A = 14 \cdot 7$
$= 98$ cm^2
Area $B = 10 \cdot 6$
$= 60$ cm^2

Total area $= 98 + 60 = 158$ cm^2

Pages 294–295 Section 9.2

***15.** 504 m^2 **17.** 45.82 cm^2 or 4582 mm^2 ***19.** 162 cm^2 or 16 200 mm^2 **21.** 27 **23.** $2\frac{3}{4}$ **25.** 6 **27.** 4.56 **29.** 2.8386 **31.** 28 **33.** $5\frac{4}{9}$ **35.** 27.09 **37.** 4.35 ***39.** $10\frac{2}{3}$

******Model Solutions:*

15. $A = bh$
$= 28 \cdot 18$
$= 504$ m^2

19. $A = \frac{1}{2}bh$
$A = \frac{1}{2} \cdot 18 \cdot 18 = 162$ cm^2 or
$A = \frac{1}{2} \cdot 180 \cdot 180 = 16\,200$ mm^2

39. $\frac{1}{2} \cdot 9x = \frac{1}{2} \cdot 8 \cdot 12$

$9x = 96$

$x = 10\frac{2}{3}$

$BC = 10\frac{2}{3}$

Pages 297–298 Section 9.3

***11.** 378 m^2 **13.** 1.1025 m^2 or 11 025 cm^2
15. 10.2 ***17.** 117 **19.** 36 **21.** 361.46
23. $12\frac{19}{32}$ **25.** $7\frac{7}{16}$ **27.** 23.24

29. Given:
Trapezoid $ABCD$ with bases $\overline{AB}$ and $\overline{CD}$, diagonals $\overline{AC}$ and $\overline{BD}$ intersect at E.

Prove:
Area $\triangle ADE$ = area $\triangle BCE$

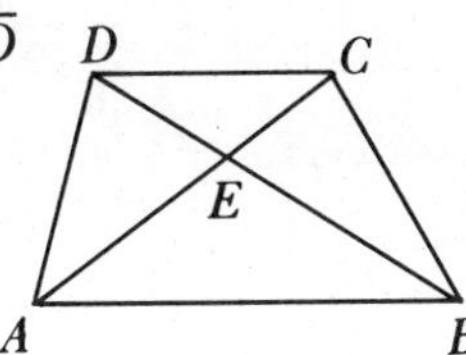

Proof:

STATEMENTS	REASONS
1. Trap. $ABCD$ with bases $\overline{AB}$ and $\overline{CD}$, diagonals $\overline{AC}$ and $\overline{BD}$ intersect at E.	1. Given
2. $\overline{AB} \parallel \overline{CD}$	2. Def. of trap.
3. Height of $\triangle ADB$ from base $\overline{AB}$ = height of $\triangle BCA$ from base $\overline{AB}$. Let height = h.	3. $\parallel$ lines are equidistant.
4. Area $\triangle ADB = \frac{1}{2}AB \cdot h$, area $\triangle BCA = \frac{1}{2}AB \cdot h$	4. Area Thm. for a $\triangle$
5. Area $\triangle ADB$ = area $\triangle BCA$	5. Substitution
6. Area $\triangle ADB$ = area $\triangle ADE$ + area $\triangle AEB$, area $\triangle BCA$ = area $\triangle BCE$ + area $\triangle AEB$	6. Area Add. Post.
7. Area $\triangle ADE$ + area $\triangle AEB$ = area $\triangle BCE$ + area $\triangle AEB$	7. Substitution (steps 5 and 6)
8. Area $\triangle ADE$ = area $\triangle BCE$	8. Subtract area $\triangle AEB$ from both sides.

***** *Model Solutions:*

11. $A = \frac{1}{2}h(b_1 + b_2)$
$= \frac{1}{2} \cdot 18(12 + 30)$
$= 9(42)$
$= 378$ m^2

17. $A = \frac{1}{2}d_1d_2$
$= \frac{1}{2} \cdot 18 \cdot 13$
$= 9 \cdot 13$
$= 117$

Page 299 Quick Quiz

1. $58\frac{1}{2}$ **2.** 27.2 **3.** 418 **4.** 147

Pages 302–303 Section 9.4

5. 4.123 **7.** 6.325 **9.** 5.916 **11.** 9.950
13. 5.657 **15.** 4 **17.** 8 **19.** 9
21. $\frac{1}{5}$ **23.** $\frac{5}{7}$ ***25.** $3\sqrt{2}$ **27.** $4\sqrt{2}$
29. $10\sqrt{2}$ **31.** $5\sqrt{5}$ **33.** $4\sqrt{3}$ **35.** $\frac{1}{2}\sqrt{3}$
37. $\frac{1}{5}\sqrt{3}$ **39.** $\frac{1}{3}\sqrt{3}$ **41.** $\frac{1}{3}\sqrt{3}$ **43.** $\frac{1}{5}\sqrt{5}$
***45.** 13.4 **47.** 13.9

***** *Model Solutions:*

25. $\sqrt{18} = \sqrt{9} \cdot \sqrt{2}$
$= 3\sqrt{2}$

45. $\sqrt{180} = \sqrt{36} \cdot \sqrt{5}$
$= 6\sqrt{5}$
$\approx 6(2.236)$
≈ 13.416
≈ 13.4

Page 303 Algebra Review

*1. $b = \pm 8$ 3. $a = \pm 9$

5. $x = \pm 25$ 7. $z = \pm 3\sqrt{10}$

**Model Solution:*

1. $6^2 + b^2 = 10^2$
$36 + b^2 = 100$
$b^2 = 64$
$b = \pm 8$

Pages 306–307 Section 9.5

*11. 13 13. $4\sqrt{2}$ 15. 9 17. $5\sqrt{7}$

*19. Yes 21. No 23. Yes *25. 50 m

27. 28 m 29. Yes; Converse of Pythagorean Thm.

31. 127.3 ft

**Model Solutions:*

11. $5^2 + 12^2 = c^2$
$25 + 144 = c^2$
$169 = c^2$
$13 = c$

19. $15^2 \stackrel{?}{=} 9^2 + 12^2$
$225 \stackrel{?}{=} 81 + 144$
$225 = 225$
Yes

25. Let c = length of cable in meters.
$c^2 = 30^2 + 40^2$
$c^2 = 900 + 1\,600$
$c^2 = 2\,500$
$c = 50$ m

9

Pages 311–313 Section 9.6

*5. $7\sqrt{2}$ 7. $\frac{1}{2}\sqrt{2}$ 9. 2 11. $3\sqrt{6}$

*13. a. 7 b. $7\sqrt{3}$ 15. a. $\frac{1}{2}$ b. $\frac{1}{2}\sqrt{3}$

17. a. $\frac{1}{4}$ b. $\frac{1}{4}\sqrt{3}$ 19. a. $\frac{1}{2}\sqrt{2}$ b. $\frac{1}{2}\sqrt{6}$

21. $5\sqrt{2}$ 23. 4 25. a. $6\sqrt{3}$ b. 12

27. a. 3 b. $2\sqrt{3}$ 29. $a = 4$, $c = 8$

31. $x = 8$ 33. $4\sqrt{3}$ 35. $5\sqrt{2}$

37. 39.6 cm 39. 48.5 cm

**Model Solutions:*

5. Let c = hypotenuse
Then $c^2 = 7^2 + 7^2$
$c^2 = 49 + 49$
$c^2 = 98$
$c = \sqrt{98} = 7\sqrt{2}$

13. Let a = side opposite 30° angle
b = side opposite 60° angle
$a = \frac{1}{2} \cdot 14 = 7$
$b = \sqrt{3} \cdot 7 = 7\sqrt{3}$

Pages 315–316 Section 9.7

7. 3 9. 8

11. *Figure shown $\frac{1}{2}$ size.*

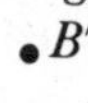

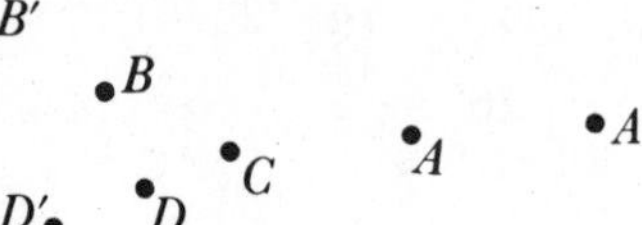

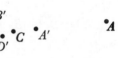

13.

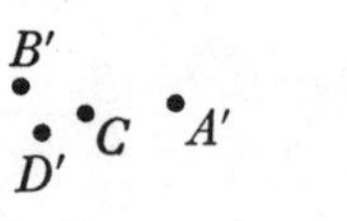

15. 17.

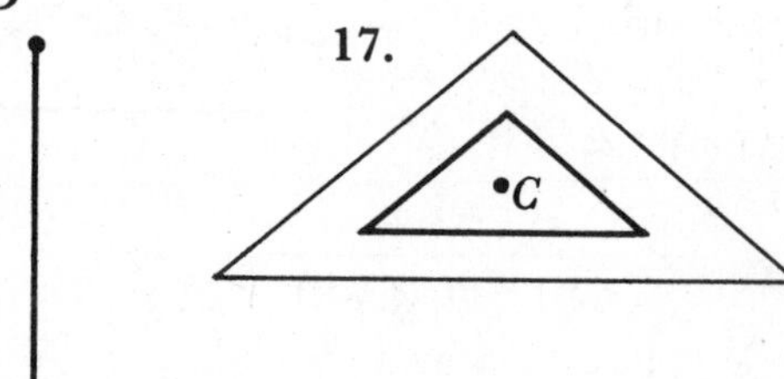

19. M 21. E

Page 316 Algebra Review

*1. $\frac{1}{2}$ 3. $\frac{1}{10}$ 5. $\frac{1}{4}$

7. $\frac{x}{y}$ 9. $\frac{2x}{3}$ 11. $\frac{1}{7x^3}$

**Model Solution:*

1. $\frac{2}{4} = \frac{2 \cdot 1}{2 \cdot 2} = \frac{1}{2}$

Pages 317–318 Chapter 9 Review

1. 224 cm^2 3. $2\frac{1}{4}$ 5. 18

7. 90 **9.** 11.97 **11.** 250
13. 6.3 **15.** 120 **17.** $3\sqrt{3}$
19. $\frac{1}{3}\sqrt{3}$ **21.** 17.3 **23.** 50
25. $9\sqrt{2}$ **27.** $b = 9, a = 9\sqrt{3}$
29. $s = 14$ **31.** 4

Page 319 Chapter 9 Test

1. 798 m^2 **2.** 20.25 m^2 **3.** $22\frac{1}{2}$
4. 4380 **5.** 876 **6.** 68
7. $5\sqrt{5}$ **8.** $\frac{1}{4}\sqrt{2}$ **9.** $\frac{8}{9}$
10. $\frac{2}{5}\sqrt{5}$ **11.** 20 **12.** 30
13. Yes; Converse of Pythagorean Theorem
14. $s = 12, r = 6\sqrt{3}$ **15.** $x = 8$ **16.** 5

Page 327 Section 10.1

13. $\frac{1}{4}$ **15.** $\frac{14}{25}$

17. $\frac{s}{4} = \frac{t}{5}, \frac{5}{t} = \frac{4}{s}, \frac{t}{s} = \frac{5}{4}, 5s = 4t$

19. $\frac{4}{3} = \frac{h}{g}, \frac{4}{h} = \frac{3}{g}, \frac{g}{3} = \frac{h}{4}, \frac{3}{4} = \frac{g}{h}$

21. $\frac{3}{7}$ **23.** $\frac{12}{5}$ **25.** $\frac{13}{15}$
27. $n = \frac{15}{8}$ ***29.** $s = \frac{3}{2}$ ***31.** $m = \frac{36}{5}$
33. $c = \frac{20}{3}$ **35.** $e = 30$ ***37.** $a = \frac{10}{7}$

**Model Solutions:*

29. $\frac{s}{7} = \frac{3}{14}$

$s = \frac{21}{14}$

$s = \frac{3}{2}$

31. $\frac{4}{m} = \frac{5}{9}$

$36 = 5m$

$\frac{36}{5} = m$

37. $\frac{2a}{5} = \frac{4}{7}$

$2a = \frac{20}{7}$

$a = \frac{20}{14} = \frac{10}{7}$

Pages 331–333 Section 10.2

15. $\frac{3}{4}$ **17.** $\frac{3}{4}$ **19.** $\frac{2}{1}$
21. Is not **23.** 2 **25.** Is not
***27.** $u = 24, z = 25, m\angle T = 40, m\angle V = 57, m\angle Y = 83$
29. $v = 49, x = 24, y = 32, m\angle M = 120, m\angle N = 60, m\angle S = 90, m\angle T = 90$
31. 17.5 cm ***33.** 0.2 m **35.** 225 cm
37. 90° **39.** 45° ***41.** $\frac{12}{5}$ **43.** 43

45. Given:
$\angle A \cong \angle M$,
$\overline{AB} \cong \overline{BC}$,
$\overline{MN} \cong \overline{NP}$,
$\frac{AB}{MN} = \frac{AC}{MP}$

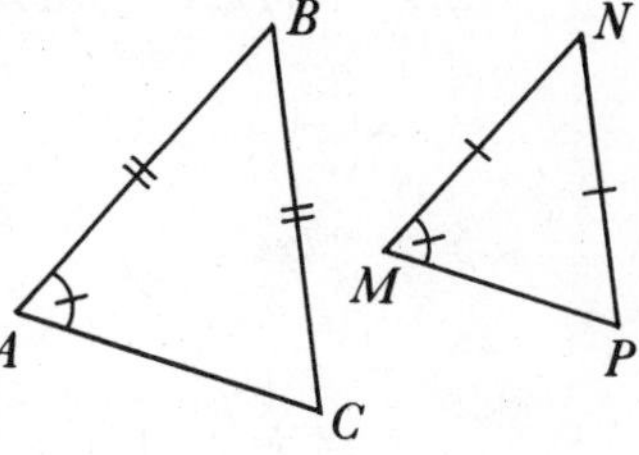

Prove:
$\triangle ABC \sim \triangle MNP$

Proof:

STATEMENTS	REASONS
1. $\angle A \cong \angle M$, $\overline{AB} \cong \overline{BC}$, $\overline{MN} \cong \overline{NP}$	1. Given
2. $\angle A \cong \angle C$, $\angle M \cong \angle P$	2. If 2 sides of △ are ≅, ∠s opp. are ≅.
3. $\angle M \cong \angle C$, $\angle C \cong \angle P$	3. ∠s ≅ to the same ∠ are ≅.
4. $\angle B \cong \angle N$	4. If 2 ∠s of 1 △ are ≅ to 2 ∠s of another △, the third ∠s are ≅.
5. $AB = BC$, $MN = NP$	5. Def. of ≅ segments
6. $\frac{AB}{MN} = \frac{BC}{NP}$	6. Use equations in step 5 to write a proportion.
7. $\frac{AB}{MN} = \frac{AC}{MP}$	7. Given
8. $\triangle ABC \sim \triangle MNP$	8. Definition of ~ polygons

10

**Model Solutions:*

27. $\frac{16}{20} = \frac{u}{30}$ | $\frac{16}{20} = \frac{20}{z}$

$\frac{4}{5} = \frac{u}{30}$ | $\frac{4}{5} = \frac{20}{z}$

$\frac{120}{5} = u$ | $4z = 100$

$24 = u$ | $z = 25$

$m\angle T = m\angle X = 40°$

$m\angle V = m\angle Z = 57°$

$m\angle Y = m\angle U = 83°$

33. $\frac{2.5}{x} = \frac{25}{2}$

$5 = 25x$

$\frac{5}{25} = x$

$0.2 = x$; 0.2 cm

41. $\frac{JP}{JM} = \frac{JN}{JK}$

$\frac{3}{5} = \frac{JN}{4}$

$\frac{12}{5} = JN$

Pages 336–337 Section 10.3

9. a and c; b and d

11. Given: $\ell \parallel n$

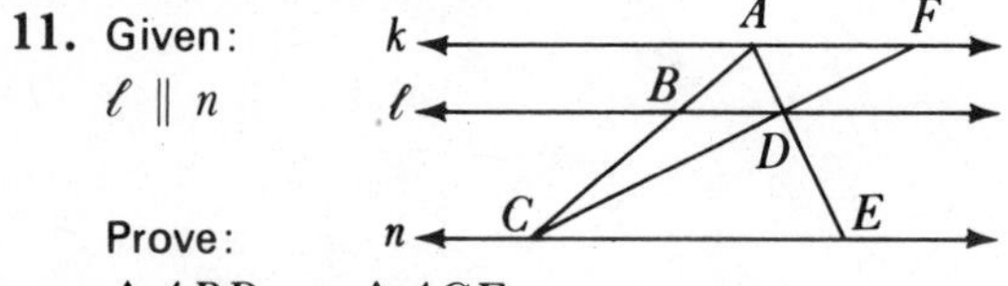

Prove: $\triangle ABD \sim \triangle ACE$

Proof: STATEMENTS	REASONS
1. $\ell \parallel n$	1. Given
2. $\triangle ABD \sim \triangle ACE$	2. If line $\parallel$ to 1 side of $\triangle$ intersects other 2 sides, $\sim$ $\triangle$ is formed.

13. Given: $k \parallel n$

Prove: $\triangle ADF \sim \triangle EDC$

(*See figure for Ex. 11.*)

Proof: STATEMENTS	REASONS
1. $k \parallel n$	1. Given
2. $\angle AFD \cong \angle ECD$, $\angle FAD \cong \angle CED$	2. If lines are $\parallel$, alt. int. $\angle$s are $\cong$.
3. $\triangle ADF \sim \triangle EDC$	3. AA Similarity Theorem

15. Given: $\overline{CD} \perp \overline{CT}$, $\overline{BP} \perp \overline{CT}$

Prove: $\triangle SPR \sim \triangle VDR$

Proof: STATEMENTS	REASONS
1. $\overline{CD} \perp \overline{CT}$, $\overline{BP} \perp \overline{CT}$	1. Given
2. $\overline{CD} \parallel \overline{BP}$	2. In plane, lines $\perp$ to same line are $\parallel$.
3. $\triangle SPR \sim \triangle VDR$	3. If line $\parallel$ to 1 side of $\triangle$ intersects other 2 sides, $\sim$ $\triangle$ is formed.

17. Given: $\angle 1 \cong \angle 2$

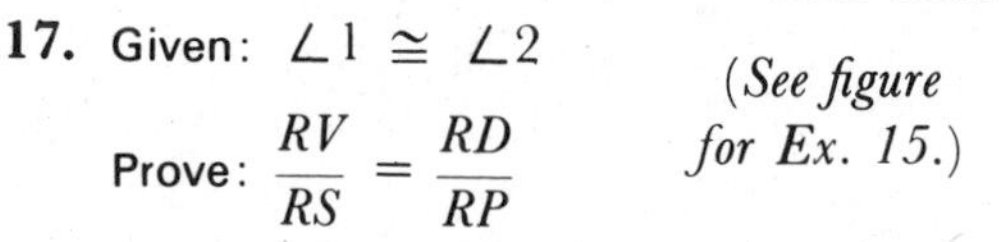

Prove: $\frac{RV}{RS} = \frac{RD}{RP}$

(*See figure for Ex. 15.*)

Proof: STATEMENTS	REASONS
1. $\angle 1 \cong \angle 2$	1. Given
2. $\overline{CD} \parallel \overline{BP}$	2. If alt. int. $\angle$s are $\cong$, lines are $\parallel$.
3. $\triangle RDV \sim \triangle RPS$	3. If line $\parallel$ to 1 side of $\triangle$ intersects other 2 sides, $\sim$ $\triangle$ is formed.
4. $\frac{RV}{RS} = \frac{RD}{RP}$	4. Def. of $\sim$ polygons

19. Given: $\triangle ABC \sim \triangle DBE$

Prove: $\ell \parallel \overline{AC}$

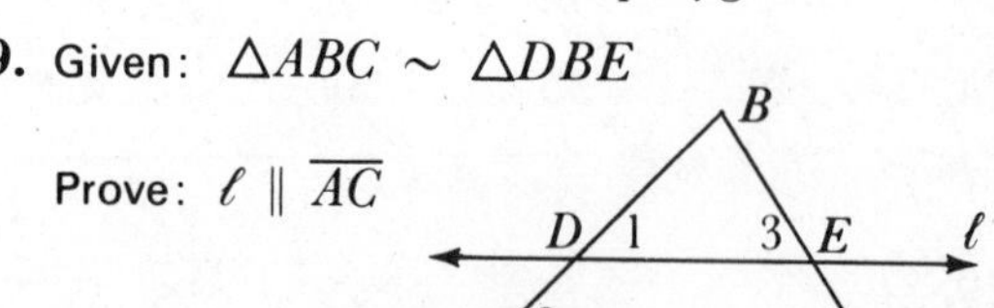

Proof: STATEMENTS	REASONS
1. $\triangle ABC \sim \triangle DBE$	1. Given
2. $\angle 1 \cong \angle 2$	2. Def. of $\sim$ polygons
3. $\ell \parallel \overline{AC}$	3. If corres. $\angle$s are $\cong$, lines are $\parallel$.

21. Def. of $\sim$ polygons

23. $\triangle DEF \sim \triangle GHJ$

Page 337 Algebra Review

*1. $9x + 8$
3. $11n - 7$
5. $4x^2$
*7. $3n - 3$
9. $2y^2$
11. $6v^2 - 3v + 2$

Model Solutions:

1. $(2x + 5) + (7x + 3)$
$= 2x + 7x + 5 + 3$
$= 9x + 8$

7. $(5n + 2) - (2n + 5)$
$= 5n + 2 - 2n - 5$
$= 5n - 2n + 2 - 5$
$= 3n - 3$

Pages 340–342 Section 10.4

17. a, b, c
19. Yes; SAS Sim. Thm.
21. Yes; SAS Sim. Thm.
23. No

25. Given: $\frac{BC}{EC} = \frac{AC}{DC}$

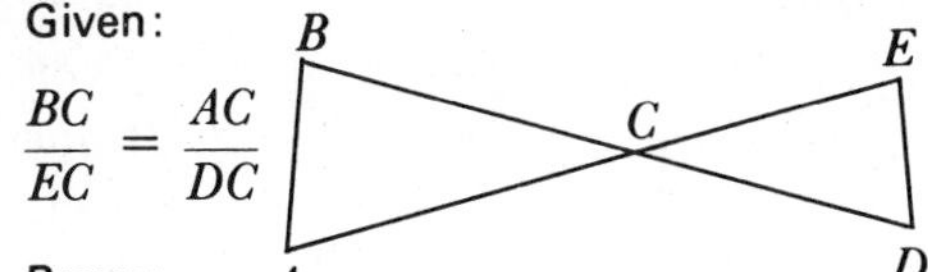

Prove: $\triangle ACB \sim \triangle DCE$

Proof: STATEMENTS	REASONS
1. $\frac{BC}{EC} = \frac{AC}{DC}$	1. Given
2. $\angle ACB \cong \angle DCE$	2. Vert. $\angle$s are $\cong$.
3. $\triangle ACB \sim \triangle DCE$	3. SAS Sim. Thm.

27. Given: $GF = \frac{1}{2}GC$, $GE = \frac{1}{2}GD$, $EF = \frac{1}{2}DC$

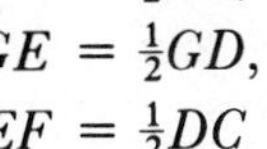

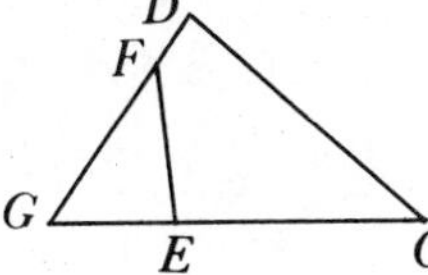

Prove: $\triangle GFE \sim \triangle GCD$

Proof: STATEMENTS	REASONS
1. $GF = \frac{1}{2}GC$, $GE = \frac{1}{2}GD$, $EF = \frac{1}{2}DC$	1. Given
2. $\frac{GF}{GC} = \frac{1}{2}, \frac{GE}{GD} = \frac{1}{2}, \frac{EF}{DC} = \frac{1}{2}$	2. Divide both sides of each given equation by the same number.
3. $\frac{GF}{GC} = \frac{GE}{GD} = \frac{EF}{DC}$	3. Substitution
4. $\triangle GFE \sim \triangle GCD$	4. SSS Sim. Thm.

29. Given: $\overline{YZ} \parallel \overline{UV}$

Prove: $\frac{XY}{XU} = \frac{YZ}{UV}$

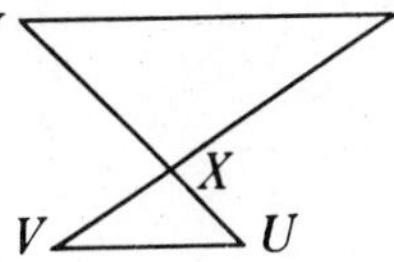

Proof: STATEMENTS	REASONS
1. $\overline{YZ} \parallel \overline{UV}$	1. Given
2. $\angle Y \cong \angle U$, $\angle Z \cong \angle V$	2. If lines are $\parallel$, alt. int. $\angle$s are $\cong$.
3. $\triangle XYZ \sim \triangle XUV$	3. AA Sim. Thm.
4. $\frac{XY}{XU} = \frac{YZ}{UV}$	4. Def. of $\sim$ polygons

*31. 6.3 m
33. 66 m
35. 20 m
37. *See pages 36 and 100.*

Model Solution:

31. Let x = height of tree.

$$\frac{x}{1.8} = \frac{14}{4}$$

$$\frac{x}{1.8} = \frac{7}{2}$$

$$x = \frac{1.8 \cdot 7}{2}$$

$$x = 6.3 \text{ m}$$

Page 343 Quick Quiz

1. n, 5
2. 3, x
3. Proportion
4. $5n$
5. $\frac{n}{x}$
6. $t = 15$
7. $\frac{2}{r}$
8. $\frac{2}{3}$
9. $m\angle D$
10. $\frac{3}{2}$
11. 9
12. *See page 334.*
13. *See page 338.*
14. *See page 339.*

10

Pages 346–347 Section 10.5

19. 8 ***21.** $4\sqrt{5}$ **23.** $8\sqrt{5}$ **25.** 9

27. Given:
$\angle Y$ and $\angle V$ are rt. $\angle$s.

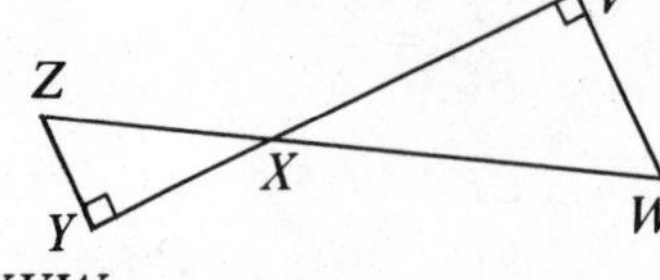

Prove:
$\triangle XYZ \sim \triangle XVW$

Proof:

STATEMENTS	REASONS
1. $\angle Y$ and $\angle V$ are rt. $\angle$s.	1. Given
2. $\angle Y \cong \angle V$	2. All rt. $\angle$s are $\cong$.
3. $\angle YXZ \cong \angle VXW$	3. Vert. $\angle$s are $\cong$.
4. $\triangle XYZ \sim \triangle XVW$	4. AA Sim. Thm.

29. Given:
$\overline{AC} \perp \overline{DE}$,
$\frac{AD}{BE} = \frac{DC}{EC}$

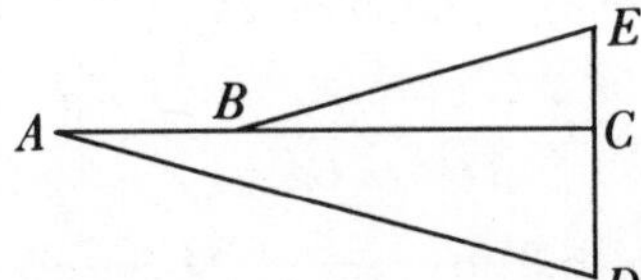

Prove:
$\triangle ADC \sim \triangle BEC$

Proof:

STATEMENTS	REASONS
1. $\overline{AC} \perp \overline{DE}$	1. Given
2. $\angle ACD$, $\angle BCE$ are rt. $\angle$s.	2. Def. of $\perp$
3. $\triangle ACD$, $\triangle BCE$ are rt. $\triangle$s.	3. Def. of rt. $\triangle$s
4. $\frac{AD}{BE} = \frac{DC}{EC}$	4. Given
5. $\triangle ADC \sim \triangle BEC$	5. HL Sim. Thm.

***31.** 913 cm **33.** *TB′* **35.** *TD′*

**Model Solutions:*

21. $\frac{20}{b} = \frac{b}{4}$

$b^2 = 80$

$b = 4\sqrt{5}$

31. Let x = height of tower.

$\frac{495}{90} = \frac{x}{166}$

$\frac{11}{2} = \frac{x}{166}$

$\frac{1826}{2} = x$

$x = 913$ cm

Page 351 Section 10.6

7. Given:
Trapezoid $WXYZ$ with $\overline{WX} \parallel \overline{YZ}$

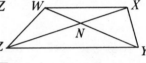

Prove:
$\triangle WNX \sim \triangle YNZ$

Proof:

STATEMENTS	REASONS
1. $\overline{WX} \parallel \overline{YZ}$	1. Given
2. $\angle XWY \cong \angle WYZ$, $\angle WXZ \cong \angle XZY$	2. If lines are $\parallel$, alt. int. $\angle$s are $\cong$.
3. $\triangle WNX \sim \triangle YNZ$	3. AA Sim. Thm.

9. Given:
$\square HIJK$,
$\frac{HI}{RH} = \frac{IR}{HK} = \frac{RH}{KR}$

Prove:
$\angle HRI$ is a rt. $\angle$.

Proof:

STATEMENTS	REASONS
1. $\frac{HI}{RH} = \frac{IR}{HK} = \frac{RH}{KR}$	1. Given
2. $\triangle HRI \sim \triangle RKH$	2. SSS Sim. Thm.
3. $m\angle HRI = m\angle RKH$	3. Def. of $\sim$ polygons
4. $HIJK$ is a $\square$.	4. Given

5. $m\angle RKH = 90$	5. □ has 4 rt. $\angle$s.
6. $m\angle HRI = 90$	6. Substitution
7. $\angle HRI$ is a rt. $\angle$.	7. Def. of rt. $\angle$

11. Given:
R is the midpoint of $\overline{XY}$,
S is the midpoint of $\overline{ZY}$.

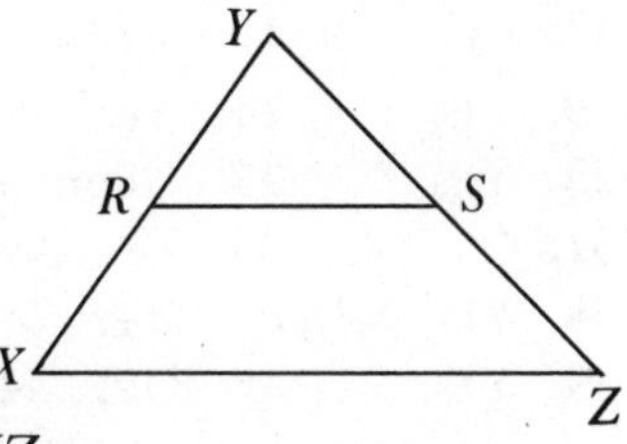

Prove:
$\triangle RYS \sim \triangle XYZ$

Proof:

STATEMENTS	REASONS
1. R is midpt. of $\overline{XY}$, S is midpt. of $\overline{ZY}$.	1. Given
2. $\overline{RS}$ is midline of $\triangle XYZ$.	2. Def. of midline
3. $\overline{RS} \parallel \overline{XZ}$	3. Midline of $\triangle$ is $\parallel$ to base.
4. $\triangle RYS \sim \triangle XYZ$	4. If line $\parallel$ to side of $\triangle$ intersects other 2 sides, $\sim \triangle$ is formed.

13. Given: $XY = \frac{5}{2}RY$,
$ZY = \frac{5}{2}SY$

(*See figure for Ex. 11.*)

Prove: $\triangle RYS \sim \triangle XYZ$

Proof:

STATEMENTS	REASONS
1. $XY = \frac{5}{2}RY$, $ZY = \frac{5}{2}SY$	1. Given
2. $\frac{XY}{RY} = \frac{5}{2}, \frac{ZY}{SY} = \frac{5}{2}$	2. Divide both sides of each given equation by same number.
3. $\frac{XY}{RY} = \frac{ZY}{SY}$	3. Substitution
4. $\angle Y \cong \angle Y$	4. $\angle$ is $\cong$ to itself.
5. $\triangle RYS \sim \triangle XYZ$	5. SAS Sim. Thm.

Pages 354–355 Section 10.7

***15.** $d = 4$ **17.** $a = 4$ **19.** $7\frac{1}{2}$
21. $3\frac{3}{4}$ ***23.** $b = 15, c = 6$ **25.** 5:2:1
27. $d = 0.5, f = 1$ **29.** Add terms in ratio.
31. Endpoints of segments on $\overline{AC}$ that are in given ratio

**Model Solutions:*

15. $\frac{a}{c} = \frac{b}{d}$

$\frac{3}{6} = \frac{2}{d}$

$3d = 12$

$d = 4$

23. $a:b:c = 1:5:2;\ a = 3$

$\frac{a}{b} = \frac{1}{5}$	$\frac{a}{c} = \frac{1}{2}$
$\frac{3}{b} = \frac{1}{5}$	$\frac{3}{c} = \frac{1}{2}$
$b = 15$	$c = 6$

Pages 358–359 Section 10.8

***13.** $\frac{3}{5}$; 6 **15.** 50; 12 **17.** $\frac{5}{3}$; 18
***19.** $\frac{\sqrt{5}}{3}$ ***21.** $\frac{3}{8}$ **23.** $\frac{2\sqrt{31}}{15}$

10

**Model Solutions:*

13. $\left(\frac{ST}{LO}\right)^2 = \frac{\text{area } \triangle STV}{\text{area } \triangle LOM} = \frac{45}{125} = \frac{9}{25}$	$\frac{TP}{OR} = \frac{ST}{LO}$
	$\frac{TP}{10} = \frac{3}{5}$
So, $\frac{ST}{LO} = \sqrt{\frac{9}{25}} = \frac{3}{5}$	$TP = \frac{30}{5}$
	$TP = 6$

19. $\left(\dfrac{\text{median } \triangle STV}{\text{median } \triangle LOM}\right)^2 = \dfrac{\text{area } \triangle STV}{\text{area } \triangle LOM}$

$= \frac{20}{36}$

$= \frac{5}{9}$

So, $\dfrac{\text{median } \triangle STV}{\text{median } \triangle LOM} = \sqrt{\dfrac{5}{9}} = \dfrac{\sqrt{5}}{3}$

21. $\dfrac{\text{area } RSTUV}{\text{area } KMNOP} = \left(\dfrac{RS}{KM}\right)^2 = \left(\dfrac{\sqrt{3}}{2\sqrt{2}}\right)^2 = \dfrac{3}{8}$

Page 359 Algebra Review

*1. $x + 3$
3. $y^3 + y + 1$
5. $2r^2 + \frac{3}{4}$
7. $3a^2b^2 + 2ab$
*9. $y + 7$
*11. $t^2 + 2t - 3$
13. $x^2 + 2x + 1$
15. $3c^2 - 2c - 1$

**Model Solutions:*

1. $\dfrac{5x^2 + 15x}{5x} = \dfrac{5x(x + 3)}{5x} = x + 3$

9. $\dfrac{y^2 + 3y - 28}{y - 4} = \dfrac{(y + 7)(y - 4)}{(y - 4)}$

$= y + 7$

11.
$$\begin{array}{r|l} & t^2 + 2t - 3 \\ t - 2 & t^3 + 0t^2 - 7t + 6 \\ & t^3 - 2t^2 \\ \hline & 2t^2 - 7t \\ & 2t^2 - 4t \\ \hline & -3t + 6 \\ & -3t + 6 \\ \hline & 0 \end{array}$$

Page 361 Section 10.9

5. $\frac{5}{3}$ 7. $\frac{4}{3}$ 9. $\triangle SVT$ 11. $\triangle RVS$

10

Pages 362–363 Chapter 10 Review

1. Equivalent
3. Is not
5. $\dfrac{b}{10}$
7. $\frac{3}{5}$
9. *See page 329.*
11. $\frac{3}{4}$
13. $6\frac{2}{3}$
15. $m\angle R$
17. Yes
19. Yes
21. Yes
23. No
25. Yes
27. Geometric mean
29. EG
31. 4
33. Yes. *See page 344.*
35. Yes. *See page 344.*
37. No
39. Yes. *See page 339.*
41. Yes. *See page 334.*
43. $\dfrac{f}{e}$
45. $f:e:d$
47. $a = 12, c = 4$
49. $\frac{6}{5}$
51. $\frac{1}{2}$

Page 364 Chapter 10 Test

1. Proportion
2. Lowest
3. Geometric mean
4. $\cong$; sides
5. $\frac{3}{5}$
6. $d = \frac{3}{2}$
7. AA Sim. Thm.
8. AA Sim. Thm.
9. SSS Sim. Thm.
10. $\triangle$s $\sim$ to the same $\triangle$ are $\sim$.
11. SAS Sim. Thm.
12. LL Sim. Thm.
13. 15
14. $m\angle S$
15. 3
16. $\frac{4}{25}$
17. 7:5:3
18. $a = 14, b = 10$
19. $\frac{2}{5}$
20. Given: $TU = 1$, $TW = 2$, $TV = 4$

W
V U T

Prove: $\triangle TUW \sim \triangle TWV$

Proof:

STATEMENTS	REASONS
1. $TU = 1$, $TW = 2$, $TV = 4$	1. Given
2. $\dfrac{TU}{TW} = \dfrac{1}{2}$, $\dfrac{TW}{TV} = \dfrac{2}{4} = \dfrac{1}{2}$	2. Use given equations to form proportions.

3. $\frac{TU}{TW} = \frac{TW}{TV}$	3. Substitution
4. $\angle T \cong \angle T$	4. $\angle$ is $\cong$ to itself.
5. $\triangle TUW \sim \triangle TWV$	5. SAS Sim. Thm.

Page 377 Section 11.1

11. $\overline{FO}$, FP, or $\overline{FM}$ 13. $\overline{PM}$
15. Any 2 of $\overline{MI}$, $\overline{MG}$, and $\overline{MT}$
17. $\overleftrightarrow{CD}$, $\overleftrightarrow{JS}$ 19. T 21. F

Page 378 Algebra Review

1. $\frac{10}{21}$ 3. $\frac{2}{5}$ 5. $\frac{a^2}{12}$ *7. $\frac{m^2r}{2}$

9. $\frac{7}{12g^3}$ 11. $\frac{2}{3y}$ *13. $\frac{cn^4}{3m^6}$

*** *Model Solutions:***

7. $$\frac{2m^3}{r} \cdot \frac{r^2}{4m} = \frac{(2m^3)(r^2)}{(r)(4m)} = \frac{(2mr)(m^2r)}{(2mr)(2)} = \frac{m^2r}{2}$$

13. $$\frac{7c^2n}{m^2n^2} \div \frac{21cm^4}{n^5} = \frac{7c^2n}{m^2n^2} \cdot \frac{n^5}{21cm^4} = \frac{(7c^2n)(n^5)}{(m^2n^2)(21cm^4)} = \frac{(7cn^2)(cn^4)}{(7cn^2)(3m^6)} = \frac{cn^4}{3m^6}$$

Pages 381–382 Section 11.2

9. Chord Thm., part b
11. $\cong$ ⊙s have $\cong$ radii.
13. Chord Thm., part c 15. Given
17. Radii of a ⊙ are $\cong$. 19. Given
21. In a plane, a seg. has exactly 1 $\perp$ bisector.
23. In the plane of a ⊙, the $\perp$ bisector of a chord contains the center of the ⊙.
25. Given:
⊙C, $\overline{CD} \perp \overline{AE}$,
$\overline{CB} \perp \overline{AF}$,
$CD = CB$

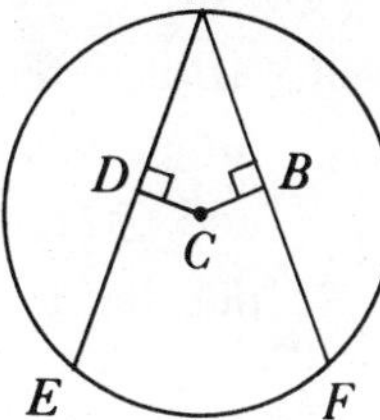

Prove:
$AD = FB$

Proof:

STATEMENTS	REASONS
1. ⊙C, $\overline{CD} \perp \overline{AE}$, $\overline{CB} \perp \overline{AF}$, $CD = CB$	1. Given
2. $\overline{AE} \cong \overline{AF}$, so $AE = AF$	2. In a ⊙, chords equidistant from the center are $\cong$.
3. $\overline{CD}$ bisects $\overline{AE}$, $\overline{CB}$ bisects $\overline{AF}$.	3. The $\perp$ from the center of a ⊙ to a chord bisects it.
4. $AD = \frac{1}{2}AE$, $FB = \frac{1}{2}AF$	4. Def. of bisect
5. $\frac{1}{2}AE = \frac{1}{2}AF$	5. Mult. both sides of equation in step 2 by $\frac{1}{2}$.
6. $AD = FB$	6. Substitution

11

Pages 385–386   Section 11.3

***9.** 8   **11.** 70

13.   **15.**

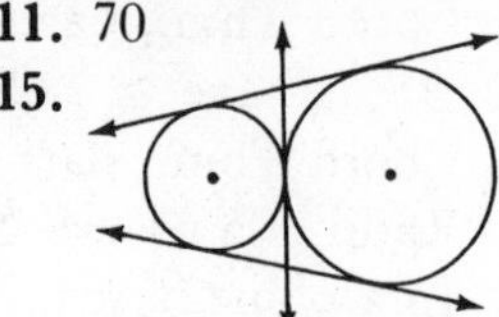

17. 5   ***19.** 30   **21.** 10

23. A line contains infinitely many points.

25. Shortest segment from point to line is the $\perp$ segment.

27. Given: $\overline{AB}$ is externally tangent to $\odot C$ and $\odot D$, $\overline{AB}$ is not parallel to $\overline{CD}$.

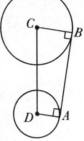

Prove: $ABCD$ is a trapezoid.

Proof:

STATEMENTS	REASONS
1. $\overline{AB}$ externally tangent to $\odot C$ and $\odot D$, $\overline{AB}$, $\overline{CD}$ not $\parallel$	*1.* Given
2. $\overline{CB} \perp \overline{AB}$, $\overline{DA} \perp \overline{AB}$	*2.* A radius is $\perp$ to a tangent at the pt. of tangency.
3. $\overline{CB} \parallel \overline{DA}$	*3.* In a plane, $\perp$s to same line are $\parallel$.
4. $ABCD$ is a trapezoid.	*4.* Def. of trapezoid

** Model Solutions:*

9. $\overline{AX} \perp \overline{AB}$, so $\triangle BAX$ is rt. $\triangle$ with rt. $\angle A$. Thus, $BA^2 + AX^2 = BX^2$

$$BA^2 + 6^2 = 10^2$$
$$BA^2 = 64$$
$$BA = 8$$

19. $\triangle NAT$ is equilateral and therefore equiangular, so $m\angle NAT = 60$.

$\overline{NA} \perp \overline{RI}$, so $m\angle NAI = 90$.

Thus, $m\angle TAI + m\angle NAT = m\angle NAI$

$$m\angle TAI + 60 = 90$$
$$m\angle TAI = 30$$

Page 391   Section 11.4

***11.** 13   **13.** 12

15. Yes   **17.** Infinitely many

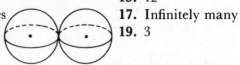

19. 3

** Model Solution:*

11. $\triangle WMX$ is a rt. $\triangle$, so

$$WX^2 = WM^2 + MX^2$$
$$= 5^2 + 12^2$$
$$= 169$$

So, $WX = 13$

Page 392   Quick Quiz

1. a. $\overline{EA}$ **b.** $\overline{BV}$

2. a. $\overleftrightarrow{MT}$ **b.** plane p

3. a. $\overleftrightarrow{SY}$ **b.** $\overleftrightarrow{GR}$

4. a. $\overline{WD}$ or $\overline{SY}$ **b.** $\overline{JO}$ or $\overline{GR}$

5. a. $\overline{EA} \perp \overline{WD}$ **b.** $\overline{BV} \perp \overline{JO}$

6. a. A **b.** B **7. a.** M **b.** H

8. 6   **9.** 12   **10.** $\odot D$ **11.** $\odot A$ **12.** 6

Pages 395–396   Section 11.5

13. Minor arc, 121   **15.** Major arc, 301

17. Semicircle, 180   **19.** 116   **21.** 116

23. Yes, $m\angle BOG = m\angle SOM$

25. Given: $\odot G$, $\overline{CE} \cong \overline{DE}$

Prove: $\widehat{ECD} \cong \widehat{EDC}$

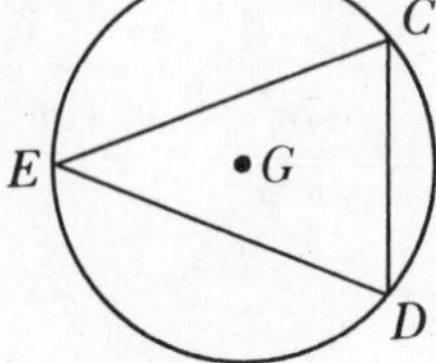

Proof:

STATEMENTS	REASONS
1. $\overline{CE} \cong \overline{DE}$	*1.* Given
2. $\widehat{EC} \cong \widehat{ED}$	*2.* In a $\odot$, $\cong$ chords have $\cong$ minor arcs.

3. $m\widehat{EC} = m\widehat{ED}$	3. Def. of $\cong$ arcs
4. $m\widehat{EC} + m\widehat{CD} = m\widehat{ED} + m\widehat{CD}$	4. Add $m\widehat{CD}$ to both sides.
5. $m\widehat{EC} + m\widehat{CD} = m\widehat{ED} + m\widehat{DC}$	5. $\widehat{CD}$ and $\widehat{DC}$ name same arc.
6. $m\widehat{EC} + m\widehat{CD} = m\widehat{ECD}$, $m\widehat{ED} + m\widehat{DC} = m\widehat{EDC}$	6. Arc Add. Post.
7. $m\widehat{ECD} = m\widehat{EDC}$	7. Substitution
8. $\widehat{ECD} \cong \widehat{EDC}$	8. Def. of $\cong$ arcs

Pages 400–402 Section 11.6

9. 87 **11.** 90 **13.** 47 **15.** 54
17. $\angle DCB$ **19.** 52 **21.** 26
23. 64 **25.** Inscribed $\angle$ Thm., Case 1
27. Angle Add. Post. **29.** Arc Add. Post.
31. *Join any 6 pts. on the $\odot$ to form a hexagon.*
33. Given: $\odot X$, $\angle B$ is inscribed in semicircle $\widehat{ABC}$, intercepts $\widehat{ADC}$.

Prove: $m\angle B = 90$

Proof:

STATEMENTS	REASONS
1. $\odot X$, $\angle B$ is inscribed in semicircle $\widehat{ABC}$, intercepts $\widehat{ADC}$	1. Given
2. $m\angle B = \frac{1}{2}m\widehat{ADC}$	2. Inscribed $\angle$ Thm.
3. $m\widehat{ADC} = 180$	3. Meas. of semicircle is 180.
4. $m\angle B = \frac{1}{2}\cdot 180 = 90$	4. Substitution and mult.

Page 402 Algebra Review

1. $\frac{2}{3}$ **3.** $\frac{17}{24}$ ***5.** $\frac{7}{x}$ ***7.** $\frac{3y^2 + 5}{y}$ **9.** $\frac{47w}{30z^2}$

***** *Model Solutions:*

5. $\frac{2}{x} + \frac{5}{x} = \frac{2 + 5}{x} = \frac{7}{x}$

7. $\frac{5}{y} + \frac{\overset{3}{\cancel{6}}y}{\underset{1}{\cancel{2}}} = \frac{5}{y} + \frac{3y}{1}\cdot\frac{y}{y} = \frac{3y^2 + 5}{y}$

Page 407 Section 11.7

***11.** $63\frac{1}{2}$ **13.** $29\frac{1}{2}$ ***15.** 54
17. $102\frac{1}{2}$ ***19.** $27\frac{1}{2}$ **21.** 35
23. $112\frac{1}{2}$ **25.** 15 **27.** 55

***** *Model Solutions:*

11. $68 + 53 + m\widehat{BD} = 180$
$m\widehat{BD} = 59$
$m\angle AGC = \frac{1}{2}(m\widehat{AC} + m\widehat{BD})$
$= \frac{1}{2}(68 + 59) = 63\frac{1}{2}$

15. $72 + m\widehat{ED} = 180$
$m\widehat{ED} = 108$
$m\angle FDE = \frac{1}{2}m\widehat{ED}$
$= \frac{1}{2}\cdot 108 = 54$

19. $m\angle SDV = \frac{1}{2}(m\widehat{SV} - m\widehat{XW})$
$= \frac{1}{2}(80 - 25) = 27\frac{1}{2}$

11

Page 410 Section 11.8

9. $x = 9$ **11.** $x = 4$ **13.** $x = 6$
15. $x = 2$ ***17.** 13 **19.** 9 **21.** $8\sqrt{3}$

***** *Model Solution:*

17. $ST\cdot TI = RT\cdot TU$	$RU = RT + TU$
$6\cdot 5 = 10\cdot TU$	$= 10 + 3$
$3 = TU$	$= 13$

Pages 411–412 Section 11.9

3. 2 ∥ lines each 2 cm from ℓ
5. Sphere X with radius 5 cm
7. The ray that bisects $\angle XYZ$
9. The ⊥ bisector of $\overline{AB}$
11. $\odot Z$, with radius 6 cm, and its interior
13. A line ∥ to and equidistant from ℓ and k
15. The exterior of $\odot R$, with radius 9 cm
17. The bisectors of the 4 angles formed by $\overleftrightarrow{XZ}$ and $\overleftrightarrow{XW}$

Page 414 Section 11.10

5. Center C, direction clockwise
7. F   9. F
11.

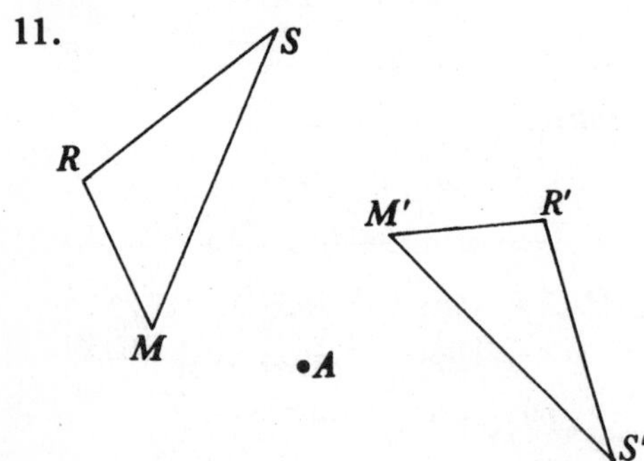

Pages 415–416 Chapter 11 Review

1. *See page 376.*   3. *See page 376.*
5. $\overline{CW}$, $\overline{ZY}$
7. When $\overline{CS} \perp \overline{RT}$ and $\overline{CX} \perp \overline{ZY}$
9. *See page 384.*   11. B, W 13. 6
15. Yes; the points are on central angle BEC or in its interior.
17. $\widehat{ABC}$, $\widehat{ADC}$
19. Any two of $\angle WVR$, $\angle WYR$, $\angle YRV$, $\angle YRW$, $\angle VRW$, $\angle RWY$, $\angle RWV$, and $\angle YWV$
21. Both are inscribed in the same arc.
23. $\frac{1}{2}$; $m\widehat{RW}$ 25. $\frac{1}{2}(m\widehat{KJ} - m\widehat{JP})$
27. $\frac{1}{2}(m\widehat{NMJ} - m\widehat{NJ})$ 29. 6   31. 38

33. $\odot C$, with radius 4.5 cm, and its interior
35. Counterclockwise   37. 110

Page 417 Chapter 11 Test

1. $\overline{PT}$	2. $\overleftrightarrow{AN}$	3. $\overline{HF}$ or $\overline{AN}$
4. $\overleftrightarrow{HO}$	5. P	6. F
7. T	8. T	9. F
10. 92	11. 92	12. 52
13. 220	14. 90	15. $6\frac{2}{3}$
16. 62	17. 34	18. 41
19. 15	20. 22	21. 12

22. The bisectors of the 4 $\angle$s formed by the 2 lines.
23. *Figure shown $\frac{1}{2}$ size.*

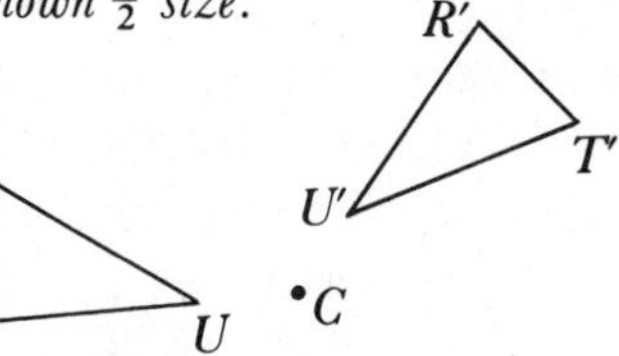

Pages 421–422 Section 12.1

*7. 120	9. 60	11. 60
13. 60	15. 30	17. 120
19. 90	21. 45	23. 2; 2; $2\sqrt{2}$
*25. $7\sqrt{3}$	27. 9	29. $10\sqrt{3}$
*31. 16	33. $13\sqrt{3}$	35. $96\sqrt{3}$
37. $48\sqrt{3}$		

* *Model Solutions:*

7. Meas. of central $\angle = \frac{360}{3} = 120$
25.

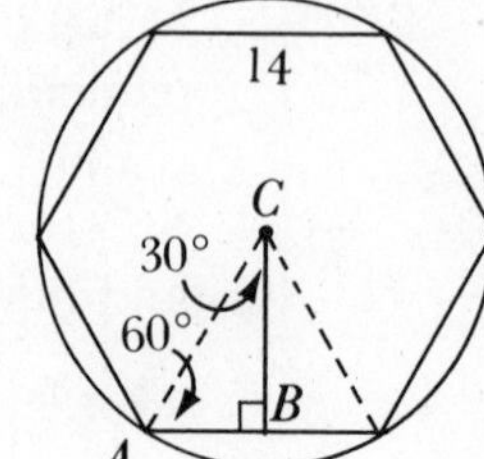

$AB = 7$
By the 30-60-90° Triangle Theorem, $CB = 7\sqrt{3}$

31.

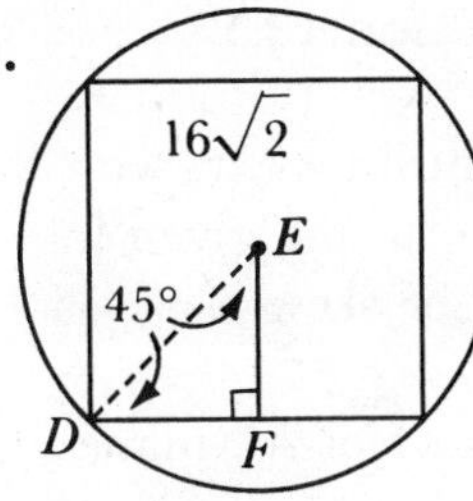

$DF = EF = 8\sqrt{2}$
By the Isos. Rt. Triangle Theorem,
$DE = \sqrt{2} \cdot 8\sqrt{2}$
$= 16$

Page 423 Algebra Review

1. $(x - 4)(x + 1)$
3. $(x - 3)^2$
5. $(x - 5)(x + 3)$
7. $(2x - 1)(x + 2)$
9. $(5x + 2)(x + 1)$
11. $(x + 7)(x - 7)$

*13. $6, -1$

15. $-2, -4$
17. $\frac{1}{2}, 1$
19. $-2, \frac{1}{4}$

***Model Solution:**

13. $x^2 - 5x - 6 = 0$
$(x - 6)(x + 1) = 0$
$x - 6 = 0$ or $x + 1 = 0$
$x = 6$ $\quad x = -1$

Pages 426–427 Section 12.2

*7. $9; 18\pi$ *9. $18; 9$ 11. $14\pi; 7\pi$

*13. 207.2 cm 15. 188.4 m 17. 2.9 m

19. $44.0; (44.0)\sqrt{2} \approx 62.2$ 21. 254.2 m

***Model Solutions:**

7. $r = \frac{1}{2}d$, $= \frac{1}{2} \cdot 18$, $= 9$ | $C = 2\pi r$, $= 2\pi \cdot 9$, $= 18\pi$

9. $C = 2\pi r$
$18\pi = 2\pi r$
$\frac{18\pi}{2\pi} = \frac{2\pi r}{2\pi}$
$9 = r$
| $d = 2r$, $= 2 \cdot 9$, $= 18$

13. $C = 2\pi r$
$= 2(3.14)(\frac{1}{2} \cdot 66)$
≈ 207.2 cm

Pages 430–431 Section 12.3

*5. $14; 44; 154$

7. $14; 88; 616$
9. $28; 56; 2464$
11. $12; 24; 75\frac{3}{7}$

*13. 672

15. 84

*17. $26\,576.96\text{ m}^2$

19. 4335.26 cm^2

***Model Solutions:**

5. $d = 2r$, $= 2(7)$, $= 14$ | $C = 2\pi r$, $= 2(\frac{22}{7})(7)$, $= 44$ | $A = \pi r^2$, $= (\frac{22}{7})(7^2)$, $= 154$

13. Area of square $= (56)^2 = 3136$
area of circle $= \pi(28)^2$
$\approx \frac{22}{7}(784) \approx 2464$
shaded area $\approx 3136 - 2464 \approx 672$

17. $A = \pi(92)^2$
$\approx 3.14(8464)$
$\approx 26\,576.96\text{ m}^2$

Pages 434–435 Section 12.4

*11. 8π

13. 20π
15. 34
17. $\frac{4}{3}\pi$
19. $\frac{8}{3}\pi$

*21. 128π

23. 96π
25. $\frac{3}{2}\pi$
27. About 0.638 m

*29. $16\pi - 32$ *31. 360

33. 147π

***Model Solutions:**

11. Arc length $= \frac{a}{360} \cdot 2\pi r$

$= \frac{\cancel{60}^{1}}{\cancel{360}_{\cancel{6}\,1}} \cdot 2\pi \cdot \cancel{24}^{4} = 8\pi$

21. Area sector $= \frac{a}{360} \cdot \pi r^2$

$= \frac{\cancel{180}^{1}}{\cancel{360}_{2}} \cdot \pi \cdot 16^2 = 128\pi$

12

29. $m\angle O = 90$

$$\text{area } \triangle AOB = \tfrac{1}{2}bh = \frac{1}{\cancel{2}_1}\cdot \cancel{8}^{4}\cdot 8 = 32$$

$$\text{area sector} = \frac{a}{360}\cdot \pi r^2$$

$$= \frac{\cancel{90}^{1}}{\cancel{360}_{4}}\cdot \pi \cdot 8^2 = 16\pi$$

$$\text{area segment} = 16\pi - 32$$

31. $\text{Area sector} = \tfrac{1}{2}\cdot 180 \cdot 4$

$$= 90 \cdot 4 = 360$$

Page 438 Section 12.5

7. Yes 9. No 11. Yes 13. No

15. Point, turn 17. Turn only

19. Draw $\overrightarrow{CP}$. Mark C' on the opposite side of P from C so that $PC = PC'$. Similarly, draw the images of A, B, and D. Join A', B', C', and D' in order.

Page 440 Chapter 12 Review

1. 10 3. $150\sqrt{3}$ 5. 880

7. 16; 16π; 64π 9. 16; 32; 256π

11. $\frac{7}{6}\pi$ 13. Yes 15. No

Page 441 Chapter 12 Test

1. 8 2. 16 3. *See page 423.*

4. 252 5. 484 6. 400

7. $38\frac{1}{2}$ 8. 6 9. $\frac{35}{9}\pi$

10. $\frac{16}{9}\pi$ 11. Yes 12. Yes

13. No 14. Yes

Pages 448–450 Section 13.1

11. T

13. F (The planes might intersect, with their line of intersection ∥ to the given line.)

15. F (The lines might be skew.)

17. T

19. Yes. If a line is ⊥ to 1 of 2 ∥ planes, it is ⊥ to the other.

21. Yes. If 2 ∥ planes are intersected by a third plane, the lines of intersection are ∥.

23. Given: $\ell \perp A$, $\ell \perp B$, C intersects A and B at m and n.

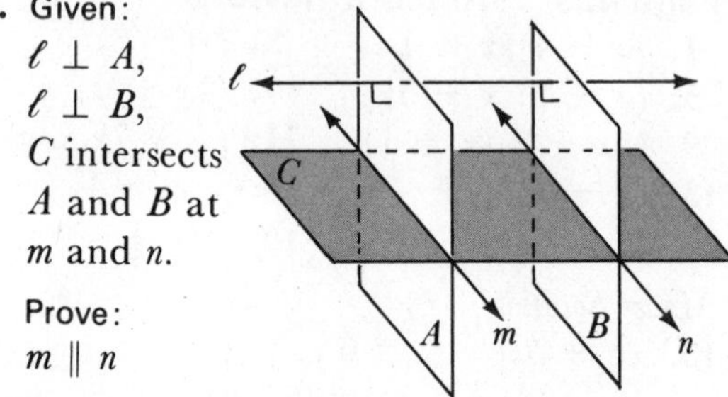

Prove: $m \parallel n$

Proof:

STATEMENTS	REASONS
1. $\ell \perp A$, $\ell \perp B$	1. Given
2. $A \parallel B$	2. Two planes ⊥ to same line are ∥.
3. C intersects A and B at m and n.	3. Given
4. $m \parallel n$	4. 3rd plane intersects 2 ∥ planes at 2 ∥ lines.

Pages 454–455 Section 13.2

9. Yes. Plane ⊥ to 1 of 2 ∥ lines is ⊥ to the other.

11. Yes. ∥ planes are everywhere equidistant.

13. T

15. F (Consider $\triangle ABC$ in plane p and lines ⊥ to p at A, B, and C.)

17. 2 planes ⊥ to the same line are ∥.

19. Def. of ≅ segments

21. Opp. sides of ▱ are ∥.

23. Opp. sides of ▱ are ≅.
25. Quadrilateral is ▱ if 2 sides are ∥ and ≅.
27. SSS Postulate
29. Given:
$A \parallel B$,
C intersects A and B at ℓ and m, $m \parallel n$

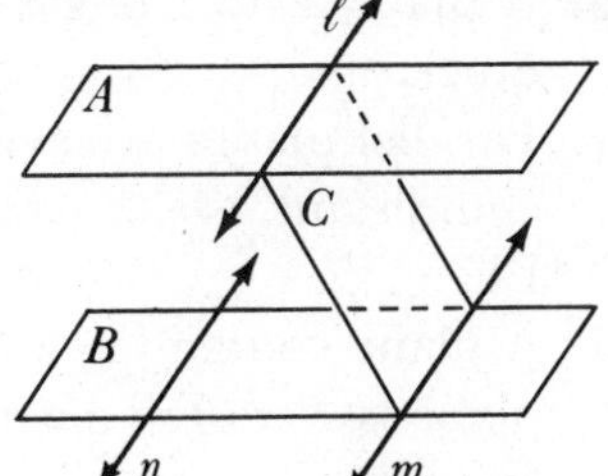

Prove:
$\ell \parallel n$

Proof:

STATEMENTS	REASONS
1. $A \parallel B$; C intersects A and B at ℓ and m.	1. Given
2. $\ell \parallel m$	2. 3rd plane intersects 2 ∥ planes at 2 ∥ lines.
3. $m \parallel n$	3. Given
4. $\ell \parallel n$	4. 2 lines ∥ to same line are ∥.

31. Given:
$C \parallel D$,
$\ell \perp C$,
$m \perp D$,
$\ell \parallel n$

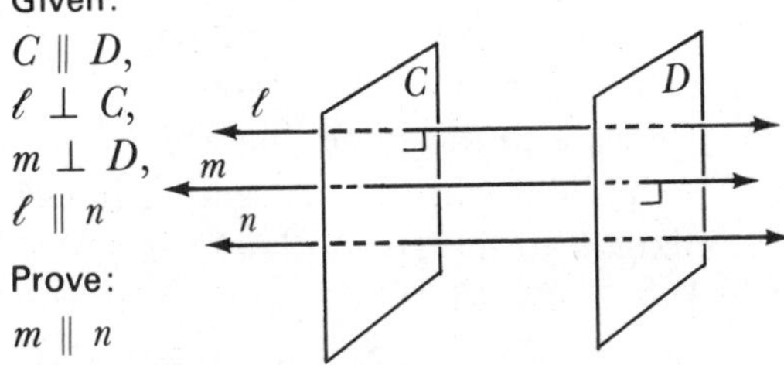

Prove:
$m \parallel n$

Proof:

STATEMENTS	REASONS
1. $C \parallel D$, $\ell \perp C$	1. Given
2. $\ell \perp D$	2. Line ⊥ to 1 of 2 ∥ planes is ⊥ to the other.
3. $m \perp D$	3. Given
4. $m \parallel \ell$	4. 2 lines ⊥ to same plane are ∥.
5. $\ell \parallel n$	5. Given
6. $m \parallel n$	6. 2 lines ∥ to same line are ∥.

Pages 459–460 Section 13.3

11. $\angle R\text{-}\overleftrightarrow{ST}\text{-}Y$, $\angle R\text{-}\overleftrightarrow{ST}\text{-}U$, $\angle R\text{-}\overleftrightarrow{ST}\text{-}X$, $\angle U\text{-}\overleftrightarrow{ST}\text{-}X$, $\angle U\text{-}\overleftrightarrow{ST}\text{-}Y$
13. Def. of meas. of dihedral ∠
15. **a.** Basic Thm. for ⊥s **b.** Def. of plane ∠
17. $\angle WXZ$ 19. $\angle \overleftrightarrow{XZ}$ *21. 55 23. 55
25. Given:
$\angle ABC$ and $\angle DEF$ are plane angles of $\angle A\text{-}\overleftrightarrow{XY}\text{-}F$,
$\overline{AB} \cong \overline{DE}$, $\overline{BC} \cong \overline{EF}$

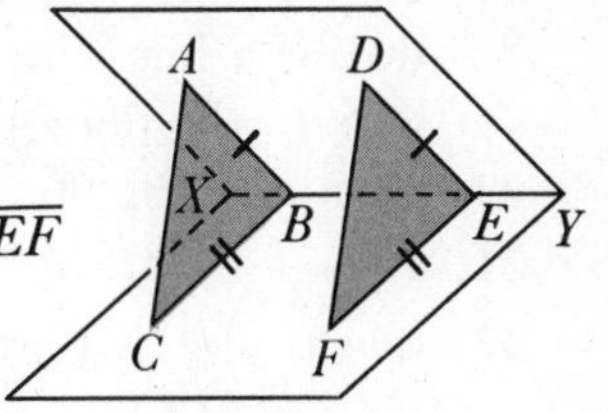

Prove:
$\overline{AC} \cong \overline{DF}$

Proof:

STATEMENTS	REASONS
1. $\angle ABC$ and $\angle DEF$ are plane ∠s of $\angle A\text{-}\overleftrightarrow{XY}\text{-}F$.	1. Given
2. $\angle ABC \cong \angle DEF$	2. Plane ∠s of a dihedral ∠ are ≅.
3. $\overline{AB} \cong \overline{DE}$, $\overline{BC} \cong \overline{EF}$	3. Given
4. $\triangle ABC \cong \triangle DEF$	4. SAS Post.
5. $\overline{AC} \cong \overline{DF}$	5. Corres. parts of ≅ △s are ≅.

27. An *acute dihedral angle* is a dihedral angle whose measure is less than 90.
29. *Complementary dihedral angles* are two dihedral angles for which the sum of the measures is 90.
31. A dihedral angle separates space into two sets—one set is convex and is called the *interior* of the dihedral angle.

* *Model Solution:*

21. $\angle DQX$ is a plane angle of $\angle D\text{-}\overleftrightarrow{BC}\text{-}X$. So $m\angle D\text{-}\overleftrightarrow{BC}\text{-}X = m\angle DQX = 55$.

Pages 464–466 Section 13.4

11. Def. of ⊥ planes.

13. If 2 planes are $\perp$, a line in 1 of them $\perp$ to their line of intersection is $\perp$ to the other.

15. F (2 walls $\perp$ to the floor intersect at a line $\perp$ to the floor.)

17. T

19. F (Consider 2 intersecting walls and the floor.)

21. F (The intersection of the ceiling and a wall is a line $\parallel$ to the floor, but the wall is $\perp$ to the floor.)

23. 90 25. 90 27. 45 29. 60

31. 120 33. 75 35. 50

37. 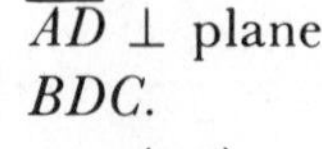
Given: $\overline{AD} \perp$ plane BDC.

Prove: $\angle A\text{-}\overleftrightarrow{DC}\text{-}B$ is a right dihedral angle.

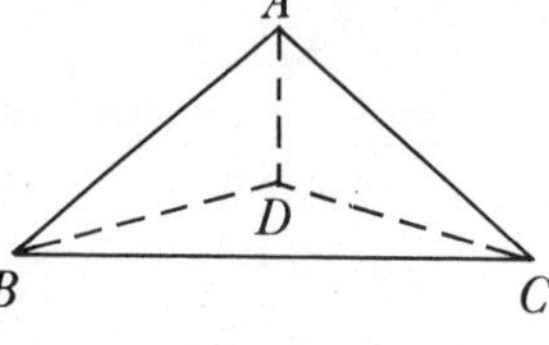

Proof: STATEMENTS	REASONS
1. $\overline{AD} \perp$ plane BDC	1. Given
2. Plane $ADC \perp$ plane BDC	2. Plane containing line $\perp$ to given plane is $\perp$ to given plane.
3. $\angle A\text{-}\overleftrightarrow{DC}\text{-}B$ is a rt. dih. $\angle$.	3. Def. of $\perp$ planes

Page 468 Section 13.5

11. Slide 13. Turn 15. Up

17. The axle of the wheel

19.

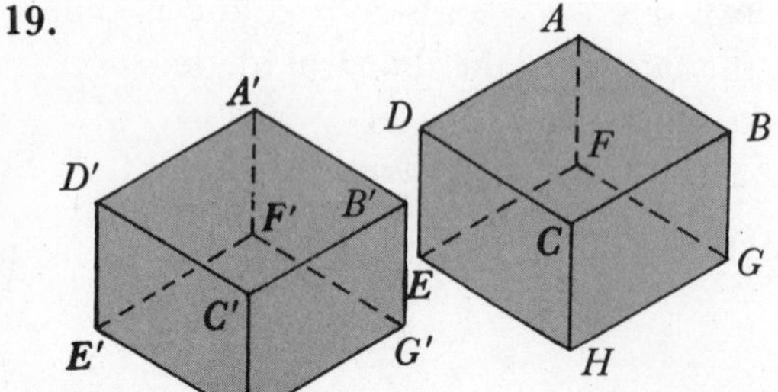

21. $\overleftrightarrow{CH}$

Page 469 Chapter 13 Review

1. A line $\perp$ to 1 of 2 $\parallel$ planes is $\perp$ to the other.
2. 2 planes $\parallel$ to the same plane are $\parallel$.
5. A plane $\perp$ to 1 of 2 $\parallel$ lines is $\perp$ to the other.
7. Parallel planes are everywhere equidistant.
9. Edge 11. Plane
13. A plane containing a line $\perp$ to a given plane is $\perp$ to the given plane.
15. Def. of $\perp$ planes 17. $\overleftrightarrow{BF}$

Page 470 Chapter 13 Test

1. *See page 445.* 2. *See page 462.*
3. *See page 457.* 4. *See page 457.*
5. Any 3 of $\angle\overleftrightarrow{AB}$, $\angle\overleftrightarrow{AC}$, $\angle\overleftrightarrow{BC}$, $\angle\overleftrightarrow{AD}$, $\angle\overleftrightarrow{BE}$, $\angle\overleftrightarrow{CF}$, $\angle\overleftrightarrow{DE}$, $\angle\overleftrightarrow{DF}$, $\angle\overleftrightarrow{EF}$
6. Def. of plane $\angle$
7. 2 planes $\perp$ to same line are $\parallel$.
8. A plane containing a line $\perp$ to a given plane is $\perp$ to the given plane.
9. 2 lines $\perp$ to the same plane are $\parallel$.
10. 2 lines $\parallel$ to the same line are $\parallel$.
11. F (They might be intersecting lines in a plane $\parallel$ to the given plane.)
12. T 13. F (Consider 2 intersecting walls and the floor.)
14. **Given:** $\overline{AD} \perp \overline{AB}$, $\overline{AD} \perp \overline{AC}$, $\overline{AD} \perp$ plane DEF.
Prove: Plane $ABC \parallel$ plane DEF.

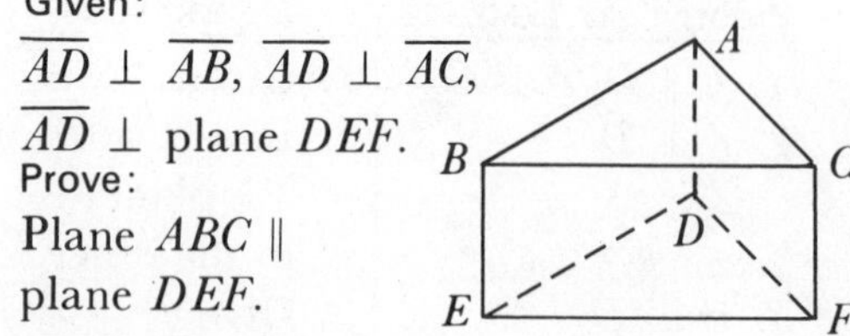

Proof: STATEMENTS	REASONS
1. $\overline{AD} \perp \overline{AB}$, $\overline{AD} \perp \overline{AC}$	1. Given
2. $\overline{AD} \perp$ plane ABC	2. Basic Thm. for $\perp$s

3. $\overline{AD} \perp$ plane DEF	3. Given
4. Plane $ABC \parallel$ plane DEF	4. 2 planes $\perp$ to same line are $\parallel$.

15. Given:
$\overline{AB} \perp$ plane BCD.
Prove:
$\angle A\text{-}\overleftrightarrow{BC}\text{-}D$ is a right dihedral angle.

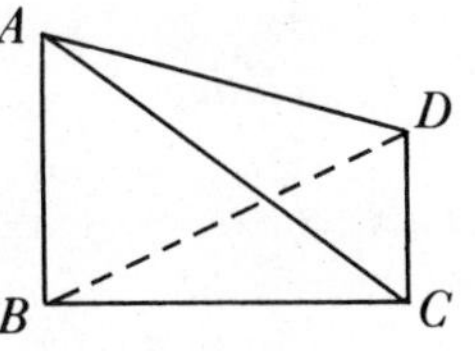

Proof:

STATEMENTS	REASONS
1. $\overline{AB} \perp$ plane BCD	1. Given
2. Plane $ABC \perp$ plane BCD	2. Plane containing line $\perp$ to given plane is $\perp$ to given plane.
3. $\angle A\text{-}\overleftrightarrow{BC}\text{-}D$ is a rt. dih. $\angle$	3. Def. of $\perp$ planes

16. Turn; turn

Page 473 Section 14.1

7. W, X, Y, Z **9.** B

11. $\angle \overleftrightarrow{WX}, \angle \overleftrightarrow{WY}, \angle \overleftrightarrow{WZ}, \angle \overleftrightarrow{XY}, \angle \overleftrightarrow{YZ}, \angle \overleftrightarrow{ZX}$

13. Convex **15.** Not convex

17. a. 6 **b.** 8 **c.** 12 **d.** 12

19. a. 6 **b.** 6 **c.** 10 **d.** 10

Pages 476–477 Section 14.2

***11.** 132.651 cm^3 **13.** e^3 m^3

***15.** 6.76 cm^3 **17.** 9 cm^3 or 9000 mm^3

19. ℓwh mm^3 **21.** 128 cm^3

***23.** 4 m^2 **25.** 16 cm

27. 90 **29.** 1 000 000

31. Volume is multiplied by 8.

***Model Solutions:**

11. $V = Bh$
$= (5.1)^2 \cdot 5.1$
$= 132.651 \text{ cm}^3$

15. $V = Bh$
$= (1.3)^2 \cdot 4$
$= 6.76 \text{ cm}^3$

23. $V = Bh$
$24 = B \cdot 6$
$4 = B$ Base area is 4 m^2.

Page 480 Section 14.3

***7.** 42 **9.** 360 **11.** 56 cm^3

13. 84 m^3 **15.** 660 cm^3 or 660 000 mm^3

***Model Solution:**

7. $V = Bh$
$= (\frac{1}{2} \cdot 4 \cdot 3)(7) = 42$

Pages 483–484 Section 14.4

***11.** 300π cm^3 **13.** 8 m **15.** 7 cm

***17.** 72π **19.** $85\frac{3}{4}\pi$

21. The one with radius 7 **23.** 35.325 cm^3

***Model Solutions:**

11. $V = \pi r^2 h$
$= \pi(5^2)(12)$
$= 300\pi \text{ cm}^3$

17. $C = 2\pi r$
$6\pi = 2\pi r$
$r = 3$

$V = \pi r^2 h$
$= \pi(3^2)(8)$
$= 72\pi$

Page 485 Quick Quiz

1. Space **2.** Rectangles

3. Bh **4.** $\pi r^2 h$ **5.** 44.4 cm^3

6. 0.14 m^3, 140 000 cm^3, or 140 000 000 mm^3

7. 64.8 cm^3 **8.** 7.2 m^3 **9.** 18π cm^3

10. 18.816π cm^3

Pages 489–490 Section 14.5

13. F **15.** F **17.** F **19.** T

***21.** 120 cm^3 **23.** 81π **25.** 4π

**Model Solution:*

21. $V = Bh$

$= (6 \cdot 2)(10) = 120 \text{ cm}^3$

Pages 494–496 Section 14.6

9. T **11.** T **13.** T

***15.** 300 cm^3 ***17.** $64\pi \text{ cm}^3$ or $64\,000\pi \text{ mm}^3$

19. 225 **21.** 125 **23.** 27

25. $5{,}920{,}266\frac{2}{3} \text{ ft}^3$ **27.** $2291\frac{2}{3} \text{ ft}^3$

**Model Solutions:*

15. $V = \frac{1}{3}Bh$

$= \frac{1}{3}(\frac{1}{2} \cdot 12 \cdot 10)(15) = 300 \text{ cm}^3$

17. $V = \frac{1}{3}\pi r^2 h$

$V = \frac{1}{3}\pi(\frac{1}{2} \cdot 8)^2(12) = 64\pi \text{ cm}^3$ or

$V = \frac{1}{3}\pi(\frac{1}{2} \cdot 80)^2(120) = 64\,000\pi \text{ mm}^3$

Pages 500–501 Section 14.7

***9. a.** 60 cm^2 **b.** 72 cm^2

***11. a.** $48\pi \text{ m}^2$ **b.** $66\pi \text{ m}^2$

13. a. 320 **b.** 520

15. a. 36 **b.** 54

17. a. 7.5 **b.** 9.75

19. a. 44π **b.** 52π

21. a. 21π **b.** $26\frac{4}{9}\pi$

23. 2700 cm^2 **25.** 440 ft^2

**Model Solutions:*

9. a. L. A. $= ph$

$= (3 + 4 + 5)5 = 60 \text{ cm}^2$

b. $B = \frac{1}{2}bh$

$= \frac{1}{2} \cdot 4 \cdot 3$

$= 6 \text{ cm}^2$

S. A. = L. A. + $2B$

$= 60 + 2 \cdot 6$

$= 72 \text{ cm}^2$

11. a. L. A. $= 2\pi rh$

$= 2\pi \cdot 3 \cdot 8 = 48\pi \text{ m}^2$

b. S. A. = L. A. + $2\pi r^2$

$= 48\pi + 2\pi \cdot 3^2 = 66\pi \text{ m}^3$

Page 502 Algebra Review

***1.** $-1, -2$ **3.** $-1, \frac{3}{5}$ **5.** $2 \pm \sqrt{3}$

7. $\dfrac{2 \pm \sqrt{2}}{2}$ **9.** $\dfrac{5 \pm \sqrt{41}}{2}$ **11.** $-\sqrt{3}$

**Model Solution:*

1. $x = \dfrac{-3 \pm \sqrt{9 - 4(1)(2)}}{2(1)}$

$= \dfrac{-3 \pm \sqrt{1}}{2} = \dfrac{-3 \pm 1}{2}$

$x = -1$ or $x = -2$

Page 506 Section 14.8

***7.** $288\pi \text{ cm}^3$, $144\pi \text{ cm}^2$

9. $121.5\pi \text{ mm}^3$, $81\pi \text{ mm}^2$

***11.** $166\frac{2}{3}\pi$ cubic units

13. 144π square units **15.** $972\pi \text{ cm}^3$

17. S. A. multiplied by 4; V multiplied by 8

19. 1:4 **21.** $686\pi \text{ cm}^3$

23. 3 units; 36π square units; 36π cubic units

**Model Solutions:*

7. $V = \frac{4}{3}\pi r^3$

$= \frac{4}{3}\pi(6^3)$

$= \frac{4}{3}(216)\pi$

$= 288\pi \text{ cm}^3$

S. A. $= 4\pi r^2$

$= 4\pi(6^2)$

$= 4(36)\pi$

$= 144\pi \text{ cm}^2$

11. S. A. $= 4\pi r^2$

$100\pi = 4\pi r^2$

$r^2 = 25$

$r = 5$

$V = \frac{4}{3}\pi r^3$

$= \frac{4}{3}\pi(5^3)$

$= \frac{4}{3}\pi(125)$

$= 166\frac{2}{3}\pi$ cubic units

Page 509 Section 14.9

5. Three **7.** Two **9.** Six

11. Infinitely many **13.** None

Pages 510–511 Chapter 14 Review

1. Four 3. Four 5. Yes
7. T 9. F 11. 960 cm^3
13. 0.4255 m^3 15. Axis 17. Height
19. T 21. F 23. T
25. 7850 mm^3 27. $\overline{AB}$, $\overline{AC}$, $\overline{AD}$, $\overline{AE}$, $\overline{AF}$
29. $\overline{AX}$ 31. 800 cm^3 33. Vertex
35. Height 37. 256π cm^3 39. 128π; 160π
41. 36π cm^3; 36π cm^2

Page 512 Chapter 14 Test

1. Polygon 2. Right prism
3. Right circular cylinder
4. Regular pyramid 5. Cone
6. Volume 7. Surface area
8. 202; 180 9. 360; 400
10. 96π; 96π 11. 140π; 225π
12. 144π; 288π 13. 243π; 486π
14. 100 cm^2; 150 cm^2; 125 cm^3
15. 96π square units 16. 9 cm
17. 9.5 cm 18. 12 19. Many

Page 519 Section 15.1

25.

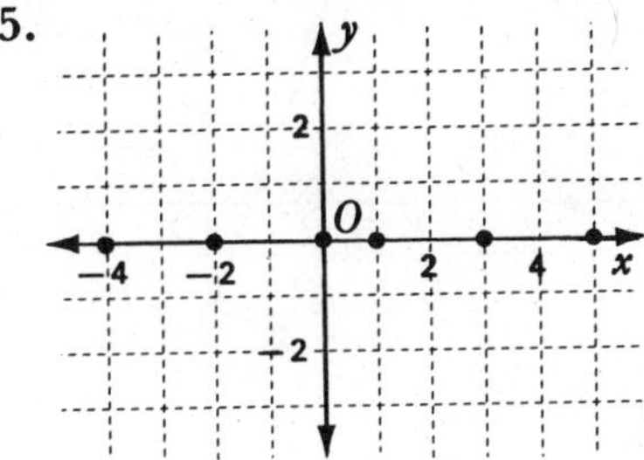

27.

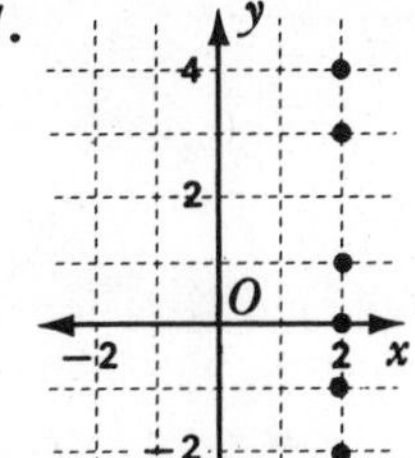

29.

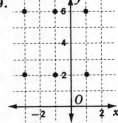

31.

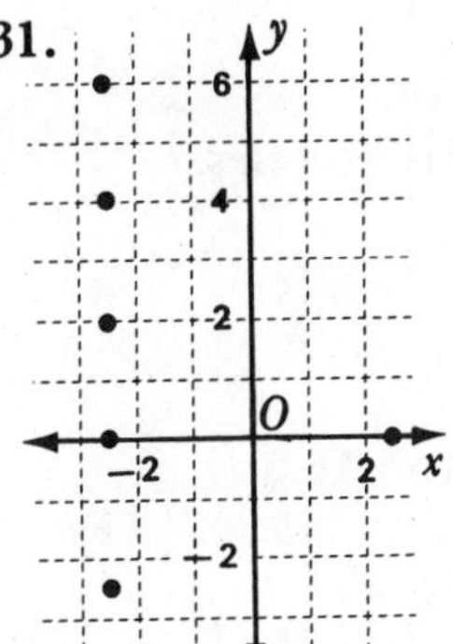

33.

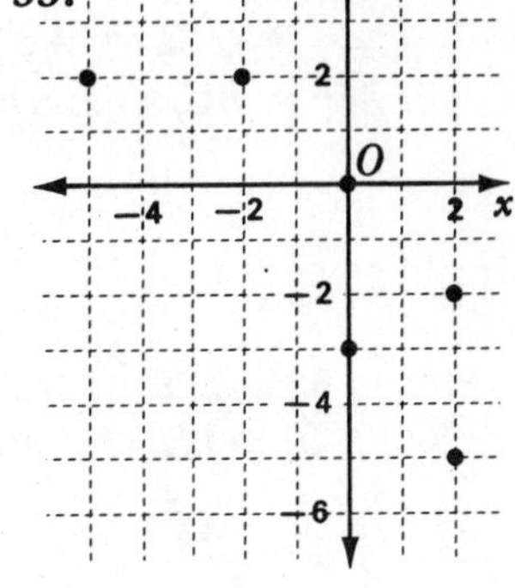

35. 0 37. x 39. Square 41. Triangle
43. Trapezoid 45. (5, 3), (5, 7)

Page 522 Section 15.2

7. (2, −3) *9. 13 11. 13
13. $2\sqrt{5}$ 15. $2\sqrt{73}$ 17. 25
19. $10\sqrt{2}$ *21. Yes. $AC = BC = 4\sqrt{2}$
23. $AC = \sqrt{34}$, $BD = 3\sqrt{2}$
25. $AB = \sqrt{13}$, $AC = \sqrt{13}$, and $BC = \sqrt{26}$; $(\sqrt{13})^2 + (\sqrt{13})^2 = (\sqrt{26})^2$

**Model Solutions:*

9. $$\begin{aligned} PQ &= \sqrt{(5 - 0)^2 + (12 - 0)^2} \\ &= \sqrt{25 + 144} \\ &= \sqrt{169} \\ &= 13 \end{aligned}$$

21. $AB = \sqrt{(5 + 3)^2 + (1 - 1)^2}$
$= \sqrt{64} = 8$
$AC = \sqrt{(1 + 3)^2 + (5 - 1)^2}$
$= \sqrt{16 + 16}$
$= \sqrt{32} = 4\sqrt{2}$
$BC = \sqrt{(1 - 5)^2 + (5 - 1)^2}$
$= \sqrt{16 + 16}$
$= \sqrt{32} = 4\sqrt{2}$
$AC = BC$, so $\triangle ABC$ is isosceles.

Pages 525–526 Section 15.3

*15. (2, 5) 17. (−6, 6) 19. $(7\frac{1}{2}, 3\frac{1}{2})$

21. $(\frac{1}{3}, \frac{3}{4})$ 23. $(\sqrt{2}, 2\sqrt{3})$ 25. $\left(\frac{a + b}{2}, 0\right)$

27. $(4\frac{1}{2}, \frac{1}{2}), (2\frac{1}{2}, -1\frac{1}{2}), (1, 3)$

29. $3\sqrt{10}, 3\sqrt{5}, 3\sqrt{13}$

31. $(-2, 1\frac{1}{2})$ is the midpoint of $\overline{AC}$ and $\overline{BD}$.

*33. (−7, −3) 35. (8, −1) 37. $(-a, 2a)$

**Model Solutions:*

15. $\frac{0 + 4}{2} = 2$ $\frac{8 + 2}{2} = 5$ (2, 5)

33. Let (x, y) be coordinates of 2nd endpt.

$\frac{3 + x}{2} = -2$	$\frac{5 + y}{2} = 1$
$3 + x = -4$	$5 + y = 2$
$x = -7$	$y = -3$

$(x, y) = (-7, -3)$

Pages 529–530 Section 15.4

*7. $\frac{2}{3}$ 9. $\frac{1}{4}$ 11. $-\frac{2}{7}$ 13. $-\frac{5}{3}$

15. $\frac{4}{3}$ 17. $-\frac{19}{18}$ 19. $\frac{19}{15}$ 21. $-\frac{5}{3}$

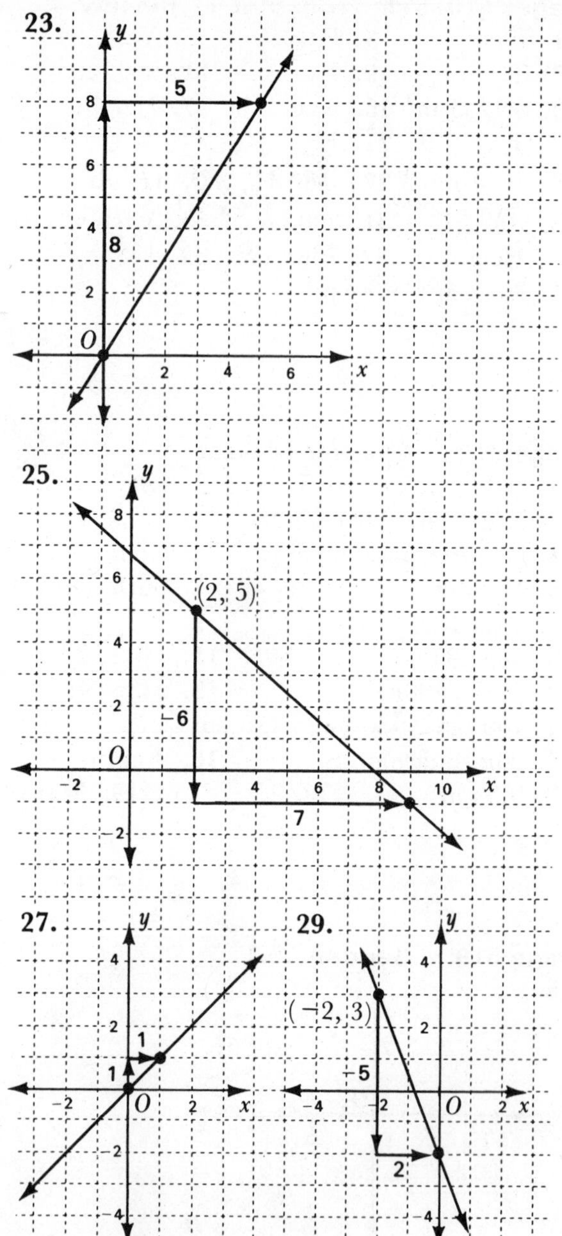

*31. Not collinear 33. Collinear

**Model Solutions:*

7. $m = \frac{5 - 7}{3 - 6} = \frac{-2}{-3} = \frac{2}{3}$ or

$m = \frac{7 - 5}{6 - 3} = \frac{2}{3}$

31. (0, 3), (4, 1) $m = \frac{1-3}{4-0} = \frac{-2}{4} = -\frac{1}{2}$

(4, 1), (6, −3) $m = \frac{-3-1}{6-4} = \frac{-4}{2}$

$= -2$

The points are not collinear. (The lines through (4, 1) and (0, 3) and through (4, 1) and (6, −3) have different slopes.)

Pages 533–534 Section 15.5

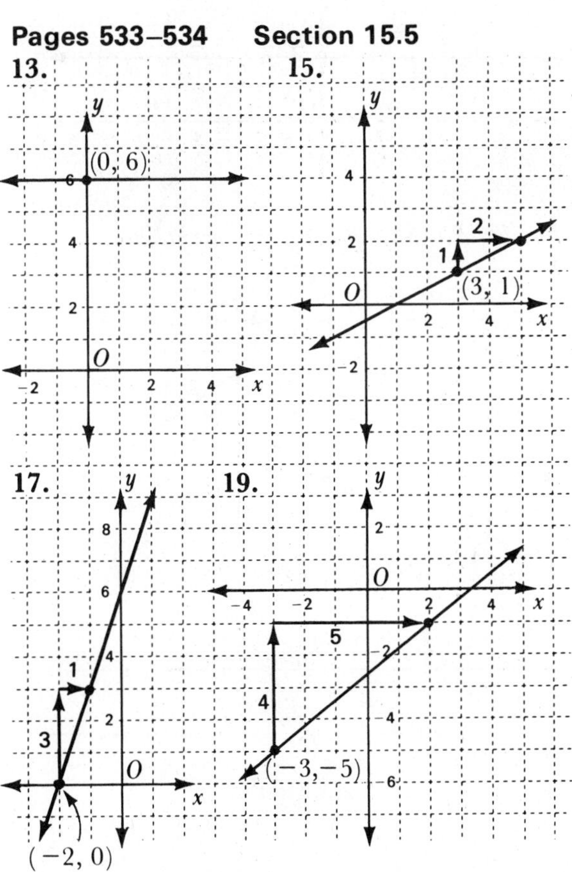

***21.** $y - 4 = \frac{2}{3}(x - 1)$; $2x - 3y = -10$
23. $y - 5 = -\frac{1}{4}(x - 4)$; $x + 4y = 24$
25. $y + 8 = \frac{3}{5}(x + 3)$; $3x - 5y = 31$
27. $y - 0 = 3(x - 4)$; $3x - y = 12$
29. $y + 7 = -\frac{2}{9}(x - 0)$; $2x + 9y = -63$

31. $y + 5 = 0(x - 0)$; $0x + y = -5$
33. $x = 7$ ***35.** $x - 4y = -7$
37. $3x + 5y = 19$ **39.** $2x - y = -2$
41. $0x + y = -1$ **43.** $x + 0y = 4$

**Model Solutions:*

21.
$$y - 4 = \frac{2}{3}(x - 1)$$
$$3(y - 4) = 2(x - 1)$$
$$3y - 12 = 2x - 2$$
$$-10 = 2x - 3y$$
$$2x - 3y = -10$$

35. $m = \frac{3-2}{5-1} = \frac{1}{4}$
$$y - 2 = \frac{1}{4}(x - 1)$$
$$4(y - 2) = x - 1$$
$$4y - 8 = x - 1$$
$$x - 4y = -7$$

Page 535 Quick Quiz

1.

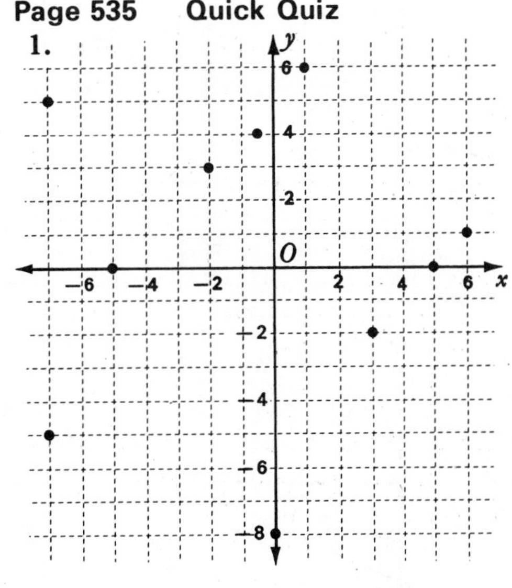

2. (−2, 3), (−7, 5), $(-\frac{1}{2}, 4)$
3. 5 **4.** $2\sqrt{10}$ **5.** (3, 2)
6. $(\frac{1}{2}, -5\frac{1}{2})$ **7.** Vertical **8.** Negative
9. 4 **10.** $\frac{1}{2}$, (3, 1)

11. **12.**

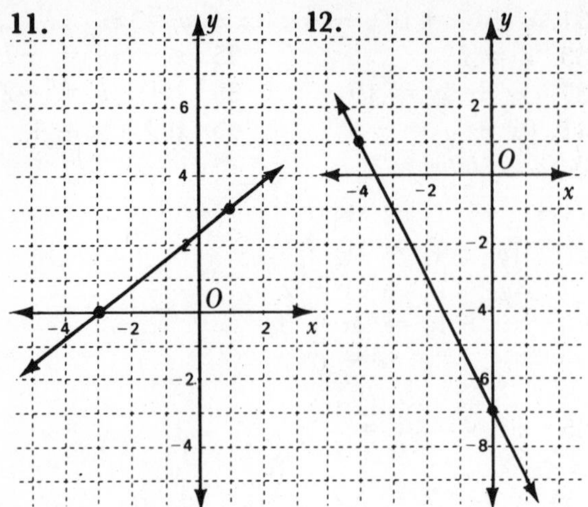

13. $x + 4y = 6$

14. $7x - 5y = -29$

Pages 537–538 Section 15.6

15. **17.**

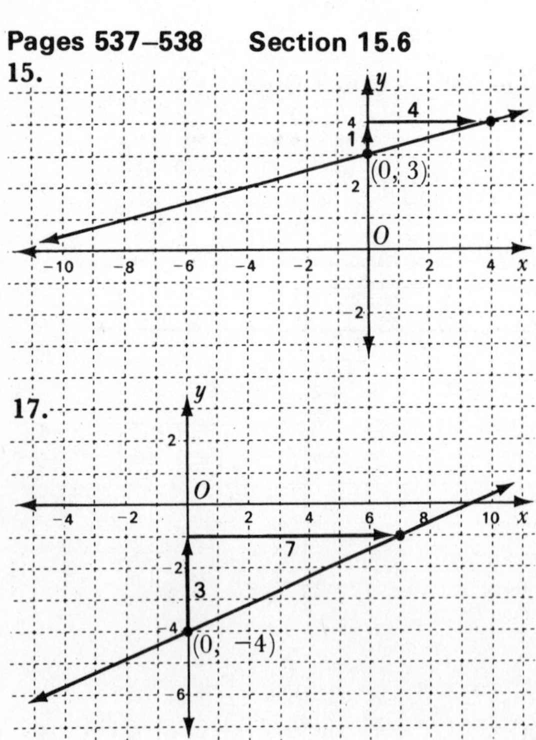

19. **21.** **23.**

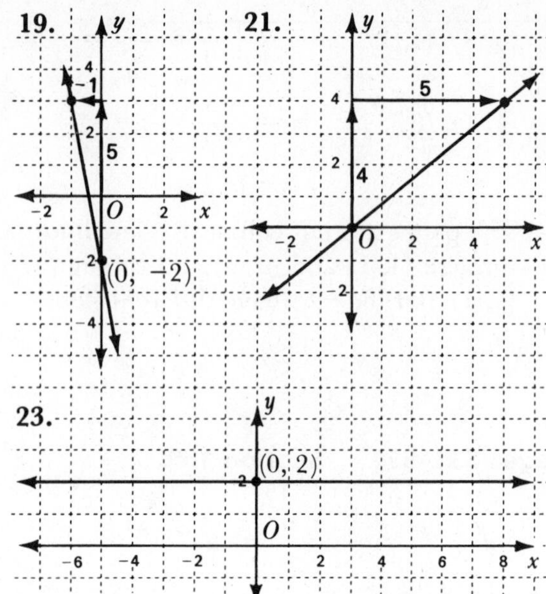

For Ex. 25–33, typical points are labeled.

25. **27.** **29.**

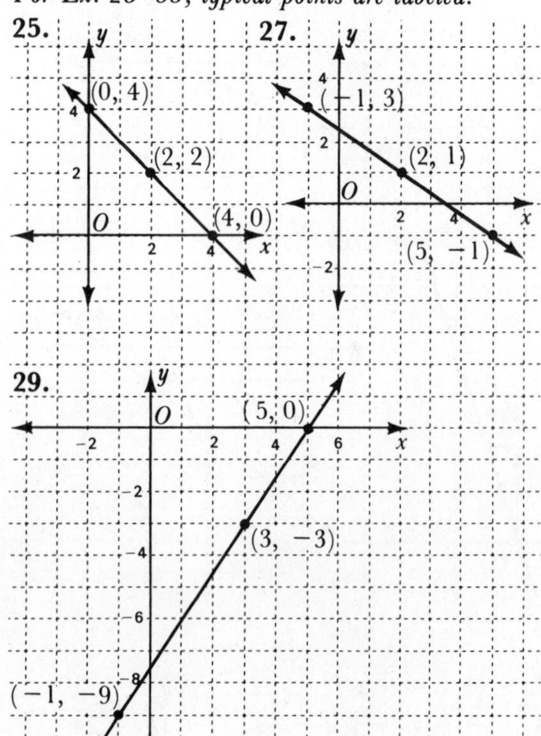

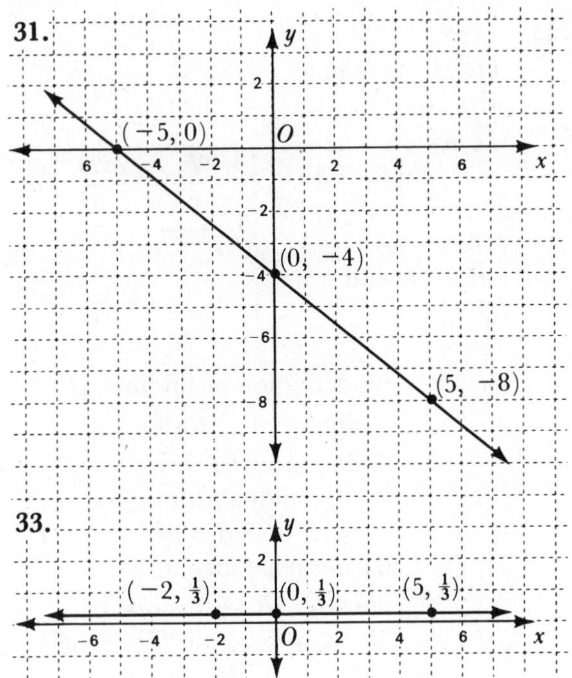

***35. a.** $y = -1x + 4$ **b.** $-1, 4$

37. a. $y = -\frac{2}{3}x + \frac{7}{3}$ **b.** $-\frac{2}{3}, \frac{7}{3}$

39. a. $y = \frac{3}{2}x + (-\frac{15}{2})$ **b.** $\frac{3}{2}, -\frac{15}{2}$

41. a. $y = -\frac{4}{5}x + (-4)$ **b.** $-\frac{4}{5}, -4$

43. a. $y = 0x + \frac{1}{3}$ **b.** $0, \frac{1}{3}$

**Model Solution:*

35. $x + y = 4$
$y = -1x + 4$
$m = -1, b = 4$

Page 538 Algebra Review

***1.** No solutions **3.** (1, 1)

***5.** (8, 11) ***7.** $(8, -\frac{26}{3})$ **9.** (5, 0)

* *Model Solutions:*

1. $2x - 3y = 12$
$-3y = -2x + 12$
$y = \frac{2}{3}x - 4$
$3y = 2x + 21$
$y = \frac{2}{3}x + 7$
Graphs are parallel lines, so there are no solutions.

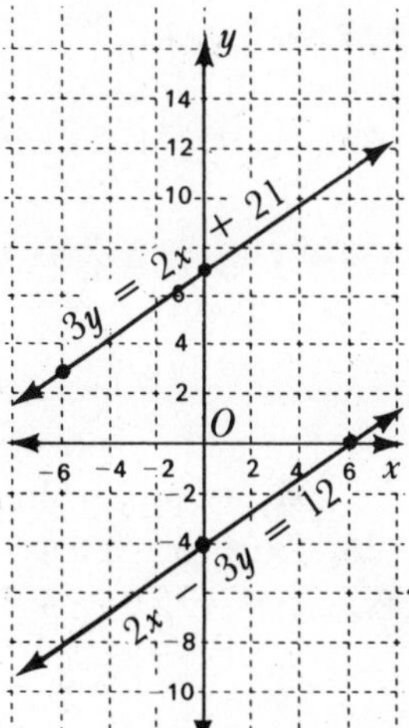

5. $y = x + 3$
$3x + 2y = 46$
$3x + 2(x + 3) = 46$
$3x + 2x + 6 = 46$
$5x = 40$
$x = 8$
$y = 8 + 3$
$= 11$
$(x, y) = (8, 11)$

7. $7x + 3y = 30$
$2x - 3y = 42$
$9x = 72$
$x = 8$
$7(8) + 3y = 30$
$56 + 3y = 30$
$3y = -26$
$y = -\frac{26}{3}$
$(x, y) = (8, -\frac{26}{3})$

Pages 541–542 Section 15.7

***15.** ∥ **17.** ⊥ **19.** Neither

21. ⊥ ***23.** ⊥ **25.** Neither

27. ∥ ***29.** $2x + 5y = 3$

31. $x - y = -9$

33. Slope of $\overline{AB}$ and $\overline{CD}$ is $\frac{1}{8}$; slope of $\overline{BC}$ and $\overline{AD}$ is $-\frac{7}{4}$.

35. Slope of $\overline{JK}$ is $\frac{2}{21}$ and slope of $\overline{KL}$ is $-\frac{21}{2}$. So $\overline{JK} \perp \overline{KL}$ and $\triangle JKL$ is a rt. $\triangle$.

37. $5, \frac{2}{5}, -\frac{3}{4}$

**Model Solutions:*

15. (0, 0), (4, 5) $m_1 = \frac{5-0}{4-0} = \frac{5}{4}$

(1, 6), (−3, 1) $m_2 = \frac{1-6}{-3-1}$

$= \frac{-5}{-4} = \frac{5}{4}$

$m_1 = m_2$, so lines are $\parallel$.

23.

$2x + y = -4$	$x - 2y = 5$
$y = -2x - 4$	$-2y = -x + 5$
$m_1 = -2$	$y = \frac{1}{2}x - \frac{5}{2}$
	$m_2 = \frac{1}{2}$

$m_1 m_2 = -2 \cdot \frac{1}{2} = -1$, so lines are $\perp$.

29. $m = -\frac{2}{5}$

$y + 1 = -\frac{2}{5}(x - 4)$

$5(y + 1) = -2(x - 4)$

$5y + 5 = -2x + 8$

$2x + 5y = 3$

Pages 545–546 Section 15.8

9. Given:
▱$ABCD$ with A at (0, 0) and $\overline{AB}$ on the x-axis

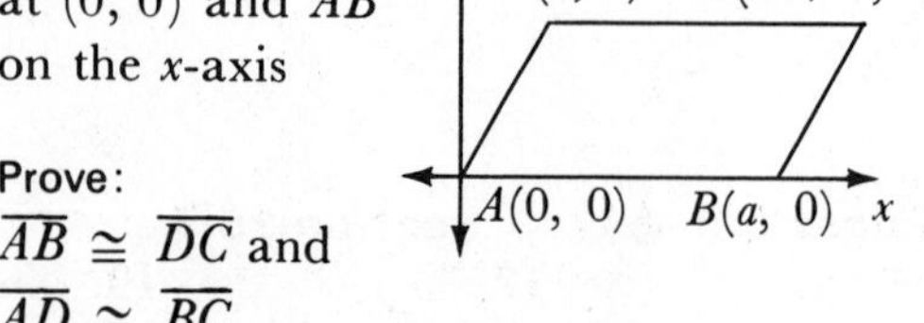

Prove:
$\overline{AB} \cong \overline{DC}$ and $\overline{AD} \cong \overline{BC}$

Proof: *1.* By the distance formula,

$AB = \sqrt{a^2} = |a|$

$DC = \sqrt{a^2} = |a|$

$AD = \sqrt{b^2 + c^2}$

$BC = \sqrt{b^2 + c^2}$

2. By substitution and definition of congruent segments, $\overline{AB} \cong \overline{DC}$ and $\overline{AD} \cong \overline{BC}$.

11. Given:
Trapezoid $JKLM$ with J at (0, 0), $\overline{JK}$ on the x-axis, and midline $\overline{AB}$

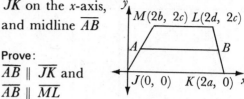

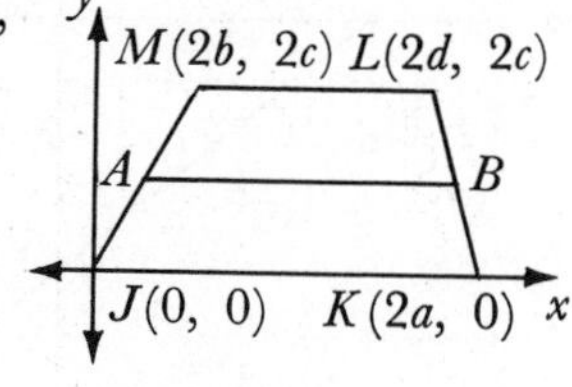

Prove:
$\overline{AB} \parallel \overline{JK}$ and $\overline{AB} \parallel \overline{ML}$

Proof: *1.* By definition of midline, A is midpoint of $\overline{JM}$ and B is midpoint of $\overline{KL}$.

2. By the midpoint formula, A is at (b, c) and B is at $(a + d, c)$.

3. By the slope formula, slope of $\overline{AB} = 0$, slope of $\overline{JK} = 0$, slope of $\overline{ML} = 0$.

4. Since nonvertical lines with equal slopes are parallel, $\overline{AB} \parallel \overline{JK}$ and $\overline{AB} \parallel \overline{ML}$.

13. Given:
$\triangle RST$ with R at (0, 0), $\overline{RS}$ on the x-axis, and midpoints W and X

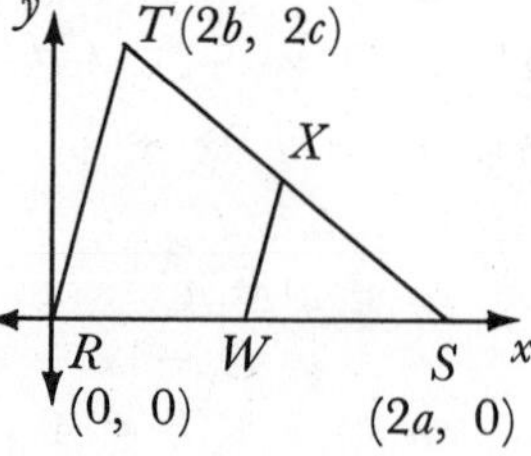

Prove:
$\overline{WX} \parallel \overline{RT}$

Proof: *1.* By the midpoint formula, W is at $(a, 0)$ and X is at $(a + b, c)$.

2. By the slope formula, slope of $\overline{WX} = \frac{c}{b}$, slope of $\overline{RT} = \frac{c}{b}$.

3. Since $\overline{WX}$ and $\overline{RT}$ have equal slopes, $\overline{WX} \parallel \overline{RT}$.